CONCORDIA UNIVERSITY

3 4211 00129 0280

S0-BHY-455

TABLE OF ATOMIC WEIGHTS, 1961 (*Continued*)

Element	Symbol	Atomic Number	Atomic Weight
Neon	Ne	10	20.183
Neptunium	Np	93	
Nickel	Ni	28	58.71
Niobium	Nb	41	92.906
Nitrogen	N	7	14.0067
Nobelium	No	102	
Osmium	Os	76	190.2
Oxygen	O	8	15.9994 ($\pm$0.0001, nat.)
Palladium	Pd	46	106.4
Phosphorus	P	15	30.9738
Platinum	Pt	78	195.09
Plutonium	Pu	94	
Polonium	Po	84	
Potassium	K	19	39.102
Praseodymium	Pr	59	140.907
Promethium	Pm	61	
Protactinium	Pa	91	
Radium	Ra	88	
Radon	Rn	86	
Rhenium	Re	75	186.2
Rhodium	Rh	45	102.905
Rubidium	Rb	37	85.47
Ruthenium	Ru	44	101.07
Samarium	Sm	62	150.35
Scandium	Sc	21	44.956
Selenium	Se	34	78.96
Silicon	Si	14	28.086 ($\pm$0.001, nat.)
Silver	Ag	47	107.870 ($\pm$0.003, exp.)
Sodium	Na	11	22.9898
Strontium	Sr	38	87.62
Sulfur	S	16	32.064 ($\pm$0.003, nat.)
Tantalum	Ta	73	180.948
Technetium	Tc	43	
Tellurium	Te	52	127.60
Terbium	Tb	65	158.924
Thallium	Tl	81	204.37
Thorium	Th	90	232.038
Thulium	Tm	69	168.934
Tin	Sn	50	118.69
Titanium	Ti	22	47.90
Tungsten	W	74	183.85
Uranium	U	92	238.03
Vanadium	V	23	50.942
Xenon	Xe	54	131.30
Ytterbium	Yb	70	173.04
Yttrium	Y	39	88.905
Zinc	Zn	30	65.37
Zirconium	Zr	40	91.22

WITHDRAWN

nat. = Variation in atomic weight due to
natural variation in the isotopic composition.
exp. = Experimental uncertainty of magnitude given.

Adopted 1961 by the International Union of Pure and Applied Chemistry.

STANDARD METHODS OF
CHEMICAL ANALYSIS

The first four editions of STANDARD METHODS OF CHEMICAL ANALYSIS were prepared under the Editorship of Dr. Wilfred W. Scott, Professor of Chemistry at the University of Southern California. After his death, the Fifth Edition was edited by Dr. N. Howell Furman, then Professor of Chemistry at Princeton University. Professor Furman also edited Volume I of the Sixth Edition, and was Advisory Editor of Volume II, which was edited by Dr. Frank J. Welcher of Indiana University. The present Volume III was also prepared under the Editorship of Dr. Welcher.

STANDARD METHODS OF
CHEMICAL ANALYSIS

SIXTH EDITION

Volume Three—Instrumental Methods
Part B

FRANK J. WELCHER, Ph.D., *Editor*

Professor of Chemistry, Indiana University

IN COLLABORATION WITH MANY CONTRIBUTORS
(SEE LIST ON PAGES FOLLOWING)

D. VAN NOSTRAND COMPANY, INC.

Princeton, New Jersey

Toronto
London

New York

KLINCK MEMORIAL LIBRARY
Concordia Teachers College
River Forest. Illinois

D. VAN NOSTRAND COMPANY, INC.
120 Alexander St., Princeton, New Jersey (*Principal office*)
24 West 40 Street, New York 18, New York

D. VAN NOSTRAND COMPANY, LTD.
358 Kensington High Street, London, W.14, England

D. VAN NOSTRAND COMPANY (Canada), LTD.
25 Hollinger Road, Toronto 16, Canada

COPYRIGHT © 1917, 1922, 1925 BY
D. VAN NOSTRAND COMPANY, INC.

COPYRIGHT © 1939, 1966 BY
D. VAN NOSTRAND COMPANY, INC.

Published simultaneously in Canada by
D. VAN NOSTRAND COMPANY (Canada), LTD.

No reproduction in any form of this book, in whole or in part (except for brief quotation in critical articles or reviews), may be made without written authorization from the publishers.

PRINTED IN THE UNITED STATES OF AMERICA

82843

CONTRIBUTORS *Sixth Edition—Volume Three*

P. Bruce Adams
Corning Glass Works

L. W. Aurand
North Carolina State University

Allen J. Bard
University of Texas

Richard C. Barras
Atlantic Refining Co.

S. A. Bartkiewicz
Humble Oil and Refining Co.

Roger G. Bates
National Bureau of Standards

Hugh F. Beeghly
Jones and Laughlin Steel Corp.

E. W. Blank
Colgate-Palmolive Research Center

David F. Boltz
Wayne State University

John A. Brabson
Tennessee Valley Authority

E. J. Brooks
Naval Research Laboratory

Robert J. Bryan
Los Angeles Air Pollution Control District

Vincent E. Caldwell
Pittsburgh Plate Glass Co.

William J. Campbell
Department of the Interior

Paul Close
Owens-Illinois Technical Center

John G. Cobler
Dow Chemical Co.

J. William Cook
Department of Health, Education and Welfare

S. Dal Nogare
E. I. duPont de Nemours and Co.

Donald G. Davis
Louisiana State University

John A. Dean
University of Tennessee

Joseph B. DiGiorgio
Sacramento State College

Jan Doležal
Charles University
Prague, Czechoslovakia

John C. Evans
Dow Chemical Co.

Robert B. Fischer
California State College at Palos Verdes

Robert Fisher
Universität Graz
Graz, Austria

Harlan Foster
E. I. duPont de Nemours and Co.

Owen R. Gates
Naval Research Laboratory

Roland S. Gohlke
Dow Chemical Co.

S. Mark Henry
Bristol Myers Corp.

Harold W. Hermance
Bell Telephone Laboratories

William G. Hime
Portland Cement Association

v

Emanuel Horowitz
National Bureau of Standards

R. Norman Jones
National Research Council of Canada

W. C. Jones, Jr.
Esso Research and Engineering Co.

Philip F. Kane
Texas Instruments, Inc.

Brian H. Kaye
I. I. T. Research Institute

Gerson Kegeles
Clark University

R. M. Kelley
Colgate-Palmolive Research Center

Duane V. Kniebes
Institute of Gas Technology

Richard M. Kniseley
Iowa State University

Stephen H. Laning
Pittsburgh Plate Glass Co.

George W. Leddicotte
University of Missouri

Gabor B. Levy
Photovolt Corp.

Ralph B. Lingeman
Indiana University Medical Center

Donald C. Malins
Department of the Interior

Helmut K. Mangold
University of Minnesota

James D. McGinness
Sherwin-Williams Research Center

Virgil C. Mehlenbacher
Swift and Co.

M. G. Mellon
Purdue University

C. M. Mitchell
Canadian Department of Mines and
Technical Surveys

John Mitchell, Jr.
E. I. duPont de Nemours and Co.

L. N. Mulay
Pennsylvania State University

A. Wendell Musser
Veterans Administration

John L. Parsons
Consultant to the Paper and Allied
Industries

Dennis G. Peters
Indiana University

James W. Robinson
Louisiana State University

Howard G. Ross
Ford Motor Co.

James W. Ross, Jr.
Orion Research, Inc.

Edward J. Rubins
University of Connecticut

Ward B. Schaap
Indiana University

Harold F. Schaeffer
Westminster College

Harald H. O. Schmid
University of Minnesota

Robert D. Schwartz
Shell Development Co.

Paul J. Secrest
Sherwin-Williams Research Center

William L. Senn, Jr.
Esso Research Laboratories

W. D. Shults
Oak Ridge National Laboratory

E. L. Steel
General Dynamics Corp.

D. P. Stevenson
Shell Development Co.

Hans J. Stolten
General Aniline and Film Corp.

Richard D. Strickland
Veterans Administration

Michael J. Taras
Detroit Department of Water Supply

Domenic J. Tessari
Sherwin-Williams Research Center

Max Tryon
National Bureau of Standards

Harold V. Wadlow
Bell Telephone Laboratories
Holmdel, New Jersey

P. A. Wadsworth
Shell Development Co.

Alan Walsh
Commonwealth Scientific and Industrial
Research Organization
Melbourne, Australia

Dean I. Walter
Naval Research Laboratory

Alfred Weissler
Air Force Office of Scientific Research

Wesley W. Wendlandt
Texas Technological College

Charles E. White
University of Maryland

William P. Whitney
Corning Glass Works

Sidney Williams
Department of Health, Education and
Welfare

J. B. Willis
Commonwealth Scientific and Industrial
Research Organization
Melbourne, Australia

Jaroslav Zýka
Charles University
Prague, Czechoslovakia

CONTENTS

INSTRUMENTAL METHODS IN CLINICAL MEDICINE

Introduction, 975; Autoanalyzer, 975; Chloride Titrator, 1019; Coagulation Timers, 1023; Flame Photometer, 1025; Fluorometry, 1031; Thin-Layer Chromatography, 1037; Gas Chromatography, 1041; Selected Bibliography, 1049.

NATURAL FATS

Visible Spectrometry, 1054; Ultraviolet Spectrometry, 1066; Infrared Spectrometry, 1072; Flame Photometry, 1073; Emission Spectrometry, 1074; X-Ray Diffraction, 1075; Refractometry, 1075; Potentiometric Titrations, 1077; Conductivity, 1080; Polarography, 1081; Nuclear Magnetic Resonance (NMR) Spectrometry, 1082; Differential Thermal Analysis, 1083; Chromatography, 1085; Gas Liquid Chromatography, 1090; Paper Chromatography, 1092; Dilatometry, 1096; Manometry, 1098; Dielectrometry, 1100; Consistency, 1101.

FERTILIZERS

X-Ray Emission Spectrometry, 1102; Automatic Analysis Trains, 1103; Automated Devarda Method, 1104; Atomic Absorption Spectrometry, 1105.

FOODS

Cereals, 1108; Chemical Preservatives, 1111; Color Additives, 1113; Food Additives, 1114; Fats, Oils, Waxes, 1125; Meat and Meat Products, 1125; Metals and Elements, 1128; Milk and Milk Products, 1131; Pesticides, 1139; Sugar, 1145; Vitamins, 1148; Miscellaneous Methods, 1157.

ORGANIC FUNCTIONAL GROUPS

Introduction, 1162; Absorption Spectrometry, 1162; Infrared Spectrometry, 1164; Near-Infrared Spectrometry, 1177; Ultraviolet Spectrometry, 1182; Gas Chromatography, 1191; Mass Spectrometry, 1198; Nuclear Magnetic Resonance Spectrometry, 1200; Polarography, 1205; Optical Rotatory Dispersion, 1207; Raman Spectrometry, 1208.

GASES, 1210

GLASS

FLAME AND ATOMIC ABSORPTION SPECTROMETRY, 1213.
THE ELECTRON MICROPROBE, 1229.
POLAROGRAPHIC AND AMPEROMETRIC TITRATIONS, 1233.
POTENTIOMETRIC TITRATIONS, 1237.

X-RAY SPECTROGRAPHIC METHODS, 1243.
SPECIAL TECHNIQUES IN X-RAY INSTRUMENTATION AND ANALYSIS
OF GLASS, 1258.

PAINT, VARNISH, AND LACQUER

Visible Spectrometry, 1265; Ultraviolet Spectrometry, 1272; Infrared Spectrometry, 1281; Flame Emission Spectrometry, 1294; Emission Spectrometry, 1298; X-Ray Emission Spectrometry, 1299; X-Ray Diffraction, 1303; Nuclear Magnetic Resonance Spectrometry, 1305; Turbidimetric Titration of Polymers, 1306; Polarography, 1307; Thermal Analysis, 1308; Gas Chromatography, 1309; Gel Permeation Chromatography, 1323.

PAPER, WOOD, AND PULP

Specific Gravity (Density) and Moisture Content of Pulpwood, 1326; Laboratory Processing of Pulp (Beater Method), 1332; Forming Handsheets for Physical Tests of Pulp, 1337; Spectral Reflectivity and Color of Pulp, 1348; Brightness of Pulp, 1351; Forming Handsheets for Optical Tests of Pulp; 1357; Physical Testing of Pulp Handsheets, 1359; Drainage Time and Drainage Factor of Pulp, 1363; Freeness of Pulp, 1366; Bacteriological Examination of Pulp, 1374; Fiber Analysis of Paper and Paperboard, 1378; Bursting Strength of Paper, 1392; Tensile Breaking Strength of Paper and Paperboard, 1395; Basis Weight of Paper and Paperboard, 1398; Thickness and Density of Paper, 1400; Internal Tearing Resistance of Paper, 1402; Folding Endurance of Paper, 1407; Contrast Gloss of Paper at 57.5°, 1411; Opacity of Paper, 1412; Bulking Thickness of Paper and Paperboard, 1419; Ink Absorption of Blotting Paper, 1421; Water Absorption of Bibulous Paper, 1422; Water Resistance of Paper and Paperboard (Dry-Indicator Method), 1423; Water Absorptiveness of Nonbibulous Paper and Paperboard (Cobb Test), 1427; Spectral Reflectivity and Color of Paper, 1429; Silver-Tarnishing Test of Paper, 1432; Water Vapor Permeability of Paper and Paperboard, 1434; Bacteriological Examination of Paper and Paperboard, 1437; Brightness of Paper and Paperboard, 1440; Stretch of Paper and Paperboard, 1446; Surface Wettability of Paper (Angle-of-Contact Method), 1449; Air Resistance of Paper, 1452; Flammability of Treated Paper and Paperboard, 1454; Degree of Curl and Sizing of Paper, 1454; Edge Tearing Resistance of Paper (Finch Method), 1456; Bacteriological Examination of Process Water and Slush Pulp, 1458; Preparation of Magnesium-Oxide Standard for Spectral Reflectivity, 1460.

PESTICIDE RESIDUE ANALYSIS

Extraction and Cleanup (Purification), 1464; Gas-Liquid Chromatography (GLC), 1472; Gas Chromatography for Organophosphates, 1488; Thin-Layer Chromatography (TLC), 1492; Paper Chromatography, 1499; Acknowledgment, 1505.

PETROLEUM AND PETROLEUM PRODUCTS

ATOMIC ABSORPTION SPECTROMETRY, 1507.
MASS SPECTROMETRY IN PETROLEUM CHEMISTRY, 1518.
NUCLEAR ACTIVATION ANALYSIS, 1528.
X-RAY EMISSION SPECTROMETRY, 1539.
COMBINATION TECHNIQUES AS APPLIED TO COMPLEX HYDROCARBON SYSTEMS, 1545.
GAS CHROMATOGRAPHY, 1554.

PLASTICS

Nuclear Magnetic Resonance Spectrometry, 1579; Crystallinity in Polymers and X-Ray Diffraction Analysis, 1582; X-Ray Fluorescence, 1586; Radiochemical Analysis, 1588; Application of Microscopy to the Study of Plastics, 1591; Ultraviolet Spectrometry, 1595; Near-Infrared Spectrometry, 1599; Infrared Spectrometry, 1602; Thermogravimetric Analysis, 1630; Differential Thermal Analysis, 1637; Chromatography, 1647; Survey of Additional Instrumental Techniques, 1660; Selected Bibliography, 1663.

RUBBER AND RUBBER PRODUCTS

INTRODUCTION, 1664.
POLYMER COMPOSITION, 1667; General Identification, 1668; Structural Characteristics, 1679; Quantitative Copolymer Composition, 1686; Internal Structures, 1690; Quantitative Composition of Polymer Mixtures, 1691.
NONRUBBER CONSTITUENTS, 1695; Qualitative Methods, 1696; Quantitative Methods, 1722.
MISCELLANEOUS ANALYSES, 1756.

SEMICONDUCTORS

Introduction, 1764; Emission Spectrography, 1770; Mass Spectrometry, 1782; Activation Analysis, 1789; The Activation Analysis of Silicon, 1792; Polarography, 1800; Vacuum Fusion Analysis, 1807; Infrared Spectrometry, 1809.

SOAPS AND SYNTHETIC DETERGENTS

Scope, 1812; Sampling, 1812; Separations, 1813; Purity of Reagents, 1814; Visible Spectrometry, 1815; Ultraviolet Spectrometry, 1821; Infrared Spectrometry, 1829; Emission Flame Photometry, 1837; X-Ray Diffraction, 1838; Turbidimetry, 1839; Potentiometric Titrations, 1840; Mass Spectrometry, 1844; Absorption Chromatography, 1845; Paper Chromatography, 1854; Gas Chromatography, 1857; Miscellaneous, 1861.

SOILS

Light Absorption Spectrometry, 1865; Emission Spectrometry, 1872; Flame Emission Spectrometry, 1874; Atomic Absorption Spectrometry, 1876; Polarography, 1876; Metal Ion-Sensitive Glass Electrodes, 1877; Electrodialysis, 1878; Automatic Analysis Trains, 1878; Chromatography, 1879; Thermogravimetry, 1880.

WATER ANALYSIS

Introduction, 1881; Spectrometric Techniques, 1883; Emission Spectrometry, 1892; Electrometric Techniques, 1894; Nuclear Techniques, 1907; Gas Chromatography, 1924; Microelectrophoresis, 1927.

DETERMINATION OF WATER

Introduction, 1935; Infrared Spectrometry, 1935; Nuclear Magnetic Resonance (NMR) Spectrometry, 1937; Colorimetric Methods, 1938; Neutron Scattering and Other Radiochemical Methods, 1940; Mass Spectrometry, 1941; Thermogravimetry, 1942; Differential Thermal Analysis, 1943; Gas Chromatography, 1945; Electrical Methods, 1946; Miscellaneous Instrumental Methods, 1952.

INDEX, 1955.

Chapter 47

INSTRUMENTAL METHODS
IN CLINICAL MEDICINE

By Ralph B. Lingeman, M.D.
Department of Pathology and Clinical Pathology
Indiana University Medical Center, Indianapolis, Indiana

and

A. Wendell Musser, M.D.
Department of Pathology, Duke University, and
Chief of Laboratory Service, Veterans Administration Hospital
Durham, North Carolina

INTRODUCTION

The number of instruments and instrumental methods in routine use in the clinical laboratory is increasing as a result of the rapid advancements that have taken place in the last decade. Instruments such as the blood clot timer and the chloride titrator have been developed either for the determination of a constituent found only in body fluids or have been developed to be sensitive to the concentration of chemical compounds in these biologic fluids. Many of the instruments and methods developed in industry and research have been adapted to the needs of chemical analysis in clinical medicine. The need for simple, relatively inexpensive instruments has limited the adaptation of many of these fine instruments to routine use in the clinical laboratory.

The criteria for instruments and instrumental methods in the routine clinical laboratory are (1) accuracies within the ranges of the normal accepted range of values; (2) rapidity of analysis; (3) simplicity in operation; (4) simplicity in maintenance; and (5) specificity for certain constituents in body fluids. An additional criterion which is quite variable from laboratory to laboratory is the initial cost of the instrument. The authors shall attempt to describe and bring to the attention of the reader a few of the more accepted and recognized instruments that are being routinely used in many hospitals.

The authors have not attempted to cover all of the applicable instruments and apologize to those readers who have been offended because of the omission of their choice of machine or brand. Those that have been included have been used to a greater or lesser degree either by the authors, acquaintances of the authors, or by reliable investigators as reported in the literature. The reader is referred to other portions of this volume for instruments that could be adapted to analysis in clinical medicine.

AUTOANALYZER®

DESCRIPTION OF INSTRUMENT

The conception and development of the Autoanalyzer® (Technicon Instruments Corp.) by Skeggs has made it possible to automate virtually every procedure available in a clinical chemistry laboratory. This system of automatic train analysis permits the analysis of large quantities of specimens and permits greater accuracy in the performance of the test procedure.

The Autoanalyzer® is constructed in modular form allowing each module to be removed and replaced as needed or the deletion of a module not needed for some analytical procedures. Each module is interconnected by plastic tubing which carries the samples and reagents in an orderly fashion from one unit to the next. (See Fig. 47-1.)

FIG. 47-1.   Autoanalyzer®. (Courtesy Technicon Instruments Corp.)

Sample Module.—The sample module introduces each sample in turn to the system. A circular plate with holes at its periphery is used to hold small polystyrene sample cups which have a capacity of 2 ml. The plate is mounted on a motorized turntable which presents each cup in turn to a fixed point where a polyethylene tube dips into each specimen, removes an aliquot and introduces it into the system.

Proportioning Pump.—The proportioning pump and its associated tubing manifold provides the mechanism for moving fluid through the system. The amounts of fluid pumped through the system are determined by the inside diameter of the manifold tubing. Air bubbles are purposely introduced into the system for the purposes of segmenting the samples and to serve as a scrubber.

The tubing manifold is placed on a Bakelite platen of the proportioning pump in a parallel manner so that a set of chain driven rollers can move over the length of the tubes, compressing them against the platen. The rollers alternately compress and release the tubing, thus providing the pressure to push the fluid through the system and the suction to withdraw samples and reagents from adjacent bottles. The pump is operated at a fixed speed.

Dialyzer Module.—In most procedures used in the clinical chemistry laboratory, protein is removed by precipitation. In the autoanalyzer, it is removed by dialysis. The dialyzer module consists of two channels separated by a semipermeable membrane. As the protein-containing sample flows through one channel, chemical constituents of the sample are dialyzed across the membrane where they are picked up by a recipient stream and carried to subsequent modules and tubing. The protein is then discarded to the waste system.

Complete dialysis is not accomplished in the dialyzer module. It is, however, exposed for a sufficient period of time so that proportions of the constituents desired are dialyzed to the recipient stream. Standards and controls are subjected to the same conditions. Dialysis can be enhanced by adjusting the osmotic pressure on either side of the semipermeable membrane. The temperature of dialysis is controlled by placing the dialyzer in a 37°C. water bath.

Heating Bath.—Some of the methods require heat to complete a chemical reaction and/or a color development. The heating bath of the autoanalyzer consists of 40 feet of coiled glass tubing suspended in an oil bath which is kept at a constant temperature of 95° ± 0.5°C. The glass coil serves to delay the flow of sample so that it remains in the heated bath for approximately 5 to 8 minutes.

Some procedures, such as enzymatic reactions, require temperatures of 37°C., with greater time delays. Heating baths set at 37°C. are available, as well as double sets of coils to provide an additional time delay within the heating bath.

Colorimeter and Recorder.—The color developed or changed in the chemical reaction being performed is observed in a colorimeter equipped with a special cuvet or flow cell. The flow cell is designed to release the bubbles that have been segmenting the samples and to allow the sample to collect in a vertical collecting tube, then to flow horizontally through a 15-mm. tubular flowcell cuvet positioned in the optical system. The outflow from the flowcell is discarded to waste.

The optical system of the colorimeter is a double beam arrangement. The wavelength of light desired is selected by means of optical glass filters. The difference in electrical output of two photocells which look at each of the two light beams is recorded by a strip chart recorder. Thus, the colorimeter and recorder read and record the amount of light absorbed by each sample as it is presented to these modules. The record of the analysis consists of a series of peaks representing the individual samples. The direction of the peaks on the recorder paper is determined by the type of colorimetric procedure utilized.

Other Modules. Flame Photometer.—The flame photometer uses an internal standard for its method of analysis. A propane-oxygen flame is used and the sample stream is fed into the base of the flame through a capillary tube. The emitted light is observed by two photocells with appropriate filters: one for sodium and one for potassium. The photocells are connected to recorders. The lower portion of the sodium scale has been suppressed electronically and only the upper (approximately 100–160 meq. per liter) range is displayed on the recorder.

Chromatographic Controls.—A chromatographic column, circulating pump, flow meter, and programming mechanism are available for chromatographic separation of chemical substances and their subsequent analysis in the autoanalyzer system. The system provides a means of programming instructions for washing the column with various solutions and buffers and at the appropriate time feeds the effluent to the autoanalyzer system for colorimetric development. This system has been used for the chromatographic fractionation of amino acids.

Hemagglutination Module.—The hemagglutination module is used in conjunction with other modules of the basic autoanalyzer system. It provides a means of mixing blood cells and antisera, allowing them to react, and then separating the unreacted cells from the agglutinated cells by decantation in the module. The unreacted cells are then hemolyzed and assayed colorimetrically and serve as a measure of the agglutination reaction. This module permits the mass typing of blood cells and the performance of other hemagglutination procedures in large quantities.

Fluorometer.—A spectrofluorometer is available to replace the colorimeter and/or flame photometer in the autoanalyzer system. This module permits the automation of those procedures that depend upon fluorescence for their quantitative analysis.

Electrophoresis.—The electrophoresis module performs electrophoretic separation of proteins. The samples to be analyzed are mixed with 64 percent sucrose and then pumped into the electrophoresis cell. At the same time, a density gradient is prepared automatically by pumping sucrose solutions of various concentrations into the same cell. All the solutions enter the vertical cell at the same time. They are mixed and produce a steep density gradient. An electric current is applied to platinum electrodes within the electrolyte chamber, causing the proteins to separate electrophoretically. After approximately 15 minutes the visualization of proteins within the cell is accomplished by moving the cell in a vertical path through a beam of ultraviolet light which falls on a photomultiplier tube. The resulting output is fed to a recorder. The protein fractions are integrated automatically during the tracing.

METHODS

The autoanalyzer system of analysis is used extensively in the fields of biology and medicine, and in industrial laboratories and research laboratories as well. New methods are continually being recorded in current literature and it could be said that any analytical procedure which depends upon the colorimetric principle can be used on the autoanalyzer.

Most of the procedures that have been set up on the autoanalyzer have been for the determination of a single chemical substance. Some of the routine procedures in the clinical chemistry laboratory are requested together in certain groups. An example is the group of serum electrolytes, in which there are individual determinations of sodium, potassium, chloride, and carbon dioxide. Several procedures have been developed so that one or more substances can be analyzed simultaneously.

The procedures to be presented in the following paragraphs are those that are the most commonly requested in the clinical chemistry laboratory. (See Standard Methods of Chemical Analysis, Volume II.)

GLUCOSE

Reagents. 0.9 Percent Sodium Chloride.—(Add 0.5 ml. of Brij-35 to each liter prepared).

Alkaline Potassium Ferricyanide.—In a 1-liter volumetric flask place 9.0 g. of sodium chloride, add approximately 500 ml. of distilled water and dissolve. Grind 0.25 g. of potassium ferricyanide to a fine powder in a mortar, and transfer it to the volumetric flask by washing. Weigh out 20 g. of sodium carbonate, dissolve it in distilled water, and add it in small portions to the flask. Mix the contents of the flask to insure complete solution and dilute to volume. Filter through glass wool and store in an amber reagent bottle. Add 0.5 ml. Brij-35 to each liter just prior to use.

In this procedure one measures a loss of color of the potassium ferricyanide reagent baseline (inverse colorimetric technic). For a "point of reference," pump water through all the reagent lines, then adjust the recorder to read 98–100 percent transmission. Place the lines in the respective reagent bottles and plot a reagent base line. This should be 13 ± 3 percent transmission.

If the base line is higher than 16 percent transmission, add a stock solution of 5 percent potassium ferricyanide in 0.9 percent sodium chloride to the ferricyanide reagent. If the base line is lower than 10 percent transmission, dilute the ferricyanide reagent with 2 percent sodium carbonate in 0.9 percent sodium chloride. If the sensitivity of the procedure is too great, (250 mg. percent standard is higher than 80 percent transmission) change the saline diluent tube size to 0.100. If too low, increase sample tube size to 0.025.

Standards. *Stock Glucose* (10 *mg. per ml.*).—Place 20 g. anhydrous dextrose in a 2-liter volumetric flask and add benzoic acid solution with mixing to dissolve the dextrose. Dilute to volume with saturated benzoic acid solution.

Working Standards.—From the basic stock glucose standard, appropriate dilutions are made to represent the following concentrations of glucose: 50, 100, 150, 200, 250, 300 mg. per 100 ml.

Procedure.—The recorder and colorimeter are turned on and allowed to warm up for 15 minutes or longer. Place the glucose manifold (see Fig. 47-2) on the platen of the pump and make the necessary connections following either the flow diagram or a system of color-coded connections. Place the 420-mμ filters in their respective places on the reference and sample side of the glucose colorimeter. The choice of aperture for the reference side of the colorimeter will be selected after reagents are pumping through the system. A Number 5 aperture is a place to start.

Place the reagent lines in a bottle of distilled water. Lower the chain assembly, locking it into place, thus starting the proportioning pump. As the fluid begins to move through the system, check all connections for leakage, and check the tubes on the platen of the pump for "snaking."

The sample plate is prepared by placing the lowest glucose standard at the starting point of the plate. The remaining standards are then placed in ascending order, counterclockwise. A sample cup of distilled water is placed after the highest standard, and the first of the numbered cups containing unknowns is started. The unknowns are interspersed with a sample cup of water after every fourth unknown.

After water has been pumped through the flow cell, the chart drive of the recorder is turned on and the pen adjusted to 100 percent on the chart paper. This is done by varying the 100 percent control on the colorimeter, and perhaps selecting either a larger or smaller aperture to keep the setting of this control above 500.

Referring to the flow diagram (Fig. 47-2) or a color coding system, place the diluent line into the reagent bottle containing 0.9 percent sodium chloride. The second reagent line is placed in a reagent bottle of potassium ferricyanide solution. The polyethylene sample line is allowed to remain in distilled water.

After the reagents have pumped through the system, a base line of reagents will be recorded on the recorder. This base line should lie somewhere between 10 and 16 percent transmission on the recorder charts. Adjustments of color intensity are given under the preparation of the ferricyanide reagent.

The sample line is removed from the water bottle and threaded through the metal crook of the sampler unit and allowed to extend approximately 1 inch beyond its tip. The arrow of the locking plate is set to point at the last sample and the plate locked into position. The sample module power switch is turned on and the action of the crook is observed as the polyethylene line dips into the first sample. The tube is adjusted just to clear the bottom of the sample cup.

At the end of approximately 10 minutes, the first standard will reach the colorimeter and its value will be recorded on the strip chart. The values are read from the strip chart and a calibration curve prepared by plotting the readings and concentrations on semilog paper. From the curve thus prepared, each unknown is read and recorded. The water samples interspersed among the unknowns serve to aid in identification of the unknowns. Recordings of glucose values above or equal to the highest standard are repeated by making an appropriate dilution.

With the conclusion of the analysis the sampler plate is turned off and the sample line and reagent lines are removed and replaced in the bottle of distilled water, which is then pumped through the system for 5 to 10 minutes. The sample cups and samples are discarded and the instrument may be turned off if no further determinations are to be performed, or prepared for the next analysis. The manifold should always be removed to avoid overstretching the Tygon tubing on the pump.

Procedural Notes.—Using the flow diagram (Fig. 47-2) and the 15 mm. tubular flow

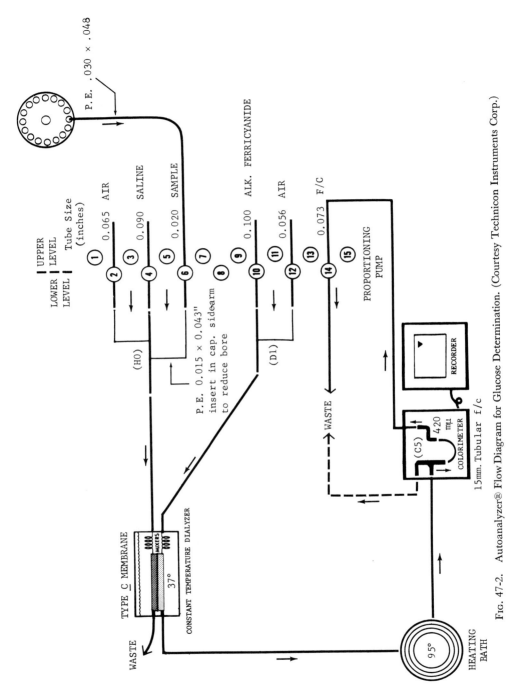

Fig. 47-2.　Autoanalyzer® Flow Diagram for Glucose Determination. (Courtesy Technicon Instruments Corp.)

cell colorimeter, the determinations can be run at 60 per hour. Glucose can be determined in serum, plasma, or whole blood which has been carefully collected with an anticoagulant (such as oxalate-fluoride mixture).

The sensitivity of the procedure can be increased by increasing the size of the sample or decreasing the flow rate of the ferricyanide reagent. These are done by altering the size of the manifold tubing. A further increase in sensitivity can be realized by lengthening the stay within the dialyzer by adding a second set of dialyzer plates. The sensitivity can be decreased by increasing the flow rate of the diluent or increasing the ferricyanide flow rate.

Normal Values.

Whole blood:	60–100 mg. per 100 ml.
Plasma or serum:	65–110 mg. per 100 ml.
Cerebrospinal fluid:	50–75 mg. per 100 ml.

ACID PHOSPHATASE

Reagents. **Acid Buffer, pH 4.8.**—Place 42 g. citric acid in a 1-liter volumetric flask and add 400 ml. of normal sodium hydroxide. Add distilled water to the 1 liter mark. Shake until dissolved. Check the pH of the solution which should be 4.8 ± 0.05 units.

Substrate Solution.—Place 3.0 g. phenyl disodium phosphate (phenol free) in a 250-ml. volumetric flask. Dilute to volume with distilled water and mix until dissolved. This solution should be stored in the refrigerator and previously warmed to room temperature before using.

Sodium Hydroxide Solution 0.37 M.

Buffered Aminoantipyrine.—Place 15 g. 4-aminoantipyrine, 30 g. sodium carbonate and 30 g. sodium bicarbonate in a 1-liter volumetric flask. Add about 500 ml. of distilled water and mix until dissolved. Dilute to volume, mix, and filter.

Buffered Potassium Ferricyanide.—Place 40 g. potassium ferricyanide, 30 g. sodium carbonate, and 30 g. sodium bicarbonate in a 1-liter volumetric flask. Add about 500 ml. of distilled water and mix until dissolved. Dilute to volume, mix, and filter.

Stock Phenol Standard (1 mg. phenol per ml.).—Weigh out 1.0 g. phenol, place in a 1-liter volumetric flask, and add about 500 ml. 0.1 N hydrochloric acid. Mix until the phenol goes completely into solution and then dilute to volume.

Note.—The concentration of the stock phenol should be checked as follows: Transfer 25 ml. of this solution to a 250-ml. volumetric flask, add 50 ml. of 0.1 N sodium hydroxide and heat to 65°C. To this hot solution add 25 ml. of 0.1 N iodine solution. Stopper the flask and allow it to stand at room temperature for 30 to 40 minutes. Add 5 ml. of concentrated hydrochloric acid. Titrate the excess of iodine with 0.1 N sodium thiosulfate solution. Each ml. of 0.1 N iodine (ml. iodine added, minus ml. of thiosulfate used in titration) corresponds to 1.567 mg. of phenol. On the basis of the titration, adjust the phenol solution, so that 1 ml. contains 1 mg. of phenol. This stock standard phenol solution is used in the preparation of the working phenol standards.

Working Phenol Standards.—Dilute the stock with 0.005 N hydrochloric acid in order to prepare working standards that will have a shelf life of at least two months.

ml. of Stock	Diluted to	μg. phenol per ml.
5	500 ml.	10
10	500 ml.	20
20	500 ml.	40
30	500 ml.	60
40	500 ml.	80
50	500 ml.	100

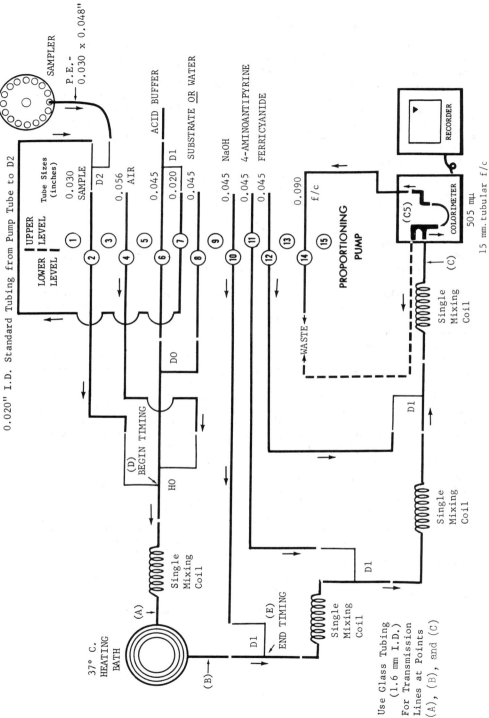

Fig. 47-3. Autoanalyzer® Flow Diagram for Acid Phosphatase Determination. (Courtesy Technicon Instruments Corp.)

Procedure.—This method is a modification of the King-Armstrong (K-A) technique for acid phosphatase. It is based on the hydrolysis of the substrate phenyl disodium phosphate by the action of the acid phosphatase enzyme in serum at pH 5.0. In the K-A modification the phenolic products are measured. This particular adaptation measures the phenol by rapid condensation with 4-aminoantipyrine followed by oxidation with potassium ferricyanide under alkaline conditions. The red colored solution that is formed is measured at 505 mμ in a 15-mm. flowcell. The colorimetric reaction can be carried out in the presence of protein at room temperature. Each sample is run twice: once *with* substrate (assay specimen) and once *without* substrate (control specimen); the former is for the assay of enzyme activity while the latter serves as the control.

The flow diagram (Fig. 47-3) gives the necessary information as to the manifold construction and connections between modules. Details of actual operation of a typical procedure are given under the method for glucose determination.

Operating Procedure Notes.—The acid phosphatase procedure can be run at 60 determinations per hour.

Determination of Incubation Time.—In order to calculate the King-Armstrong Unit values it is necessary to determine the incubation time of the manifold.

A stop watch or watch with a sweep second hand is used.

Begin by pumping all reagents that are used for determining the controls. After five minutes, temporarily introduce some potassium ferricyanide into the water line. (This can be done by placing the water line into a beaker of potassium ferricyanide.) Observe the movement of the yellow potassium ferricyanide reagent.

When it reaches the point in the HO fitting where the sample is added (point D in the flow diagram) begin timing. When you notice the yellow potassium ferricyanide mixing with the sodium hydroxide reagent (point E), stop timing, and note minutes and seconds. Convert seconds into tenths of a minute by dividing seconds by six.

Express time in minutes to the nearest tenth, (*e.g.*, 10 minutes 30 seconds equals 10.5 minutes). The time obtained is the incubation time for your specimens and is a constant for the 37°C. incubation bath and manifold, being used for this day's run. It is necessary to determine the incubation time each day acid phosphatase is to be run.

Operating Sequence.—Place serum samples (control specimens) followed by phenol standards on sample tray and run, using acid buffer and water as the diluent (no substrate). The phenol standards are placed after the serum controls to eliminate contamination of the specimens with free phenol. The control specimen value represents phenolic substances present in the serum which must be subtracted from the assay value.

Substitute substrate solution for the water in the diluent stream and place sample tube in distilled water. When the new reagent baseline is recorded it should be no lower than 95 percent transmission *vs.* the acid buffer–water baseline at 100 percent transmission. If it is lower, discard the substrate solution since it has decomposed and contains free phenol and prepare fresh reagent. If the baseline is within the tolerance described, adjust to 100 percent transmission and re-analyze the serum samples (assay specimens) for enzyme activity.

It is not necessary to repeat the phenol standards since the calibration curve is identical with acid buffer–water or acid buffer–substrate solution.

Calculation of King-Armstrong Units.—The control and assay specimens are calculated as μg. of phenol per ml. from the standard curve and the results are substituted into the following formula:

$$\text{K-A units/100 ml.} = \frac{60 \times \mu\text{g. phenol/ml. (assay-control)}}{t \times 10}$$

where: t = incubation time in minutes to nearest tenth;
        60 = factor to convert to manual incubation time; and
        10 = factor to convert μg. phenol/ml. to mg. phenol/100 ml.

Example.

Assay = 15 μg. phenol/ml.; Control = 10 μg. phenol/ml.
t = 11.6 minutes

$$\text{K-A Units}/100 \text{ ml.} = \frac{60 \times (15 - 10)}{11.6 \times 10}$$

$$= 5.17 \times 0.5$$
$$= 2.6$$

The manifold incorporates a differential sampling technique which permits the sample pump tube to be continuously washed during operation. This effectively minimizes free phenol contamination of the pump tube.

Use $\frac{1}{8}$ inch I.D. Tygon as waste tubing from the colorimeter debubbler T to the drain to reduce "surging" of fluid from the heating bath.

Normal Value.

0–4 King-Armstrong Units.

ALKALINE PHOSPHATASE

Reagents. Alkaline Control Buffer.—Place 1.58 g. anhydrous sodium carbonate in a 1-liter volumetric flask; add approximately 500 ml. of distilled water; and shake until dissolved. Add 0.84 g. sodium bicarbonate to the flask and shake until completely dissolved, and dilute to volume. Filter through a suitable material.

NOTE.—Check the pH of the solution using a pH meter. The pH should be 10.0 ± 0.05 units.

Alkaline Buffer Substrate.—Place 2.0 g. phenyl disodium phosphate (phenol-free) in a 1-liter volumetric flask. Add approximately 500 ml. of alkaline control buffer, shake until all the phenyl disodium phosphate goes into solution. Dilute to volume with alkaline control buffer. Filter through a suitable material.

NOTE.—Check the pH of the solution with a pH meter. The pH should be 10.0 ± 0.05 units. This solution should be stored in the refrigerator and previously warmed to room temperature before using.

4-Aminoantipyrine.—Place 1.0 g. 4-aminoantipyrine in a 1-liter volumetric flask; add approximately 500 ml. of distilled water and shake until dissolved. Dilute to volume with water. Filter through a suitable material.

Stock Phenol Standard (1 mg. phenol per ml.).—Weigh out 1.0 g. phenol, place in a 1-liter volumetric flask, and add about 500 ml. 0.1 N hydrochloric acid. Mix until the phenol goes completely into solution and then dilute to volume.

NOTE.—The concentration of the stock phenol should be checked as follows: Transfer 25 ml. of this solution to a 250-ml. volumetric flask, add 50 ml. of 0.1 N sodium hydroxide and heat to 65°C. To this hot solution add 25 ml. of 0.1 N iodine solution. Stopper the flask and allow it to stand at room temperature for 30 to 40 minutes. Add 5 ml. of concentrated hydrochloric acid. Titrate the excess of iodine with 0.1 N sodium thiosulfate solution. Each ml. of 0.1 N iodine (ml. iodine added, minus ml. of thiosulfate used in titration) corresponds to 1.567 mg. of phenol. On the basis of the titration, adjust the phenol solution, so that 1 ml. contains 1 mg. of phenol. This stock standard phenol solution is used in the preparation of the working phenol standards.

Working Phenol Standards.—Dilute the stock with 0.005 N hydrochloric acid in order to prepare working standards that will have a shelf life of at least two months.

ml. of Stock	Diluted to	µg. phenol per ml.
5	500 ml.	10
10	500 ml.	20
20	500 ml.	40
30	500 ml.	60
40	500 ml.	80
50	500 ml.	100
75	500 ml.	150
100	500 ml.	200

Procedure.—This method is based on the hydrolysis of the substrate phenyl disodium phosphate by the action of the alkaline phosphatase enzyme in serum. In the K-A modifications, the phenolic products are measured; whereas in the Bodansky methods, the inorganic phosphate is measured.

This particular modification (Powell and Smith of Kind and King) measures the phenol by rapid condensation with 4-aminoantipyrine followed by oxidation with alkaline potassium ferricyanide to give a red product. This is measured colorimetrically at 505 mµ in a 15-mm. flowcell. The reaction can be carried out in the presence of protein at room temperature. Each sample is run twice: once with substrate (assay specimen) and once without substrate (control specimen). The former is for assay of enzyme activity, while the latter serves as the control specimen.

The flow diagram (Fig. 47-4) gives the necessary information as to the manifold construction and connections between modules. Details of actual operation of a typical procedure are given under the method for glucose determination.

Operational Notes.—The alkaline phosphatase procedure can be run at 60 determinations per hour.

Determination of Incubation Time.—In order to calculate the King-Armstrong Unit values it is necessary to determine the incubation time of the manifold. A stop watch or watch with a sweep second hand is used. Begin by pumping all reagents that are used for determining the controls. After 5 minutes, temporarily introduce some potassium ferricyanide reagent into the buffer-substrate line. (This can be done by placing the buffer-substrate reagent line into a beaker of potassium ferricyanide.) Observe the movement of the yellow potassium ferricyanide reagent. When it reaches the point in the HO fitting where the sample is added (point D on the flow diagram), begin timing. When you notice the yellow potassium ferricyanide mixing with the potassium ferricyanide reagent (point E) stop timing, and note minutes and seconds. Convert seconds into tenths of a minute by dividing seconds by six.

Express time in minutes to the nearest tenth (*e.g.*, 6 minutes 30 seconds equals 6.5 minutes). The time obtained is the incubation time for your specimens, and is a constant for the 37°C. incubation bath and manifold being used for this day's run. It is necessary to determine the incubation time each day alkaline phosphatase is to be run.

Operating Sequence.—Place serum samples (control specimens) followed by phenol standards on sample tray and run using alkaline control buffer (without substrate) as diluent. The phenol standards are placed after the serum controls to eliminate contamination of the specimens with free phenol. The control specimen value represents phenolic substances present in the serum which must be subtracted from the assay value.

Substitute alkaline buffer-substrate as diluent and place sample tube in distilled water. When the new reagent baseline is recorded, it should be no lower than 95 percent transmission *vs.* the control buffer baseline at 100 percent transmission. If it is lower, discard

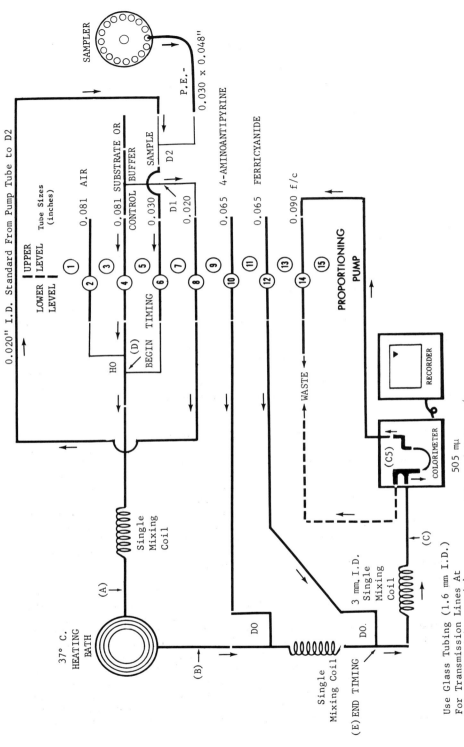

FIG. 47-4. Autoanalyzer® Flow Diagram for Alkaline Phosphatase Determination. (Courtesy Technicon Instruments Corp.)

the buffer-substrate, since it has decomposed and contains free phenol, and prepare fresh reagent. If the baseline is within the tolerances described, adjust to 100 percent transmission and re-analyze the serum samples (assay) specimens for enzyme activity.

It is not necessary to repeat the phenol standards, since the calibration curve is identical with alkaline control buffer or buffer-substrate.

Calculation of King-Armstrong Units.—The control and assay specimens are calculated as μg. of phenol per ml. from the standard curve and the results are substituted into the following formula:

$$\text{K-A Units/100 ml.} = \frac{15 \times \mu\text{g. phenol/ml. (assay-control)}}{t \times 10}$$

where: t = incubation time in minutes to nearest tenth;
   15 = factor to convert to manual incubation time; and
   10 = factor to convert μg. phenol/ml. to mg. phenol/100 ml.

Example.

Assay = 100 μg. phenol/ml.; Control = 10 μg. phenol/ml.
t = 6.9 minutes

$$\text{K-A Units/100 ml.} = \frac{15 \times (100 - 10)}{6.9 \times 10}$$

$$= 2.8 \times 9$$
$$= 19.6$$

The manifold incorporates a differential sampling technique which permits the sample pump tube to be continuously washed during operation. This effectively minimizes free phenol contamination of the pump tube.

Use ⅛ inch I.D. Tygon as waste tubing from the colorimeter debubbler T to the drain to reduce "surging" of fluid from the heating bath.

Normal Value.
4 to 10 King-Armstrong Units.

BILIRUBIN

Reagents. **Control Hydrochloric Acid, 0.18 M.**
Methanol, 55 percent.
Sodium Nitrite.—Place 0.5 g. sodium nitrite in a 100-ml. volumetric flask. Dilute to mark with distilled water and mix well. Filter and bottle in 4-ounce amber bottle.

NOTE.—Store this solution in the refrigerator and prepare fresh each week. This solution is not stable.

Sulfanilic Acid.—Place 10 g. sulfanilic acid in a 1-liter volumetric flask and add 15 ml. concentrated hydrochloric acid. Mix well until the sulfanilic acid goes into solution. Add distilled water to the mark and mix well. Filter and bottle in 1-liter amber bottle.

Protein-Bilirubin Standards.—Prepare a solution of bilirubin (Eastman Organic Chemicals) in redistilled chloroform at a concentration of 100 mg. bilirubin per 100 ml. Transfer 25 ml. of bilirubin in chloroform standard to a 400-ml. beaker. Evaporate to near dryness by using a stream of air until there is no odor of chloroform. Immediately add 10 ml. of 0.1 N sodium hydroxide, swirl for 2 seconds and pour rapidly into 90 ml. of clear, unhemolyzed, bilirubin-negative serum while swirling. Adjust the pH to 7.4 with 1 N hydrochloric acid. Determine the total bilirubin value of the stock protein-

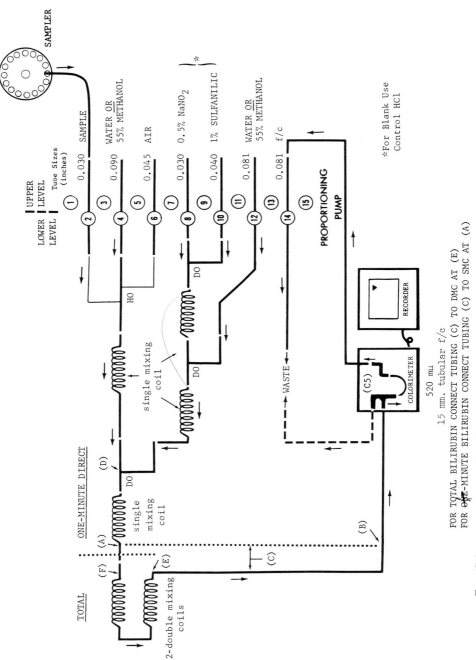

520 mu
15 mm. tubular f/c

FOR TOTAL BILIRUBIN CONNECT TUBING (C) TO DMC AT (E)
FOR ONE-MINUTE BILIRUBIN CONNECT TUBING (C) TO SMC AT (A)

FIG. 47-5. Autoanalyzer® Flow Diagram for Bilirubin Determination. (Courtesy Technicon Instruments Corp.)

bilirubin standard in triplicate by the method of Malloy and Evelyn. The stock protein-bilirubin standard may be kept several weeks frozen in small aliquots. From this stock prepare a series of working standards as desired. Make dilutions with water just prior to their being used. Once established, the standardization curve does not vary from day to day any appreciable amount for a given manifold and reagents. A few points on the curve should be checked daily with each run of samples.

Procedure.—The quantitative determination of bilirubin is based on the formation of the red-violet color of azobilirubin which forms when bilirubin reacts with diazotized sulfanilic acid. One-minute (direct-reacting) bilirubin is determined in an aqueous medium, while total bilirubin is measured in a methanolic reaction mixture.

A blank and assay series are run for both the one-minute (direct) bilirubin (aqueous medium) and total bilirubin (methanolic medium). Sample, air and reagent (water for direct bilirubin, 55 percent methanol for total bilirubin) are introduced and mixed. An aqueous or methanolic solution of diazotized sulfanilic acid is added to the diluted sample. After mixing and allowing time for color development, the color of the reaction mixture is measured at 520 mμ in a flowcell having a 15-mm. light path.

The flow diagram (Fig. 47-5) gives the necessary information as to the manifold construction and connections between modules. Details of actual operation of a typical procedure are given under the method for glucose determination.

Operational Notes.—The bilirubin procedure can be run at 60 determinations per hour.

Samples should be fresh, clear, non-hemolyzed, non-turbid sera. Bilirubin on standing may be altered by light, by chemical action and by enzymes.

Specimens whose bilirubin values are greater than the highest standard run should be diluted with water and redetermined. Since water is used as the diluent, the proteins slowly precipitate from the serum. In order to minimize the effect of protein precipitation, the specimen should be diluted just prior to running the analysis.

Operating sequence: One-minute direct bilirubin is determined using distilled water as diluent for serum (Line 4) and diluent for diazo reagent (Line 12). Connect single mixing coil (point A on flow diagram) to colorimeter debubbler (B) with sufficient length of transmission tubing (C) to give one minute time delay between addition of diluted diazo reagent (D) and entrance to colorimeter (B).

One-minute control specimens are analyzed using control hydrochloric acid in place of the nitrite (Line 8) and sulfanilic acid (Line 10) reagents. One-minute assay specimens are analyzed using the sodium nitrite and sulfanilic acid reagents through their respective lines.

Total bilirubin is determined using 55 percent methanol as diluent for serum (Line 4) and diluent for diazo reagent (Line 12). Connect transmission tubing (C) from colorimeter (B) to double mixing coil (E). Connect single mixing coil (A) to double mixing coil (F).

Total bilirubin control specimens and standards are analyzed using control hydrochloric acid in place of nitrite (Line 8) and sulfanilic (Line 10) reagents. Total bilirubin assay specimens and standards are analyzed using the sodium nitrite and sulfanilic acid reagents through their respective lines.

Calculations.—In general, the method of calculation is the same as ordinarily employed in classical manual methods. The control and assay series for the standards are run for total bilirubin. The percent transmission values obtained are converted to optical density (O.D.) values. The O.D. of the control is subtracted from the O.D. value of the corresponding assay determination of the standard. The optical density *difference* that is obtained *vs.* concentration is plotted on square section graph paper to give a calibration graph. For serum samples, the percent transmission values of the control and assay series are changed to optical density units. The control value is subtracted from the corresponding assay optical density value. The difference in optical densities obtained for the samples are converted to milligrams bilirubin per 100 ml. by reading the corresponding concentration from the calibration graph.

Optical density values may be obtained directly if optical density recorder paper is used.

Normal Values.

One minute—0.0 to 0.2 mg. per 100 ml.
Total   —0.2 to 0.8 mg. per 100 ml.

CALCIUM

Reagents. Hydrochloric Acid, 1 N.—Add 83 ml. concentrated hydrochloric acid to approximately 500 ml. water in a 1-liter volumetric flask. Dilute to volume and mix. Add 0.5 ml. Brij-35 and mix.

Cresolphthalein Complexone, 0.007 percent.—Place approximately 500 ml. of 1 N hydrochloric acid in a 1-liter volumetric flask. Add 0.070 g. of Cresolphthalein Complexone and mix until completely dissolved. Add 50 g. sodium acetate and mix until dissolved. Dilute to volume with 1 N hydrochloric acid and mix. Add 0.5 ml. Brij-35 and mix.

Base.—Place approximately 500 ml. of distilled water in a 1-liter volumetric flask. Add 0.5 g. potassium cyanide and mix until dissolved. Add 150 ml. diethylamine, dilute to volume and mix.

Stock Calcium Standard (50 mg. calcium per 100 ml.).—Weigh 1.250 g. calcium carbonate and transfer to a 1-liter volumetric flask. Add approximately 100 ml. of distilled water. Carefully add 7 ml. of concentrated hydrochloric acid and swirl flask until all of the calcium carbonate has been dissolved. Dilute to volume and mix.

Stock Magnesium Standard (100 mg. magnesium per 100 ml.).—Place approximately 500 ml. of distilled water in a 1-liter volumetric flask. Add 8.36 g. magnesium chloride and mix until dissolved. Dilute to volume and mix.

Working Calcium Standards (containing 2 mg. magnesium per 100 ml.).*— Dilute the stock standards with distilled water. Add 1 drop concentrated hydrochloric acid per 100 ml.

ml. Stock Calcium	+	ml. Stock Magnesium	Diluted to	mg./100 ml. Calcium	mg./100 ml. Magnesium
10		2	100 ml.	5.0	2
15		2	100 ml.	7.5	2
20		2	100 ml.	10.0	2
25		2	100 ml.	12.5	2
30		2	100 ml.	15.0	2

Procedure.—Calcium is dialyzed under acidic conditions into a recipient stream of Cresolphthalein Complexone solution. A colored complex between calcium and the dye is formed upon the addition of diethylamine, which alkalinizes the reaction mixture. The developed color is measured at 580 mμ in a flowcell with a 15-mm. light path.

The flow diagram (Fig. 47-6) gives the necessary information as to the manifold construction and connections between modules. Details of actual operation of a typical procedure are given under the method for glucose determination.

Operational Notes.—The calcium procedure can be run at 60 determinations per hour. Calcium can be determined in serum or heparinized plasma. Do not use EDTA,

* See Operational Notes.

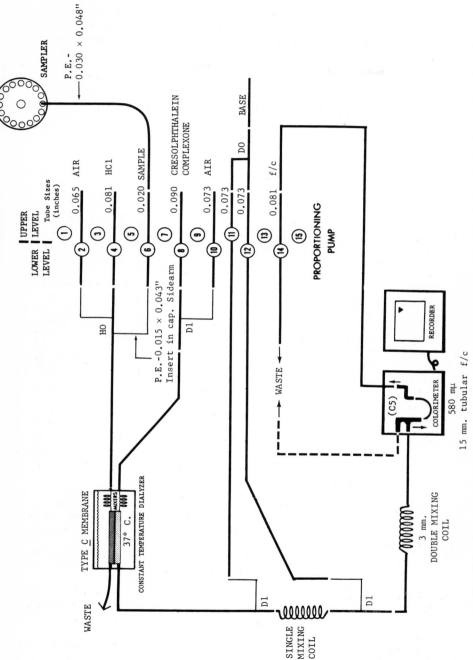

Fig. 47-6. Autoanalyzer® Flow Diagram for Calcium Determination. (Courtesy Technicon Instruments Corp.)

991

citrate, or oxalate as anticoagulant. Magnesium (2 mg. per 100 ml.) is added to the working calcium standards equivalent to the level normally present in serum. This compensates for the slight color reaction of the dye with magnesium. Urine may be analyzed directly, but abnormally high magnesium levels will result in a positive error. Precipitation of calcium with oxalate and analysis of the dissolved precipitate must be used in these cases. The reagent baseline must be set with water being aspirated through the sample line. With air through the sample line a higher percent transmission is recorded. Be sure to use 0.5 ml. of Brij-35 per liter of hydrochloric acid and Cresolphthalein Complexone Reagent to obtain good bubble patterns and low noise.

Normal Values.

9 to 11.5 mg. per 100 ml. (serum)
0.1 to 0.3 g. per 24 hours (urine)

CARBON DIOXIDE

Reagents. Acid Diluent.—Place approximately 500 ml. of distilled water in a 1-liter volumetric flask. Add 2.8 ml. concentrated sulfuric acid and mix. Add 1.0 ml. Dow Corning Antifoam B and dilute to volume with distilled water. Shake well before using.

Carbonate-Bicarbonate Buffer.—To 1 part 1 M sodium carbonate, add 2 parts 1 M sodium bicarbonate. Mix well. Place approximately 2.3 ml. of carbonate-bicarbonate buffer and approximately 0.8 ml. of 1.0 percent phenolphthalein in methyl alcohol in a 1-liter volumetric flask. Dilute to volume with carbon dioxide-free distilled water and mix well. This reagent should be protected from prolonged exposure to the carbon dioxide in air. The volume of carbonate-bicarbonate buffer will control the sensitivity of the reagent, while the volume of phenolphthalein is used to adjust the percent transmission of the reagent base line.

Sodium Carbonate Standards.—Dilute a 1 M stock sodium carbonate standard with distilled water to prepare working solutions containing 10 meq. per liter bicarbonate, 20 meq. per liter bicarbonate, 30 meq. per liter bicarbonate, and 40 meq. per liter bicarbonate.

Procedure.—The method determines carbonate, bicarbonate and physically dissolved carbon dioxide present in serum or plasma. A sample is aspirated, segmented with carbon dioxide-free air, then mixed with a stream of acid diluent containing an anti-foam reagent. The stream passes through mixing coils, where the released carbon dioxide enters the air phase. Emerging from the coils the stream feeds into a trap (liquid-gas separator), the liquid goes to waste and the gas phase containing carbon dioxide is aspirated. This gaseous stream now segments a weak alkaline buffer reagent stream containing an appropriate pH color indicator (phenolphthalein). The carbon dioxide is absorbed by the alkaline solution, causing a decrease in pH which is reflected by a change in color of the indicator. The indicator stream passes into a 15-mm. tubular flow cuvet where the color is measured at 550 mμ.

The flow diagram (Fig. 47-7) gives the necessary information as to the manifold construction and connections between modules. Details of actual operation of a typical procedure are given under the method for glucose determination.

Operational Notes.—The carbon dioxide procedure can be run at a speed of 60 specimens per hour. Carbon dioxide can be determined in serum and plasma. The method of handling the specimen will determine whether a carbon dioxide content or carbon dioxide combining power (saturation) is performed.

The standards are of a concentration range of 10 to 40 meq. of bicarbonate per liter. The standards should not be exposed to air longer than necessary as they will absorb

TOTAL CHOLESTEROL

Reagents. 0.05 percent Ferric Chloride in 95 percent Acetic Acid.

Color Reagent.—Place 1000 ml. of 0.05 percent ferric chloride reagent in a 2-liter Erlenmeyer flask. Add 150 ml. of concentrated sulfuric acid to the flask. Then swirl it gently and allow to stand until air bubbles leave solution. Add another 150 ml. in the same manner. Add 130 ml. in the same manner. Cap flask with aluminum foil and allow to cool. When reagent has cooled, transfer it to an amber glass reagent bottle. Reagent is stable for at least a month.

Isopropanol.—Reagent grade 99 percent isopropanol.

Cholesterol Standards. *Stock Standard (5 mg. cholesterol per ml.).*—Place 500 mg. cholesterol in a 100 ml. beaker. Add approximately 50 ml. isopropanol. Mix well and heat the isopropanol on a hot plate to put the cholesterol into solution. Cool and transfer the isopropanol-cholesterol solution to a 100 ml. volumetric flask. Rinse the beaker with isopropanol, transferring the rinsings to the flask. Dilute to mark with isopropanol. Bottle in 4-oz. amber bottle with foil lined cap.

Working Standards.—From stock standard prepare working standards containing concentrations of 10, 20, 30, 40, and 50 mg. cholesterol per 100 ml. using redistilled isopropanol. Bottle the dilute standards in 4-ounce amber bottles with foil lined caps.

Note.—These standards are based upon using a 1:10 isopropanol extract in the cholesterol determination. They then correspond to 100, 200, 300, 400, and 500 mg. cholesterol per 100 ml. when multiplied by a dilution factor of 10.

Manifold.—The cholesterol manifold has several features not found in the usual autoanalyzer manifold. It contains three types of pump tubing, a differential sampling system, and special pulse suppressors.

Tubing.—(a) Tygon—air line; (b) Acidflex tubing, a black tubing used for pumping and transmitting concentrated acid solutions; (c) Solvaflex, a yellow tubing used for pumping the sample and solvent wash.

Since Acidflex tubing has no shoulder, it is held in the endblock with double tapered nipples (N9). The free end of the nipple is then connected to glass fittings by means of a 1.5-inch length of 0.081-inch Acidflex.

The free end of the Acidflex connector is slipped directly over the glass fitting by first moistening the glass and then grasping the tubing with a cloth. Where 0.081-inch Acidflex tubing is used to sleeve a nipple to a glass fitting, the sleeving should be slipped over the nipple first.

Acidflex tubing is also used to make the connection between the manifold, heating bath, and colorimeter. It is essential to make the changes shown in the flow diagram before operating the manifold. The Acidflex connections have no effect on other determinations and should be left permanently in place.

Sample Pick Up.—The sample line in this manifold is constantly being washed by a small stream of isopropanol to prevent contamination between specimens. The actual amount of specimen aspirated from each sample cup is the differential between the sample line and the wash line:

0.056 sample line flow rate....................	1.1 ml./min.
0.035 wash line flow rate....................	0.4 ml./min.
Actual sample aspirated....................	0.7 ml./min.

The 50 percent milligram peak should fall between 20 and 30 percent transmission. If it does not reach this level, sensitivity can be increased by decreasing the wash pump tube one size.

Pulse Suppressors.—Because of the high viscosity of the cholesterol color reagent special "pulse suppressors" are used. (a) Air line—a length of 0.005-inch I.D. Tygon pump tubing; (b) Color reagent: two special glass pulse suppressors with a 1-mm. outlet constriction are connected to the outlet lines of the color reagent pump tubes.

Procedure.—This quantitative procedure for the determination of cholesterol is based on the reaction of concentrated sulfuric acid and ferric chloride in acetic acid with steroids having the 5-ene, 3B-ol grouping.

A 1:10 isopropanol extract of serum is prepared. An aliquot of this is then diluted with a segmented stream of a premixed color reagent containing sulfuric acid and 0.05 percent ferric chloride in acetic acid. After a second addition of reagent the mixture enters a 95°C. heating bath to develop the colored reaction product. The color is then measured at 520 mμ in a flowcell with a 15-mm. light path.

The flow diagram (Fig. 47-9) gives the necessary information as to the manifold construction and connections between modules. Details of actual operation of a typical procedure are given under the method for glucose determination.

Operational Notes.—The cholesterol procedure can be routinely run at 40 determinations per hour.

Preparation of Extract.—Add 4.5 ml. of 99 percent isopropanol (ACS Reagent grade) to a series of test tubes *via* an automatic buret. Blow 0.5 ml. of serum into the isopropanol and cap the tube. Mix immediately so as to produce a finely divided precipitate. Let stand for 5 minutes, then filter or centrifuge taking care not to lose solvent by evaporation. The supernatant extract is then stored in a stoppered tube until ready for use. For analysis, an unmeasured aliquot is placed in the polystyrene cups. When running a plate of samples, be sure to use the plastic cover plate to prevent evaporation. Smaller quantities of serum may be used, keeping the 1:10 ratio.

The use of the strongly acid color reagent requires several precautions:

a. The operator should wear glasses or safety goggles.
b. Be sure to have sufficient flow of water flushing out the waste sink to minimize the corrosive effects of the acids on the sink drains.
c. Never use the high pump speed with a two speed pump. Do not stop pump rollers on tubing as they will distort on standing.
d. Always pump water through manifold for five minutes prior to operation. During this time check for leaks, pressure build up, pinched tubing, and poor connections.
e. Following water rinse, allow air to flush through system until no segmented liquid stream is present in the mixing coil. This will prevent acid mixing with water and generating excessive heat and pressure.
f. Run color reagent through system. Also run isopropanol through wash line and sample pick up to establish baseline.
g. At the end of the run remove the glass aspirating line from the color reagent by gently pulling it through a wad of paper towels. Handle carefully; it may spatter acid. Also remove line from isopropanol.
h. Allow air to flush through system until no segmented stream appears in the mixing coil. Then flush water through system for at least 7 minutes.

In the event of a nipple connection leaking during a run, immediately stop pump by cutting power. With a hemostat clamp off the Solvaflex connection between the 0.056 sample line and the HO fitting (point a on flow diagram). Then transfer reagent lines to an empty beaker and release pump rollers, allowing reagent to flow back into beaker. When reagent stops flowing back disconnect line from heating bath inlet nipple and dip it into a beaker. Inspect manifold and reinsert leaking nipple being careful not to get acid on fingers. Then remove hemostat from point A and flush air through manifold. If

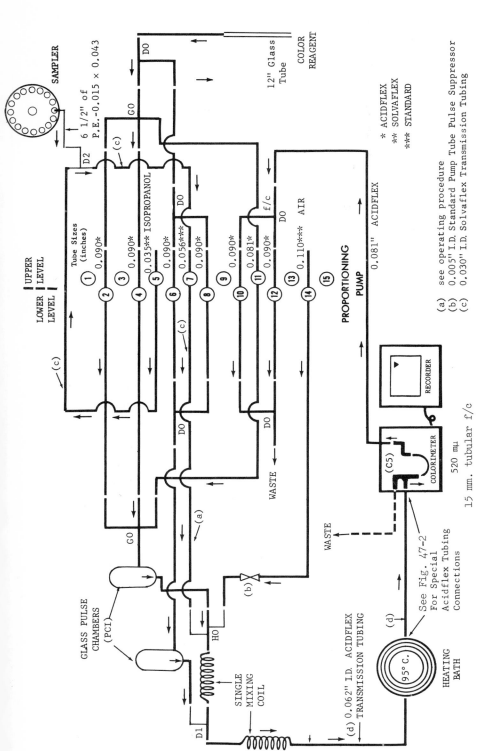

FIG. 47-9. Autoanalyzer® Flow Diagram for Total Cholesterol Determination. (Courtesy Technicon Instruments Corp.)

999

no further leaking occurs pump water through manifold for 5 minutes and follow with an air flush. Then reconnect to heating bath and continue air flush to remove color reagent in heating bath. Finally, repeat step d for 10 minutes before continuing run.

Normal Values.

150 to 250 mg. per 100 ml.

CREATININE

Reagents. **0.9 percent Saline.**—Add 0.5 ml. Brij-35 to each liter.

Sodium Hydroxide, 0.5 M.

Saturated Picric Acid.—To 13 g. of Reagent grade picric acid in a 1-liter volumetric flask add distilled water to the mark. Allow the excess picric acid to remain in contact with the water and shake occasionally. Filter and store in a polyethylene bottle.

Stock Creatinine Standard (1 mg. creatinine per ml.).—Weigh 1.00 g. creatinine, transfer to a 1-liter volumetric flask, and dissolve and dilute to volume with 0.1 N hydrochloric acid.

Working Creatinine Standards.—Dilute the stock creatinine standard with 0.1 N hydrochloric acid to produce working standards in the following concentrations: 1, 3, 5, 7, and 10 mg. creatinine per 100 ml.

Procedure.—The sample stream, segmented with air, is diluted with 0.9 percent sodium chloride. This combined stream enters the sample side of the dialyzer. The recipient stream consists of water segmented with air. After emerging from the dialyzer it is joined with a stream formed by a combination of saturated picric acid and 0.5 N sodium hydroxide. The streams are mixed, sent through a time delay coil and then into the Colorimeter. The developed color is read at 505 mμ using a 15-mm. tubular flow cuvet.

The flow diagram (Fig. 47-10) gives the necessary information as to the manifold construction and connections between modules. Details of actual operation of a typical procedure are given under the method for glucose determination.

Operational Notes.—The creatinine method can be run at 60 determinations per hour. The samples should consist of clear serum or urine. Lower values are experienced with whole blood and plasma.

Standards covering a range of 1 to 10 mg. creatinine per 100 ml. are adequate. Serum containing values of creatinine higher than this range should be diluted.

The 40-foot time delay coil used for color development should be immersed in a container of water at room temperature to protect against rapid fluctuations in ambient temperature.

When running the creatinine determination, a check should be made of the noise level. This can be done by continually aspirating a 5 mg. per 100 ml. creatinine standard. The noise level should be no greater than ±0.5 transmission line. If the noise level is greater, a check of the manifold and dialyzer should be made to insure that a good bubble pattern is being obtained. Noise is generally related to a poor bubble pattern, which gives poor proportioning of reagents.

For optimal bubble pattern and low noise, use 0.5 ml. of Brij-35 per liter of saline and distilled water recipient.

The noise with serum may sometimes be due to the formation of a precipitate. If this occurs, it is advisable to try a different lot of picric acid. It may also be helpful to clean the picric-sodium hydroxide lines and coils as well as the flow cell with 10 percent acetic acid.

Normal Values.

Serum—1.0 to 1.5 mg. per 100 ml.
Whole blood—1.0 to 2.0 mg. per 100 ml.
Urine—1.0 to 1.7 g. per 24 hours.

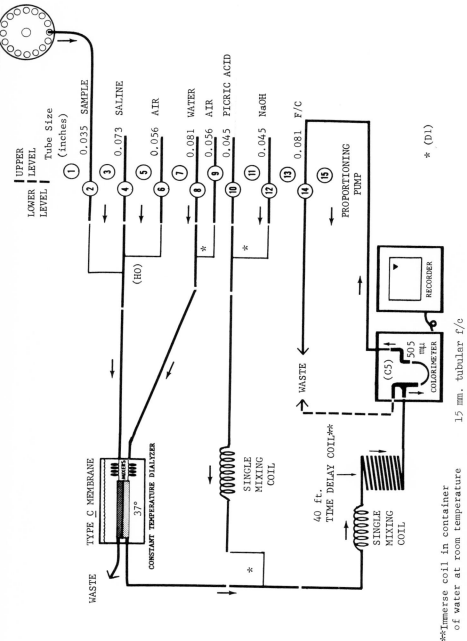

FIG. 47-10. Autoanalyzer® Flow Diagram for Creatinine Determination. (Courtesy Technicon Instruments Corp.)

**Immerse coil in container
of water at room temperature   15 mm. tubular f/c

1001

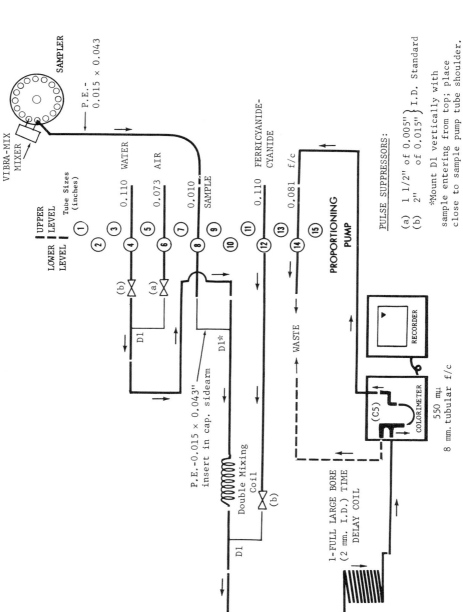

Fig. 47-11. Autoanalyzer® Flow Diagram for Hemoglobin Determination. (Courtesy Technicon Instruments Corp.)

HEMOGLOBIN

Reagents. Distilled Water Diluent.—Add 0.5 ml. Brij-35 per liter.

Ferricyanide-Cyanide.—Place 2.4 g. sodium bicarbonate, 2.4 g. potassium ferricyanide, and 0.3 g. potassium cyanide in a 1-liter volumetric flask. Add distilled water to the mark and mix until dissolved. Filter and transfer to amber glass reagent bottle. Date bottle.

NOTE.—This reagent slowly deteriorates and should be prepared fresh weekly.

Stock Standard.—Technicon Hemoglobin Standard, a stable aqueous solution prepared from blood, is recommended as a primary standard for the autoanalyzer hemoglobin determination. It is supplied in 5 ml. vials with the hemoglobin concentration (obtained by spectrophotometric analysis) indicated on the label.

Working Standards.—Prepare serial dilutions of the Hemoglobin Standard with 0.9 percent saline to establish a calibration curve as follows:

ml. of Stock	Diluted to	g.% Hemoglobin
2	5 ml.	0.4 × Stock g.%
3	5 ml.	0.6 × Stock g.%
4	5 ml.	0.8 × Stock g.%

Since optical density versus concentration is linear for this test, a mid-range working standard may be run with blood samples to re-establish the standard curve.

NOTE.—Store hemoglobin stock and working standards in the refrigerator to insure stability. Working standards are stable for at least two weeks.

Procedure.—The determination is based on the oxidation of hemoglobin to methemoglobin by potassium ferricyanide and subsequent conversion to cyanmethemoglobin by potassium cyanide. This technique will determine all forms of hemoglobin except sulf-hemoglobin. The manual procedure is described in Standard Methods of Clinical Chemistry, Volume II, page 52, Academic Press, New York, 1958.

In this automated procedure, mixed whole blood samples are aspirated. The samples are then diluted and red cells hemolyzed with an air-segmented stream of distilled water. Ferricyanide-cyanide reagent is then added, and the stream is passed through a time delay coil for color development. The color is measured at 550 mμ using an 8-mm. tubular flowcell.

The flow diagram (Fig. 47-11) gives the necessary information as to the manifold construction and connections between modules. Details of actual operation of a typical procedure are given under the method for glucose determination.

Operational Notes.—The hemoglobin procedure can be run at 60 determinations per hour. The whole blood specimens must be well mixed prior to aspiration by utilizing the Vibra-Mix accessory on the sampler module.

INORGANIC PHOSPHATE

Reagents. Aminonaphthol. *Stock Solution.*—Dissolve 150 g. sodium bisulfite ($NaHSO_3$) and 5.0 g. anhydrous sodium sulfite in about 800 ml. of distilled water. Heat to about 50°C. and then add 2.5 g. aminonaphthol (1-amino-2-naphthol-4-sulfonic acid), stirring until almost dissolved. Dilute to 1250 ml., filter, and store in an amber bottle.

Working Solution.—Dilute 100 ml. of stock solution to 1 liter with distilled water and filter. Add 0.5 ml. *Levor II* and mix.

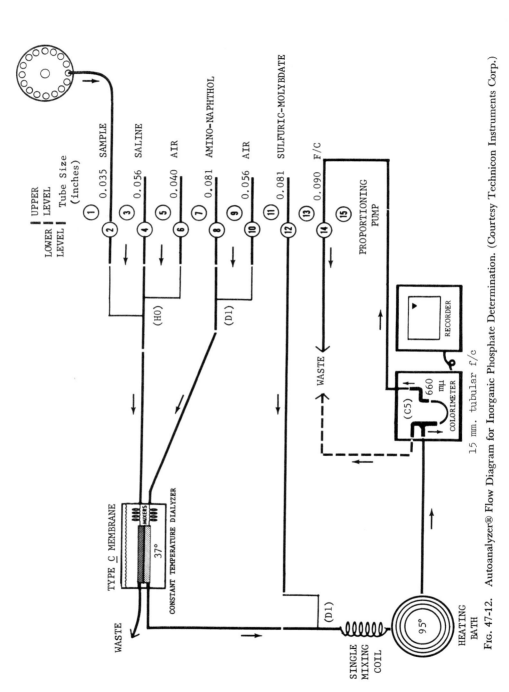

Fig. 47-12. Autoanalyzer® Flow Diagram for Inorganic Phosphate Determination. (Courtesy Technicon Instruments Corp.)

Note.—The working solution is stable at room temperature, for approximately two months, though there is a gradual increase in color. It is important to use a 1:10 dilution of the stock solution, otherwise the acidity of the test will be incorrect.

Sulfuric-Molybdate.—Place 7.5 g. ammonium molybdate in a 1-liter volumetric flask, add approximately 500 ml. of distilled water and dissolve. Slowly add 98.0 g. sulfuric acid (sp. gr. 1.84), mix well, and set aside to cool to room temperature. Dilute to volume with distilled water, and filter.

Phosphate Standards.—From a stock standard containing 1 mg. phosphate per ml., prepare working standards containing 1, 3, 5, and 7 mg. per 100 ml.

Procedure.—This method is a modification of the Fiske and Subbarow procedure, which is based upon the formation of phosphomolybdic acid which is reduced by 1-amino-2-naphthol-4-sulfonic acid.

This modification uses the reductant (1-amino-2-naphthol-4-sulfonic acid) as the recipient stream for the dialyzable phosphate. After dialysis, an acidic solution of ammonium molybdate is added, with the formation of phosphomolybdic acid, immediately followed by reduction. The reaction mixture is sent through the heating bath giving rise to a blue color, the optical density being proportional to the amount of phosphate present. The colored product is measured at 660 mμ in a tubular flow cuvet with a 15-mm. light path.

The flow diagram (Fig. 47-12) gives the necessary information as to the manifold construction and connections between modules. Details of actual operation of a typical procedure are given under the method for glucose determination.

Operational Notes.—The inorganic phosphate procedure can be run at 60 determinations per hour. Inorganic phosphate should be determined on unhemolyzed serum or plasma. Urinary phosphate can be determined on a diluted specimen (dilution approximately 1:5 to 1:10).

For optimal bubble pattern use 0.5 ml. of *Levor II* per liter of aminonaphthol working solution and per liter of saline.

Normal Values.

Adults—3 to 4.5 mg. per 100 ml. (serum).
Children—4 to 6 mg. per 100 ml. (serum).
Approximately 1.0 g. per 24 hours (urine).

TOTAL PROTEIN

Reagents. **Alkaline Iodide.**—Add 8 g. sodium hydroxide to approximately 800 ml. distilled water in a 1-liter volumetric flask. Stir until dissolved. Add 5 g. potassium iodide and stir until dissolved. Dilute to volume with distilled water, filter, and store in a 1-liter polyethylene bottle.

Biuret. *Stock Solution.*—To 45 g. of sodium potassium tartrate ($KNaC_4H_4O_6 \cdot 4H_2O$) in a 1-liter volumetric flask add 400 ml. of 0.2 N sodium hydroxide. Dissolve the tartrate and while stirring add 15 g. copper sulfate ($CuSO_4 \cdot 5H_2O$). Continue stirring until the copper sulfate is dissolved. Add 5 g. potassium iodide. Dissolve and dilute to 1 liter with 0.2 N sodium hydroxide. Filter and store in a polyethylene bottle.

Working Solution.—Dilute 200 ml. of stock biuret solution to 1 liter with Alkaline Iodide solution.

Blank Solution.—Dissolve 9 g. sodium potassium tartrate and dilute to 1 liter with Alkaline Iodide solution.

Note.—Use this reagent in place of working biuret reagent for determining blank values on serum samples. Readjust reagent baseline, determine grams percent protein equivalent blank from standard curve, and subtract from biuret value.

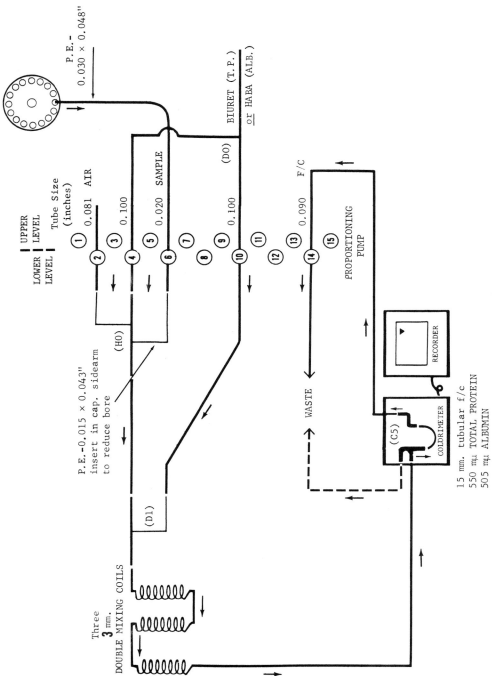

Fig. 47-13. Autoanalyzer® Flow Diagram for Total Protein and Albumin Determinations. (Courtesy Technicon Instruments Corp.)

Stock Protein Standard (10 g. protein per 100 ml.).—Protein used is crystalline Bovine Albumin, Fraction V from Armour Pharmaceutical Company, Kankakee, Illinois. To account for nonprotein material in the Bovine Albumin powder (*e.g.*, ash, moisture), the Kjeldahl nitrogen factor must be used to calculate the weight needed for a 10 gram percent protein standard. For example, Albumin lot no. 2706 has a nitrogen content of 155 mg. nitrogen per gram. The pure protein material has a nitrogen content of 160. Therefore, the weight of albumin to be used from this lot is:

$$10 \text{ g.} \times \frac{160}{155} = 10.32 \text{ g.}$$

In general, for 10 gram percent standard use:

$$10 \text{ g.} \times \frac{160}{\text{Kjeldahl N content on bottle label}}$$

Working Protein Standards.—Prepare working standards by diluting the stock protein solution with saline to the following concentrations: 2, 4, 6, 8, and 10 g. protein per 100 ml.

Place 0.5 ml. aliquots of the working standards in the polystyrene sample cups and cover with a polyethylene cap. Place in deep freeze for storage. For use, thaw immediately before running the test, taking care to mix the contents of the cup well.

Procedure.—This method is a modification of the biuret reaction as proposed by Weichselbaum. This reaction depends upon the formation of a purple colored complex of copper, in an alkaline solution, with two or more carbamyl groups (—CO—NH—), which are joined directly together or through a single atom of nitrogen or carbon.

The sample stream is diluted with an air-segmented stream of biuret reagent. The developed color is measured at 550 mμ using a flow cuvet with a 15-mm. light path.

The flow diagram (Fig. 47-13) gives the necessary information as to the manifold construction and connections between modules. Details of actual operation of a typical procedure are given under the method for glucose determination.

Operational Notes.—The total protein procedure can be run at 60 determinations per hour.

The samples should consist of nonhemolyzed sera or plasma. Turbid sera are not satisfactory without blank correction, as the turbidity will interfere with the colorimetric measurement.

For blank correction the serum samples are run using blank solution in place of biuret reagent, and the resultant blank value is subtracted from the biuret value.

When running the total protein procedure, a check should be made of the noise level. This is done by continually aspirating a 6 g. per 100 ml. standard. The noise level should be no greater than ±0.5 transmission line. The same manifold is used for both albumin and total protein. When changing from one procedure to another, merely wash manifold well with distilled water.

Normal Value.

6 to 8 g. per 100 ml.

ALBUMIN

Reagents. **Disodium EDTA-Sodium Chloride.**—Place 20 g. disodium EDTA in a 1000-ml. beaker. Add 800 ml. water and stir until the disodium EDTA goes into solution. Check the pH using a pH meter. The pH should be 5.0 ± 0.05. If adjustment is necessary, use either 1 M hydrochloric acid or 1 M sodium hydroxide. Add 100 g.

sodium chloride and stir until dissolved. Transfer to a 1-liter volumetric flask. Rinse beaker and transfer washings to the volumetric flask. Dilute to mark with water. Check that the pH is 5.0 ± 0.05, and filter.

HABA Dye. *Stock Solution (.0001 M).*—Dissolve 240 mg. 2-(4′hydroxyazobenzene) benzoic acid (HABA) in 970 ml. 0.01 M sodium hydroxide. Add 10 ml. of 37 percent neutral formalin and mix. Add sufficient 1 M acetate buffer pH 3.8 to adjust pH to 5.0 ± 0.05. Dilute to 1 liter with distilled water, and filter.

Working Solution.—Place 200 ml. of stock HABA in a liter volumetric flask. Add 100 ml. of disodium EDTA-sodium chloride and mix. Dilute to 1000 ml. with distilled water, and mix. Filter.

Note.—Check the pH of the solution using a pH meter. The pH should be 5.0 ± 0.05 units.

Blank Solution.—Dilute 100 ml. of disodium EDTA-sodium chloride reagent to 1 liter with distilled water.

Note.—Use this reagent in place of working HABA solution for determining blank values on serum samples. Readjust reagent baseline, determine grams percent albumin equivalent of blank from standard curve, and subtract from HABA value.

Stock Albumin Standard (10 g. albumin per 100 ml.).—Albumin used is crystalline Bovine Albumin, Fraction V from Armour Pharmaceutical Company, Kankakee, Illinois. To account for nonprotein material in the Bovine Albumin powder (*e.g.*, ash, moisture), the Kjeldahl nitrogen factor must be used to calculate the weight needed for a 10 gram percent standard.

For example, Albumin lot no. 2706 has a nitrogen content of 155 mg. nitrogen per g. The pure protein material has a nitrogen content of 160. Therefore, the weight of albumin to be used from this lot is:

$$10 \text{ g.} \times \frac{160}{155} = 10.32 \text{ g.}$$

In general, for 10 grams percent standard use:

$$10 \text{ g.} \times \frac{160}{\text{Kjeldahl nitrogen content on bottle label}}$$

Working Albumin Standards.—Dilute the stock albumin solution with *saline* to prepare standards of the following concentrations: 2, 4, 6 g. albumin per 100 ml. Place 0.5 ml. aliquots of the working standards in the polystyrene sample cups and cover with a polyethylene cap. Place in deep freeze for storage. For use, thaw immediately before running the test, taking care to mix the contents of the cup well.

Procedure.—A quantitative method for albumin based on its dye-binding capacity with 2-(4′-hydroxyazobenzene) benzoic acid has been proposed for the automation of serum albumin determinations.

The sample stream is diluted with an air-segmented stream of a buffered, stabilized dye solution. The color is measured at 505 mμ using a flow cuvet with a 15-mm. light path.

The flow diagram (Fig. 47-13) gives the necessary information as to the manifold construction and connections between modules. Details of actual operation of a typical procedure are given under the method for glucose determination.

Operational Notes.—The albumin procedure can be run at 60 determinations per hour. The samples should consist of non-hemolyzed sera or plasma. Turbid and icteric sera are not satisfactory without blank correction as they will give falsely elevated results.

For blank correction the serum samples are run using the blank reagent in place of HABA and the resultant blank value is subtracted from the HABA value.

When running the albumin procedure, a check should be made of the noise level. This is done by continually aspirating a 4 g. per 100 ml. standard. The noise level should be no greater than ±0.5 percent transmission.

The same manifold is used for both albumin and total protein. When changing from one procedure to another, merely wash manifold well with distilled water.

Normal Values.

3.5–5.0 g. per 100 ml. (serum).

SODIUM AND POTASSIUM

Reagents. **Lithium Nitrate.**—(125 meq. lithium nitrate per liter in 0.25 N sulfuric acid). Add 0.5 ml. of Brij-35 per liter.

Sodium-Potassium Standards are prepared by diluting appropriate stock solutions so as to provide the following concentrations:

meq. $Na^+/l.$	meq. $K^+/l.$
100	8
110	8
120	8
130	2
140	4
150	6
160	8

Procedure.—In this procedure the undiluted stream supplied by the sampler, merges with an air segmented stream of acid lithium nitrate diluent, mixes and enters the dialyzer. The dialyzed portion of the sample enters into an air segmented distilled water stream flowing through the lower half of the dialyzer. This segmented recipient stream enters a glass "T" where the segmenting air exits to waste, and the solid stream enters the burner.

On the two-channel module sodium and potassium are determined simultaneously from the same sample. On the one channel module sodium and potassium are run separately and in sequence. The proportioning pump automatically makes the correct dilution with lithium which serves as an internal standard. Two light-sensitive cells, located in a detector assembly, measure sodium or potassium on one side, lithium on the other, and their ratio is charted on the recorder.

The flow diagram (Fig. 47-14) gives the necessary information as to the manifold construction and connection between modules. Details of actual operation of a typical procedure are given under the method for glucose determination.

Operational Notes.—The procedure for sodium and potassium in biological specimens can be run at 40 determinations per hour. The standards range from 100 to 160 meq. sodium per liter and 2 to 8 meq. potassium per liter. The potassium and sodium standards are mixed together. The various combinations do not influence each other. There is a definite order of preference for running the standards. It is as follows:

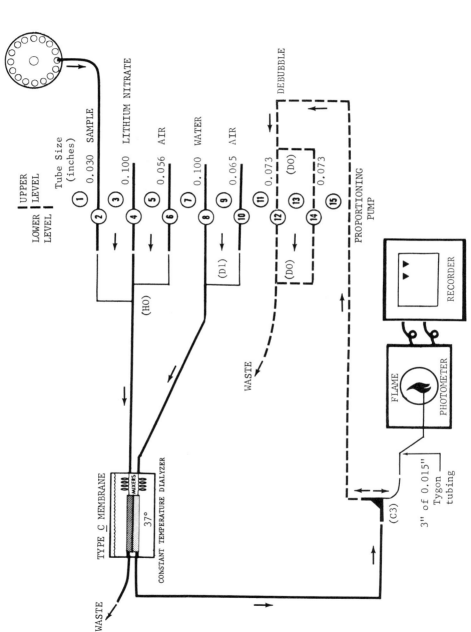

Fig. 47-14. Autoanalyzer® Flow Diagram for Sodium and Potassium Determination. (Courtesy Technicon Instruments Corp.)

1010

Fill the first three sampler cups with 160 meq. sodium per liter + 8 meq. potassium per liter standard. The next seven cups (in sequence) as follows:

$$100 \text{ meq. Na}^+ \text{ per liter} + 8 \text{ meq. K}^+ \text{ per liter}$$

110	"	"	"	"	8	"	"	"	"
120	"	"	"	"	8	"	"	"	"
130	"	"	"	"	2	"	"	"	"
140	"	"	"	"	4	"	"	"	"
150	"	"	"	"	6	"	"	"	"
160	"	"	"	"	8	"	"	"	"

Put a 140-meq. sodium per liter + 4-meq. potassium per liter standard in every 10th cup, then fill the remaining cups with unknowns to be analyzed.

NOTE.—*Do not leave a blank space in sampler.* Always fill with a standard.

Whether running a continuous sample or sampling repetitively, the 160-meq. sodium per liter or the 8-meq. potassium per liter standard should be positioned between 90–95 percent on the recorder scale. This will give proper sensitivity and range for both procedures.

If for experimental purposes it is necessary to run sodium levels lower than 100 meq. per liter, use the sodium filters and the K position on the control panel. Adjust the highest standard used to read 99 percent on the scale. This will give proper range and sensitivity.

Noise level on both sodium and potassium should not exceed ±0.75 lines. Noise greater than this may be due to: a) worn manifold, b) aged membrane, c) dirty or uncentered capillary, d) improper flow into capillary.

Sodium is reproducible ±1 meq. sodium per liter while the potassium is reproducible ±0.1 meq. potassium per liter.

Normal Values.

Sodium: 135 to 142 meq. per liter.
Potassium: 4.5 to 5.5 meq. per liter.

SERUM GLUTAMIC-OXALACETIC TRANSAMINASE (SGOT)

Reagents. Substrate.—Add approximately 800 ml. of distilled water to a 1-liter beaker. Place beaker on a magnetic mixer. Then, slowly add 33.5 g. dipotassium hydrogen phosphate (K_2HPO_4) and mix until in solution. Leave stirrer on until all chemicals are in solution. Add 1.0 g. monopotassium dihydrogen phosphate (KH_2PO_4) and dissolve thoroughly. Add 2.66 g. L-aspartic acid and dissolve thoroughly. Add 0.731 g. alpha-ketoglutaric acid and dissolve thoroughly. Add 1.0 g. tetrasodium EDTA and dissolve thoroughly. Add 10 g. polyvinylpyrrolidone and dissolve thoroughly.

Check pH of solution. The pH should be 7.40. If necessary, adjust to pH 7.40 with 0.1 M sodium hydroxide or 0.1 M hydrochloric acid. Transfer contents of beaker to 1-liter volumetric flask. Rinse beaker with distilled water and add washings to flask. Bring volume up to mark with distilled water. Mix.

Filter substrate and transfer to a polyethylene bottle. Add 0.5 ml. of chloroform and store in refrigerator. Immediately before using add 1 ml. of Triton X-405 per liter of substrate. Mix well. Solution should be warmed to room temperature before using.

Control Buffer.—Add approximately 800 ml. of distilled water to a 1-liter beaker. Place beaker on a magnetic mixer. Then slowly add 28.6 g. dipotassium hydrogen phosphate (K_2HPO_4) and mix until in solution. Leave stirrer on until all chemicals are in solution. Add 4.9 g. monopotassium dihydrogen phosphate (KH_2PO_4) and dissolve thoroughly. Add 1.0 g. tetrasodium EDTA and dissolve thoroughly. Add 10 g. polyvinylpyrrolidone and dissolve thoroughly. Check pH of solution. The pH should be 7.40. If necessary, adjust to pH 7.40 with 0.1 M sodium hydroxide or 0.1 M hydrochloric acid.

Transfer contents of beaker to a 1-liter volumetric flask. Rinse beaker with distilled water and add washings to flask. Bring volume up to mark with distilled water. Mix. Filter and transfer to a polyethylene bottle. Add 0.5 ml. of chloroform and store in refrigerator. Immediately before using add 1 ml. of Triton X-405 per liter control buffer. Mix well.

SGOT Dye.—To 1000 ml. of 0.01 M hydrochloric acid in a 1-liter mixing cylinder add 1 ml. of Triton X-405. Mix well. Add 1.5 g. 6-benzamido-4-methoxy-m-toluidine diazonium chloride (Azoene Fast Violet B-Alliance Color and Chemical Co.) dye to solution and mix until dye is thoroughly dissolved. Immediately filter and transfer solution to a 1-liter amber bottle. Store in refrigerator. Solution is stable under refrigeration for at least a week. If it turns pink, discard. Before using dye solution, shake well. Keep dye bottle in an ice water bath during determination.

Standards.—The determination is standardized with a serum of high enzyme activity. A frozen serum pool or a lyophilized serum control, such as Versatol-E, is used with appropriate dilutions.

Example.—A Versatol-E with a label value of 332 Reitman-Frankel units is reconstituted according to the manufacturer's instructions. Dilutions are prepared with 0.9 percent saline.

ml. of Versatol-E	+	ml. of Saline	Reitman-Frankel Units
0.1		0.9	33
0.2		0.8	66
0.3		0.7	100
0.4		0.6	133
0.5		0.5	166
1.0		0	332

Measurements should be made with 1-ml. graduated pipets. For convenience, dilutions can be prepared in sample cups. The cups can be sealed with polyethylene caps for mixing by inversion.

Procedure.—The method is based on the procedure of A. L. Babson, *et al.* The oxalacetic acid produced by the action of the enzyme is reacted with a diazonium salt, 6-benzamido-4-methoxy-m-toluidine diazonium chloride (Azoene Fast Violet B).

Serum samples are incubated in a 37°C. heating bath coil and then mixed with dye. Color is developed in a 37°C. heating bath coil and the product is read at 550 mμ in a 15-mm. flowcell. Each sample is run twice: once with substrate (assay specimen) and once without substrate (control specimen).

The flow diagram (Fig. 47-15) gives the necessary information as to the manifold construction and connections between modules. Details of actual operation of a typical procedure are given under the method for glucose determination.

Operational Notes.—The SGOT determination can be run at the rate of 40 determinations per hour. Before beginning run, be sure that tap water is flowing through the jacketed mixing coil between the 37°C. heating bath and the colorimeter.

Begin by aspirating substrate for 8 minutes while pumping water through the dye and sample lines. Then switch dye line to dye. When substrate-dye mixture reaches colorimeter, set baseline to 99 percent transmission and run assay specimens.

At the end of the assay run, place sample line in water. Switch substrate line to control buffer. Allow five minutes before running control specimens. The baseline will shift

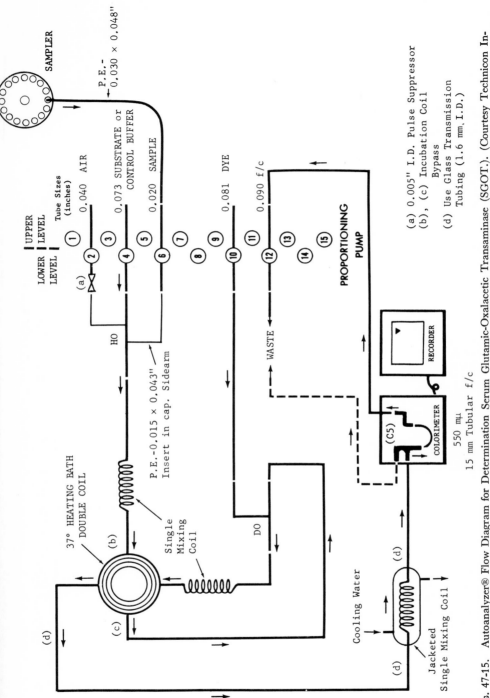

FIG. 47-15. Autoanalyzer® Flow Diagram for Determination Serum Glutamic-Oxalacetic Transaminase (SGOT). (Courtesy Technicon Instruments Corp.)

1013

towards 100 percent transmission with control buffer, so baseline must be readjusted to 99 percent transmission.

Calculation of Results.—The assay and control percent transmission values for the standards and specimens are converted to optical density. The control optical density is subtracted from the assay optical density to give the corrected optical density (O.D.). The corrected O.D. of the standards are plotted *vs.* their Reitman-Frankel units, and corrected O.D. of the specimens are read from this curve.

Control values for normal sera will generally be equivalent to 6 or 7 Reitman-Frankel units. The user may find it convenient to determine an average control value for normal sera and subtract it from the assay value. Control values should be run on the standards and on hemolyzed and icteric sera.

During the determination a small amount of dye may deposit on the walls of the tubular flowcell. This can be removed by flushing system with Ferric Alum reagent for five minutes (see Reagents under method for urea nitrogen). First bypass incubation heating bath at points (b) and (c) on flow diagram and remove substrate line from liquid. Then pump Ferric Alum reagent through dye line, followed by a water bath.

Normal Values.

8–40 units per ml. serum.

UREA NITROGEN

Reagents. 0.9 percent Sodium Chloride.—Add 0.5 ml. Brij-35 to each liter prepared.

Ferric Alum-Acid.—Dissolve 5.0 g. ferric ammonium sulfate $(FeNH_4(SO_4)_2 \cdot 12H_2O)$ in 500 ml. of distilled water in a 2-liter Erlenmeyer flask. Place the flask in an icewater bath and add 500 ml. 85 percent orthophosphoric acid and mix. While mixing, slowly add to the contents of the flask 500 ml. of concentrated sulfuric acid. Set aside, allow to cool, and filter through glass wool and store in an amber reagent bottle.

Diacetylmonoxime.—In a 1-liter volumetric flask place approximately 500 ml. of distilled water and add to it 5.0 g. of diacetylmonoxime (2,3-butanedione-2-oxime). Add 150 g. of sodium chloride and dissolve. Dilute to volume, filter, and store in amber reagent bottles.

Diacetylmonoxime and Urea.—Pipet 10 ml. of the 100 mg. per 100 ml. urea nitrogen standard into a 1-liter volumetric flask. Dilute to volume with diacetylmonoxime reagent. Add 0.5 ml. of Brij-35, mix and store in an amber reagent bottle. The diacetylmonoxime and urea is used as the dialyzer recipient. This reagent may not be stable for periods in excess of one week.

Standards. *Standard Diluent.*—0.01 N sulfuric acid containing 40 mg. per liter of phenyl mercuric acetate (Eastman P-4267).

Stock Urea Nitrogen.—(10 mg. urea nitrogen per ml.). Place 21.43 g. urea, reagent grade, in a 1-liter volumetric flask. Add approximately 500 ml. of the standard diluent, swirl until complete solution of the urea is obtained and then dilute to volume.

Working Urea Nitrogen Standards.—Working standards are prepared from the stock standard in the following concentrations using standard diluent:

10 mg. urea nitrogen per 100 ml.
30 mg. urea nitrogen per 100 ml.
50 mg. urea nitrogen per 100 ml.
70 mg. urea nitrogen per 100 ml.
100 mg. urea nitrogen per 100 ml.
150 mg. urea nitrogen per 100 ml.

Procedure.—The procedure is a modification of the carbamido-diacetyl reaction as applied to the determination of urea nitrogen. It is based on the direct reaction of urea and diacetylmonoxime (2,3-butanedione-2-oxime) under strongly acidic conditions. In acid solution diacetylmonoxime is hydrolyzed to diacetyl, which reacts directly with urea in the presence of an acidic ferric alum reagent to form triazine derivatives by an oxidative and condensation reaction. The colored product of the reaction is measured at 480 mμ in a flow cuvet with a 15-mm. light path.

Urea nitrogen can be determined in whole blood, serum, plasma, cerebrospinal fluid, or urine. No prior treatment of urine specimens is necessary as ammonia does not enter into the chemical reaction. Therefore, the determination of urea nitrogen in urine samples for urea clearance tests can be run without prior removal of ammonia. The diffusion rate of urea from these biological materials is similar to that obtained from aqueous standards.

The flow diagram (Fig. 47-16) gives the necessary information as to the manifold construction and connections between modules. Details of actual operation of a typical procedure are given under the method for glucose determination.

Operating Procedure Notes.—The urea nitrogen procedure can be run at 60 determinations per hour.

The urea is added to the diacetylmonoxime in order to have a linear calibration curve and increased sensitivity for low urea levels. This causes a low percent transmission reagent base line when compared with water. For adjustment of 100 percent transmission base line, pump reagents as indicated in the flow diagram and adjust to 98–100 percent transmission, using the proper aperture and 100 percent control setting.

The sensitivity of the reaction can be increased by increasing the sample size and/or decreasing the diluent flow rate. By increasing the time that the samples remain in the heating bath, a further increase in sensitivity can be achieved.

Normal Values.

Whole blood: 10–20 mg. per 100 ml.
Plasma or serum: 10–20 mg. per 100 ml.
For elderly persons, 25 mg. is considered normal.

URIC ACID

Reagents. **Saline, 0.9 percent.**—Add 0.5 ml. Aerosol 22 to each liter and mix before use.

Phosphotungstic Acid.—Place 40 g. sodium tungstate in a 1-liter flask with a ground glass joint. Add 300 ml. distilled water and dissolve the sodium tungstate. Place several glass beads in the flask. Add 32 ml. of 85 percent orthophosphoric acid and mix. Attach a reflux condenser and boil gently for two hours. Cool to room temperature. Transfer to a 1-liter volumetric flask. Rinse reaction flask and transfer rinsings to the volumetric flask. Dilute to mark with water. Add 32 g. lithium sulfate and mix well. Filter through filter paper and store in 1-liter amber bottle.

NOTE.—The reagent is stable if kept in the refrigerator. Do *not* dilute the phosphotungstic acid.

Cyanide-urea. *Stock Sodium Cyanide.**—Place 100 g. sodium cyanide in a 1-liter volumetric flask. Add 950 ml. water and mix well. Add 2 ml. concentrated ammonium hydroxide and dilute to mark with water. Mix well. Filter and store in 1-liter polyethylene bottle.

Stock Urea Solution.—Place 200 g. urea in 1-liter volumetric flask, dissolve and dilute to volume with water.

* Label this solution: POISON—DO NOT PIPET BY MOUTH.

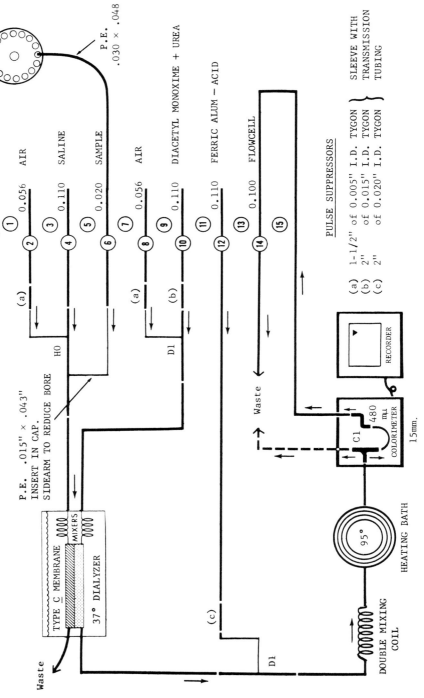

Fig. 47-16. Autoanalyzer® Flow Diagram for Urea Nitrogen Determination. (Courtesy Technicon Instruments Corp.)

1016

Working Cyanide-urea Solution.*—On day of use, mix one part of stock sodium cyanide with one part of stock urea.

Stock Uric Acid Standard (1 mg. uric acid per ml.).—Place 1.0 g. uric acid in a 1-liter volumetric flask. In a separate 250-ml. flask, dissolve 0.6 g. lithium carbonate ni 150 ml. of water. Shake 5 minutes until dissolved. Filter off any insoluble material. Heat the solution or filtrate to 60°C.

Pour the warm lithium carbonate solution into the 1-liter volumetric flask while warming it under hot tap water. Shake so as to dissolve the uric acid promptly. In 5 minutes all the uric acid should be dissolved. Shake the flask under cold running water without undue delay. Add 20 ml. of 37 percent formalin, and half fill the volumetric flask with distilled water.

With shaking add slowly from a pipet 25 ml. 1 N sulfuric acid. Dilute to volume, mix thoroughly and transfer to a 1-liter amber bottle. This stock solution contains 1 mg. uric acid per ml.

Working Uric Acid Standards.—From the stock standard prepare working standards of the following concentrations: 2, 4, 6, 8, 10, 12 mg. uric acid per 100 ml. Store the dilute standards in the refrigerator.

Procedure.—The quantitative measurement of uric acid involves the reduction of a phosphotungstate complex to a phosphotungstite complex. The presence of cyanide intensifies the color and prevents turbidity.

The sample is diluted with physiological saline and segmented with air. This diluted sample stream enters one side of the dialyzer. The physiological saline recipient stream is segmented with air, enters the dialyzer opposite the sample stream and proceeds in concurrent fashion. The recipient stream now containing the dialyzed uric acid is joined by a stream of sodium cyanide and mixed, followed by the addition of the phosphotungstic acid reagent. After mixing and allowing time for color development, the blue color of the reaction mixture is measured at 660 mμ in a flow cuvet having a 15-mm. light path.

The flow diagram (Fig. 47-17) gives the necessary information as to the manifold construction and connections between modules. Details of actual operation of a typical procedure are given under the method for glucose determination.

Operational Notes.—The uric acid procedure can be run at 60 determinations per hour. The samples should consist of clear, nonhemolyzed serum or plasma. Urine specimens can be run but should be prediluted 1:10 with water. Specimens whose uric acid values are greater than the highest standard run should be diluted with physiological saline and redetermined.

Occasionally turbidity is encountered when an old sodium cyanide solution is used. To eliminate turbidity when it occurs, flush the manifold thoroughly with distilled water, then rerun the procedure with a freshly prepared reagent.

When phosphotungstic reagent and sodium cyanide reagent age, they will be subjected to a gradual decrease in sensitivity. With freshly prepared reagents, full sensitivity will be restored.

When running the uric acid procedure, a check should be made of the noise level. This is done by continually aspirating a 6 mg. uric acid per 100 ml. standard and examining the record trace for noise. The noise level should be no greater than ±0.5 transmission line. If the noise level is greater, a check of the manifold and dialyzer should be made to insure that a good bubble pattern is being obtained. Noise is generally related to a poor bubble pattern which gives poor proportioning of reagents.

For optimal bubble pattern and low noise use 0.5 ml. Aerosol 22 per liter of saline.

---

* Label this solution: POISON—DO NOT PIPET BY MOUTH.

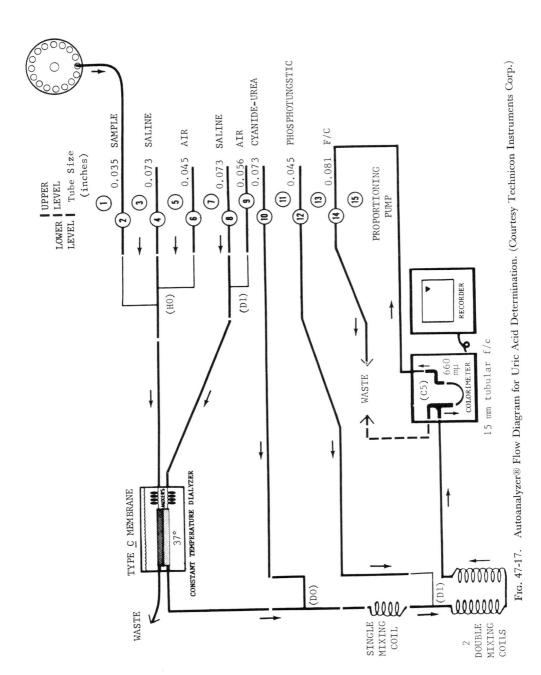

Fig. 47-17. Autoanalyzer® Flow Diagram for Uric Acid Determination. (Courtesy Technicon Instruments Corp.)

Normal Value.

2.0 to 4.0 mg. per 100 ml. (serum)
0.4 to 1.0 g. per 24 hours (urine)

CHLORIDE TITRATOR

Description of Instrument.—The chloride titrator (Figs. 47-18 and 47-19) conceived and developed by Cotlove *et al.* was designed for the rapid and accurate determination

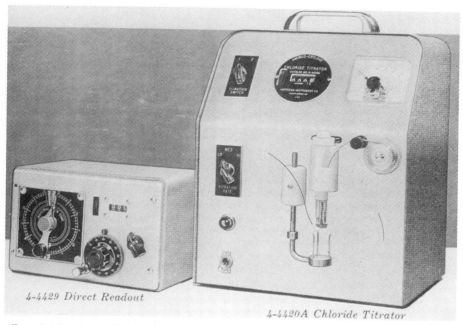

4-4429 Direct Readout

4-4420A Chloride Titrator

Fig. 47-18.   Amico-Cotlove Chloride Titrator. (Courtesy American Instrument Co. Inc.)

of the concentration of chloride in biological fluids by titration with silver ions. In developing this instrument, the emphasis was placed on automation, rapidity, accuracy, sensitivity, and ease of operation in performing the analyses.

The operation of the titrator is based on the principle of coulometric generation of reagent and of amperometric indication of the end point. During the actual analysis of a fluid sample, a constant direct current is passed between a pair of silver generator electrodes causing an electrochemical oxidation of the generator anode to silver ions which are continuously released at a steady rate into the titration solution. When all of the chloride has combined with the silver ions, there is a sudden appearance of free silver ions. These ions cause an abrupt increase in current between a pair of silver indicator electrodes.

When the indicator current reaches a preselected magnitude, a sensitive meter relay circuit is actuated, which removes the potential from the generator electrodes and at the same time stops a timer which runs concurrently with the generation of the silver ions. Since the silver ions are generated at a constant rate, the amount used to precipitate the chloride is proportional to the elapsed time, and hence, the chloride content of the titrated solution can be determined. Figure 47-19 shows a simplified diagram of the basic components of the titrator.

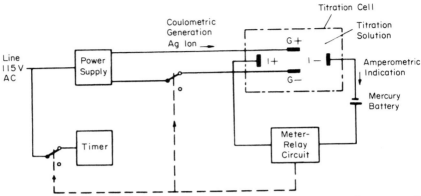

Fig. 47-19.   Basic Components of Chloride Titrator. (Courtesy American Instrument Co., Inc.)

The titrator can measure concentrations of chloride as small as 0.25 μeq. and has an accuracy approximating 0.5 percent of the mean value. Provisions are provided for changing the rate of titrations so as to keep most titration times within 60 seconds. Fluids containing large quantities of chloride can be appropriately diluted prior to analysis. The high titration rate is ideally suited for samples with a chloride content ranging from 4 to 50 μeq.; the medium rate for samples with a content ranging from 1 to 12 μeq.; and the low rate for samples with a content ranging from 0.25 to 3 μeq. The ability to change the titration rate can also provide means of avoiding excessively short titration times.

The titration medium contains 0.1 M nitric acid and 10 percent (1.75 M) acetic acid and 25 mg. percent gelatin as final concentrations (within plus or minus 10 percent). The presence of gelatin is required to smooth out the indicator current and to prevent reduction of silver chloride. Thymol blue acts as an indicator to show solution is acid and thymol crystals of the gelatin reagent act as a preservative. The reagent is kept refrigerated and will keep indefinitely at this temperature. Only enough is removed for each day's run of analyses.

Readout Device.—The original instrument has been modified to simplify further its operation and to permit direct readout of the values obtained. This device can be added to the basic instrument and is extremely useful when large numbers of samples are to be processed. The procedure described includes the use of the readout device with the basic chloride titrator.

Reagents. Nitric-acetic Reagent.—To 900 ml. of distilled water (chloride free) add 6.4 ml. of concentrated nitric acid and 100 ml. of glacial acetic acid. Mix thoroughly. (Volumes are approximate; use only Reagent grade acids).

Gelatin Reagent. *Dry Mixture.*—Weigh and mix dry reagents as follows: 60 g. gelatin (Knox unflavored gelatin), 1 g. thymol blue, 1 g. thymol crystal. Store in dark screw-cap bottle. *Solution.* Weigh 6.2 g. of dry mix. Place in 2-liter container (beaker or flask) and add approximately 1 liter of hot water and heat gently with continued swirling until the solution is clear. Keeps indefinitely at 4°C.

Standard—100 meq. per liter chloride.—Dissolve 5.8 g. of dried reagent grade sodium chloride in water and dilute to 1 liter. Other standard concentrations can be made by calculating required amount of sodium chloride for concentrations desired or by preparing a concentrated stock solution (1000 meq. per liter) and diluting to desired concentration.

Procedure.—Turn on main instrument switch. (Indicator light will light and stirrer motor will start.) Wait 10 seconds and then stop stirrer motor by performing manual shut off as follows: Turn titration switch to #2; turn adjustable (red) pointer of meter to coincide with indicator (black) pointer. A click will be heard and stirrer motor will stop. Move the adjustable pointer to about 20 microamperes (the indicator pointer will follow because of the activation of the electromagnet.) Allow the instrument to warm up for 10 minutes.

Prepare samples as follows: Using a Seligson stopcock pipet (or 0.1-ml. TC pipet) measure 0.1 ml. of sample (serum, urine, or spinal fluid). Wash sample into titration vial (20 × 40 mm.) with 4 ml. of acetic-nitric acid reagent (rinse TC pipet in reagent previously pipeted in vial). Add 4 drops of gelatin reagent to each vial. Prepare standards and blanks as follows: Measure and dilute standards in same manner as for the unknowns. Prepare at least four 100-meq. per liter chloride standards. Prepare at least 4 blanks using 4 ml. of acid reagent and 4 drops of gelatin reagent.

Polish electrodes as follows: Moisten (distilled water) a strip of seam binding tape ($\frac{1}{4}$ to $\frac{1}{2}$ inch wide) and rub across a piece of Bon Ami soap. (Note: silver paste and folded facial tissue may also be used). Polish the electrodes (with shoe shining motion) until bright. Clean all surfaces of the electrode pair (at the operator's left), the generator electrode (at the right) and the bottom end of the plastic rod (between indicator electrodes on left) especially at the crotch. Wipe off excess soap or paste and rinse thoroughly with chloride free distilled water. Check condition of the silver wire generator electrode. It must present an adequate surface immersed in the solution. The end must be positioned so that it is almost flush with the upper edge of the stirrer. Readjust wire when it becomes shortened about $\frac{1}{8}$ inch or less than the diameter of a straight pin (clip thinned portion off and reposition).

Set titration rate switch to Hi. Turn switch on readout device to blank and reset counter to zero. Titrate blanks and standards as follows: Place titration vial containing a sample or blank in vial holder and position with electrodes and stirrer in solution. Turn the titration switch to position #1. (The stirrer will start; the indicator pointer will fall within an interval of 10–30 seconds to a stable value of less than 5 microamperes). Reset timer on titrator to zero and/or reset counter on readout device. Set the adjustable (red) pointer 10 divisions (microamperes) above the reading of the indicator pointer. Turn the titration switch to position #2. (The timer will start with the simultaneous generation of silver ions.) Record value from readout counter and from timer to nearest 0.1 second when the timer has shut off (occurs automatically). Remove the vial and rinse electrodes with distilled water by directing stream of water from a squeeze bottle onto the electrodes after surrounding them with a 250-ml. beaker to catch the rinse water and to avoid spraying the instrument. Proceed to next titration.

With readout device switch at blank position, proceed to titrate 4 blanks. Discard the first two results (time from timer) and average second two times. Set adjustable stop of timer on readout device to average blank time. (When readout is not used, record average blank time for subsequent calculation). Set readout device switch to standard-unknown position and proceed to titrate 4 standards. Discard first two results (read from readout counter) and record values of second two. These values must agree with each other and with known value of standard by plus or minus 1 meq. Instrument must be recalibrated (see calibration) when value read does not agree with known value of standard. Proceed to titrate unknown samples, recording values from readout, or calculating values as shown below. Repeat standard at end of unknowns and after every 10th unknown.

Calculations.—For use when readout device is not used, or is turned to the off position. Gross seconds equal Timer reading. Average net seconds of standards equal average gross seconds of standard minus average blank seconds.

$$\text{Calibration factor } K = \frac{\text{ml. of NaCl reagent} \times \text{conc. of reagent in meq.}}{\text{average net seconds of standard}}$$

$$\text{Concentration of Cl unknown (meq./liter)} = \frac{K \times \text{net seconds of unknown}}{\text{ml. of unknown}}$$

where net seconds of unknown equal gross seconds minus average blank seconds. Example: Net time of standard = 50 seconds. Net time of unknown = 40 seconds. Standard = 100 meq per liter chloride. Sample and standard volume = 0.1 ml.

$$K = \frac{0.1 \times 100}{50} = 0.200 \qquad Cl = \frac{0.200 \times 40}{0.1} = 80 \text{ meq./liter}$$

Calibration. **Without Use of Readout Device.**—A calibration curve may be prepared for each group of unknowns by titrating a series of standards (using concentrations of 70, 85, 100, 115, and 130 meq. per liter) and plotting the net seconds for each standard on the ordinate and concentration on the abscissa. Concentrations of unknowns (reading in net seconds) can be read directly from the curve.

Using Readout Device.—To adjust readout to concentration of standard, titrate a group of 4 blanks and 2 standards, discarding all values *except* the average of the second pair of blanks. (Readout in blank position). Set readout timer to average blank time. Prepare 20 solutions of standard (100 meq. per liter). Record setting of calibration dial and titrate standard with readout switch in standard position. Record value on readout counter to correspond to dial setting (it is best to set dial at 50 when gross misadjustment is suspected). Increase and decrease dial setting by units of 10 so that values above and below standard value are obtained. Plot a curve of values read against dial settings. Pick a dial setting range 10 to 20 units above and below standard value. Titrate a second group of standards varying dial settings by units of 2 covering the range of settings selected from previous curve. Plot results as before and pick dial setting for standard value from curve. Set and lock dial setting at this value. Titrate several standards to check setting. Once dial is set it should not be necessary to change setting unless gross adjustment or technique change is needed.

Precautions.—Do not titrate a sample unless the solution is acid and gelatin reagent is present (indicated by the presence and red color of thymol blue; blue at pH 9.6; yellow between pH 8.0 and 2.8; and red at pH 1.2 and below). Avoid the use of gelatin reagent which has been at room temperature for more than a day or two. Samples to be titrated should be at room temperature (20°–30°C.). Do not place samples already at room temperature near sources of heat (such as on top of instrument). Check generator electrode for proper size and position. Polish new electrode after every several hundred determinations (once per week). Indicator electrodes must be completely immersed in solution. Stirring must be adequate. Stirrer should rotate freely at approximately 700 r.p.m. (blade is a blur at this speed). Adjustable meter pointer must be set at 10 microamperes (within one division) above the indicating pointer. The line switch must be in the "Off" position whenever the instrument is disconnected from a.c. power to prevent a continuing battery drain of approximately 5 milliamperes.

Normal Values.—The normal values for chloride concentration in the fluids of the human body are as follows: blood serum—96–105 meq. per liter; spinal fluid—118–130 meq. per liter; urine—6–10 g. per 24 hours.

COAGULATION TIMERS

Description of Instrument.—For many years all coagulation studies were carried out by hand in glass tubes. In recent years many mechanical means of arriving at the end point of a coagulation study have been brought forth. Almost all of these had some merit in attempting to eliminate the variable of the human; however, almost all instruments also had definite disadvantages, *i.e.*, improper temperature, erratic temperature control, delayed reaction times, etc. The instrument described below is one of these types and the authors have found it to be the most reliable of the mechanical means of quantitating coagulation times.

The instrument shown in Fig. 47-20 offers reproducible and accurate results, automatic operation, and simple operation. The clot-timer consists of four principal parts:

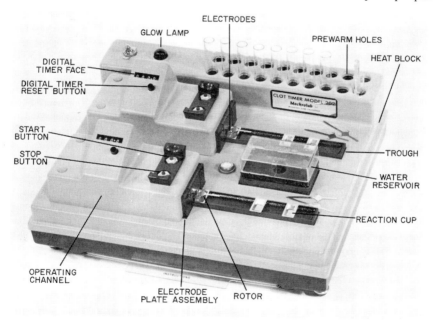

Fig. 47-20.   Coagulation Timer. (Courtesy Mechrolab, Inc.)

one heat block assembly; one base plate and power supply assembly; two operating channels. The heat block assembly consists of an aluminum block. On its upper rear surface are twenty holes designed to receive 13-mm. test tubes for prewarming plasma and reagents. Two operating channels are mounted on the left side of the instrument. The electrode plate assembly accurately positions two platinum electrodes which are the sensing element of the detector circuit, and provides for accurate rotational motion of the rotor. The rotor is inserted through a hole in the electrode plate into a coupling which transmits the movement of the motor.

The clot-timer operates on the principle that the gel formation results in a change in viscosity and surface tension of the reaction mixture. The reagents, plasma, cups, and rotors are prewarmed. The reagents are added to the cups. The cups are placed flush against the electrode plate and the rotor inserted into the coupling hole. Prewarmed plasma is pipeted onto the surface of the rotor. The start button is pushed and the rotor turns and allows the plasma to fall into the reaction mixture of the cup. Simultaneously the clock begins to run. The side arms of the rotor revolve through the reaction mixture in a rhythmic fashion resulting in mixing of the solution. When the fibrin gel begins to form, the arm picks up a small drop of liquid as it emerges from the solution and transfers this drop to the electrodes thus closing the detector circuit and stopping the timer. The time is read directly to the nearest one-tenth of a second.

Background of Method.—The coagulation test most often used in the central clinical laboratory is the Quick one-stage prothrombin test. The one-stage prothrombin test involves the interaction of calcium, thromboplastin reagent and plasma; and therefore, it is roughly a measure of primarily the plasma prothrombin and less completely the fibrinogen. Many commercial preparations are available which combine the thromboplastin and calcium.

Procedure.—Prothrombin time by means of the clot-timer.

Preparation of Instrument.

1. Place instrument on a level bench and adjust front feet until the bubble in the level is centered. It should be located in an area which is relatively free of excessive drafts, particularly those arising from air conditioning units, which will tend to disturb the temperature equilibrium across the surface of the heat block.
2. Plug the instrument into a power source of the type specified on the name plate.
3. Turn the power switch to the "On" position. The lamp will glow red. Do not start tests until lamp is cycling. Allow the heat block to reach operating temperature. Temperature of the block may be checked by placing a thermometer in a 13-ml. test tube into one of the prewarmed holes, and adding a few milliliters of water to the tube.
4. Fill the plastic reservoir with distilled water and invert in the holder. The water level of the troughs may have to be adjusted in order that the cups do not float.
5. Pipets and test tubes should be rinsed extremely well after cleaning; prothrombin times are very sensitive to contamination by detergents.
6. Prepare a supply of reagent solution which is adequate for the number of tests to be carried out. The reagent must be fresh and it must have been properly stored.
7. Press the timer reset button to return all dials to zero.
8. Carefully wipe the electrodes with soft tissue to insure that they are thoroughly clean.

Procedure for Series of Prothrombin Times.

1. Place test tubes which contain plasma to be tested in the prewarmed holes in the rear of the heat block. Five minutes in the hole is sufficient to prewarm plasma.
2. Place six clean reaction cups at the right-hand end of each trough. These cups will reach thermal equilibrium about three minutes after they have been placed in the trough.
3. Place some reaction rotors near the right-hand side of the plastic cover in a convenient spot.
4. Mix reagent solution and pipet a 0.2-ml. aliquot of reagent solution into the first two cups in each trough. On the first run, allow sixty seconds for warm-up of reagent.

5. With the channel raised, insert the long end of a prewarmed reaction rotor into the coupling hole above the reaction cup. Gently push in the rotor until its end reaches the stop. Make certain that the rotor arms are horizontal and that the smooth face of the square plate faces upward. Lower the channel. Repeat the above in the second channel.

6. Slide the prewarmed cup of reagent solution into position against the electrode plate of each channel. Check that the timers are set to zero.

7. Pipet a 0.1-ml. sample of prewarmed plasma onto the square plate of the reaction rotor. Deliver the sample by a short pipet, calibrated to read 0.1 ml. between two lines.

8. Momentarily press down the start button. Do this as soon as possible after pipeting plasma onto the rotor plate, to prevent possible evaporation. Both the rotor and digital timer will start to operate. Repeat steps 7 and 8 on the second channel.

9. While the channels are running, pipet additional aliquots of reagent solution into more reaction cups. Do not fill more than two or three cups ahead in each channel, to prevent loss of reagent solution by evaporation.

10. Rotation of the rotor deposits plasma in the reagent solution and then stirs the mixture at a regular rate. When the fibrin gel begins to form, a rotor arm transfers a small drop from the reaction cup to the electrodes thus closing the detector circuit and stopping the timer. Read the prothrombin time to the nearest one-tenth of a second.

11. Return the timer to zero and clean each channel for the next run.

Reagents.—Several commercial preparations of thromboplastin plus calcium chloride are available. Useable results may be obtained with several of these preparations.

Normal Values.—Usual prothrombin times vary normally from 12 to 14 seconds according to the type of thromboplastin and its method of preparation. Many ways of reporting prothrombin times have been used. In the opinion of the authors, the use of seconds only, affords a more precise control than the reporting of percentage of normals. Prothrombin times are used in great numbers to control the therapeutic use of anticoagulants. The therapeutic range varies from one and one-half to two and one-half times normal, according to the drug used.

FLAME PHOTOMETER

Description of Instrument.—The application of emission flame spectrophotometry to chemical analyses in clinical medicine has made the analysis of certain substances such as sodium and potassium in biological fluid both rapid and fairly accurate. Several instruments have been designed specifically for use within the routine clinical laboratory. All of them employ certain basic techniques which will be outlined below.

Each flame photometer consists of a gas burner, a system of atomizing and introducing the sample into the flame, a system of isolating certain wavelengths of light emitted by the burning substance, and a system of detecting the amount of light emitted for each substance. The gas burners vary in type and size from simple adaptations of the standard Fisher burner to the complicated burners which incorporate a capillary tube which aspirates the sample into the base of the flame. The burners vary also depending upon the type of gases being burned. The very hot flames produced by burning mixtures of acetylene-oxygen, hydrogen-oxygen, and propane-oxygen, provide the best sources of excitation. However, with proper pressure regulation, illuminating gas and compressed air can provide adequate heat.

The system of atomizing the samples and introducing them into the flame is divided into the open and closed types of systems. The open type of system introduces the sample through a capillary tube directly into the base of the flame where it is vaporized and burned. This type of system is subject to error due to the introduction of airborne particles into the system. The closed system vaporizes the sample by a blast of compressed air which is then used as the carrying medium into the base of the flame. The entire system is enclosed and is not easily contaminated from the surrounding air.

The isolation of the wavelength of light being emitted by the substance burning in the flame is accomplished either by the use of optical filters or a monochrometer system.

The detection system of the flame photometer may either be a simple barrier-layer type photocell, or, as most of the newer units use, more sensitive detecting devices such as photomultiplier systems.

The direct system of analysis measures the intensity of the emitted light relating the intensity to the concentration of the material being analyzed. The indirect or internal standard method of analysis introduces lithium into the materials being analyzed to serve as a reference point. The instruments using the indirect method require a double

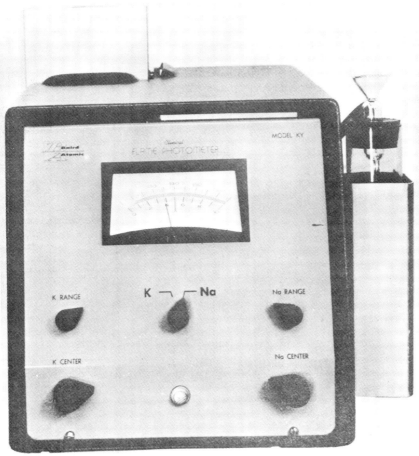

FIG. 47-21.   Clinical Flame Photometer. (Courtesy Baird-Atomic, Inc.)

detection system which is balanced against each other and by appropriate electronic construction can be used to detect the differences in the output signals of the detectors. The indirect system has the chief advantage of compensating for fluctuations in flame intensity due to variations in gas and air pressure.

The clinical flame photometer Model KY-1 shown in Fig. 47-21 is an example of a flame photometer which utilizes a closed atomizing system and an internal standard method of analysis. Figure 47-22 is a block diagram of the electronic components of

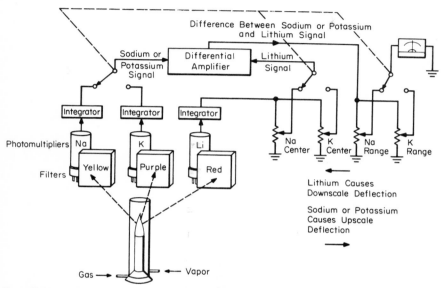

FIG. 47-22.   Diagram Showing Block Components of Clinical Flame Photometer. (Courtesy Baird-Atomic, Inc.)

the instrument shown in Fig. 47-21. Three separate photomultiplier detector systems are used to observe the flame. Each detector is designed to respond only to light emitted by a specific element as shown. A switch selects either the sodium or potassium detector and compares its output with that of the lithium detector. The difference in signal output represents the concentration of either sodium or potassium present in the sample. By calibrating the instrument with standard solutions, a meter can be used to read the concentrations of either sodium or potassium directly.

The burner of this instrument can be used with illuminating, manufactured, or propane gasses and compressed air. It has a sensitivity for sodium of 0.02 p.p.m., for potassium 0.01 p.p.m., and for lithium 0.2 p.p.m.

SODIUM AND POTASSIUM IN SERUM AND URINE
(Baird-Atomic Flame Photometer, Model KY-1)

Reagents. Sodium Stock Standard (50 meq. per liter).
Potassium Stock Standard (20 meq. per liter).
Lithium Solution (5000 p.p.m.).—Place exactly 26.595 g. of lithium carbonate, Reagent grade, in a 1-liter volumetric flask. Add 250 ml. of distilled water and 0.5 ml. of bromthymol blue. Slowly add the minimum amount of glacial acetic acid to change

the color of the solution to a golden yellow. Under no circumstances should excess acid be added. When the lithium is all in solution, dilute to volume with distilled water. Store in appropriately marked polyethylene container.

Potassium Dilute Standard (5 meq. per liter).—Place exactly 12.5 ml. of potassium stock standard (20 meq. per liter) in a 50-ml. volumetric flask and dilute to volume with distilled water.

Sodium Dilute Standard (20 meq. per liter—for GP standards).—Place exactly 10 ml. of sodium stock standard (50 meq. per liter) in a 25-ml. volumetric flask and dilute to volume with distilled water.

Lithium Water.—Add 19 liters of deionized distilled water to 1 liter of 5000 p.p.m. lithium water.

Working Standards for serum determinations are prepared as follows:

Working Std. Conc.	Ml. Na Stock Std. (50 meq./liter)	Ml. K Dilute Std. (5 meq./liter)	Final Vol. q.s. with Li-H₂O
120/1	12	1	1000
140/5	14	5	1000
160/9	16	9	1000

General purpose standards for urine, sweats, etc., are prepared according to the following table:

General Purpose Standard (GP)	Ml. Na Dilute Std. (20 meq./liter)	Ml. K Stock Std. (20 meq./liter)	Final Vol. q.s. with Li-H₂O
GP 1	1	1	1000
GP 5	5	5	1000
GP 9	9	9	1000

NOTE.—Store all standards in polyethylene bottles.

Procedure. **Determination of Serum Sodium and Potassium.**—Light and adjust flame (see Operational Notes). Allow flame to warm up for 15 minutes. Allow demineralized water to run through the funnel for 10–15 minutes before analyzing unknowns. This allows the glass and flame to come to equilibrium. Adjust the K range and Na range knobs so that the pointed edge of the knob is straight up. Adjust the K center knob so that the pointed edge is to the right. Adjust the Na center knob so that the pointed edge is to the left. With no solution in the funnel, set the selector switch on K. The meter should read between 4.8 and 5.2 on the lower scale. If not, adjust with K zero control on the back of the instrument. Turn the selector switch to Na. The meter should read between 139 and 141 on the upper scale. If not, adjust with the Na zero control on the back of the instrument.

Fill the funnel with the 140/5 standard. Set the selector switch on K, and adjust the K center knob so the meter reads 5 on the lower scale. Turn the selector switch to Na, wait 30 seconds for the meter needle to stabilize, and adjust the Na center knob so that the meter reads 140 on the upper scale.

Remove the 140/5 standard from the funnel and rinse 2 or 3 times with demineralized distilled water.

NOTE.—When removing the liquid from the atomizer, do not touch the side of the funnel with the aspirator; the aspirator tip may contaminate the funnel. Leave some liquid to run through the capillary.

Fill the funnel with the 160/9 standard, wait 30 seconds for the meter needle to stabilize, and with the selector switch set on Na, adjust the Na range knob so that the meter reads 160 on the upper scale. Turn the selector switch on K, allow 30 seconds for the meter to stabilize, and adjust the K range knob so the meter reads 9 on the lower scale.

Remove the 160/9 standard and rinse the funnel 2 or 3 times with demineralized distilled water. Fill the funnel with 120/1 standard. Without touching either the range or center knobs, K should read 1 (± 1 division) on the lower scale, and Na should read 120 (± 2 divisions) on the upper scale. If not, repeat.

NOTE.—The instrument is now standardized, and the center and range controls should not be moved. The standardization of the instrument should be checked after every 3 or 4 specimens have been analyzed.

Remove the 120/1 standard from the funnel and rinse 2 or 3 times with demineralized distilled water. Fill the funnel with the diluted serum (see below). Set the selector switch on K, and on the lower scale read the concentration of potassium in meq. per liter, representing the original undiluted sample. Set the selector switch on Na, and on the upper scale read the concentration of sodium in meq. per liter, representing the original undiluted sample.

Preparation of Serum Sample.—Measure 0.1 ml. of serum by using the Seligson automatic pipet, and add 20 ml. of lithium water. This is the 1:200 dilution used for serum sodium-potassium.

Determination of Urine Sodium and Potassium.—Light and adjust the flame and controls as for serum determination. Fill the funnel with the general purpose (GP) standard Number 5. Set the selector switch to K and adjust the K center knob so the meter reads 5 on the lower scale. Set the selector switch to Na and adjust the Na center knob so the meter reads 5 on the lower scale.

Remove the GP 5 standard from the funnel and rinse 2 or 3 times with demineralized distilled water. Fill the funnel with general purpose (GP) standard Number 9. Allow 30 seconds for the meter needle to stabilize. Set the selector switch on K, allow 30 seconds for the meter needle to stabilize, and adjust the K range knob so the meter reads 9 on the lower scale.

Remove the GP 9 standard from the funnel and rinse 2 or 3 times with demineralized distilled water. Fill the funnel with GP standard Number 1. Without touching either the range or center knobs, K should read 1 (± 1 scale division) on the lower scale, and Na should read 1 (± 1 scale division) on the lower scale. If not, repeat.

Remove GP standard Number 1 from the funnel and rinse 2 or 3 times with demineralized distilled water. Fill the funnel with the diluted urine. Set the selector switch on K. If the 1:500 dilution reads below 2 on the lower scale, make a 1:100 dilution. The lower scale reading multiplied by the proper factor gives the concentration of potassium in meq. per liter in the original undiluted sample (see Calculations below).

Set the selector switch on Na. If the 1:500 dilution reads below 1 on the lower scale, make a 1:100 dilution. The lower scale reading multiplied by the proper dilution factor gives the concentration of sodium in meq. per liter in the original undiluted sample.

Calculation of Sodium and Potassium in Urine for 24 Hours (milliequivalents).— The reading taken from the lower scale (K) $\times$ the appropriate dilution factor $\times$ the volume in liters equals meq. per 24 hours (to be reported). If the sample is only a single specimen, record the volume, multiply the reading by the appropriate dilution factor and report as meq. per liter.

To convert values to grams per 24 hours use the following example:

Potassium.

meq./L. $\times$ 0.039 $\times$ 24 hr. vol. in liters = g. K/24 hours

24-hour volume of urine is 1000 ml. (1 liter)

A 1:1000 dilution reads 5 on the lower scale.

5 $\times$ 20 = 100 meq. per liter.

100 $\times$ 0.039 $\times$ 1.0 = 3.9 g. K/24 hours.

Sodium.

meq./L. $\times$ 0.023 $\times$ 24 hr. vol. in liters = g. Na/24 hours

24-hour volume of urine is 1000 ml. (1 liter)

A 1:1000 dilution reads 7.4 on the lower scale.

7.4 $\times$ 20 = 148 meq. Na/liter

148 $\times$ 0.023 $\times$ 1.0 = 3.4 g. Na/24 hours.

Preparation of Urine Sample.—Measure and record the volume of the specimen. Prepare a 1:500 dilution using the Seligson automatic pipet (see table below). More or less concentrated solutions (as indicated by the results of the analysis of the initial dilution) are prepared as shown in the following table:

Dilution:	Ml. of Specimen	Ml. of Lithium Water
1:1000	0.1	100
1:500	0.1	50
1:100	0.1	10

Calculation for dilution factors:

1. 1:1000 reading from the K scale $\times$ 20 = meq./liter
2. 1:500 reading from the K scale $\times$ 10 = meq./liter
3. 1:100 reading from the K scale $\times$ 2 = meq./liter

Operational Notes.—The electronic unit of the photometer is allowed to operate continuously. The red light on the front panel of the instrument is "on" when the instrument is operating. Check to see if the light is "on."

Igniting the Gas.—Turn on the air supply and adjust it to 6 p.s.i. Rest a burning applicator stick or a lighted match on the chimney rim so that the flame is inside the chimney, and turn on the gas. Note: When using propane, the flow of gas from the tank is controlled by three valves: (a) the main valve of the tank; (b) a regulator valve attached to the tank, and (c) a needle valve attached to the side of the regulator. To turn the gas on open the main valve; open the needle valve; regulate the gas pressure by turning the handle of the regulator valve in. The pressure should be 2.5 to 5.0 p.s.i., depending on the amount of gas in the tank. If the gas does not ignite, reduce the air pressure and repeat. After the gas ignites, return the air pressure to 6 p.s.i.

Flame Adjustment.—Observe the flame for proper height and pattern. CAUTION: Do not look down the chimney when the flame is lit. The correct flame should burn with small blue cones forming over each of the burner grid openings, and appear as though they are about to break away from the grid. To check the height of the flame, fill the funnel with the 140/5 standard and observe the colored flame. The tip of the flame should be level with the top of the instrument cabinet. Minor variations in the flame height and pattern can be corrected by slowly changing the gas pressure and/or changing the needle valve opening located at the base of the burner. If the correct flame cannot be obtained, refer to the Instrument Manual for correct adjustment procedure.

Allow demineralized water to run through the funnel for 10 to 15 minutes before analyzing unknowns. This allows the glass and flame to come to equilibrium. After 15 minutes the instrument is ready for standardization as outlined above.

Normal Values.

Serum—Sodium—132–144 meq. per liter
Potassium—3.3–4.6 meq. per liter
Urine—Sodium—186–216 meq. per liter
4.28–4.98 g. per 24 hours
Potassium—65–79 meq. per 24 hours
2.55–3.04 g. per 24 hours.

FLUOROMETRY

Fluorescence is brought about by the illumination of light upon a substance. The substance absorbs this light and emits light at an equal or longer wavelength, usually of a longer wavelength. Electrons of a molecule are excited to a higher energy level; and while in this state, the electrons lose some of their energy as a result of molecular collisions. The electrons lose energy in stages to return to the so-called ground state. The final emission to ground state is called fluorescence. Strongly fluorescent materials convert a much higher percentage of the excitation energy into fluorescent energy.

The amount of fluorescent light detected is related to the concentration of the fluoresing species by the following equation:

$$F = P_0 \left(1 - 10^{-abc}\right) \phi$$

where: F = power of the fluorescent radiation;
P_0 = power of the incident light;
a = absorptivity of absorbing species;
b = pathlength;
c = concentration of absorbing species; and
ϕ = ratio of light emitted to light absorbed.

Substances that transmit more than 80 percent of P_0 follow the formula: $F = P_0(2.3\ abc)\phi$. Fluorescence intensity is proportional to concentration for dilute solutions.

There are six basic elements to a fluorometer: (1) a source of excitation light, (2) a primary filter to select and isolate the required spectral region of the source light for excitation of the sample, (3) a cell to contain the sample and orient it properly in the light path, (4) a secondary filter to select the desired spectral region of the resulting fluorescence from the sample, (5) a detector, and (6) a readout device. The excitation light consists usually of a mercury lamp. Three precautions should be remembered when choosing filters for fluorescence: (1) negligible amounts of overlap between the transmittance curves of the primary and secondary filters, (2) cautionary use of interference filters, and (3) slight fluorescence of some glass filters and many gelatin filters. The sample cups are made of low fluorescent materials.

Fluorometric methods may be grouped into four classifications: (1) direct, (2) indirect, (3) rearrangement, and (4) complexing. Direct reactions are those in which a substance dissolved in a proper solvent fluoresces upon excitation. Indirect reaction involves a compound which does not fluoresce itself but converts a non-fluorescing compound to a fluorescing one. Rearrangement reactions are those in which internal rearrangement of a compound occurs and results in the formation of a fluorescent compound. Complexing denotes the reaction of a substance with a reagent resulting in the formation of a fluorescent compound.

In most cases, the calculation of concentration from fluorescence intensities can be made using the following equation:

$$\frac{F_s - F_b}{F_{std} - F_b} \times k = \text{concentration of the material in the specimen}$$

where: F_s = fluorescence of the sample;
F_b = fluorescence of the blank;
F_{std} = fluorescence of the standard; and
k = a proportionality constant.

"k" will include the concentration of the standard used and whatever multipliers are necessary to convert to the desired units of concentration. When an internal standard is used in a determination, concentrations can be calculated as follows:

$$\frac{F_s - F_b}{F_{ststd} - F_s} \times k = \text{concentration of the unknown}$$

where: F_{ststd} = fluorescence of sample plus an internal standard.

Individual points of operation of selected instruments may be obtained from the operational manuals of those instruments.

CORTICOSTEROIDS

Procedure.—The method may be used with heparinized plasma or with urine. If urine is used, the sample must be washed with 4 volumes of petroleum ether. The sample is then diluted with 4 volumes of water and immediately extracted with 10 volumes of dichloromethane. The extract is then washed with 0.1 M sodium hydroxide. For plasma or urine, 1 volume of hydroxide is used for 12 volumes of dichloromethane extract. Finally, two-thirds of the original volume of dichloromethane can easily be recovered. The corticoids are re-extracted almost quantitatively from this dichloromethane by 0.25 volume of a mixture of sulfuric acid and ethanol (75:25 v/v). After exactly 5 minutes of incubation in the above mixture, fluorometry is done using a 470 mμ interferential primary filter and a narrow band secondary filter giving peaks around 560 mμ (510–600).

The corticoid level of plasma can be preserved at 4°C. However, as far as urine is concerned, only fresh samples should be used since a specific fluorescence increases markedly on storage, even in a deep freezer.

Normal Values.

Urine: 300 μg. per 24 hours
Plasma: 95 μg. per 100 ml.

CATECHOLAMINES

Procedure.—The sample is composed of a single voiding during a period of hypertension. Place 10.0 ml. of clear urine (centrifuge, if not clear) in a 6 × ¾-inch test tube and add 5.0 ml. of 0.2 M sodium acetate. Add 7 percent sodium carbonate to obtain a pH of 8.5. After having prepared a chromatographic column with activated alumina (washed with distilled water and 0.2 M sodium acetate) which has been suspended in 0.2 M sodium acetate, quickly and carefully decant the specimen onto the column. A minimum of disturbance to the surface of the column will be obtained if the solution is poured down the side of the column while the column is turned rapidly between the fingers. The sample should be added while there is still about one-fourth inch of the original 0.2 M sodium acetate above the top of the alumina. The column must never run dry. Wash the column 4 times with 5 ml. portions of 0.2 M sodium acetate and twice with 10-ml. portions of water. Elute with 0.2 M sodium acetate, collecting

25 ml. of eluate in a graduated cylinder. Start collecting in a cylinder immediately upon addition of the acid to the column. Mix eluate thoroughly and transfer 2.0 ml. of eluate to each of three test tubes (5 × ½-inch): 1. blank; 2. sample; 3. sample plus standard. Add 1.0 ml. of water to sample and blank tubes. Add 1.0 ml. of dilute standard (1 ml. equals ⅛ μg.). Add 0.5 M sodium phosphate to all tubes to obtain pH 6.5. Mix thoroughly. Approximately 0.9 ml. of sodium phosphate will be required, but will vary slightly with different specimens. Add 0.15 ml. of 0.25 percent potassium ferricyanide to the blank tubes. Mix and allow to stand for three minutes. Then add 0.9 ml. of 20 percent sodium hydroxide; mix thoroughly. Allow to stand for 20 minutes. While the blank tubes are standing, add 0.15 ml. of 0.25 percent potassium ferricyanide to sample and sample plus standard tubes. Mix and allow to stand for three minutes. Then add 1.0 ml. of freshly prepared ascorbic acid-sodium hydroxide reagent (prepare within 3 minutes of use as follows: mix 1.0 ml. of 2 percent ascorbic acid with 9.0 ml. of 20 percent of sodium hydroxide). Mix. Centrifuge the tubes which contain sample and sample plus standard, decant centrifugate into the fluorometer tubes, place in the fluorometer and read in 4 to 5 minutes. When the blanks have stood for the required 20 minutes, add 0.1 ml. of 2 percent ascorbic acid solution, mix, centrifuge and read in 4 to 5 minutes.

If it is desired to test for adrenaline only, substitute 1.0 ml. of 1 M acetate buffer, pH 3.5, for the sodium phosphate. The pH of the solution must now be 3.5. Add 0.1 ml. of 5 percent zinc sulfate, mix, and allow tubes to stand for exactly four minutes before adding the sodium hydroxide or sodium hydroxide ascorbic acid reagents. For the internal standard, use ⅛ μg. of adrenaline instead of noradrenaline. There is much less adrenaline than noradrenaline in both normal and pathologic urines and it is usually not necessary to make this separate determination.

Calculations are to be done according to the formulas given in the beginning of this section.

Normal range.

> Random sample = up to 18 μg. per 100 ml. of urine.
> 24-hour sample = 32–103 μg. per 24 hours.

ESTROGENS (Barlow Method)

Procedure.—Total 24-hour-urine samples are collected without preservative and aliquots are either hydrolyzed fresh or frozen until used.

In the assays, 10-percent aliquots of the 24-hour samples are diluted with distilled water to a volume of 100 ml. or 200 ml., and 15 ml. concentrated hydrochloric acid per 100 ml. is added. The mixture is brought to boiling, refluxed for one hour, and then cooled rapidly under running tap water.

Tritiated estrone-6,7-H³, estradiol-17B-6,7-H³, and estriol-6,7-H³ of high specific activities are added to the cooled hydrolysis mixture. Approximately 3000–5000 c.p.m. of each estrogen is added to 0.1 ml. ethanol. The fluorescent contribution of these estrogens of high specific activity is not detectable.

The hydrolyzates with added tritiated estrogens are extracted in separatory funnels with ether (one time with volume equal to diluted urine volume and two times with one-half volumes). The acidic fraction is removed by shaking with concentrated carbonate solution (150 ml. of 20 percent sodium hydroxide and 1 liter of 8 percent sodium bicarbonate)—forty ml. per 100 ml. diluted urine volume.

The ether extract is then shaken with 8 percent sodium hydroxide solution (10 ml. per 100 ml. original diluted urine). This aqueous layer is not discarded but partially neutralized by adding 8 percent sodium bicarbonate solution (40 ml. per 100 ml.

original diluted urine) and again shaken with the ether layer. The aqueous layer is now discarded. Another 10 ml. of 8 percent sodium bicarbonate solution per 100 ml. of original diluted urine is shaken with ether to remove any residual alkali. This is discarded. The ether is washed one time with water (5 ml. per 100 ml. original diluted urine).

The ether layer is evaporated in a round-bottom flask to near dryness *in vacuo* at 40°C. and 1 ml. of ethanol is added to dissolve the residue. The flask contents are transferred to a separatory funnel containing light petroleum (25 ml.) with portions of benzene (total of 25 ml.). The benzene-light petroleum mixture is extracted two times with 25 ml. of water and then 2 times with 25 ml. of 1.6 percent sodium hydroxide. Both of these extracts are saved.

Four g. of solid sodium bicarbonate are dissolved in the water extract which contains the estriol. The estriol is then quantitatively extracted from this saturated bicarbonate solution with ether (once with 50 ml. and twice with 25 ml.). The ether extracts are pooled and washed with 2.5 ml. of water to remove excess sodium bicarbonate. The ether is evaporated to dryness *in vacuo* at 40°C.

The 1.6 percent sodium hydroxide extract, which contains the estrone and estradiol-17B, is partially neutralized with 6 N sulfuric acid to about pH 8 by pH paper. Since this is a brittle end point one is likely to overacidify. To avoid this, 2 g. of solid sodium bicarbonate is added to stabilize the pH. This aqueous mixture is also extracted with ether (once with 50 ml. and twice with 25 ml.). The pooled ether extract is washed with 2.5 ml. of water and evaporated to dryness *in vacuo* at 40°C. The dried residues are transferred with portions of ether to glass test tubes and the ether is evaporated to dryness under a nitrogen jet at 40°C.

Estrone, estradiol-17B, and estriol are used as paper chromatography standards and in dilute concentration in ethanol (made fresh monthly) as fluorescent reference standards.

The dried residues are chromatographed in Bush systems on Whatman No. 1 paper against standard estrogens. Chromatography is carried out at room temperature. Usual equilibration time is 1.5 hours and running time is 2–2.5 hours. The estrone-estradiol-17B fraction is chromatographed in heptane-toluene-methanol-water (50:50:70:30). Estrone and estradiol-17B are widely separated in this system having R_f's of 0.8 and 0.38, respectively. The estriol fraction is chromatographed in a modified Bush C system— ethyl acetate-toluene-methanol-water (15:85:50:50). Estriol has an R_f of 0.33 under these conditions.

The standard estrogens are located by developing the paper with potassium ferricy-anide-ferric chloride (1:1) and the areas of the unknowns corresponding to the standards are eluted with anhydrous methanol. The methanol is slowly run down the cut out area, and the drops are collected directly into a glass-stoppered (8-ml.) "acetylation tube." The eluate is evaporated to dryness at 40°C. under nitrogen jets.

The residue in the glass-stoppered tube is further dried in a vacuum desiccator over calcium chloride for 1 hour prior to addition of 0.05 ml. of acetic anhydride and 0.1 ml. of pyridine. The tubes are tightly stoppered, gently shaken to mix the reagents and to dissolve any residue adhering to the sides of the tube, and placed in an oven at 37°C. overnight. The following morning, the acetylated estrogens are extracted from the acetylation mixture by a partition described by Kliman and Peterson. Five-tenths ml. of aqueous ethanol and 2.5 ml. of 25 percent (v/v), methylene dichloride are pipeted into the acetylation mixture. After shaking, the layers are allowed to settle or the tube is centrifuged for a few seconds, and the aqueous layer is aspirated off. The methylene dichloride is washed twice with 0.5 ml. of water, which is also aspirated off. A few drops of absolute ethanol are used to wash down the side of the tube and the tube contents are evaporated to dryness at 40°C. under a nitrogen jet.

The dried residues of acetylated estrogens are now chromatographed on small (2-g.) alumina columns (9–10 percent water). Estrone acetate, estradiol-17B diacetate, and estriol triacetate are each chromatographed on a separate column. The running time for a column is about forty minutes. Two or even three columns may be run simultaneously on the same automatic fraction collector; one column dropping through the photocounter turns the turntable, and the rates of the other columns are adjusted to its flow rate by varying the heights of the eluting solvents in the reservoirs.

All columns are prepared by adding alumina to the chromatography tube, which is partially filled with water-saturated light petroleum (40–60°C.). The alumina is leveled by gentle tapping of the tube and overlaid by about $\frac{1}{4}$ inch of acid-washed sand to protect the surface. Each acetylated residue is transferred to the columns in three portions (each, 1 ml. or less) of eluting solvent, each portion being added when the previous portion reaches the sand surface. The estrone acetate column is developed with 70 percent benzene in light petroleum; the estradiol-17B diacetate column is developed with 50 percent benzene in light petroleum; and the estriol triacetate column is developed with 70 percent benzene in light petroleum. Both the benzene and light petroleum are water saturated. Ten 2-ml. fractions are collected from the estrone acetate and the estradiol-17B diacetate columns. Twelve 2-ml. fractions are collected from the estriol triacetate column. Mild suction is used during the preparation of columns and during the application of residue to columns, but fractions are collected without suction. From each column fraction precise aliquots are taken for fluorometry and for radioactive counting (usually 1.0 ml. and 0.5 ml., respectively).

The fluorescence method is that of Engel *et al.* and Bates and Cohen. The fluorometer is equipped with filters for incident light to pass 436 mμ. mercury emission line. For fluorescent light a filter to pass peak transmission of 491 mμ. is used. The aliquots for fluorometry are pipeted directly into calibrated fluorometry tubes and evaporated to dryness at 40°C. under nitrogen jets. The following reagents are then added: 0.2 ml. 5 percent ethanol in toluene (special Spectrograde toluene—kept at 5°C. when not in use), and 1.0 ml. of 90 percent sulfuric acid. The tubes are placed in a boiling water bath for 10 minutes and cooled in a pan of cold tap water for 3 minutes. Then 6.0 ml. of 65 percent sulfuric acid are added and the tube contents are mixed gently with footed, glass stirring rods. A reagent blank and two standards for each of the three estrogens (0.05 and 0.1 μg.) are similarly prepared. The tubes are read in a fluorometer within thirty minutes.

The column fraction aliquots for radioactive counting are directly pipeted into 20-ml. scintillation counting vials and evaporated to dryness. Five ml. of the phosphor solution (3.0 g. of 2,5-diphenyloxazole and 0.3 g. of 1,4-bis-2-(5-phenyloxazolyl) plus benzene in one liter of Reagent grade toluene) is added and each fraction aliquot is counted in the liquid scintillation spectrometer.

From the fluorescence and radioactive counts of known aliquots of each column fraction the specific activity of the material in each fraction containing significant amounts of estrogen is determined. This figure and the known number of counts for each tritiated estrogen originally added may be substituted into the formula:

$$\text{Micrograms in } \tfrac{1}{10}\text{-day-urine hydrolyzate} = \frac{\text{c.p.m. added}}{\text{S.A. of estrogen in column fraction}}$$

Multiply by 10 to obtain μg. per day.

From the specific activity of the estrogen in a single column fraction one can calculate the total amount of that estrogen present when the tritiated estrogens were added. The final calculation is based on peak tubes of constant specific activity. The peak of fluorescence and radioactivity must coincide, and constant specific activity in more than one fraction confirms the accuracy and specificity of the measurement.

Normal Vales: Total.

4–60 μg./24 hour (female)
4–25 μg./24 hour (male)

SEROTONIN (5-HYDROXYTRYPTAMINE)

Procedure.—The sample consists either of platelets or platelet-rich plasma. Samples of blood are collected by means of a siliconed syringe with siliconed needles and transferred to round-bottomed centrifuge tubes containing 1 ml. of EDTA-saline (1 percent ethylenediaminetetracetate in 0.9 percent sodium chloride). Blood is added to the 10-ml. graduation mark and the tube is stoppered and mixed by gentle inversion.

For the preparation of platelet-rich plasma, the blood is centrifuged at 750 r.p.m. (136 × g.) for 20 minutes. The platelet-rich plasma is carefully removed with a siliconed pasteur pipet and transferred to a siliconed tube and an aliquot taken for platelet count. If platelet-rich plasma 5-hydroxytryptamine is to be determined 2 ml. are transferred to an unsiliconed tube for freezing and thawing prior to analysis. For the determination of platelet suspension 5-hydroxytryptamine, two ml. of platelet-rich plasma are centrifuged at 3000 r.p.m. for 30 minutes in a refrigerated centrifuge at 5°C. The platelet-poor plasma is removed by careful decantation and after draining the tube and removing the adherent plasma with filter paper, the platelet button is resuspended in 1.8 ml. of water and 0.2 ml. of EDTA-saline. Partial disruption of the platelets in both platelet-rich plasma and platelet suspension is achieved by freezing the samples rapidly in a mixture of cardice and alcohol at lower than minus 40°C. and thawing to room temperature.

After partial disruption of the platelets 2 ml. of 20 percent trichloroacetic acid are added, dropwise with shaking, and the tube is stoppered and shaken vigorously for one minute. The mixture is centrifuged at 3000 r.p.m. for 10 minutes and the clear supernatant liquid is decanted into a large glass-stoppered centrifuge tube graduated to 4 ml. The volume is adjusted to 4 ml. with glass-distilled water, an equal volume of peroxide-free ether is added and the tube is stoppered and shaken vigorously for one minute. After centrifuging, the ether phase is removed by means of suction and the extraction, centrifuging, and removal of ether is repeated once more with a fresh 4 ml. of ether. Four ml. of borate buffer (pH 9.5–9.8; 94.2 g. of boric acid in one liter of distilled water) are added followed by 5 g. of sodium chloride dropped into the tube through a paper funnel to avoid subsequent leakage through an ill-fitting all glass joint. Fifteen ml. of redistilled butanol are now added and the mixture is shaken vigorously for 3 minutes, followed by centrifuging at 2500 r.p.m. for 5 minutes. Ten ml. of the upper butanol layer are transferred to another glass-stoppered centrifuge tube containing 20 ml. of isoöctane. Three ml. of 3 M hydrochloric acid are then added and extraction is performed by vigorous shaking for 3 minutes. After centrifuging, the upper solvent layer is removed with suction and the acid layer is transferred to an optical cell of approximately 1-ml. capacity.

Standards and a reagent blank are prepared according to the following table:

	Std. Solution (B≡ 0.5 μg./ml.)	Water (ml.)	EDTA-Saline (ml.)	20% TCA (ml.)	5HT≡ (μg. per tube)
Std. 1	0.3	1.5	0.2	2.0	0.15
Std. 2	0.6	1.2	0.2	2.0	0.30
Std. 3	1.2	1.6	0.2	2.0	0.60
Reagent Blank	0.0	1.8	0.2	2.0	0.0

The standards and reagent blank are taken through the whole procedure omitting the freezing, thawing and centrifuging after the addition of the trichloroacetic acid.

A spectrophotofluorometer is used with an activating wavelength of 295 mμ. and a fluorescent wavelength of 540 mμ.

After subtraction of the blank reading from the standard and test figures, a standard curve is prepared and the sample values obtained from this. These values are corrected by the following expression: Curve reading $\times \dfrac{10}{V \times 9}$, where V equals the volume of the platelet-rich plasma taken for analysis. The remaining factors correct for the dilution due to EDTA-saline present in the original whole blood.

Normal Values.

Platelet-rich plasma serotonin level: 0.035–0.290 μg./ml.
Platelet suspension serotonin level: 0.065–0.600 μg. per 10^9 platelets

THIN-LAYER CHROMATOGRAPHY

Thin-layer (300 microns) chromatography is adsorption chromatography performed on open layers of adsorbent materials supported on glass plates. Separation is usually accomplished in a few minutes. This procedure may not only be used for quantitative analysis, but also for preparative fractionation preliminary to other analytical methods. The method is quite sensitive and usually has sharp resolution. A descending development technique permits elution and collection of individual fractions.

Generally the technique of applying adsorbents is completed by applying a slurry or pasty mass to a glass plate in a very thin layer. (Air drying for a few minutes after application allows the thin layers to set before the plates are moved.) Several aids to application are described in the literature, most of which resemble a fitted trowel. The usual solvent is distilled water; but other solvents have been used, some with chemical additives. Heating thin-layers at temperature slightly above 100°C. activates the adsorbents. Samples are spotted on thin-layers with micropipets by means of application techniques similar to those used in paper chromatography. The prepared plates are placed in a jar in which there is a small amount of suitable solvent. The solvent will ascend in the adsorbent layer, thus making a chromatographic separation.

Any of the packing materials of column chromatography can be used in thin-layer chromatography if the materials are available in powders that will cling to the plates. Many adsorbent materials are available, but silica gel and aluminum oxide are most commonly used. The materials must be finely ground and activated. Occasionally a binder, such as starch or gypsum (calcinated calcium sulfate), must be added in order that the adsorbent material adhere to the glass plates. Some investigators treat adsorbents chemically to alter the chromatographic characteristics of the materials.

The samples to be separated are applied to the plate with a micropipet in the form of dots along a line 2.5 cm. from the lower end of the plate. The volume limits for each dot are 0.5 μl.–500 μl. Most investigators feel that 1.5 cm. between each dot is best. A line is drawn interrupting the adsorbent layer 10 cm. from the starting points.

The plates are developed with solvents in solvent-saturated atmospheres within glass developing chambers. A commercially available descending chromatography tube permits collection of separate fractions by continuous elution off the bottom of the plate. The selection of the solvent is based upon the principles of adsorption chromatography. Polar solvents cause a greater migration than nonpolar ones. The R$_f$-value of a substance increases with increasing polarity of the solvent. Often it is advantageous to adjust the polarity of a solvent by adding small quantities of a polar solvent (0.5–10 percent) to a nonpolar one.

Most investigators recommend that universal reference material be run on the same plate as comparisons. The following mixture of azo-dyes is recommended: oil yellow (p-dimethylaminoazobenzene), Sudan G (dihydroxyazobenzene), and indophenol (dimethyl-p-aminophenylnaphthoquinoneimine). A mixture of six dyes is used as a test mixture for alumina-azo-benzene, p-methoxyazobenzene, Du Pont oil yellow (amino-azotoluene), Sudan III (aminoazobenzeneazo-β-naphthol), p-aminoazobenzene, and p-hydroxyazobenzene.

Multiple means of developing the plates are used. Reagents and dyes are conveniently sprayed onto the chromatogram in order to either develop a color or to produce a complex which is visible in ultraviolet light. Fluorescent indicators may be used in the adsorbent material. Inorganic adsorbents may be developed with strong chemicals. Several recent innovations have been published in the literature. One useful, interesting one involves the scanning densitometrically of cut sections of a thin-layer chromatogram.

AMINO ACIDS

Reagents. Silica Gel G.—Mix 30 g. of gel with 60 ml. of water.

Butanol-acetic Acid Mixture.—Mix n-butanol, acetic acid, and water in the ratio 3:1:1.

Phenol-water Mixture.—3:1.

Copper—Ninhydrin Reagent.—*Solution I*. Mix 0.25 g. of ninhydrin, 100 ml. of methanol, 20 ml. of glacial acetic acid, and 4 ml. of 2,4,6-collidine. *Solution II*. Prepare a 1 percent w/v solution of copper(II) nitrate in methanol. Mix immediately before use 25 ml. of Solution I and 1.5 ml. of Solution II.

Ethylenediaminetetraacetic Acid Solution.—Dissolve 0.5 g. of ethylenediaminetetraacetic acid in 100 ml. of water. Adjust the pH to 7.2.

Procedure.—Four chromoplates are prepared with Silica Gel G. The thin-layer plates are dried in air for at least 3 hours. A jar is prepared by lining two sides with filter paper. Fifty ml. of the butanol-acetic acid mixture are poured into the jar. Wait 15 minutes to saturate the jar.

Five μl. of urine are spotted on to a corner of the plate about 2 cm. from the edges as for paper chromatography. The plate is placed in the tank, and an additional 50 ml. of solvent are carefully added. The solvent is allowed to ascend at room temperature for 2 to 2.5 hours. When the front has ascended 11 to 13 cm. the plate is withdrawn and gently dried with a fan. It is then run at right angles in a similar manner with the phenol-water mixture as the second solvent for 2 to 2.5 hours, the front moving again 11 to 13 cm. The plate is removed and dried in an oven at 100°C. for about 15 minutes to remove traces of phenol.

The amino-acids may be stained by spraying with the copper-ninhydrin reagent. After spraying with ninhydrin the plates are heated carefully at 105°C. for 2 to 5 minutes. The unknown is compared with standards.

By using techniques described in previous sections, the spots may be eluted and reacted quantitatively with the ninhydrin reagent. The spot may be eluted off with an ethylenediaminetetraacetic acid solution. Five ml. of ninhydrin reagent are added and the mixture is placed in a boiling water bath for 20 minutes. Then cool to room temperature and add 50 percent ethanol to a volume of 10 ml. Read optical densities of unknown and standards at 570 mμ. Use distilled water as a blank. A curve may be drawn from the standards or the unknowns calculated from the standards.

BARBITURATES

Reagents. Solvent.—Chloroform (stabilized with 1 percent v/v ethanol), n-butanol, and concentrated ammonia are mixed in the ratio 70:40:5.

Standards. *Stock Standards.*—Stock solutions are prepared containing 0.25 percent of the compounds listed below in 75 percent v/v ethanol.

1. 5-ethyl-5-phenylbarbituric acid
2. 5-allyl-5-phenylbarbituric acid
3. 5,5-diethylbarbituric acid
4. 5,5-diallylbarbituric acid
5. 5-ethyl-5-(1-methyl-1-butenyl) barbituric acid
6. 5-allyl-5-isopropylbarbituric acid
7. 5-ethyl-5-isoamylbarbituric acid
8. 5-ethyl-5-(methylbutyl)barbituric acid
9. 5(1-cyclohexen-1-yl)-1,5-dimethylbarbituric acid

Working Standard Solution I.—Mix equal volumes of stock solutions of compounds 1 3, 5, 8, and 9.

Working Standard Solution II.—Mix equal volumes of stock solutions of compounds 2 4, 6, and 7.

Only compounds 2, 4, 5, 6, and 9 react with permanganate as described below.

Procedure.—The plates are prepared in the usual manner with Silica Gel G. The solvent is poured into jars and the walls are covered with wetted filter paper. The atmosphere of the jar is saturated with ammonia by placing a beaker of concentrated ammonia in the jars. The lid is sealed with silicone grease.

The serum sample is prepared in the following manner: 3 ml. of serum are acidified with 0.1 ml. of concentrated hydrochloric acid, 2 g. of anhydrous sodium sulfate is added and the solution is shaken for 3 minutes with 15 ml. of chloroform, which is then centrifuged or filtered. A 5-ml. aliquot of the extract is used for the quantitative determination and the remainder (8–10 ml.) is evaporated in a small porcelain dish on a bath of hot water. The residue is dissolved in 0.2 ml. of 75 percent v/v ethanol, and 40 μl. of this solution are applied with a micropipet to the plate under a stream of hot air, together with 20 μl. of Standard Solution I to the left and 20 μl. of Standard Solution II to the right. Two sets of spots are applied in the following order: Standard I-test Standard II-standard I-test-standard II. If two test samples are to be analyzed simultaneously, they are placed beside one another. The distance between the spots is 15–20 mm. and the starting line is 20 mm. from the lower edge of the plate. The diameter of the spots should not exceed 8 mm.

The plate is placed diagonally in the jar and taken out when the solvent front has moved 15–18 cm. from the starting line (about one hour). The solvent front is immediately marked with a pencil and the plate is dried for 5 minutes in an oven at 90–105°C. The plate is placed in a fume hood and the left half is covered with a glass plate while the right half is sprayed with 0.05 percent potassium permanganate. The glass plate is moved to cover the right half and the left half is sprayed with 0.1 percent *s*-diphenylcarbazone in 95 percent (v/v) ethanol until a slight rose color is observed, and thereafter with 0.33 percent mercuric nitrate in 0.04 M nitric acid. The barbiturates which react with permanganate give yellow spots on a rose background which disappear after 5–10 minutes. All nine drugs react with the mercury reagent and give a rose color on a light purple background. By comparing standards with unknown, identification can be made. Some of the barbiturates have nearly the same R_f, but react with different developing solutions. Elution and ultraviolet spectrophotometry may be used to quantitate the unknown quantities of barbiturates.

SERUM LIPIDS

Reagents. Aluminum Oxide, Analytical Grade.—This is washed with distilled water, dried, and its pH adjusted to 4 with hydrochloric acid.

Standards.—Cholesterol, cholesterol palmitate, palmitic acid, and crude lecithin purified 10 times by repeated precipitation. The above are dissolved in chloroform and applied to the chromoplates in amounts of 1 mg.; and with palmitic acid 1 mmole. Bloor's extract from 50 ml. of human serum is used.

Petroleum Ether-Ether, 95:5.

Ethanol-ether, 1:1 and 3:1.

Ferric Chloride Solution.—This is a 0.37 M solution in 0.1 M hydrochloric acid.

Sodium Hydroxide Solution, 3.5 M.

Hydrochloric Acid, 4 M.

Hydroxylamine Solution, 2 M.

Extraction Mixture (Trout Method).—Isopropanol, heptane, and 1 N sulfuric acid are mixed in the ratio of 40:10:1 by volume.

Dole's Titration Mixture.—A solution of 0.01 percent thymol blue and 90 percent ethanol in water, prepared by dilution of a stock 0.1 percent solution of thymol blue in water with 9 parts of redistilled ethanol.

Procedure.—The aluminum oxide is poured on a glass plate 16 × 23 cm., and is smoothed to a homogeneous layer 1–1.5 cm. thick. The chromatograms are developed in glass chambers by the ascending method at an angle of 30 degrees.

Five ml. of serum are run, with continuous stirring, into a 100-ml. volumetric flask containing about 75 ml. of a mixture of 3 volumes of 95 percent ethanol and 1 volume of ether, both redistilled. The mixture is heated to boiling on a water bath (with frequent stirring to avoid superheating), kept at the boiling temperature for a few seconds, then cooled to room temperature, made up to volume, and filtered through a fat-free filter paper. The extract is evaporated and re-extracted with 50 ml. of petroleum ether. One ml. of this extract is used for the determination.

Two cm. from the edge of the chromatoplate a mixture of standards and samples is applied in the form of a strip. The chromatoplates are developed in a system of petroleum ether-ether (95:5). Afterwards the chromatoplates are removed and dried at room temperature. The detection is carried out either under ultraviolet light at 365 mμ. or by spraying the chromatoplate with a solution of bromthymol blue. In this system cholesterol esters and triglycerides are separated. Phospholipids, fatty acids and cholesterol remain at the beginning. Cholesterol ester fractions and triglyceride fractions are removed from the layer by a vacuum pump and eluted from the adsorbent. The cholesterol esters are eluted with 4 ml. of chloroform and the adsorbent rinsed with three, 2-ml. portions of chloroform. The combined eluates are evaporated to dryness and cholesterol is estimated by any standard method. Triglycerides are similarly eluted with ethanol-ether (1:1). After evaporation the triglycerides are determined by the Stern and Shapiro method or they are first subjected to hydrolysis with 50 percent potassium hydroxide and after neutralization the liberated fatty acids are determined by Trout's method.

The method of Stern and Shapiro is given below. The spot on the chromatoplate is eluted into a glass-stoppered measuring cylinder containing approximately 8 ml. of a 3:1 alcohol-ether mixture. This mixture is brought to a boil, cooled, made up to 10 ml., filtered, and 3 ml. of the filtrate measured into a 16-mm. test tube. A blank containing 3 ml. of the alcohol-ether mixture is included in every run. Then 0.5 ml. of 2 M hydroxylamine solution and 0.5 ml. of 3.5 M sodium hydroxide solution are added and mixed. The tubes are stoppered and allowed to stand for 20 minutes at room temperature. After this period 0.6 ml. of 4 M hydrochloric acid is added, and, after mixing 0.5 ml. of ferric chloride solution (0.37 M dissolved in 0.1 M hydrochloric acid) is introduced. The tubes are mixed again and the color developed is read in a spectrophotometer at 525 mμ. A standard stock solution is made up of 295 mg. triolein in 25 ml. of 3:1 alcohol-ether. A calibration curve is drawn.

The Trout method is modified slightly in that the chromatoplate is eluted with "extraction" mixture so that the spot is contained in 10 ml. of the mixture; then 6 ml. of heptane and 4 ml. of water are introduced, and the mixture is shaken for at least 2 minutes. A 4- or 5-ml. aliquot of the upper, or "heptane," layer is removed to a glass-stoppered centrifuge tube and vigorously shaken for 5 minutes with an equal volume of 0.05 percent aqueous sulfuric acid. The tube is then centrifuged at about 300 $\times$ g. for 5 minutes. To a final tube containing Dole's "titration" mixture is transferred 3.0 ml. of the washed heptane layer, and it is then titrated with 0.018 M sodium hydroxide while being agitated by a stream of nitrogen. The heptane layers from appropriate titration blanks and palmitic acid standards are similarly washed before titration.

From the remaining chromatoplate, part of the aluminum oxide layer is removed from the site of the triglyceride fraction. The surface of the glass plate is supplemented by new aluminum oxide and smoothed to form a homogeneous layer. The chromatoplate prepared in this manner is developed in a system of petroleum ether-ether-acetic acid (94.5:5:0.5). In this system the fatty acids, cholesterol, and phospholipids are separated. The fractions are removed as described above. Cholesterol is eluted and estimated as for the cholesterol esters. Fatty acids are eluted by the extraction mixture with sulfuric acid and water and estimated by titration. Phospholipids are subjected to hydrolysis and the liberated fatty acids are estimated by the Trout method.

Normal Values.

Total lipids—300–600 mg. %
Cholesterol—17.0 % of total lipids
Triglycerides—26.5 % of total lipids
Free fatty acids—5.0 % of total lipids
Phospholipids—46.9 % of total lipids

GAS CHROMATOGRAPHY

Gas chromatography is discussed in greater detail in Chapter 38 of this volume. We will attempt to present the simplified application of this instrument to the clinical laboratory. During the past ten years many authors have emphasized the usefulness of gas chromatography in the clinical laboratory, and often have been vigorously opposed on the grounds that the instrument is much too complicated and fastidious for routine determinations. Several excellent investigators have proven this later statement to be false.

Instrumentation.—In biomedical work, there are four critical performance standards against which a gas chromatograph is measured: sensitivity, efficiency, peak symmetry, and component loss. Several instruments that fulfill these requirements are available. The following description is a composite of several models. Figure 47-23 displays the internal arrangement of one of these instruments.

Capillaries separate the carrier gas flow into two streams. One stream flows through the gas sample valve, the sample inlet, and the column, to the sample measuring side of the detector cell. The other stream goes to the reference side of the detector block. A gas sample, or a liquid sample of suitable vapor pressure, is introduced into the carrier gas stream by means of the gas sample valve, or by syringe injection. Often the liquid sampler is a microsyringe designed to introduce small, precisely measured quantities of liquids into the flow systems of gas chromatographs. The heated sample inlet vaporizes the sample. The carrier gas pushes the sample through the chromato-graphic column which separates it into its component parts. Fractions are adsorbed and absorbed by the column's packing and pass through the column at characteristic individual rates. They emerge from the column in a time sequence directly proportional to their affinities for the packing. The fractions of least affinity emerge first. With proper resolution in the column, the stream emerging from the column is composed of carrier gas and dilute bands of the components.

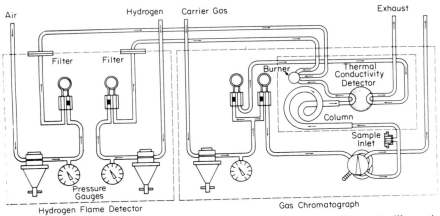

Fig. 47-23.   Gas Chromatograph Using Hydrogen Flame Detector. (Composite illustration, part of which was obtained through the courtesy of Beckman Instruments, Inc.)

The presence of sample components is detected by primarily three methods—thermal conductivity cell, hydrogen flame detector, and electron capture detector. The latter two detectors are designed for those applications that require extremely high sensitivity for detecting trace concentrations of organic compounds with fast response and sharp resolution. The less expensive standard models have a thermal conductivity detector. The elements of the thermal conductivity detector are arranged in a Wheatstone bridge configuration, and measure the difference in thermal conductivity between the sample-carrying stream of carrier gas and the reference stream of pure carrier gas. Sample gas passes into the sample-measuring side of the detector cell altering the transfer of heat from a heated filament to the cell wall. This change in the temperature of the filament alters its resistance and creates a voltage imbalance, between the reference side and the sample side of the detector. The imbalance is recorded on a standard strip chart recorder. The area under the resulting peak serves as a quantitative index of the sample component. The retention time, i.e., the interval between the sample injection and the elution of a sample component, can be interpreted to identify the component.

Very little has been said about two very important items—the carrier gas and the columns. Helium is the most widely used carrier gas. Other gases, such as argon, may be used. Columns may be made or purchased to suit the requirement of the procedure undertaken.

The accessories and modifications are now available for the standard instrument. These may be selected to fulfill the requirements of specific determinations. In the next few pages, several methods will be discussed which are either being used in clinical laboratories or will be considered for routine use in the near future.

BLOOD GASES

Procedure.—The method used is that of Wilson and Jay. This method makes use of modifications of the standard chromatograph. These modifications include the placement of an analytical cuvet, with a 0.5-ml. pipet attached to it, into the carrier gas stream. The top of the pipet is connected to a manifold which has compressed air for delivering blood to the cuvet, an open chamber for measuring the volume of blood delivered at the ambient pressure, and suction for cleansing the pipet.

Two ml. of a solution of equal parts of saponin and potassium ferricyanide and 0.5 N lactic acid (plus 0.2 ml. of antifoam) are introduced into the chamber. Helium is passed through the chamber until the chromatographic curve returns to the base line. The pipet is then filled with blood from a mercury-sealed syringe through the three-way stopcock at the bottom of the pipet, the manifold being open to room air. A reading is taken from the pipet to the nearest thousandth of a ml. The sample is delivered to the deaerated analytical chamber with compressed air pressure from the manifold. After this is completed, the manifold is again opened to room air and the blood allowed to settle in the pipet for four minutes; then the delivered volume of sample is determined. The carrier stream of helium picks up the gases liberated in the cuvet and carries them through the sampling valve and into a column 120 inches in length that contains 30- to 60-mesh molecular sieves. This column holds the carbon dioxide indefinitely and resolves the oxygen and nitrogen. The oxygen is followed by the nitrogen as it leaves the column and passes into the thermal conductivity cell where the output of the detector records the peaks. To obtain resolution of the carbon dioxide from the oxygen and nitrogen, a second sample of blood is injected into the cuvet and the gases then allowed to traverse an 18-inch column of activated charcoal.

The quantity of oxygen or carbon dioxide expressed in ml. per 100 ml. of blood is calculated in the following manner:

$$C_{BO_2} \text{ or } C_{BCO_2} = (V_L/V_B) \times F_{SO_2} \text{ or } F_{SCO_2}/(A_S \times A_u)$$

where: C_{BO_2} or C_{BCO_2} = O_2 or CO_2 content in blood in volumes percent;

$\qquad V_L$ = volume of sampling loop in gas chromatograph corrected to standard temperature, pressure, dry;

$\qquad V_B$ = volume of blood injected into analytic chamber;

$\qquad F_{SO_2}$ or F_{SCO_2} = known volume percent of O_2 or CO_2 used in calibration procedure of standard gas sample;

$\qquad A_S$ = area under curve obtained when standard containing known content of O_2 or CO_2 was analyzed; and

$\qquad A_u$ = area under curve obtained when blood sample was analyzed for unknown content, O_2 of CO_2.

The authors report that the method is simple, rapid and reliable.

Normal Values.

O₂ Content	CO₂ Content
O_2 Content	CO_2 Content
15–23 Vol % arterial blood	53–76 Vol % venous serum or plasma
10–18 Vol % venous blood	56–65 Vol % arterial serum or plasma
	47–62 Vol % venous blood
	45–54 Vol % arterial blood

HOMOVANILLIC ACID (HVA)—3-METHOXY-4-HYDROXY-PHENYLACETIC
ACID AND VANILMANDELIC (VMA)—
3-METHOXY-4-HYDROXYMANDELIC ACID

Procedure.—A fresh morning-sample of urine is collected. The urine is analyzed for creatinine by a standard method. A 300-ml. portion of urine is acidified to pH 1.5 with hydrochloric acid, saturated with sodium chloride, and extracted four times with 100-ml. portions of ethyl acetate. The combined ethyl acetate extracts are shaken thoroughly with successive small volumes of 1 N sodium bicarbonate (15 to 20 ml. total) until the pH of the emergent aqueous phase is 7.5 to 8.0. The pooled bicarbonate extracts are acidified to pH 1.5, saturated with sodium chloride, and extracted with four successive 5-ml. portions of ethyl acetate. The combined ethyl acetate extracts are diluted with ethyl acetate so that 1 ml. corresponds to 10 to 15 mg. of creatinine in the original urine; the extracts are dried over anhydrous sodium sulfate and stored at 10°C.

It is necessary to convert the aromatic acids to methyl esters. The mixture from above is reacted with 4 ml. of 1.2 percent diazomethane in anhydrous ethyl ether for fifteen minutes at 25°C. The diazomethane reagent, prepared from N'-nitro-N-methyl-N-nitrosoguanidine, is redistilled with ether and stored over anhydrous sodium sulfate at 4°C. for periods up to two weeks. After methylation of the acids with diazomethane, the ether solution is evaporated to dryness with a stream of nitrogen in a hood. The residue is dissolved in 200 μl. of absolute ethanol and stored for short periods at 4°C. prior to gas chromatography.

The material is then analyzed on a gas chromatograph using a 6-foot $\frac{1}{4}$ inch inner diameter U tube containing 8 percent ethylene glycol adipate polyester coated on 80–100 mesh Chromosorb W (Applied Sciences Laboratories, Inc.). Operating conditions are: column 204°, high voltage 1250 volts, argon inlet pressure 12 p.s.i., outflow rate 75 ml. per minute. A large peak is found at the relative retention time of 0.40—the methyl 3-methoxy-4-hydroxyphenylacetate derivative of homovanillic acid. A second derivative of homovanillic acid is prepared by reaction with diazomethane-methanol (1:1, v/v) overnight. Again a large peak is encountered at the exact relative retention time (0.26) of a standard containing homovanillic acid treated in the same way. Vanilmandelic acid cannot be separated from hippuric acid on the silicone column when the aromatic acid extract is treated with diazomethane for 15 minutes because the methyl 3-methoxy-4-hydroxymandelic derivative of vanilmandelic acid has a retention time of 0.98 relative to the methyl ester of hippuric acid. For this reason it is most convenient to determine both homovanillic acid and vanilmandelic acid in a sample of aromatic acids treated with diazomethane-methanol overnight. In this case the methyl-3, 4-dimethyloxymandelate derivative of vanilmandelic acid has a retention time of 1.21 relative to the methyl ester of hippuric acid and is easily separated. The area is calculated for the standard peaks and compared to the unknowns.

Normal Values. (mg. per mg. creatinine).

	Homovanillic Acid	Vanilmandelic Acid
Normal excretion of adults (mean)	3.6	1.4
Normal excretion of children (range)	3.9–39.9	1.2–9.5

PREGNANEDIOL

Procedure.—The gas chromatograph is equipped with a 6-foot U-tube column (5 mm.) containing Gas Chromosorb P., 80–100 mesh coated with the liquid phase,

1.5 percent SE-52. The column temperature is maintained at 210°C.; the strontium-90 detector cell at 265–270°C.; the flash heater at 280–285°C. The applied voltage is kept at 600 volts and the gas flow is maintained at an exhaust outlet of 80 ml. per minute.

The standard consists of pregnanediol (10 mg.) dissolved in Reagent grade methanol to a concentration of 1 mg. per ml. Four μl. are injected into the column.

Specimens consist of either blood or urine. A 25-ml. sample of blood is drawn from the subjects and transferred to tubes containing heparin. Samples are prepared for analysis two hours after collection. For satisfactory results with plasma or blood, it is necessary to employ a 1:10 dilution with water prior to hydrolysis. Twenty-four-hour urines are collected with no preservative. Aliquots are frozen until processed. Twenty-five-ml. aliquots of pregnancy urines and 50-ml. aliquots of nonpregnancy specimens are analyzed.

The specimen is hydrolyzed by the schema shown in Table 47-1.

TABLE 47-1.   ISOLATION OF PREGNANEDIOL: ENZYMATIC HYDROLYSIS

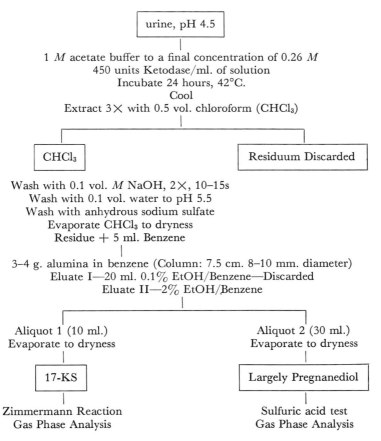

Comparison of the areas under the peaks by triangulation is completed for unknown and standards. To calculate the area of a peak, the two shoulders of the peak are connected by a line and a perpendicular is drawn from the apex to the base of the theoretical triangle. The area is the product of the height of the perpendicular and the width at its midpoint.

Normal Values

0.0–1.5 mg./24 hours (male)
0.0–10 mg./24 hours (nonpregnant female)
5–120 mg./24 hours (pregnant female)

17-KETOSTEROIDS

Dehydroepiandrosterone (DHEA), etiocholanolone (E), and androsterone (A), 11-oxy-etiocholanolone (11-OE), 11B-OH-androsterone (11B-OHA) and 11B-OH-etiocholan-

TABLE 47-2. ISOLATION OF URINARY 17-KETOSTEROIDS

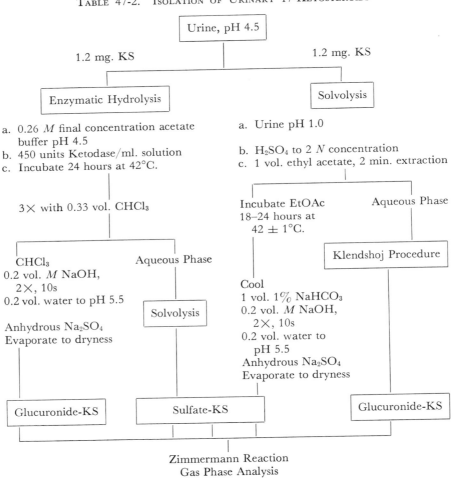

olone (11B-OHE) serve as reference standards. The steroids are dissolved in Reagent Grade methanol to a concentration of 1 mg. per ml. and 8 μl. are injected into the column.

The column and unit controls are the same as those for the pregnanediol except that a 1 percent SE—52 column is used and the exhaust flow is 50 ml. per minute.

The specimen consists of twenty-four-hour urine sample collected without preservative. Aliquots are frozen until the time of processing. The schema for isolation of the urinary 17-ketosteroids is shown in Table 47-2.

Procedure.—The Klendshoj procedure is described in the following paragraph. Pipet 10 ml. of urine into a 50-ml. Pyrex glass-stoppered bottle. Add 3 ml. of concentrated hydrochloric acid, and place in a boiling water bath for ten minutes. Cool and add 10 ml. of ethylene dichloride. Stopper and shake for 15 minutes with a mechanical shaker. Separate the bottom layer and filter into a dry 50-ml. Pyrex bottle. Add 20 pellets of sodium hydroxide and shake for 15 minutes. Filter the solvent into a dry test tube. Pipet 2 ml. of the ethylene dichloride into a dry test tube and evaporate the solvent on the water bath at 100°C.

Bush and Willoughby reported a preliminary purification of crude extracts by paper chromatography which permits the separation of the steroids into three areas, namely the corticoids, 11-oxy- and 11-desoxy-17-ketosteroids. Corticosterone, 11-oxy-etiocholanolone, and DHEA serve as the reference standards. Zones on the unknowns corresponding to these are eluted and analyzed by gas chromatography.

The steroid residues are dissolved in 50 μl. of methanol and 8 μl. equivalent to 8–20 ml. urine are injected into the columns. The triangular area of the unknown is compared with the standards.

The Zimmermann reaction involves the interaction of alcoholic m-dinitrobenzene and potassium hydroxide. A saturated solution of aqueous potassium hydroxide (approximately 12 M) is prepared and kept in a rubber-stoppered Pyrex bottle at room temperature. This solution is suitable for use at least two months. A portion of the potassium hydroxide solution is diluted with ethanol just before use so that its concentration is 2.5 M. A 2 percent alcoholic solution of m-dinitrobenzene is prepared just before use. With each set of unknowns appropriate standards are run. 0.2 ml. of m-dinitrobenzene and of alcoholic potassium hydroxide solutions are added to each tube, followed by shaking. Thorough solution and mixing of the reagents and dried extract is essential. The mixture is allowed to stand in the dark for approximately 30 minutes at 25°C. $\pm$ 1. Quantitation of the 17-ketosteroids is then carried out.

Normal values.

8–25 mg./24 hours (male)
5–18 mg./24 hours (female)

ESTROGENS

Procedure.—The column and unit controls are set up as for the 17-ketosteroids with the exception that the argon gas flow is maintained at 20–25 p.s.i. with an exhaust flow of 80 ml. per minute.

Estrone, 17B-estradiol and estriol are used as standards and are dissolved in Reagent grade methanol to a concentration of 2 mg. per ml. Eight μl. are injected into the column.

Twenty-four-hour urine specimens are collected with no preservative. Aliquots are frozen until the time of processing. 25–100 ml. samples are prepared for gas chromatography in Table 47-3.

The final residue is taken up in 50 microliters of pyridine-acetic anhydride (1:1).

Table 47-3.   Isolation of Urinary 17-Ketosteroids and Estrogens

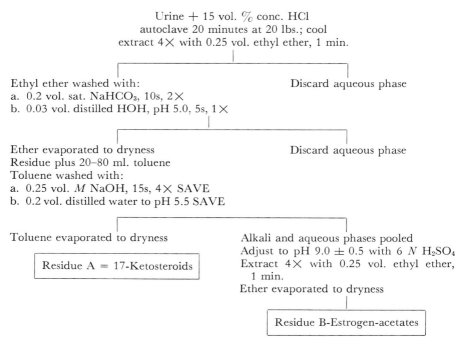

Urine + 15 vol. % conc. HCl
autoclave 20 minutes at 20 lbs.; cool
extract 4× with 0.25 vol. ethyl ether, 1 min.

Ethyl ether washed with: Discard aqueous phase
a. 0.2 vol. sat. NaHCO₃, 10s, 2×
b. 0.03 vol. distilled HOH, pH 5.0, 5s, 1×

Ether evaporated to dryness   Discard aqueous phase
Residue plus 20–80 ml. toluene
Toluene washed with:
a. 0.25 vol. M NaOH, 15s, 4× SAVE
b. 0.2 vol. distilled water to pH 5.5 SAVE

Toluene evaporated to dryness   Alkali and aqueous phases pooled
                                                  Adjust to pH 9.0 ± 0.5 with 6 N H₂SO₄
    Residue A = 17-Ketosteroids   Extract 4× with 0.25 vol. ethyl ether,
                                                      1 min.
                                                  Ether evaporated to dryness

                                                      Residue B-Estrogen-acetates

Eight μl. equivalent to 4–16 ml. of urine are injected into the column. To identify the steroids on the chromatograms, reference estrogen acetates are added to the acetates of the unknowns and the mixtures are rechromatographed.

Normal Values (total).

4–60 μg./24 hours (female)
4–25 μg./24 hours (male)

17-HYDROXYCORTICOSTEROIDS

Procedure.—The column and unit controls were set the same as for estrogens. The standards consist of cortisol, cortisone, tetrahydrocortisol, and tetrahydrocortisone. The steroids are dissolved in methanol to a concentration of 1 mg. per ml. and 4 μl. are injected into the column.

Twenty-four-hour urine samples are collected with no preservative. The specimens are stored in the cold and 50 ml. are used for the reduced steroids and 1000 ml. for cortisol analysis. Enzymatic hydrolysis, described under the pregnanediol method, is used with tetrahydrocortisol and tetrahydrocortisone.

One liter of each twenty-four-hour urine collection is subjected to hydrolysis with hydrochloric acid at pH 1 for 36 hours (originally this procedure used also for aldosterone determinations). The acidified urine is then continuously treated with chloroform (2:1) in an extractor of the Cohen type for a period of 12 hours. After neutralization to pH 7 with 1 percent sodium hydroxide, the chloroform extract is dried with anhydrous sodium sulfate and brought to dryness under reduced pressure. The dried extract is taken up in chloroform, purified by passing through a Florisil Column, and eluted with 25 percent methanol in chloroform. Eluate III, 25 percent methanol in chloroform, contains the corticoids. After evaporation, the residue is taken up in 50 μl. of methanol and 1–8 μl. are injected into the column.

Normal Values.—0.8–9.7 mg./24 hours (total).

SELECTED BIBLIOGRAPHY

Abegg, H., "An Apparatus for the Introduction of Small Test Mixtures into Gas Chromatographic Columns," J. Chromatogr., 9, 519–521, 1962.

Annino, J. S., Clinical Chemistry, 2nd Ed., Little, Brown and Co., Boston, Mass., 1960.

Baird-Atomic, Inc., Instruction Manual for the Baird-Atomic Flame Photometer Model KY-1, Cambridge, Mass.

Barlow, J. J., "A Sensitive Method of High Specificity for Determination of Urinary Estrogens," Anal. Biochem., 6, 435–450, 1963.

Baron, D. N., and Economidis, "Thin-layer Chromatography for Amino-acids and Sugars," J. Clin. Path., 16, 484–486, 1963.

Bates, R. W., and Cohen, H., "Experimental Basis for Selecting Optimal Conditions for Quantitative Fluorometry of Natural Estrogens," Endocr., 47, 166–181, 1950.

Bates, R. W., and Cohen, H., "Fluorescence Spectra of Natural Estrogens and their Application to Biological Extracts," Endocr., 47, 182–192, 1950.

Baumgarten, W., "Panel Discussion Assay Technics," Amer. J. Cardiol., 6, 447, 1960.

Bennett, R. D., Heftmann, E., "Devices for Continuous Development and Sample Application in Preparative Thin-layer Chromatography," J. Chromatogr., 12, 245–248, 1963.

Bennett, R. D., and Heftmann, E., "Thin-layer Chromatography of Corticosteroids," J. Chromatogr., 9, 348–352, 1962.

Bican-Fister, T., Kajganovic, V., "Separation and Identification of Sulfonamides by Thin Layer Chromatography," J. Chromatogr., 11, 492–495, 1963.

Bodansky, O., and Schwartz, M. K., "Alkaline and Acid Phosphatases," in J. H. Quartel (Ed.), Methods in Medical Research, 9, Yearbook and Medical Publ., Inc., p. 86–91, Chicago, 1961.

Bongiovanni, A. M., and Clayton, G. W., Jr., "Simplified Method for Routine Determination of Pregnanediol and Pregnanetriol in Urine," Johns Hopk. Hosp., 94, 180–186, 1954.

Bloor, W. R., "The Oxidative Determination of Phospholipid (Lecithin and Cephalin) in Blood and Tissues," J. Biol. Chem., 82, 273–286, 1929.

Boy, J., "Automatic Determination of Blood Cholesterol," J. Clin. Path., 16, 178–180, 1963.

Brambel, C. E., "The So-called Prothrombin Tests; Their Relative Practical Values with a Discussion as to What We Are Actually Measuring," in Blood Clotting and Allied Problems, Third Conference, p. 135, Josiah Macy Foundation, New York, 1950.

Brenner, M., "Thin Layer Chromatographic Detection of Amino Acids in Urine," Experientia, 19, 213–217, 1963.

Brown, D. E., "Flame Photometry," Am. J. Clin. Path., 26, 807–816, 1956.

Brown, J. B., "Chemical Method for Determination of Oestriol, Oestrone, and Oestradiol in Human Urine," Biochem. J., 60, 185–193, 1955.

Burstein, S., and Lieberman, S., "Hydrolysis of Ketosteroid Hydrogen Sulfates by Solvolysis Procedures," J. Biol. Chem., 233, 331–335, 1958.

Bush, I. E., "Methods of Paper Chromatography of Steroids Applicable to Study of Steroids in Mammalian Blood and Tissues," Biochem. J., 50, 370–378, 1952.

Bush, I. E., and Willoughby, M., "The Excretion of Allo-tetrahydrocortisol in Human Urine," Biochem. J., 77, 689–700, 1957.

Caneclides, R. M., and Tomlinson, M., Sr., "A Comparison of Anticoagulants and/or Preservatives Affecting Blood Glucose Determination by Automation," Amer. J. of Med. Tech., 28, 195–201, 1962.

Chambliss, K. W., Nouse, D. C., "Blood Oxygen Determination by Gas Chromatography," Clin. Chem., 8, 654–659, 1962.

Chasson, A. L., Grady, H. J., and Stanley, M. A., "Determination of Creatinine by Means of Automatic Chemical Analysis," Am. J. Clin. Path., 35, 83–88, 1961.

Cohn, G. L., Pancake, E., "A Standardized Technique for the Separation of Steroids by Thin Layer Chromatography," Nature (London), 201, 75–76, 1964.

Cooke, K. B., and Patson, J. V., "Some Modifications to the Autoanalyzer Method for Serum Alkaline Phosphatase," Abstract, Proc. Assoc. Clin. Biochem., 6, 150–151, 1961.

Cooper, J. A., Abbott, J. P., Rosengreen, B. K., and Claggett, W. R., "Gas Chromatography of Urinary Steroids, 1. A Preliminary Report on the Demonstration and Identification of Pregnanediol in Pregnancy Urine, by Means of Gas Chromatography," Amer. J. Clin. Path., 38, 388–391, 1962.

Cooper, J. A., and Creech, B. G., "The Application of Gas-liquid Chromatography to the Analysis of Urinary 17-Ketosteroids," Anal. Biochem., 2, 502–506, 1961.

Cotlove, E., and Mishi, Hiroshi H., "Automatic Titration with Direct Read-out of Chloride Concentration," Clin. Chem., 7, 285, 1961.

Cotlove, E., Tranthan, H. V., and Bowman, R. L., "An Instrument and Method for Automatic, Rapid, Accurate, and Sensitive Titration of Chloride in Biological Samples," J. Lab. and Clin. Med., 51, 461, 1958.

Crawford, N., and Rudd, B. T., "A Spectrophotofluorimetric Method for the Determinations of Serotonin (5-Hydroxytryptamine) in Plasma," Clin. Chim. Acta., 7, 114–121, 1962.

Crofford, O. B., and Lacy, W. W., "Rapid Micro Method for Determination of Blood Sugar in Mice," J. Lab. and Clin. Med., 61, 708–712, 1963.

Crout, R., and Sjoerdsma, A., "Catecholamines in the Localization of Pheochromocytoma," Circulation, 22, 516–525, 1960.

Crowley, L. V., "Automated Determination of Uric Acid by a Carbonate, Abstract, Clin. Res., 10, 85, 1962.

Demole, E., "Recent Progress in Thin Layer Microchromatography," J. Chromatogr., 6, 2–21, 1961.

DeMoor, P., Osinski, P., Deckx, R., and Steeno, O., "The Specificity of Fluorometric Corticoid Determinations," Clin. Chim. Acta, 7, 475–480, 1962.

Dole, V. P., "A Relation Between Non-esterified Fatty Acids in Plasma and the Metabolism of Glucose," J. Clin. Invest., 35, 150–154, 1956.

Eilers, R. J., Grady, H. J., Crocker, C., and Knowles, S., "Simultaneous Determination of Serum Creatinine and Urea Nitrogen by Means of Automatic Chemical Analysis," Abstract., Am. J. Clin. Path., 39, 301, 1963.

Engle, L. L., Slaunwhite, W. R., Jr., Carter, P., and Nathanson, I. T., "The Separation of Natural Estrogens by Counter-current Distribution," J. Biol. Chem., 185, 255–263, 1950.

Epstein, E., Boginski, E. S., and Zak, B., "Methods for the Determination of Serum Phosphate," Clin. Chem., 9, 441, 1963.

Failing, J. F., Buckley, M. W., and Zak, B., "Automatic Determination of Serum Proteins," Am. J. Clin. Path., 33, 83–88, 1960.

Failing, J. F., Buckley, M. W., and Zak, B., "A Study on an Ultramicro and Automated Procedure for Serum Proteins," Am. J. Med. Tech., 27, 177–185, 1961.

Fales, H. M., Haahti, E. O., Luukkainen, T., Vandenheuvel, W. J., and Horning, E. C., "Milligram-scale Preparative Gas Chromatography of Steroids and Alkaloids," Anal. Biochem., 4, 296–305, 1962.

Fingerhut, B., Ferzola, R., Marsh, W. H., Levine, J. B., "An Automated Method for a Colorimetric Determination of Serum Glutamic Oxalacetic Transaminase," Ann. N. Y. Acad. Sci., 102(1), 137–143, 1962.

Fiske, C. H., and Subbarow, Y., "The Colorimetric Determination of Phosphorus," J. Biol. Chem., 66, 375–400, 1925.

Folin, O., and Wu, H., "A System of Blood Analysis," J. Biol. Chem., 38, 81–110, 1919.

Galla, S. J., and Ottenstein, D. M., "Measurement of Inert Gases in Blood by Gas Chromatography," Ann. N. Y. Acad. Sci., 102, 4–14, 1962.

Glenn, E. M., and Nelson, D. H., "Chemical Method for the Determination of 17-Hydroxycosteroiden," Aufsteigende und Absteigende Technik., Hoppe Seyler, Z. Physiol. Chem., J. Clin. Endocr., 13, 911–921, 1953.

Goldel, L., Zimmermann, W., and Lommer, D., "Dunnschichtchromatographie von Corticosteroiden," Aufsteigende und Absteigende Technik., Hoppe Seyler, Z. Physiol. Chem., 333, 35–45, 1963.

Grady, H. J., and Lamar, M. A., "Glucose Determination by Automated Chemical Method," Clin. Chem., 5, 542–550, 1959.

Hamilton, L. H., "Gas Chromatography for Respiratory and Blood Gas Analysis," Ann. N. Y. Acad. Sci., 102, 15–28, 1962.

Hofmann, A. F., "Thin Layer Adsorption Chromatography of Proteins on Hydroxylapatite," Biochim. Biophys. Acta., 60, 458–460, 1962.

Hofmann, A. F., "Thin Layer Adsorption Chromatography on Microscope Slides," Anal. Biochem., 3, 145–149, 1962.

Instruction Manual for Model 202 Clot Timer, Mechrolab Inc., Mountain View, Calif.

Isreeli, J., Pelavin, M., and Kessler, G., "Continuous Flame Photometry," Ann. N. Y. Acad. Sci., 87(2), 636–649, 1960.

Jacobs, S. L., Sobel, C., and Henry, R. J., "Specificity of the Trihydroxyindole Method for Determination of Urinary Catecholamines," J. Clin. Endocr. and Metab., 21, 305–314, 1961.

Jenkins, P., "A Reliable System for the Introduction of Samples to Gas Chromatographic Columns, Particularly Suited for Quantitative Capillary Column Analysis, "Nature (London), 197, 72–73, 1963.

Johnson, J., "Protein Free Filtrate or Dialysate; Some Experiences with Automation in a Clinical Chemistry Laboratory with Special Reference to the Routine Blood Glucose Determinations," Amer. J. of Med. Tech., 24, 271–280, 1958.

Johnsen, S. G., "Fractionation of Urinary 17-Ketosteroids," Acta Endocr. (Kobenhavin), 21, 176, 1956.

Jones, G. E., Turner, D., Sarlos, I. J., Barnes, A. C., and Cohen, R., "The Determination of Urinary Pregnanediol by Gas Liquid Chromatography," Fertil. Steril., 13, 544–549, 1962.

Jung, I., Bourgoin, C., Foussard, J. C., Audrin, P., and Morand, P., "Application of Thin Layer Chromatography to Hormonal Determinations and Estimations, I. Separation and Determination of Urinary Estrogens: Estrone, Estradiol, Estriol.," Rev. Franc. Etud. Clin. Biol., 8, 406–409, 1963.

Kenny, A. P., and Jamison, A., "Direct Estimation of Serum Total Cholesterol on the Autoanalyzer., "Proc. Assoc. Clin. Biochem., 2(8), 213–214, 1963.

Kessler, G., and Wolfman, M., "An Automated Procedure for the Simultaneous Determination of Calcium and Phosphorus in Serum and Urine," Abstract. Clin. Chem., 8, 429, 1962.

Kessler, G., and Wolfman, M., "An Automated Procedure for the Simultaneous Determination of Calcium and Phosphorus," Abstract. Clin. Chem., 10, 686–703, 1964.

Keyser, J. W., "Determination of Plasma and Serum Albumin by Dye Methods," Proc. Assoc. Clin. Biochemists, 2, 40–41, 1962.

Klendshoj, N. C., Feldstein, M., and Sprague, A., "A Determination of 17-Ketosteroids in Urine," J. Clin. Endocr., 13, 922–927, 1953.

Kliman, B., and Peterson, R. E., "Double Isotope Derivative Assay of Aldosterone in Biological Extracts," J. Biol. Chem., 235, 1639–1648, 1960.

Kroman, H. S., Bender, S. R., "An Improved Method for the Gas Chromatographic Separate of Estrogens," J. Chromatogr., 10, 111–112, 1963.

Lees, T. M., and Demuria, P. J., "A Simple Method for the Preparation of Thin Layer Chromatography Plates," J. Chromatogr., 8, 108–109, 1962.

Lehman, J., and Karamustafaoglu, V., "Rapid Differentiation of Barbiturates in Blood Serum by Thin-layer Chromatography," Scand. J. Clin. & Lab. Invest., 14, 554–558, 1962.

Lie, K. B., and Nyc, J. F., "The Chromatography of Lipids in Test Tubes Coated with a Thin Layer of Silica Acid," J. Chromatogr., 8, 75–81, 1962.

Lipsky, S. R., and Landowne, R. A., "Effects of Varying the Chemical Composition of the Stationary Phase on the Separation of Certain C_{19}, C_{21}, and C_{27} Steroids by Gas Chromatography," Anal. Chem., 33, 818–828, 1961.

Lisboa, B. P., and Diczfalusy, E., "Colour Reaction for the Sitre Characterisation of Steroid Oestrogens on Thin Layer Chromatograms," Acta Endocr. (Kobenhavin), 43, 545–560, 1963.

Marsh, W. H., Fingerhut, B., and Kirsch, E., "Adaptation of an Alkaline Phosphatase Method for Automatic Colorimetric Analysis," Clin. Chem., 5, 119–126, 1959.

Marsh, W. H., Fingerhut, B., Kirsch, E., "Determination of Urea Nitrogen with the Diacetyl Method in an Automatic Dialyzing Apparatus," Amer. J. Clin. Path., 28, 681–688, 1957.

Marshall, M. B., and Whitman, D. H., "A Source of Error in Automatic Plasma Albumin Estimation," Guys Hosp. Reports., 11, 313–320, 1962.

Matthews, J. S., Pereda, V. A. L., and Aguilera, P. A., "The Quantitative Analysis of Steroids by Thin-layer Chromatography," J. Chromatogr., 9, 331–338, 1962.

McEwen, D. J., "Improved Sampling Valve for Gas Chromatography," J. Chromatogr., 9, 266–269, 1962.

McGuckin, W. F., "Experience with the Autoanalyzer in the Analysis of Blood for Sugar and Urea," Abstract. Clin. Chem., 5, 262, 1959.

McGuckin, W. F., and Power, M. H., "Determination of Blood Sugar by an Automated Method," Abstract. Clin. Chem., 4, 541, 1958.

Nash, N., Allen, P., Bebenue, A., et al., "A Technique for the Recovery of Compounds for Thin-layer Chromatograph Strips for Infra-red Analysis," J. Chromatogr., 12, 421–423, 1963.

Nelson, D. H., and Samuels, L. T., "Method for Determination of 17-Hydroxycorticosteroids in Blood: 17-Hydroxycorticosterone in Peripheral Circulation," J. Clin. Endocr., 12, 519–526, 1952.

Nelson, M. G., and Lamont, A., "Haemoglobinometry by an Automatic Analytical Procedure," J. Clin. Path., 14, 448–450, 1961.

Niall, M. M., and Owen, J. A., "The Necessity for Plasma or Serum Blanks in Determining Albumin or Total Protein with the Autoanalyzer," Proc. Assoc. Clin. Biochem., 1(5), 130–131, 1961.

Nybom, N., "A New System for Thin Layer Chromatography," Nature (London), 198, 1229–1230, 1963.

Patti, A. A., Bonanno, P., Frawley, T. F., and Stein, A. A., "Preliminary Studies on the Application of Gas Phase Chromatography to the Separation and Identification of Steroids in Biological Fluids. I. Pregnanediol. II. 17-Ketosteroids. III. Estrogen. IV. 17OH Corticosteroids," Acta Endocr. (Kobenhaven), 42 (Suppl. 77), 1–34, 1963.

Patti, A. A., Bonanno, P., Frawley, T. F., and Stein, A. A., "Gas-phase Chromatography in Separation and Identification of Pregnanediol in Urine and Blood of Pregnant Women," Obstet. Gynec., 21, 302–307, 1963.

Patti, A. A., Bonanno, P., Frawley, T. F., and Stein, A. A., "Preliminary Studies on the Application of Gas Phase Chromatography to the Separation and Identification of Steroids in Biological Fluids," Acta Endocr. Supp., 77, 3–34, 1963.

Peereboom, J. W., Beekes, H. W., "The Analysis of Mixtures of Animal and Vegetable Fats. III. Separation of Some Sterols and Sterol Acetates by Thin Layer Chromatography," J. Chromatogr., 9, 316–320, 1962.

Peters, J. H., "The Determination of Creatinine and Creatine in Blood and Urine with the Photoelectric Colorimeter," J. Biol. Chem., 146, 179–186, 1942.

Rink, M., and Herrmann, S., "Separation of Sugars Occurring in Urine by Means of Thin Layer Chromatography," J. Chromatogr., 12, 415–416, 1963.

Ross, E. J., "Urinary Excretion of Cortisol in Cushing's Syndrome; Effect of Corticotropin," J. Clin. Endocr., 20, 1360–1365, 1960.

Saroff, H. A., Karmen, A., and Healy, J. W., "Gas Chromatography of the Amino Acid Esters in Ammonia," J. Chromatogr., 9, 122–123, 1962.

Shaffert, R. R., Kingsley, G. R., and Getchell, G., "Automated Determination of Serum Glutamic Oxalacetic and Glutamic Pyruvic Transaminase," Abstract. Clin. Chem., 8, 429, 1962.

Schwartz, M. K., Kessler, G., and Bodansky, O., "A Comparison of Acid and Alkaline Phosphatase Determination by Manual and Automatic Technic," Abstract. Clin. Chem., 5, 368–369.

Schwartz, M. K., Kessler, G., and Bodansky, O., "Comparison of Serum Alkaline Phosphatase Activities Determined with Sodium-B-glycerophosphate and Sodium Phenylphosphate as Substrates," Am. J. Clin. Path., 33, 295–280, 1960.

Shaw, K. N. F., McMillian, A., and Armstrong, N. D., "The Metabolism of 3,4-Dihydroxyphenylalamine," J. Biol. Chem., 226, 255–266, 1957.

Skeggs, L. T., Jr., "An Automatic Method of Colorimetric Analysis," Amer. J. Clin. Path., 28, 311–322, 1957.

Slaunwhite, W. R., Jr., Engel, L. L., Scott, J. F., and Ham, C. L., "Fluorescence and Absorption Spectra of Estrogens Heated in Sulfuric Acid," J. Biol. Chem., 201, 615–620, 1953.

Snodgrass, P. J., Fuiva, K., and Hviid, K., "Validation of Automatic Photometric Analysis of Sodium and Potassium," J. Lab. Clin. Med., 60, 983–990, 1962.

Smith, L. L., and Foell, T., "Thin Layer Chromatography of Steroids on Starch-bound Silica Gel Chromatoplate," J. Chromatogr., 9, 339–344, 1962.

Sobel, C., and Henry, R. J., "Determination of Catecholamines (Adrenaline and Noradrenaline) in Urine and Tissue," Amer. J. Clin. Path., 27, 240–245, 1957.

Squibb, R. L., "An Improved Technique for the Preparation of Scanning of Thin Layer Chromatograms," Nature (London), 198, 317, 1963.

Stern, I., and Shapiro, B., "A Rapid and Simple Method for the Determination of Esterified Fatty Acids and for Total Fatty Acids in Blood," J. Clin. Path., 6, 158–160, 1953.

Stitch, S. R., Halkenston, I. D. R., and Hillman, J., "The Enzymic Hydrolysis of Steroid Conjugates," Biochem. J., 63, 710–715, 1956.

Sweeley, C. C., and Williams, C. M., "Microanalytical Determination of Urinary Aromatic Acids by Gas Chromatography," Anal. Biochem., 2, 83–88, 1961.

Szentirmai, A., Howath, B. I., Hauk, M., "A Rapid Screening Test for Determination of Total I-amino Acids in Urine and Serum," Clin. Chim. Acta, 7, 459–462, 1962.

Teraniski, R., Corse, J. W., Day, J. C., and Jennings, W. G., "Volman Collector for Gas Chromatography," J. Chromatogr., 9, 244–245, 1962.

Trout, D. L., Estes, E. H., Jr., and Friedberg, S. J., "Titration of Free Fatty Acids of Plasma," J. of Lipid Res., 1, 199–202, 1960.

Turner, D. A., Seegar, Jones, G. E., Sarlos, I. J., Barnes, A. C., and Cohen, R., "Determination of Urinary Pregnanediol by Gas Chromatography," Anal. Biochem., **5**, 99–106, 1963.

Udenfriend, S., Fluorescence Assay in Biology and Medicine, Academic Press, New York, 1962.

Vacikova, A., Felt, V., and Malikova, J., "Chromatography of Serum Lipid Fractions on a Thin Layer of Al_2O_3," J. Chromatogr., **9**, 301–306, 1962.

Vaedtke, J., and Gajewska, A., "Thin Layer Partition Chromatography; A quick Method of Chromatography for Steroids," J. Chromatogr., **9**, 345–347, 1962.

Vandenhenvel, W. J. A., Sweely, C. C., and Horning, E. C., "Separation of Steroids by Gas Chromatography," J. Amer. Chem. Soc., **82**, 3481–3482, 1960.

Weichselbaum, T. E., "An Accurate and Rapid Method for the Determination of Proteins in Small Amounts of Blood Serum and Plasma," Am. J. Clin. Path. (Tech. Sec.), **10**, 40–49, associated with Am. J. Clin. Path., **16**, 1946.

Williams, C. M., and Greer, M., "Diagnosis of Neuroblastoma by Quantitative Gas Chromatographic Analysis of Urinary Homovanillic and Vanilmandelic Acid," Clin. Chim. Acta, **7**, 880–883, 1962.

Winsten, S., "The Use of a Single Manifold Sugar and Urea Determination on the Autoanalyzer," Ann. N. Y. Acad. Sci., **102(1)**, 127–136, 1962.

Wollenweber, P., "Dunschicht-chromatographische Trennungen von Amino-sauren an Cellulose-Schichten," J. Chromatogr., **9**, 369–371, 1962.

Wollenweber, P., "Thin Layer Chromatographic Separation of Amino Acids on Cellulose Layers," J. Chromatogr., **9**, 369–371, 1962.

Wotiz, H. H., "Studies in Steroid Metabolism XIII, Factors Influencing the Gas Chromatographic Stability of Steroids," Biochim. Biophys. Acta, **63**, 180–185, 1962.

Wotiz, H. H., and Martin, H. F., "Studies in Steroid Metabolism," J. Biol. Chem., **236**, 1312–1317, 1961.

Yamaguchi, S., Seki, I., Okuda, S., and Tsuda, Y., "Gas Chromatography of the Morphine Alkaloids and the Related Compounds," Chem. Pharm. Bull. (Tokyo), **10**, 755–757, 1962.

Zoellner, N., Wolfram, G., and Amin. G., "On Quantitative Evaluation of Thin Layer Chromatograms of Cholesterol Esters," Klin. Wschr., **40**, 273–275, 1962.

Zoellner, N., and Wolfram, G., "Studies on Thin Layer Chromatography of Lipoids," Klin. Wschr., **40**, 1098–1101, 1962.

Zoellner, N., and Wolfram, G., "Thin Layer Chromatographic Systems for the Separation of Plasma Lipoids," Klin. Wschr., **40**, 1101–1107, 1962.

Chapter 48

NATURAL FATS

By Virgil C. Mehlenbacher

Quality Assurance Department
Swift and Co.
Chicago, Illinois

VISIBLE SPECTROMETRY

METALS

Visible absorption spectrometry provides a convenient means of determining almost any substance that can be treated in such a way as to form a colored solution in which the intensity of the color is proportional to the concentration of the substance. In the specific case of fats, methods of this type have been used for determination of metals, and of certain nonmetals such as phosphorus, antioxidants, tocopherol, gossypol, sesamin, and related compounds.

The general procedure usually involves these basic steps; (a) treatment of the properly prepared sample with a reagent to form a colored solution; (b) measurement of the transmittance of the colored solution at the appropriate wavelength; and (c) estimation of the concentration by comparison with similar measurements of standards of known concentration.

Apparatus.—The methods presented here for metals were designed for use with a Coleman Jr. spectrometer. Other instruments may be used, although some adjustments may be necessary. It is essential that the same instrument be used for preparation of the concentration-transmittance graph and for analysis.

NICKEL

Procedure.—Weigh a sample of suitable size, depending on the nickel content, and prepare the ash by heating over a burner and then in a muffle furnace at 500°–550°C. to remove all carbonaceous matter. Dissolve the ash in 1 ml. of concentrated hydrochloric acid. Slightly more acid may be used if needed for complete solution but amount of acid should be kept at a minimum. Evaporate almost to dryness at 160°C., but stop heating before complete dryness is reached. Dissolve the residue in distilled water and transfer to a 50-ml. volumetric flask. The total volume should not exceed 15 ml. at this point. Add three ml. of saturated bromine water and allow to stand one minute. Add ammonium hydroxide (sp. gr. 0.90) a drop at a time until the excess bromine is destroyed, as indicated by the disappearance of the brown color. Then add 5 ml. of ammonium hydroxide. If iron is absent, proceed to the addition of dimethylglyoxime.

If iron is present, filter the solution at this point. Dissolve the precipitate with a minimum of hydrochloric acid (1 + 1, v/v), wash the filter paper with distilled water, and collect the filtrate and washings in a beaker. Reprecipitate the iron with sufficient ammonium hydroxide to make the solution definitely basic, but avoid a large excess. Refilter and wash the precipitate with distilled water. Combine the filtrate and washings, evaporate the solution to a volume of a few ml. and then transfer to a 50-ml. volumetric flask. Proceed from here with the addition of dimethylglyoxime.

Add 10 ml. of dimethylglyoxime solution (0.1 g. in 100 ml. of 95 percent ethanol) followed by 15–20 ml. of 95 percent ethanol. Mix, make up to volume with distilled water and mix again. Avoid exposure to bright light or direct sunlight in carrying out the reactions and the color development.

Allow the solution to stand 5 minutes to permit the full development of color and then immediately transfer a portion into a cuvet. Measure the transmittance at 445 mμ after adjusting the instrument to read 100 percent transmittance with an identical cuvet containing distilled water. Prepare and conduct simultaneously a blank determination that is similar in all respects except for omission of the sample. The transmittance of the blank should be 98 ± 1 percent. Determine the equivalent nickel content by reference to a concentration-transmittance graph.

Preparation of Concentration-Transmittance Graph.—Prepare a nickel solution by dissolving 2.2617 g. of nickel sulfate ($NiSO_4 \cdot 6H_2O$) in distilled water in a 500-ml. volumetric flask. Add 30 ml. of concentrated hydrochloric acid and bring to volume with distilled water. This solution contains 1000 μg. of nickel per ml. Transfer 50 ml. of this nickel solution to 500-ml. volumetric flask and make up to volume with distilled water. Make another 50 to 500 dilution in a similar manner. The final dilution then contains 10 μg. of nickel per ml. Transfer 8 aliquots, from 1.0 to 10.0 ml. inclusive, of this solution to 50-ml. volumetric flasks. Dilute each to 15 ml. with distilled water, and prepare a blank by placing 15 ml. of water in another flask. These should then cover the range of 0–100 μg. of nickel. Treat each of the standards and the blank as directed for the determination of nickel, beginning with the addition of bromine. Finally, plot percent transmittance against micrograms of nickel on semilogarithmic paper.

Calculation.—The nickel content found from the graph divided by the weight of the sample equals the nickel content of the sample in parts per million or μg. per g.

IRON

Procedure.—Prepare a hydroquinone solution containing 2.5 g. of hydroquinone and 1 ml. of hydrochloric acid (1 + 1, v/v) diluted to 100 ml. with distilled water.

Ash 5 g. of sample, or more if the sample contains less than 5 p.p.m. of iron. Add 5 ml. of hydrochloric acid (1 + 1, v/v) and heat just to boiling. Transfer the sample quantitatively to a 50-ml. volumetric flask, and make to volume with distilled water. Mix thoroughly, and transfer 10 ml. into a cuvet. A smaller aliquot may be used if necessary to come within the limits of the concentration-transmittance graph.

Add 2 ml. of the hydroquinone solution, 5 ml. of 1,10-phenanthroline solution (0.1 percent in distilled water), and 5 ml. of aqueous sodium acetate solution (20 percent w/w). These reagents should be added with a volumetric pipet, and the solution should be thoroughly mixed after addition of each reagent.

Conduct a blank determination along with the sample to make certain that none of the reagents is contaminated, and also to use as a reference solution against which the transmittance of the sample is measured. The transmittance of the blank is usually about two percent less than that of distilled water. If it is as much as 5 percent less, the cause should be determined and corrected. Determine the transmittance of the sample solution at 503 mμ with the instrument adjusted to read 100 percent transmittance with the blank. Determine the iron content of the solution by reference to a concentration-transmittance graph prepared as follows:

Preparation of Concentration-Transmittance Graph.—Dissolve 0.1000 g. of pure iron wire in 10 ml. of 10 percent sulfuric acid. Add 3 ml. of nitric acid (sp. gr. 1.43) and dilute to 1 liter with distilled water in a volumetric flask. Pipet 100 ml. of the standard iron solution into a 1-liter volumetric flask and dilute to volume with hydrochloric acid (1 + 19, v/v). This solution then contains 10 μg. of iron per ml.

Pipet 0.5, 1.0, 2.0, 3.0, 4.0, and 5.0 ml. of the dilute iron standard into a series of cuvets, and add sufficient dilute hydrochloric acid to bring the total volume in each to 10 ml. In one cuvet place 10 ml. of the acid only. From this point on, process all cuvets as directed for developing and measuring the color, beginning with the addition of hydroquinone. Construct a concentration-transmittance graph on semilogarithmic paper, relating transmittance to μg. of iron.

Calculation.—The iron found from the graph divided by the weight of sample in the dilution tested gives the iron content of the sample in parts per million or μg. per g.

COPPER

Procedure.—Prepare a solution of 125 g. of ammonium citrate in 500 ml. of distilled water, and add to this 100 ml. of ammonium hydroxide (sp. gr. 0.90).

Ash 5 g. of sample and add 40 ml. 0.1 M hydrochloric acid solution. If the residue does not dissolve, cover the dish with a watch glass, heat the mixture just to boiling, and then cool it to room temperature. Transfer the solution to a 125-ml. separatory funnel and rinse the dish twice with 10-ml. portions of 0.1 M hydrochloric acid, adding the washings to the separatory funnel. Add 15 ml. of the ammonium citrate-ammonium hydroxide solution to the separatory funnel, mix thoroughly, and then add 5 ml. of aqueous sodium diethyldithiocarbamate solution (0.2 percent, w/v) and mix again. Add 15 ml. of carbon tetrachloride with a pipet, and shake vigorously to obtain complete extraction of the colored compound. Allow the solution to stand until the carbon tetrachloride layer separates. Filter the carbon tetrachloride portion through filter paper and measure the transmittance at 430 mμ with the spectrometer adjusted to 100 percent transmittance with carbon tetrachloride.

Prepare and conduct a blank determination using 60 ml. of 0.1 M hydrochloric acid. Proceed otherwise as described for the sample, beginning with the addition of the ammonium citrate-ammonium hydroxide solution. The transmittance of the blank should be at least 95 percent.

Preparation of Concentration-Transmittance Graph.—Prepare a graph relating transmittance to copper content from the analysis of samples of copper sulfate ($CuSO_4 \cdot 5H_2O$) solutions of known concentration. Dissolve 0.3930 g. of $CuSO_4 \cdot 5H_2O$ in 0.1 M hydrochloric acid in a 1-liter volumetric flask. Make to volume with 0.1 M acid and mix thoroughly. Similarly make a second dilution of 50 to 500 ml. and finally a third dilution of 50 to 250 ml. The final dilution should then contain 2 mg. of copper per ml. Plot a graph of concentration $vs.$ transmittance. The dilutions selected for preparing the graph should cover the range of 0–40 μg. of copper.

PHOSPHORUS

Procedure.—Add 140 ml. of sulfuric acid (sp. gr. 1.84) to 300 ml. of distilled water. Cool to room temperature, and add 12.5 g. of sodium molybdate. Dilute to 500 ml. with distilled water, mix thoroughly, and allow this molybdate solution to stand for at least 24 hours before using.

Weigh 3.0–3.2 g. of sample and 0.5 g. of zinc oxide into a Vycor crucible. Heat the mixture on a hot plate until the mass thickens, then increase the rate of heating slowly until the mass is completely charred. Place the crucible in a muffle furnace and maintain at 550°–600°C. for 2 hours. Remove the crucible from the furnace and allow to cool to room temperature. Add 5 ml. of distilled water and 5 ml. of hydrochloric acid (sp. gr. 1.19) to the residue. Cover the crucible with a watch glass and heat at gentle boiling for 5 minutes.

Filter the solution into a 100-ml. volumetric flask. Wash the inside of the watch glass and the sides of the crucible into the filter paper with about 5 ml. of hot distilled water, using a wash bottle with a fine jet. Wash the crucible and the filter paper with four additional 5-ml. portions of hot distilled water. Cool the solution to room temperature and neutralize to a faint turbidity by dropwise addition of potassium hydroxide solution (50 percent, w/v). Add hydrochloric acid dropwise until the zinc oxide precipitate is dissolved, then add 2 additional drops. Dilute to volume with distilled water and mix thoroughly.

Pipet 10 ml. of this solution into a clean, dry 50 ml. volumetric flask. Add 8.0 ml. of hydrazine solution (0.015 percent, w/v) and 2.0 ml. of sodium molybdate solution in that order. Insert a stopper and invert the flask 2 or 3 times. Loosen the stopper and heat for 9.5–10.5 minutes in a vigorously boiling water bath. Remove the flask from the bath and cool to 20°–30°C. in a water bath, dilute to volume with distilled water, and mix thoroughly.

Transfer the solution to a clean, dry cuvet. Measure the transmittance at 650 mμ with the instrument adjusted to read 100 percent transmittance with a cuvet containing distilled water. If the transmittance of the solution is less than 15 percent use an aliquot less than 10-ml., and dilute to 10-ml. before proceeding. Prepare and conduct a reagent blank as described above, but without the sample.

Preparation of Concentration-Transmittance Graph.—Prepare two solutions as follows:

> a. **Standard Stock Solution.**—Dissolve 1.0967 g. of dry potassium dihydrogen phosphate in distilled water. Dilute to 250 ml. in a volumetric flask and mix thoroughly. This solution contains 1 mg. of phosphorus per ml.
> b. **Standard Working Solution.**—Pipet 5 ml. of the standard stock solution into a 500-ml. volumetric flask and dilute to volume with distilled water. This solution contains 0.01 mg. of phosphorus per ml.

Pipet 0.0, 1, 2, 4, 6, 8, and 10 ml. of the standard working solution into 50-ml. volumetric flasks. Dilute each to 10 ml. with distilled water, using a measuring pipet and proceed as directed for the determination of phosphorus, beginning with the addition of hydrazine sulfate.

Plot the percent transmittance of each standard against its phosphorus content in mg. on one-cycle semilogarithmic paper.

Calculation.—Read the phosphorus content of the sample and the blank from the concentration-transmittance graph and calculate the phosphorus content of the sample.

$$\text{percent phosphorus} = 10(A - B)/WV$$

where: A = phosphorus content of sample aliquot in mg.;
B = phosphorus content of blank aliquot in mg.;
W = weight of sample in g.; and
V = volume of aliquot.

ANTIOXIDANTS

The only standard method available for the analysis of fat antioxidants is a procedure for the determination of propyl gallate. The methods most commonly used for the estimation of NDGA, BHA, and BHT or combinations of these are based on publications by Mahon and Chapman,[1] and more recent reports by Anglin, Mahon, and Chapman.[2]

[1] Mahon, J. H., and Chapman, R. A., Anal. Chem., **23**, 1116, 1120, 1951; **24**, 534, 1952.
[2] Anglin, C., Mahon, J. H., and Chapman, R. A., J. Agri. and Food Chem., **4**, 1018, 1956.

Current efforts directed toward standardization of methods for the determination of antioxidants are based on these publications.

One of the problems in estimating antioxidants, and particularly mixtures of anti-oxidants, in fat is removal of them from the fat for analysis. The earlier publication prescribed removal by extraction, while according to the more recent methods, the antioxidants are removed by distillation. The latter seems to provide better and more complete separations.

PROPYL GALLATE[3]

Reagents. Petroleum Ether Reagent.—Mix 1 volume of petroleum ether, b.p. 30°–60°C. with 3 volumes of petroleum ether, b.p. 60°–100°C., (Skellysolve B and H are satis-factory). Shake this mixture with one-tenth its volume of sulfuric acid for 5 minutes. Discard the acid layer and wash the ether several times with water and then with 1 percent sodium hydroxide solution. Continue washing with water until the washings are substantially neutral. Finally, distill the washed petroleum ether mixture in all-glass apparatus.

Ferrous Tartrate Reagent.—Dissolve 0.100 g. of ferrous sulfate ($FeSO_4 \cdot 7H_2O$), and 0.500 g. of sodium potassium tartrate ($NaKC_4H_4O_6 \cdot 4H_2O$) in water and dilute to 100 ml. This reagent must be used within 3 hours of preparation.

Procedure.—Dissolve 40 g. of the sample in the petroleum ether reagent and dilute to 250 ml. with this reagent. Gentle warming may be necessary to obtain complete solu-tion. Transfer 100 ml. of this solution to a 250-ml. separatory funnel and extract with 20 ml. of aqueous ammonium acetate (1.67 percent, w/v), by inverting the funnel con-tinuously for $2\frac{1}{2}$ minutes. Allow complete separation of the phases and then drain the lower layer into a 100-ml. volumetric flask. Exercise care to prevent any oil droplets from passing into the flask. If emulsification occurs, extract with a 1.67 percent ammo-nium acetate in 5 percent alcohol instead of the aqueous solution and add 2 drops n-octane to the 100-ml. aliquot before extracting.

Repeat the extraction in a similar manner twice more combining the extracts in the 100-ml. flask. Finally, extract the fat solution with 15 ml. of water for 30 seconds and combine with previous extracts. Add exactly 2.5 ml. of aqueous ammonium acetate solution (1.25 percent, w/v) and dilute to 100 ml. with water. Filter to remove any turbidity and measure the color on the same day the extraction is made.

Accurately transfer an aliquot, not exceeding 20 ml. in quantity, to a 50-ml. Erlen-meyer flask and dilute (if necessary) to exactly 20 ml. with the 1.25 percent ammonium acetate. Add exactly 4 ml. of water and 1 ml. of the ferrous tartrate reagent. Mix well and measure the transmittance at 540 mμ relative to a blank consisting of 20 ml. of 1.25 percent aqueous ammonium acetate, 4 ml. of water, and 1 ml. of the ferrous tartrate reagent. Determine the propyl gallate content of the aliquot by referring to a concentra-tion-transmittance graph prepared from the analysis of samples of known concentration.

Preparation of Concentration-Transmittance Graph.—Dissolve 50 mg. of pure propyl gallate and make to 1 liter in water. This solution then contains 1 μg./ml. Select at least 7 aliquots of this solution covering the range of 50–1000 μg., place in 50-ml. Erlenmeyer flasks, and add 2.5 ml. of aqueous ammonium acetate solution (10 percent, w/v). Dilute to exactly 24 ml. with water. Add 1 ml. of the tartrate reagent, mix and allow to stand for 3 minutes, and then measure the transmittance at 540 mμ, relative to a solution containing 20 ml. of 1.25 percent acetate solution, 4 ml. of water, and 1 ml. of tartrate reagent. Plot μg. of propyl gallate against transmittance.

[3] Association of Official Agricultural Chemists, Official Methods of Analysis, 9th Ed., Washington D. C., 378, 1960.

THIOBARBITURIC ACID (TBA) METHOD FOR RANCIDITY

The color formed as a result of a reaction between thiobarbituric acid and certain fat oxidation products is used as an index of the extent to which oxidation has progressed. The method presented here was designed for use with either a Coleman Model 6 or a Spectronic 20 spectrometer.

Reagents. The reagents required for the TBA determination are as follows.

Trichloroacetic Acid Solution.—Dilute 115 g. of 85 percent phosphoric acid to 500 ml. with distilled water and add 150 g. of trichloroacetic acid.

Thiobarbituric Acid Solution.—Dissolve 3.0 g. of 2-thiobarbituric acid in 1 liter of distilled water. Warm to effect solution if necessary. The solution may be slightly yellow in color.

Standard Tetraethoxypropane Solution.—Dissolve 0.2000 g. ($\pm$0.0004 g.) of tetraethoxypropane in 40 percent ethanol, make up to 1 liter with the same alcohol, and mix thoroughly. Make a further dilution of 100 ml. to 1000 ml., this time using distilled water, and finally a third dilution of 100 to 500 ml., also with distilled water. The final solution then contains 4 mg. of the reagent per ml.

Procedure.—Weigh 5 to 10 g. ($\pm$0.01 g.) of sample into a 250-ml. Erlenmeyer flask. Add 40 ml. of water, 15 ml. trichloroacetic acid solution and 20 ml. of thiobarbituric acid solution. Prepare two blanks using 40 ml. of water, 15 ml. of trichloroacetic acid, and 20 ml. of thiobarbituric acid solution in each, and handle exactly as the samples.

Shake vigorously for 1 minute, attach a reflux condenser, and then heat on a steam bath or in a boiling water bath for 30 to 35 minutes, shaking at 10-minute intervals for approximately 5 seconds each time. Remove from the heat source and place in an ice-water bath for 10 to 15 minutes.

Remove the reflux condenser and add 50 ml. of isoamyl alcohol-pyridine solution (2 + 1, v/v) with a pipet. Stopper and shake vigorously for 30 seconds; then set aside and allow the isoamyl alcohol-pyridine solution to separate. Filter 12 to 15 ml. of the isoamyl alcohol-pyridine solution through Whatman No. 12 filter paper.

Determine the transmittance of this solution at 535 mμ with instrument adjusted to read zero percent transmittance when no light reaches the photocell and 100 percent transmittance with distilled water. Refer to a standard graph to determine the equivalent tetraethoxypropane.

Preparation of Standard Graph.—Pipet 2, 5, and 10 ml. of the standard tetraethoxypropane into separate 250-ml. Erlenmeyer flasks and at the same time prepare three blanks. Process all of these as directed for the sample. Determine the transmittance on filtered portion of each of the blanks. Select the blank that is closest to the average for the three blanks and adjust the instrument to 100 percent transmittance at 535 mμ with this blank. Then measure the transmittance of the standard solutions.

Plot on semilogarithmic paper, the percent transmittance of standard solutions on the logarithmic scale against the μg. of tetraethoxypropane in 50 ml. of solution on the linear scale.

Calculations.—TBA Number = mg. of tetraethoxypropane per 1000 g. of sample = $A - B/W$.

where: A = μg. of tetraethoxypropane in 50 ml. solution of sample read from calibration graph;

W = grams of sample taken for test; and

B = average of μg. of tetraethoxypropane in the 50-ml. blank solution read from the calibration graph, or the μg. of tetraethoxypropane in the 50-ml. sample blank solution read from the calibration graph, or whichever is appropriate.

WATER—INSOLUBLE COMBINED LACTIC ACID[4]

Lactic acid is reacted with commercial monoglyceride to produce lactylated compounds which have properties desirable for certain commercial food products. The method given here is applicable to the determination of the lactylated compounds in shortening.

Reagents. p-Phenylphenol Solution.—Dissolve 1.5 percent p-phenylphenol (Eastman) in 2 percent sodium hydroxide solution. Filter. Prepare fresh daily.

Lithium Lactate Standard Solution.—Dissolve 1.067 g. of lithium lactate (Harleco) in distilled water and dilute to 1 liter. This solution contains the equivalent of 1 mg. lactic acid per ml. It will keep several months stored in the refrigerator.

Procedure.—Weigh 0.5–0.6 g. of melted fat into a 25-ml. extraction cylinder and add 10 ml. of chloroform. Prepare and conduct a blank containing 10 ml. of chloroform. Add 10 ml. of distilled water and extract by inverting the cylinder 25–30 times. Remove the water layer by means of a siphon, and then repeat the extraction with water twice more.

Transfer the chloroform solution to a 60-ml. beaker, rinsing the cylinder 2 times with 3-ml. portions of chloroform and finally with 3 ml. of acetone. Evaporate the solvent on a steam bath under a stream of clear, dry air until no odor of chloroform remains.

Add 5 ml. of alcoholic potassium hydroxide (40 g. per liter of 95 percent alcohol) and heat until most of the alcohol has evaporated. Add 2–3 ml. of water and continue heating until no odor of alcohol remains. Add 5–10 ml. of water and heat to complete solution of the soap. Add 3 ml. of sulfuric acid (1 + 1, v/v) and heat until the fatty acids are completely melted. Then cool to 60°C. and add 20–25 ml. of petroleum ether. Transfer quantitatively to a 60-ml. separatory funnel using about 5 ml. of distilled water at 60°C. to wash the beaker. Draw the water layer from the funnel through a fluted filter paper into a 100-ml. volumetric flask. Rinse the beaker again, using 10 ml. of distilled water, transfer to the separatory funnel and, after cooling to room temperature, swirl the contents of the funnel to extract the ether layer.

Draw off the water layer into the 100-ml. flask as before and repeat the extraction once more.

Dilute the contents of the flask to 100 ml., and from this prepare another dilution such that the final concentration of lactic acid is 2–8 mg. per ml. of solution.

Place 1 ml. of the diluted sample solution in a Pyrex test tube and add 0.10 ml. of 4 percent $CuSO_4 \cdot 5H_2O$, followed by 6 ml. of concentrated sulfuric acid. Shake for 10 seconds to mix, insert a glass stopper loosely and place in a water bath at 80°C. for exactly 5 minutes. Transfer immediately to an ice-water bath and hold for 5 minutes to cool the sample to below 20°C.

Add 0.10 ml. of p-phenylphenol making certain that none of the reagent gets on the sides of the tube. Shake immediately to mix and place in a 30°C. bath for 30 minutes. Shake once during this interval. Place in an 80°C. bath for exactly 90 seconds. Cool for 5 minutes in an ice-water bath and then determine the transmittance at 570 mμ against the blank.

Determine the concentration of lactic acid by reference to a curve relating transmittance to concentration.

Preparation of Concentration-Transmittance Graph.—Prepare a tenfold dilution of the lithium lactate standard solution. Dilute this solution further to give solutions containing 1, 2, 4, 6, and 8 μg. of lactic acid per ml. Pipet 1 ml. of each of these solutions into a Pyrex test tube. Proceed as directed for the sample, beginning with the addition of copper sulfate. Use 1 ml. of distilled water as a blank. Plot the absorption

[4] Fett, H. M., J. Am. Oil Chemists' Soc., **38**, 447–449, 1961.

at 570 mμ against the lactic acid concentration in micrograms. The curve obtained obeys Beer's Law in this range.

$$\text{Percent Lactic acid} = 100 \frac{(\mu g. \text{ lactic acid found} \times \text{dilution factor})}{\text{sample weight in grams} \times 10^6}$$

SESAMOL AND SESAMIN[5]

Sesamol and sesamin occur naturally in sesame oil. The methods presented here are applicable to sesame oil and sesamin concentrates. The calculations provided with these methods were derived for use with a Beckman spectrometer and may require modification if some other instrument is used.

Procedure for Free Sesamol.—Weigh 10.0 g. of sesame oil or 0.25 g. of sesamin concentrate into a 100-ml. volumetric flask. Add sufficient chloroform-isoöctane (1 + 4, v/v) to bring the volume of the solution to 100 ml. If the sample dissolves slowly, add the chloroform first and then finish with the isoöctane. Both the chloroform and the isoöctane must be optically pure.

Transfer 50 ml. of the sample solution into a 250-ml. centrifuge tube and then add 10 ml. of potassium hydroxide solution (10 g. pure potassium hydroxide + 80 ml. water + 20 ml. anhydrous ethanol). Insert a stopper in the tube, shake the contents vigorously for 3 minutes, and then whirl in a centrifuge at 2000 r.p.m. for 10 minutes. Separate the alkaline and solvent layers and use the former for the estimation of free sesamol. Filter the alkaline solution before proceeding.

Place 50 ml. of sulfuric acid (sp. gr. 1.37 at 15°C.) in a 50-ml. volumetric flask and add to it 1 ml. of furfural reagent (2 g. of freshly distilled furfural in 100 ml. of ethanol) followed by 0.6 ml. of the alkaline extract. Insert a stopper in the flask and invert it several times to mix the contents. Fill a 1-cm. absorption cell with the sample solution and determine the absorbance at 518 mμ, 50–75 minutes after mixing. Determine the absorbance on a blank prepared similarly but using 1 ml. of optically pure ethanol (99 percent) instead of furfural reagent.

$$\text{Percent free sesamol} = 10.75 \cdot A_{518}/C$$

where: A_{518} = absorbance at 518 mμ; and
  C = concentration of original sample solution in g./liter.

Procedure for Bound Sesamol.—Use the chloroform-isoöctane portion for the determination of bound sesamol, but filter it to remove any turbidity. Place 50 ml. of sulfuric acid (sp. gr. 1.37 at 15°C.) into a 125-ml. Erlenmeyer flask. Add to the flask 1 ml. of furfural reagent and 2 ml. of the sample solution. Insert a stopper in the flask and shake the contents for 30 minutes in a mechanical shaker. Transfer the mixture into a 100-ml. separatory funnel where it is allowed to separate. The acid (lower) layer may be slightly turbid. This should gradually clear and must have disappeared when the color is measured. Fill a 1-cm. absorption cell with the sample solution and determine the absorbance at 518 mμ, 50–75 minutes after shaking was started. Determine the absorbance on a blank using 1 ml. of 99 percent ethyl alcohol instead of the furfural reagent.

$$\text{Percent bound sesamol} = 15.9375 \cdot A_{518}/C$$

where: C = concentration of original sample solution in g./liter.

Procedure for Sesamin.—The chloroform-isoöctane solution used for the determination of bound sesamol is used also for estimating sesamin but it is diluted, if necessary, with additional chloroform-isoöctane. Fill a 1-cm. absorption cell with the test solution

[5] Suarez, C., O'Connor, R. T., Field, E. T., and Bickford, W. G., Anal. Chem., **24**, 668, 1952.

and measure the absorbances at 287–288, 255, and 320 mμ. In practice, the maximum and minimum absorption are determined at 287–288 and 255 mμ. The third wavelength is then selected so that it will be at the same distance above the maximum as the minimum is below the maximum.

$$\text{Percent sesamin} = 4.541\,a_{288} - 0.953\,C_1 - 2.271(a_{255} + a_{320})$$

where: C_1 is the percent of sesamolin(bound sesamol) determined; and
a is the absorptivity at the indicated wavelength.

TOCOPHEROLS[6]

Procedure.—Place a 1-ml. aliquot of the sample containing 50 to 300 μg. dissolved in absolute ethanol (redistilled over potassium hydroxide and potassium permanganate) in an opaque 2-oz. glass-stoppered bottle. Add 1 ml. of each of 0.1 percent $FeCl_3 \cdot 6H_2O$ and 0.25 percent α,α'-dipyridyl solutions in ethanol in this order and then add 22 ml. of purified ethanol. Determine the color in an Evelyn colorimeter (1.9-cm. cell) 10 minutes after adding the iron chloride solution, using a 520 mμ filter. Refer to a curve previously prepared from samples of known tocopherol α (or hydroquinone) content multiplied by 0.91 to obtain the assay of mixed tocopherols. If a spectrometer is employed, use a 1-cm. cell with a 2-ml. aliquot of sample and 1 ml. each of 0.2 percent $FeCl_3 \cdot 6H_2O$ and 0.5 percent of α,α'-dipyridyl reagent.

GOSSYPOL[7]

Gossypol is an oil-soluble pigment found in cotton-seed and in cottonseed oil. This method presented here utilizes *p*-anisidine as the reagent for the estimation of gossypol and gossypol-like substances in cottonseed oil.

Reagent. Dissolve about 40 g. of *p*-anisidine in 1 liter of water at approximately 75°C. Add about 2 g. of sodium sulfite and 20 g. of decolorizing carbon and stir the mixture for about 5 minutes. Filter the mixture through a double layer of medium retentivity paper on a Büchner funnel with the aid of suction. If the filtrate is turbid due to the presence of carbon, refilter the solution through the same paper. Place the water-white solution in a refrigerator, or water bath, at 32°–36°F. for at least 4 hours, or preferably overnight, for crystallization, Filter the mixture through a Büchner funnel with the aid of suction and wash the crystals once with a minimum amount of cold water at 32°–36°F. Dry the crystals in a vacuum desiccator over phosphorus pentoxide or concentrated sulfuric acid for 16 hours and then transfer them to a screw-capped brown bottle. Store the bottle and contents in a refrigerator. When maintained under these conditions, purified *p*-anisidine is stable for one year. Recrystallize the *p*-anisidine when the reagent blank is below 95 percent transmittance, or the absorbance is greater than 0.022.

Weigh 1 g. of purified *p*-anisidine into a small glass-stoppered brown bottle, add 48 ml. of the isopropanol-hexane solvent (3 + 2, v/v) and 2 ml. of glacial acetic acid, and swirl the solution to dissolve the *p*-anisidine. Prepare this solution daily as needed.

Procedure.—The quantity of sample to use for analysis depends on the gossypol content of the sample. Refer to Table 48-1 for such details as weight of sample, size of flask, and quantity of aliquot. The actual portion of the sample used in analysis should contain about 0.1 mg. of gossypol.

After weighing the sample into the flask, add some isopropanol-hexane solvent (3 + 2, v/v) to dissolve the oil, and then add a sufficient quantity of the solvent to make up to

[6] Rawlings, H. W., Kuhrt, N. H., and Baxter, J. G., Oil and Soap, **25**, 24, 1948.
[7] American Oil Chemists' Society, Official and Tentative Methods, 2nd Ed., Chicago, Ill., 1946, Method Ca 13–56.

TABLE 48-1. SIZE OF SAMPLE, FLASK, AND ALIQUOTS REQUIRED
FOR THE DETERMINATION OF GOSSYPOL

Expected Gossypol Content, %	Sample Weight, g.	Size of Flask for Oil Sample, ml.	Aliquot for Analysis, ml.
0.00–0.01..............	5.0	25	5–10
0.01–0.03..............	3.0	25	5
0.03–0.05..............	1.0	25	5
0.05–0.10..............	1.0	25	2
0.10–0.20..............	0.8	25	2
0.20–0.40..............	0.5	25	2
0.40–0.60..............	0.25	25	2
0.60–0.80..............	0.4	50	2
0.80–1.0..............	0.25	50	2
Over 1.0..............	0.25–0.50	100	2

the designated volume. Mix the solution well. Transfer with a pipet two aliquots of the sample solution, each containing about 0.1 mg. of gossypol into 25-ml. volumetric flasks. Add to one of the flasks 5 ml. of a solution consisting of glacial acetic acid and isopropanol-hexane solvent (1 + 24, v/v) and then add sufficient isopropanol-hexane to bring the volume to 25 ml. Designate the contents of this flask as A. To the other 25-ml. flask add 5 ml. of p-anisidine reagent. Designate the contents of this flask as B. Prepare a reagent blank consisting of 5 ml. of p-anisidine solution and 5 ml. of solvent. Place solution B and the reagent blank in a water bath at 75°C. and heat at this temperature for one hour with stoppers inserted in the flasks.

Remove solution B and the reagent blank from the water bath and cool to room temperature. Add isopropanol-hexane solution to each flask to bring to volume, and then mix the contents of each.

To measure the color, use a spectrometer which will isolate a band at 460 mμ or a photoelectric colorimeter with a filter with maximum transmission between 450 and 465 mμ. Adjust the instrument to 100 percent transmission with the isopropanol-hexane solvent and determine the percent transmission of the reagent blank. This should be above 95 percent. Then adjust the instrument to 100 percent transmission with solution A and determine the percent transmission of solution B. Convert transmission readings to absorbances.

Calculate the corrected absorbance of solution B by subtracting the absorbance of the reagent blank from the measured absorbance of solution B. Refer to a graph prepared with sample of pure gossypol to determine the gossypol content of the sample aliquot.

Prepare a calibration curve relating pure gossypol content to absorbance as follows.

Weigh 100 mg. of pure gossypol and dissolve it in isopropanol-hexane, warming if necessary until the gossypol dissolves. Transfer the solution quantitatively to a 250-ml. volumetric flask, and add solvent to bring the volume to 250 ml. Transfer with a pipet, 25 ml. of this solution, after mixing into a 500-ml. volumetric flask and again dilute to volume with the isopropanol-hexane solvent. This solution should contain 0.02 mg. of gossypol per ml.

Use a pipet to place duplicate 1-, 2-, 3-, 4-, 5-, 6-, 7-, 8-, 9-, and 10-ml. aliquots of the standard gossypol solution into 25-ml. volumetric flasks. To one set of aliquots and to a reagent blank, add 5 ml. of *p*-anisidine reagent. To the other set of aliquots, add 5 ml. of the acetic acid solution, make to volume with the solvent, and then mix. Determine the absorbance of the reagent blank and then the absorbances of the gossypol standards using the diluted gossypol standard as reference solutions and following the directions prescribed above for the sample. Plot the corrected absorbance of each gossypol standard against the corresponding gossypol content in mg. per ml.

$$\text{Percent gossypol} = \frac{10 \times \text{mg. gossypol per ml. from graph}}{\text{g. of sample in aliquot analyzed}}$$

COLOR[8]

The photometric method for estimating the color of vegetable oil is designed to yield results of essentially the same numerical value as obtained with the Wesson Method. This method is adapted specifically to the Coleman Jr. spectrometer.

The apparatus and reagents needed for the spectrometric estimation are the following:

Apparatus.—The spectrometer must be capable of adjustment to the following readings with nickel sulfate solutions at 25 to 30°C., after setting the zero point and after adjusting the instrument to 100 percent transmittance with carbon tetrachloride.

$m\mu$	*Percent Transmittance*
400	less than 4.0
460	26.2 ± 2.0
510	73.9 ± 1.0
550	54.8 ± 1.0
620	5.2 ± 0.5
670	1.1 ± 0.5
700	less than 2.0

The cuvets are glass, cylindrical in shape, and matched, having dimensions of approximately 21.8 mm. inside diameter and 24.5 mm. outside diameter. All cuvets used with a given instrument should be checked with carbon tetrachloride and with the nickel sulfate solution at 500 $m\mu$, and be within ±0.6 percent of the same transmittance.

Reagents.—Dissolve 200 g. of $NiSO_4 \cdot 6H_2O$ (Analytical Reagent Grade) is distilled water. Add 10 ml. of concentrated hydrochloric acid and dilute to exactly 1000 ml. in a volumetric flask. The nickel content of the solution must fall between 4.40 and 4.46 g. of nickel per 100 ml. at 25° to 30°C.

The filter paper should have fine porosity, such as that of E & D No. 512, Whatman No. 12, Reeve-Angel No. 871, or S & S No. 596. The carbon tetrachloride should be redistilled if its transmittance differs from that of distilled water by 0.5 percent at 400 $m\mu$.

Calibration of the Spectrophotometer.—Turn on the spectrometer and allow at least a 20-minute warm-up period before standardizing or making any measurements. After the initial warm-up period, rotate both the control knobs on top of the instrument counterclockwise to their stop position. Adjust the galvanometer by means of the galvanometer adjustment or by sliding the scale so that an exact zero reading is obtained. Set the wavelength dial to 460 $m\mu$. Recheck the zero reading of the instrument, insert a cuvet filled with carbon tetrachloride in the instrument and set the 100 percent transmittance point exactly. Fill a cuvet with the standardizing $NiSO_4$ solution and read the transmittance of the solution. The reading must fall between 24.2 and 28.2 percent. Repeat in a similar manner at the other wavelengths listed above. All readings must fall within the indicated limits.

[8] *Ibid.*, Method Cc 13c–50.

Procedure.—Add 0.5 g. of diatomaceous earth (AOCS grade) to 300 g. of the sample. Agitate for $2\frac{1}{2}$ minutes at 250 r.p.m. at room temperature (or at 10°–15°C. above the melting point of the fat if necessary) and then filter to remove the earth. The samples must be absolutely clear. Suspended material, even if colloidal size, will cause light scattering.

Adjust the temperature of the oil to 25–30°C. Fill a cuvet, using a sufficient amount of oil to insure a full column in the light beam. Determine the absorbance to nearest 0.001 at 460, 550, 620, and 670 mμ.

Calculations.

$$\text{Photometric color} = 1.29\,A_{460} + 69.7\,A_{550} + 41.2\,A_{620} - 56.4\,A_{670}$$

where: A = absorbance at the indicated wavelengths.

Procedure for Commercial Fatty Acids.[9]—Follow the procedure described for fats and oils except that two measurements are made, one at 440 mμ and the other at 550 mμ. The color is designated as the Photometric Index, which is expressed as follows:

$$\text{Photometric Index} = 100 \times A_{440} \text{ and } 100 \times A_{550}$$

where: A = absorbance at the indicated wavelength.

CHLOROPHYLL[10]

Chlorophyll may, under certain conditions of growth and maturation, be present in cottonseed and soybean oils. It may also be found in such animal fats as tallow and under certain conditions of animal growth and fat expression. When chlorophyll is present in a significant quantity, it complicates visual methods of color measurement such as with the Wesson Method.

The chlorophyll content of vegetable oils is determined from spectrometric absorption measurements at 630 mμ, 670 mμ, and 710 mμ. This method is applicable to refined and bleached oils but is not applicable to hydrogenated and deodorized oils because the chlorophyll absorption does not occur at 670 mμ in these.

This method is designed to be used with a Beckman Model B spectrometer; however, other instruments may be employed. Follow the manufacturer's instructions for adjusting the instrument and making absorbance determinations. The Coleman Jr. spectrometer is not applicable if the chlorophyll content is less than 0.1.

Procedure.—Determine the absorbance of the sample in 50-mm. matched cells with the spectrometer previously adjusted to read 100 percent transmittance with carbon tetrachloride. The carbon tetrachloride should be redistilled if the transmittance differs from the transmittance of distilled water by 0.5 percent at 400 mμ. Samples with absorbances greater than 0.8 should be measured in cells smaller than those designated here. When the determination is made with a Coleman Jr. spectrometer use 25-mm. cuvets to contain the samples. Make measurements at 630, 670, and 710 mμ with the Beckman or Cary spectrometer, and at 630 and 670 mμ with the Coleman instrument. Calculate the chlorophyll content of the sample as follows.

Using Beckman Model B Spectrometer:

$$\text{Chlorophyll, in p.p.m.} = \frac{A_{670} - (A_{630} + A_{710}/2)}{0.0964L*}$$

[9] *Ibid.*, Method Td 2a–64.
[10] *Ibid.*, Method Cc 13d–55.
   * The Beckman DU spectrometer is also applicable, in which case this value becomes 0.1016L.

where: A = absorbance; and
L = cell length in cm.

Using Cary Spectrometer:

$$\text{Chlorophyll, in p.p.m.} = \frac{A_{670} - (A_{630} + A_{710}/2)}{0.1086L}$$

Using Coleman Jr. Spectrometer:

$$\text{Chlorophyll, in p.p.m.} = \frac{A_{670} - A_{630}}{0.0668}$$

ULTRAVIOLET SPECTROMETRY

POLYUNSATURATED FATTY ACIDS[11]

Ultraviolet absorption spectrometry is applied to the analysis of fats principally for the purpose of determining polyunsaturated fatty acids. Conjugated carbon to carbon linkages produce intense and characteristic absorption bands in the spectral range of 200–400 mμ, while the absorption of isolated double bonds is weak in the same region. Isolated double bonds are converted to conjugated configurations by being heated in the presence of an alkali.

According to the method of the American Oil Chemists' Society, which is presented here, the natural or preformed conjugated constituents are determined by measuring the ultraviolet absorption in an appropriate solvent at specified wavelengths. Measurements at the same wavelengths are again made after isomerization. From the values thus obtained, the polyunsaturated fatty acids are calculated by means of simultaneous equations. The mathematical constants involved in the calculations are based on absorptivities of pure *cis*-acids determined under the same conditions.

The American Oil Chemists' Society method is applicable to the estimation of the *cis*-isomers of polyunsaturated fatty acids from dienoic through pentaenoic, providing only small amounts of preformed conjugated materials and only small quantities of pigments that may undergo change during isomerization are present.

The method is not applicable, or is applicable only with special precautions, to modified drying oils, hydrogenated oils, or other fats containing *trans*-isomers of the unsaturated fatty acids; to fish oils or similar fats containing acids more unsaturated than pentaenoic; to crude oils or unusual samples containing pigments whose absorption undergoes change during isomerization causing unknown interferences; or to fats and oils containing large quantities of preformed conjugated fatty acids apparatus.

Apparatus.—The spectrometer should cover the range of 220–360 mμ with a wavelength scale capable of being read to 0.1 mμ. Adjust the hydrogen lamp with no cell in the beam so that the meter balances at the lowest possible wavelength (usually 211 mμ or less). Slit widths are critical for absorption measurements at 262, 268, and 274 mμ where, at the final balancing adjustment, these widths must be 0.8–0.9 mm.

The absorption cells should be matched pairs of quartz cells, with lengths of 1.000–10.000 (± 0.005) cm. When they are filled with water or isoöctane, their readings must match within 0.01 absorbance units.

The isomerization bath is a constant temperature bath capable of being maintained at 180 $\pm$ 0.5°C. with capacity sufficient to immerse the desired number of 1- $\times$ 10-in.

[11] *Ibid.*, Method Cd 7–59.

Pyrex test tubes to a depth of $4\frac{1}{2}$ in. The bath liquid should be the bath wax of the Fisher Scientific Co., DC 550 fluid, Dow Corning Corp., Midland, Mich.

Other items of equipment are distributing heads for the test tubes and a connecting manifold which permits passing nitrogen over the contents of the tubes during isomerization.

Reagents. Isomerization Reagent.—Dissolve 60 g. of potassium hydroxide (85% ACS grade pellets) in 750 ml. of ethylene glycol which has been previously heated to 190°C. to drive off the water. Add the potassium hydroxide cautiously when the glycol is 150°C., and protect the solution with nitrogen. Reheat the reagent to 190°C. for 10 minutes. Titrate the glycol solution with 1 M hydrochloric acid. The solution should contain 6.5 to 6.6 percent potassium hydroxide. Make appropriate adjustments if the strength is not between these limits. Store the reagent under nitrogen in a refrigerator.

Prepare 21 percent potassium hydroxide in a similar manner, but use 210 g. of potassium hydroxide instead of 60 g.

Absolute Synthetic Methanol or Ethanol.—Check the absorbance of a 1-cm. layer of methanol against distilled water at 200 mμ and through the range of wavelengths employed in the analysis. The absorbance at 220 mμ compared with distilled water set at zero absorbance must be less than 0.04 and the percent curve should be smooth in the range of 262 to 322 mμ. If the alcohol does not comply with the foregoing specifications, purify it as follows, and determine the absorbance of the purified material.

Place 2000 ml. of methanol into a 3-liter distilling flask, double-neck type. Add to the flask 10 g. of potassium hydroxide (Reagent grade) and 25 g. of zinc powder. Place a glass stopper in one outlet of the flask and a reflux tube in the other. Reflux on the steam bath for 3 hours. Remove from the steam bath and replace the reflux tube with a trap, a 75° connecting tube, and a condenser. Place the flask in a water bath or electric heating mantle and heat to distill the methanol. Collect the distillate in a 2-liter Erlenmeyer flask. If the absorbance of the purified methanol complies with specifications, store in a glass stoppered bottle for future use.

Isoöctane (2,2,4-trimethylpentane), Spectro Grade.—Hexane and cyclohexane are also satisfactory but all must comply with the absorbance requirements. Place about $3\frac{1}{2}$ in. of glass wool above the stopcock at the lower end of a 32 $\times$ $1\frac{3}{4}$ in. filter tube. Add about 12 in. of silica gel. Fasten the tube vertically to a ring stand and pour the isoöctane into the tube, filling it about three-fourths full. Insert a cork stopper covered with aluminum foil loosely in the top of the tube and allow the isoöctane to filter through the silica gel. Renew the silica gel in the tube as often as necessary to yield isoöctane conforming to the required absorbance limits.

Check the absorbance of a 1-cm. layer of the isoöctane against distilled water through the range of wavelengths used in the analysis. The absorbance compared with distilled water set at zero absorbance must not be more than 0.070 percent at all wavelengths and the resultant absorbance *vs.* wavelength curve must be smooth; otherwise, repeat the filtration and recheck the absorbance.

Procedure for Conjugated Polyunsaturated Acids.—Weigh sufficient sample into a 1-ml. Pyrex cup to give an absorbance reading of 0.2 or more. This usually requires about 200 mg. Place approximately 75 ml. of purified isoöctane, hexane, or cyclohexane in a 150-ml. beaker. Hold the cup just above the solvent and allow it to drop to the bottom of the beaker. Rotate the beaker and warm the contents if necessary to promote solution of the sample.

Cool the beaker and contents to room temperature and transfer the solution quantitatively to a 100-ml. glass-stoppered volumetric flask and add sufficient solvent to bring the volume to 100 ml. Mix thoroughly. Determine the absorbance of the solution in the ultraviolet absorption spectrometer, following the manufacturer's instructions for operating the instrument. Use a matched cell containing only solvent as the blank cell.

Determine the absorbance readings at *346*, 322, *315*, 308, 274, *268*, 262, and *233* mμ, diluting the original solution and/or using other cell lengths if necessary so that the observed densities are between 0.2 and 0.8. Record the cell length, grams of sample in a liter of the final dilution used for the measurement, and the absorbance reading for each wavelength. Readings are not necessarily required at all wavelengths for all samples. If the history of the sample is known, it is not necessary to make readings at wavelengths higher than those which correspond to the most highly unsaturated acids known to be present. It is convenient to make readings on both sides of the wavelengths italicized to ascertain that a maximum is present. A component is assumed to be absent if a maximum is not found in the characteristic region and no further calculations need be made in this region.

Procedure for Nonconjugated Polyunsaturated Acids Using 6.6 Percent Potassium Hydroxide and 25-Minute Isomerization.—This method is preferred when the sample contains only linoleic and linolenic unsaturated acids. Weigh about 100 mg. of sample into a 1-ml. Pyrex glass cup and weigh 11.0 ± 0.1 g. of the 6.6 percent potassium hydroxide-glycol reagent into a 1 × 10 in. test tube. Prepare and conduct two blanks with each group of samples. Cover the test tube with a distributing head attached to a manifold which will permit passing nitrogen (containing no more than 0.01 percent oxygen) over the contents of the tubes at the rate of 50–100 ml./min. Start and adjust the flow of nitrogen and allow the gas to sweep through the tube for about one minute to replace the air, and then immerse the tube and contents to a depth of $4\frac{1}{2}$ in. in the isomerization bath maintained at 180.0° ± 0.5°C. Maintenance at this temperature is important and should be checked frequently. Remove the distributing head after 20 minutes of heating and drop the 1-ml. glass cup containing the weighed sample into the test tube. Observe the exact time when the cup is dropped into the tube and replace the distributing head. Conduct the potassium hydroxide-glycol blank in a similar manner but use a clean 1-ml. glass cup and omit the sample. Keeping the distributing head in place, remove each test tube from the bath and swirl vigorously for a few seconds and then return to the bath. After heating for 1 minute, remove and examine the solution in each tube. If the solution is clear, indicating complete saponification, return the tube to the bath. If the solution is not clear, swirl the test tube two or three times and again return it to the bath. Repeat the inspection after 1 minute of heating, and continue the swirling, heating, and inspection until saponification is complete. Exactly 25 minutes after dropping the sample into the test tube, remove the tube from the bath, wipe it clean, and place it in a 3000-ml. beaker containing cold water. Continue to pass nitrogen over the solution during the cooling process. When the solution has cooled to room temperature, remove the head, wash with about 20 ml. of methanol, and collect the washings in the test tube. Use a long glass stirring rod to mix and quantitatively transfer the contents of the test tube to a 100-ml. glass-stoppered volumetric flask. Dilute to volume with methanol and mix thoroughly.

Determine the absorbance readings at 346, 322, 315, 308, 274, 268, 262, and 233 mμ, using dilutions such that the absorbance values will lie between 0.2 and 0.8.

Procedure for Nonconjugated Polyunsaturated Acid Using 21 Percent Potassium Hydroxide-Glycol Reagent and 15-Minute Isomerization.—This method is preferred for the analysis of samples containing linoleic, linolenic, and arachidonic acids, and it is essential when linoleic, linolenic, arachidonic, and pentaenoic acids are present.

The procedure is carried out as directed in the preceding method except that the reagent is 21 percent potassium hydroxide in ethylene glycol, the sample size is 80 mg., and the isomerization period is 15 minutes.

Calculations. **Absorptivity for Conjugated Constituents.**

1. Calculate the absorptivity, a, for each wavelength using subscripts 233, 268, 315, and 346 to designate each individual a.

$$\text{Absorptivity} = a = A/(b \times c)$$

where: A = observed absorbance;
b = cell length in cm.; and
c = grams of sample in a liter of the final dilution used for the absorbance measurement.

In the equations which follow, subscripts 2, 3, 4, and 5, refer to diene, triene, tetraene, and pentaene constituents, respectively.

2. Absorptivity at 233 mμ corrected for absorption by acid or ester groups = a_2 = $a_{233} - a_0$
where: $a_0 = 0.07$ for esters, and 0.03 for soaps and fatty acids.
3. Absorptivity at 268 mμ corrected for background absorption = $a_3 = 2.8[a_{268} - \frac{1}{2}(a_{262} + a_{274})]$
4. Absorptivity at 315 mμ corrected for background absorption = $a_4 = 2.5[a_{315} - \frac{1}{2}(a_{308} + a_{322})]$
5. Absorptivity at 346 mμ = $a_5 = a_{346}$

Conjugated Acids. NOTE.—If the quantities within the brackets are zero or negative, no characteristic absorption maxima are present and the corresponding constituent is reported as absent. As preformed constituents are usually present in small quantities, background absorption corrections are usually required. If large quantities of preformed constituents are present this method is not applicable. However, no background corrections are to be applied to readings in the pentaenoic region, 346 mμ.

1. Conjugated diene, percent, = $C_2 = 0.91\ a_2$
2. Conjugated triene, percent, = $C_3 = 0.47\ a_3$
3. Conjugated tetraene, percent, = $C_4 = 0.45\ a_4$
4. Conjugated pentaene, percent, = $C_5 = 0.39\ a_5$

Absorptivities for Nonconjugated Constituents—6.6 percent Potassium Hydroxide—25-Minute Isomerization.

1. Calculate the absorptivity, a', for each wavelength.

$$\text{Absorptivity} = a' = A/(b \times c)$$

2. Absorptivity at 233 mμ corrected for conjugated diene acids originally present is $a'_2 = a'_{233} - a_2 - 0.03$.
3. Absorptivity at 268 mμ corrected for background absorption and for undestroyed conjugated triene is: $a'_3 = 4.03\ [a'_{268} - 1/2\ (a'_{262} + a'_{274})] - a_3$
4. Absorptivity at 315 mμ corrected for background absorption and for undestroyed conjugated tetraene is: $a'_4 = 2.06\ [a'_{315} - 1/2\ (a'_{308} + a'_{322})] - a_4$

Nonconjugated Acids—6.6 percent Potassium Hydroxide—25-Minute Isomerization.

1. Without background corrections:
   a. Linoleic acid, percent = $X = 1.086\ a'_2 - 1.324\ (a'_{268} - a_{268}) + 0.040\ (a'_{315} - a_{315})$
   b. Linolenic acid, percent = $Y + 1.980\ (a'_{268} - a_{268}) - 4.92\ (a'_{315} - a_{315})$

    c. Arachidonic acid, percent $= Z = 4.69 \, (a'_{315} - a_{315})$

2. When background corrections are required:

    a. Linoleic acid, percent $= X = 1.086a'_2 - 1.324a'_3 + 0.40a'_4$
    b. Linolenic acid, percent $= Y = 1.980a'_3 - 4.92a'_4$
    c. Arachidonic acid, percent $= Z = 4.69a'_3$

Absorptivities for Nonconjugated Constituents—21 percent Potassium Hydroxide—15-Minute Isomerization.

1. Calculate absorptivities a' for each wavelength 233, 268, 315, and 346 mμ. Remember that spectrometric readings are to be taken on both sides of these analytical wavelengths to ascertain that a maximum is present. If no maximum is found the component is to be reported as zero without further measurement or calculation.
2. Absorptivity at 233 m$\mu = a'_2 = a'_{233} - a_2$
3. Absorptivity at 268 m$\mu = a'_3 = a'_{268} - a_{268}$
4. Absorptivity at 315 m$\mu = a'_4 = a'_{315} - a_{315}$
5. Absorptivity at 346 m$\mu = a'_5 = a'_{346} - a_{346}$

Nonconjugated Acids—21 percent Potassium Hydroxide—15-Minute Isomerization. NOTE.—The spectrophotometric method of analysis will not differentiate between acids that have the same number of double bonds but different chain length, *e.g.*, between C_{20} and C_{22} pentaenes. The first two sets of equations below are for samples containing C_{20} pentaene acid and for samples containing C_{22} pentaene acid, respectively. If chain length is unknown, the assumption is made that these pentaene acids are present in equal quantities, and the third set of equations given below is to be used. This assumption, although not necessarily true in all fats, is in agreement with the approximate proportions found in beef suprarenal lipids.

Equations (Acids in Sample).

1. Samples containing C_{20} pentaene acid:
    a. Linoleic acid, percent $= X = 1.09a'_2 - 0.57a'_3 - 0.26a'_4 + 0.002a'_5$
    b. Linolenic acid, percent $= Y = 1.10a'_3 - 0.88a'_4 + 0.31a'_5$
    c. Arachidonic acid, percent $= Z = 1.65a'_4 - 1.55a'_5$
    d. Pentaenoic acids, percent $= P = 1.14a'_5$
2. Samples containing C_{22} pentaene acid:
    a. Linoleic acid, percent $= X = 1.09a'_2 - 0.57a'_4 - 0.26a'_4 - 0.12a'_5$
    b. Linolenic acid, percent $= Y = 1.10a'_3 - 0.88a'_4 - 0.02a'_5$
    c. Arachidonic acid, percent $= Z = 1.65a'_4 - 1.86a'_5$
    d. Pentaenoic acids, percent $= P = 1.98a'_5$
3. Samples containing pentaene acids of unknown chain length (Calculated as 50% C_{20} and 50% C_{22} pentaenoic acids):
    a. Linoleic acid, percent $= X = 1.09a'_2 - 0.57a'_3 - 0.57a'_3 - 0.26a'_4 - 0.03a'_5$
    b. Linolenic acid, percent $= Y = 1.10a'_3 - 0.88a'_4 + 0.19a'_5$
    c. Arachidonic acid, percent $= Z = 1.65a'_4 - 1.67a'_5$
    d. Pentaenoic acids, percent $= P = 1.45a'_5$

Total Composition.

1. Total conjugated polyunsaturated acids, percent $= C_2 + C_3 + C_4 + C_5$
2. Total nonconjugated polyunsaturated acids, percent $= X + Y + Z + P$
3. Oleic acid,

$$\text{percent} = \text{I.V. of samp.} - 1.811\ (C_2 + X) + 2.737\ (C_3 + Y)$$
$$+ \frac{3.337\ (C_4 + Z) + 4.014\ (C_5 + P)}{0.899}$$

4. Saturated acids, percent = percent total fatty acid − (percent oleic acid + percent conjugated acid + percent nonconjugated acid)

NOTE.—The percent total fatty acid of most naturally occurring oils is 95.6.

5. To calculate to a fatty acid basis, multiply the percentage value by

$$\frac{100}{\text{percent total fatty acid}}$$

CONJUGATED DIENOIC ACID IN DEHYDRATED CASTOR OIL, DEHYDRATED CASTOR FATTY ACIDS, AND THEIR METHYL OR ETHYL ESTERS[12]

Procedure.—Prepare a solution of the sample in isoöctane of such a concentration that the absorbance reading will be within 0.2 and 0.8 (about 0.01 g. per liter). Adjust the weight of the sample or dilution if necessary. Determine the absorbance at 233 mμ using a matched cell containing solvent only as a blank.

Percent Conjugated Dienoic Acid:

$$= 0.84\ (A/bc - k)$$

where: k = 0.07 for esters and 0.03 for acids;
A = absorbance at 233 mμ;
b = cell length in cm; and
c = concentration of dilution measured.

ELEOSTEARIC ACID IN TUNG OIL:

Procedure.—Prepare a solution of the sample in cyclohexane such that the absorbance reading will be within the range of 0.2 − 0.8 (approximately 0.005 g. per liter). Determine the absorbance at 269.0 mμ and 271.5 mμ. The following calculations are based on using a Beckman DU spectrometer with slit width adjusted to 0.3 − 0.4 mm. at the designated wave lengths.

$$\text{percent } \alpha \text{ eleostearic acid} = 2.186a_{271.5} - 1.820a_{269.0}$$
$$\text{percent } \beta \text{ eleostearic acid} = 1.914a_{269.0} - 1.704a_{271.5}$$

where a is the absorptivity at the designated wavelengths.

DIFFERENTIATION BETWEEN BLEACHED AND UNBLEACHED LARD:[13]

Procedure.—Calculate absorptivities from ultraviolet absorption measurements at 264, 268, and 272 mμ. Two criteria are employed as a means of detecting bleached (refined) lard. These are: $T = 100\ [a_{268} - (a_{264} + a_{272})/2]$ should not exceed 1; and $Q = T/a_{268}$ should not exceed 7 (usually 3–4), where a equals absorptivities at the indicated wavelengths.

[12] *Ibid.*, Method Ti 1a–64.

[13] Kaufmann, H. P., Thieme, J. C., and Volbert, F., Fette-Seifen Anstrichmittel, **58**, 1046, 1956.

INFRARED SPECTROMETRY

ISOLATED *TRANS*-ISOMERS[14]

The principal application of infrared spectrometry to fat analysis is for the estimation of isolated *trans*-isomers. The unsaturated fatty acids of most naturally occurring vegetable oils contain double bonds in the *cis*-configuration. However, these may be converted to *trans*-isomers in processing, especially in hydrogenation. Fats and oils of animal and marine origin may contain small amounts of *trans*-isomers.

The basis of the infrared method of analysis is estimation of the intensity of the absorption at 10.3 μ. The intensity of the absorption of the sample is compared with the intensity of the absorption of a sample of known *trans*-isomer content. From these measurements the concentration of the *trans*-isomer in the sample may be calculated.

The method of the American Oil Chemists' Society presented here is applicable to the determination of isolated *trans*-bonds in natural or processed long-chain acids, esters, and triglycerides which contain less than 5 percent conjugated materials. Long-chain fatty acids containing less than 15 percent isolated *trans*-isomers must be converted to their methyl esters before analysis by this method.

The method is not applicable, or is applicable only with special precautions, to fats and oils containing more than 5 percent conjugated unsaturation or to materials containing functional groups which modify or interfere with the intensity of the C—H deformation about the *trans*-double bond.

Apparatus.—The infrared spectrometer should cover the spectral range of 9 to 11 μ with a wavelength scale capable of being read to 0.01 μ. The instrument should be equipped with a compartment to hold the cells.

The absorption cells should have sodium chloride or potassium bromide windows with internal cell lengths of 0.2 to 2.00 mm. Pairs must match within 0.01 absorbance units.

Standards.—The accuracy of the infrared method depends on the purity of the primary standard so this must be of the highest possible (99 + percent). None of the materials used as primary standards, that is, elaidic acid, methyl elaidate, or trielaidin is readily available in this grade of purity. Therefore, secondary standards of acids, esters, or glycerides are employed. These are samples of known *trans*-isomer content, calibrated against primary standards and available through the American Oil Chemists' Society. Elaidic acid is used as the standard for the analysis of fatty acids; methyl elaidate and trielaidin are standards for esters and glycerides respectively.

Procedure.—Melt solid fats on a steam bath and mix before sampling. Filter samples that appear cloudy. If a sample appears cloudy after dilution due to the presence of water, add a small quantity of anhydrous sodium sulfate, mix, and allow to settle before removing the portion to be analyzed.

Weigh accurately 0.2000 ±0.0002 g. of the standard or the sample into a glass stoppered 10-ml. volumetric flask. Dissolve in, and dilute to volume with, carbon disulfide (dry, ACS grade) and mix thoroughly. The transmittance at the *trans*-absorption maximum should be between 20 and 70 percent. If it is outside this range, use a different weight of sample or a different cell thickness. Fill a clear absorption cell with carbon disulfide (dry, ACS grade) and fill a matching cell with the sample or standard in solution. With the cell in an upright position, inject the sample from the bottom using a hypodermic syringe with a blunted needle allowing any air bubbles to pass up through the cell. Determine the transmittance or absorbance curve with an infrared spectrometer

[14] American Oil Chemists' Society, Official and Tentative Methods, 2nd Ed., 1946, Method Cd 14–61.

over the region 9 to 11 μ. The exact programming of the instrument to obtain this curve will depend upon the particular instrument selected. Manufacturer's directions for operation should be followed. Transmittances of both sample and standard curves are determined in the same manner.

Once the curve is obtained for the standard, all samples subsequently analyzed must be measured with the same instrument with all programming controls set at identical positions. The curve for the standard need not be repeated as long as the same instrument is used without adjustments or replacement parts and with the same programming controls. Otherwise, analysis of the standard should be repeated and it is advisable to repeat analysis of the standard periodically under any circumstances.

Calculations.—Obtain from the charts, the transmittances at the 10.36 μ maximum of both the sample and standard. Using the base line technique, calculate the fractional transmittance of the sample. This is the distance from the zero line of the chart to the absorption peak, divided by the distance from the zero line to the base line. The base line for acids is a line drawn from 10.10 to 10.65 μ, for esters from 10.02 to 10.59 μ, and for glycerides from 10.05 to 10.67 μ. Convert transmittances to absorbances and calculate the absorbtivities.

$$a = A/bc$$

where: A is the absorbance (log $100/T$);

T is percent transmittance;

b is the internal cell length in cm.; and

c is the concentration in grams per liter of the sample dilution tested.

Calculate the percent *trans*-isomer as methyl elaidate, elaidic acid, or trielaidin using the equation:

$$\text{percent } trans\text{-isomer} = 100a_s/a_k$$

where a_s and a_k are the absorptivities of the sample and the appropriate standard, respectively.

FLAME PHOTOMETRY

SOAP IN OIL[15]

The usual source of soap in refined oils and fats is the sodium hydroxide or sodium carbonate used to neutralize the free fatty acids in the refining process. Traces of the sodium salts of the fatty acids are difficult to remove. Chemical methods for the estimation of dissolved soap are presented in the chapter, "Natural Fats," in Standard Methods of Chemical Analysis, Volume II, Part B. Two instrumental methods for the determination are given in this chapter. The photometric method depends on measurement with a flame photometer of the sodium ion extracted from the sample as sodium chloride. A method depending on electrical resistance of the soap solution appears later in this chapter.

Procedure.—Mix 100 g. of the sample with 1 ml. of concentrated hydrochloric acid in a Waring Blendor for about 1 minute. Add 50 ml. of petroleum ether and mix again for 1 minute. Add 50 ml. of water and blend again for 1 minute. Transfer the mixture to a 250-ml. separatory funnel and allow the liquid phases to separate. Use the water layer for the photometric determination. Aspirate a few ml. of the water extract in the

[15] Edmonds, S. M., and Mattikow, M., J. Am. Oil Chemists' Soc., **35**, 680, 1958.

flame photometer and determine the intensity of the sodium (D) line. Refer to a graph to determine the soap content.

Prepare standards by mixing 1 ml. of concentrated hydrochloric acid with varying amounts of sodium hydroxide (see Table 48-2). Dilute each to 50 ml. with water and aspirate. Prepare and run a blank determination with each sample or group of samples. The instrument should be checked with standards daily because of the possibility of instrument drift.

TABLE 48-2. STANDARDS FOR DETERMINATION OF SOAP IN OIL

Ml. 0.01 M NaOH	Sodium Oleate (p.p.m.) (Using 100-g. Sample)
0.0	blank
0.5	15
1.0	30
2.0	60
4.0	120

The photometric method is reported to be accurate up to levels of 150 p.p.m. Above this, results tend to be low, possibly because of incomplete removal of the soap by the prescribed analytical procedure.

EMISSION SPECTROMETRY

Emission spectrometric techniques have been successfully employed to determine trace quantities of such metals as iron, copper, manganese, and tin. A spectrometric procedure was reported by Melvin and Hawley[16] for the determination of iron and copper in fats and oils. In this procedure, an internal standard was employed, and the sample of fat was decomposed by slow pyrolysis on a hot plate at 350–450°C. The ashing was then completed in a muffle furnace at 450°C.

LINE-WIDTH METHOD[17]

The line-width spectrometric procedure was applied to the determination of copper, iron, manganese, nickel, and tin in vegetable oils by O'Connor[17] and co-workers. This method is based on the principle that if all factors which affect line-width except concentration are kept constant, the width of the line of the spectrogram will be dependent only on the concentration. It has been demonstrated that the method can be applied to the determination of metals present in fats to the extent of only one part in 10 million.

Procedure.—Exactly 5 mg. of the ash are weighed into the electrode crater of the emission spectrometer and the sample is completely consumed by arcing in a direct-current arc at 235 volts, 20 amperes, for exactly 90 seconds. The excited sample is photographed covering the ultraviolet region from 2500 to 3500 A. Any spectrometer that will cover this range with equal or higher dispersion can be used. The processed plates are measured with a recording microdensitometer through the selected lines of the elements to be determined. From densities of each of the lines of the elements being determined, and by use of previously prepared curves, the concentrations of the elements may be obtained.

[16] Melvin, E. H., and Hawley, J. E., J. Am. Oil Chemists' Soc., **28**, 346, 1951.
[17] O'Connor, R. T., Heinzelman, D. C., and Jefferson, M. E., J. Am. Oil Chemists' Soc., **25**, 408, 1948.

X-RAY DIFFRACTION

X-ray diffraction is employed in fat analysis to characterize certain crystal forms which have functional significance. There is no standard procedure. The method given here is basic; however, modern automatic apparatus simplifies these operations considerably.

Procedure.—Mount the specimen by pressing as thin and as even a layer as possible of the sample onto the center of the mount or disc, but avoid working the sample any more than necessary. Operate the x-ray diffraction apparatus according to directions for the specific instrument and expose and process the film. Then, utilizing an illuminating device, measure the diameter of each circle to the nearest 0.01 mm. with a vernier scale. Calculate the short spacings $d(A)$ as directed below.

Theta (θ) is obtained from a trigonometric table, using the relationship

$$\tan 2\theta = d/2s$$

where: $d/2$ = distance on the film from the center of the pattern to the line;

s = distance from the film to the sample;

2θ = the angle of diffraction; and

$d(A)$ is calculated from the equation:

$d = \lambda/2 \sin$

where: λ = wavelength of Cu K_a = 1.5374 A.

If targets other than copper are used, of course, the wavelength will be different.

REFRACTOMETRY

The refractive index of fats is a very helpful characteristic from an analytical viewpoint. Some of the more common usages are: (a) as a process control test where changes in unsaturation are involved *e.g.*, in hydrogenation; (b) as an index of the iodine value of vegetable oils; (c) as a measure of the oil content of oilseed meals and various other oil bearing materials; (d) as a standard of identity. The refractive index is constant, within limits, for a given kind or type of fat. See Table 48-3.

TABLE 48-3.   REFRACTIVE INDEXES OF SOME FATS

Fat	Refractive Index at 40°C.	Fat	Refractive Index at 40°C.
Castor	1.466–1.473	Peanut	1.460–1.464
Coconut	1.448–1.450	Perilla	1.473–1.479
Corn	1.476–1.477	Safflower	1.467–1.469
Cottonseed	1.464–1.468	Sesame at 25°C.	1.472–1.474
Kapok	1.460–1.466	Soybean	1.468–1.474
Lard	1.448–1.460	Sunflower	1.465–1.469
Linseed	1.472–1.475	Tallow (Beef)	1.450–1.458
Olive	1.460–1.464	Tallow (Mutton)	1.452–1.458
Palm	1.453–1.459	Tung at 25°C.	1.514–1.520
Palm Kernel	1.449–1.452	Walnut	1.469–1.471

The refractive index of fats is related to such characteristics as unsaturation, molecular weight, free fatty acid content, and hydroxyl content. In the case of many of the most commonly used oils such as cottonseed, soybean, and linseed, with relatively low free fatty acid and hydroxyl content and essentially the same saponification values, the degree of unsaturation is the predominating influence. Pickering and Cowlishaw[18] developed the relation expressed by the equation

$$n_D{}^{40} = 1.4515 + 0.0001171 \text{ (I.V.)}$$

Subsequent and more recent studies have been reasonably confirmatory. A hand-held refractive reading directly in iodine value units and designed specifically for soybean and linseed oils depends on a similar relationship.[18a]

A refractometer on which the scale can be estimated to the fourth decimal point is satisfactory for most purposes. However, for the determination of oil content an instrument which can be estimated to the fifth decimal point is preferable.

A standard method for determining the oil content of flaxseed follows. This method is basic in design and with proper modification of the tables should be applicable to a wide variety of oil-bearing materials.

Procedure for Refractive Index.—Melt the sample, unless it is already liquid, and pour it through a filter paper to remove impurities and traces of moisture. Adjust the temperature of the refractometer to the desired temperature, then place several drops of the sample on the lower prism. Close the prisms and tighten them firmly with the screw-head. Allow to stand for 1 to 2 minutes or until the sample comes to the temperature of the instrument. Adjust the instrument and light to obtain the most distinct reading possible, and then determine the refractive index. The light source should preferably be a sodium vapor lamp which will provide monochromatic light. Take several readings and calculate the average.

Since the refractive index is a function of temperature, variations in temperature must either be compensated for by correction, or the instrument must be thermostatically controlled with motor-driven pump to circulate water continuously through the refractometer. The temperature should be maintained at the selected level $\pm 0.1°C$. Temperatures of 25°C., 40°C., and 60°C., are employed; however, it is advisable to limit these to as few a number as possible. A temperature of 40°C. suffices for most fats and oils except high-titer fats. Some of these, such as certain hydrogenated oils, must be maintained at 60°C., or even 70°C., in order to remain completely liquid. Temperature corrections may be made according to the following formula:

$$R = R' + K \, (T' - T)$$

where: R = reading reduced to desired temperature T;
R' = reading at temperature T';
T = the desired temperature;
T' = temperature at which reading R' is made;
K for fats on the Butyro scale = 0.55;
K for oils on the Butyro scale = 0.58;
K for fats on the Abbe scale = 0.000365;
K for oils on the Abbe scale = 0.000385.

For conversion of Butyro readings to refractive index see the chapter, "Natural Fats," in Volume II, Part B.

Procedure for Oil Content of Flaxseed.[19]—Mix about 74 parts of α-chloronaph-

[18] Pickering, G. F., and Cowlishaw, G. E., J. Soc. Chem. Ind., **41**, 74T, 1922.
[18a] Hunt, W. H., Neustadt, M. H., Shurkus, A. A., and Zeleny, L., J. Am. Oil Chemists' Soc., **28**, 5, 1951.
[19] Association of Official Agricultural Chemists, Official Methods of Analysis, 9th Ed., Washington, D. C., 1960, 379.

thalene with about 26 parts α-bromonaphthalene by weight and then carefully adjust the composition of the mixture to a refractive index of 1.63940 at 25.0°C. Temperature readings must be to the nearest 0.1°C. It is preferable to make the index readings exactly at 25°C., but if this is impossible, corrections may be made. The correction factor is 0.00045 per 1°C., to be added if the temperature is above 25.0°C. and to be subtracted if the reading is below 25.0°C. Maintain this solution in a glass-stoppered, dark colored bottle and away from direct sunlight. The refractive index should remain constant for long periods of time, but it is advisable to check it from time to time.

Grind about 25 g. of the sample in a suitable mill to such fineness that, after extraction with ether, 95 percent of it will pass through a No. 40 sieve.

Weigh accurately 2.5 g. of finely ground sample into a clean porcelain mortar which has been preheated to about 70°C. in an oven or on an electric hot plate. Add about 1 g. of pure sea sand or a similar abrasive and exactly 5 ml. of the prepared solvent mixture. This mixture has a high specific gravity so it is important to measure its volume accurately. This may be accomplished with an accurately calibrated 5-ml. pipet having a delivery time not exceeding 15 seconds.

Grind the mixture of solvent and sample in the mortar vigorously for 3 minutes constantly scraping the particles of meal into the bottom that are thrown against the sides. Filter into a test tube through S & S No. 588 folded paper or an equivalent fat free paper that yields a clear filtrate. When the filtrate has cooled to room temperature, determine its refractive index at 25.0°C. with an accuracy of ±0.00002. If the reading is made at a temperature other than 25.0°C., correct as previously directed using a temperature coefficient of 0.00042 per 1°C. Refer to the Conversion Table 48-4 to find the oil percentage corresponding to the refractive index of the filtrate. This is the uncorrected value for oil content.

Since the refractive index of linseed oil may vary from lot to lot it is necessary to make an adjustment for the difference between the refractive index of the oil being examined and the refractive of the oil used to prepare the conversion table.

Place about 2 g. of ground sample in a fine paper filter in glass funnel and pour over it about 15 ml. of petroleum ether, collecting the clear filtrate in a small, shallow evaporating dish. Carefully evaporate the ether on a steam bath and then place the dish in an oven for 20 minutes at 105°C. Remove and cool to room temperature. If more convenient or otherwise preferred, the oil may be obtained by pressing a small sample of the ground seed in a laboratory hydraulic press and filtering the oil obtained if it is not entirely clear. Determine the refractive index of the oil at 25.0°C. The temperature coefficient for pure oil is 0.000357 per 1°C., to be added if the temperature at which the reading is taken is above 25.0°C. and to be subtracted if the temperature is less than 25°C.

From the refractive index value of the oil, subtract 1.47780 (the refractive index at 25.0°C. of the oil used in obtaining the data in Table 48-4). Using this difference, determine from Table 48-5, the correction to be applied to the uncorrected value for oil content as determined above. If the difference is positive add the correction, and if the difference is negative subtract the correction.

POTENTIOMETRIC TITRATIONS

Several potentiometric titration techniques are applicable for the analysis of fats. The titrations required in the determinations of free fatty acids, saponification value, iodine value, determination of moisture by the Karl Fischer method, and determination of monoglycerides with periodic acid may be performed potentiometrically. Titration curves for free fatty acids and saponification values resemble conventional acid-base titration curves, although it should be remembered that these methods are carried out

TABLE 48-4. CONVERSION TABLE—OIL CONTENT OF FLAXSEED

$n_D{}^{25}$	Oil	$n_D{}^{25}$	Oil	$n_D{}^{25}$	Oil	$n_D{}^{25}$	Oil
	percent		percent		percent		percent
1.61837	28.0	1.61554	32.5	1.61279	37.0	1.61012	41.5
1.61831	28.1	1.61548	32.6	1.61273	37.1	1.61006	41.6
1.61824	28.2	1.61542	32.7	1.61267	37.2	1.61000	41.7
1.61818	28.3	1.61535	32.8	1.61261	37.3	1.60995	41.8
1.61811	28.4	1.61529	32.9	1.61255	37.4	1.60989	41.9
1.61805	28.5	1.61523	33.0	1.61249	37.5	1.60983	42.0
1.61799	28.6	1.61517	33.1	1.61243	37.6	1.60977	42.1
1.61792	28.7	1.61511	33.2	1.61237	37.7	1.60971	42.2
1.61786	28.8	1.61504	33.3	1.61231	37.8	1.60966	42.3
1.61779	28.9	1.61498	33.4	1.61225	37.9	1.60960	42.4
1.61773	29.0	1.61492	33.5	1.61219	38.0	1.60954	42.5
1.61767	29.1	1.61486	33.6	1.61213	38.1	1.60948	42.6
1.61760	29.2	1.61480	33.7	1.61207	38.2	1.60942	42.7
1.61754	29.3	1.61473	33.8	1.61201	38.3	1.60937	42.8
1.61748	29.4	1.61467	33.9	1.61195	38.4	1.60931	42.9
1.61742	29.5	1.61461	34.0	1.61189	38.5	1.60925	43.0
1.61735	29.6	1.61455	34.1	1.61183	38.6	1.60919	43.1
1.61729	29.7	1.61449	34.2	1.61177	38.7	1.60913	43.2
1.61723	29.8	1.61443	34.3	1.61171	38.8	1.60908	43.3
1.61716	29.9	1.61437	34.4	1.61165	38.9	1.60902	43.4
1.61710	30.0	1.61431	34.5	1.61159	39.0	1.60896	43.5
1.61704	30.1	1.61424	34.6	1.61153	39.1	1.60890	43.6
1.61697	30.2	1.61418	34.7	1.61147	39.2	1.60884	43.7
1.61691	30.3	1.61412	34.8	1.61141	39.3	1.60879	43.8
1.61685	30.4	1.61406	34.9	1.61135	39.4	1.60873	43.9
1.61679	30.5	1.61400	35.0	1.61130	39.5	1.60867	44.0
1.61672	30.6	1.61394	35.1	1.61124	39.6	1.60861	44.1
1.61666	30.7	1.61388	35.2	1.61118	39.7	1.60856	44.2
1.61660	30.8	1.61382	35.3	1.61112	39.8	1.60850	44.3
1.61653	30.9	1.61376	35.4	1.61106	39.9	1.60844	44.4
1.61647	31.0	1.61370	35.5	1.61100	40.0	1.60839	44.5
1.61641	31.1	1.61363	35.6	1.61094	40.1	1.60833	44.6
1.61635	31.2	1.61357	35.7	1.61088	40.2	1.60827	44.7
1.61628	31.3	1.61351	35.8	1.61082	40.3	1.60821	44.8
1.61622	31.4	1.61345	35.9	1.61076	40.4	1.60816	44.9
1.61616	31.5	1.61339	36.0	1.61071	40.5	1.60810	45.0
1.61610	31.6	1.61333	36.1	1.61065	40.6	1.60804	45.1
1.61604	31.7	1.61327	36.2	1.61059	40.7	1.60799	45.2
1.61597	31.8	1.61321	36.3	1.61053	40.8	1.60793	45.3
1.61591	31.9	1.61315	36.4	1.61047	40.9	1.60787	45.4
1.61585	32.0	1.61309	36.5	1.61041	41.0	1.60782	45.5
1.61579	32.1	1.61303	36.6	1.61035	41.1	1.60776	45.6
1.61573	32.2	1.61297	36.7	1.61029	41.2	1.60770	45.7
1.61566	32.3	1.61291	36.8	1.61024	41.3	1.60764	45.8
1.61560	32.4	1.61285	36.9	1.61018	41.4		

TABLE 48-5. CORRECTION TABLE—OIL CONTENT OF FLAXSEED

[Values to be added when $(n_D^{25} - 1.4778)$ is positive, subtracted when $(n_D^{25} - 1.4778)$ is negative]

(Corrections in terms of percent of oil indicated)

$nM - 1.4778$	28	29	30	31	32	33	34	35	36	37	38	39	40	41	42	43	44	45	46	47	48
.0001	0.02	0.02	0.02	0.02	0.02	0.02	0.02	0.02	0.02	0.02	0.02	0.02	0.02	0.02	0.02	0.02	0.03	0.03	0.03	0.03	0.03
.0002	.03	.03	.03	.03	.04	.04	.04	.04	.04	.04	.04	.04	.05	.05	.05	.05	.05	.05	.05	.05	.06
.0003	.05	.05	.05	.05	.05	.06	.06	.06	.06	.06	.06	.07	.07	.07	.07	.07	.08	.08	.08	.08	.08
.0004	.06	.06	.07	.07	.07	.07	.08	.08	.08	.08	.09	.09	.09	.09	.10	.10	.10	.10	.11	.11	.11
.0005	.08	.08	.08	.09	.09	.09	.10	.10	.10	.11	.11	.11	.11	.12	.12	.12	.13	.13	.13	.14	.14
.0006	.09	.10	.10	.10	.11	.11	.11	.12	.12	.13	.13	.13	.14	.14	.15	.15	.15	.16	.16	.16	.17
.0007	.11	.11	.12	.12	.12	.13	.13	.14	.14	.15	.15	.16	.16	.17	.17	.17	.18	.18	.19	.19	.20
.0008	.12	.13	.13	.14	.14	.15	.15	.16	.16	.17	.17	.18	.18	.19	.19	.20	.20	.21	.21	.22	.22
.0009	.14	.14	.15	.15	.16	.17	.17	.18	.18	.19	.19	.20	.21	.21	.22	.22	.23	.23	.24	.25	.25
.0010	.15	.16	.17	.17	.18	.19	.19	.20	.20	.21	.22	.22	.23	.24	.24	.25	.26	.26	.27	.27	.28
.0011	.17	.17	.18	.19	.20	.20	.21	.22	.22	.23	.24	.25	.25	.26	.27	.27	.28	.29	.29	.30	.31
.0012	.18	.19	.20	.21	.21	.22	.23	.24	.24	.25	.26	.27	.27	.28	.29	.30	.31	.31	.32	.33	.34
.0013	.20	.21	.22	.22	.23	.24	.25	.26	.27	.27	.28	.29	.30	.31	.31	.32	.33	.34	.35	.36	.36
.0014	.21	.22	.23	.24	.25	.26	.27	.28	.29	.29	.30	.31	.32	.33	.34	.35	.36	.37	.37	.38	.39
.0015	.23	.24	.25	.26	.27	.28	.29	.30	.31	.32	.32	.33	.34	.35	.36	.37	.38	.39	.40	.41	.42
.0016	.24	.25	.27	.28	.28	.30	.31	.32	.33	.34	.35	.36	.37	.38	.39	.40	.41	.42	.43	.44	.45
.0017	.26	.27	.28	.29	.30	.31	.32	.33	.35	.36	.37	.38	.39	.40	.41	.42	.43	.44	.45	.47	.48
.0018	.28	.28	.30	.31	.32	.33	.34	.35	.37	.38	.39	.40	.41	.42	.44	.45	.46	.47	.48	.49	.50
.0019	.29	.30	.32	.33	.34	.35	.36	.37	.39	.40	.41	.42	.44	.45	.46	.47	.48	.50	.51	.52	.53
.0020	.31	.32	.33	.34	.36	.37	.38	.39	.41	.42	.43	.45	.46	.47	.48	.50	.51	.52	.53	.55	.56
.0021	.32	.33	.35	.36	.37	.39	.40	.41	.43	.44	.45	.47	.48	.50	.51	.52	.54	.55	.56	.58	.59
.0022	.34	.35	.37	.38	.39	.41	.42	.43	.45	.46	.48	.49	.50	.52	.53	.55	.56	.57	.59	.60	.62
.0023	.35	.37	.38	.40	.41	.43	.44	.45	.47	.48	.50	.51	.53	.54	.56	.57	.59	.60	.61	.63	.64
.0024	.37	.38	.40	.41	.43	.44	.46	.47	.49	.50	.52	.54	.55	.57	.58	.60	.61	.63	.64	.66	.67
.0025	.38	.40	.42	.43	.45	.46	.48	.49	.51	.53	.54	.56	.57	.59	.61	.62	.64	.65	.67	.69	.70
.0026	.40	.41	.43	.45	.46	.48	.50	.51	.53	.55	.56	.58	.60	.61	.63	.64	.66	.68	.69	.71	.73
.0027	.41	.43	.45	.46	.48	.50	.52	.53	.55	.57	.58	.60	.62	.64	.65	.67	.69	.70	.72	.74	.76
.0028	.43	.45	.46	.48	.50	.52	.53	.55	.57	.59	.60	.62	.64	.66	.68	.69	.71	.73	.75	.77	.78
.0029	.44	.46	.48	.50	.52	.54	.55	.57	.59	.61	.63	.65	.66	.68	.70	.72	.74	.76	.77	.79	.81
.0030	.46	.48	.50	.52	.53	.55	.57	.59	.61	.63	.65	.67	.69	.71	.73	.74	.76	.78	.80	.82	.84

in nonaqueous media. The iodometric titration involved in the determination of iodine value has been performed with the deadstop end point. Commercial apparatus available from laboratory supply houses for the Fischer volumetric titration of water involves a deadstop end point. The titration of the excess periodic acid in the estimation of monoglyceride is accomplished by the use of a pH meter and titration to a predetermined pH value.

Chemical methods for the determinations mentioned above are given in the chapter, "Natural Fats," in Volume II, Part B of Standard Methods of Chemical Analysis.

CONDUCTIVITY

SOAP IN OIL[20]

The estimate of soap in refined oil by measuring the electrical resistance of a water extract of the soap is the Official Method of the American Oil Chemists' Society. Resistance in ohms is correlated with concentration of soap (Fig. 48-1).

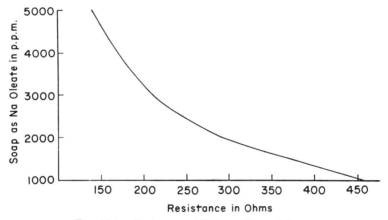

FIG. 48-1.   Resistance of Sodium Oleate Solutions.

Apparatus.—The apparatus needed to determine soap by this method includes a tetraethyl lead extractor (ASTM D-526), a conductivity bridge (Leads Northup No. 4960), a conductivity cell (Leads Northup No. 4920), and a water deionizer. The conductivity water employed in the analysis should have a minimum resistance of 35,000 ohms at 30°C.

Procedure.—Introduce 50 ml. of conductivity water through the graduated filling tube into the tetraethyl lead extractor. Add 100 ml. of the sample at 75–80°F. to the extractor, then rinse the filling tube with an additional 50 ml. of conductivity water. Apply 110 volts (a.c.) from the voltage regulator to the Nichrome wire heater on the extractor. Boil the oil-water mixture for 4 minutes after the first bubble breaks through the oil layer. Allow the mixture to separate one minute after turning off the heater.

Flush out the tip of the extraction tube with a few drops of the water extract, then draw off 60 to 80 ml. of the water extract into a clean 100-ml. beaker. Cool the extract

[20] American Oil Chemists' Society, Official and Tentative Methods, 2nd Ed., Chicago, Ill., 1946, Method Cc 15–60.

in an ice-water bath to 30°C. (±0.5°C.). Transfer about 25 ml. to a clean 30-ml. beaker, and rinse the conductivity cell by immersing it several times in the 30-ml. beaker containing the water extract. Empty the beaker and refill with a fresh portion of water extract. Determine the resistance of the water extract, according to the manufacturers instructions furnished with the conductivity bridge, adjusting the block selector to give a slidewire scale reading between 0.3 and 3.0.

Observe the resistance (R_m) in ohms of the water extract on the conductivity bridge scale at 30°C. (±0.5°C.) and convert to specific resistance (R_s) by the following formula:

$$R_s = \frac{R_m}{K_c}$$

where K_c equals the conductivity cell constant.

The cell constant should be about 0.10 and is determined with an 0.01 M potassium chloride solution according to instructions furnished by the manufacturer. Refer to a standard reference curve to obtain the sodium oleate content equivalent to the resistance.

Preparation of the Standard Reference Curve.—Determine the sodium content of a soapy refined oil obtained directly from the primary centrifugal refining machines, by ashing about 50 g. at 500–550°C., dissolving the ash in distilled water and titrating with 0.05 M hydrochloric acid, using methyl orange indicator. Calculate the alkali (Na_2O) found in this manner to sodium oleate. Dilute the sample of soapy oil with soap-free, double water-washed oil to give a series of oils containing about 20, 50, 100, 200, and 500 p.p.m. soap (sodium oleate).

Extract these solutions with conductivity water as outlined above. Measure the conductivities of the extracts and plot against p.p.m. soap to give a standard reference curve. A separate curve should be prepared for each different kind of soap (cottonseed, peanut, soybean, etc.) if a high degree of accuracy is desired. For control purposes, soap in caustic refined soybean and cottonseed oils may be estimated by the equation:

$$\text{Soap as sodium oleate in p.p.m.} = \frac{340}{0.0001\ R_s}$$

This eliminates the need of preparing reference curve, but it is applicable only if the procedure described is followed exactly.

POLAROGRAPHY

TIN IN FATS

The method given for determining tin in fats is designed for use with Sargent's Model XXI Visible Recording Polarograph.

Procedure.—Weigh into a evaporating dish 0.1, 1, or 10 g. of the well-mixed sample of fat, the quantity depending on the tin content. For less than 100 p.p.m. of tin, weigh 10 ± 0.01 g.; for 100 p.p.m. to 1 ± 0.001 g.; and for more than 1 percent weigh 0.1 ± 0.0001 g.

Adjust the surface temperature of a hot plate to approximately 130°C. Add 50 ml. of alcoholic potassium hydroxide (50 g. per liter) to the sample in the evaporating dish and evaporate the solution to dryness on the hot plate. Direct a current of dry air into the dish during evaporation to reduce the drying time. When dryness is reached, increase the temperature of the hot plate to approximately 250°C., and allow the dish to remain at this temperature for approximately 1 hour. Place the dish in a muffle furnace (previously warmed to 200–225°C.) and gradually raise the temperature of the furnace to approximately 600°C. This usually requires approximately 1 hour. Remove the dish from the muffle furnace and allow it to cool. One hour at the ashing temperature is ordinarily sufficient to carbonize the saponified sample. It is not necessary to burn off completely all of the carbon.

Cover the dish containing the ash with a watch glass and carefully add 10 ml. of hydrochloric acid (1 + 1, v/v) pouring the acid through the lip of the dish. Place the dish on a hot plate and heat the solution to boiling. If a large quantity of carbonaceous material is present, it is advantageous to crush the cake with the flattened end of a glass stirring rod. Remove the dish from the hot plate and rinse down the inside of the watch glass and the sides of the dish with 3–5 ml. of hot distilled water, using a wash bottle with a fine jet. Filter the solution through filter paper into a 25-ml. volumetric flask. Wash the dish and the residue in the paper with three 3-ml. portions of hot distilled water. Cool the flask and contents to room temperature and fill the flask to the 25-ml. mark with distilled water.

Pass a stream of nitrogen gas through the solution for about 10 minutes to remove all of the oxygen and then polarograph a convenient quantity of the sample (10 ml. plus 1 drop of saturated cresol red solution) at about 25°C. The polarogram should cover a voltage range of 0.2 to 0.8 volts, with the controls adjusted to provide a voltage span of 0 to 2 volts. Determine the diffusion current and estimate the concentration of tin by reference to a standard curve relating tin concentration to diffusion current.

Preparation of Standard Diffusion Current-Concentration Graph.—Prepare a standard tin solution containing 1 mg. of tin per ml. of hydrochloric acid (1 + 1, v/v). Dilute 10 ml. of the standard tin solution to 100 ml. with hydrochloric acid (1 + 1, v/v). Select varying quantities (e.g., 0.5, 1.0, and 2.0 ml.) of this diluted solution, such that the range of the tin content of these samples will extend over the range anticipated for the samples that are to be subsequently analyzed. Dilute each to 2.5 ml. with hydrochloric acid (1 + 1, v/v). Add to each dilution 7.5 ml. of saturated ammonium chloride solution and one drop of saturated cresol red solution. Polarograph these standard samples and determine the diffusion current of each solution and then construct a graph relating the diffusion current to µg. of tin per ml. of the standard tin solutions.

$$\text{Tin, in } \mu\text{g./gram} = 25 \times S/\text{wt. of sample (grams)}$$

where S = µg./gram of tin per ml. determined from graph.

NUCLEAR MAGNETIC RESONANCE (NMR) SPECTROMETRY
SOLID FAT CONTENT[21]

Plastic fats such as shortening are, within the normal room-temperature range, mixtures of liquid and solid fractions. The ratio of liquid to solid in any given fat depends, among other things, on the temperature of the fat. The hardness of a given fat at any given temperature is partly determined by the solid fat content at that temperature. The basis for the determination of solid fat content at any given temperature is the fact that change in volume due to phase transformation is relatively greater than change in volume due to thermal expansion.

The solid fat content (SFC) of fats is conventionally determined dilatometrically from measurements of melting dilation. This method is presented later in this chapter. The NMR method presented here can be performed in much less time than the dilatometric procedure, and, furthermore, it can be applied to the sample as is, without melting and

[21] Taylor, J. R., Pohle, W. D., and Gregory, R. L., J. Am. Oil Chemists' Soc., **41**, 177–180, 1964.

recrystallization. The standard method is not recommended when the solid fat index (SFI) exceeds 50 but there appears to be no such limitation to NMR.

Procedure.—The determination is performed with a low resolution NMR spectrometer. In the case reported, using a model 105 NMR instrument and model 1042 integrator by Schlumberger, it was found preferable to modify the derivative curve to allow use of the integrator for determining the area under the curve. This provided more accurate measurement than peak-to-peak height.

Weigh 4–7 ($\pm$0.01) g. of sample into NMR tubes. The sample size may be varied, within limits, for a suitable signal response but the weight must be known. Examine the sample instrumentally according to the manufacturer's operating directions, and with the following instrument parameters.

Sweep time................. 1 minute
Sweep amplitude.............. 1 gauss
Modulation amplitude.......... 0.5 gauss
Sensitivity................... 100

An SFC curve may be obtained in a manner similar to that described for SFI. Melt the fat at 60°C. and then place it in a 0°C. bath for 10 minutes. Following this, place 1 tube in each of 5 water baths regulated at 50°C, 70°C, 80°C, 92° and 100°F. for 30 minutes and then immediately examine by NMR. At completion of the cycle the integrator automatically records the area under the curve in millivolts on the strip chart. Results are calculated to a mv./g. basis.

OIL CONTENT OF OILSEEDS[22]

Nuclear Magnetic Resonance spectrometry has been successfully applied to the estimation of the oil content of certain vegetable oil seeds. The optimum conditions of sample preparation and moisture content were not determined but the accuracy was judged to be comparable to conventional methods. The correlation coefficient obtained between instrument and oil content obtained by standards methods on a limited number of samples was 0.993. The time advantage was significant, the analysis of a single sample requiring about 3 minutes. The method was applied to intact seeds and to carbon tetrachloride solutions of the oil.

Procedure.—Place a weighed quantity of the seed in the sample cell sufficient to occupy a space of about 35 ml. Examine the sample instrumentally, following the manufacturer's directions for operation of the spectrometer, and using the parameters shown in Table 48-6. The integrator reading is adjusted to a unit weight basis in order to calculate percent oil content.

DIFFERENTIAL THERMAL ANALYSIS

FAT CRYSTALLIZING CHARACTERISTICS BY THE DIFFERENTIAL COOLING CURVE[23]

The conventional cooling curve is a graphical representation of time *vs.* temperature changes as a substance is being subjected to a cooling process. Phase transformations that occur during cooling are signified by changes in the slope of the cooling curve.

The differential cooling curve technique is based upon the difference in cooling rate between a standard oil, which will not crystallize when cooled to 0°C., and an unknown

[22] Conway, T. F., and Earle, F. R., J. Am. Oil Chemists' Soc., 40, 265–268, 1963.
[23] Jacobson, G. A., Tiemstra, P. J., and Pohle, W. D., J. Am. Oil Chemists' Soc., 38, 399–402, 1961.

TABLE 48-6.   PARAMETERS FOR DETERMINING OIL CONTENT

	Carbon Tetrachloride Solution	Intact Seed
Analyzer: Schlumberger Model 104		
Time constant (sec.).....................	2	2
Radio-frequency attenuator (decibels)......	32	32
Sweep time (min.)......................	2	2
Sweep amplitude (gauss)	1	1
Sensitivity.............................	50	200
Modulation amplitude (gauss)............	0.5	0.5
Integrator: Model 104-3		
Weight setting.........................	3000	2400
Readout multiplier.....................	10	20
Threshold (millivolts)...................	0.1	Off
Signal multiplier......................	5	5
Sample temperature: 25–27°C.		
Modulation frequency: 33.1 cycles per second (square wave).		
Field strength: 1717 gauss.		

fat, which will crystallize under the same conditions. The evolution of heat associated with phase transformations in the sample results in a temperature differential between the sample and the standard.

The differential cooling curve technique provides a measure of the net thermal effect of the commingled phenomena associated with phase transformation, but these in turn are related to glyceride and fatty acid composition. Therefore, by the selection of suitable standards for comparison, and by careful interpretation of results, reliable judgments can be made relative to composition and melting and solidification aspects. Some analytical applications that have been reported include process control, determination of trisaturants in lard, and identification of certain types of fat.

When an automatic recording is made of the temperature differential during the controlled cooling and solidification period, fats of different crystallizing habits produce curves of different shapes. Three characteristics of these curves reflect differences in the glyceride composition, namely the height, the overall shape and the positioning of the peaks along the horizontal (time) axis. These criteria are useful for diagnostic purposes.

Apparatus.—The apparatus employed to measure the difference in temperature includes copper constantan thermocouples, a recording potentiometer, standardized test tubes, and baths for heating and cooling. The constantan leads of the two thermocouples are connected (series opposed), and the copper leads are connected to the recording potentiometer. Connected in this manner the thermocouple assembly measures directly the difference in temperature between the two tubes.

The test tubes should be standardized as to internal and external dimensions and maintained within ±0.1 mm. tolerances. Placement of the thermocouple assemblies in the test tubes is critical. The thermocouples should be maintained at the same depth and centered in the tubes. It is convenient to fit the thermocouples into properly-dimensioned disc supports for insertion into the withdrawal from the test tubes. This also aids in maintaining uniform spacing.

Procedure.—Fill two 15- × 125-mm. test tubes to a depth of 6 cm. with the reference oil and the sample, respectively. A winterized cottonseed oil serves as a satisfactory standard or reference oil. Insert the thermocouples and place them 3 cm. from the bottom and in the center of the tube. Place the tubes in a boiling water bath until the contents are at equilibrium (at least 10 minutes) and then transfer them to an ice-water bath (0°C.) for the cooling phase. Immediately start the recorder. The temperature difference between the two tubes as measured by the thermocouple is recorded as a graph by the recording potentiometer in units of fractions of a millivolt.

CHROMATOGRAPHY

The development of chromatography is one of the most important advances in analytical chemistry of recent years. Certainly, in the case of fats, this technique provides means of making separations and qualitative and quantitative determinations not previously possible; at least, not without the expense of considerable time and labor. Chromatography is in some instances combined with infrared and mass spectrometry for purposes of separation and identification.

The techniques that have been used include gas-liquid and thin layer chromatography, and separations on paper and in a column. However, at the present time, there are only two standard techniques, both of which are presented here. There are, nevertheless, innumerable reports in the literature pertaining to other chromatographic methods, but these must be subjected to the evaluation of future use.

NEUTRAL OIL[24]

The price of crude soybean oil is, in part, determined by the neutral oil content of the oil, when traded in accordance with the rules of the National Soybean Processors' Association. Neutral oil as determined by column chromatography includes triglycerides and the natural unsaponifiable material.

The chromatographic column must conform to the specifications of the American Oil Chemists' Society (see Fig. 48-2).

Reagents. **Solvent.**—Ether-methanol, preparing by mixing 25 ml. of methanol (ACS grade) with 975 ml. of absolute ethyl ether (ACS grade).

Aluminum Oxide.—Activated alumina, Mesh 80–200, Aluminum Company of America, East St. Louis, Illinois, Grade F-20, or equivalent. Dry at 200–205°C. for 4 hours before use. The alumina may be used up to 72 hours after drying, provided it is kept in a tightly sealed container, preferably in a desiccator.

Preparation of Sample.—The sample container must be vigorously shaken and the sample must be thoroughly mixed in order to incorporate and uniformly distribute meal or other sediment. In order to achieve this, the oil must be brought up to a temperature of at least 20°C. (50°C. for soybean oil and 38°C. until completely melted for coconut oil) before shaking. Inspect the inside of the container to be sure that no sediment remains clinging to the sides or bottom. If any sediment is found, remove it completely, cut this can open if necessary, and incorporate thoroughly with the oil. The uniform incorporation and distribution of settlings and suspended matter are very significant in determining the accuracy of the result of the analysis.

Preparation of the Column.—With the dispensing buret removed, add about 10 ml. of solvent to the column. Open the stopcock momentarily to fill the delivery tube with solvent. Weigh 20 ± 1 g. of activated alumina into a beaker, add enough of the solvent to slurry the alumina readily. Mix thoroughly and transfer the slurry into the tube with the aid of a funnel. Tap the column during the addition of the slurry so that the alumina

[24] American Oil Chemists' Society, Official and Tentative Methods, 2nd Ed., Chicago, Ill., 1946, Method Ca 9f–57.

will be tightly packed at the bottom of the column. Wash down any alumina remaining on the wall of the tube with a few ml. of the solvent. Drop the filter pad into the tube and position it on the alumina with a stirring rod. Draw off the solvent until approximately 5 mm. of solvent remain above the top level of the alumina. Keep the surface of the alumina covered with solvent throughout the entire chromatographic procedure.

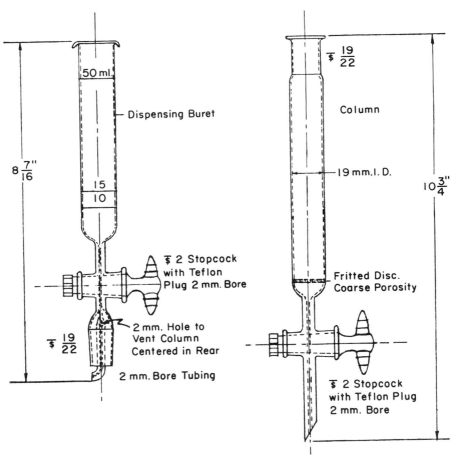

Fig. 48-2.   Column for Neutral Oil Determination.

Procedure.—Place a tared 250-ml. Soxhlet flask under the delivery tube of the column. Weigh a sample of approximately 5 g. to an accuracy of ±0.0002 g. in a 50-ml. beaker or other suitable container. If the loss exceeds 5 percent, reduce the size of the sample proportionally. From a polyethylene wash bottle, add 10 ml. of the solvent and dissolve by stirring with a stirring rod. Remove the rod and wash with about 5 ml. of solvent. Transfer the sample in the solvent to the column, and wash the beaker thoroughly with an additional 50 ml. of solvent. Wash down the top of the column with 3 successive 10-ml. washes, making sure that the level of the solvent above the alumina drains to

5 mm. between the successive washes. When the last wash has gone into the alumina, except for the 5 mm. remaining above the column, attach the buret containing 50 ml. of the solvent to the column. Start the solvent into the column.

Collect the percolate at a rate of 4 to 6 ml. per minute until all of the solvent has passed through the column. This collection rate of about 5 ml. per minute should be observed throughout the entire handling of the sample. The level of solvent in the column should be constant as closely as possible. Finally, wash the end of the delivery tube going into the Soxhlet flask with a few ml. of the solvent.

Evaporate the ether-methanol solution on a steam or water bath with the aid of a gentle stream (2–5 liters per minute) of clean, dry air or nitrogen. The air jet of suitable size to deliver the predetermined volume of air per minute should be inserted against the inside of the neck of the flask as a slight angle to a depth equal to approximately two-thirds the length of the neck. In addition to speeding up the evaporation of solvent, the air prevents loss of neutral oil by creeping over the top of the flask. Excessive air will increase the rate of oxidation, thus giving unrealistic yields of neutral oil. A controlled volume of air, in the range specified, will not contribute to detectable oxidation under the conditions of the test. However, the aeration should be discontinued before the removal of the last traces of solvent. When all but the last traces of ethyl ether fumes have disappeared, remove the sample from the steam bath and immediately place it in a 105°C. forced draft oven for 1 hour. Remove from the oven, cool, and weigh the flask and contents.

Calculations.

$$\text{Percent Neutral Oil} = \frac{100 \ (\text{weight of residue})}{\text{weight of sample}}$$

$$\text{Loss} = 100 - \text{Percent Neutral Oil}$$

BUTYRIC ACID IN BUTTER FAT[25]

An important application of the determination of butyric acid content is for the purpose of detecting adulteration of butterfat with fats which contain little or no butyric acid: However, a normal butyric acid content on a given sample is not necessarily conclusive, since butyrin from other sources may be present. The following reagents are required for the chromatographic separation of butyric acid from butterfat.

Reagents. **Silicic Acid.**—Heat the acid in a shallow pan or evaporating dish for 18 hours at 175°C. and store it in a desiccator or in a tightly sealed container.

Bromocresol Green-Glycol Solution.—Dissolve 700 mg. of bromocresol green in 700 ml. of ethylene glycol by warming on a steam bath. Cool and then add about 200 ml. of water. Prepare 0.1 M ammonium hydroxide by diluting about 6.6 ml. of ammonium hydroxide (sp. gr. 0.90) to 1 liter with water. Add 40 ml. of this solution to the indicator solution, and then add additional water to make 1 liter. Store this ink-blue solution in a glass-stoppered bottle.

Packing Material.—Mix 100 g. of silicic acid with about 95 ml. of bromocresol green-glycol solution until a homogeneous olive-green powder is obtained. The mixing may be done in small batches in a mortar or in larger batches in a mechanical mixer. Prepared packing material may be stored in a tightly stoppered container for several months.

Hexane-Butanol Mixture.—Add 1 volume of *n*-butanol to 100 volumes of *n*-hexane.

Isopropanol-Potassium Hydroxide Solution.—Dissolve 25 g. of potassium hydroxide

[25] Association of Official Agricultural Chemists, Official Methods of Analysis, 9th Ed., Washington, D. C., 1960, 365.

in 400 ml. of isopropanol by warming on a steam bath with occasional swirling. Decant the supernatant alcoholic solution from the small amount of aqueous solution clinging to the bottom of the flask. Cool and decant the supernatant isopropanol-potassium hydroxide solution, which contains about 50 mg. of potassium hydroxide per ml. Store in a refrigerator.

Potassium Hydroxide Solution, Approximately 0.05 M.—Dilute 60 ml of the isopropanol-potassium hydroxide solution with 440 ml. of isopropanol and 500 ml. of methanol. Store in an amber bottle.

Dilute Sulfuric Acid Solution (2 + 1, v/v).

Thymol Blue Solution.—Dissolve 300 mg. of thymol blue in 25 ml. of 0.05 M alcoholic potassium hydroxide solution and add 75 ml. of isopropanol.

Preparation of the Sample.—Place 0.5–0.7 g. of the sample and 5 ml. of isopropanol-potassium hydroxide solution in a 20 × 150 mm. test tube, and heat in a boiling water bath to saponify the fat. Continue heating to evaporate the isopropanol, leaving the solid soap.

Determine the amount of dilute sulfuric acid equivalent to 5 ml. of isopropanol-potassium hydroxide solution in 10 ml. of water containing 2 drops of thymol blue solution. Place the tube containing the saponified fat in a cold water bath and add the indicated quantity of dilute sulfuric acid. If the top of the column turns blue when the fatty acid solution is added, the use of more sulfuric acid is indicated. The top of the chromatographic column should be yellow.

Break up the lumps in the bottom of the tube with a glass stirring rod. After thoroughly mixing the mass in the test tube, a yellow mixture of fatty acids clinging to a viscous aqueous layer of potassium sulfate should result. Add 10 ml. of the hexane-butanol solution and mix thoroughly with a glass rod. Decant the hexane-butanol solution of fatty acids, which is now ready to be chromatographed.

Preparation of the Column.—Prepare a chromatographic column by fusing a 15-cm. section of glass tubing (38 mm. O.D.) to a 20-cm. section of glass tubing (22 mm. O.D.) which, in turn, is fused to a 5-cm. length of 7-mm. tubing. Overlay 35 g. of packing material with the hexane-butanol mixture in a mortar and mix with a pestle to form a slurry. Place a small glass wool plug loosely in the constricted end of the column and gently tamp it into place with a glass rod. Place a finger over the constricted end of the column and add the hexane-butanol mixture until the reservoir is half full. With the aid of a teaspoon, underlay the prepared slurry beneath the solvent. Move the spoon up and down along the side of the reservoir to allow the flocculent slurry to settle to the bottom of the column. After adding all of the packing material, remove the finger, and allow the solvent to flow out and the packing material to settle. Apply 5–10 lb. of air pressure to the top of the column to speed up the flow of solvent and to facilitate uniform packing of the slurry. Release the pressure just before the last portion of solvent sinks into the column. If the column looks uniformly packed, it is ready for use. If the column does not appear to be uniformly packed, add more hexane-butanol solution to the reservoir and again apply pressure as before. A suitably prepared column should have a flow rate of about 3.5 ml. per minute without the use of pressure. If the flow rate is less than 3 ml. per minute, add more bromocresol green-glycol solution to the packing material and remix. If the flow rate is more than 4 ml. per minute, add more silicic acid to the packing material and remix. The hexane-butanol mixture recovered during preparation of the column may be used subsequently to prepare other columns or for the chromatography of the acids.

Separation of Butyric Acid.—Decant the hexane-butanol solution of fatty acids on to the top of the packed column and immediately start collecting eluate in a 250-ml. Erlenmeyer flask. Note the previous remarks about the color of the top of the column.

As soon as the fatty acid solution completely settles into the packing, wash down the inside of the reservoir with three 5-ml. portions of the hexane-butanol mixture. Allow each washing to sink into the packing before refilling the reservoir. The yellow band should be observed at the very top of the column; this band contains the inorganic acids and should not move. If the sample contains butterfat, a second distinct yellow band due to butyric acid will appear and will slowly migrate down the column, breaking away from the inorganic band. Long-chain fatty acids, C_6 and higher, pass rapidly through the column and do not form yellow bands. There will be an eluate volume of 20–30 ml. between the elution of the last traces of long-chain acids and the first traces of butyric acid. When the lower edge of the yellow butyric acid zone is 1 cm. from the lower end of the chromatographic column, change the fraction collector. The first fraction contains long-chain fatty acids and usually measures 100 ± 10 ml. The next 120-ml. fraction will contain butyric acid.

Add 1 drop of thymol blue indicator solution for each 10 ml. of eluate to be titrated. Titrate each fraction to the first permanent appearance of a purple-blue end point with 0.05 M alcoholic potassium hydroxide. Use a buret graduated in 0.01 ml. for titration of the butyric acid fraction. Avoid undue exposure to the air and titrate with a minimum of agitation to avoid the absorption of carbon dioxide.

Express the butyric acid as the percent of sum of the two titrations, calculated to nearest 0.1 percent.

Since the molecular weight of butyric acid is relatively small compared with the molecular weights of the fatty acids which constitute the major portion of butterfat, it is convenient to calculate the results in terms of molar percent instead of the conventional manner, that is, percent by weight.

$$\text{Molar percent butyric acid} = 100A/A + B$$

where: A = titration of butyric acid (second) fraction; and
B = titration of long-chain acids (first) fraction.

MINERAL HYDROCARBONS

The following method is applicable to the estimation of saturated hydrocarbons in natural fats. The presence of saturated hydrocarbons is most commonly the result of mineral oil contamination during processing or transportation.

Apparatus.—The chromatographic column used in this determination should have a diameter of 25–35 mm. and be provided with a Teflon stopcock.

Reagents.—The aluminum oxide should be Alcoa grade, F-20 or equivalent, 80–200 mesh. Dry the alumina 4 hours at 200°C. before use. The moisture content of the dried oxide should not exceed 3 percent for effective retention of the glycerides.

Procedure.—Weigh 10 g. (±0.01 g.) of melted, well-mixed sample into a 125-ml. Erlenmeyer flask. Dissolve in 50–100 ml. of petroleum ether, warming gently if necessary.

Prepare the column by tamping a plug of glass wool into the bottom of the chromatographic column in such a manner that some of the glass wool is in the constricted portion above the stopcock. Fill the column about two-thirds full with petroleum ether and add 200 g. of alumina through a powder funnel. Tap the side of the column to aid in packing. Cover with about one-half inch of anhydrous sodium sulfate. Fix the elution rate at 80–90 drops per minute (3.0–3.5 ml.) using the stopcock for control.

When the solvent head is reduced to about 1 cm., add the sample solution. Allow the solvent layer to penetrate until about 1 cm. of head remains. Rinse the Erlenmeyer flask with 50 ml. of petroleum ether and add to the column. Repeat 3 times, adding each washing to the column when the solvent head is reduced to about 1 cm., and wash down the sides of the column on transferring. Continue adding petroleum ether to the column until a total of 400 ml. has passed through the column.

NOTE.—An inverted volumetric flask can serve as a convenient reservoir for this final addition of solvent. Collect the eluate in a 500-ml. Erlenmeyer flask.

Place on a steam bath and reduce the volume to 50–75 ml. A stirring rod placed in the flask will help prevent super-heating and subsequent boiling over. A gentle stream of air will aid in solvent removal. Transfer to a tared 250-ml. Soxhlet flask, rinsing with three 20-ml. portions of petroleum ether in transferring. Remove the remaining solvent by evaporation on a warm surface employing a gentle stream of air and keeping the solution below the boiling point. Cool to room temperature in a desiccator and weigh the residue. Repeat with additional heating periods of 20 minutes each until change in residue weight is less than 0.5 mg. Conduct a blank determination in a similar manner but excluding the sample.

Calculations.

$$\text{Hydrocarbons, percent} = \frac{A - B}{C} \times 100$$

where: A = weight of sample residue;
B = weight of blank residue; and
C = weight of sample.

GAS LIQUID CHROMATOGRAPHY

DETERMINATION OF FATTY ACIDS[26]

The method of the American Oil Chemists' Society is applicable to animal and vegetable fatty acids having 8–24 carbon atoms. Saturated and the various unsaturated acids are determined separately. The fats or fatty acids are converted to their methyl esters and chromatographed as such. This method is not applicable to the determination of epoxy or oxidized fatty acids.

Apparatus.—The gas chromatographic instrument should have the following characteristics. Several makes are commercially available.

a. Temperature of sample inlet port 50°C. above column temperature.
b. Column—4 to 10 ft. in length, $\frac{1}{4}$ in. O.D. glass, stainless steel, aluminum, or copper, packed with 20 percent polyester (polydiethylene glycol succinate is recommended) on 60–80 mesh acid-washed Chromosorb P or W and operated at a constant temperature between 190° and 210°C.
c. Detector of the thermal conductivity type and, if separately thermostated, maintained at column temperature or up to 25°C. hotter.
d. Recorder—0–1 millivolt range, 1 second full scale deflection with chart speed of $\frac{1}{2}$ in. per minute. Attenuator switch to change the recorder range.

Procedure.—Adjust the instrument to operating temperature with helium gas flowing through it, and record a base line to check the stability of the instrument. Condition a new column by holding it at operating temperature for 24 hours with helium flowing through it. The proper gas flow rate will permit elution of the C_{18} and shorter chain acids in 30 minutes. The inlet pressure and gas flow necessary to accomplish this will vary between columns and instruments but will be relatively constant for a given apparatus. The inlet gas pressure should not exceed 40 pounds per square inch. A constant

[26] American Oil Chemists' Society, Official and Tentative Methods, 2nd Ed., Chicago, Ill., 1946, Method Cc 1–62.

gas flow should be maintained throughout the run, and should be measured periodically with a soap bubble flow meter or other device.

Measure a few microliters of the fat ester sample (0.5–4.0 μl.) in a hypodermic syringe, capacity 0.01 ml. Pierce the septum of the inlet port and quickly discharge the sample. Withdraw the needle and note on the recorder chart the small peak due to air which marks the sample introduction reference point. The sample size must be adjusted so that the major peak is not attenuated more than 8 times and should preferably be less. Observe the recorder pen to make sure that the peaks do not go off scale and change the setting of the attenuator as necessary to keep the peaks on the chart paper. Mark the setting on the chart. After all the peaks have been traced and the pen has returned to the base line, remove the chart for calculation.

Calculations.—Determine the area of each peak. This is conveniently accomplished by drawing lines tangent to the sides of the peak and intersecting the base line. For attenuated peaks the tangents should be drawn to the outer side of the peak (these should be two-thirds of chart paper width). Determine the area of the resulting triangle by multiplying the height (corrected for any change in attenuation) by half the base. Obtain the sum of the areas of all peaks and calculate the percentage represented by each. Report this figure as the percentage of each component.

Identify the peaks by relative position on the chart. The esters appear in order of increasing number of carbon atoms. That is, C_{16} is ahead of C_{18} and then the C_{18} esters appear in the order stearate, oleate, linoleate, and linolenate. The C_{20} saturated (arachidic) ester usually appears after C18:3 (linolenic) ester but may be reversed on some columns, or the positions may change with column usage. Identities must be established with known mixtures. At constant gas flow the ratios of times (chart distances) from the air peak to various sample component peaks can be used for identification of the peaks. Compare these ratios with those calculated from known mixtures run periodically on the same column under the same conditions.

Calibration factors should be determined to correct for nonlinearity of instrument response and for molecular weight differences. Such factors are determined by analyzing known mixtures having composition similar to that of the unknown sample. For ordinary work, the percentage area of a peak may be considered as the percentage of the corresponding component in the sample.

Instrument and column performance are monitored by noting the separation of the oleate and stearate ester peaks which is expressed as peak resolution.

$$\text{Peak Resolution} = \frac{2Y}{S + O}$$

where: Y = the distance between the peak maxima for stearate and oleate esters;
S = the base width of the stearate peak; and
O = the base width of the oleate peak.

These values should be determined on a sample containing approximately equal quantities of oleate and stearate esters using a sample size such that these peaks are 25–50 percent of the chart width. If the peak resolution is equal to or greater than 1.0, the column and instrument are in satisfactory condition. All columns when used will show a gradual loss in peak resolution; when the value becomes less than 1.0, a new column should be installed.

Preparation of the Esters. **Triglycerides.**—Add 0.15 g. of sodium hydroxide (pellets) to 22.8 g. of anhydrous methanol. Heat to 70°C. to dissolve the alkali. This reagent may be stored for future use.

Place 0.8 ml. of the methanol-alkali reagent in a test tube and heat to 70°C. Add

2.0 g. of the sample of triglyceride, preheated to 80°C. Stir and heat at 80°C. until glycerol separates. Allow to stand at 80°C. for 5 minutes and then decant the methyl esters. Evaporate any remaining methanol from the esters under reduced pressure after decanting.

Fatty Acids.—Place 1 liter of reagent grade methanol in a 2-liter flask. Weigh the flask and contents and then cool them in an ice bath. With the flask still in the bath, bubble boron trifluoride through a glass tube into the methanol until 125 g. are taken up. This operation should be performed in a good fume hood, and the gas should not be allowed to flow so fast that white fumes emerge from the flask. The boron trifluoride must be flowing through the tube before it is placed in the methanol and until it is removed from it, or the liquid may be drawn into the gas cylinder valve system.

Esterification Procedure.—Place 100–200 g. of fatty acids in a 20 × 150-mm. test tube, and add 3 ml. of boron trifluoride-methanol reagent. Place the mixture on a steam bath and allow to boil for 2 minutes. Recover the esters by the appropriate procedure following.

For Acids of More Than 10 Carbons.—Wash the boiled mixture into a 125-ml. separatory funnel with 30 ml. of petroleum ether (b. p. 40–60°C., Reagent grade, redistilled) and add 20 ml. of distilled water. Shake the funnel vigorously and allow the layers to separate. Drain and discard the aqueous-methanol layer. Remove the petroleum ether layer and filter through filter paper into a 50-ml. beaker.

For Acids of Less Than 10 Carbons.—Transfer the boiled mixture into the separatory funnel with 20 ml. of water, mix the contents and allow the layers to separate. Remove the top ester layer from the lower aqueous layer, and filter or centrifuge to remove small amounts of entrapped water.

Prepare a solution of about 7 percent of the methyl esters in hexane for injection into the column.

PAPER CHROMATOGRAPHY

SEPARATION OF FATS AND FATTY ACIDS[27]

Preparation of the Paper.—Cut Whatman No. 1 paper (for chromatography) into strips 11.5 × 46 cm. and dry them for 2 hours at 120°C. Store the papers over calcium chloride after drying. Prepare a 5 percent (w/v) solution of silicone (Dow Corning fluid 200, 10 cs. at 25°C.) in ether and place in a chromatographic jar. Dip the papers in the solution and then aerate them until the ether has been evaporated. These papers are then ready for use and may be stored without special precautions.

Procedure.—Prepare a 1 percent solution of the sample in either methanol, ethyl ether, or acetone. Place a small spot of this solution, about 2.5 cm. from one end of the paper. Suspend the paper in a suitable glass jar (15 cm. wide × 46 cm. high), so that the lower end of the paper, at which the sample is located, dips into the solvent. Cover the jar and allow it to remain for 17 to 24 hours at 30° ± 1°C. Remove the paper from the jar and allow it to dry in a free circulation of air until all of the solvent has been removed.

Accurate temperature control during this operation is essential. Higher temperatures increase the migration rate; decreasing the concentration of the more polar component of the solvent lowers the R_f values. The reverse is also true, so by the manipulation of these factors, the migration rates can be so regulated that any fatty acid between C_{10} and C_{22} will have an R_f value between 0.2 and 0.8. This is the most useful area of the chromatogram for quantitative analysis.

The solvents employed in this method are given in Tables 48-7 and 48-8. The follow-

[27] Schlenk, H., Gellerman, J. L., Tillotson, J. A., and Mangold, H. K., J. Am. Oil Chemists' Soc., **34**, 377–386, 1957.

TABLE 48-7. Rf VALUES OF VARIOUS ESTERS AND FATTY ACIDS AT 30°C.

	Acids			Methyl Esters		Aldehydes	Alcohols
	85 CH_3COOH 15 H_2O	75 CH_3COOH 25 H_2O	42.0 HCOOH 40.5 CH_3COOH 17.5 H_2O	85 CH_3COOH 15 H_2O	75 CH_3COOH 25 H_2O	85 CH_3COOH 15 H_2O	75 CH_3COOH 25 H_2O
Saturated							
Lauric	0.79			0.60		0.72	0.74
Myristic	0.73			0.44		0.59	0.62
Pentadecanoic	0.64			0.33			
Palmitic	0.59			0.26		0.49	0.46
Heptadecanoic	0.53			0.22			
Stearic	0.40			0.17		0.38	0.30
Arachidic							
Behenic							
Unsaturated							
Palmitoleic		0.40	0.36	0.55			
Palmitolinoleic		0.54	0.56	0.65			
Palmitolinolenic		0.63	0.71	0.74			
Hexadecatetraenoic		0.70	0.80				
Oleic	0.54	0.36	0.20	0.28	0.13	0.43	0.45
Elaidic	0.52						
Linoleic	0.66	0.40	0.35	0.38	0.20	0.54	0.58
Linolenic	0.73	0.55	0.52	0.50	0.26	0.64	0.69

Other esters 90 CH_3COOH,10 H_2O

Allyl palmitate	0.53
Allyl stearate	0.37

TABLE 48-8. SOLVENTS FOR DEVELOPING PAPER CHROMATOGRAMS OF FATS

Acetic Acid + Water	Tetrahydrofuran + Water	Chloroform + Methanol + Water	Carbon Tetrachloride + Methanol + Water
Alcohols Aldehydes Acids Esters Other monochain lipids	Monoglycerides	Diglycerides, triglycerides, lipid contaminants of synthetic glycerides	

ing additional information may serve as a guide to the selection of solvents. A mixture of acetic acid and water (85 + 15, v/v) covers the broadest spectrum with regard to chain length, unsaturation, and functional groups, and is, therefore, recommended for the analysis of unknown mixtures of fatty acids and esters, although some highly unsaturated fatty acids migrate too close to the solvent front with this solvent. Acetic acid and water (75 + 25, v/v) is recommended for the unsaturated C_{16} acids. Formic and acetic acids and water (42 + 40.5 + 17.5, v/v) are sometimes preferable for unsaturated acids containing more than three double bonds. The resolving power of this mixture is about the same as the acetic acid and water (75 + 25, v/v).

Identification.—A scheme of identification is given in Table 48-9. If the paper is to

TABLE 48-9. INDICATORS FOR THE IDENTIFICATION OF FATS ON PAPER CHROMATOGRAMS

Reagent	Compounds Detected	Appearance
a. I_2 vapor	Unsaturated fats	Yellow or brown spots on light background
b. α-Cyclodextrin, then I_2	All fats except di- and triglycerides	White spots with saturated, blue to dark brown spots with unsaturated fats, purple background
c. Lead tetraacetate	α-Monoglycerides	White spots on brown background
d. Lipase, then b or c	Di- and triglycerides, preferably saturated	As b or c

be exposed to iodine, it is first humidified in a water-saturated atmosphere at 50°C. It is then suspended in a glass jar containing a small dish at the bottom, in which are placed some iodine crystals. Expose the chromatogram to the iodine vapor for 5 minutes immediately after humidifying. When α-cyclodextrin is to be applied, spray the dry chromatogram with a 1 percent solution of α-cyclodextrin in water containing 30 percent methanol; then dry the sprayed paper and expose to iodine vapor as directed above. A densitometer is employed for the quantitative estimation.

FREE GOSSYPOL[28]

Procedure.—Prepare a standard gossypol solution by weighing 25 ± 0.1 mg. of pure gossypol into a 250-ml. volumetric flask. Add a small quantity of acetone to dissolve the

[28] Sehramm, G., and Benedict, J. H., J. Am. Oil Chemists' Soc., 35, 371, 1958.

gossypol, and then make the volume to 250 ml. with acetone. This solution contains 0.1 mg. of gossypol per milliliter of solution, and will remain stable for one week.

Weigh 10 g. of sample into a 50-ml. beaker and add 25 ml. of heptane (b.p. 98–99°C.). Transfer this solution quantitatively into a 250-ml. separatory funnel using additional heptane to wash the contents of the beaker into the funnel. The final total volume of heptane should be about 100 ml.

Extract the heptane solution twice, using 25 ml. of aqueous N,N-dimethylformamide (b.p. 152–154°C.) each time. The aqueous dimethylformamide is prepared by mixing 600 ml. of dimethylformamide with 300 ml. of distilled water. After each extraction draw off the lower layer into a 250-ml. centrifuge bottle and then add 150 ml. of water and 50 ml. of chloroform-heptane (1 + 9, v/v). Somewhat less than 150 ml. of water may be used if necessary to accommodate the capacity of the bottle. Insert a stopper in the flask, shake the contents vigorously, and then centrifuge at 2000 r.p.m. for 10–15 minutes. Siphon off the upper layer using as little vacuum as possible. Repeat the extraction twice more, using 50 ml. of chloroform-heptane each time. Collect and combine the three extracts and dry them with small portions of anhydrous sodium sulfate. The final solution should be clear. Filter the solution into a 400-ml. beaker, wash the sodium sulfate with several volumes of the chloroform-heptane solution, and combine these with the filtered portion. Evaporate the solution on a steam bath until the column is reduced to less than 5 ml., or 10 ml. if more than 1 percent gossypol. Transfer this portion immediately to a graduated cylinder with the aid of small amounts of acetone and then dilute to 5 ml. with acetone. Store the graduate and contents at 0.5°C. until ready to chromatograph.

Prepare a glass jar (250 cm. in diameter × 450 cm. in height) by inserting a piece of Whatman No. 1 paper (413 × 572 cm.) along the inner wall. Place a mixture consisting of 160 ml. of n-pentane, 40 ml. of chloroform, and 10 ml. of glacial acetic acid in the jar. Swirl the solvent around in the jar so that all of the paper lining the jar is soaked, and cover with a glass plate. Do this just before starting each chromatogram. Use the solvent for no longer than 3 days.

To a piece of Whatman No. 3MM paper (413 × 572 cm.), apply portions of a standard gossypol solution and the sample. The spots are made along the long side of the paper and 5 cm. apart. It is convenient to make the spots with pencil dots. Apply 50, 20, and 5 μl. of the standard gossypol solution to the first three dots, and 50 μl. of the sample on the other dots. Form the paper into a cylinder and staple the edges together, making sure the edges do not touch. Place the paper cylinder in the center of the jar with the spotted end at the bottom. Cover the jar and allow irrigation to proceed for $1\frac{1}{2}$ hours in an ascending fashion. Then remove the paper from the jar, mark the solvent front, and allow the paper to dry at room temperature.

Spray the chromatogram from the bottom line up to the solvent front with freshly prepared phloroglucinol (2 g. in 10 ml. of 95 percent ethanol plus 5 ml. of concentrated hydrochloric acid). Prepare the phloroglucinol solution fresh daily. Make sure the paper is thoroughly wetted. After spraying and when the paper is dry, compare the samples with the standards by visual observation. If no purple spot is present at the gossypol position, no gossypol is present. When a reddish spot is present in the same location (R_f value) as the standard, estimate the gossypol content of the sample by comparison with the standard, taking into account the area of the spot and the density of the color. Additional portions and different quantities of the standard may be utilized if desirable. Recoveries are about 50 percent by this method.

Table 48-10 provides a guide to the volume to apply to the paper depending upon the free gossypol content.

TABLE 48-10. VOLUMES TO BE USED IN FREE GOSSYPOL DETERMINATION

Volume Applied	Estimated Free Gossypol µg./g.
50 µl.	10– 50
25 µl.	50–100
10 µl.	100–250
5 µl.	250–500

TOCOPHEROLS[29]

Procedure.—Prepare the stationary phase by dissolving 25 g. of ammonium carbonate in 600 ml. of distilled water and then adding 25 g. of zinc carbonate and 150 ml. of ammonium hydroxide (sp. gr. 0.88). Immerse the paper in this solution for 3 minutes and then allow the paper to dry. Saponify the sample, remove the unsaponifiable fraction, dissolve this fraction in ethanol, and spot the alcohol solution on the paper. Chromatograph the unsaponifiable fraction using the ascending technique with cyclohexane as the mobile phase. Allow the chromatogram to develop until the solvent front attains a height of 22–25 cm., which usually requires 45–60 minutes. Dry the paper, cut out and remove the spots, and determine the tocopherol in each with ferric chloride and α,α'-dipyridyl. If a clean separation does not result when the unsaponifiable fraction is used directly, remove the sterols by passing the fraction through Floridan earth. A 95 percent recovery is reported for this method.

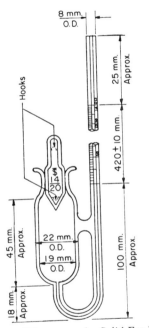

FIG. 48-3. Dilatometer for Solid Fat Index.

DILATOMETRY

SOLID FAT INDEX[30]

The dilatometric method for obtaining an index of solid fat content is the official Method of the American Oil Chemists' Society. Values obtained by this method are arbitrary and dependent on the composition of the fat as well as on the manner in which the samples are solidified in the determination.

Apparatus.—Pyrex dilatometers with glass stoppers, constructed in accordance with the specifications shown in Fig. 48-3. The stems should be made from precision-bore capillary tubing graduated in 0.005-ml. increments from 0 to 1.400 ml., with an

[29] Green, J., Marcinkiewicz, S., and Watt, P. R., J. Soc. Food Agri., **6**, 274, 1955.
[30] American Oil Chemists' Society, Official and Tentative Methods, 2nd Ed., Chicago, Ill., 1946, Method Cd 10–47.

overall accuracy of at least ±0.005 ml. The scale should be marked from 0 to 1400 at intervals of 50. The dilatometers should have identification numbers on the stems and stoppers. Springs are necessary to attach the stoppers securely to the dilatometers. Clamps of thermometer type are needed for holding the dilatometers in the constant temperature baths.

Constant temperature water baths accurate to ±0.05°C. with provision for adequate circulation. Solid fat indexes at 10°, 21.1°, 26.7°, 33.3°, and 37.8°C. are commonly used to characterize shortenings and margarine oils. Therefore, the baths required would be 0°, 10°, 21.1°, 26.7°, 33.3°, 37.8°, and 60°C.

New dilatometers should be checked for accuracy of calibration. This may be done as follows: clean and dry the dilatometer thoroughly and clamp it securely in an inverted position. Clamp a 2-way capillary stopcock with buret tip (2 mm. I.D.) in place at the end of the dilatometer stem, and make a seal with Pyseal cement. After the cement has hardened, immerse the tip of the stopcock into a reservoir of clean mercury which is at room temperature. Using vacuum, draw the mercury into the dilatometer stem until the calibrated portion is full. Withdraw successive 0.200-ml. portions of mercury into a tared 50-ml. beaker and record the weight of each portion. Calculate the true volume in milliliters contained in each measured scale interval as follows:

$$\frac{\text{Weight of mercury} \times \text{sp. vol. of Hg at } T_R \times 1000}{\text{Final scale reading} - \text{initial scale reading}}$$

where T_R is room temperature.

$$1 \text{ ml.} = 1000 \text{ in scale reading}$$

Procedure.—Deaerate about 50 ml. of indicator solution (1 percent potassium dichromate in distilled water) for 3 minutes in a suitable flask. This is accomplished by applying a vacuum such that the pressure will be slightly above the vapor pressure of the solution at the temperature of deaeration. The indicator may also be deaerated by vigorous boiling for 15 minutes at atmospheric pressure, but if this method is used, be sure to cool the indicator to room temperature before using it. Heat the sample to 80°C. and deaerate under reduced pressure until no gas bubbles are visible, and for at least 2 minutes. Maintain the sample in a liquid state and agitate vigorously during deaeration. Use both indicator and sample as soon as possible after deaeration.

Pipet exactly 2 ml. of the indicator solution into the dilatometer bulb. Lubricate the stopper lightly with silicone grease and weigh the assembled dilatometer to the nearest 0.01 g. Carefully overlay the indicator with the sample and fill until the sample overflows. Insert the stopper so that the indicator solution rises to approximately the 1200 mark on the stem when the stopper is securely sealed. The reading should then be 1200 ± 100 at 60°C.; if not, repeat the filling operation. Wash the fat from the outer surface of the dilatometer with petroleum solvent. Attach retaining springs and reweigh the dilatometer as soon as the solvent has evaporated.

Immerse the dilatometer to the 300-mark in the 60°C. bath and observe the reading after 15 minutes, and then at 5-minute intervals until the change is less than 2 units in 5 minutes. The samples must be completely melted at the lower temperature. If any seeding or clouding occurs, remelt the sample in the 60°C. bath and raise the temperature of the other bath. When the sample is not entirely liquid at 37.8°C., bath temperatures of 60°C. and 80°C. are suitable for determining the slope of the liquid line. The value of 22.2 in the denominator of the expression for the calculation of thermal expansion must then be changed to agree with the difference between the two bath temperatures. Transfer the dilatometer to the 0°C. bath, immerse to the 300-mark, and hold for 15 minutes. Transfer to the 26.7°C. bath and hold for 30 minutes. Transfer back to the 0°C. bath and hold for 15 minutes. Move the dilatometer from the 0°C. bath to the 10°C. bath. Immerse to the 300-mark, and observe the reading at 30 minutes. Repeat at the next higher temperature and so on until readings have been obtained at all of the desired temperatures. Thermal equilibrium is essential and in some instances it may be advisable to hold the fat at each temperature longer than indicated.

For accurate volumetric measurements, it is necessary to make corrections for the thermal expansion of the glassware and the confining liquid. See Table 48-11.

Solid fat index at temperature T
$$= \text{(total dilation)} - [(\text{thermal expansion}) \times (60 - T)]$$
Thermal expansion of sample per degree C. in ml./kg.
$$= R(60) - R(37.8) - Vc(37.8)/W(60 - 37.8)$$
Total dilation between T and 60°C. in ml./kg.
$$= R(60) - R(T) - Vc(T)/W$$

where:
T = observed temperature;
$Vc(T)$ = volume correction from Table 48-11;
$R(T)$ = observed dilatometer reading at T; and
W = weight of sample.

TABLE 48-11. VOLUME CORRECTIONS FOR GLASS AND CONFINING LIQUID

Bath Temperature	60°C. Reading				
	1000	1100	1200	1300	1400
0°C.	22.0	20.3	18.6	16.9	15.2
5.	22.2	20.5	18.7	17.0	15.3
10.	21.8	20.1	18.4	16.7	15.1
15.	21.0	19.5	17.8	16.2	14.6
20.	19.8	18.4	16.8	15.3	13.8
25.	18.4	17.0	15.6	14.1	12.7
30.	16.6	15.3	14.0	12.7	11.4
35.	14.4	13.3	12.2	11.1	10.0
40.	12.0	11.0	10.2	9.2	8.3
45.	9.4	8.7	8.0	7.2	6.5
50.	6.6	6.1	5.6	5.1	4.5
55.	3.2	3.0	2.8	2.5	2.3
60.	0	0	0	0	0

MANOMETRY

FAT STABILITY[31]

The absorption of oxygen under accelerated conditions has long been one of the methods used to measure the resistance of fats to oxidation. A recent modification of the absorption procedure is employment of the ASTM oxygen bomb which is commonly used in the petroleum industry. Several variants of the original ASTM bomb method

[31] Pohle, W. D., Gregory, R. L., and Van Giessen, B., J. Am. Oil Chemists Soc., **40**, 603–605, 1963.

have now been investigated and reported. One of the latest published methods of this type, using a copper catalyst to accelerate the oxidation reaction, is presented here.

Preparation of Copper Catalyst.—Weigh 10 ± 0.1 g. of coconut oil fatty acids and dissolve in 150 ml. of 95 percent ethanol. Neutralize to the phenophthalein end point with 50 percent aqueous potassium hydroxide. Add 100 ml. of aqueous copper chloride solution, (4.0 percent $CuCl_2 \cdot 2H_2O$, w/v) slowly with stirring to the fatty acid salt solution. Filter, using a Buchner funnel with two layers of rapid-filtering filter paper. Wash the precipitate twice with 50-ml. portions of water and finally with 50 ml. of 95 percent ethanol. Allow to stand overnight at room temperature covered with a clean towel, and then complete drying in an oven at 100°C. Remove the precipitate from the oven, cool and grind into a fine powder.

Analysis of Copper Catalyst.—Ash 0.500 ± 0.001 g. of the copper salt of coconut oil acids. Cool the ash to room temperature and dissolve it in 0.1 M hydrochloric acid. Transfer quantitatively to 1-liter volumetric flask, dilute to volume with 0.1 M hydrochloric acid and mix thoroughly. Dilute 50 ml. again to 500. Pipet 50 ml. of the final dilution into a 125-ml. separatory funnel and determine the copper as directed earlier in the chapter.

$$\text{Percent Copper} = (A - B) \times 0.4$$

where: A = μg. of copper in carbon tetrachloride solution of the sample; and
B = μg. of copper in carbon tetrachloride solution of blank.

Preparation of Catalyst Solution.—Calculate the amount of the copper salt of coconut oil acids which when dissolved in chloroform and diluted to 100 ml. will contain 375 mg. of copper per ml.

$$\text{Grams of copper salt of coconut oil acids} = \frac{0.0375}{A}$$

where A = percent of copper in copper salt of C/N acids divided by 100.

Weigh the calculated amount of the copper salt of the fatty acids to the nearest milligram. Transfer to a 100-ml. volumetric flask, and dissolve in about 90 ml. of chloroform. Warm slightly if necessary. Dilute to volume at room temperature and mix thoroughly.

Procedure.—Weigh 7.5 ± 0.1 g. of sample into a beaker and melt. Add 0.5 ml. of the copper solution, using a 1-ml. measuring pipet graduated in 0.01-ml. subdivisions. Mix thoroughly by swirling or stirring and immediately weigh 6.4 ± 0.1 g. on to a pad of Kimpak 2 × 3¾ × ¼ in. Distribute evenly over the top of the pad. Weighing is carried out by placing the Kimpak on a watch glass on a torsion balance sensitive to 0.01 g. The torsion balance is brought to exact balance, the appropriate weight is then added, and the liquid sample is poured evenly over the Kimpak until the scale is again in balance. Roll the pad into a cylinder with the sample side on the inside and fit the cylinder into the glass liner of the bomb. Insert the glass liner into the stainless steel bomb. Place the glass cover on the glass liner. Attach the cap containing the pressure line and valve to the bomb and tighten. Attach an oxygen cylinder and raise the pressure in the bomb to 50 ± 5 lbs., close the valve on the bomb, detach the connecting tube, open the valve on the bomb, and allow the oxygen to escape into the atmosphere. Attach the oxygen cylinder and raise the pressure in the bomb to 50 ± 5 lbs., close the valve, and disconnect the bomb assembly from the oxygen cylinder. Immerse the bomb assembly in a bucket of water to check for leaks. If any bubbles are observed escaping from the bomb, remove from the bucket, tighten any joints or seals that leak, adjust the pressure to 50 ± 5 lbs. and test again for leaks. When no leaks are evident place the bomb in a boiling water bath and start the recorder. Record the time indicated on the chart that the bomb was placed in the bath and the time at the end of the first 60-minute period in which the pressure drops 2 p.s.i. All time intervals are read to the nearest 5 minutes. Report the difference in time in minutes to the nearest 5 minutes.

DIELECTROMETRY

DETERMINATION OF FAT CONTENT[32]

The dielectrometric method for the quantitative estimation of fat in various source materials depends on the fact that when a fat-solvent solution is placed between the plates of a high-frequency oscillator, the characteristics of the oscillator are determined in part by the concentration and type of fat in the solvent. The apparatus is designed so that the changes induced in the radio-frequency impedance of a condenser by altering the characteristics of the dielectric medium between the plates of the condenser are related to frequency and indicated by a frequency meter. When oil is added to a standardized solvent, there is an increase in frequency which can be related to the concentration of the oil or fat in the solvent.

The items required for application of the dielectrometric method to the determination of fat content include (a) a standardized fat solvent, (b) a mill or some other comminuting device in which the sample can be ground and extracted simultaneously, (c) an electronic testing device for measuring the frequency of the oil-solvent solution, and (d) a conversion chart relating oil content to meter reading. A separate chart should be prepared for each type of material to be analyzed. The conversion chart can be prepared by analyzing a sufficient number of samples to cover the desired range by a standard method such as the Official Method of the American Oil Chemists' Society. Analyze the same samples with the electronic tester, following the directions provided with the instrument. Finally plot meter reading versus oil content.

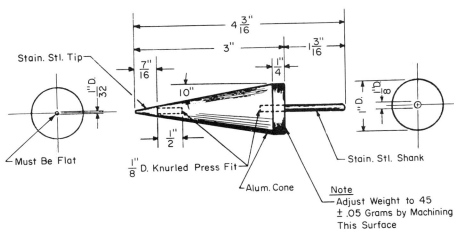

FIG. 48-4.   Penetration Cone for Consistency.

The Steinlite 300-LOS Tester was designed originally to determine the oil content of soybeans. This instrument has since been applied to additional commodities such as

[32] Fred Stein Laboratories, Atchison, Kansas.

flaxseed, peanuts, oil-seed meals, potato chips, and chocolate. The method is simple and relatively rapid.

Procedure.—Weigh the amount of sample shown on the conversion chart and place in Stein Mill extraction cup. Add solvent and grind the sample-solvent mixture for the time specified. Filter the mixture into a flask and then transfer the filtrate into the test cell. Obtain the meter reading and the temperature. Convert the meter reading directly to oil content by reference to the conversion chart, making the proper correction for temperature.

CONSISTENCY[33]

The consistency of fats is related to hardness which is a critical functional factor, especially as it refers to plastic fats. The procedure presented here is the standard method of the American Oil Chemists' Society and utilizes an ASTM penetrometer (D 5, D 217, and D 937 with shaft; D 5 wt. 47.5 g.) with a special cone, as shown in Fig. 48-4.

Procedure.—Condition the sample at the desired temperature and for such time as is necessary to attain uniformity. Adjust the level of the penetrometer so that the cone is in a vertical position. Place the sample on the penetrometer table and make certain that it remains steady and secure during testing. Adjust the cone to its "zero" position. Adjust either the indicator assembly or the table, depending upon the type of instrument, until the tip of the cone nearly touches the surface of the sample at a point close to the middle of the surface. Lock the movable assembly in this position. Using the slow motion adjustment, adjust the cone so that the tip just touches the surface of the sample. Observation of the shadow of the cone tip is an aid to making an accurate setting. Operating the release mechanism rapidly, release the cone shaft and hold it free for exactly 5 seconds. Gently depress the indicator shaft until it is stopped by the cone shaft and read the penetration in tenths of a millimeter directly from the indicator scale.

[33] American Oil Chemists' Society, Official and Tentative Methods, 2nd Ed., Chicago, Ill., 1946, Method Cc 16–60.

Chapter **49**

FERTILIZERS

By John A. Brabson
Tennessee Valley Authority
Wilson Dam, Alabama

Until recently, fertilizers have been analyzed by time-honored, manually-conducted chemical methods. The increasing cost of manpower, together with the fact that conventional analytical methods are too slow for the control of continuous manufacturing processes, has drawn the attention of many laboratories to instrumental methods of analysis. In addition, some of the instrumental methods permit a great saving of time where large numbers of samples accumulate, as in a state chemist's laboratory.

Many of the methods mentioned in this chapter are too new to have stood the test of time, so that they cannot be considered standard methods by any definition. The instruments themselves are subject to rapid modification and change; detailed procedures, which may be obsolete tomorrow, are, therefore, not given. The methods mentioned, however, are potentially valuable in expediting the analysis of fertilizers, but, because of the high costs of instrumentation, the reader is cautioned to compare the instruments mentioned here with other, newer instruments which may be even better suited to his needs.

X-RAY EMISSION SPECTROMETRY

Surveys of the literature and inquiries to manufacturers of x-ray emission spectrometric equipment point up the absence of publications on the analysis of fertilizers. The technique is being used, however, for the analysis of phosphate rock[1] and, to some extent, for the control of fertilizer processes. Mention is made of it here because of its potential usefulness in the analysis of fertilizers.

Fertilizers are not ideal materials for analysis by x-ray emission because they are usually mixtures of compounds which vary widely in physical properties or in particle size. Fine grinding is required to ensure a homogeneous sample and to provide the proper conditions for analysis, but fine grinding of some fertilizer materials is not practical. Powdered specimens usually are briquetted before analysis.

To minimize the effect of the matrix composition on the results, standards should be similar to the samples to be analyzed. This puts a severe limitation on the use of x-ray emission for general fertilizer analysis because of the wide ranges in composition. As a practical matter, this technique is best suited to control of an operation in which only a few grades of fertilizer are manufactured and the results can be checked frequently by chemical methods of analysis.

The equipment is expensive; hence, there is a tendency to use it without adequate testing of its performance. Considerable preliminary work is essential at each installation

[1] Philips Electronics and Pharmaceutical Industries Corp. Norelco Application Data Number 126, June, 1964.

to identify the variables that affect the results significantly and to find a means of compensating for these variables.

AUTOMATIC ANALYSIS TRAINS

The Technicon "AutoAnalyzer"[2] automates some spectrophotometric and flame photometric methods of fertilizer analysis. In the United States, determinations of total phosphorus[3] and ammonium carbonate-soluble potassium[4,5] are automated after sample solutions are prepared by official procedures. Each procedure is standardized with solutions of pure salts and is applicable over a wide range of composition. In England,[6] the AutoAnalyzer is used to monitor the water-soluble phosphorus, ammoniacal and nitrate nitrogen, and potassium in the product of a continuous operation. Production samples are analyzed frequently, and the method is standardized regularly against a sample of similar material which has been analyzed by official methods.

TOTAL PHOSPHORUS[3]

The sample containing a maximum of 35 percent P_2O_5 is decomposed with a mixture of nitric and hydrochloric acids, diluted to volume, and aliquoted into a cup of the sampler. Molybdovanadate reagent, prepared as directed for the official spectrophotometric method, is the color-forming reagent. The sample solution and a measured amount of molybdovanadate solution are pumped into a capillary "h" fitting, where the color reaction occurs. Diluent water is added in a second "h" fitting and, after passage through two mixing coils and a time delay coil, the colored solution passes into the flow cuvet of the colorimeter. The transmission at 420 mμ is measured and plotted on a recorder. Concentrations are read from a standard curve which is prepared from analyses of solutions of primary-standard-grade potassium phosphate, monobasic, corresponding to the range 2.50 to 35.0 percent P_2O_5 in a sample.

The flow cuvet is modified to give a broad, smooth plateau on the read-out curve during the peak response. Addition to the usual air segmentation of a water wash separates the samples and flushes out the flow cuvet, so that the curve returns to a water baseline between samples. The instrument can analyze twenty samples or standards per hour.

WATER-SOLUBLE PHOSPHORUS[6]

A common solution of 1 g. of fertilizer in 1 liter of water is used for the determination of water-soluble phosphorus, water-soluble ammoniacal and nitrate nitrogen, and potassium.

The reaction between molybdovanadate solution and orthophosphate is used as in the method for total phosphorus. A more dilute molybdovanadate solution is used, however, and no dilution step is necessary after the color-reaction step. The samples are separated by air segmentation alone. Instead of preparing a set of standards from reagents, the instrument is calibrated by analysis of solutions of similar fertilizers which have been analyzed by official procedures. When samples and standards are analyzed alternately, the method is in effect a standard method.

[2] Technicon Instruments Corp., Chauncey, N. Y.
[3] Ferretti, R. J., and Hoffman, W. M., J. Assoc. Offic. Agr. Chemists, **45**, 993, 1962.
[4] Association of Official Agricultural Chemists, Official Methods of Analysis, 9th Ed., 1960.
[5] Gehrke, C. W., Ussary, J. P., and Kramer, G. H., Jr., J. Assoc. Offic. Agr. Chemists, **47**, 459, 1964.
[6] Docherty, A. C., in "Analytical Symposium: Self Actuated Devices and New Methods for Control," Proceedings No. 79, The Fertiliser Society, London, 1963.

WATER-SOLUBLE NITRATE NITROGEN[6]

The determination of nitrate nitrogen is based on the reaction of 2,4-xylenol with nitrates in the presence of strong sulfuric acid. The reagent is prepared continuously by passing an acetic acid solution of 2,4-xylenol and 80 percent sulfuric acid through a mixing coil. The mixed reagent then is mixed with the sample solution in a constant ratio and the mixture is passed through double mixing coils to a colorimeter that is set at 420 mμ. The system is calibrated by alternate analyses of samples and standards.

WATER-SOLUBLE AMMONIACAL NITROGEN[6]

A less concentrated sample solution is used for the determination of ammoniacal nitrogen and potassium than for the determination of phosphorus, and for the determination of potassium the solution must be free of solids. The solution is diluted and the internal standard lithium is added prior to a dialysis step in which solids are removed. After further dilution the solution is divided into two portions for the ammoniacal nitrogen and potassium determinations.

The indo-phenol color reaction is the basis for the determination of ammoniacal nitrogen. The diluted sample solution is mixed successively with a solution of sodium phenoxide and a solution of sodium hypochlorite, and 10 minutes is allowed for color development, after which the solution passes to a colorimeter that is set at 625 mμ. This system also is calibrated by alternate analyses of samples and fertilizers of known ammoniacal nitrogen content.

WATER-SOLUBLE POTASSIUM[6]

A portion of the dilute dialyzed sample is fed to the flame photometer, and emission of potassium is measured relative to that of the constant amount of lithium that was added as the internal standard. Phosphate does not interfere at the very high temperature (2775°C.) of the oxy-propane flame. The relation between potassium concentration and peak height is not quite linear, and the results are read from a calibration graph.

AMMONIUM CARBONATE-SOLUBLE POTASSIUM[4,5]

Solutions of fertilizers are prepared by extraction with ammonium carbonate solution as described in the official direct-intensity flame photometric procedure.[4] Addition of the internal standard lithium nitrate, recommended for the AutoAnalyzer, makes further cleanup of the solutions unnecessary for samples containing less than 16 percent K$_2$O. The accuracy of the results for high-potash materials is increased by passing aliquots of the ammonium carbonate extracts through anion-exchange columns before adding the internal standard. The method is calibrated with solutions of primary-standard potassium nitrate.

AUTOMATED DEVARDA METHOD[7,8]

The Devarda method, long recognized as one of the best methods for determining nitrate nitrogen or mixtures of ammoniacal and nitrate nitrogen, has been automated for use in control of fertilizer manufacturing processes. By using a small volume of solution for the reduction and distillation, heating the spray trap, and passing inert gas through the system, the distillation time is shortened to 1 minute. The heat evolved in

[7] Potrafke, K. A., Kroll, M., and Blom, L., Anal. Chim. Acta, **31**, 128, 1964.
[8] Kateman, G., Willemsen, L. L. M., Wijenberg, J. B. G., and Stornebrink, P. J., Anal. Chim. Acta, **31**, 139, 1964.

the reaction between Devarda alloy and sodium hydroxide makes external heating unnecessary.

In practice, the operator weighs the sample and transfers it to a reaction vessel along with the required amounts of Devarda alloy, water, and an antifoaming agent. The vessel is placed on the platform of a distillation head which is raised into position when a start button is pushed.

Raising the platform to its uppermost position energizes a switch which actuates circuits that deliver alkali to the reaction vessel, add a constant amount of standard acid to the absorber, and back-titrate the excess standard acid from a previous sample with standard alkali. The alkali buret sends counting pulses to an electromechanical counter at the rate of 100 per milliliter. The counter then prints the results of the titration on a card or paper tape.

Approximately 3.5 minutes is required for a complete analysis. Three samples, however, are handled simultaneously—while one is weighed, another is distilled, and a third is titrated—so that it is possible for one operator to analyze 50 samples per hour.

The method can be used to determine ammoniacal nitrogen also, but, since there is then no exothermic reaction, heat is provided by a glass-covered platinum resistance heater.

The procedure is applicable to such materials as ammonium nitrate, nitrolime, and nitric phosphates, but not to samples containing other forms of nitrogen such as urea.

ATOMIC ABSORPTION SPECTROMETRY

Although the principles of absorption flame spectrometry have been known for many years, they have been applied to the analysis of agricultural materials only in the past decade, following the pioneering work of Allan[9] in New Zealand and David[10] in Australia. Its high sensitivity and relative freedom from interference combine to make atomic absorption spectrometry especially useful for the determination of micronutrients and secondary elements in fertilizers.

The discussion of this technique is based on the author's experience with the Perkin-Elmer Model 303 photometer. Other photometers probably have about the same sensitivities, although the optimum ranges of concentrations of the sample solutions may differ somewhat with different instruments.

Atomic absorption spectrometry is the subject of much study, new developments are frequent, and sensitivities are being increased by such refinements as scale expansion, concentration by extraction into an organic solvent of the element to be determined, and improvements in atomization of the sample solution into the flame. The current literature should be consulted for the latest improvements in the technique.

MICRONUTRIENTS

Copper.—The sample is decomposed with boiling 3 N hydrochloric acid, the mixture is evaporated to dryness, and the residue is taken up in 0.1 N hydrochloric acid.[11,12] The solution is diluted to contain 2 to 20 p.p.m. copper, and readings on it can be compared directly with those on standard solutions of a copper salt; the copper line at 3247 A is used. When a 2-g. sample is diluted to 100 ml., results as low as 0.01 percent

[9] Allan, J. E., Analyst, **83**, 466, 1958.
[10] David, D. J., Analyst, **83**, 655, 1958.
[11] Allan, J. E., Spectrochim. Acta, **17**, 459, 1961.
[12] "Analytical Methods for Atomic Absorption Spectrophotometry," Perkin-Elmer Corp., Norwalk, Conn., 1964.

copper can be reported with confidence. For determinations of lower concentrations, the copper is complexed with ammonium pyrrolidine dithiocarbamate and extracted with an organic solvent.[13] Lines of lower sensitivity than that at 3247 A can be used for higher concentrations of copper if dilution of the sample solution is undesirable.

Zinc.—Solutions prepared as for the determination of copper are diluted to contain 0.5 to 5 p.p.m. of zinc.[14] Readings are compared against those of standard zinc nitrate solutions; the zinc line at 2138 A is used. Results as low as 0.001 percent zinc can be reported with confidence when a 2-g. sample is diluted to 100 ml. The sensitivity of the determination can be increased fivefold by complexing the zinc with ammonium pyrrolidine dithiocarbamate and extracting the complex with methyl isobutyl ketone. By aliquoting and diluting, zinc contents as high as 5 percent can be determined with a precision of ± 0.1 percent.

Manganese.—Solutions prepared as for the determination of copper[11] are diluted to contain 2 to 20 p.p.m. of manganese. When other acids such as perchloric are used in the initial digestions, the standards should be prepared with the same acids. The manganese line at 2794.8 A, which is recommended for maximum sensitivity,[15] permits the determination of 0.01 percent manganese when a 2-g. sample is diluted to 100 ml., but less sensitive lines can be used for determinations of larger quantities of manganese. The same absorbance was obtained for 10 p.p.m. of manganese when the manganese was present alone, and when the solution contained also 3000 p.p.m. of potassium, 3000 p.p.m. of calcium, 1000 p.p.m. of sodium, 1000 p.p.m. of magnesium, and 500 p.p.m. of phosphorus.

Iron.—The line at 2483.3 A is recommended for maximum sensitivity for the determination of iron.[15] In all other details, the comments under manganese apply equally to iron.

Molybdenum.—Atomic absorption spectrometry is a promising technique for determination of molybdenum in fertilizers, but the sensitivity to this element is rather low.[16] Sample solutions are prepared by digesting large samples with mixtures of nitric and hydrochloric acids and diluting to 10 to 100 p.p.m. of molybdenum. Strongly reducing conditions, provided by adjustment of the acetylene-air ratio, are essential. In the determination of 10 to 40 p.p.m. of molybdenum, serious interference is caused by 500 p.p.m. of calcium, strontium, or manganese; somewhat less interference is caused by 500 p.p.m. of sulfate, magnesium, or iron, but addition of 1000 p.p.m. of aluminum as the chloride completely suppresses all these interferences. Standards should contain the same amounts of suppressant and nitric acid as the sample solution, and it may also be necessary to compensate for other major elements such as phosphorus. With a 2-g. sample diluted to 100 ml., results can be reported with confidence in the range 0.02 to 0.5 percent.

Cobalt.—Determination of cobalt in fertilizers by atomic absorption spectrometry has been described as feasible,[17] but the literature contains no reports of such determinations. The 2407 A line is recommended for maximum sensitivity, and the flame should be strongly oxidizing.[18] The optimum range is 10 to 40 p.p.m. and the sensitivity is about 1 p.p.m. for 1 percent absorption. Experiments in the author's laboratory showed no interference from phosphorus when the ratio P:Co was as high as 40.

[13] Malissa, H., and Schoffmann, E., Mikrochim. Acta, 187, 1955.
[14] Allan, J. E., Analyst, **86**, 530, 1961.
[15] Allan, J. E., Spectrochim. Acta, 800, 1959.
[16] David, D. J., Analyst, **86**, 730, 1961.
[17] David, D. J., Rev. Univ. Ind. Santander, **4**, No. 3/4, 207, 1962.
[18] Allan, J. E., Nature, **187**, 1110, 1960.

SECONDARY ELEMENTS[9,10,19,20,21,22]

Calcium.—Applications of atomic absorption spectrometry to the determination of calcium have been almost entirely devoted to plant materials, soil extracts, and biological materials,[19,20,21,22] but the results are directly applicable to the analysis of fertilizers. The major interfering element is phosphorus, and its effect is intensified by aluminum. Willis[22] found that addition of 10,000 p.p.m. of lanthanum as the chloride virtually eliminated the interference from 250 p.p.m. of phosphorus in the determination of 10 p.p.m. of calcium, and acceptable results were obtained with 500 p.p.m. of phosphorus.

The suppression of phosphate interference with lanthanum has been used in the author's laboratory for determining calcium in wet-process phosphoric acid in which the ratio P:Ca occasionally exceeds 100. To ensure suppression of phosphorus interference, the sample solution is diluted to contain 10,000 p.p.m. of lanthanum, no more than 400 p.p.m. of phosphorus, and 1 to 20 p.p.m. of calcium. It is preferable to have the readings on the lower portion of the calibration curve and to avoid excessive phosphorus rather than to use a larger sample to increase the concentration of calcium. Scale expansion can be used if necessary to increase the sensitivity of the calcium determination.

Magnesium.—Magnesium was one of the first elements studied by the pioneers in atomic absorption spectrometry because of the inadequacy of chemical and emission flame photometry techniques for determination of this element,[9,10] Allan[9] found aluminum to be the major interfering element in the determination of magnesium in plants and soil extracts, and that even a ratio Al:Mg of 1 could not be tolerated. The determination of 0.3 to 10 p.p.m. of magnesium was not affected by 200 p.p.m. of either potassium or calcium or by phosphorus when the ratio P:Mg was as high as 60.

Both strontium and lanthanum have been used to eliminate aluminum interference. In the author's laboratory, 10,000 p.p.m. of lanthanum prevented interference by 4 p.p.m. of aluminum and 87 p.p.m. of phosphorus in the determination of 0.4 p.p.m. of magnesium.

For concentrations of magnesium in samples and standards of 0.2 to 2.0 p.p.m. the 2852 A line is used, and for higher concentrations of magnesium the less sensitive line at 2025 A is preferred.

[19] David, D. J., Analyst, **84**, 536, 1959.
[20] *Ibid.*, **85**, 495, 1960.
[21] Willis, J. B., Nature, **186**, 249, 1960.
[22] Willis, J. B., Anal. Chem., **33**, 556, 1961.

Chapter 50

FOODS

By L. W. Aurand

Department of Food Science
North Carolina State University
Raleigh, North Carolina

CEREALS

Cereals are those members of the grass family that are grown for their edible grains and include wheat, rye, barley, corn, oats, and rice. Buckwheat, although not a true cereal, is usually included with them. Sorghums are cereals; however, they are used primarily for animal feeding.

The cereals are, in general, the cheapest sources of food energy and normally constitute about one-third or more of the caloric and protein intake of humans. In the United States, wheat is the most extensively used cereal for human food. By-products in the manufacture of food products from wheat constitute an important group of animal feeds. Since wheat is the most widely used cereal in the United States, it will be the only one considered in detail.

ANALYSIS OF FLOUR

STARCH DETERMINATION BY A SACCHARIMETRIC METHOD[1,2]

Reagent. **Calcium Chloride Solution.**—Dissolve 2 parts of calcium chloride ($CaCl_2 \cdot 6H_2O$) in 1 part of water and adjust to a density of 1.30 at 20°C. Add phenolphthalein indicator and then 0.1 N sodium hydroxide solution until faintly pink.

Procedure.—Weigh a 2.000-g. sample of flour into a 50-ml. round-bottom centrifuge tube. Wash with ether to remove lipid material; then add 10 ml. of 65 percent ethanol solution (d_4^{20} 0.88) and stir thoroughly with a glass rod. Centrifuge the suspension and pour off the liquid. Repeat the washing until 60 ml. of the ethanol solution have been used, stirring after each addition of the wash liquid with the same glass rod.

Stir the residue with 10 ml. of distilled water and pour the suspension into a 250-ml. Erlenmeyer flask. Transfer the remaining material in the tube to the flask by washing with 60 ml. of the calcium chloride solution containing 2 ml. of an 0.8 percent acetic acid solution. Place the glass rod in the flask supported on a wire gauze over a burner and, with frequent stirring, quickly bring the mixture to boiling. Boil briskly for 15 to 17 min., being careful to prevent foaming and burning. During the boiling, rub down particles on the sides of the flask with the glass rod.

At the completion of boiling, quickly cool the solution and pour into a 100-ml. volumetric flask. Transfer the remaining material in the Erlenmeyer flask to the volumetric flask by rinsing with the calcium chloride solution and dilute to volume with the rinse solution.

---

[1] Assoc. Offic. Agr. Chemists., Official Methods of Analysis, 9th Ed., 1960, p. 165.
[2] Am. Assoc. Cereal Chem., General Laboratory Methods, 6th Ed., St. Paul, Minn., 1957.

Thoroughly mix the contents of the volumetric flask and pour about 10 ml. of the contents on a fluted filter (Whatman No. 42 or its equivalent). Permit the filter to run dry and discard the filtrate. Continue the filtration through the filter, collecting 40 to 50 ml. of filtrate in a dry flask.

Fill a 200-mm. saccharimeter tube with the clear filtrate and obtain 10 readings on the saccharimeter. Refill the saccharimeter tube with a fresh sample of filtrate and take readings on it. Average the readings to obtain the average degrees Ventzske (°V) and calculate the percentage of starch from the formula: °V × 4.3225 = percent starch. (*Note.* This formula holds only if an exactly 2-g. sample was used, and if the mixture was diluted to a volume of 100 ml. and polarized in a 200-mm. tube).

DETERMINATION OF STARCH AND SUGARS IN CEREALS[3]

Reagents. Anthrone Solution.—Dissolve 1 g. of anthrone in 1 liter of sulfuric acid solution containing 760 ml. of concentrated sulfuric acid that has been cooled to room temperature. The required quantity of reagent is prepared daily.

Perchloric Acid Solution (52 percent).—Prepared by adding 270 ml. of 72 percent perchloric acid to 100 ml. of water.

Glucose Standard Solution.—A standard aqueous solution containing 1 mg. of DL-glucose per ml. is prepared every two or three days and diluted daily to give a solution of 0.1 mg. of glucose per ml.

Extraction of Sugars from Sample.—Weigh approximately 0.2 g. of finely ground sample into a 50-ml. centrifuge tube, add 2 drops of 80 percent alcohol to aid mixing, and then 5 ml. of water. Stir thoroughly, then add 25 ml. of hot 80 percent alcohol and stir, set aside for 5 min., and centrifuge. Decant the alcoholic solution and repeat the alcohol procedure by adding 30 ml. of hot 80 percent alcohol to the residue. Combine the two alcohol extracts and remove the alcohol by evaporation under reduced pressure in a boiling water bath. Dilute the remaining aqueous extract so that final concentration of sugar is equivalent to about 0.1 mg. of glucose per ml.

Extraction of Starch from Sample.—Add 5 ml. of water to the residue of sample which has been extracted with alcohol, and, while stirring, add 6.5 ml. of perchloric acid solution. Stir continuously for 5 min. and then occasionally for 15 min. Add 20 ml. of water and centrifuge. Transfer supernatant liquid into a 100-ml. volumetric flask. Add 5 ml. of water to the residue and repeat the extraction with perchloric acid. Wash contents of the tube into the flask containing the first extract. Dilute to volume with water and filter, discarding the first 5 ml. of the filtrate. Dilute an aliquot portion to a final concentration equivalent to about 0.1 mg. glucose per ml.

Procedure.—Using 25 × 150 mm. boiling tubes, prepare in duplicate, the blank containing 2 ml. of water; in triplicate, the test extract alone containing 1 ml. of diluted extract and 1 ml. of water; in triplicate, 1 ml. of diluted extract plus 1 ml. of glucose standard (containing 0.1 mg. glucose 1 ml.). To all tubes add 10 ml. of the anthrone reagent and mix the contents thoroughly. Heat the tubes (fitted with rubber stoppers containing a piece of capillary glass tubing) in a boiling water bath for 12 min., and then cool to room temperature. Read the absorbance in a spectrometer set at 630 mμ with the reagent blank as standard.

Calculation.—Take the average of the two sets of triplicates and calculate the equivalent quantity of glucose in the test extract by comparison with the test extract plus glucose standard (0.1 mg.). For both extracts use this value and a dilution factor to calculate the percentage of sugars and starch in the original material. Use conversion factor of 0.9 for the starch extract since 0.9 g. starch yields approximately 1.0 g. of glucose on hydrolysis.

[3] Clegg, K. M., J. Sci. Food Agr., **7**, 40, 1956.

DETERMINATION OF CALCIUM IN FLOUR[4]

Reagents. **Standard Calcium Solution.**—Dissolve 8.3626 g. calcium carbonate in the minimum volume of acetic acid and dilute to 250 ml. with distilled water.

Buffer Solution (pH 4.0).—Mix equal volumes of 0.2 M sodium acetate and 0.8 M acid solution.

Chloranilic Acid Solution.—Dissolve 1 g. chloranilic acid in 1 liter of hot buffer solution. Cool and filter.

Sodium Dithionite Solution.—Dissolve 15 g. of sodium dithionite in 100 ml. of distilled water. Prepare immediately before use.

Procedure.—To a series of 100-ml. Erlenmeyer flasks (ten for standards and one for each sample) add 40 ml. of chloranilic acid solution. For the standards, add 0.0, 0.1, 0.2, 0.3, and 0.4 ml. of the standard calcium solution, each in duplicate. Add 3.00 g. of flour to each sample. Stopper flasks and shake them, first vigorously and then gently, in a mechanical shaker for 30 min. *Loosen stoppers at intervals to release gas pressure.* Allow the flasks to stand overnight in a cool place. By means of a pipet, transfer 10 ml. of the supernatant solution to a colorimeter tube and read the extinction, E_1, at 540 mμ, using water as a reference solution. Decolorize by adding 1 drop of sodium dithionite solution and reread the extinction, E_2. The second reading is a measure of the turbidity of the extract, and $E_1 - E_2$ is the extinction due to the color of the solution.

DETERMINATION OF IRON IN FLOURS[5]

Reagents. **Glycerol-ethyl Alcohol Mixture (1:1).**

Hydrochloric Acid (5 M).—Dilute 445 ml. concentrated hydrochloric acid to 1 liter.

Sodium Acetate (2 M).

o-**Phenanthroline Solution (0.25 percent).**—Dissolve 0.25 g. in distilled water and dilute to 100 ml.

Procedure.—Weigh out a 10.0-g. sample into a porcelain dish, add 10 ml. of glycerol-alcohol mixture and, after carefully igniting in a muffle furnace to prevent splattering, ash overnight at 600°C. Cool, add 1.0 ml. concentrated nitric acid, evaporate at the furnace entrance and ignite in the muffle furnace for 1 hr. Cool, add 5 ml. of 5 M hydrochloric acid to the ash, place on a steam bath for 15 min., and filter through a hardened filter paper into a 100-ml. volumetric flask. Add 3 ml. dilute hydrochloric acid (1 in 100) to the dish, bring to a boil, and pass through the filter paper. Repeat the process a few times and then wash the dish and filter paper with hot water. Cool and dilute to volume. Pipet 10 ml. into a 25-ml. volumetric flask, and add 1 ml. of 2 percent sulfur dioxide solution and titrate with sodium acetate solution using a small piece of Congo red paper. Add 2 ml. of *o*-phenanthroline solution and dilute to volume. Allow color to develop overnight and read the absorbance at 520 mμ against a blank prepared in the same manner as the test solution. Determine the iron concentration from a standard curve.

Preparation of Standard Curve.—Dissolve 0.7024 g. ferrous ammonium sulfate, $Fe(NH_4)_2(SO_4)_2 \cdot 6H_2O$, in water, add 2 drops of 5 M hydrochloric acid, and dilute to 1 liter. Dilute 50 ml. of the stock solution to 1 liter so that 1 ml. of solution is equivalent to 0.005 mg. iron. For the standard curve, pipet aliquot amounts of the latter solution (over the range 0.05 mg. iron) into series of 25-ml. volumetric flasks, and add the appropriate reagents. Plot absorbance against concentration (in mg.) of iron.

[4] Sawyer, R., Tyler, J. F. C., and Weston, R. E., Analyst, **81,** 362, 1956.
[5] Pringle, W. J. S., Analyst, **71,** 491, 1946.

CHEMICAL PRESERVATIVES

DETERMINATION OF BENZOIC ACID[6]

Reagents. **Saturated Sodium Chloride Solution.**

Concentrated Hydrochloric Acid.

Benozic Standard Solutions.—Prepare solutions of benzoic acid in ethyl ether containing 20, 40, 60, 80, 100, and 120 mg. per liter.

Procedure.—Transfer either 10 g. or 10 ml. of the food product to a separatory funnel and dilute to 200 ml. with sodium chloride solution. Add hydrochloric acid until solution is acid to litmus and mix. Extract with 70-, 50-, 40-, and 30-ml. portions of ethyl ether. Wash combined ether extracts with 50-, 40-, and 30-ml. portions of acidified water (1 + 1000) and discard washings. Dilute combined ether extracts to 200 ml. with ethyl ether and determine absorbance in well-stoppered cuvet at wavelengths of 268 mμ (A), 272 mμ (B), and 276 mμ (C). Average absorbance at A and C (minimum) and subtract this volume from absorbance at B (maximum). Correct for dilution and determine the concentration of benzoic acid from standard curve.

Preparation of Standard Curve.—Determine absorbances of above standard solutions in well-stoppered cuvets at points A, B, and C. For each concentration, average absorbances at A and C and subtract this value from absorbance at B. Plot difference against concentration.

To convert benzoic acid to sodium benzoate, multiply benzoic acid concentration by factor of 1.18.

This method is applicable to catsup, tomato products, jams, jellies, soft drinks, and fruit juices. Reference 21 CFR (Code of Federal Regulations) Subpart B 121.101. The tolerance in processed foods is 0.1 percent.

DETERMINATION OF BORIC ACID[7]

Reagents. **Concentrated Hydrochloric Acid.**

Dilute Hydrochloric Acid.—Dilute 5 ml. of concentrated hydrochloric acid to 100 ml. with water.

Concentrated Sulfuric Acid.

Carmine Solution (0.05 percent).—Dissolve 0.05 g. Carmine No. 40 N.F. in 54 ml. concentrated sulfuric acid.

Boric Acid Standard Solution.—Dissolve 0.5716 g. of boric acid in distilled water and dilute to 1 liter. One ml. contains 0.100 mg. of boron.

Preparation of Sample.—Weigh a 5-g. portion of dried sample and transfer to a glazed paper. Add 0.1 g. calcium oxide for each gram of sample and mix. Transfer to a platinum dish, ignite in a muffle furnace at 500° to 550°C., cool, and moisten with water. Add 15 ml. 6 M hydrochloric acid and heat on a steam bath for 30 min. Filter and wash the residue with water. Dilute to a volume of 100 ml.

Procedure.—Pipet 2 ml. of the sample into an Erlenmeyer flask, add 10 ml. of concentrated sulfuric acid, mix, and cool. Add 10 ml. of carmine solution, mix well, and allow to stand for 45 min. Read absorbance at a wavelength of 585 mμ against a blank of 2 ml. distilled water carried through the entire procedure. Determine the boron concentration from a standard curve.

Preparation of Standard Curve.—Dilute portions of standard solution to obtain standards over the range of 0 to 10 p.p.m. of boron. Treat 2 ml. of each solution, as

[6] Assoc. Offic. Agr. Chemists, Official Methods of Analysis, 9th Ed., 1960, p. 385.
[7] Hatcher, J. T., and Wilcox, L. V., Anal. Chem., **22,** 567, 1950.

described above, and read the absorbance at 585 mμ. Plot absorbance readings against concentration of boron.

Reference 21CFR Subpart A 121.90. Tolerance 0.10 mg. per day.

DETERMINATION OF SORBIC ACID IN FOOD PRODUCTS[8]

Reagents. Sulfuric Acid Solution, 0.05 M.

Sorbic Acid Standard Solution.—Dissolve 50 mg. sorbic acid in a 100-ml. volumetric flask containing 25 ml. ethanol and dilute to volume with distilled water. Each ml. contains 0.5 mg. or 500 μg. of sorbic acid.

Procedure.—To a sample of food product, containing between 0.50 to 2.00 mg. of sorbic acid, in a macro-Kjeldahl flask are added 200 g. of magnesium sulfate heptahydrate (MgSO$_4$·7H$_2$O) and 200 ml. of 0.05 M sulfuric acid. The mixture is distilled on a Kjeldahl distillation rack until about 95 ml. of distillate have been collected in a 100-ml. volumetric flask.

The distillate is acidified with 1.00 ml. of 1 M hydrochloric acid and diluted to volume with distilled water. The absorbance of the distillate is determined against 0.01 M hydrochloric acid at 263 mμ using quartz cells and the hydrogen discharge lamp. The absorbance of a comparable blank sample without added sorbic acid is determined and then subtracted from absorbance of sample. The micrograms of sorbic acid are determined by reference to standard curve.

Preparation of Standard Curve.—Into a series of 100-ml. flasks, containing 1.00 ml. of 1 M hydrochloric acid, pipet 0, 1.0, 2.0, 3.0, 4.0, and 5.0 ml. of sorbic acid standard solution and dilute to volume with distilled water. Determine absorbance and plot against micrograms of sorbic acid on ordinary graph paper.

DETERMINATION OF SULFUR DIOXIDE IN DRIED FRUITS[9]

Reagents. Formaldehyde Solution (0.015 percent).—Prepared from formalin (36 percent).

Acid-bleached Pararosaniline Hydrochloride.—Transfer 100 mg. of pararosaniline hydrochloride and 200 ml. of distilled water to a 1000-ml. volumetric flask. Add 160 ml. of hydrochloric acid (1:1) and dilute to volume.

Sodium Tetrachloromercurate.—Place 23.4 g. sodium chloride and 54.3 g. mercuric chloride in a 2000-ml. volumetric flask. Add approximately 1500 ml. distilled water and shake to dissolve. Dilute to volume.

Standard Sodium Bisulfite Solution.—Prepare a solution containing 100 μg. of sulfur dioxide per ml. from sodium bisulfite (58.5 percent as SO$_2$). Standardize with 0.01 N iodine before use.

Preparation of Sample.—Weigh 10 g. of dried fruit and place in a Waring Blendor. Add 290 ml. distilled water and blend for 3 to 5 min. Transfer a 10-g. aliquot to a 100-ml. volumetric flask containing 4.0 ml. of 0.5 M sodium hydroxide. Mix. Add 4.0 ml. of 0.25 M sulfuric acid, 20.0 ml. sodium tetrachloromercurate, and dilute to volume with distilled water. Mix and filter through Whatman No. 2 (or equivalent) filter paper.

Procedure.—Transfer a 2-ml. aliquot of the above filtrate to a colorimeter tube containing 5 ml. pararosaniline hydrochloride. Add 10 ml. of the formaldehyde solution, mix and allow to stand at room temperature for 25 min. Read absorbance at 560 mμ and determine micrograms of sulfur dioxide from standard curve. Carry out a blank determination on the dried fruit in the same way, but use 10 ml. of water in place of the formaldehyde solution. Use blank to set spectrometer at zero absorbance.

[8] Alderton, G., and Lewis, J. C., Food Research, **23**, 338, 1958.
[9] Nury, F. S., Taylor, D. H., and Baeke, J. E., Agr. Food Chem., **7**, 351, 1959.

Preparation of Standard Curve.—Into a series of 100-ml. volumetric flasks, containing 20 ml. of sodium tetrachloromercurate solution, pipet different volumes of the sodium bisulfite solution ranging in concentration from 0 to 50 μg. of sulfur dioxide per ml. Use 2 ml. of the standard solutions for analysis as described above. Plot absorbance *vs.* micrograms of sulfur dioxide.

NOTE.—The above procedure can be used to determine free sulfur dioxide of dried fruits by omitting acid and base treatment in a preparation of sample and the analysis carried out without delay.

COLOR ADDITIVES

Under the Color Additive Amendment of 1960 all colorants added to foods are classified as "Color Additives." Obviously only those colors approved by the Federal Food and Drug Administration can be used. Two classes of colors are available: (a) Natural colors (vegetable, animal, and mineral); and (b) synthetic colors (products of chemical synthesis). Synthetic colors occupy the most favored position among colorants in the food industries because of the variety of available shades, their brilliance and uniformity, and solubility. Synthetic colors are given specific letters and numbers for identification. The names of the eleven primary certified colors are:

FD & C	Blue No. 1	(Brilliant Blue FCF)
FD & C	Blue No. 2	(Sodium Indigo Disulfonate)
FD & C	Green No. 1	(Guinea Green B)
FD & C	Green No. 2	(Light Green SF Yellowish)
FD & C	Green No. 3	(Fast Green FCF)
FD & C	Red No. 2	(Amaranth)
FD & C	Red No. 3	(Erythrosine)
FD & C	Red No. 4	(Ponceaux 5X)
FD & C	Violet No. 1	(Wool Violet 5BN)
FD & C	Yellow No. 5	(Tartrazine)
FD & C	Yellow No. 6	(Sunset Yellow FCF)

IDENTIFICATION OF PERMITTED WATER-SOLUBLE COAL-TAR DYES PRESENT IN FOODS

Preliminary Treatment of the Food.—Suggested methods of treating various kinds of foods are given below:

(a) Soluble foods, as icings, jams, syrups and other saccharine foods, may be taken up in hot water (30 ml.) and strained if necessary. Acidify slightly with acetic acid.

(b) Solid foods, as fruits, meat products, cakes, and macaroni: Grind 10 g. of sample with 70 percent alcohol, containing 3 to 5 percent ammonia, allow to stand for a few hours, and centrifuge. Pour the separated liquid into a dish and evaporate on the water bath. Take up the residue in 30 ml. water containing acetic acid.

(c) Food products with a relatively high fat content, as sausages, meat, and fish pastes: Remove fat from food product by extracting with petroleum ether. The color is obtained in aqueous solution by treatment of sample with hot water. Acidify with acetic acid.

(d) Nonalcoholic liquids, as soft drinks: Since most of the food products in this group are acidic, they can be treated directly with wool. Otherwise, acidify slightly with acetic acid.

(e) Alcoholic liquids, as wine: Liquids containing alcohol should be evaporated on the water bath until the alcohol is removed. Acidify if necessary.

Extraction of the Color from the Food.—The wool should be prepared by boiling pure white knitting wool in dilute sodium hydroxide solution and then thoroughly washing in boiling water.

Add a 20-cm. strip of wool to about 50 ml. of the prepared, slightly acidified solution and boil for at least 10 min., replacing the water lost by evaporation. Remove the wool, and, if colored, rinse thoroughly in boiling water to remove any color which may be adherent to the fiber. Transfer the wool strip to a small beaker and boil gently with dilute ammonia (1 part of concentrated ammonia to 50 parts of water). If the color is stripped by the alkali, the presence of a coal-tar dye is indicated. Remove the wool, add dilute hydrochloric acid to the solution until it is faintly acid and boil. Immerse a fresh strip of wool and boil again for 10 min. Re-extract the dye from the wool with a small volume of dilute ammonia, filter, and evaporate to near dryness. In general, a distinct color indicates the presence of a coal-tar dye because natural colors are not usually removed by dilute ammonia.

Separation of the Extracted Color.—Colors can be separated using any of the usual paper chromatographic techniques. For example, apply the prepared dye solution about 2 cm. from the bottom edge of a piece of Whatman No. 1 chromatographic paper and dry. Develop chromatogram by ascending technique with a solvent, such as n-butanol (20 vols.), water (12 vols.), glacial acetic acid (5 vols.). Cut out the separate lines of color, extract with water or aqueous acetone, and evaporate to dryness.

Identification of the Separated Color.—Infrared spectrometry is of considerable value in identifying food colors and judging their purity. The spectrum of the purified material may be determined after grinding it with potassium bromide and pressing it into a pellet. The spectrum of the unknown is compared with a number of known spectra. If a match can be found, the identity of the unknown is established.

An alternative method for confirming the identity of dyes is the use of a spectrometer. Dilute the pure neutral dye residue to a suitable intensity of color and determine the absorption curve on the spectrometer in region of 400–750 mμ, in neutral (0.02 percent ammonium acetate), acid (0.1 M hydrochloric acid), and alkaline (0.1 M sodium hydroxide) solution and compare the maxima with those obtained with known dyes.

If the dye appears to be a nonpermitted dye, chemical tests should be made. (See Assoc. Offic. Agr. Chemists, Official Methods of Analysis, 9th Ed., 1960, p. 581.)

FOOD ADDITIVES

Food additives fall into two general categories depending on whether they may become components of foods, directly or indirectly. Direct additives are substances added to food intentionally and for a specific technical purpose. Indirect additives are substances which may become components of food as a result of its contact with processing equipment, storage facilities, or packaging materials.

Regulations governing food additives are promulgated by the Food and Drug Administration and are incorporated in Title 21, Chapter 1 of the Code of Federal Regulations, Part 121. This part is divided in subparts and sections in the following manner:

Subpart A—Definitions and procedural and interpretive regulations.
Subpart B—Exemption of certain food additives from the requirement of tolerances.
Subpart C—Food additives permitted for animal feed or animal feed supplements.
Subpart D—Food additives permitted in food for human consumption.
Subpart E—Substances for which prior sanctions have been granted.
Subpart F—Food additives resulting from contact with containers or equipment and food additives otherwise affecting food.
Subpart G—Radiation and radiation sources intended for use in the production, processing, and handling of food.

FOOD ADDITIVES—DIRECT

DETERMINATION OF RESIDUAL SOLVENTS IN SPICE OLEORESINS[10]

Equipment. A **gas chromatography unit** equipped with a differential type detector, with the column thermostated separately from the cell. The cell is preferably thermostated at 150°C. The columns (6–8 ft.) are either of 17 percent (w/w) Ucon 75-H-90,000 on 35–80 mesh firebrick or 20 percent Ucon LB-135 on 35–80 mesh firebrick. (Ucon lubricants may be obtained from Union Carbide and Chemicals Company.) The operating conditions are: column temperature of 70°–80°C. and a helium gas flow rate of 50–70 ml. per minute.

Volatile oil apparatus for oils heavier than water, made according to the specifications found in the Journal of the American Pharmaceutical Society, XVII, No. 4, p. 346.

Reagents. Toluene.—Purity of the toluene for the purposes of this analysis may be determined by a gas chromatographic analysis using the columns and conditions described above, and injecting the same quantity of toluene as will be injected in the analysis for solvents.

Potassium Carbonate, Anhydrous.

Sodium Sulfate, Anhydrous.

Detergent.—A detergent (*e.g.*, Tide) free of volatile compounds and an antifoam compound free of volatile compounds. If volatile compounds are present in the detergents and antifoam available, they may be removed by lengthy boiling of their aqueous solutions.

Benzene Reference Solution.—Prepare a solution of toluene containing 2500 p.p.m. of benzene.

Acetone Reference Solution.—Prepare a solution containing 0.63 percent (v/w) acetone in water.

Procedure. Preparation of Sample.—Place 50.0 g. oleoresin, 1.0 ml. toluene containing 2500 p.p.m. benzene, 10 g. sodium sulfate, 50 ml. water, and a small amount of detergent and antifoam in a 250-ml. flask. Attach the distilling head and receiver, and collect approximately 15 ml. of distillate. Add 15 g. potassium carbonate to the distillate, cool while shaking and allow the two phases to separate. All of the solvents except methanol will be present in the toluene layer.

Draw off the aqueous layer, and place in a 50-ml. flask with boiling chips. Add 1.0 ml. of the acetone reference solution. Attach a distilling head and distill off approximately 1.0 ml. The distillate will contain the methanol, if present, in the oleoresin, and acetone as the internal standard.

Gas Chromatography.—Use Ucon 75-H-90,000 for separation of acetone and methanol from their aqueous solution. Use it for separation and analysis of hexane, acetone, and trichloroethylene in the toluene layer from the distillate. Elution order on the column is acetone, methanol, water, hexane, isopropyl alcohol plus methylene chloride, benzene, trichloroethylene, and ethylene dichloride plus toluene. Use a Ucon LB-135 column for separation of mixture methylene chloride plus isopropyl alcohol, and ethylene dichloride. Elution order on this column is as follows: hexane plus acetone, methylene chloride, isopropanol, benzene, ethylene dichloride, trichloroethylene, and toluene.

Inject a sample of sufficient size to give a measurable deflection of the internal standards of benzene, in the toluene phase, or of acetone, in the aqueous phase. If a katharometer is used as a detector, approximately 40 μl. will give adequate deflection. If an argon ionization detector is used, approximately 0.4 μl. or less will be sufficient.

[10] Todd, P. H., Jr., Food Technology, **14**, 301, 1960.

Calibration of Instrument.—Determine the response of the detector in the instrument to known amounts of solvents in toluene. The levels of the solvents and benzene in toluene should be of the same magnitude as will be present in the analysis. Calculate the areas of the solvents in relation to benzene. Determine the calibration factor C of the detector as follows:

$$\text{Solvent } (S) = \frac{\text{weight percent solvent}}{\text{weight percent benzene}} \times \frac{\text{area of benzene}}{\text{area of solvent}}$$

Calculation of Residual Solvent in Oleoresin.—The level of the internal standards, related back to the 50 g. of oleoresin used, is: benzene, 43.4 p.p.m.; acetone, 100 p.p.m. The level of residual solvent using benzene as an internal standard is calculated as follows:

$$\text{Residual solvent, p.p.m.} = \frac{43.4 \times S(\text{solvent}) \times 100}{\text{percent recovery of solvent}} \times \frac{\text{area of solvent}}{\text{area of benzene}}$$

The level of residual methanol using acetone as an internal standard is

$$\text{Residual methanol, p.p.m.} = \frac{100 \times S(\text{methanol})}{0.07} \times \frac{\text{area of methanol}}{\text{area of acetone}}$$

NOTE.—Food additive regulation Sec. 121.093, 121.1040, 121.1041, 121.1042, 121.1043, 121.1044, 121.1045. For enforcement the tolerance for residual solvents in spice oleoresins are: methylene chloride 30 p.p.m., ethylene dichloride 30 p.p.m., trichloroethylene 30 p.p.m., acetone 30 p.p.m., isopropyl alcohol 50 p.p.m., methyl alcohol 50 p.p.m., and hexane 25 p.p.m.

DETERMINATION OF AMPROLIUM (1-4 AMINO-2-n-PROPYL-5-PYRIMIDINYL METHYL-2-PICOLIUM CHLORIDE HYDROCHLORIDE) IN EGGS, MEAT AND MEAT PRODUCTS OF POULTRY[11]

Reagents. Ethanol, Absolute (U.S.P.).

n-Amyl Alcohol, Reagent Grade.

Hydrogen Peroxide (3 percent).—Dilute 3.0 ml. of Reagent Grade hydrogen peroxide (30 percent) to a final volume of 100 ml. Prepare fresh daily.

Potassium Ferricyanide (2 percent).—Dissolve 2.0 g. of potassium ferricyanide in distilled water and dilute to 100 ml. Store in a refrigerator.

Silver Nitrate (2 percent).—Dissolve 2.0 g. of silver nitrate per 100 ml. of aqueous solution.

Sodium Hydroxide (30 percent).—Dissolve 30.0 g. of sodium hydroxide per 100 ml. of aqueous solution at room temperature.

Trichloroacetic Acid (5 percent).—Dissolve 5.0 g. of trichloroacetic acid per 100 ml. of aqueous solution.

Amprolium Standard Stock Solution.—Weigh accurately 20 mg. of Amprolium Reference Standard and dilute with distilled water to 100 ml. and mix. Dilute 10.0 ml. of this solution with water to exactly 1000 ml. and mix. Each 5.0 ml. is equivalent to 1.00 μg. of amprolium.

Amprolium Standard Working Solution.—Transfer 5.00, 10.00, and 20.00 ml. of the Amprolium Standard Stock solution to each of three 50-ml. volumetric flasks. Add to each 25 ml. of trichloroacetic acid reagent, dilute with water to 50 ml. and mix. Each 5.00 ml. is equivalent to 0.10, 0.20, or 0.40 μg. of amprolium.

[11] Methods of Analysis and Tolerances for Food Additives, U.S. Food and Drug Administration, Department of Health, Education, and Welfare, Washington 25, D.C.

Procedure.—In the analysis of individual birds, use the entire liver (30.50 g.), the entire kidney (5–15 g.), or 50 g. of muscle tissue or of skin and associated fat. Weigh the sample and add a measured volume of trichloroacetic acid solution equivalent to 2 ml. per gram of sample, but not less than 15 ml. Homogenize in a Waring Blendor. Transfer to a 50-ml. centrifuge tube and centrifuge at high speed. Filter the supernatant liquid through a small Pyrex-wool plug fitted in a funnel stem to remove any coarse suspended matters. Transfer a 5.0-ml. aliquot of the filtrate to a 15-ml. centrifuge tube. Add 2.00 ml. of sodium hydroxide solution, mix, add 0.20 ml. of silver nitrate solution, shake, and let stand for exactly 2 min. Add 1.00 ml. of potassium ferricyanide solution, mix. and let stand for exactly 1 min. Add 0.20 ml. of the hydrogen peroxide solution, shake, and let stand for 3 min. Add 2.00 ml. of *n*-amyl alcohol, shake 30 sec., and centrifuge at high speed until the amyl alcohol layer is clear.

Transfer 1.00 ml. of the *n*-amyl alcohol layer to a small colorimeter tube, add 0.20 ml. of absolute ethanol, and mix. Determine fluorescence intensity with a fluorometer using an activation wavelength of 400 mμ and a fluorescence wavelength of 460 mμ.

Run a reagent blank using 5.00 ml. of trichloroacetic acid solution in place of the filtered sample extract. Subtract this reading from the sample reading.

To 15-ml. centrifuge tubes add 5.00 ml. of each Amprolium Standard Working solution, respectively, equivalent to 0.1, 0.2, and 0.4 μg. of amprolium, and continue in the same manner as with 5.0 ml. of the filtered sample extract.

Calculate the amprolium content of the samples. Sensitivity of the method is of the order of 0.05 p.p.m.

NOTE.—For enforcement of food additive regulation 121.1022, the tolerance of amprolium is as follows: 1 p.p.m. in uncooked poultry liver and kidney, 0.5 p.p.m. in uncooked poultry muscle, and zero p.p.m. in eggs.

DETERMINATION OF BUTYLATED HYDROXYANISOLE (BHA) AND BUTYLATED HYDROXYTOLUENE (BHT) IN BREAKFAST CEREALS

Apparatus. **Steam Still.**—A three-necked, 500-ml. distilling flask, outer joints $\overline{S}$ 24/40, inner joint $\overline{S}$ 34/45 (Pyrex #4960).

Steam Generator.—A 1000-ml. flat bottom boiling flask with $\overline{S}$ 29/42 joint, with glass hooks (Pyrex #4102).

Freidrichs Condenser.—Drip type, both joints $\overline{S}$ 24/40 (Pyrex #2460).

Kjeldahl Bulb.—Length of bulb 120 mm., diameter 55 mm., with two $\overline{S}$ 24/40 joints. (The joints must be sealed on the bulb and the bulb inserted between steam still and condenser.)

Steam Inlet Tube.—Enters the left neck of the steam still and is equipped with a $\overline{S}$ 24/40 inner joint and an 18/9 socket joint.

Steam Generator Connecting Tube.—Between steam generator and steam inlet. Equipped with a $\overline{S}$ 29/42 inner joint and an 18/9 ball joint.

Collecting Adapter.—For use below the Freidrichs condenser, with a $\overline{S}$ 24/40 outer joint.

Reagents. **Ethyl Alcohol (95 percent).**

Sodium Borate Solution.—Dissolve 2.0 g. of sodium borate ($Na_2B_4O_7 \cdot 10H_2O$) in 100 ml. of distilled water.

2,6-Dichloroquinonechloroimide Solution (Distillation Products Industries, Organic Chemical No. 2483, also named *N*,2,6-Trichloro-*p*-benzoquinoneimide).—Dissolve 0.010 g. in 100 ml. of absolute ethanol. This solution should be prepared fresh every three days and stored in dark.

2,2′-Bipyridine Solution.—Dissolve 0.200 g. of 2,2′-bipyridine in 1 ml. of 95 percent ethanol and dilute to 100 ml. with distilled water. Prepare fresh daily.

Ferric Chloride Solution.—Dissolve 0.200 g. in 100 ml. of distilled water. Prepare fresh daily.

n-Butanol Reagent.—Mix 5 parts of n-butanol with 2 parts absolute ethanol (v/v).

BHA Stock Solution.—Dissolve 0.1000 g. of BHA in absolute ethanol, and dilute to mark in a 100-ml. volumetric flask. Prepare an intermediate solution by diluting a 10-ml. aliquot to 100 ml. in a volumetric flask with distilled water and mixing.

BHA Standard Solution.—Place a 10-ml. aliquot of the intermediate solution in a 250-ml. volumetric flask, add 190 ml. of distilled water, and dilute to volume with 95 percent ethanol.

BHT Standard Solution.—Prepare in a similar manner. The intermediate of BHT requires that 40 ml. of 95 percent ethanol be added before dilution to the mark with water to keep the BHT in solution.

Procedure.—Set up apparatus, except that in the beginning the steam generator should be disconnected at the ball-and-socket joint. Place about 700 ml. of distilled water in the steam generator and heat it to boiling. Place a 250-ml. volumetric flask under the condenser so that the collecting adapter is well into its neck (about 200 ml. level).

Place 20 g. of the sample in the stream still, add 135 ml. of distilled water, and stopper the flask. Connect the steam generator and heat strongly, collecting 200 ml. of distillate over 10–20 min. Rinse the condenser with 50 ml. of 95 percent ethanol and make up to 250 ml. with 95 percent ethanol.

For BHA content, pipet a 10-ml. aliquot of the distillate into a small glass-stoppered bottle of approximately 20-ml. capacity. Pipet 10 ml. of 20 percent ethanol into a second bottle to serve as a blank. Add 2 ml. of sodium borate solution and 2 ml. of the 2,6-dichloroquinonechloroimide to each bottle and mix well. Measure the absorbance at 610 mμ in 1-cm. cells vs. the blank in not less than 5 nor more than 10 min. after mixing. Calculate p.p.m. of BHA as follows:

$$\text{p.p.m. BHA} = \frac{A}{B} \times 25$$

where A = absorbance of sample, and
B = absorbance of standard.

For BHT, pipet 10 ml. of 20 percent ethanol into a taped, 20-ml. glass-stoppered bottle. Pipet 10 ml. of the distillate into a second bottle. Pipet 5 ml. of 20 percent ethanol and 5 ml. of BHA standard solution into a third bottle. Pipet 5 ml. of BHA standard solution and 5 ml. of BHT standard solution into a fourth bottle. Add 2 ml. of 2,2'-bipyridine reagent and 2 ml. of ferric chloride solution to each bottle and mix well. Let stand for *exactly* 30 min., then add 5 ml. of n-butanol reagent, and mix well. *Exactly* 35 min. after adding the ferric chloride reagent, place solution in 1-cm. cells and measure absorbance, at 515 mμ, of each solution using the blank as the reference standard at *exactly* 38 min. after adding the ferric chloride reagent. Calculate BHT content as follows:

$$\text{p.p.m. BHT} = \frac{C - \dfrac{A \times D}{B} \times 25}{E - D}$$

where C = absorbance of sample,
D = absorbance of BHA standard, and
E = absorbance of BHA–BHT standard.

NOTE.—The absorbance of the BHA standard by the Gibbs method and BHA–BHT standard by the Emmerie-Engel method should be determined simultaneously with each pair of samples.

Food Additives Regulation. 121.1034 and 121.1035. The tolerance for BHA and BHT in dry cereals 50 p.p.m.

DETERMINATION OF CALCIUM DISODIUM ETHYLENEDIAMINETETRAACETIC ACID (CALCIUM DISODIUM EDTA)

This method is applicable to dressings (nonstandardized), fermented malt beverages, French dressing, mayonnaise, oleomargarine, potato salad, salad dressing, sandwich spread, sauces, pecan pie filling, and spice extractives in soluble carriers.

Principle.—The sample is clarified by filtering after treating with barium carbonate and filter aid. The filtrate is treated with magnesium to remove interferences; calcium EDTA is then determined in a filtered portion of the sample. In a strongly acidic solution calcium EDTA reacts with zirconium, chelating an amount of zirconium equivalent to the calcium EDTA present. The excess zirconium is determined by its reaction with Xylenol Orange producing a red-colored complex. The decrease in absorbance at 535 mμ is portional to the calcium EDTA present.

Reagents. Filter Aid.—Celite, J-M analytical filter aid.

Ammonium Hydroxide, concentrated reagent.

Barium Carbonate, Reagent Grade.

Hydrochloric Acid, 5 M.—Dilute 417 ml. of concentrated hydrochloric acid to 1 liter.

Magnesium Chloride Solution.—Dissolve 200 g. of magnesium chloride ($MgCl_2 \cdot 6H_2O$) in 800 ml. of distilled water.

Phosphoric Acid Solution.—Dilute 10 ml. of 85 percent phosphoric acid to 1 liter.

Hydroxylamine Hydrochloride.—Dissolve 100 g. of hydroxylamine hydrochloride in water and dilute to 1 liter.

Calcium Disodium EDTA Stock Solution.—Dissolve 1.101 g. of the calcium disodium EDTA dihydrate in water and dilute to 1 liter. One ml. is equivalent to 1 mg. of calcium disodium EDTA.

Calcium Disodium EDTA Standard Solution.—Dilute 25.0 ml. of the stock solution to volume in a 500-ml. volumetric flask.

Zirconium Stock Solution.—Dissolve 3.454 g. of zirconium oxychloride ($ZrOCl_2 \cdot 8H_2O$) in 100 ml. of concentrated hydrochloric acid and dilute to one liter. One ml. is approximately equivalent to 1 mg. of zirconium.

Zirconium Standard Solution.—Dilute 6 ml. of the zirconium stock solution and 20 ml. of concentrated hydrochloric acid to 1 liter. Prepare fresh daily.

Xylenol Orange Reagent.—Dissolve 1.00 g. of Xylenol Orange in anhydrous methanol and dilute to 1 liter with methanol.

Preparation of Sample.—Each sample of product should be blended in a Waring Blendor until no visible evidence of separation occurs. If products consist of an oil and water mixture, sampling should be done while the sample is still being stirred in the Blendor.

Procedure. Sample Recovery Curve.—Weigh 10.00 g. of sample into a series of 250-ml. beakers, and add 0, 5, 10, 12, 15, and 17 ml. of the calcium disodium EDTA standard solution from a buret. Dilute each to 100 ml. with distilled water. Add to each beaker, 4.0 g. of filter aid and 2.0 g. of barium carbonate. Mix with the aid of stirring rod and heat almost to boiling on a hot plate with continuous stirring. Transfer the samples to the steam bath and digest for one-half hour with stirring at 10-min.

intervals. Remove the beakers from the steam bath, cool, and filter on a Büchner funnel prepared with Whatman No. 3 (or equivalent paper) and 2.0 g. of filter aid added as a slurry. Collect the filtrate in a beaker, wash the contents of the funnel with four successive 25-ml. portions of water and combine washings with filtrate. Add 3.0 ml. of 5 M hydrochloric acid and 10 ml. of magnesium chloride solution. Neutralize the resulting solution to a pH of 9.0 with concentrated ammonium hydroxide, and add 0.5 ml. in excess. Then add 5.0 ml. of the phosphoric acid solution, stirring vigorously. Quantitatively transfer the filtrate to a 250-ml. volumetric flask and dilute to volume. Allow to stand for 1 hr. Filter 75–100 ml. of the above solutions through a Whatman No. 42 filter (or equivalent). Discard the first few ml. of filtrate and collect the remaining filtrate.

Determination of Calcium Disodium EDTA.—Add 4.0 ml. of 5 M hydrochloric acid, 5.0 ml. of 10 percent hydroxylamine hydrochloride, 5.0 ml. of the zirconium standard solution, and 4.0 ml. of the Xylenol Orange reagent to each of several 50-ml. volumetric flasks. Prepare a color blank for each sample by adding all reagents except the zirconium standard solution. Pipet a 25-ml. aliquot of the filtrate into the flasks to be used as sample color reagent flask and sample color reagent blank. Dilute each flask to volume and mix well. Allow to stand for 15 min. Determine the absorbance of each sample at 535 mμ using its color blank as the reference standard. Read the micrograms of calcium disodium EDTA from a standard curve.

Preparation of Standard Curve.—Prepare a 50-ml. volumetric flask as above for each sample. Also prepare another 50-ml. volumetric flask for each sample to be used as a color blank.

Dilute 34 ml. of the calcium disodium EDTA standard solution to 500 ml. with distilled water. Pipet into each previously prepared volumetric flask 0, 5, 10, 15, 20, and 25 ml. of the freshly prepared standard (equivalent to 0, 17, 34, 51, 68, and 85 μg. of calcium disodium EDTA), dilute to volume, and mix well.

Allow standards to stand for 15 min. Determine the absorbance at 535 mμ of each sample using its color blank as the reference standard. Plot the absorbance against the micrograms of calcium disodium EDTA on ordinary coordinate paper.

Calculation of Results.—

$$\text{p.p.m. Calcium disodium EDTA} = \frac{\text{micrograms of calcium disodium EDTA found}}{\text{grams of sample} \times \text{aliquot}}$$

NOTE.—Food Additives Regulation-121.1017. Tolerances for dressings, nonstandardized, 75 p.p.m.; fermented malt beverages, 25 p.p.m.; French dressing, 75 p.p.m.; mayonnaise, 75 p.p.m.; oleomargarine, 75 p.p.m.; potato salad, 100 p.p.m.; pecan pie filling, 100 p.p.m.; salad dressing, 75 p.p.m.; sandwich spread, 100 p.p.m.; sauces, 75 p.p.m.; spice extractives in soluble carriers, 60 p.p.m.

DETERMINATION OF COUMARONE-INDENE RESINS ON CITRUS FRUITS

Coumarone-indene is one of the main components used as a protective surface coating material for citrus fruits to reduce shrinkage during transit and storage.

Reagents. Chloroform.

Concentrated Sulfuric Acid.

Coumarone-indene Stock Solution.—Weigh 1.00 g. of the resin and transfer to a 100-ml. volumetric flask. Dissolve in chloroform and dilute to volume.

Coumarone-indene Intermediate Solution.—A 10-ml. aliquot of the stock solution is diluted to 100 ml. with chloroform.

Coumarone-indene Standard Solution.—A 5-ml. aliquot of the intermediate solution is further dilute to 100 ml. with chloroform. Each 1-ml. aliquot will contain 50 μg. of resin.

Procedure.—The resin is removed from the coated citrus by tumbling a weighed amount of fruit (usually 3 or 4 fruits) in a glass jar for 2 min. with 200 ml. of chloroform. Two separate aliquots of 1 and 2 ml. of the strippings are used for the analysis. Add 10.0 ml. of concentrated sulfuric acid to each sample and heat on a steam bath for approximately 20 min. Transfer the colored acid solution to matched tubes and read absorbance at 505 mμ. Concentration of the resin is determined by referring to the standard curve.

Prepare a standard curve using 0, 1.0, 3.0, and 5.0 ml. of the standard solution (0, 50, 150, 250 μg. of resin) and 5 ml. of chloroform in the blank. Add 10 ml. of concentrated sulfuric acid and repeat procedure as above. Plot absorbance readings against concentration of the resin on ordinary graph paper.

NOTE.—Due to citrus peel oils, a correction factor of 10 percent must be applied to the resin recovery value. The fungicides, diphenyl and orthophenylphenol, which may be present as a residue on the peel, do not interfere with the method. Food Additive Regulation 121.1050. The tolerance for coumarone-indene resin on citrus fruits is 200 p.p.m.

DETERMINATION OF FORMALDEHYDE IN MAPLE SYRUP[12]

Reagent. **Nash's Reagent.**—Dissolve 0.50 g. ammonium acetate in a small amount of water, then add 3.0 ml. acetic acid, 2.0 ml. of acetylacetone, and dilute to 1 liter with water.

Procedure.—Transfer 20–25 ml. of maple syrup to a tared 50-ml. micro-Kjeldahl flask having a standard taper 19/38 outer joint. Connected to the flask is a delivery tube having a ₮ 19/38 inner joint, bent at a right angle and provided with a drawn-out tip. Heat the maple syrup at a very slow rate and collect 2–3 ml. of distillate. Transfer 1.0 ml. of the distillate to a colorimeter tube (13 mm.), and then add 1.0 ml. distilled water and 2.0 ml. Nash's reagent. Heat the tube and contents at 37°C. for 30 min. Cool and read absorbance at 415 mμ. The concentration of formaldehyde (p.p.m.) in the syrup is determined by referring to a standard curve.

Preparation of Standard Curve.—Prepare a standard curve by adding sufficient formaldehyde to maple syrup to produce formaldehyde concentrations of 1, 2, 4, 6, and 8 mg. per g. of syrup. Each of the standards are distilled slowly and the first 2–3 ml. of distillate collected. Develop color as described above. Plot absorbance readings against concentration of formaldehyde.

A blank correction is made for the water and reagent by substituting 1 ml. water for 1 ml. syrup distillate. A blank should also be run for test sample of maple syrup.

DETERMINATION OF SEQUESTRENE (DISODIUM DIHYDROGEN EDTA) IN SALAD DRESSING

This method is applicable to French dressing, mayonnaise and sandwich spread.

Reagents. **Aqueous Ammonium Hydroxide (28 percent).**

Dimethylglyoxime.—Dissolve 1.5 g. in ethanol and dilute to 100 ml.

Nickel Solution.—Dissolve 13.3 g. nickel(II) sulfate hexahydrate in distilled water and dilute to 1 liter.

Potassium Dithiooxalate Solution.—Dissolve 0.1 g. in distilled water and dilute to 100 ml. Prepare fresh daily.

Sequestrene Stock Solution.—A sample of 0.382 g. of disodium dihydrogen EDTA· 2H$_2$O (mol. wt. 372) is placed in a 100-ml. volumetric flask and diluted to volume with distilled water. This is equivalent to 0.300 g. of Sequestrene AA (mol. wt. 292).

[12] Nash, T., Biochem. J., **55**, 416, 1953.

Sequestrene Working Standard.—A 10-ml. aliquot of the Sequestreme stock solution is diluted to 100 ml. with distilled water. Each ml. of solution contains 0.30 mg. of Sequestrene AA.

Procedure.—Weigh 30.0-g. samples and thoroughly mix with 40 ml. distilled water.

TABLE 50-1. TOLERANCES FOR SOME FOOD ADDITIVES

Substance	Food Additive Regulation (21 CFR 121)			
	Subpart	Section	Tolerance	Application
Acetone	D	121.1042	30 p.p.m.	Spice oleoresins
Amprolium	D	121.1020	1 p.p.m.	Uncooked poultry liver and kidney
Amprolium	D	121.1020	0.5 p.p.m.	Uncooked poultry muscle
Amprolium	D	121.1020	0	Eggs
Benzoic acid	B	121.101	0.1%	Processed foods[a]
Boric acid	A	121.90	0.1 mg./day	Processed foods[a]
Butylated hydroxyamisole	D	121.1035	50 p.p.m.	Dry cereals
Butylated hydroxytoluene	D	121.1034	50 p.p.m.	Dry cereals
Calcium disodium EDTA	D	121.1017	75 p.p.m.	Dressings, non-standardized
Calcium disodium EDTA	D	121.1017	25 p.p.m.	Fermented malt beverages
Calcium disodium EDTA	D	121.1017	75 p.p.m.	French dressing
Calcium disodium EDTA	D	121.1017	75 p.p.m.	Mayonnaise
Calcium disodium EDTA	D	121.1017	75 p.p.m.	Oleomargarine
Calcium disodium EDTA	D	121.1017	100 p.p.m.	Potato salad
Calcium disodium EDTA	D	121.1017	100 p.p.m.	Pecan pie filling
Calcium disodium EDTA	D	121.1017	75 p.p.m.	Salad dressing
Calcium disodium EDTA	D	121.1017	100 p.p.m.	Sandwich spread
Calcium disodium EDTA	D	121.1017	75 p.p.m.	Sauces
Captan	D	121.1061	100 p.p.m.	Raisins[b]
Coumarone-indene	D	121.1050	200 p.p.m.	Citrus fruits
Formaldehyde	D	121.1079	2 p.p.m.	Maple syrup
Disodium EDTA	D	121.1056	75 p.p.m.	French dressing
Disodium EDTA	D	121.1056	75 p.p.m.	Mayonnaise
Disodium EDTA	D	121.1056	100 p.p.m.	Sandwich spread
Hexane	D	121.1045	25 p.p.m.	Spice oleoresins
Isopropyl alcohol	D	121.1043	50 p.p.m.	Spice oleoresins
Methyl alcohol	D	121.1044	50 p.p.m.	Spice oleoresins
Methylene chloride	D	121.1039	30 p.p.m.	Spice oleoresins
Sodium nitrite	D	121.1064	200 p.p.m.	Meat curing preparations

[a] For method, see "Preservatives" in this chapter.
[b] For method, see "Pesticides" in this chapter.

Adjust pH of the slurry to 6.5, and then dilute to a volume of 100 ml. Add 15 ml. of the nickel solution and allow to stand for 10 min. Add 5 ml. of the ammonium hydroxide solution and let stand for 5 min. Then 15 ml. of dimethylglyoxime solution is added, and the solution allowed to stand for 5 min. for complete precipitation to occur. Five g. of Darco KB are added and the mixture shaken for 1 hr. The suspension is then filtered through Whatman No. 12 (or the equivalent) filter paper. To 60 ml. of the filtrate, 3 ml. concentrated hydrochloric acid and 1 g. Darco KB are added and the mixture is shaken for 5 min. The suspension is again filtered through Whatman No. 12 filter paper. To 52.5 ml. of the filtrate is added 10 ml. of the potassium dithiooxalate solution and the absorbance of the solution read at 508 $m\mu$ against a reagent blank. Determine the concentration of Sequestrene by referring to a standard curve.

Preparation of Standard Curve.—To 100-ml. volumetric flasks add 5, 10, and 15 ml. of the Sequestrene working standard, corresponding to 1.5, 3.0 and 4.5 mg. of Sequestrene AA. Add 80 ml. distilled water, adjust to pH 6.5, and dilute to volume. The solutions are then carried through the same procedure as described above beginning with the addition of the nickel solution. Plot absorbance against mg. of Sequestrene AA used in the reading step (62.5 ml.).

Food Additive Regulation 121.1056. Tolerances for sandwich spread, 100 p.p.m.; sauces, 75 p.p.m.; dressing, nonstandardized, 75 p.p.m.

FOOD ADDITIVES—INDIRECT

In contrast to the food processor who intentionally adds a chemical to his food product, the manufacturer of packaging materials has as his problem the characterization of all components which may migrate to the food contained within the packaging material. The exact composition of the migrants can only be determined by lengthy extraction studies with different solvents. In many cases a practicable method of analysis is not available because the amounts of migrants are in the p.p.m. range. As a consequence, it is now an accepted practice to determine total extractables by gravimetric methods, and to further divide these extractables into chloroform-soluble and chloroform-insoluble extractables.

DETERMINATION OF EXTRACTABLES FROM RESINOUS AND POLYMERIC COATINGS FROM PACKAGING MATERIALS (FOOD ADDITIVE REGULATION 121.2514)

Reagents. **Water.**—All water used in extraction procedure should be freshly deionized distilled water.

Heptane.—Reagent grade, freshly redistilled before use, using only material boiling at 208°F.

Alcohol, 8 percent by Volume.—Prepared from undenatured 95 percent ethyl alcohol diluted with deionized distilled water.

Chloroform.—Reagent Grade. Freshly redistilled before use or a grade having a consistently low blank.

Equipment.—**Pressure Cooker,** 21-quart capacity with pressure gauge, safety release and removable rack, 12.5 in. inside diameter and 11 in. inside height, 20 p.s.i. safe operating pressure.

Rinsing Equipment, soda fountain pressure-type hot water, metal tube attached to a hot water line delivering 190°F. water and bent so as to direct a stream of water upward.

Water Bath, range 100°F.–212°F. ± 2°F.

Constant Temperature Chamber. 70°F. ± 2°F.

Procedure.—**Selection of Extractant Conditions.**—It is necessary to ascertain the type of food product (Table 50-2) that is being packaged before proceeding with the test procedure recommended by the F & DA for determining the amount of extractives (Table 50-3). Aqueous products at the temperatures and time conditions shown are for the most severe "conditions of use." Aqueous products with free oil or fat and water-oil emulsions (Types III, IV-A, and VII) will require determinations of both water and heptane extractants. Low-moisture fats and oils (Type V) require only the heptane extractant. Alcoholic beverages (Type VI-A) require only the 8 percent alcohol extractant.

Selection of Coated-container Samples.—For consumer-sized containers up to 1 gal., quadruplicate samples of representative containers should be selected from the lot to be examined.

Cleaning Procedure Preliminary to Determining the Amount of Extractables from Coated Containers.—The samples must be carefully rinsed to remove extraneous material prior to the actual extraction procedure. Invert the container over the top of the fountain and direct a strong stream of hot water against the bottom and all sides for 1 min., drain, and allow to dry.

Exposure Conditions. (See Table 50-3.)

Determinative Step.

(*i*) *Total Extractables.*—Evaporate the extractant from Table 50-3 to about 100 ml. in a Pyrex flask. Transfer to a clean, tared platinum dish and wash the flask 3 times with the solvent used in the extractant procedure. Evaporate to a few milliliters on a low-temperature hot plate. The last few milliliters should be evaporated in an oven maintained at 212°F. Cool the platinum dish in a desiccator for 30 min., weigh the residue to nearest milligram (*e*). Calculate the extractives in milligrams per square inch and in p.p.m. for the particular size of container being tested and for the specific food-simulating solvent used.

Water and 8 percent alcohol:

$$\text{Milligrams extractive per square inch} = \frac{e}{s}$$

$$\text{Extractives residue} = Ex = \frac{(e)(a)(1000)}{(c)(s)}$$

Heptane:

$$\text{Milligrams extractive per square inch} = \frac{e}{(s)(F)}$$

$$\text{Extractives residue} = Ex = \frac{(e)(a)(1000)}{(c)(s)(F)}$$

where e = extractives residues in p.p.m. for any container size,
Ex = milligrams extractives per sample tested,
a = total coated area, including closure, in square inches,
c = water capacity of container, in grams,
s = surface of coated area test, in square inches,
F = five, the ratio of the amount of extractives removed from a coated container by heptane under exaggerated time-temperature test conditions compared to the amount extracted by a fat or oil from a container tested under exaggerated conditions of thermal sterilization and use, and
e' = chloroform-soluble extractives residue (substituted for e in the above formulas when necessary).

If, when calculated by the above formulas, the concentration of extractives residue (*Ex*) exceeds 50 p.p.m., one should determine chloroform-soluble extractives residue (*i.e.*, ratio of organic to inorganic extractables).

(*ii*) *Chloroform-Soluble Extractives Residue.*—The dried residue is extracted twice with two 50-ml. portions of chloroform and the extract filtered through Whatman No. 41 filter paper into a tared platinum evaporating dish and dried as before. Weigh the residue (*e'*). The value is substituted for *e* in the formulas above. The chloroform-soluble extractables may be characterized by infrared spectrometry or chemical methods.

(*iii*) *Chloroform-Insoluble Extractables.*—To determine the inorganic matter, ash the residue in the platinum evaporating dish by heating over a Meker burner to destroy the organic matter and hold at red heat for 1 min. Cool for 3 min., and place in a desiccator for 30 min. Weigh to the nearest 0.1 mg. Determine the composition of this inorganic residue by emission spectroscopy or chemical methods.

TABLE 50-2. TYPES OF FOOD[a]

   I. Nonacid (pH above 5.0) aqueous products; may contain salt or sugar or both, and including oil-in-water emulsions of low or high fat content.
  II. Acidic (pH 5.0 or below), aqueous products; may contain salt or sugar or both, including oil-in-water emulsions of low or high fat content.
 III. Aqueous, acid or nonacid products containing free oil or fat; may contain salt, and including water-in-oil emulsions of low or high fat content.
  IV. Dairy products and modifications:
      A. Water in-oil emulsion, high or low fat.
      B. Oil-in-water emulsion, high or low fat.
   V. Low-moisture fats and oils.
  VI. Beverages:
      A. Containing alcohol.
      B. Nonalcoholic.
 VII. Bakery products.
VIII. Dry solids (no end test required).

   [a] Tables 50-1 and 50-2 are portions of Food Additive Regulation 121.2514, Resinous and Polymeric Coatings, Code of Federal Regulations, Title 21 (21 CFR).

FATS, OILS, WAXES

See Vol. IIB, Chapter 33, pp. 1411–1482
Instrumental Methods

   I. Refractive Index, p. 1447.
  II. Polyunsaturated Fatty Acids (Spectrophotometric), p. 1470.
 III. Gas Chromatography, p. 1475.
  IV. Isolated *Trans*-isomers. Infrared spectrometry, p. 1478.

MEAT AND MEAT PRODUCTS

In the processing of meat products certain ingredients are added to meat, *e.g.*, the curing process involves the use of salt, nitrate, and/or nitrite. Cereal flours, milk powder, and curing adjuncts are also used in some prepared meat products. An analysis for these materials is necessary not only for quality control but also to determine that the product will meet certain governmental regulatory requirements.

TABLE 50-3. TEST PROCEDURES FOR DETERMINING THE AMOUNT OF EXTRACTIVES FROM RESINOUS OR POLYMERIC COATINGS, USING SOLVENTS SIMULATING TYPES OF FOODS AND BEVERAGES[a]

Condition of Use	Types of Food (see Table 50-2)	Time and Temperature of Extractant		
		Water	Heptane[b,c]	% Alcohol
A. High temperature, heat sterilized (e.g., over 212°F.)	I, IV-B	250°F., 2 hr.	—	—
	III, IV-A, VII	250°F., 2 hr.	150°F., 2 hr.	—
B. Boiling water sterilized	II	212°F., 30 min.	—	—
	III, VII	212°F., 30 min.	120°F., 30 min.	—
C. Hot filled or pasteurized above 150°F.	II, IV-B	Fill boiling, cool to 100°F.	—	—
	III, IV-A	Fill boiling, cool to 100°F.	120°F., 15 min.	—
	V	—	120°F., 15 min.	—
D. Hot filled or pasteurized below 150°F.	II, IV-B, VI-B	150°F., 2 hr.	—	—
	III, IV-A	150°F., 2 hr.	100°F., 30 min.	—
	V	—	100°F., 30 min.	—
	VI-A	—	—	150°F., 2 hr.
E. Room temperature filled and stored (no thermal treatment in the container	II, IV-B, VI-B	120°F., 24 hr	—	—
	III, IV-A	120°F., 24 hr.	70°F., 30 min.	—
	V, VII	—	70°F., 30 min.	—
	VI-A	—	—	120°F., 24 hr.
F. Refrigerated storage (no thermal treatment in the container	I, II, III, IV-A IV-B, VI-B, VII	70°F., 48 hr.	—	—
	VI-A	—	—	70°F., 48 hr.
G. Frozen storage (no thermal treatment in the container)	I, II, III, IV-B VII	70°F., 24 hr.	—	—
H. Frozen Storage: ready-prepared foods intended to be reheated in container at time of use:				
1. Aqueous or oil-in-water emulsion of high or low fat	I, II, IV-B	212°F., 30 min.	—	—
2. Aqueous, high or low free oil or fat	III, IV-A, VII	212°F., 30 min.	120°F., 30 min.	—

[a] Tables 50-1 and 50-2 are portions of Food Additive Regulation 121.2514, Resinous and Polymeric Coatings, Code of Federal Regulations, Title 21 (21 CFR).

[b] Heptane extractant not to be used on wax-lined containers.

[c] Heptane extractivity results must be divided by a factor of five in arriving at the extractivity for a food product.

DETERMINATION OF SODIUM CHLORIDE (SALT)

Reagent.—Silver Nitrate, 0.1 M.—Dissolve slightly more than theoretical quantity of AgNO$_3$ (16.99 g. per liter) in halogen-free water and dilute to volume. Dilute about 40 ml., accurately measured, of the silver nitrate solution with about 100 ml. of halogen-free water, heat the solution and add slowly, with continuous stirring, diluted hydrochloric acid until precipitation of the silver is complete. Boil the mixture cautiously for about 5 min.; then allow to stand in the dark until the precipitate has settled and the supernatant has become clear. Transfer the precipitate quantitatively to a tared filtering crucible, and wash it with small portions of water slightly acidified with nitric acid. Dry the precipitate at 110°C. to constant weight. Each 14.332 mg. of silver chloride obtained is equivalent to 1 ml. of 0.1 M silver nitrate.

Procedure.—A 10-g. sample of meat is comminuted in a Waring Blendor with 125 ml. halogen-free water made to 200 ml., mixed and filtered. Transfer a 10-ml. aliquot to a 250-ml. beaker, dilute to about 100 ml. and add 5 ml. of nitric acid (1:4). Titrate with 0.1 M silver nitrate on a titration apparatus using silver-mercurous sulfate electrodes. Add the silver nitrate rapidly at first, with stirring, and then dropwise until a maximum deflection per drop is obtained.

This method is useful for colored solutions and unfiltered blended samples may be titrated without appreciably affecting the results.

DETERMINATION OF NITRITE

Reagents. Griess-Ilosvay Reagent. *Solution A.*—Dissolve 0.5 g. of sulfanilic acid in 30 ml. glacial acetic acid and 120 ml. distilled water.

Solution B.—Dissolve 0.1 g. α-naphthylamine in 120 ml. distilled water by boiling, cool, and add 30 ml. glacial acetic acid.

Solution C.—Mix the two solutions and filter if necessary.

Nitrite Standard Solution.—Dissolve 0.493 g. of pure sodium nitrite in nitrite-free water and dilute to 1 liter. Dilute 10 ml. of this solution to 1 liter, so that 1 ml. of final solution = 0.001 mg. nitrite (as N).

NOTE.—The best range for the test is from 0.0005 to 0.001 mg. N.

Procedure.—Mix 5 g. of finely comminuted meat with 40 ml. of water. Heat to 80°C. and transfer quantitatively to a 500-ml. volumetric flask using an additional 260 ml. of hot water. Place the flask on a steam bath and let stand for 2 hr., with occasional shaking. Then add 5 ml. saturated mercuric chloride solution, cook, dilute to mark with nitrite-free water, and mix. Filter and determine the nitrite on a suitable aliquot of the filtrate. The aliquot is diluted to the mark in a 50-ml. volumetric flask, 2 ml. of the reagent is added, and the contents are mixed thoroughly. Allow to stand for 1 hr. and determine the absorbance at a wavelength of 520 mμ.

Calculate the results as sodium nitrite in p.p.m. by comparison with the standard curve prepared by measuring the color developed in a similar manner in solutions of known amounts of nitrite.

DETERMINATION OF NITRATE[13]

Reagents. Brucine Solution.—Dissolve 10 g. brucine alkaloid in approximately 80 ml. of 95 percent ethanol, with the addition of 3 ml. of distilled water. Bring to a volume of 100 ml. with 95 percent ethanol.

Phosphoric Acid–Sulfuric Acid Mixture.—Mix with care equal volumes of orthophosphoric acid, 85 percent, and concentrated sulfuric acid. Cool before using.

Urea Solution.—Saturated solution of urea in water.

Nitrate Standard Solution.—Dissolve 1.00 g. sodium nitrate in water and dilute to 1 liter. Next prepare a more dilute standard solution by diluting the above solution 1:10.

Procedure.—Thoroughly mix 10 g. of sample with 40 ml. distilled water for 3 min. in a Waring Blendor. Transfer the slurry quantitatively to a 250-ml. beaker, using a maximum of 20 ml. water. Heat on a steam bath for 1 hr., with occasional stirring. Cool and filter the extract through Whatman No. 42 filter paper (or equivalent) into

[13] Landmann, W. A., Saeed, M., and Phi, K., J. Assoc. Offic. Agr. Chemists, **43**, 531, 1960.

a 100-ml. volumetric flask. Wash beaker, filter, and precipitate thoroughly with successive 10-ml. portions of water. Add enough water to bring to volume and mix. Prepare a reagent blank and sample blank by using 1.0 ml. water and 1.0 ml. sample solution, respectively. To each of the tubes add 0.1 ml. saturated urea solution and 1.0 ml. phosphoric acid–sulfuric acid mixture. Allow to stand at room temperature for 5 min.; then cool in a water bath (10°C.). Add 1.0 ml. brucine reagent to all solutions except the sample blank. To the sample blank add 1.0 ml. of 95 percent ethanol. Add 9.0 ml. of the acid mixture, mix thoroughly, and allow to stand for 1 min. The temperature of the solutions should not rise above room temperature.

Place all tubes simultaneously into a vigorously boiling water bath. After 2 min., remove all tubes at the same time and immediately place them into the cold water bath until they reach room temperature (3–5 min.). Transfer suitable portions of the solution to a cell and determine absorbance at wavelength of 425 mμ, setting the instrument to zero absorbance with blank of water.

Determine nitrate present by comparison with standard curve prepared as follows: Dilute 0.50, 1.0, 2.0, 4.0, 6.0, 8.0 and 10.0 ml. of the diluted standard solution to the mark in a series of 10-ml. volumetric flasks. Treat 10 ml. of each solution with brucine and proceed as outlined above.

METALS AND ELEMENTS

PREPARATION IN FOOD SAMPLE FOR ESTIMATION OF ELEMENTS

Into a 300-ml. Pyrex Kjeldahl flask, place a 5- to 10-g. sample, 20 ml. concentrated nitric acid, and 20 ml. water. Boil for approximately 10 min., cool, and cautiously add 10 ml. concentrated sulfuric acid. Boil again. Maintain oxidizing conditions during digestion by adding small quantities of nitric acid whenever liquid begins to darken. Continue digestion until organic matter is oxidized and white fumes are in evidence. Cool, add 10 ml. saturated ammonium oxalate solution, and boil until fumes of sulfur dioxide are again produced. The ammonium oxalate treatment assists in removing nitro compounds from the solution so that the final solution is colorless. A reagent blank is prepared by the same procedure.

METHODS OF ANALYSIS

DETERMINATION OF ARSENIC[14]

Reagents. Standard Arsenic Solution.—Dissolve 0.132 g. arsenious oxide in 2 ml. M sodium hydroxide, dilute with approximately 25 ml. water, neutralize with 2 ml. M hydrochloric acid, and dilute to 100 ml. Dilute 5 ml. of this solution to 1 liter with water. (1 ml. contains 0.005 mg. arsenic.)

Chloride-hydrazine-bromide Reagent.—Mix together 100 g. sodium chloride, 10 g. hydrazine sulfate, and 0.4 g. potassium bromide.

Ammonium Molybdate Solution.—Dissolve 10 g. ammonium molybdate $(NH_4)_6Mo_7O_{24} \cdot 4H_2O$ in 2.5 M sulfuric acid and dilute to a final volume of 1 liter.

Molybdate-Hydrazine Reagent.—Dilute 10 ml. of the ammonium molybdate solution with 80 ml. of water, add 1 ml. of 0.15 percent hydrazine sulfate, and dilute to 100 ml. Solution should be freshly prepared.

Sand.—Clean white sea sand (30-mesh) by washing successively with hot 10 percent

[14] Eastoe, J. E., and Eastoe, B., J. Sci. Food Agr., **4,** 310, 1953.

sodium hydroxide solution, hot nitric acid, and hot water. Dry the sand in an oven.

Distillation Apparatus.—Use either Ramberg-Sjöström arsenic apparatus or 300-ml. Kjeldahl flask provided with a 13-mm. outlet tube having a constricted tip (*ca.* 5 mm.), and connected with the flask by means of a rubber stopper. The rubber stopper must be previously boiled in 10 percent NaOH for 15 min. and then in HCl for 15 min.

Procedure.—Wet oxidize 5 g. of the sample in a Kjeldahl flask. Add 30 ml. of saturated ammonium oxalate solution to the digest and heat until fumes of SO_3 evolve. Cool and add 20 ml. of water while gently swirling flask. Cool, dry neck of flask over a small flame, add 5 g. of the chloride-hydrazine-bromide reagent and 10 ml. of hydrochloric acid. Immediately distill into a flask containing 10 ml. of dilute nitric acid (1:5) with the end of the condenser tube immersed in the acid solution. Collect about 10 ml. of the distillate, transfer quantitatively to a 50-ml. beaker, add 10 ml. concentrated nitric acid and evaporate to dryness on a hot plate. Dissolve the residue in the molybdate-hydrazine reagent, transfer to a 25-ml. volumetric flask, and dilute to volume with the reagent. Mix and heat in a boiling water bath for 10 min. Cool and determine the absorbance of the solution at 845 mμ. A blank should be determined at the same time.

Prepare the standard curve using 0, 1.0, 2.0, 3.0, 4.0 and 5.0 ml. of the standard arsenic solution (0–25 μg. of arsenic). Evaporate each volume with nitric acid to dryness, dilute to 25 ml. with the reagent, mix, and heat in boiling water for 10 min. Cool and read at 845 mμ.

NOTE.—Precautions should be taken to remove residual arsenic from all glassware before use for the determination.

DETERMINATION OF COPPER BY THE CARBAMATE METHOD[15]

Reagents. Carbamate Solution.—Dissolve 1 g. sodium diethyldithiocarbamate in 100 ml. of redistilled water, and filter.

Citrate-EDTA Solution.—Dissolve 20 g. ammonium citrate and 5 g. ethylenediaminetetraacetic acid (EDTA) in 100 ml. of redistilled water.

Ammonium Hydroxide, concentrated.

Copper Standard Solution.—Dissolve 0.3928 g. copper sulfate ($CuSO_4 \cdot 5H_2O$) in redistilled water and dilute to 1 liter. Prepare working standard by diluting stock olution one hundred times (1 ml. contains 1 μg. of copper).

Procedure.—Weigh a sample containing 10–20 g. of solids and ash at about 600°C. in a silica dish. Extract the ash by heating with 10 ml. of mixture of hydrochloric acid, nitric acid, and water (2:1:3). Quantitatively transfer the extract to a separatory funnel with water (*ca.* 40 ml.). Cool and add 10 ml. citrate-EDTA reagent. Add 2 drops of cresol red, and 6 M ammonium hydroxide dropwise until color turns pink. Cook, add 1 ml. of the carbamate solution, and mix. Add 10 ml. carbon tetrachloride from a buret, stopper the separatory funnel, and shake vigorously for 2 min. Allow the layers to separate and drain the lower layer through cotton pledget into a flask. Re-extract with 5 ml. carbon tetrachloride and add the lower layer to the first extract. Mix the combined extracts and determine the absorbance at 500 mμ, using a 1-cm. cell.

For the standard curve, use volumes of the working standard equivalent to 0–50 μg. copper, diluting in each case to a total volume of 50 ml. Add 10 ml. of the citrate-EDTA solution and proceed as above. Plot absorbance against micrograms of copper on ordinary graph paper. Each reading is equivalent to the number of micrograms of copper per 15 ml. of solvent.

[15] Cheng, K. L., and Bray, R. H., Anal. Chem., **25,** 655, 1953.

DETERMINATION OF LEAD BY THE DITHIZONE METHOD[16]

This method is applicable to all foods in which no tin is encountered.

Reagents.—All reagents must be free from lead. The following "lead-free" reagents are commercially available: hydrochloric acid, sulfuric acid, nitric acid, citric acid, ammonium hydroxide, and potassium cyanide.

Nitric Acid, 1 percent.—Dilute 10 ml. concentrated nitric acid to 1 liter with redistilled water.

Sodium Hexametaphosphate Solution, 10 percent.

Potassium Cyanide.—A 10 percent (w/v) solution in water.

Chloroform.—Shake 250 ml. of chloroform with 25 ml. of water containing 1 ml. of 10 percent potassium cyanide solution and 20 drops of 5 M ammonium hydroxide. Allow phases to separate and discard the aqueous phase. Wash chloroform with water. Filter the chloroform.

Diphenythiocarbazone (Dithizone) Stock Solution.—Dissolve 100 mg. dithizone in chloroform and dilute to 100 ml. Filter, and store in a refrigerator.

Dithizone Working Solution.—Shake 6 ml. of the dithizone solution (0.17 percent) with 9 ml. water and 1 ml. of 5 M ammonium hydroxide solution. Discard the lower layer and clear the remaining aqueous layer by filtering. This solution must be freshly prepared on day of use.

Ammoniacal Sulfite-Cyanide Solution.—Mix 350 ml. of ammonium hydroxide (sp. gr. 0.90), 75 ml. of 2 percent (w/v) sodium sulfate (Na$_2$SO$_4$) solution, 30 ml. of 10 percent potassium cyanide solution, and 605 ml. of water.

Ammonium Citrate Solution.—Dissolve 25 g. and dilute to 100 ml. with water.

If sample contains appreciable amounts of calcium, magnesium or phosphate, the following additional reagents are needed.

Sulfuric Acid.—Add 1 volume of concentrated sulfuric acid to 1 volume of water.

Perchloric Acid.

Sodium Iodide Solution.—Dissolve 20 g. sodium iodide and dilute to 100 ml. with water.

Sodium Metabisulfite Solution.—Prepare, fresh, a 1.25 percent solution in water.

Diethylammonium Diethylthiocarbamate Solution.—Dissolve 1 g. of the reagent in 100 ml. of chloroform and store in an amber-colored bottle. Discard after 1 week.

Preparation of Sample.—Sample should not contain more than 40 μg. of lead. If appreciable amounts of calcium are present, sulfuric acid should not be used and should be replaced by perchloric acid. After the completion of oxidation by wet-ashing, cool, and add 5 ml. of water. Transfer quantitatively to a 100-ml. Erlenmeyer flask, rinsing twice with 1-ml. portions of water. Add 10 ml. of 5 M hydrochloric acid to the Kjeldahl flask, boil and drain into the Erlenmeyer flask, rinsing with two 1-ml. portions of water. If the contents in the Kjeldahl flask contain insoluble matter, filter solution and washings through a Whatman No. 1 (or equivalent) filter paper.

Procedure. Method A.—Use for samples in which concentrations of calcium, magnesium, and phosphate are low. Cool the solution, and add 5–10 ml. of the ammonium citrate and 10 ml. of fresh sodium hexametaphosphate solution. Add sufficient ammonium hydroxide solution to bring solution to a pH 9.0–9.5 (blue-green with thymol blue). Add 1 ml. of potassium cyanide solution *and 1 ml. of 20 percent hydroxylamine reagent, if much iron is present.* Transfer the solution to a separatory funnel containing 10 ml. of chloroform, rinsing with water to produce a volume of approximately 50 ml. in the aqueous layer. Add 0.5 ml. of dithizone working solution and shake for 1 min. If the lower layer is red, add dithizone working solution until the color, after shaking, is purple,

[16] Society of Analytical Chemistry (Analytical Methods Committee), Analyst, **84**, 127, 1959.

blue, or green. Transfer the lower layer to another separatory funnel and wash with 1 or 2 ml. of chloroform. Continue extracting the lead from the first separatory funnel by shaking successively 3 ml. of chloroform and 0.2 ml. of dithizone working solution for 0.5 min. Allow the chloroform layer to separate and add each extract to the second separatory funnel. The final extract should be green. Add 10 ml. of the dilute nitric acid to the combined extracts and shake for 1 min. Reject the chloroform layer and to the acid extract add 30 ml. of ammoniacal sulfate–cyanide solution, exactly 10 ml. of chloroform, and 0.5 ml. of dithizone working solution. Shake vigorously for 1 min. and measure the absorbance of the filtered lower layer against chloroform in a 1-cm. cell at 520 mμ.

Method B.—Use for samples in which concentrations of calcium, magnesium, and phosphate are high. To the prepared solution add 2 drops of methyl red solution and make just alkaline with ammonium hydroxide solution. Make the solution just acid with 5 M hydrochloric acid and add a further 10 ml. Warm the solution to 60°C., add 2 ml. of sodium iodide solution, and reduce any liberated iodine with 2 ml. of fresh sodium metabisulfite solution. Cool, transfer to a separatory funnel and adjust the volume to 50–75 ml. in order to produce an acid concentration of approximately one molar with respect to hydrochloric acid. Add 10 ml. of carbamate reagent and shake vigorously for 0.5 min. Transfer the chloroform layer to a 100-ml. Erlenmeyer flask. Wash the aqueous layer twice with small amounts of chloroform without mixing, and then repeat extraction with 10 ml. of carbamate reagent, adding the washings and extract to the main extract in the flask. To the combined extracts, add 2.0 ml. of dilute sulfuric acid and evaporate the chloroform. Add 0.5 ml. of perchloric acid and heat until the fuming solution is clear and colorless. Cool, add 10 ml. of water and 5 ml. of 5 M hydrochloric acid, boil for 1 min., cool, and add 2 ml. of ammonium citrate solution.

Continue as in Method A above at the sentence "Add sufficient ammonium hydroxide to bring solution to a pH 9.0–9.5."

A reagent blank involving the whole procedure must be performed.

Preparation of Standard Curve.—Dissolve 1.60 g. of lead nitrate in water, add 100 ml. of concentrated nitric acid, and dilute to a final volume of 1 liter (Solution A). Prepare stock solution containing equivalent of 10 μg. of lead per ml. by diluting 1 volume of Solution A to 100 volumes with water. To a series of separatory funnels add 0, 1.0, 1.5, 2.0, 3.0, and 4.0 ml. of stock solution and dilute each to 10 ml. with 1 percent acid. Proceed as described above under "Procedure." Measure the absorbance of each chloroform solution against chloroform with a spectrometer at 520 mμ. Plot absorbance against micrograms of lead on ordinary graph paper.

MILK AND MILK PRODUCTS

PREPARATION OF SAMPLE FOR ANALYSIS

Milk fat will rise sufficiently on a milk sample to destroy its uniformity in 5 min. In order, then, to secure a representative sample for analysis, it is necessary to mix the milk thoroughly just before removal of the sample. This is best accomplished by pouring the milk from its container into another vessel and back again several times. If this is not feasible, the milk should be stirred thoroughly. Shaking the milk is to be avoided, as this tends to cause separation of the milk fat.

METHODS OF ANALYSIS

SACCHARIMETRIC DETERMINATION OF LACTOSE

Reagents. Acid Mercuric Nitrate Solution.—Dissolve mercury in twice its weight of nitric acid and dilute this volume with 5 equal volumes of water.

Phosphotungstic Acid Solution.—Dissolve 5 g. of phosphotungstic acid in 95 ml. of water.

Procedure for Single Dilution Method.—Obtain the specific gravity of the milk sample. The volume of sample to be used for the determination will vary with the specific gravity. This volume must be measured at the same temperature as that at which the specific gravity was taken. The correct volume will be found in Table 50-4. The amount of sample is based upon twice the normal weight of lactose (normal weight 32.9 g. per 100 ml. of solution) for the Ventzke sugar scale.

Transfer the volume of sample indicated in Table 50-4 into a 102.6-ml. volumetric

TABLE 50-4. VOLUMES OF MILK CORRESPONDING TO DOUBLE THE NORMAL WEIGHT OF LACTOSE

Specific Gravity of Milk	Volume of Milk for Double the Normal Weight of Lactose (Ventzke Scale)	Specific Gravity of Milk	Volume of Milk for Double the Normal Weight of Lactose (Ventzke Scale)
1.024	64.25	1.031	63.80
1.025	64.20	1.032	63.75
1.026	64.15	1.033	63.70
1.027	64.05	1.034	63.65
1.028	64.00	1.035	63.55
1.029	63.95	1.036	63.50
1.030	63.90		

flask and add 20 ml. of the acid mercuric nitrate solution. Dilute to the mark with 5 percent phosphotungstic acid solution. Let stand for 15 min. or longer with frequent shaking. Filter the mixture through a dry filter, discarding the first 10 ml. of filtrate. Collect the filtrate and fill a 400-mm. saccharimeter tube. Place the tube in the saccharimeter and obtain the reading on the A scale with the K scale set at zero. The reading obtained must be corrected, since the sample was twice the normal weight and was viewed in a tube twice the length specified for reading directly. The observed reading is then 2 × 2 too great and must be divided by 4 to give the percentage of lactose present in the sample.

Procedure for the Double Dilution Method.—Transfer accurately weighed samples of the well-mixed milk, each equal to twice the normal weight of lactose, into a 100-ml. and a 200-ml. volumetric flask, respectively. Add to each flask 20 ml. of the acid mercuric nitrate solution. To the 200-ml. flask add 15 ml. of the 5 percent phosphotungstic acid solution and dilute to the mark with water. Dilute the contents of the 100-ml. flask to the mark with the 5 percent phosphotungstic acid solution. For a period of 15 min. shake both flasks frequently; then filter each through a dry filter, discarding the first 10 ml. of filtrate. Place each solution in a 400-mm. saccharimeter tube and determine their reading in a saccharimeter.

Calculation of Percentage Lactose Using the Double Dilution Method.—The readings obtained for each solution are in error, due to the volume of the precipitate formed by the clarifying agent. Since both solutions contained the same quantity of milk, they both should give the same volume of precipitate. However, the effect of the precipitate error will be twice as great in the 100-ml. solution as in the 200-ml. solution. In this way, half of the effect of the precipitate error may be obtained from the saccharimeter readings on the 100- and the 200-ml. solutions. The total effect may then be calculated and applied as a correction to the readings.

For example, suppose the readings obtained on a milk sample by following the above directions were 20.2 for the 100-ml. solution and 9.85 for the 200-ml. solution. If no error was introduced by the precipitate, the reading on the 200-ml. solution should be exactly one-half that of the 100-ml. solution. On multiplying the reading for the 200-ml. solution by 2, a value is obtained which is less than the reading on the 100-ml. solution. This difference obtained represents one-half the error of the precipitate.

$$9.85 \times 2 = 19.70 \text{ (twice the reading on the 200-ml. solution)}$$
$$20.20 - 19.70 = 0.50 \text{ (one-half of the precipitate error)}$$
$$0.50 \times 2 = 1.00 \text{ (total precipitate error)}$$
$$20.20 - 1.00 = 19.20 \text{ (corrected reading on the 100-ml. solution)}$$

The reading obtained by these calculations must be corrected further, since the sample was twice the normal weight and was viewed in a tube twice the length specified for reading directly. The reading is then 2×2 too great and must be divided by 4 to give the correct percentage of lactose in the sample.

$$19.20 \div 4 = 4.80 \text{ (percentage of lactose in the sample)}$$

DETERMINATION OF LACTOSE BY FOLIN-WU METHOD

Reagents. **Sodium Tungstate Solution.**—Dissolve 10 g. of sodium tungstate in 90 g. of water.

Standard Lactose Solution.—Dissolve exactly 0.3000 g. of pure lactose monohydrate in water and dilute to a liter.

Alkaline Copper Reagent.—Place 40 g. of pure anhydrous sodium carbonate in a 1000-ml. volumetric flask and dissolve it in 400 ml. of water. Dissolve in this solution, first 7.5 g. of tartaric acid, and then 4.5 g. of crystalline copper sulfate. Dilute to volume and mix thoroughly.

Phosphomolybdic Acid Solution.—Place 35 g. of molybdic acid, 5 g. of sodium tungstate, 200 ml. of 10 percent sodium hydroxide solution, and 200 ml. of water in a beaker. Boil vigorously for 20 to 40 min. to remove the ammonia in the molybdic acid. Cool and transfer to a 500-ml. volumetric flask, adding sufficient water to bring the volume to about 350 ml. Add 125 ml. of concentrated phosphoric acid (85 percent) and dilute to volume with water.

Sulfuric Acid Solution (0.33 *M*).—Prepare from a 1 *M* solution by dilution.

Procedure.—Pipet accurately 1.00 ml. of milk into a 100-ml. volumetric flask, add 2 ml. of the 10 percent sodium tungstate solution, and then, drop by drop, 2.0 ml. of 0.33 *M* sulfuric acid solution. Mix thoroughly and filter, discarding the first 5 to 10 ml. of filtrate.

Pipet accurately 1.00 ml. of the filtrate and 1.0 ml. of water into a Folin-Wu sugar tube. Pipet, into a similar tube, exactly 2.00 ml. of the standard lactose solution. Add 2.0 ml. of the alkaline copper reagent to each tube and place the tubes in a beaker of boiling water for 8 min. Cook and add 4.00 ml. of the phosphomolybdic acid solution. Let stand for 1 min.; then dilute to the 25-ml. mark with a 1:4 dilution of the phosphomolybdic acid solution. Make a parallel determination on 2 ml. of water as a blank.

Mix thoroughly, transfer to colorimeter tube, and read within 15 min. in a colorimeter at 420 mμ. The intensity of the colored solution is directly proportioned to the amount of lactose present. Calculate the milligrams of lactose in 1.0 ml. of the milk sample,

$c = c' A/A'$, where c' is concentration of standard, A is absorbance of unknown, and A' is absorbance of standard. If the specific gravity of the milk is known, calculate the percentage of lactose in the milk.

DETECTION OF ADDED WATER BY COPPER SULFATE SERUM REFRACTION METHOD

Reagents. Copper Sulfate Solution.—Dissolve 72.5 g. of crystallized copper sulfate in water and dilute to a volume of 1 liter. Adjust the concentration of this solution so that it will give a reading of 36 on the scale of the immersion refractometer at 20°C. or have a sp. gr.$_4^{20}$ of 1.0443.

Procedure.—Add 4 volumes of milk to 1 volume of the copper sulfate solution, shake thoroughly, and filter. Discard the first filtrate that comes through, as it will be cloudy. Collect the clear filtrate and determine either the refraction at 20°C. with an immersion refractometer, or the sp. gr.$_4^{20}$, or the total solids content.

Minimum values for the copper serum of normal milk are: refraction at 20°C. on the immersion refractometer, 36; a sp. gr.$_4^{20}$ of 1.0245; and a total solids content of 5.28 percent.

THE CRYOSCOPIC METHOD FOR DETERMINATION OF ADDED WATER[17]

Apparatus. Cryoscope.—A cylindrical-shaped Dewar flask of 1-liter capacity and 28-cm. internal depth, surrounded by metal casing, is tightly closed by means of a large cork approximately 3 cm. thick. Through the center of the cork is a tightly fitted, medium, thin-walled glass or metal tube, 250 mm. in length by 33 mm. outside diameter. At one side of the cork is inserted a narrow metal inlet tube, the lower end of which is formed into a perforated loop near the bottom of flask. At the opposite side is a metal tube of T-shape construction and 6 mm. internal diameter, intended to afford escape for vapors and also for introducing volatile fluid into apparatus. At the back portion of cork is fitted a control thermometer, the bulb of which extends nearly to the bottom of the flask. The freezing test tube is of thin glass, approximately 240 mm. long by 29 mm. outside diameter, and fits closely into a larger tube, which is sealed into cork. In the rubber stopper of the freezing tube is fitted the standard thermometer. The length of the thermometer permits insertion of bulb nearly to the bottom of the tube and at the same time allows complete exposure of scale above the stopper. At the right side of the thermometer a stirring device made of noncorrodible low conductivity metal is fitted into the stopper through a short section of thin-walled metal tubing. The lower end extends nearly to the bottom of test tube and is provided with a horizontal loop encircling the thermometer. At the left of the thermometer is a freezing starter attachment inserted through the opening in the stopper formed by means of a short section of metal tubing. This device consists of a noncorrodible metal rod, at the lower end of which is an opening 10 mm. long for the purpose of carrying a small fragment of ice. At one side of the cryoscope is installed an air-drying arrangement which consists of a Folin absorption bulb inserged through a tightly fitting stopper and extending nearly to the bottom of a large-sized test tube. A short section of glass tubing is inserted through the second opening in the stopper and is connected to the vaporizing tube which enters the cryoscope. Sulfuric acid is poured into the drying tube to a level slightly above the small inner bulb. At the opposite side of the apparatus is arranged a drain tube for the purpose of conducting vapors away from the operator. By means of a pressure and suction pump, dry air may be forced into the apparatus at a suitable rate and mixed vapors conducted out through

---

[17] Assoc. Offic. Agr. Chemists, Official Methods of Analysis, 9th Ed., 1960, p. 193.

the base of the drain tube into the sink. An adjustable lens is mounted in a convenient position in front of the thermometer for the purpose of magnifying the scale.

Standard Thermometer.—A solid-stem instrument having a total length of 58 cm., with a scale portion measuring approximately 30 cm. The total scale range is 3°, from +1 to −2°, and each division is subdivided into tenths and hundredths. The length of a degree division approximates 1 cm., making the subdivisions of such magnitudes easy to observe and read to an estimated 0.001°. Standardize the thermometer as directed below. Check at frequent intervals, once a week or as often as may be necessary, to keep accurate record of any changes that may occur.

Control Thermometer.—A solid-stem instrument approximately 58 cm. long and having a scale range of +20° to −30°. Test in a bath of melting crushed ice for the purpose of determining whether the zero-mark on the scale is correct. Scale graduations should be accurate to within 0.10°.

Procedure.—Insert a funnel tube into a vertical portion of the T-tube at one side of the apparatus and pour in 400 ml. of ethyl ether previously cooled to 10°C. or lower. Close the vertical tube by means of a small cork and connect the pressure pump to the inlet tube of the air-drying attachment. Adjust the pump so as to pass air through the apparatus at moderate rate. Continuous vaporization of ethyl ether will cause a lowering of temperature in the flask from ordinary room temperature to 0°C. in 5 to 10 min. Continue lowering the temperature until the control thermometer registers near −3°C. At this stage, by lowering the gauge tube into the ethyl ether tube, then closing the top by means of the forefinger and raising to a suitable height, an estimate can be made as to the additional quantity of ether necessary to restore the 400-ml. volume. When the volume of ethyl ether has been adjusted to 400 ml., an additional 10 to 15 ml. are sufficient on an average for each succeeding determination. Pour into a freezing test tube sufficient water (30 to 35 ml.), boiled and cooled to 10° or lower, to submerge the thermometer bulb. Insert the thermometer together with the stirrer and lower the test tube into the larger tube. A small quantity of ethanol, sufficient to fill the lower space between the two test tubes, will serve to complete the conduction medium between the freezing bath and the liquid to be tested. Keep the stirrer in steady up-and-down motion at a rate of approximately one stroke every 1 or 2 sec. Maintain a passage of air through the apparatus until the temperature of the cooling bath reaches −2.5°C., at which time the top of the mercury thread in the thermometer usually recedes to a position near the freezing point of water. Maintain the temperature of the cooling bath at −2.5°C. and continue manipulation of the stirrer until super-cooling of the sample of 1.0° to 1.2°C. is observed. As a rule, at this time the liquid will begin to freeze, as may be noted by the rapid rise of the mercury. Manipulate the stirrer slowly 3 or 4 times as mercury column approaches its highest point. By means of a suitable light-weight cork mallet, tap the upper end of the thermometer cautiously a number of times until the top of the mercury column remains stationary for at least 1 min. Observe the exact reading on the thermometer scale, taking the necessary precautions to avoid parallax, and estimate to 0.001°. When observation has been satisfactorily completed, make a duplicate determination; then remove the thermometer and stirrer and empty the water from the freezing tube.

Using the same procedure, make freezing-point determinations on two sucrose solutions, recording the results.

1. Sucrose solution made by dissolving 7 g. of pure sucrose in water and making solution to a volume of 100 ml. at 20°C.

2. Sucrose solution made by dissolving 10 g. of pure sucrose in water and making the solution to a volume of 100 ml. at 20°C.

Rinse the clean freezing tube with approximately 25 ml. of the sample of milk, cooled to 10°C. or lower; measure into the tube 30 to 35 ml. of milk or enough to submerge the thermometer bulb; and insert the tube into the apparatus. Maintain the temperature of the cooling bath at 2.5°C. below the probable freezing point of the sample. Make a determination of the milk, following the same procedure as that used in determining the freezing point of water. As a rule, however, it is necessary to start the freezing action in milk by inserting the freezing starter (kept in contact with ice for several minutes, and in the open end of which has been wedged a fragment of ice) at the time when the mercury column has receded to 1.0° to 1.2° below the probable freezing point. A rapid rise of the mercury begins almost immediately. Remove the starter and manipulate the stirrer slowly and carefully 2 or 3 times while the mercury approaches its highest point. Complete the adjustment of the mercury column in the same manner as in the preceding determination; then, avoiding parallax, observe the exact reading on the thermometer scale and estimate to 0.001°. The algebraic difference between the average of readings obtained on the water and the reading obtained on the sample of milk represents the freezing-point depression of the milk. To determine the true freezing point (T') of milk, subtract from the freezing-point depression, freezing-point depression of 7 percent sucrose solution as determined by the laboratory thermometer. Multiply the difference by the correction factor for the thermometer. Add to the product 0.422 (freezing point of 7 percent sucrose solution by Bureau of Standards Thermometer). See example under calculations.

Calculations.—Calculate the percentage of added water by the following formula:

$$W = \frac{100(T - T')}{T}$$

where T = average freezing point of normal milk ($-0.55°$), and
T' = true freezing point on given sample.

A tolerance of 3 percent may be allowed on results for added water determined on the basis of the average freezing-point depression of $-0.55°$. Owing to narrow variations found in market milks of genuine character, it is not necessary to deduct tolerance figure from results showing added water in excess of 3 percent. Make freezing-point determinations only on samples of milk that show an acidity of not more than 0.18 percent calculated as lactic acid.

Calculation of True Freezing Point of Milk Sample:

1. Observed freezing points: water = $+0.056$; 7 g. sucrose/100 ml. = -0.369; 10 g. sucrose/100 ml. = 0.565; milk sample = 0.491.

2. Freezing-point depressions: 7 g. sucrose/100 ml. = 0.425; 10 g. sucrose/100 ml. = 0.621; milk sample = -0.547.

3. Intervals and thermometer correction: theoretical interval for sucrose 7 to 10 g./100 ml. = 0.199; actual found for sucrose 7 to 10 g./100 ml. = (0.621 − 0.425) = 1.196. Therefore the correction factor for the thermometer is 0.199 − 0.196 = 1.015.

4. True freezing point of milk.

$$[-0.547 - (-0.425)] \times 1.015 + (-0.422) = 0.546$$

THERMISTOR CRYOSCOPIC METHOD FOR DETERMINATION OF ADDED WATER

Apparatus. Assembled Cryoscope.—Consists of chilling chamber, completely insulated freezing bath isothermal freezing mechanism, and 0.001° thermistor thermometer. The thermometer scale ranges from 0 to $-1°C$. with successive 0.001°C.

graduations at 1.2-mm. intervals. The thermometer is adjusted to read directly the accepted freezing values of 7 percent and 10 percent sucrose standards.

Procedure.—Use thoroughly mixed samples of milk having titratable acidity not over 0.18 percent. Transfer 2-ml. sample to a clean 16 × 50 mm. test tube. Precool sample by placing tube in ice bath. Place test tube with temperature probe, stirrer, and freezing assembly into instrument bath. Cool sample. *Switch* to *Position 1,* or *"Cool"* or *"Stir."* Measure knob to expected value for sample, or to Base Breezing Point, T. Stop bath circulation at prescribed point by switching to Position 2 or "Supercool" or by isolating sample above bath. Freeze sample by switching to Position 3 or "Freeze." Adjust Rotate "Measure" knob to adjust galvanometer spot to zero (Position 5). Make reading only when spot reverses direction from right to left (end of "plateau"). This is the most repeatable point, and the one around which the instrument should be calibrated. It represents the true freezing point, T'. An alternative procedure—Leave "Measure" knob at base freezing point (Base T). Depress high-sensitivity switch (Position 5) and observe galvanometer spot move to right of zero. The reading corresponds with scale graduations indicating directly the approximate percentage of added water in the milk.

Calculations.—Calculate added water as follows:

$$\text{Percent added water} = \frac{100 \, (T - T')}{T}$$

where T = base freezing point of authenticated samples, and
T' = true freezing point of test sample.

PHOSPHATASE TEST FOR PROPER PASTEURIZATION[18]

Reagents. Barium Buffer Substrate (pH 10.6).—Prepare a barium borate-hydroxide buffer by dissolving 25.0 g. of barium hydroxide $[Ba(OH)_2 \cdot 8H_2O]$ in distilled water and diluting to 500 ml. In another flask dissolve 11.0 g. of boric acid (H_3BO_3) and dilute to 500 ml. Warm each solution to 50°C., mix the two solutions together, stir, cool to approximately 20°C., filter, and stopper the filtrate tightly. For use with milk, the above buffer should be diluted with an equal volume of water.

Then prepare the buffer substrate by dissolving 0.20 g. of phenol-free crystalline disodium phenyl phosphate in 100 ml. of the above prepared barium borate-hydroxide buffer.

Zinc-copper Precipitant.—Dissolve 3.0 g. of zinc sulfate $(ZnSO_4 \cdot 7H_2O)$ and 0.6 g. of copper sulfate $(CuSO_4 \cdot 5H_2O)$ in water and dilute to 100 ml. with water.

Color Development Buffer.—Dissolve 6.0 g. of sodium metaborate $(NaBO_2)$ and 20 g. of sodium chloride in water and dilute to 1 liter with water.

Color Dilution Buffer.—Dilute 100 ml. of the Color Development Buffer (above) to a volume of 1 liter with water.

BQC (Gibbs Reagent).—Dissolve 0.040 g. of 2,6-dibromoquinone-chloroimide powder in 10 ml. of absolute ethyl or methyl alcohol and transfer to a dark-colored dropping bottle. If kept in the ice tray of a refrigerator, the solution will remain stable for at least a month. Discontinue using it when it begins to turn brown.

Butyl Alcohol (B.P. 116°–118°C.).—Adjust the pH by mixing a liter of the alcohol with 50 ml. of the Color Development Buffer (above).

A 0.05 Percent Copper Sulfate Solution.—Dissolve 0.05 g. of copper sulfate in water and dilute to a volume of 100 ml. with water.

Phenol Standards.—First prepare a stock solution of phenol. Transfer 1.0 g. of phenol, accurately weighed, into a 1-liter volumetric flask, dissolve in water, and dilute

[18] Assoc. Offic. Agr. Chemists, Official Methods of Analysis, 9th Ed., 1960, p. 198.

to the mark with water. Thus, 1 ml. of this solution contains 1 mg. of phenol. The solution is stable for several months if kept in a refrigerator.

Next prepare a more dilute stock solution by diluting 10 ml. of the stock solution prepared as described above to a volume of 1 liter with water.

Prepare still more dilute standard solutions by diluting 5-, 10-, 30-, and 50-ml. volumes of the dilute stock phenol solution to a volume of 100 ml. with water, giving solutions containing 0.5, 1.0, 3.0, and 5.0 μg. of phenol per ml., respectively. Store these standard solutions in a refrigerator.

Measure the appropriate quantities of the phenol standard solutions into a series of tubes (preferably graduated at 5.0 and 10.0 ml.) to provide a range of standards as needed containing 0 (blank), 0.5, 1.0, 3.0, 5.0, 10.0, and up to 30 or 40 μg. of phenol if necessary. To improve the stability of the standards and increase their brightness, add 1.0 ml. of 0.05 percent copper sulfate solution to each tube. Then add 5.0 ml. of the Color Dilution Buffer (above) and dilute to a 10-ml. volume with water. Add 2 drops of BQC, mix, and allow to stand for 30 min. at room temperature to develop the color. If the butyl alcohol extraction method is used in the test, extract the standards in a manner similar to that described for the samples.

Read absorbance in spectrometer at 610 mμ, subtracting value of blank from value of each phenol standard, and prepare a standard curve.

Procedure.—Pipet a 1.0-ml. sample of milk into each of 3 test tubes and reserve one of these tubes for control. Heat the control sample, for about a minute, to at least 85°C. in a beaker of boiling water, having the beaker covered so that the entire tube is heated to approximately 85°C., and cool to room temperature.

Add 10 ml. of the barium buffer substrate to each tube, stopper, and mix. Incubate the tubes in a water bath at 37°C. for 1 hr., occasionally shaking the tubes. Place the tubes in a beaker of boiling water for nearly a minute, heating to approximately 85°C., and then cool to room temperature.

Pipet 1 ml. of the zinc-copper precipitant into each tube and mix thoroughly. Filter through a 5-cm. funnel, using a 9-cm. Whatman No. 42 or No. 2 filter paper (or equivalent). Collect 5 ml. of the filtrate in a tube graduated at 5.0 and 10.0 ml. Add 5 ml. of the Color Development Buffer. Then add 2 drops of BQC to the solution, mix, and allow to stand for 30 min. at room temperature to develop the color. Determine the intensity with the spectrometer at 610 mμ. Subtract reading of blank from that of test sample and convert result to phenol equivalents by reference to standard curve. In tests yielding 0.5 to 5 units of color, extract with butyl alcohol by adding 5 ml. of the alcohol, invert the tube slowly several times, centrifuge if necessary to clear the alcohol layer, and compare with the standards in the alcohol.

Calculation and Evaluation of Results.—Using a 1.0-ml. fluid sample and adding 11 ml. of liquid (total liquid 12 ml., with 5 ml. of the filtrate used in test) multiply the value of the reading by 1.2 to convert to phenol equivalents per 0.5 ml. of sample. For milk, a value of greater than 2 μg. per 0.5 ml. of sample indicates underpasteurization.

DETERMINATION OF LACTIC ACID[19]

Reagents. Copper Sulfate Solution (25 percent).—Dissolve 25 g. of copper sulfate ($CuSO_4 \cdot 5H_2O$) in water and dilute to 100 ml. with water.

Copper Sulfate Solution (5 percent).—Dissolve 5 g. of copper sulfate ($CuSO_4 \cdot 5H_2O$) in water and dilute to 100 ml. with water.

Calcium Hydroxide Solution.—Grind 300 g. of calcium oxide with water to a cream in a mortar, transfer to a container with water, and dilute with 1400 ml. of water.

[19] Davidson, Jr., J. Dairy Res., **16**, 209, 1949.

p-Hydroxydiphenyl Reagent.—Dissolve 1.5 g. of *p*-hydroxydiphenyl in 10 ml. of 5 percent (w/v) sodium hydroxide, heat and stir until dissolved, and then dilute to 100 ml. with water. Store in a dark glass bottle.

Lactate Standards.—First, prepare a *primary standard*. Transfer 0.1067 g. of lithium lactate, accurately weighed, into a 1-liter volumetric flask, dissolve in water, and dilute to the mark with water.

Next prepare more *dilute standard solutions* by transferring 3-, 6-, 9-, and 12-ml. volumes of the primary standard solution to four 100-ml. volumetric flasks and diluting to the mark with water. These solutions contain the equivalent of 3, 6, 9, and 12 μg. lactic acid per ml.

Procedure.—Dilute 5 ml. of milk or reconstituted milk product with water to approximately 35 ml. in a 50-ml. volumetric flask. Add, while swirling, 0.5 ml. of 5 percent copper sulfate solution. Raise the temperature of the flask contents to 45°–47°C. by rapid swirling in a water bath at approximately 90°C. and, after addition of 5 ml. of 25 percent copper sulfate solution, maintain for 10 min. at 45°–47°C. Add 5 ml. calcium hydroxide suspension, dilute to the mark with water, shake vigorously, and hold for an additional 10 min. at 45°–47°C. Cool to 20°C., adjust to volume, and filter.

Measure 1 ml. of filtrate into a Pyrex tube (1 in. × 6 in.). Add 1 drop of 5 percent copper sulfate solution and exactly 6 ml. of concentrated sulfuric acid. Place the tube in boiling water for 5 min. and cool to 20°C. in iced water. Add 2 drops of *p*-hydroxy-diphenyl reagent, mix thoroughly to ensure a fine suspension of the reagent which is insoluble in acid, and hold at 30°C. for 15 min. Add another drop of reagent, mix well again and hold for an additional 15 min. at 30°C. Transfer the tubes to a boiling water bath for 1.5 min. to dissolve excess suspended reagent, and cool to room temperature. Measure the absorbance with the spectrometer at 570 mμ.

One ml. each of the working standards solution, containing 3, 6, 9, and 12 μg. lactic acid, are pipeted into 1 in. × 6 in. Pyrex tubes and the color developed as described above for the filtrates. Read absorbance in a spectrometer at 570 mμ, and prepare a standard curve.

Calculation of Results.—There are two correction factors to be applied after due allowance has been made for milk dilution: (a) for the volume occupied by the precipitate in the volumetric flask, and (b) for the partial retention of lactic acid by the precipitate. Consequently, an overall multiplication factor of 1.06 should be applied to all results read off the standard curve.

PESTICIDES

Insecticides, fungicides, miticides, rodenticides, repellents, and herbicides are embraced in the general term pesticide which has been defined[20] as "a product, substance, or mixture of substances—gaseous, liquid, or solid—which may be used to destroy, prevent, control, repel, or mitigate any form of plant or animal life or viruses (except viruses, fungi or bacteria on or in living man and other animals), and weeds." The use of any of the pesticides may create a residue problem on foodstuffs. Consequently, the use of any pesticide in connection with the growing, processing, or marketing of foods is under governmental control, with use permitted only on specified foodstuffs under specific conditions of application and with definite permitted tolerances, or no tolerances, for residues in the product.

Following is a list of some of the common pesticides and the principal products on which they are used:

[20] Food Protection Committee, Food and Nutrition Board, "Statements Prepared on Safe Use of Chemical Additives in Foods," December 1952, p. 4.

Insecticides

Primarily used for protection of certain fruit and vegetable crops.

Chlorinated Insecticides

Aldrin	Dieldrin	Methoxychlor
BHC	Endrin	Strobane
Chlordane	Heptachlor	TDE
DDT	Lindane	Toxaphene

Phosphorous Insecticides

Malathion	Methyl parathion	Parathion

Inorganic Insecticides

Calcium arsenate	Cryolite	Lead arsenate

Insecticides from Plant Sources

Nicotine sulfate	Rotenone	Ryania
Pyrethrins		

Fungicides

Primarily used for protection of certain fruit and vegetable crops.

Organic Foliage Fungicides

Captan	Maneb	Zineb
Dichlone	Nabam	Ziram
Ferbam	Thiram	

Inorganic Foilage Fungicides

Bordeaux mixture	Cuprous oxide
Copper oxychloride	Lime sulfur
Copper zinc chromate	Sulfur
Tribasic copper sulfate	

Fumigants

Primarily used for protection of stored grains and other foods and for industrial fumigation.

Acrylonitrile	Carbon tetrachloride	Ethylene dichloride
Calcium cyanide	Chloropicrin	Ethylene oxide
Carbon disulfide	Cyanide (HCN)	Methyl bromide

Miticides

Primarily for the protection of certain nuts, fruits and vegetables.

Aramite	EPN	TEPP
Chlorobenzilate		

Rodenticides

Antu	Dicoumarol	Thallium sulfate
Coumachlor	Red squill	Warfarin

METHODS OF ANALYSIS

DETERMINATION OF CHLORINATED INSECTICIDES[21]

Reagents. Acetonitrile, Reagent Grade.—If Technical Grade is used, purify by the following procedure: to approximately 4000 ml., add 1 ml. 85 percent phosphoric acid, 30 g. phosphorous pentoxide, and distill at 81°–82°C.

Acetonitrile, Saturated Solution.—Saturate acetonitrile with redistilled petroleum ether (B.P. = 30°–60°C.).

Ethanol, Absolute.

Alcoholic Sodium Hydroxide (2 percent, w/v).—Dissolve 2 g. sodium hydroxide in absolute ethanol and dilute to 100 ml.

Celite 545.—Johns-Manville Company.

Eluting Mixture (6 + 94).—Dilute 60 ml. purified ethyl ether to 1000 ml. with redistilled petroleum ether. Add 25 g. anhydrous sodium sulfate to remove moisture.

Eluting Mixture (15 + 85).—Dilute 150 ml. purified ethyl ether to 1000 ml. with redistilled petroleum ether. Add 25 g. anhydrous sodium sulfate to remove moisture.

Ethyl Ether.—Ether must be peroxide-free and contain 2 percent (v/v) ethanol. Purify as follows: transfer a suitable volume to a separatory funnel and wash twice with protions of water equal to approximately one-half the volume of ether. Shake the washed ether with 50–100 ml. saturated sodium chloride solution and discard all aqueous layers. Draw the washed ether into a standard taper flask, add a large excess of anhydrous sodium sulfate, and shake vigorously to remove water (15–30 min. on a mechanical shaker). Add 2 percent (v/v) ethanol.

Florisil, Activated, 60–100 Mesh.—(Purchase Florisil activated at 650°C.).

Hexane.

Magnesium Oxide.—Sea Sorb #43 (Westvaco) treat as follows: slurry about 500 g. with distilled water, heat on a steam bath for 30 min., and filter with suction. Dry overnight at 105°–130°C. and pulverize to pass 60-mesh sieve. Store in closed bottle.

Magnesia-Celite Mixture.—Thoroughly mix treated magnesium oxide with Celite 545, 1 + 1 by weight.

A. Foods Containing More Than 2 Percent Fat[22]

Extraction. a. *Animal and Vegetable Fats.*—Warm until liquid and filter through a dry filter. Take 5 g. of fat for isolation.

b. *Animal Tissues.*—Grind a suitable quantity with sufficient anhydrous sodium sulfate to combine with the water present and to disintegrate the sample. Transfer the mixture to a centrifuge bottle, add 100 ml. of petroleum ether, shake vigorously, and centrifuge at about 1500 r.p.m. Pour off the solvent layer into a beaker and repeat the extraction twice with 50-ml. portions of petroleum ether. Evaporate the combined extracts to obtain the fat. Take 5 g. of fat for isolation.

c. *Butter.*—Warm at about 50°C. until oil separates. Decant through dry filter. Take 5 g. of oil for isolation.

d. *Cheese.*—Place 100 g. diced cheese, 2 g. sodium oxalate, and 100 ml. of ethanol in a Waring Blendor and blend 2–3 min. Pour into a 500-ml. centrifuge bottle, and add 50 ml. ethyl ether and 50 ml. petroleum ether, shaking vigorously after addition of each solvent. Centrifuge at about 1500 r.p.m. for 5 min. Remove solvent layer and repeat extraction procedure twice with 50-ml. portions of the mixed ethers. Evaporate the combined extracts to obtain fat. Take 5 g. of fat for isolation.

[21] Pesticide Analytical Manual, Food and Drug Administration, U. S. Department of Health, Education, and Welfare, Washington 25, D. C.

[22] Mills, P. A., J. Assoc. Offic. Agr. Chemists, **46**, 186, 1963.

e. *Milk.*—To 100 g. of fluid milk in a centrifuge bottle, add ethyl ether and shake vigorously; then add 50 ml. petroleum ether and shake vigorously. Centrifuge at about 1500 r.p.m. and transfer solvent layer to a 1-liter separatory funnel containing 500–600 ml. of water. Repeat extraction by centrifuging twice with 50-ml. portions of the mixed ethers (1 + 1). Mix combined extracts and water cautiously. Drain and discard water. Rewash twice with additional 100-ml. portions of water, discarding the water each time. Pass the ether residue through a column of anhydrous sodium sulfate and collect in a 400-ml. beaker. Wash column with small portions of petroleum ether and evaporate combined extracts to obtain fat. Use total fat extracted from 100 g. of milk for isolation.

f. *Nuts.*—Weigh 100 g. of finely copped nutmeats into a Waring Blendor. Add 100 ml. of ethyl alcohol and proceed as with cheese. Combine extracts, and make to volume. Take an aliquot containing not more than 5 g. for isolation.

g. *Oils.*—Take 5 g. for isolation.

Isolation of Chlorinated Insecticides. *Partioning.*—Transfer quantitatively the total fat extracted from either milk or 5 g. of fat extracted from other products to 125-ml. separator, using small portions of petroleum ether. Adjust to total volume of 25 ml. Add 25 ml. of saturated acetonitrile, shake thoroughly, separate and drain acetonitrile layer into a 1-liter separator containing 500–600 ml. water. Extract petroleum ether solution three more times with 25-ml. portions of saturated acetonitrile and combine extracts. Add 100 ml. of petroleum ether, shake cautiously, and allow layers to separate. Discard aqueous layer and wash petroleum ether with two 100-ml. portions of water (if emulsions form, add 5 ml. of saturated sodium chloride). Discard washings and draw off petroleum ether layer through a layer of anhydrous sodium sulfate into a 400-ml. beaker. Rinse column three times with 10-ml. portions of petroleum ether. Evaporate to about 10 ml. at room temperature and use for column clean up.

Column Cleanup.—Prepare a 25 mm. outside diameter × 300 mm. chromatographic column that contains about 4 in. of activated Florisil topped with about a 0.5 in. layer of anhydrous sodium sulfate. Pre-wet the column with 35–40 ml. petroleum ether, and place a receiver under it. Transfer the above petroleum ether extract to the column, letting it pass through at a rate of about 5 ml. per minute. Rinse the container with two successive 5-ml. portions of petroleum ether, pour rinsings on column, rinse walls of chromatographic tube with an additional small quantity of petroleum ether, and elute column at a rate of 5 ml. per minute with 200 ml. of the 6 + 94 eluting mixture.

Change receivers and elute column at rate of 5 ml. per minute with 200 ml. of 15 + 85 eluting mixture.

Evaporate each eluate to a suitable volume.

NOTE.—All of the chlorinated insecticides listed above with the exception of dieldrin and endrin will be recovered in the 6 + 94 elution. Dieldrin and endrin will be recovered in the 15 + 85 elution after 6 + 94 elution.

B. Foods Containing Less Than 2 Percent Fat (Approximate Water Content known)[23]

Extraction.—Weigh 100 g. of chopped or blended sample into a Waring Blendor, and add 200 ml. of acetonitrile and approximately 10 g. of Celite. Mix at high speed for 1–2 min. and filter with suction through a 12-cm. Büchner funnel into a 500-ml. suction flask. Transfer filtrate to a 250-ml graduated cylinder and record volume (F). Transfer measured filtrate to a 1000-ml. separatory funnel. Carefully measure 100 ml. of petroleum ether (R) into the same graduate used for the filtrate and pour into the separatory funnel. Shake vigorously for 1–2 min., add 10 ml. of saturated sodium chloride solution, and about 600 ml. of water. Mix gently. Allow to separate, discard the aqueous

[23] Mills, P. A., J. Assoc. Offic. Agr. Chemists, **46,** 186, 1963.

layer, and wash the solvent layer with two successive 100-ml. portions of water. Discard washings, transfer solvent layer to a 100-ml. stoppered graduate, and record volume (*P*). Add about 15 g. anhydrous sodium sulfate and shake vigorously. Evaporate to about 10 ml. at room temperature and place on the column.

Column Cleanup.—Same as described in A above. Calculate sample represented by eluants as follows:

$$\text{Sample represented by eluants} = S \times (F/T) \times (P/R)$$

where S = grams of sample taken,
F = volume of filtrate,
T = total volume (ml. water contained in sample + ml. acetonitrile added—correction in ml. for volume contraction),
P = ml. petroleum ether extract, and
R = ml. petroleum ether used to dissolve residue.

Determinative Step.—A suitable gas-liquid chromatograph, equipped with an electron-capture detector with tritium source, can be used for analysis of chlorinated pesticides. The columns of Pyrex glass ($\frac{1}{4}$ in. $\times$ 6 ft.) with 10 percent (w/w) silicone fluid (Dow Corning 200, 12,500 centistokes) on 80–90 mesh Anakrom ABS. The operating conditions are as follows: column temperature 190°–215°C., detector 210°–230°C., and a nitrogen flow rate of 60–100 ml. per minute. (The flask heater and detector temperatures to be approximately 25° above temperature of column but in no case to exceed 230°C.). The sensitivity of the instrument should be such that 0.01 p.p.m. of endrin can be detected with a normal sample injection of approximately 5 μl. A standard mixture of aldrin, heptachlor epoxide, p,p'-DDT and endrin should be injected each day before any run to check column behavior.

A suitable gas-liquid chromatograph (Microtek) equipped with a microcoulometric detector (Dohrmann Instrument Company) may also be used for analysis of pesticides. The column consists of 6 ft., $\frac{1}{4}$-in. outside diameter aluminum tubing with 15–20 percent w/w silicone fluid (Dow Corning 200 Fluid, 12,500 Centistokes) cm. 30–60 mesh Chromosorb P. The operating conditions are as follows: column temperature, 220°C.; column flow rate of helium 120 ml. per minute; injection port, 240°C.; transfer time,

TABLE 50-5. RETENTION TIMES OF SELECTED CHLORINATED PESTICIDES
RELATIVE TO ALDRIN

Pesticide	Ratio	Pesticide	Ratio
Ethylene dichloride	0.12	Captan	1.12
Methylene chloride	0.12	Phaltan	1.16
Chloropicrin	0.13	β-Chlordane	1.51
TCNB	0.35	Dieldrin	1.65
Hexachlorobenzene	0.51	Aramite	1.66
BHC	0.45,[a] 0.55	Tech. DDT	1.71, 2.0, 2.5
Lindane	0.55	Chlorobenzilate	1.89
Dichlone	0.59	Endrin	2.0, 2.9
Heptachlor	0.81	Methoxychlor	3.2
Chlorthion	0.96	Chlordane (tech.)	0.54, 0.73, 0.79, 0.94, 1.12, 1.34,
Aldrin	1.00		1.47, 1.80, 2.25
		Toxaphene	No definite peaks.

[a] When more than one peak is present, major peak is italic.

250°C.; combustion inlet block, 250°C.; furnace temperature, 800°C. minimum; and halogen detector.

The retention times for different compounds are related to the retention time of some standard. In most cases aldrin is the reference standard. The ratios obtained will be constant even though the actual retention times vary for different trials. The ratios reported in Table 50-5 were obtained by dividing the retention time of the compound by the retention time of aldrin which was run concurrently.

A microcoulometric gas chromatograph (Dohrmann Instrument Company) equipped with a sulfur detector (Model T-200-P) can be used to determine sulfur containing pesticides. The column is of Pyrex glass (6 ft. $\times \frac{1}{4}$ in. outside diameter) with 10 percent (w/w) silicone fluid (Dow Corning 200 fluid, 12,500 centistokes) on 80–90 mesh Anakrom ABS. The operating conditions are the same as those for the gas-liquid chromotograph above except that nitrogen is the carrier gas. The ratios reported in Table 50-6 were obtained by dividing the retention time of the compound by the retention time of sulphenone which was run concurrently.

TABLE 50-6. RETENTION TIMES OF PESTICIDES
RELATIVE TO SULPHENONE (SULFUR DETECTOR)

Pesticide	Ratio
Systox	0.27, *0.37*[b]
Methyl parathion	0.60
Malathion	0.71
Parathion	0.78
Captan	0.95
Sulphenone[a]	1.00
Aramite	1.48, 1.58
EPN	3.15
Guthion	3.75

[a] Retention time for Sulphenone reference is approximately 5.9 min.
[b] Whenever more than one peak is present, the major peak is italic.

DETERMINATION OF PARATHION[24]

Reagents. n-Hexane.
Acetonitrile.
Ethanol, Anhydrous.
Sodium Sulfate, Anhydrous.

Extraction and Isolation.—Weigh a suitable amount of the plant tissue into a wide-mouth, screw-cap jar. Add 300 ml. n-hexane and shake the sealed container vigorously for 3–5 min. Filter the hexane into a 1-liter round-bottomed standard taper flask. Wash plant tissue with two successive 100-ml. portions of hexane and filter into flask as before. Concentrate to about 100 ml., allow to cool, and transfer quantitatively to a 500-ml. separatory funnel. Add 100 ml. of acetonitrile to the separatory funnel and shake for 3–5 min. Allow the two phases to separate and drain the lower acetonitrile phase into a 500-ml. round-bottomed standard taper flask. Extract the hexane with three additional 100-ml. portions of acetonitrile. Combine extracts and discard hexane layer after fourth extraction. Attach the flask to a condenser and evaporate just to dryness. Dissolve the residue in ethanol, transfer quantitatively to a 10-ml. volumetric flask, and make to volume.

[24] Jones, L. R., and Riddick, J. A., Anal. Chem., **24**, 569, 1952.

Determination Step.—Either an isothermal electron capture cell or a thermal conductivity cell can be used for analysis. For electron capture gas chromatography, a column, 7 ft. × 4 mm. inside diameter, packed with 10 percent Dow Corning 200 Silicone fluid (12,500 centistokes) on 80–90 mesh Anakrom ABS. The operating conditions are as follows: column temperature, 200°C.; injection temperature, 225°C.; carrier gas flow rate 120 ml. per minute. For thermal conductivity,[25] a 6-ft. column, $\frac{1}{4}$ in. outside diameter, packed with 25 percent Dow Corning high-vacuum silicone fluid on 30–60 mesh Chromosorb P. The operating conditions are as follows: column temperature, 220°C.; carrier gas flow rate (helium), 120 ml. per minute.

SUGAR

In sugar analysis it is necessary to be familiar with optical methods involving the polariscope and, more particularly, the saccharimeter. These instruments make use of the fact that all natural sugars possess asymmetric carbon atoms and consequently have the power of rotating the vibration plane of polarized light about an axis parallel to its direction of propagation. The angle through which this rotation occurs for substances in solution is directly proportional to the concentration of the substance, the length of the column of solution through which the light passes, and the rotating power of the substance.

METHODS OF ANALYSIS
SACCHARIMETRIC DETERMINATION OF A SINGLE SUGAR

Procedure.—Dissolve a weight of sample, equivalent to the normal weight of sugar present, in 100 ml. of solution at 20°C. The reading obtained at 20°C. when using a 200-mm. saccharimeter tube will be the percentage of sugar in the sample. Frequently it is advisable to use sample weights equivalent to fractions or multiples of the normal weight. Thus, if the sample weight was one-half the normal weight and the other conditions remained the same, the reading obtained would be one-half as great as it should be for the normal weight; therefore it would have to be multiplied by two in order to give the correct percentage. Similarly, if a 400-mm. saccharimeter tube was used, the reading would be twice as great as it should be and would have to be divided by two for the percentage value.

Frequently samples contain interfering substances which must be removed before a saccharimeter reading can be obtained. In making clarification, prepare a saturated solution of neutral lead acetate solution and add to the sugar solution before diluting to volume. After bringing the solution to volume, pour the clarified solution on a dry rapid filter. Reject the first portions of the filtrate and use the remainder. Remove the lead with potassium oxalate or sodium carbonate. The clarifying procedure introduces a precipitate error which must be compensated for by calculating the volume of precipitate and correcting for it (double dilution procedure).

SACCHARIMETRIC DETERMINATION OF A SUGAR
IN A MIXTURE OF SUGARS[26]

The most common example is the determination of sucrose in the presence of invert sugar, as in honey, molasses, syrup, or other similar products. In this instance, the direct saccharimetric reading of a solution of the two sugars is the resultant rotation of the sucrose and invert sugars. Supplementing this reading by another, in which the rotation

[25] Coulson, D. M., Cavanagh, L. A., and Stuart, J., J. Agr. Food Chem., **7**, 250, 1952.
[26] Bates and Associates, Cir. Natl. Bur. Standards, C440, 126, 1942.

of the invert sugar is kept constant but that of the sucrose is changed by hydrolysis, permits calculation of the amount of sucrose, since the change in rotation can be measured and is an exact function of the quantity of sucrose. The change of rotation of the normal solution of pure sucrose upon hydrolysis is known as the *Clerget divisor*—a numerical value influenced by concentration, temperature, and impurities. By use of the Clerget method, sucrose and raffinose can be determined in a mixture of the two if they are the only optically active substances present in solution.[27]

(a) *Hydrolysis by Hydrochloric Acid.*[28]—Prepare 100 ml. of a clear solution containing 26 g. of the sample and 2.315 g. of sodium chloride and take the reading (P), using a 200-mm. tube at 20°C.

Pipet 50 ml. of the 26 percent sugar solution into a 100-ml. volumetric flask and add 25 ml. of water. Then add slowly, while rotating the flask, 10 ml. of hydrochloric (sp. gr. 1.12) and place in a water bath maintained at 60°C. for 10 min., agitating the flask for the first 3 min. Then immerse the flask in water at 20°C.

When the temperature of the contents is decreased to about 35°C., dilute to neck of flask and leave the flask in the water for an additional 30 min. before making to volume. Mix well and polarize the solution in a 200-mm. tube at 20°C. Double the reading of this solution to give that for a normal weight (I). Calculate sucrose by use of the formula:

$$\text{Percent sucrose} = S = \frac{100(P - I)}{132.56 + 0.0794(m - 13) - 053(t - 20)}$$

where $P =$ direct reading, normal solution,
$\quad I =$ invert reading, normal solution,
$\quad t =$ temperature at which readings are made, and
$\quad m =$ weight in grams of total solids from original sample of inverted solution.

If the original solution contains exactly 26 g. of sample and the readings are made at 20°C., the formula becomes:

$$S = \frac{100(P - I)}{132.56}$$

(b) *Hydrolysis by Invertase.*—The hydrolysis by invertase is required for samples high in fructose, such as honey, fruit products, sorghum syrup, and molasses. Detailed procedures on the enzyme hydrolysis of sucrose are given in the Official Methods of Analysis of the Association of Official Agricultural Chemists.[29]

SPECTROMETRIC METHOD FOR SUGAR ANALYSIS[30,31]

This method is an adaptation of the Somogyi method for the determination of sugars.

Reagents. Alkaline Copper Tartrate Stock Reagent.—Dissolve 28 g. anhydrous disodium phosphate and 40 g. sodium potassium tartrate in 700 ml. distilled water. Add 100 ml. M sodium hydroxide and stir in 80 ml. 10 percent copper sulfate. Add 180 g. anhydrous sodium sulfate, dissolve, and make up to 1 liter.

Arsenomolybdate Reagent (Nelson Color Reagent).—Dissolve 25 g. ammonium molybdate in 450 ml. water, add 21 ml. concentrated sulfuric acid and 3 g. disodium arsenate dissolved in 25 ml. water. Place in an incubator at 37°C. for two days.

Procedure.—Mix 2 ml. alkaline copper tartrate stock reagent and 2 ml. of clear sugar

[27] Bates and Associates, Cir. Natl. Bur. Standards, C440, 142, 1942.
[28] Assoc. Offic. Agr. Chemists, Official Methods of Analysis, 9th Ed., 1960, p. 424.
[29] Assoc. offic. Agr. Chemists, Official Methods of Analysis, 9th Ed., 1960, p. 422.
[30] Somogyi, M., J. Biol. Chem., 160, 61, 1945.
[31] Nelson, N., J. Biol. Chem., 153, 375, 1944.

solution in a test tube (18 × 15 mm.), cover and heat in boiling water for 10 min. Cool, add 2 ml. arsenomolybdate reagent and dilute to either 10 ml. or 25 ml. The degree of dilution depends on the intensity of color. Measure absorbance at 500 mμ. Compare with standards.

NOTE.—Limitation of the method is that it can be used only when the sugar solution is colorless, and it is serviceable only as a micromethod.

ENZYMATIC DETERMINATION OF GLUCOSE

Principle.—When glucose oxidase oxidizes glucose, gluconic acid and hydrogen peroxide are formed. The hydrogen peroxide is utilized by peroxidase to oxidize a chromogen forming a colored product. Thus, the amount of color formed is directly proportional to the amount of glucose initially present. The method described here gives linear results to about 0.2 mg. glucose and can be used to accurately determine the glucose content of an aliquot containing about 0.02 to 0.2 mg. glucose.

Reagents. **Acetate Buffer.**—Dissolve 14.3 g. sodium acetate ($NaC_2H_3O_2 \cdot 3H_2O$) in approximately 900 ml. deionized water. Adjust pH to 5.1 with glacial acetic acid (about 2.5 ml. will be required). Make up to a final volume 1000 ml. with water.

Enzyme Reagent.—Dissolve 57.6 mg. Fermco[32] glucose oxidase (130,000 units per gram) and 13.4 mg. horseradish peroxidase (R.Z. 1.0 or equivalent) in 10.0 ml. of acetate buffer.

Chromogen Solution.—Dissolve 200 mg *o*-dianisidine dihydrochloride in 10 ml. water. For prolonged storage, store in amber bottles at −10°C. or lower.

Mixed Enzyme-chromogen Reagent.—Add 1.0 ml. chromogen solution to 80 ml. of buffer and mix. Add 0.5 ml. enzyme reagent and make up to 100 ml. with buffer.

Sulfuric Acid Reagent.—Add 50 ml. concentrated sulfuric acid to 250 ml. deionized water.

Standard Glucose Solution.—Dissolve 1.00 g. anhydrous glucose (dextrose) in water saturated with benzoic acid and make up to 100 ml. Store in the refrigerator. Dilute 10.0 ml. of the standard solution to 1000 ml. with water. This final dilution (working standard) contains 0.1 mg. glucose per ml. and should be prepared fresh daily.

Procedure.—Dilute the unknown so that it contains about 1 mg. glucose per. ml.

The volumes below are calculated to produce a maximum absorbance of 0.70 with a 10-mm. light path when using 0.2 mg. glucose.

Standard Curve	Working Standard Glucose (ml.)	Glucose (mg.)	Water (ml.)	Mixed Enzyme-chromogen Reagent (ml.)
1	0.0	0.0	2.0	1.0
2	0.4	0.04	0.6	1.0
3	0.8	0.08	1.2	1.0
4	1.2	0.12	0.8	1.0
5	1.6	0.16	0.4	1.0
6	2.0	0.20	0.0	1.0
Unknown	0.1[a]		1.9[a]	1.0

[a] These volumes may be varied depending on the glucose concentration of the unknown, but the combined volume of the unknown solution and water must be 2.0 ml.

Allow the reaction to proceed at 30°C. for 30 min. at the end of which time 8.0 ml. sulfuric acid reagent is added to stop the reaction and develop the color of the oxidized

[32] Fermco Laboratory, Inc., 4941 So. Racine Avenue, Chicago 9, Ill.

chromogen. Read absorbance at 540 mμ and obtain concentration of glucose in the unknown sample from a standard curve.

Calculations.—A standard curve is drawn by plotting absorbance *vs.* mg. of glucose. The mg. of glucose in the original sample is:

$$\text{mg./ml. or g. Glucose in original sample} = \frac{\text{mg. glucose in unknown tube} \times \text{dilution}}{\text{ml. of unknown tube}}$$

PRECAUTION.—Possible inhibitors for the reaction are competing hydrogen donors for the peroxidase reaction, such as ascorbate.

SUGAR ANALYSIS BY REFRACTOMETRIC METHOD

The refractive index of a sugar solution may be determined easily by one of several types of refractometers. In pure solutions, the refractive index is a direct measure of the sugar concentration. Other dissolved substances will also effect the refractive index. However, the effect on refractive index by these substances is not as great as the effect on density; consequently, the determination of sugar concentration in a solution by its refractive index is a convenient method for determining water content of sugar solutions.

Determine the refractive index of the solution at 20°C. with a refractometer and obtain corresponding percentage of dry matter (as sucrose) from Table 50-7. If the readings are made at temperatures other than 20°C., apply corrections in Table 50-8 and obtain the percentage of dry matter.

VITAMINS

DETERMINATION OF VITAMIN A IN FOOD PRODUCTS[33]

Reagents. Chloroform.—Wash 3 times with an equal volume of water, dry over anhydrous sodium sulfate, distill, and store over anhydrous sodium sulfate.

Antimony Trichloride Solution.—Weigh an unopened bottle of antimony chloride (25–30 g.), open it, and transfer to a glass-stoppered, wide-mouthed, amber-colored bottle containing 100 ml. of chloroform. Reweigh the opened bottle and obtain weight of antimony trichloride added to the chloroform by difference. This solution should be filtered if turbid.

Alcoholic Potassium Hydroxide Solution (0.5 M).—Dissolve about 35 g. of potassium hydroxide in 20 ml. of water and add sufficient alcohol to make 1000 ml. of solution.

Aqueous Potassium Hydroxide Solution (0.5 M).

Diethyl Ether.—Freshly distilled over sodium hydroxide pellets.

Vitamin A Standard.—A chloroform solution containing 100 U.S.P. units of vitamin A per ml. This is prepared by dissolving a weighed amount of distilled vitamin A esters in chloroform.

[33] Oser, B. L., Melmick, D., and Pader, M., Ind. Eng. Chem., Anal. Ed., **15**, 724, 1943.

---

[a] Reproduced with permission from the Assoc. Offic. Agr. Chemists, Official Methods of Analysis, 9th Ed., 1960, pp. 714–715.

[b] The values in this table for the range 0 to 49.8 percent sucrose are in accordance with the International Scale of Refractive Indices of Sucrose at 20°C., 1936, adopted as official at the 1938 meeting of the Association. Values of indices for range 0–24 percent sucrose are given to five decimal places, and those for range 24.2–49.8 percent to four decimal places. Values for range 50–85 percent are those adopted as official at the 1959 meeting and are given to five decimal places.

[c] Intern. Sugar J., **39**, 225, 1937.

Refractive Index at 20°	Sucrose (%)	Refractive Index at 20°	Sucrose (%)	Refractive Index at 20°	Sucrose (%)	Refractive Index at 20°	Sucrose (%)	Refractive Index at 20°	Sucrose (%)
1.33299	0.0	1.34629	9.0	1.36053	18.0	1.3758	27.0	1.3920	36.0
.33328	0.2	.34660	9.2	.36086	18.2	.3761	27.2	.3924	36.2
.33357	0.4	.34691	9.4	.36119	18.4	.3765	27.4	.3928	36.4
.33385	0.6	.34721	9.6	.36152	18.6	.3768	27.6	.3931	36.6
.33414	0.8	.34752	9.8	.36185	18.8	.3772	27.8	.3935	36.8
.33443	1.0	.34783	10.0	.36218	19.0	.3775	28.0	.3939	37.0
.33472	1.2	.34814	10.2	.36251	19.2	.3779	28.2	.3943	37.2
.33501	1.4	.34845	10.4	.36284	19.4	.3782	28.4	.3947	37.4
.33530	1.6	.34875	10.6	.36318	19.6	.3786	28.6	.3950	37.6
.33559	1.8	.34906	10.8	.36351	19.8	.3789	28.8	.3954	37.8
.33588	2.0	.34937	11.0	.36384	20.0	.3793	29.0	.3958	38.0
.33617	2.2	.34968	11.2	.36417	20.2	.3797	29.2	.3962	38.2
.33646	2.4	.34999	11.4	.36451	20.4	.3800	29.4	.3966	38.4
.33675	2.6	.35031	11.6	.36484	20.6	.3804	29.6	.3970	38.6
.33704	2.8	.35062	11.8	.36518	20.8	.3807	29.8	.3974	38.8
.33733	3.0	.35093	12.0	.36551	21.0	.3811	30.0	.3978	39.0
.33762	3.2	.35124	12.2	.36585	21.2	.3815	30.2	.3982	39.2
.33792	3.4	.35156	12.4	.36618	21.4	.3818	30.4	.3986	39.4
.33821	3.6	.35187	12.6	.36652	21.6	.3822	30.6	.3989	39.6
.33851	3.8	.35219	12.8	.36685	21.8	.3825	30.8	.3993	39.8
.33880	4.0	.35250	13.0	.36719	22.0	.3829	31.0	.3997	40.0
.33909	4.2	.35282	13.2	.36753	22.2	.3833	31.2	.4001	40.2
.33939	4.4	.35313	13.4	.36787	22.4	.3836	31.4	.4005	40.4
.33968	4.6	.35345	13.6	.36820	22.6	.3840	31.6	.4008	40.6
.33998	4.8	.35376	13.8	.36854	22.8	.3843	31.8	.4012	40.8
.34027	5.0	.35408	14.0	.36888	23.0	.3847	32.0	.4016	41.0
.34057	5.2	.35440	14.2	.36922	23.2	.3851	32.2	.4020	41.2
.34087	5.4	.35472	14.4	.36956	23.4	.3854	32.4	.4024	41.4
.34116	5.6	.35503	14.6	.36991	23.6	.3858	32.6	.4028	41.6
.34146	5.8	.35535	14.8	.37025	23.8	.3861	32.8	.4032	41.8
.34176	6.0	.35567	15.0	.37059	24.0	.3865	33.0	.4036	42.0
.34206	6.2	.35599	15.2	.3709	24.2	.3869	33.2	.4040	42.2
.34236	6.4	.35631	15.4	.3713	24.4	.3872	33.4	.4044	42.4
.34266	6.6	.35664	15.6	.3716	24.6	.3876	33.6	.4048	42.6
.34296	6.8	.35696	15.8	.3720	24.8	.3879	33.8	.4052	42.8
.34326	7.0	.35728	16.0	.3723	25.0	.3883	34.0	.4056	43.0
.34356	7.2	.35760	16.2	.3726	25.2	.3887	34.2	.4060	43.2
.34386	7.4	.35793	16.4	.3730	25.4	.3891	34.4	.4064	43.4
.34417	7.6	.35825	16.6	.3733	25.6	.3894	34.6	.4068	43.6
.34447	7.8	.35858	16.8	.3737	25.8	.3898	34.8	.4072	43.8
.34477	8.0	.35890	17.0	.3740	26.0	.3902	35.0	.4076	44.0
.34507	8.2	.35923	17.2	.3744	26.2	.3906	35.2	.4080	44.2
.34538	8.4	.35955	17.4	.3747	26.4	.3909	35.4	.4084	44.4
.34568	8.6	.35988	17.6	.3751	26.6	.3913	35.6	.4088	44.6
.34599	8.8	.36020	17.8	.3754	26.8	.3916	35.8	.4092	44.8

Footnotes on page 1148.

TABLE 50-7 (cont.)

Refractive Index at 20°	Sucrose (%)	Refractive Index at 20°	Sucrose (%)	Refractive Index at 20°	Sucrose (%)	Refractive Index at 20°	Sucrose (%)	Refractive Index at 20°	Sucrose (%)
1.4096	45.0	1.42646	53.0	1.44420	61.0	1.46299	69.0	1.48288	77.0
.4100	45.2	.42689	53.2	.44465	61.2	.46347	69.2	.48339	77.2
.4104	45.4	.42733	53.4	.44511	61.4	.46396	69.4	.48390	77.4
.4109	45.6	.42776	53.6	.44557	61.6	.46444	69.6	.48442	77.6
.4113	45.8	.42819	53.8	.44603	61.8	.46493	69.8	.48493	77.8
.4117	46.0	.42862	54.0	.44649	62.0	.46541	70.0	.48544	78.0
.4121	46.2	.42906	54.2	.44695	62.2	.46590	70.2	.48596	78.2
.4125	46.4	.42949	54.4	.44741	62.4	.46639	70.4	.48648	78.4
.4129	46.6	.42993	54.6	.44787	62.6	.46688	70.6	.48699	78.6
.4133	46.8	.43036	54.8	.44833	62.8	.46737	70.8	.48751	78.8
.4137	47.0	.43080	55.0	.44879	63.0	.46786	71.0	.48803	79.0
.4141	47.2	.43124	55.2	.44926	63.2	.46835	71.2	.48855	79.2
.4145	47.4	.43168	55.4	.44972	63.4	.46884	71.4	.48907	79.4
.4150	47.6	.43211	55.6	.45019	63.6	.46933	71.6	.48959	79.6
.4154	47.8	.43255	55.8	.45065	63.8	.46982	71.8	.49011	79.8
.4158	48.0	.43299	56.0	.45112	64.0	.47032	72.0	.49063	80.0
.4162	48.2	.43343	56.2	.45158	64.2	.47081	72.2	.49115	80.2
.4166	48.4	.43387	56.4	.45205	64.4	.47131	72.4	.49167	80.4
.4171	48.6	.43432	56.6	.45252	64.6	.47180	72.6	.49220	80.6
.4175	48.8	.43476	56.8	.45299	64.8	.47230	72.8	.49272	80.8
.4179	49.0	.43520	57.0	.45346	65.0	.47279	73.0	.49325	81.0
.4183	49.2	.43564	57.2	.45393	65.2	.47329	73.2	.49377	81.2
.4187	49.4	.43609	57.4	.45440	65.4	.47379	73.4	.49430	81.4
.4192	49.6	.43653	57.6	.45487	65.6	.47429	73.6	.49483	81.6
.4196	49.8	.43698	57.8	.45534	65.8	.47479	73.8	.49536	81.8
.42008	50.0	.43742	58.0	.45581	66.0	.47529	74.0	.49589	82.0
.42050	50.2	.43787	58.2	.45629	66.2	.47579	74.2	.49641	82.2
.42092	50.4	.43832	58.4	.45676	66.4	.47629	74.4	.49695	82.4
.42135	50.6	.43877	58.6	.45724	66.6	.47679	74.6	.49748	82.6
.42177	50.8	.43922	58.8	.45771	66.8	.47730	74.8	.49801	82.8
.42219	51.0	.43966	59.0	.45819	67.0	.47780	75.0	.49854	83.0
.42261	51.2	.44011	59.2	.45867	67.2	.47831	75.2	.49907	83.2
.42304	51.4	.44057	59.4	.45914	67.4	.47881	75.4	.49961	83.4
.42347	51.6	.44102	59.6	.45962	67.6	.47932	75.6	.50014	83.6
.42389	51.8	.44147	59.8	.46010	67.8	.47982	75.8	.50068	83.8
.42432	52.0	.44192	60.0	.46058	68.0	.48033	76.0	.50121	84.0
.42475	52.2	.44238	60.2	.46106	68.2	.48084	76.2	.50175	84.2
.42517	52.4	.44283	60.4	.46154	68.4	.48135	76.4	.50229	84.4
.42560	52.6	.44328	60.6	.46202	68.6	.48186	76.6	.50283	86.6
.42603	52.8	.44374	60.8	.46251	68.8	.48237	76.8	.50337	84.8
								.50391	85.0

TABLE 50-8. CORRECTIONS FOR DETERMINING PERCENTAGE OF SUCROSE IN SUGAR SOLUTIONS BY MEANS OF EITHER ABBÉ OR IMMERSION REFRACTOMETER WHEN READINGS ARE MADE AT TEMPERATURES OTHER THAN 20°C.[a]
(International Temperature Correction Table, 1936)[b]

Temp. (°C.)	Sucrose (%)										
	0	5	10	15	20	25	30	40	50	60	70
	Subtract from the percentage of sucrose										
10	0.50	0.54	0.58	0.61	0.64	0.66	0.68	0.72	0.74	0.76	0.79
11	.46	.49	.53	.55	.58	.60	.62	.65	.67	.69	.71
12	.42	.45	.48	.50	.52	.54	.56	.58	.60	.61	.63
13	.37	.40	.42	.44	.46	.48	.49	.51	.53	.54	.55
14	.33	.35	.37	.39	.40	.41	.42	.44	.45	.46	.48
15	.27	.29	.31	.33	.34	.34	.35	.37	.38	.39	.40
16	.22	.24	.25	.26	.27	.28	.28	.30	.30	.31	.32
17	.17	.18	.19	.20	.21	.21	.21	.22	.23	.23	.24
18	.12	.13	.13	.14	.14	.14	.14	.15	.15	.16	.16
19	.06	.06	.06	.07	.07	.07	.07	.08	.08	.08	.08
	Add to the percentage of sucrose										
21	0.06	0.07	0.07	0.07	0.07	0.08	0.08	0.08	0.08	0.08	0.08
22	.13	.13	.14	.14	.15	.15	.15	.15	.16	.16	.16
23	.19	.20	.21	.22	.22	.23	.23	.23	.24	.24	.24
24	.26	.27	.28	.29	.30	.30	.31	.31	.31	.32	.32
25	33	.35	.36	.37	.38	.38	.39	.40	.40	.40	.40
26	.40	.42	.43	.44	.45	.46	.47	.48	.48	.48	.48
27	.48	.50	.52	.53	.54	.55	.55	.56	.56	.56	.56
28	.56	.57	.60	.61	.62	.63	.63	.64	.64	.64	.64
29	.64	.66	.68	.69	.71	.72	.72	.73	.73	.73	.73
30	.72	.74	.77	.78	.79	.80	.80	.81	.81	.81	.81

[a] From the Assoc. Offic. Agr. Chemists, Official Methods of Analysis, 9th Ed., 1960, p. 716.
[b] Int. Sugar J., 39, 24s, (1937).

Procedure.—Weigh an amount of fat or oil containing at least 50 U.S.P. units into a saponification flask, add the alcoholic potassium hydroxide (10 ml. per g. of sample) and attach to a reflux condenser. Heat on a water bath for 30 min. Wash condenser with ml. of water. Cool, dilute with 50–100 ml. of water, and transfer to a separatory funnel. Extract 4 times with 50–100 ml. of ether. Combine the ether extracts, pour two 50-ml. portions of water through the combined ether extracts and discard the water without shaking. Wash the ether extract with 50 ml. of the 0.5 M aqueous potassium hydroxide, shaking gently. Allow to separate, draw off aqueous layer, and discard. Wash with 50-ml. portions of water until free of alkali. Allow ether extract to stand 5 min., discard separated water, filter through 305 g. of anhydrous sodium sulfate, placed on filter paper in a funnel, into a 250-ml. flask. Rinse the separatory funnel with small portions of ether and add the rinses to the 250-ml. flask. Evaporate the ether to dryness on a water bath, removing the flask from direct heat toward end of the evaporation (viscous oily residue). Take up the residue immediately in chloroform, adjusting the concentration to 5–15 U.S.P. units per ml.

Transfer 2 ml. of chloroform to a colorimeter tube or cuvet and add 9 ml. of the antimony trichloride reagent with the aid of a fast delivery pipet and zero the instrument (Blank). To another tube or cuvet containing 1 ml. of the unknown solution and 1 ml. of chloroform are added 9 ml. of the antimony trichloride solution. The tube is immediately stoppered, swirled, and the absorbance read with the instrument set at 620 mμ (A). The reading should be made within 3–6 sec. after the addition of the antimony trichloride solution. To another tube or cuvet, add 1 ml. of the unknown solution, 1 ml. of a known vitamin A solution in chloroform approximately equal in concentration to that of the unknown, and treat as above (B).

Calculations.

$$\text{U.S.P. units per ml. unknown} = \frac{A}{B - A} \times \text{concentration of standard (U.S.P. units/ml.)}$$

$$\text{Vitamin A/g. sample} = \text{U.S.P. units/ml. unknown} \times \frac{\text{final volume}}{\text{sample weight}}$$

If the unknown is colored, a blank correction is made by measuring the absorbance at 620 mμ of 1 ml. of unknown plus 10 ml. of chloroform.

DETERMINATION OF THIAMINE IN FOOD PRODUCTS[34,35]

Reagents. Acid Potassium Chloride Solution.—Dissolve 250 g. of potassium chloride in sufficient water to make 1000 ml. Add 8.5 ml. of concentrated hydrochloric acid to the 1000 ml. of potassium chloride solution.

Sodium Hydroxide Solution, 15 percent.—Dissolve 15 g. of sodium hydroxide in sufficient water to make 100 ml.

Potassium Ferricyanide Solution, 1 percent.—Dissolve 1 g. of potassium ferricyanide ($K_3Fe(CN)_6$) in sufficient water to make 100 ml. Prepare fresh on the day of use.

Oxidizing Reagent.—Dilute 4.0 ml. of 1 percent potassium ferricyanide solution to 100 ml. with 15 percent sodium hydroxide solution. The solution must be used within 4 hr.

Isobutyl Alcohol.—The fluorescence of the isobutyl alcohol should not exceed 10 percent of the fluorescence of the quinine standard (below). Redistill in an all-glass apparatus and collect the fraction boiling in the range 105°–108°C.

Sodium Acetate Solution.—Prepare a 2 M solution of sodium acetate by dissolving 275 g. of $NaC_2H_3O_2 \cdot 3H_2O$ in water and dilute to 1000 ml.

Activated Zeolite.—Place 100–500 g. of 60- to 80-mesh zeolite in a suitable beaker. Stir continuously for 15 min. each with 4 portions of hot 3 percent acetic acid. The acid should cover the material. Then wash similarly 3 times with hot 25 percent potassium chloride solution. Finally wash the zeolite repeatedly with water, filter on a Büchner funnel with the aid of suction, allow to dry at 100°C., and bottle.

Enzyme Solution.—Prepare a fresh 6 percent aqueous solution from a suitable source of enzyme. Mylase-P, Polidase-S, Clarase, or Takadiastase are generally suitable.

Standard Thiamine Stock Solution.—Transfer about 25 mg. of U.S.P. Thiamin Hydrochloride Reference Standard, previously dried at 105° for 2 hr. and accurately

---

[34] Assoc. Offic. Agr. Chemists, Official Methods of Analysis, 9th Ed., 1960, p. 655.
[35] Society Public Analysts Analytical Methods Committee, Analyst, **76**, 127, 1951.

weighed, to a 1000-ml. volumetric flask. Dissolve the weighed samples in 300 ml. of dilute alcohol solution (1:3), adjusted to a pH 3.5–4.3 with diluted hydrochloric acid, and dilute to volume with the acidified dilute alcohol. Store in a light resistant bottle in a refrigerator and renew each month.

Standard Thiamine Solution.—Pipet a volume of Standard Thiamine Stock Solution, equivalent to 100 μg. of U.S.P. Thiamine Hydrochloride Reference Standard, into a 100-ml. volumetric flask, and dilute with acid potassium chloride solution to volume. Dilute 10 ml. of this solution with acid potassium chloride solution to 50 ml. Each ml. of the resulting standard preparation contains 0.2 μg. of thiamine hydrochloride.

Quinine Sulfate Stock Solution.—Dissolve 0.025 of quinine sulfate $(C_{20}H_{24}N_2O_2)_2\cdot H_2SO_4\cdot 2H_2O$, in sufficient 0.05 M sulfuric acid to make 250 ml. Store in a dark-brown bottle at a temperature below 5°C.

Quinine Sulfate Standard Solution.—Dilute 10 ml. of stock quinine sulfate solution to 1 liter with 0.1 N sulfuric acid. This solution is stable for three months if stored in a brown bottle at a temperature below 5°C.

Bromocresol Green pH Indicator.—Dissolve 100 mg. of bromocresol green with 7.2 ml. of 0.05 M sodium hydroxide and dilute with water to 200 ml.

Preparation of the Extract.—Accurately weigh or pipet into a flask of suitable size a sample estimated to contain not more than 50 μg. of thiamine. Add 65 ml. of approximately 0.05 M sulfuric acid and digest for 30 min. at 95°–100° on a steam bath, with frequent mixing. Cool the extract to below 50°C. and adjust pH to 4.0–4.5 with sodium acetate solution. Add 5 ml. of the freshly prepared enzyme solution, mix, and incubate at 45°–50°C. for 2 hr. Make up to 100 ml. by the addition of water, mix thoroughly, and filter. Discard the first 10 ml. of filtrate and collect remainder.

Purification.—Plug the bottom of an adsorption column (Thiochrome tube) and introduce an aqueous suspension of activated zeolite to give a 6-cm. column. Allow the water to drain, keep a small layer of liquid above surface of column, and pour in 10 ml. of 3 percent acetic acid. Allow to drain as before.

Transfer 10 to 50 ml. of the original extract, *containing about 5 μg. of thiamine*, to the prepared chromatographic tube. Wash the column with three 10-ml. portions of boiling hot water and discard washings.

Elute the thiamine from the zeolite by passing through the column hot acid potassium chloride solution. Collect eluate in a 25-ml. volumetric flask. Add a second 10-ml. aliquot when all of the first portion has entered the column and collect the eluate as before. Cool and dilute to volume with acid-potassium chloride solution. *This is the "sample eluate."* Repeat with an aliquot of the standard thiamine solution using 5.0 μg. of thiamine in place of the unknown.

Oxidation to Thiochrome.—*In this and all subsequent stages undue exposure of the solutions to light must be avoided.* Pipet 5 ml. of the sample eluate into each of two reaction vessels. To the first add quickly with mixing 5 ml. of the alkaline potassium ferricyanide solution; to the second, add 5 ml. of 15 percent sodium hydroxide solution. Add 25 ml. of water-saturated isobutyl alcohol and shake the tubes vigorously for 1.5 min. Centrifuge the tubes at low speed until clear supernatant extract can be obtained from each tube. Remove the stoppers, drain off the lower layer, add approximately 2 g. of anhydrous sodium sulfate to each tube, and shake vigorously for a moment.

Add 5 ml. of the standard thiamine solution into each of two reaction vessels. Treat these tubes in the same manner as directed for tubes containing the "sample eluate."

CAUTION.—To avoid changes in experimental conditions the oxidation of all solutions used in a given assay should be carried out in immediate succession. Similar precautions must be taken in measurement of their fluorescence.

Thiochrome Fluorescence Measurement.—Filter should have a narrow transmittance range; input filter with maximum about 365 mμ, and output filter with maximum about 435 mμ. Use the quinine sulfate standard solution to govern reproducibility of fluorometer. Measure fluorescence of the isobutyl alcohol extract from the oxidized sample eluate and call this reading A. Next, measure fluorescence of the extract from sample eluate which has been treated with 5 ml. of 15 percent sodium hydroxide solution and call this reading b (sample blank). Measure fluorescence of the extract from the oxidized thiamine standard solution (S). Finally, measure fluorescence of the extract of the thiamine standard solution which has been treated with 5 ml. of 15 percent sodium hydroxide and call this reading d (standard blank).

Calculation.

Micrograms of thiamine hydrochloride in 5 ml. sample eluate $= (A - b)/(S - d)$

DETERMINATION OF RIBOFLAVIN IN FOOD PRODUCTS[36]

This method is applicable to whole-grain products, grits, meal, flaked and puffed cereals, farina, and bread.

Reagents. Sulfuric Acid Solution (0.05 M.).

Sodium Acetate (2.5 M).—Dissolve 340 g. sodium acetate trihydrate and dilute to 1 liter.

Potassium Permanganate, 4 percent.—Prepare fresh daily.

Hydrogen Peroxide, 3 percent.—Dilute 30 percent hydrogen peroxide (Superoxol) 1:10 with water.

Riboflavin Stock Solutions. *Riboflavin Stock Solution I.*—Dry Riboflavin Reference Standard (U.S.P.) over phosphorous pentoxide in desiccator for 24 hr. Dissolve 50 mg. in 0.02 M acetic acid in a 500-ml. volumetric flask and make up to volume. Store under toluene in an amber bottle and refrigerate. 1.0 ml. = 100 μg. riboflavin.

Riboflavin Stock Solution II.—To 100 ml. of Riboflavin Stock Solution I add 0.02 M acetic acid solution to make 1 liter. Store under toluene in amber bottle and refrigerate. 1.0 ml. = 10 μg. riboflavin.

Riboflavin Stock Solution III.—Dilute 10 ml. of Riboflavin Stock Solution II with water to make 100 ml. 1 ml. = 1 μg. riboflavin. Prepare fresh daily, and protect from light.

Procedure. Sodium Hydrosulfite.—Accurately weigh a sample into a 100-ml. volumetric flask, using the following plan:

For Samples Containing (mg./lb.)	Weight of Sample (g.)
0.0–0.8	5
0.8–2.0	4
2.0–4.0	2

Add 75 ml. of 0.05 M sulfuric acid, mix, and either autoclave at 15 lb. for 30 min. or immerse flask in boiling water for 30 min. Shake flask every 5 min. and cool. Add 5 ml. of 2.5 M sodium acetate solution. Mix. Let stand for 1 hr. Dilute mixture to volume and filter through medium-fast paper such as Whatman No. 2 or No. 4 (or equivalent), discarding first 10 to 15 ml. of filtrate.

To each of four test tubes add 10 ml. of sample solution. To each of two of these tubes add 1 ml. of the standard riboflavin solution and 1 ml. of water (Solution A). To each of the two remaining tubes add 2 ml. of water (Solution B). Mix. To each tube add, with mixing, 0.5 ml. of 4.0 percent potassium permanganate solution. Let stand 2 min.;

[36] Am. Assoc. Cereal Chem., Cereal Lab. Methods, 7th Ed., 1962, Method 86–70.

then to each tube add, with mixing, 0.5 ml. of 3 percent hydrogen peroxide solution. Shake after adding peroxide to the solution.

Adjust fluorometer so that glass standard or sodium fluorescein solution gives suitable galvanometer deflection as directed for the instrument. Determine fluorescence of solutions A and B. Measure fluorescence with no more than 10 sec. of exposure in fluorometer. To Solution B add, with mixing, 20 mg. sodium hydrosulfite and determine blank fluorescence, C. (Do not use reading C after colloidal sulfur begins to form.)

Calculations.—

$$\text{Riboflavin mg./lb.} = \frac{B - C}{A - B} \times \frac{R}{S} \times \frac{V}{V_1} \times 0.454$$

where A = fluorometer reading of sample plus riboflavin standard,
  B = fluorometer reading of sample plus water,
  C = fluorometer reading after addition of sodium hydrosulfite,
  R = standard riboflavin,
  V = original volume of sample solution in ml.,
  V_1 = volume of sample solution taken for measurement in ml., and
  S = sample weight in grains.

DETERMINATION OF ASCORBIC ACID (VITAMIN C) IN FOOD PRODUCTS[37]

Reagents. Oxalic Acid Solution, 0.4 percent.

Stock Ascorbic Acid Solution.—Weigh accurately 100 mg. of the reference standard ascorbic acid, transfer to a 100-ml. volumetric flask, and dilute to mark with 0.4 percent oxalic acid solution.

Ascorbic Acid Standard Solutions.—Transfer 5, 10, 15, 20, and 25 ml. of the stock ascorbic acid solution to each of a series of 500-ml. volumetric flasks, and dilute to the mark with 0.4 percent oxalic acid solution. These solutions, numbered 1 to 5, contain 1, 2, 3, 4, and 5 mg. of ascorbic acid per 100 ml., respectively.

Indophenol Standard Solution.—Dissolve 12 mg. of 2,6-dichlorophenolindophenol in warm water. Filter and dilute to 1 liter with water.

Preparation of Standard Curve.—To four colorimeter tubes add the following: 10 ml. water (W); 1 ml. of 0.4 percent oxalic acid (*No. 1*); 1 mg. of working standard No. 1 plus 9 ml. of water (S); 1 ml. of working standard No. 1 (*No. 2*). Transfer tube W to a colorimeter set at 520 mμ and set instrument at zero on absorbance scale. To tube marked *No. 1* add 9 ml. of standard dye solution, mix, and record reading (L_1) exactly 15 sec. after adding the dye solution. Then adjust the instrument to zero with tube S in the colorimeter. To tube *No. 2* add 9 ml. of the standard dye solution, mix, and record reading (L_2) exactly 15 sec. after adding the dye solution. Treat each of the standard solutions in the same manner and construct standard curve by plotting absorbance of total dye minus that of the standard solutions ($L_1 - L_2$) *vs.* concentrations of the standard solutions (mg./100 ml.).

Procedure.—Blend 50 g. of sample for 30 min. in a Waring Blendor with 350 ml. of 0.4 percent oxalic acid solution and filter. Obtain L_1 reading as described above. To tube S add 1 ml. filtrate plus 9 ml. water and adjust instrument to zero. To tube *No. 2* add 1 ml. filtrate plus 9 ml. of dye and record L_2 reading after 15 sec. Calculate $L_1 - L_2$ and obtain the concentration of ascorbic acid from the standard curve.

[37] Loeffler, H. J., and Ponting, Ind. Eng. Chem., Anal. Ed., **14,** 846, 1942.

DETERMINATION OF NIACIN IN FOOD PRODUCTS
(CYANOGEN BROMIDE METHOD)[38,39]

Reagents. Concentrated Hydrochloric Acid.

Sulfuric Acid, 5 M.

Sulfuric Acid, M.

Sulfuric Acid, 0.1 M.

Sodium Hydroxide, 10 M.

Sodium Hydroxide, 0.5 M.

Lloyd Reagent (Hydrated Aluminum Silicate).

Phenolphthalein Solution, 1 percent in 70 percent ethanol.

Phosphoric Acid Solution, 20 percent.

Standard Niacin Stock Solution.—Dissolve 500 mg. of U.S.P. reference standard niacin, previously dried stored in desiccator, in 5 ml. of 5 M sulfuric acid in a 500-ml. volumetric flask. Dilute to the mark with water. *Keep under refrigeration and protect from light.*

Standard Niacin Solution.—Dilute 5 ml. of standard niacin stock solution to 200 ml. with water. Prepare fresh daily.

Cyanogen Bromide Solution, 0.5 M.—(CNBr is very poisonous. Prepare and use only in hood. If solution comes in contact with skin, wash with water at once.) Dissolve 53 g. CNBr crystals in water in an Erlenmeyer flask calibrated at 1000 ml. Dilute to mark.

Hydrochloric Acid, 8 M.

Hydrochloric Acid, 0.5 M.

p-Methylaminophenol Sulfate (Metol or Photol).—Dissolve 10 g. in 200 ml. 0.5 M HCl in amber colored bottle. Prepare fresh daily. Do not use discolored solution.

Procedure.—Weigh sample (usually 5 g.) and transfer to a centrifuge tube. Dilute to 15 ml. with water and add 5 ml. concentrated hydrochloric acid. Place centrifuge tubes in a rack in a boiling-water bath for 1 hr., stirring occasionally. Cool to room temperature by placing in cold-water bath. Dilute to 25 ml. with water and stir well. Filter into small beakers, using Whatman No. 40 (or equivalent) filter paper.

Pipet a 10-ml. aliquot to a 50-ml. beaker. Add 2 ml. of 10 M sodium hydroxide, cool, and adjust pH to 1.0. Then transfer quantitatively to a centrifuge tube containing 2 g. of Lloyd reagent, using a small amount of 0.1 M sulfuric acid as wash solution. Stir for 1 min. Wash sides of tube and stirring rod with 0.1 M sulfuric acid. Centrifuge 5 min. at 2000 r.p.m. Discard supernatant liquid. Wash residue with 10 ml. of 0.1 M sulfuric acid, stirring sufficiently to break up clumps of the Lloyd reagent. Wash sides of tube and stirring rod with 0.1 M sulfuric acid and centrifuge as before. Discard supernatant liquid. Add 15 ml. of 0.5 M sodium hydroxide. Stir for 1 min. Dilute to 21.2 ml. with water and stir to mix thoroughly. Centrifuge as above. Drain supernatant liquid into a centrifuge tube containing 1 g. of pulverized lead nitrate and 1 drop of phenolphthalein solution. Stir until pink color disappears. Centrifuge as above. Decant liquid into centrifuge tube containing 1 drop of phenolphthalein solution. Add tribasic potassium phosphate crystals to give a pink color. Carefully add 20 percent phosphoric acid to change pH to 4.5 (1 drop is usually sufficient). Centrifuge. Supernatant liquid is used for color readings (sample extract).

Cereal products may contain substances which react with aromatic amines to give a yellow color not due to niacin. This error is eliminated by use of a correction series as described below.

[38] Assoc. of Vitamin Chemists, Methods of Vitamin Assays, 2nd Ed., 1951, p. 184.
[39] Am. Assoc. Cereal Chemists, Cereal Lab. Methods, 7th Ed., 1962, Method 86–50.

	Instrument Blanks		Stand-ard Niacin (ml.)	Sample Tubes	
	Total Color (ml.)	Amine Corr. (ml.)		Total Color (ml.)	Amine Corr. (ml.)
Sample extract	0	0	0	4	4
Niacin standard solution	0	0	1	0	0
Water	7	9	6	3	5
KH_2PO_4	1	1	1	1	1
CNBr	2	0	2	2	0
p-Methyl animophenol sulfate	10	10	10	10	10

First transfer 4-ml. aliquots of sample extract to colorimeter tubes. Add 1 ml. of standard niacin solution to a colorimeter tube. To all tubes add 1 ml. of 10 percent monobasic potassium phosphate (KH_2PO_4). Add required volume of water to the tubes. Place all tubes in water bath at 70° for 5 min. Under diffused light in hood add 2 ml. of cyanogen bromide solution from a buret to required tubes at 15-sec. intervals. Mix by swirling 5 min. after adding cyanogen bromide to first tube, and transfer it to water bath at 25°. Transfer other tubes, in order, at 15-sec. intervals. Add p-methylaminophenol sulfate solution as indicated, and mix. Place tubes in dark place for 1 hr.

Transfer the "total color blank" to a suitable colorimeter set at 420 mμ and set instrument at zero on absorbance scale. Then read sample tubes of that series. No correction is needed for standard niacin solution. Correct absorbance of sample by subtracting absorbance of amine correction.

Calculations.

$$\text{Niacin mg./lb.} = \frac{25}{A} \times \frac{B}{S} \times D \times 0.454$$

where A = absorbance of standard niacin solution,
B = corrected absorbance of sample,
S = sample weight, and
D = dilution factor. (If volumes given above are used, dilution factor is $\frac{25}{10} \times \frac{20}{4} = \frac{25}{2}$.)

MISCELLANEOUS METHODS

NITROGEN DETERMINATION BY A CONTINUOUS DIGESTION AND ANALYSIS SYSTEM

The food industry constantly employs nitrogen analysis to determine the protein content of various foods and food products, and thus assess their nutritive value. Similarly, a great many foods are sold or purchased on the basis of their protein content. Thus, a rapid and accurate analysis is essential. The availability of automatic analyzing systems[40, 41, 42] provides a means to determine nitrogen by the Kjeldahl procedure, that is, the liberated ammonia present in a digested sample.

[40] Ferrari, A., Russo-Alesi, F. M., and Kelly, J. M., Anal. Chem., **31,** 1710, 1959.
[41] Ferrari, A., Ann. N. Y. Acad. Sci., **87,** 792, 1960.
[42] Lundgren, D. P., Ann. N. Y. Acad. Sci., **87,** 904, 1960.

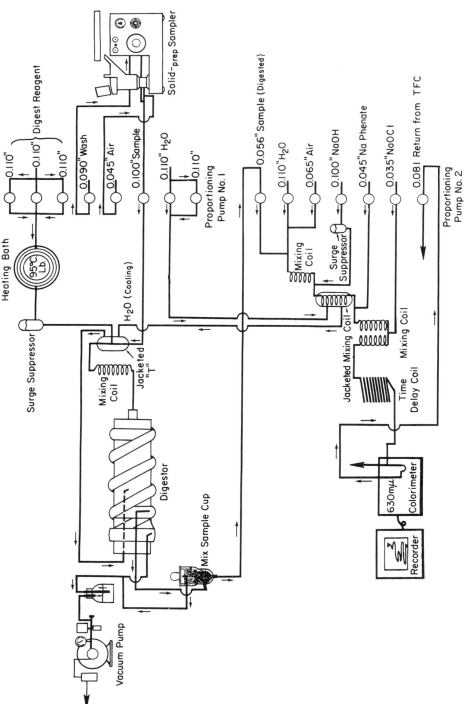

FIG. 50-1. Nitrogen Analysis Performed by the Automatic Auto Analyzer. (Reproduced with permission from Technicon Controls, Inc., Chauncey, N.Y.)

1158

Reagents. **Digestion Solution.**—Dissolve 3.0 g. selenium dioxide in 50 ml. of hot water, cool, then carefully add to 900.0 ml. of sulfuric acid (sp. gr. 1.85). Add 20 ml. perchloric acid (68–70 percent) carefully to the sulfuric acid–selenium dioxide mixture. When cool make up to a final volume of 1000 ml. with water.

Neutralizing Solution.—Dissolve 350 g. sodium hydroxide in 700 ml. distilled water. Dissolve 50 g. disodium EDTA in sufficient water (100 ml.), then add to the sodium hydroxide solution and dilute to 1 liter.

Sodium Phenate Reagent.—Transfer approximately 281 ml. of liquefied phenol to a 2-liter Erlenmeyer flask. Place flask in a cold water bath, add 500 ml. 40 percent sodium hydroxide with constant stirring. When phenol crystals are dissolved, transfer to a 1000-ml. volumetric flask and dilute to volume with distilled water. Store in polyethylene bottles. Proper cooling, stirring, and slow addition of sodium hydroxide will give a light-colored solution with a corresponding low reagent blank.

Sodium Hypochlorite Solution.—Any solution containing 4–6 percent chlorine can be used. Clorox (made by Purex Company) has been found to be completely satisfactory.

Ammonium Sulfate Stock Solution.—Dissolve 100 g. ammonium sulfate in distilled water and dilute to 1 liter. (1.0 ml. = 0.1 g. ammonium sulfate). To make reference standards equivalent to 1.0, 2.0, 4.0, 6.0, 8.0, and 10.0 percent protein, dilute 7.54, 15.10, 30.20, 45.20, 60.30, and 75.40 ml. of stock solution to 100 ml. with water. The following equation was used to compute the above.

$$\frac{\text{g. protein}}{100 \text{ ml.}} \times \frac{1}{6.25} \times \frac{132.146}{28.016} = \text{g. ammonium sulfate/100 ml.}$$

Procedure.—The flow diagram (Fig. 50-1) outlines the nitrogen analysis performed by the Automatic Auto Analyzer.[43] The system is controlled by 2 multichannel proportioning pumps which deliver fixed volume ratios of sample and reagents to the other components in the system. The sequence is as follows:

The samples are placed in the automatic sample changer. Pump No. 1 delivers through appropriate channels the desired volume of digestion solution, as well as aspirating the sample from the sampler. The combined streams of sample and digestant solution may be decreased or increased by varying the temperature and time of passage through the furnace. On emerging from the digestor, the digested sample is continuously diluted with water added by a glass pipet. The diluted sample is then aspirated by a small vacuum pump into a mixing chamber. After thorough mixing, an aliquot is pumped through the channel of Pump No. 2 and the excess digested sample goes off as waste. The aliquot of diluted digestion mixture is introduced into a stream of sodium hydroxide solution, and ammonia-free air is introduced for segmentation. After mixing, the solution passes through a mixing coil and is joined by a stream of alkaline phenol, mixed, sodium hypochlorite solution is added and mixed. After a time delay of approximately 5 min. the resultant reaction passes into the colorimeter, where its absorbance is recorded at 630 mμ. Determine the percent protein from a standard curve.

Standard Curve.—The working standards are presented to the Auto Analyzer for analysis. Plot absorbance of the working standards against percent protein.

KARL FISCHER METHOD FOR MOISTURE DETERMINATION

The method is most suitable for materials in which only traces of moisture are present.

Reagents. **Karl Fischer Reagent.**—Add 125 g. iodine to a solution containing 670 ml. absolute methanol and 170 ml. pyridine. Pass dry sulfur dioxide into 100 ml. of cooled

[43] Technicon Controls, Inc., Chauncey, N. Y.

pyridine, contained in a 250-ml. graduated cylinder, until the volume is 200 ml. Slowly add the latter solution, with shaking, to the cooled iodine solution. Shake well to dissolve the iodine and transfer to an automatic buret. Allow to stand overnight before standardizing (one ml. = approximately 8 mg. water).

Standard Water Solution.—Pipet 2 ml. water, between 20° and 25°C. into a dry 1000-ml. volumetric flask. Dilute to volume with absolute methanol. Retain sufficient amount of the same methanol for blank determinations.

Standardization of Karl Fischer Reagent Using Sodium Tartrate Dihydrate.[44] Select a sample of sodium tartrate dihydrate, the water content of which has been established as 15.66 ± 0.05 percent by heating at 150°C. for 3 hr. The sodium tartrate dihydrate sample size is determined from the water equivalence of the Karl Fischer reagent and the size of the buret used, since 1 g. of the salt contains 156.6 mg. of water. For example, a 300-mg. sample will require 9.4 ml. of a solution whose strength is equivalent to about 5 mg. of water per ml.

Pipet 25 ml. absolute methanol into a clean, dry titration flask and titrate to the end point with the Karl Fischer reagent. Quickly add the sodium tartrate and titrate again. Determine the weight of sodium tartrate by difference. The weight of sodium tartrate multiplied by 0.1566 and divided by the milliliters of Karl Fischer reagent gives the strength of Karl Fischer reagent in equivalent milligrams of water per milliliter.

Standardization of the Water in Methanol.—After titration of the methanol with Karl Fischer reagent, the water equivalence of the methanol is calculated as follows:

$$\text{Mg. water/ml. methanol} = \frac{\text{ml. Karl Fischer reagent} \times \text{equivalence}}{\text{ml. methanol}}$$

Equipment.—Since Karl Fischer reagent reacts with water, exposure to atmospheric moisture must be avoided. Consequently, the Karl Fischer reagent and the standard water in methanol solution should be stored in automatic burets, protected with a desiccant. The titration is carried out in a flask fitted with a two-hole stopper, one hole for the buret tip and the other hole fitted with a vent tube filled with a desiccant. Stirring is accomplished by means of a magnetic stirrer. A source of dry purge gas is also needed to displace moist air over the sample. Typical suitable purge gases are dry air and dry nitrogen.

The electrometric method used for water determination involves the use of the "dead-stop" end point, wherein the electrodes are either a self-polarizing platinum-tungsten pair, or an externally polarized platinum-platinum pair.

The externally polarized electrode system is recommended. A convenient apparatus for determining the end point is a pH meter, such as the Beckman Expanded Scale pH meter. The pH meter should be equipped with a polarizing jumper and two platinum electrodes. (An instrument designed specifically for automatic titration of water is the Beckman Aquameter.) A simple and convenient apparatus[45] may be constructed as follows:

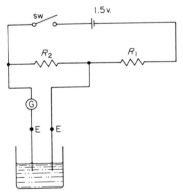

Fig. 50-2.   Electrical Circuit for Karl Fischer Water Determination.

[44] Neuss, J. D., O'Brien, M. G., and Frediani, H. A., Anal. Chem., **23**, 1332, 1951.

Two platinum electrodes, connected in series with a potentiometer-type resistor (2000 ohms) and a galvanometer, are polarized with a potential of 10–15 millivolts, just sufficient to balance the back e.m.f. (see Fig. 50-2). When a solution is titrated with Karl Fischer reagent by means of this simple apparatus, no current flows through the galvanometer, until the end point is reached, which is indicated by a displacement of the galvanometer index. The displacement is increased by further additions of Karl Fischer reagent. On the other hand, when the reverse titration is made, *i.e.*, when the Karl Fischer reagent is titrated with standard water in methanol solution, the galvanometer will be deflected off the scale. Then, as successive drops of the titrant are added immediately preceding the end point, the galvanometer index approaches the zero point of the scale until, coincident with the disappearance of the last trace of Karl Fischer reagent, it comes to zero and remains there, after an excess of titrant has been added.

Procedure. **(A) Direct Titration.**—Add about 25 ml. of dry methanol to the titration flask and titrate to the end point with the standardized Karl Fischer reagent. Do not record the volume consumed since it is the starting point for all titrations. Weigh sufficient sample to contain between 10 to 50 mg. of water and quickly transfer to the titration flask. Stir vigorously and titrate again to the end point noting the buret readings both before and after this titration.

$$\text{Percent water} = \frac{\text{ml. Karl Fischer reagent} \times \text{equivalence}}{\text{weight of sample in grams} \times 10}$$

(B) Reverse Titration.—Add about 25 ml. of dry methanol to the titration flask and titrate to the end point with the standardized Karl Fischer reagent. Introduce the sample and a measured amount of Karl Fischer reagent known to be more than required to react with the water present; allow sufficient time for complete reaction. Titrate to the end point with standardized water in methanol solution and calculate the percent water present as follows:

Percent water =

$$\frac{(\text{ml. Karl Fischer reagent} \times \text{equivalent}) - (\text{ml. standard methanol} \times \text{equivalent})}{\text{weight of sample in grams} \times 10}$$

MOISTURE ELECTRICAL METHODS

The proportion of water in foods affects their electrical properties and, as a consequence, electrical instruments are available which measure the frequency, resistance and dielectric properties. For example, the Tag-Heppenstall Moisture Meter or Steinlite Moisture Tester are available for the rapid estimation of water in whole grains.[46] The manufacturers of these instruments furnish conversion tables for their use. Such instruments are useful for making rapid checks of the moisture content wherein accuracies not greater than ±1 per cent are required.

[45] Foulk, C. W., and Bawden, A. T., J. Am. Chem. Soc., **48**, 2044, 1926.
[46] Am. Assoc. Cereal Chemists, Cereal Laboratory Methods, 7th Ed., 1962, Method 44-10.

Chapter 51

ORGANIC FUNCTIONAL GROUPS

By Hans J. Stolten
Central Research Laboratory
General Aniline & Film Corp.
Easton, Pennsylvania

INTRODUCTION

Instrumental methods of analysis have not only become well established in analytical chemistry, but some have essentially achieved the status of classical techniques. Many excellent treatises have been published on every aspect of each of these analytical tools; to cover them, even cursorily, in a chapter of this type is an overwhelming undertaking. Restricting the coverage to those techniques useful in the quantitative analysis of organic functional groups renders the problem only slightly less formidable. Therefore, the following discussions are treated in such a manner that the practicing organic analyst, when faced with a particular analytical problem, may find the brief exposition and selected illustrations sufficiently informative to enable him to decide on the utility of a given technique as an aid to the solution of his problem. The instrumental methods described are those of absorption spectrometry including the infrared, near infrared, and ultraviolet regions of the spectrum, gas chromatography, mass spectrometry, nuclear magnetic resonance, polarography, optical rotatory dispersion, and Raman spectrometry. This order essentially corresponds to one based on the numerical frequency with which these methods are employed in the analytical laboratory at the present time.[1]

ABSORPTION SPECTROMETRY

The general quantitative procedures applicable to all types of absorption spectrometry are described here in order to avoid needless repetition in the illustrative methods for each technique.

Theory and Calculations.—In its simplest terms the application of absorption spectrometry in quantitative organic functional group analysis involves the location of a reasonably unique absorption peak, in a given region of the spectrum, for the functional group of interest and the relation of the intensity of this peak to the concentration of the functional group responsible for it. This relation is treated mathematically by a combination of the Beer-Bouquer-Lambert laws into an equation of the form: $A = abc$

where: A = absorbance due to the functional group at the wavelength selected;
  a = absorptivity of the group at the same wavelength;
  b = cell thickness (sample path length); and
  c = concentration of the sample containing the functional group in convenient units, *i.e.*, w/v.

[1] Industrial Research, Vol. 6, pp. 50–51, June, 1964.

The absorbance, A, is defined as $\log_{10} P_0/P$, i.e., the logarithm to the base 10 of the ratio of the incident radiant power to the transmitted radiant power. The absorptivity, a, is obtained by calibration from absorbance measurements made on a pure material under the conditions of the analysis. An unknown sample is then analyzed by measuring the absorbance, A, and calculating the value of the concentration, c, employing the known values of a and b, i.e., $c = A/ab$.

When the analysis involves a mixture of different components, it is rarely possible to apply the above treatment to the absorption maximum for each component since interferences in the form of overlapping peaks usually occur. In this case, when the absorption maximum of each component is known, and it is assumed that the absorbancies of each component are additive at the wavelengths measured, the mathematical treatment takes the form:

$$A\lambda_1 = a_1\lambda_1 c_1 + a_2\lambda_1 c_2 + \cdots + a_n\lambda_1 c_n$$
$$A\lambda_2 = a_1\lambda_2 c_1 + a_2\lambda_2 c_2 + \cdots + a_n\lambda_2 c_n$$
$$A\lambda_n = a_1\lambda_n c_1 + a_2\lambda_n c_2 + \cdots + a_n\lambda_n c_n$$

where c_1, c_2, and c_n are the concentrations of the components of the mixture, $A\lambda_1$, $A\lambda_2$, and $A\lambda_n$ are the absorbances of the mixture at each wavelength, and $a_1\lambda$, $a_2\lambda$, and $a_3\lambda$ are the absorptivities of the components at the corresponding wavelengths. Since the path length or cell thickness b is the same for each component, it does not appear in the equations, or it may be combined as a constant with the absorptivities, a. These equations may be solved for the concentration values, c, by any standard mathematical treatment such as matrix inversion, successive approximation, determinants, or graphical procedures.

The procedure used for the measurement of the absorbance values will depend on the type of spectrometer employed. The most widely used technique is the baseline method[2] which applies to any recorded spectrum. This technique involves the recording or selection of a portion of the spectrum containing the absorption peak to be measured. Two wavelengths, on each side of the peak, are chosen at which the transmitted radiant power is at a maximum. A straight line, tangent to the spectrum curve, is drawn between these points. At the wavelength of the absorption peak, the distance from the zero transmitted power line to the baseline is P_0 and the distance from the zero transmitted power line to the absorption maximum is P. The absorbance is calculated by $A = \log_{10} P_0/P$. The same baseline is used for subsequent measurements.

Sample Handling.—Spectra, in the ultraviolet region, are usually obtained on either gases or liquids. Quartz cells ranging in thickness from 0.1 to 100 mm. are available for either phase; these considerably facilitate sample handling in this region. The same is essentially true of the near infrared region where glass cells of fixed thickness may also be used.

The manipulation of samples in the infrared region is somewhat more complicated, and several techniques are available for the wide variety of materials encountered.

Gases are most easily handled. Cells of path lengths of 10 mm. to 40 meters are available equipped with windows of appropriate materials such as sodium chloride or potassium bromide.

Liquids and solutions are contained in fixed-thickness, sealed liquid cells. The cell windows consist of salt plates (sodium chloride, potassium bromide, silver chloride, Irtran, etc.) separated by lead, copper, or aluminum spacers of 0.005 to 0.3 mm. thickness. Variable thickness cells are also available, as are microcells capable of yielding spectra on samples as small as 0.5 μl.

[2] Wright, N., Ind. Eng. Chem., Anal. Ed., **13,** 1, 1941.

Solid materials are handled in any of the ways described below.

(a) **Mull Technique.**—In this procedure a small amount of solid is ground with a drop or two of a mineral oil (Nujol or perfluorocarbon) in a mortar and pestle. The mull is placed in a demountable cell with appropriate windows and a suitable spacer.

(b) **Pressed Pellet Technique.**[3]—One or two mg. of sample are mixed with approximately 300 mg. of a salt such as potassium bromide by grinding in a mortar and pestle or by means of a grinder-mill or vibratory shaker. The mixture is placed in an evacuable die and subjected to pressures of 10,000 to 20,000 p.s.i. in a hydraulic press. A clear disc results which is mounted in a special holder for insertion into the spectrometer.

(c) **Cast Film Technique.**—Thin films, suitable for infrared spectrometry, may be cast from solution directly on the salt plate of the cell window. The film thickness is determined by the concentration of the solute in the solvent.

(d) **Attenuated Total Reflectance.**[4,5]—The recent development of ATR attachments for infrared spectrometers enables spectra to be obtained on materials such as pastes, hard solids, fibers, and coated opaque substances which are difficult or impossible to handle by the above techniques. The incident radiation which is internally reflected in an ATR crystal interacts with a material in close contact with the reflecting surface in such a manner as to absorb the radiation and produce a spectrum quite similar to a transmission spectrum. The crystal, in the form of a truncated prism, may consist of silver chloride, KRS-5 (thallium bromide-thallium iodide) and Irtran. The intensity of the spectrum is affected both by the area of contact and the efficiency of the contact between the sample and the internal reflection crystal. The spectrum is essentially independent of the thickness of the sample.

In the infrared, near-infrared, and ultraviolet regions of the spectrum, spectra are most commonly obtained by means of double-beam instruments. These permit the compensation for radiant power losses due to cells, solvents, and matrices simultaneously, while recording the spectrum of the sample. Thus in the ultraviolet and near-infrared regions, where solvents are usually employed, the sample spectrum is obtained with a matched cell containing only solvent including any reagents which may be required in a given method in the reference beam. In the infrared region, a matched cell containing solvent (reagents), a piece of window material equivalent in thickness to that of the two cell windows, a potassium bromide pellet, or an ATR crystal plate in an appropriate mounting is placed in the reference beam depending on whether solutions, neat liquids, or solids are employed. With single-beam instruments the same type references are used and two spectral scans are made; the first with the particular reference material in the beam, and the second with the sample in the beam. The absorptions due to the sample are obtained by the differences between the two spectral curves.

In the examples described for each of the following methods, it is assumed that the appropriate reference materials are employed as described above.

INFRARED SPECTROMETRY

Infrared spectrometry is one of the most useful and the most widely used techniques employed in the elucidation of the structure as well as in the qualitative and quantitative analysis of organic molecules. Its utility is based on the fact that absorption peaks due to a specific configuration of atoms in a molecule occur at certain essentially invariant wavelengths in the infrared spectrum. The literature is rich in the applications of

[3] Stimson, M. M., J. Am. Chem. Soc., **74**, 1805, 1952.
[4] Harrick, N. J., Anal. Chem., **36**, 188, 1964.
[5] Fahrenfort, J., Spectrochim. Acta, **17**, 698, 1961.

infrared spectrometry,[6,7,8,9,10,11,12] and, due to the wide variety of problems encountered, it is impossible to illustrate the analysis of functional groups in each case. Instead, some typical analyses and some of those illustrating ingenuity beyond the obvious are described. No calibration curves are presented since they would be obtained with the actual reagents with the particular instrument on hand.

HYDROCARBONS-ALKANES (PARAFFINS)

Characteristic Absorptions

Functional Group	Microns (μ)	$cm.^{-1}$
$>CH$	3.45–3.47	2900–2880
$>CH_2$	3.43–3.51	2920–2850
$-CH_3$	3.35–3.48	2990–2870
$>CH_2$	6.82–7.12	1468–1404
	7.40–8.70	1351–1150
$-CH_3$	7.18–7.38	1392–1355
	8.30–9.20	1205–1088
	10.00–11.30	1000– 895
$(CH_3)_2\overset{\mid}{C}-$	7.19–7.24(1)	1390–1380(1)
	7.24–7.38(2)	1380–1355(2)
$(CH_3)_3C-$	7.22–7.30(1)	1385–1370(1)
	7.30–7.38(2)	1370–1355(2)
$-(CH_2)_{3+n}-$	13.00–14.00	770–715

The determination of methine, methylene, and methyl groups in the carbon-hydrogen stretching vibration region of 3.3–3.5 μ by infrared techniques requires the use of lithium fluoride, calcium fluoride, or grating optics in order to achieve the resolution necessary for the discrimination of these bands. While this procedure is useful at times, these groups are more readily determined by the techniques of mass spectrometry and nuclear magnetic resonance. There are many more instances where use is made of the absorption peaks in the carbon-hydrogen bending vibration region of 6.75–14.00 μ. Of these, the analysis of hydrocarbon copolymers and the determination of chain branching in alkylbenzenesulfonates are typical applications.

Example: *THE ANALYSIS OF ETHYLENE-PROPYLENE COPOLYMERS*

Several similar infrared spectrometric procedures are used for the analysis of the composition of ethylene-propylene copolymers which differ only in the selection of the

[6] Bellamy, L. J., The Infrared Spectra of Complex Organic Molecules, 2nd Ed., John Wiley, New York, 1958.

[7] Cross, A. D., Introduction to Practical Infrared Spectroscopy, Butterworth Scientific Publications, London, 1960.

[8] Nakanishi, Koji, Infrared Absorption Spectroscopy-Practical, Holden-Day, Inc., San Francisco, 1962.

[9] Cole, A. R. H., Applications of Infrared Spectroscopy, Chapter III, in A. Weissberger, Ed., Technique of Organic Chemistry, Vol. XI, Interscience, New York, 1963.

[10] Silverstein, R. M., and Bassler, G. C., Spectrometric Identification of Organic Compounds, John Wiley, New York, 1963.

[11] Potts, W. J., Jr., Chemical Infrared Spectroscopy, Vol. 1: Techniques, John Wiley, New York, 1963.

[12] Rao, C. N. R., Chemical Applications of Infrared Spectroscopy, Academic Press, New York, 1963.

individual absorption maxima for the analysis of the components. Wei[13] and Drushel and Iddings[14] make use of the methyl wagging vibration at 8.7 μ and the methylene chain rocking vibration at 13.9 μ. The logarithm of the ratio of the absorbances at 8.7 μ and 13.9 μ is directly proportional to the molar concentration of propylene in the copolymer. Cornish[15] uses the ratios of the absorbances of the 7.25-μ and 6.82-μ maxima, due to the methyl and methylene bending vibrations, as a measure of polypropylene units. The use of ratios simplifies sample preparation since their values are independent of sample thickness.

Procedure. **Sample Preparation.**—Thin films (0.02–0.05 mm.) of the ethylene-propylene copolymer are prepared by (a) squeezing in a hydraulic press (10,000 lbs./ft.²) at elevated temperature (400°F.), (b) casting from solution on a sodium chloride plate or potassium bromide disc, and (c) placing a section of the copolymer in an attenuated internal reflectance device.

Absorbance Measurement.—The partial infrared spectrum of the sample is obtained between 6.0 and 15.0 μ. Baselines are drawn between the following approximate points of minimum absorption:

(1)   6.5 and   7.6 μ;
(2)   8.1 and   8.8 μ;
(3)   13.0 and 14.5 μ.

From these baselines, the absorbance is measured at the following absorption maxima:

(1)   6.82 and 7.25 μ;
(2)   8.7 μ;
(3)   13.9 μ.

Calculations.—The ratio of the absorbances $A_{7.25\mu}/A_{6.82\mu}$ is calculated, referred to a calibration curve, and the corresponding value of the copolymer propylene content is read from the plot.

The logarithm of the ratio of the absorbances $A_{8.7\mu}/A_{13.9\mu}$ is calculated, referred to a calibration curve, and the corresponding value of the propylene content of the copolymer is read from the plot.

Calibration curves are prepared by plotting these ratios against the molar concentrations of propylene for a series of copolymers, or a mixture of homopolymers, of known composition.

Example: *THE ESTIMATION OF THE DEGREE OF CHAIN BRANCHING IN ALKYLBENZENE-SULFONATES*

The extent of the linearity of the alkyl chain in alkylbenzene-sulfonates may readily be determined by measuring the ratio of the absorbances at 7.32 and 7.10 μ.[16] The absorbance at 7.32 μ is attributed to the bending vibrations of the methyl groups in the branched chain structures found in tetrapropylene derived alkylbenzenesulfonates. The 7.10-μ absorbance is associated with the sulfonate group, and its precise location depends on the nature of the alkyl chain.[17] The ratio of the absorbances at 7.32 μ and 7.10 μ is directly proportional to the extent to which the alkyl chain is branched. The use of ratios simplifies sample preparation since their values are independent of sample thickness.

[13] Wei, P. E., Anal. Chem., **33**, 215, 1961.
[14] Drushel, H. V., and Iddings, F. A., *Ibid.*, **35**, 28, 1963.
[15] Corish, P. J., *Ibid.*, **33**, 1798, 1961.
[16] Frazee, C. D., and Crisler, R. O., JAOCS, **41**, 334, 1964.
[17] Ogden, C. P., Webster, H. L., and Halliday, J., Analyst, **86**, 22, 1961.

Procedure. **Sample Preparation.**—(a) A 1:1 mull of the sample and hexachloro-1,3-butadiene is prepared and placed in a demountable sodium chloride cell of approximately 0.01 mm. thickness. (b) A potassium bromide pressed pellet containing the sample is prepared.

Absorbance Measurement.—The partial infrared spectrum of the sample is obtained between 6.5 and 7.9 μ. A baseline is drawn between 6.6 and 7.5 μ, the approximate points of minimum absorption. From this baseline the absorbances are measured at the absorption maxima of 7.10 and 7.32 μ.

Calculations.—The ratio of the absorbances $A_{7.32\mu}/A_{7.10\mu}$ is calculated, referred to a calibration curve, and the corresponding value of the degree of alkyl chain branching is read from the plot.

A calibration curve is prepared by plotting: (a) the value of this ratio for a known sample of linear alkylbenzenesulfonate as zero percent branched; (b) the value of this ratio for a tetrapropylene derived (branched) alkylbenzenesulfonate as 100 percent branched; (c) the values of this ratio for a series of known mixtures of these materials against the branched alkylbenzenesulfonate content.

HYDROCARBONS-ALKENES (OLEFINS)

Characteristic Absorptions

Functional Group	Microns (μ)	cm.$^{-1}$
=CH	3.23–3.34	3100–2998
—C=C— (unconjugated)	5.95–6.16	1680–1620
—C=C— (conjugated)	6.15–6.30	1625–1585
—CH=CH$_2$	7.04–7.10	1420–1410
	7.70–7.75	1300–1290
	10.05–10.15	995– 985
	10.92–11.05	915– 905
RCH=CHR$_1$ (*trans*)	10.30–10.42	970– 959
RR$_1$C=CH$_2$	10.90–11.30	917– 885
RR$_1$C=CHR$_2$	11.78–12.12	850– 825
RCH=CHR$_1$ (*cis*)	13.3–15.4 (14.5)	752– 650 (690)

The olefinic carbon-hydrogen stretching vibrations are of limited usefulness in quantitative analysis for the same reasons which apply to the comparable paraffinic absorptions. The carbon-hydrogen bending vibrations are more useful and are employed in the general analysis of olefin group types,[18] as well as in specific analyses for alpha-olefins.[19] Absorptions due to the carbon-carbon double bond stretching vibrations range from very weak to nonexistent for the isolated double bond, depending on the location of this group in the molecule. The intensity of this absorption reaches a maximum in the case of a terminal bond as occurs in a vinyl group. *Cis*-compounds generally absorb more strongly than *trans*-compounds. Conjugation, especially with an aromatic ring, increases the intensity of a terminal olefinic group sufficiently to permit quantitative analysis with reasonable sensitivity.

[18] Saier, E. L., Pozefsky, A., and Coggeshall, N. D., Anal. Chem., **26**, 1258, 1954.
[19] Saier, E. L., Cousins, L. R., and Basila, M. R., *Ibid.*, **35**, 2219, 1963.

Example: *THE DETERMINATION OF N-VINYLPYRROLIDONE IN 2-PYRROLIDONE*

The intensity of the absorption due to the vinyl group at 6.15 μ readily permits the analysis of 2-pyrrolidone for concentrations of N-vinylpyrrolidone over the range 0 to 10 percent.

Procedure. Sample Preparation.—Solutions of N-vinylpyrrolidone in 2-pyrrolidone, over the concentration range 0–10 percent, are placed in a sealed liquid cell, with sodium chloride windows, 0.01 mm. in thickness.

Absorbance Measurement.—The partial infrared spectrum of the sample is obtained between 5.0 and 6.7 μ. A baseline is drawn between the following approximate points of minimum absorption: 5.4 and 6.6 μ. From this baseline the absorbance is measured at the absorption maximum of 6.15 μ.

Calculations.—The absorbance at 6.15 μ is referred to a calibration curve and the corresponding concentration of N-vinylpyrrolidone is read from the plot.

A calibration curve is prepared by plotting this absorption against the concentration of N-vinylpyrrolidone in a series of solutions in 2-pyrrolidone of known concentration.

HYDROCARBONS-ALKYNES (ACETYLENES)

Characteristic Absorptions

Functional Group	Microns (μ)	cm.$^{-1}$
≡CH	2.95–3.05	3390–3280
C≡CH	4.67–4.76	2120–2100
—C—C≡C—C—C	4.43–4.56	2255–2190
—C≡C—C≡CH	4.54–4.90	2203–2040

The absorption due to the carbon-carbon triple bond stretching vibrations is very variable in intensity, depending on the location of the triple bond in the molecule.[20] This absorption is absent when the bond is symmetrically located and is barely detectable when located three or more positions from the end of the molecule. Consequently the most intense absorption occurs when the bond is terminally located as in mono-substituted acetylenes. Under these conditions the carbon-hydrogen stretching vibration of the triple bond group also appears with an intensity sufficient to be analytically useful.

Example: *THE DETERMINATION OF 2-BUTYNE-1,4-DIOL IN 2-BUTENE-1,4-DIOL*

Since the most intense carbon-carbon triple bond absorption is relatively weak as far as absorption intensities in general are concerned, use can be made of the effect that the triple bond unsaturation has on neighboring functional groups. In butynediol the carbon-carbon triple bond is symmetrically located and does not exhibit any absorption. However, its effect on the carbon-hydroxyl stretching vibration is sufficient to shift the wavelength of this absorption so that it is distinguishable from that due to the carbon-hydroxyl absorption of butenediol and, therefore, may be used to analyze butenediol for butynediol content. Acetonitrile solutions of butynediol exhibit a unique absorption

[20] Wotiz, J. H., and Miller, F. A., J. Amer. Chem. Soc., **71**, 3441, 1949.

band at 8.91 μ, which is analytically suitable for the determination of butynediol in butenediol over the concentration range of 1 to 8 percent.

Procedure. Sample Preparation.—0.5000 g. of a sample of butenediol containing 1–8 percent butynediol is dissolved in 10 ml. of acetonitrile. An aliquot of this solution is placed in a sealed liquid cell, with sodium chloride windows, 0.125 mm. in thickness.

Absorbance Measurement.—The partial infrared spectrum of the sample solution is obtained between 8.0 and 11.0 μ. A baseline is drawn between the following approximate points of minimum absorption: 8.81 and 9.32 μ. From this baseline the absorbance is measured at the absorption maximum of 8.91 μ.

Calculations.—The absorbance of 8.91 μ is referred to a calibration curve and the corresponding concentration of 2-butyne-1,4-diol is read from the plot.

A calibration curve is prepared by plotting this absorption against the concentration of 2-butyne-1,4-diol in a series of solutions in 2-butene-1,4-diol of known concentration.

HYDROCARBONS—AROMATIC

Characteristic Absorptions

Functional Group	Microns (μ)		cm.$^{-1}$	
CH	3.23–3.34		3095–3000	
phenyl group	6.18–6.23	(1)	1620–1602	(1)
phenyl group	6.67–6.72	(2)	1500–1489	(2)
phenyl group conjugated	6.30–6.33	(3)	1588–1579	(3)
substituted phenyl groups				
1, 4	8.26–9.27	(1)	1210–1079	(1)
1, 3	8.55–8.77	(1)	1170–1140	(1)
1, 2	8.90–9.22	(1)	1123–1085	(1)
mono	9.05–9.44	(1)	1105–1060	(1)
1, 3, 5	11.70–12.35	(1)	855– 810	(1)
1, 4	11.99–12.60	(2)	834– 794	(2)
1, 2, 4	12.05–12.58		830– 797	
1, 3	12.40–13.35	(2)	806– 750	(2)
1, 2, 3	12.42–13.00		805– 769	
1, 2	13.00–14.00	(2)	769– 714	(2)
mono	13.20–13.90	(2)	758– 720	(2)
1, 3, 5	13.70-14.80	(2)	730– 676	(2)

The aromatic nucleus, or phenyl ring, constitutes a functional group. Some functional groups, such as the hydroxyl, when occurring in alcohols, are classified as primary, secondary, and tertiary by virtue of their attachment to a primary, secondary, or tertiary carbon atom. Other functional groups, such as amines, are also classified in this manner, but on the basis of the number of the hydrogen atoms of the amine substituted by other groups. On this same basis, the phenyl ring may be considered a functional group with a larger number of classifications due to the greater number of hydrogens and the varying multiplicities and symmetries with which they can be substituted. The qualitative and quantitative analysis of isomeric aromatic hydrocarbons is a classic illustration of the use that is made of the very characteristic and intense out-of-plane bending vibration absorption bands of these materials.

Example: *THE ANALYSIS OF ISOMERIC XYLENES*

Each of the compounds *p*-, *m*-, and *o*-xylene exhibits a specific absorption maximum suitable for the determination of the content of each isomer in a sample containing these three components. The absorbance maximum for *p*-xylene occurs at 12.60 μ, for *m*-xylene at 13.04 μ, and for *o*-xylene at 13.51 μ. These peaks are attributable to the phenyl ring carbon-hydrogen out-of-plane bending vibrations in each case.

Procedure. Sample Preparation.—A series of 0.20, 0.40, 0.60, 0.80, and 1.00 percent by volume solutions are prepared in spectrographic grade cyclohexane from (a) a pure standard of *p*-xylene, (b) a pure standard of *m*-xylene, and (c) a pure standard of *o*-xylene. A solution containing 1.00 to 3.00 percent by volume in Spectrographic Grade cyclohexane is prepared from (d) a sample containing a mixture of three isomeric xylenes.

An aliquot of each of the 5 solutions of (a), of (b), of (c), and of solution (d) is placed in a sealed liquid cell, which is equipped with sodium chloride windows, 0.20–0.22 mm. in thickness.

Absorbance Measurement.—The partial infrared spectrum of each of the 16 solutions is obtained between 12.0 and 14.0 μ. A baseline is drawn between the following approximate points of minimum absorption: 12.26 and 14.0 μ. From this baseline the absorbances are measured, on each spectrum, at the following absorption maxima:

$$(1) \quad 12.60 \ \mu;$$
$$(2) \quad 13.04 \ \mu;$$
$$(3) \quad 13.51 \ \mu.$$

Calculations.—The absorbances at each of these three wavelengths, for each solution in (a), (b), and (c) above, is plotted against the concentration of (a) *p*-xylene, (b) *m*-xylene, and (c) *o*-xylene. From the slope of each line, the absorptivity at each wavelength is calculated for each isomer.

The absorbances, at each of these three wavelengths, of the sample solution (d) is equated to the sum of the individual absorbances of each component at that wavelength by means of the following equations:

$$A\lambda_1 = ap\lambda_1 Cp + am\lambda_1 Cm + ao\lambda_1 Co$$
$$A\lambda_2 = ap\lambda_2 Cp + am\lambda_2 Cm + ao\lambda_2 Co$$
$$A\lambda_3 = ap\lambda_3 Cp + am\lambda_3 Cm + ao\lambda_3 Co$$

where: $\lambda_1 = 12.60 \ \mu;$
$\lambda_2 = 13.04 \ \mu;$
$\lambda_3 = 13.51 \ \mu;$

$A\lambda_1, A\lambda_2, A\lambda_3$ = the absorbances of the sample solution at each wavelength;
$ap\lambda_1, ap\lambda_2, ap\lambda_3$ = absorptivities of *p*-xylene at each wavelength;
$am\lambda_1, am\lambda_2, am\lambda_3$ = absorptivities of *m*-xylene at each wavelength;
$ao\lambda_1, ao\lambda_2, ao\lambda_3$ = absorptivities of *o*-xylene at each wavelength; and
Cp, Cm, and Co = the concentration in volume percent of *p*-, *m*-, and *o*-xylene in the sample solution (d).

The three simultaneous equations are solved for Cp, Cm, and Co by any of the procedures mentioned under "Absorption Spectrometry: Theory and Calculations," in the beginning of the chapter.

OXYGEN-CONTAINING FUNCTIONAL GROUPS— CARBONYL GROUPS

Characteristic Absorptions

Functional Group	Microns (μ)	cm.$^{-1}$
O O ‖ ‖ —C—O—C—	5.35–5.70 (1) 5.55–5.80 (2)	1870–1755 (1) 1800–1725 (2)
lactone	5.50–5.75	1818–1740
COCl	5.51–5.65	1816–1770
COOR	5.70–5.80	1755–1725
O ‖ —C—C—C—	5.73 5.87	1745–1702
CHO	5.75 5.85	1740–1710
COOH	5.70–5.90	1755–1692
COO$^-$	6.21–6.45 (1) 6.90–7.70 (2)	1610–1550 (1) 1449–1300 (2)

The carbonyl group absorption peaks resulting from the carbon-oxygen double bond stretching vibrations are generally quite intense, reasonably specific, and subject to relatively few interferences. Due to these spectral properties of the carbonyl group, there are many infrared analyses for the determination of acid, acid halide, aldehyde, anhydride, ester, ketone, and similar functional groups.

Example: *THE ANALYSIS OF ACID CHLORIDES FOR FREE FATTY ACID CONTENT*

Aliphatic carboxylic acids, in carbon tetrachloride solution, exhibit an intense absorption maximum at 5.84 μ. Substitution of the hydroxyl group by a chlorine atom shifts the absorption of the carbonyl group to 5.55 μ. These absorption peaks are sufficiently resolved to permit their use for the quantitative determination of 0 to 5 percent fatty acid in the corresponding acid chloride.

Procedure. **Sample Preparation.**—A solution of approximately 25 percent by weight of the sample of acid chloride is prepared in dry carbon tetrachloride. (The carbon tetrachloride is distilled and stored over a dessicant.) Special precautions are taken to prevent hydrolysis of the acid chloride by atmospheric moisture. An aliquot of the solution is placed in a sealed liquid cell, with sodium chloride windows, 0.125 mm. in thickness. The operations of solution preparation and filling of the cell are most conveniently performed in a suitable dry box.

Absorbance Measurement.—The partial infrared spectrum of the sample solution is obtained between 4.80 and 6.60 μ. A baseline is drawn between the following approximate points of minimum absorption: 4.80 and 6.10 μ. From this baseline the absorbance is measured at the absorption maximum of 5.84 μ. From the partial spectrum of a solution of a standard sample of acid chloride containing no free acid, the absorbance at 5.84 μ. is measured from the same baseline.

Calculations.—The difference in absorbance at 5.84 μ between the sample solution and the standard solution is referred to a calibration curve, and the corresponding concentration of free acid is read from the plot.

A calibration curve is prepared by plotting this absorbance difference against the concentration of free fatty acid in a series of solutions of known concentration.

Example: *THE ANALYSIS OF HYDROLYZED METHYL VINYL ETHER-MALEIC ANHYDRIDE COPOLYMERS (PVM/MA)*

The copolymer *PVM/MA*, in tetrahydrofuran solution, exhibits two absorption peaks due to the carbon-oxygen double bond stretching vibrations of the anhydride carbonyl groups at 5.36 and 5.58 μ. The carbonyl of the free acid carboxyl group resulting from the hydrolysis of the anhydride absorbs over the range of 5.74 to 5.78 μ, depending on the degree of hydrolysis (concentration of carboxyl groups.) These absorption peaks are sufficiently resolved to permit the quantitative determination of the extent of the hydrolysis.

Procedure. **Sample Preparation.**—A 0.5000-g. sample of PVM/MA, in which 0–75 percent of the anhydride groups have been hydrolyzed to free carboxylic acid groups, is dissolved in 25 ml. of dry tetrahydrofuran. An aliquot of this solution is placed in a sealed liquid cell, with sodium chloride windows, 0.135 mm. in thickness.

Absorbance Measurement.—The partial infrared spectrum of the sample solution is obtained between 5.2 and 6.1 μ. A baseline is drawn between the following approximate points of minimum absorption: 5.26 and 5.96 μ. From this baseline the absorbance is measured at the absorption maximum between 5.74 and 5.78 μ. From the partial spectrum of a solution of a standard, unhydrolyzed, sample of *PVM/MA* the absorbance at 5.76 μ is measured from the same baseline.

Calculations.—The difference in the absorbance between 5.74 and 5.78 μ of the sample solution and that at 5.76 μ of the standard solution is referred to a calibration curve and the corresponding degree of hydrolysis is read from the plot.

OXYGEN-CONTAINING FUNCTIONAL GROUPS— NONCARBONYL GROUPS

Characteristic Absorptions

Functional Group	Microns (μ)	cm.$^{-1}$
—OH unbonded	2.70–2.90	3701–3450
bonded	2.90–3.12	3450–3210
H$_2$C—OH	9.30–9.90	1075–1010
H C—OH	8.90–9.10	1123–1100
—C—OH	8.50–9.15	1178–1092
⬡—OH	8.10–8.90	1235–1123
C—O—C aliphatic	8.70–9.45	1150–1059
aromatic alkyl-aryl vinyl	7.85–8.15	1272–1228

A calibration curve is prepared by plotting this absorbance difference against the degree of hydrolysis in a series of solutions of PVM/MA in which the number of anhydride groups hydrolyzed to carboxyl groups is known. (It is not possible to prepare a calibration curve from a series of solutions prepared by mixing known amounts of unhydrolyzed and completely hydrolyzed samples of PVM/MA because of the total insolubility of the latter in tetrahydrofuran; rather, the extent of hydrolysis of samples hydrolyzed to different degrees must be determined by chemical means.)

The absorption peaks due to the oxygen-hydrogen, carbon-hydroxyl and carbon-oxygen-carbon stretching vibrations are sufficiently intense and characteristic to be useful for the quantitative analysis of compounds containing these functional groups.

Example: THE DETERMINATION OF MOISTURE IN N-METHYLPYRROLIDONE

Water in N-methylpyrrolidone exhibits a unique and intense absorption peak due to the oxygen-hydrogen stretching vibration at 2.84 μ.

Procedure. Sample Preparation.—A sample of N-methylpyrrolidone, containing 0.01 to 2.00 percent water, is placed in a sealed liquid cell, with sodium chloride windows, 0.175 mm. in thickness.

Absorbance Measurement.—The partial infrared spectrum of the sample is obtained between 2.00 and 3.40 μ. The percent transmittance at 2.12 μ is measured as P_0, and the percent transmittance at 2.84 μ is measured as P. The absorbance at 2.84 μ is calculated by: $A_{2.84\mu} = \log_{10} P_{0\ 2.12\mu}/P_{2.84\mu}$.

Calculations.—The absorbance at 2.84 μ, as determined above, is referred to a calibration curve and the corresponding concentration of water is read from the plot.

A calibration curve is prepared by plotting this absorbance against the concentration of water in a series of N-methylpyrrolidone samples of known moisture content.

Example: THE ANALYSIS OF PROPARGYL HALIDES FOR RESIDUAL PROPARGYL ALCOHOL

The carbon-hydroxyl stretching vibration of the primary hydroxyl group of propargyl alcohol exhibits a unique and intense absorption maximum at 9.75 μ suitable for the determination of residual quantities of this material in either propargyl chloride or propargyl bromide.

Procedure. Sample Preparation.—The sample of propargyl halide, containing 0.01 to 1.00 percent propargyl alcohol, is placed in a sealed liquid cell, with sodium chloride windows, 0.13 mm. in thickness.

Absorbance Measurement.—The partial infrared spectrum of the sample is obtained between 9.0 and 10.0 μ. A baseline is drawn between the following approximate points of minimum absorption: 9.50 and 9.96 μ. From this baseline the absorbance is measured at the absorption maximum of 9.75 μ.

Calculations.—The absorbance at 9.75 μ is referred to a calibration curve and the corresponding concentration of propargyl alcohol is read from the plot.

A calibration curve is prepared by plotting this absorbance against the concentration of propargyl alcohol in a series of propargyl chloride or propargyl bromide samples of known propynol content.

Example: ESTIMATION OF THE ETHYLENE OXIDE CHAIN LENGTH IN ALKYLPHENOL ETHOXYLATES

The condensation products of alkylphenols and two or more moles of ethylene oxide contain both an aryl-alkyl carbon-oxygen-carbon group and an aliphatic carbon-oxygen-carbon group. The former exhibits an absorption maximum at 8.04 μ and the latter a broad absorption maximum centered about 8.92 μ. A very simple and rapid method for the estimation of the number of moles of ethylene oxide per mole of alkylphenol is based on the measurement of the ratio of these absorbances, i.e., $A_{8.92\mu}/A_{8.04\mu}$, which is a measure of the ratio of aliphatic to aryl-alkyl ether functional groups.

Procedure. Sample Preparation.—A sample of alkylphenol ethoxylate containing more than two moles of ethylene oxide (but less than the number of moles of ethylene oxide which would result in a solid product) is placed in a demountable cell with sodium chloride windows separated by a spacer approximately 0.01 mm. in thickness.

Absorbance Measurement.—The partial infrared spectrum of the sample is obtained between 6.6 and 10.4 μ. A baseline is drawn between the following approximate points of minimum absorption: 7.08 and 10.4 μ. From this baseline the absorbances are measured at the absorption maxima of 8.04 and 8.92 μ.

Calculations.—The ratio of the absorbances $A_{8.92\mu}/A_{8.04\mu}$ is calculated, referred to a calibration curve, and the corresponding number of moles of ethylene oxide per mole of alkylphenol is read from the plot.

A calibration curve is prepared by plotting the value of this absorbance ratio against the number of moles of ethylene oxide per mole of alkylphenol for a series of alkylphenol ethoxylates of known mole ratio.

NITROGEN-CONTAINING FUNCTIONAL GROUPS

Characteristic Absorptions

Functional Group	Microns (μ)	cm.$^{-1}$
N—H (unbonded)	2.85–3.05	3510–3280
N—H (bonded)	2.98–3.25	3355–3080
—C≡N	4.35–4.55	2300–2200
—N=C=O	4.35–4.80	2300–2081
Amide I (C=O)		
H$_2$N—$\overset{\vert}{C}$=O	5.90–6.05	1695–1655
RHN—$\overset{\vert}{C}$=O	5.95–6.10	1680–1639
RR'N—$\overset{\vert}{C}$=O	6.00–6.15	1667–1625
Amide II (N—H)		
O=$\overset{\vert}{C}$—NH$_2$	6.05–6.30	1655–1588
O=$\overset{\vert}{C}$—NHR	6.35–6.60	1575–1515
—NO$_2$	6.05–6.70 (1)	1655–1493 (1)
	7.30–8.00 (2)	1370–1250 (2)

The absorption bands due to the nitrogen-hydrogen stretching and bending vibrations of the amine and amide groups have an analytical utility comparable to their oxygen-hydrogen counterparts. Despite the sensitivity limitations of the nitrile and isocyanate absorption peaks, their usefulness stems from their freedom from interferences due to their occurrence in the sparsely occupied region of the infrared spectrum. Although amides are functional groups containing nitrogen, most quantitative applications involve the intense absorption of the amide I band due to the carbon-oxygen double bond stretching vibration. The properties of this band are essentially the same as those described for the other carbonyl-containing functional groups. When free from interferences, the intensities of the asymmetric and symmetric stretching vibrations of the nitro group provide excellent sensitivity for the analysis of compounds containing this group.

Example: *THE DETERMINATION OF 2-PYRROLIDONE IN N-VINYLPYRROLIDONE*

The nitrogen-hydrogen stretching vibration of 2-pyrrolidone exhibits a characteristic absorption maximum at 3.02 μ which can be distinguished from a sharp absorption peak at 2.96 μ due to N-vinylpyrrolidone and from an absorption at 2.84 μ associated with water.

Procedure. **Sample Preparation.**—A sample of N-vinylpyrrolidone, containing 1 to 5 percent 2-pyrrolidone, is placed in a sealed liquid cell, with sodium chloride windows, 0.175 mm. in thickness.

Absorbance Measurement.—The partial infrared spectrum of the sample is obtained between 2.00 and 3.40 μ. The percent transmittance at 2.12 μ is measured as P_0, and the percent transmittance at 3.02 μ is measured as P. The absorbance at 3.02 μ is calculated by: $A_{3.02\mu} = \log_{10} P_{0\,2.12\mu}/P_{3.02\mu}$.

Calculations.—The absorbance at 3.02 μ, as determined above, is referred to a calibration curve and the corresponding concentration of 2-pyrrolidone is read from the plot.

A calibration curve is prepared by plotting this absorbance against the concentration of 2-pyrrolidone in a series of solutions in N-vinylpyrrolidone of known concentration.

Example: *THE DETERMINATION OF NONYLPHENOXYPROPIONITRILE IN NONYLPHENOL*

The characteristic nitrile absorption maximum at 4.44 μ provides a simple and rapid analysis of the extent of the conversion of nonylphenol to nonylphenoxypropionitrile.

Procedure. **Sample Preparation.**—A solution, 25 percent by weight of the sample containing 1 to 100 percent nonylphenoxypropionitrile, is prepared in carbon tetrachloride. An aliquot of the solution is placed in a sealed liquid cell, with sodium chloride windows, 0.100 mm. in thickness.

Absorbance Measurement.—The partial infrared spectrum of the solution is obtained between 2.00 and 5.00 μ. A baseline is drawn between the following approximate points of minimum absorption: 4.3 and 4.6 μ. From this baseline the absorbance is measured at the absorption maximum of 4.44 μ.

Calculations.—The absorbance at 4.44 μ is referred to a calibration curve and the corresponding concentration of nonylphenoxypropionitrile is read from the plot.

A calibration curve is prepared by plotting this absorbance against the concentration of nonylphenoxypropionitrile in a series of solutions of known concentration.

Example: *THE DETERMINATION OF 2,6-TOLUENE DIISOCYANATE (2,6-TDI) AND 2,4-TOLUENE DIISOCYANATE (2,4-TDI) IN MIXTURES*

Toluene diisocyanates exhibit the characteristic absorption due to the stretching vibrations of the isocyanate group at 4.40 μ. Although *TDI* isomers are indistinguishable at this wavelength, the isocyanate groups, by virtue of their positions on the toluene molecule, give rise to unique absorptions between 9.5 and 10.5 μ. Thus 2,6-*TDI* has an absorption maximum at 9.85 μ due to the vibrations of the vicinal trisubstituted phenyl ring, and 2,4-*TDI* has the absorption of the unsymmetrically trisubstituted phenyl ring at 10.05 μ. The relative amounts of each of these isomers are determined at these wavelengths.

Procedure. Sample Preparation.—Samples of pure 2,6-TDI, pure 2,4-TDI, and the unknown mixture of these isomers are successively placed in a sealed liquid cell, with sodium chloride windows, 0.03 mm. in thickness.

Absorbance Measurement.—The partial infrared spectrum of each of these samples is obtained between 9.5 and 10.5 μ. A baseline is drawn between the following approximate points of minimum absorption: 9.5 and 10.3–10.5 μ. From this baseline the absorbances are measured, on each spectrum, at the following absorption maxima

$$(1) \quad 9.85 \ \mu.$$
$$(2) \quad 10.05 \ \mu$$

Calculations.—From these absorbance values it is seen that the absorbance of 2,6-*TDI* at 10.05 μ is 0.045 times its absorbance at 9.85 μ and that the absorptivity of 2,6-*TDI* at 9.85 μ is 5.5 times the absorptivity of 2,4-*TDI* at 10.05 μ. Therefore, the corrected absorbance at each wavelength is

$$A_{9.85\mu} \text{ corr.} = A_{9.85\mu}/5.5 \text{ and}$$
$$A_{10.05\mu} \text{ corr.} = A_{10.05\mu} - 0.045A_{9.85\mu}$$

The percent of 2,6-*TDI* is calculated by:

$$\text{Percent } 2,6\text{-}TDI = \frac{A_{9.85\mu} \text{ corr.}}{A_{9.85\mu} \text{ corr.} + A_{10.05\mu} \text{ corr.}} \times 100$$

and the percent of 2,4-*TDI* is obtained by subtracting the percent 2,6-*TDI* from 100 percent.

MISCELLANEOUS

Characteristic Absorptions

Functional Group	Microns (μ)		$cm.^{-1}$	
P—OH	3.70–4.00		2700–2500	
S—H	3.80–4.10		2635–2440	
Si—H	3.85–3.90		2600–2562	
P—H	4.10–4.35		2440–2300	
C—F	7.00–10.00		1428–1000	
—SO$_3$	7.00–7.50	(1)	1428–1334	(1)
	8.30–8.70	(2)	1204–1150	(2)
>SO$_2$	7.40–7.75	(1)	1350–1290	(1)
	8.60–8.90	(2)	1162–1122	(2)
SiO	9.00–10.00		1111–1000	
>SO	9.35–9.80		1070–1020	
Si—C	11.80–14.30		847–700	
C—Cl	13.20–15.4		758–649	

The characteristic absorptions of these various functional groups are listed under miscellaneous since they are primarily used in the qualitative infrared applications of functional group analysis. However, when the need arises on those occasions when other analytical methods are not applicable, the absorptions of these groups, or those arising from the effect of these groups as molecular substituents, may be used for quantitative analysis in methods similar to those described above.

NEAR-INFRARED SPECTROMETRY

The development of detectors sufficiently more sensitive than thermocouples in the 1.0- to 3.0-μ (near-infrared) region of the spectrum led to the availability of an instrumental analytical technique which bridged the gap between the useful ultraviolet-visible and infrared regions. Almost all the absorption bands in this region arise from the overtones of the carbon-hydrogen, oxygen-hydrogen, and nitrogen-hydrogen stretching vibrations and the combinations of these with the other types of molecular vibrations.[21,22] This region loses some of the variety and specificity for functional groups exhibited by the 3.0- to 15.0-μ infrared region, but the analyst is compensated for this qualitative loss by enhanced quantitative capabilities. Although the intensities of the bands are considerably less (by one or two orders of magnitude) than those of the infrared region, they are readily measured by the use of cells and techniques comparable to those employed in the ultraviolet region. The analytical utility of the near infrared region of the spectrum, then, lies in the quantitative determination of functional groups which contain characteristic hydrogen atoms.

The selection of solvents is important in this region since fairly dilute solutions of solutes are employed to minimize the effects of hydrogen bonding which tend to limit the discrimination of bands subject to this phenomenon. The best solvent from the standpoint of lack of interference is carbon tetrachloride (absence of hydrogen atoms) followed closely by carbon disulfide which has only one band in the vicinity of 2.2 μ. Solubility considerations necessitate the use of solvents such as chloroform, methylene chloride, and similar materials.

In the table of characteristic absorptions are listed some of those which are of proven analytical value.[23,24] The wavelengths listed are approximations of the centers of the wavelength regions in which the absorptions due to the given functional groups occur. In general, the intensities of the absorption bands diminish with decreasing wavelength. The most intense band for a given functional group, however, is not always the most useful, for, as often occurs, the weaker bands are more specific.

Characteristic Absorptions

Functional Group	Microns (μ)			
—CH$_3$	1.13;	1.68;	2.30	
>CH$_2$	1.12;	1.68;	2.36	
>CH	1.22;	1.73;		
=CH$_2$		1.62;	2.12	
≡CH		1.55;		
C—H (aromatic)	1.30;	1.68;	2.43	
O=C—H			2.08	
—OH (alcohol)	1.41;		2.05;	2.75
—OH (phenol)	1.41;	1.95;		2.77
—OH (water)	1.40;	1.90;		2.68
—NH$_2$	1.02;	1.48;	2.02;	2.85
>NH	1.07;	1.52;		2.90
=NH	1.02;	1.57		

[21] Kaye, W., Spectrochim. Acta, 6, 257, 1954.
[22] Goddu, R. F., Near-Infrared Spectrophotometry, Vol. 1: Advances in Analytical Chemistry and Instrumentation, C. N. Reilley, Ed., Interscience Publishers, New York, 1960.
[23] Wheeler, O. H., Chem. Rev., 59, 629, 1959.
[24] Goddu, R. F., and Delker, D. A., Anal. Chem., 32, 140, 1960.

HYDROCARBONS

Example: *THE DETERMINATION OF TERMINAL UNSATURATION*[25]

Aliphatic hydrocarbons containing temirnal methylene groups exhibit absorption bands in the vicinity of 1.6 and 2.1 μ arising from the first overtone of the terminal methylene carbon-hydrogen stretching vibrations and from the combination of the carbon-hydrogen stretching and other vibrations respectively. These bands are quite intense and occur in a region relatively free from interferences by the saturated carbon-hydrogen bands. The more intense 1.6-μ band is analytically useful for the determination of terminally unsaturated compounds in a variety of hydrocarbon mixtures.

Procedure. **Sample Preparation.**—For the determination of the amount of terminal unsaturation of an alpha-olefin, the undiluted sample is placed in a quartz or Corex cell 1.00 cm. in thickness.

For the determination of small to trace amounts of an alpha-olefin in saturated hydrocarbons, the undiluted sample is placed in quartz or Corex cells to 10.00 cm. in thickness.

Absorbance Measurement.—The near-infrared spectrum is obtained between the following approximate points of minimum absorption: 1.5 to 1.9 μ, with a matched cell containing carbon tetrachloride in the reference beam. A baseline is drawn between these points of minimum absorption. From this baseline the absorbance of the sample is measured at the absorption maximum of 1.62 μ.

Calculations.—The absorbance of the sample at 1.62 μ is referred to a calibration curve and the corresponding concentration of the alpha-olefin is read from the plot.

A calibration curve is prepared by plotting this absorbance against the concentration of the terminally unsaturated hydrocarbon in a series of solutions of known concentration.

OXYGEN-CONTAINING FUNCTIONAL GROUPS— CARBONYL GROUPS

Example: *THE DETERMINATION OF ALIPHATIC FORMATES*[26]

The combination of the carbon-hydrogen and carbon-oxygen double bond stretching vibrations of aliphatic formates produce an absorption band at 2.15 μ. In carbon tetrachloride solutions the intensity of this absorption band is linear with concentration. Interferences due to overlapping carbon-hydrogen bands occur with aromatic compounds, aldehydes, and materials containing a terminal methylene group, and, to a lesser extent, with alcohols.

Procedure. **Sample Preparation.**—Sufficient sample of the formate is dissolved in 25 ml. of carbon tetrachloride to provide a concentration in the range of 0.06–0.72 moles/liter. An aliquot of this solution is placed in a quartz cell 1.00 cm. in thickness.

Absorbance Measurement.—The near-infrared spectrum of the sample is obtained between 1.0 and 2.7 μ. A baseline is drawn between the following approximate points of minimum absorption across the 2.15-μ band: 2.09 and 2.20 μ. From this baseline the absorbance is measured at the absorption maximum of 2.15 μ.

Calculations.—The absorbance at 2.15 μ is referred to a calibration curve, and the corresponding concentration of the formate is read from the plot.

A calibration curve is prepared by plotting this absorbance against the concentration of formate in a series of solutions in carbon tetrachloride over the range 0.06–0.72 moles/liter.

[25] Goddu, R. F., Anal. Chem., **29**, 1790, 1957.
[26] Powers, R. M., Tetenbaum, M. T., and Han Tai, Anal. Chem., **34**, 1132, 1962.

Example: *THE DETERMINATION OF AROMATIC ALDEHYDES IN THE PRESENCE OF AROMATIC KETONES*[27]

Aromatic aldehydes exhibit two strong absorption bands at 2.21 and 2.25 μ and a weaker band at 1.25 μ The analytical band at 2.21 μ results from the combination of the formyl carbon-hydrogen and the carbon-oxygen double bond stretching vibrations. In carbon tetrachloride solutions the intensity of this absorption is linear with concentration over the range 0.006–0.600 moles/liter. This band is relatively free from interference, with the exception of epoxides and cyclopropyl groups.

Procedure. **Sample Preparation.**—Approximately 2 g. of sample are dissolved in 50 ml. of carbon tetrachloride. An aliquot of this solution is placed in a quartz cell 1.00 cm. in thickness.

Absorbance Measurement.—The near-infrared spectrum of the sample is obtained between 2.0 and 2.8 μ. A baseline is drawn between the following approximate points of minimum absorption across the 2.21-μ band: 2.18 and 2.23 μ. From this baseline the absorbance is measured at the absorption maximum of 2.21 μ.

Calculations.—The absorbance at 2.21 μ is referred to a calibration curve and the corresponding concentration of the aldehyde is read from the plot.

A calibration curve is prepared by plotting this absorbance against the concentration of aldehyde in a series of solutions in carbon tetrachloride over the range 0.006–0.600 moles/liter. 1.00-, 5.00-, and 10.00-cm. quartz cells are used to cover this range.

Example: *THE QUANTITATIVE ANALYSIS OF ACETIC ACID–ACETIC ANHYDRIDE MIXTURES*[28]

Acetic acid in acetic anhydride exhibits an absorption band at 1.505 μ due to the intermolecularly bonded hydroxyl groups of the acetic acid dimer or higher homologs. This band occurs at an absorption minimum for acetic anhydride. The absorbance of this band is not linear with concentration and, therefore, the percent transmittance of acetic acid, over the range 0–10 percent in acetic anhydride, is used instead.

Procedure. **Sample Preparation.**—The undiluted, untreated sample of acetic anhydride containing 0–10 percent acetic acid is placed in a Corex cell 1.00 cm. in thickness.

Transmittance Measurement.—The near infrared spectrum of the sample is obtained between 1.450 and 1.600 μ with a clean, dry, empty 1.00-cm. Corex cell in the reference beam. The percent transmittance is measured at the transmission minimum of 1.505 μ. A background spectral scan is obtained between 1.450 and 1.600 μ with clean, dry, empty 1.00-cm. Corex cells in both the sample and reference beams and the percent transmittance is measured at 1.505 μ.

Calculations.—The corrected percent transmittance is calculated by the following equation:

$$\text{Percent } T_{1.505\mu} \text{ (corrected)} = \frac{\% \ T_{1.505} \text{ (sample)}}{\% \ T_{1.505} \text{ (empty cells)}} \times 100$$

This value of the percent transmittance is referred to a calibration curve and the corresponding concentration of acetic acid is read from the plot.

A calibration curve is prepared by plotting the corrected percent transmittance

[27] Powers, R. M., Harper, J. L., and Han Tai, Anal. Chem., **32**, 1287, 1960.
[28] Fernandez, J. E., McPherson, R. T., Finch, G. K., and Bockman, C. D., Anal. Chem., **32**, 158, 1960.

against the concentration of acetic acid in a series of mixtures with acetic anhydride over the range 0–10 percent acetic acid.

OXYGEN-CONTAINING GROUPS—NONCARBONYL GROUPS

EXAMPLE: THE DETERMINATION OF HYDROXYL VALUES OF ALCOHOLS[29]

In dilute carbon tetrachloride or tetrachloroethylene solution, alcohols exhibit oxygen-hydrogen stretching vibration overtone bands at 1.41 μ and combination bands at 2.0 μ. The overtone band at 1.41 μ is used to determine the hydroxyl values of alcohols, which, in this procedure, are defined as the milligrams of hydroxyl per gram of sample.

Procedure. Sample Preparation.—The solvents employed in this method are dried by adding 0.5 lb. anhydrous silica gel to a liter of solvent, shaking, and filtering.

A series of solutions containing 25, 50, 75, 100, 125 and 150 mg. of hydroxyl are prepared with a standard alcohol (*e.g.*, pure dodecyl alcohol) in 50 ml. of carbon tetrachloride or tetrachloroethylene.

A sample containing 40 mg. of hydroxyl is dissolved in 50 ml. of the same solvent. If the sample contains water, add 0.5–1.0 g. anhydrous sodium sulfate, allow to stand 15 min., and filter through coarse filter paper into a dry flask. An aliquot of each of the 7 solutions is placed in a Corex cell 10.00 cm. in thickness.

Absorbance Measurement.—The near-infrared spectrum of each of the seven solutions is obtained between 1.3 and 1.6 μ against a 10.00-cm. Corex cell filled with solvent in the reference beam. A baseline is drawn between the following approximate points of minimum absorption: 1.33 and 1.55 μ. From this baseline the absorbance is measured, on each spectrum, at the absorption maximum of 1.41 μ.

Calculations.—The absorbances of the 6 standard solutions are plotted against the milligrams of hydroxyl per milliliter of solution. The absorbance of the sample solution is referred to the calibration curve and the milligrams hydroxyl per milliliter of solution is read from the plot. This value is divided by the concentration of the sample in grams per milliliter to obtain the hydroxyl value of the sample as defined above.

NITROGEN-CONTAINING FUNCTIONAL GROUPS

EXAMPLE: THE DETERMINATION OF PRIMARY AND SECONDARY ALIPHATIC AMINES IN THE PRESENCE OF TERTIARY AMINES[30]

Primary amines exhibit intense bands in the vicinity of 2.0 μ arising from the combination of the nitrogen-hydrogen stretching and bending vibrations. Secondary and tertiary amines do not have a band in this region. Primary and secondary amines have an absorption band in the vicinity of 1.5 μ due to the first overtones of the nitrogen-hydrogen stretching vibrations. Tertiary amines do not exhibit any absorption in this region. In this procedure the primary amine concentration is determined at 2.023 μ and the secondary amine at 1.5385 μ after correction for the absorption of the primary amine at this wavelength. There is no interference with this determination due to the presence of amines, nitriles, alcohols, and esters in concentrations to 10 percent.

Procedure. Sample Preparation.—Reference solutions are prepared containing:

A. 0.0, 0.250, 0.400, 0.550, 0.700, and 0.850 g. of primary amine plus 5.000 g. of the corresponding tertiary amine in 50 ml. of chloroform.

B. 0.0, 0.100, 0.300, 0.550, 0.800, and 1.000 g. of secondary amine plus 5.000 g. of the corresponding tertiary amine in 50 ml. of chloroform. The sample solution is prepared containing:

[29] Crisler, R. O., and Burill, A. M., Anal. Chem., **31**, 2055, 1959.
[30] Lohman, F. H., and Norteman, W. E., Jr., Anal. Chem., **35**, 707, 1963.

C. 5.000–6.000 g. of the tertiary amine, containing the primary and secondary amines to be determined, in 50 ml. of chloroform.

An aliquot of each of these solutions is placed in a 10.00-cm. fused silica cell.

Absorbance Measurement.—The near-infrared spectrum of each solution in A and of solution C is obtained between: 1.950 and 2.100 μ and 1.500 and 1.600 μ with the 0.0 concentration solution in a matched cell in the reference beam.

The near-infrared spectrum of each solution in B is obtained between 1.500 and 1.600 μ with the 0.0 concentration solution in a matched cell in the reference beam.

During these spectral scans stop the wavelength drive at exactly 2.023 μ and at exactly 1.5385 μ while allowing the chart drive to move the chart one division before completing the scan. This draws a horizontal line at the analytical wavelengths from which the net absorbance is measured.

The net absorbances of the solutions in A and C are measured at 2.023 and 1.5385 μ, and the net absorbances of the solutions in B are measured at 1.5385 μ as follows.

The net absorbance at 2.023 μ is measured as the distance between an extension of the 2.023-μ line in the spectrum and a horizontal line drawn through a point formed by the intersection of a line drawn tangent to the spectral curve in the vicinity of 1.900 μ and a vertical line drawn tangent to the short wavelength side of the absorption peak.

The net absorbance at 1.5385 μ is measured as the distance between an extension of the 1.5385-μ line in the spectrum and a horizontal line drawn tangent to the spectral curve in the vicinity of 1.600 μ.

Calculations.—The net absorbances of the reference solutions in A at 2.023 μ and at 1.5385 μ are plotted against the corresponding concentrations of primary amine in grams per 50 ml. of chloroform to obtain calibration curves for primary amine at each wavelength.

The net absorbances of the reference solutions in B at 1.5385 μ are plotted against the corresponding concentrations of secondary amine in grams per 50 ml. of chloroform to obtain a calibration curve for secondary amine.

The net absorbances of the sample solution are measured at 2.023 and 1.5385 μ. The primary amine content of the sample is obtained by referring the absorbance at 2.023 μ to the appropriate calibration curve and reading the concentration from the plot. This concentration is converted to an absorbance at 1.5385 μ by means of the primary amine calibration curve at this wavelength. This absorbance value is subtracted from the net absorbance of the sample solution at 1.5385 μ. This corrected absorbance is referred to the calibration curve for secondary amine and the corresponding secondary amine content of the sample is read from the plot.

MISCELLANEOUS

EXAMPLE: THE DETERMINATION OF WATER[31]

Water in most organic materials exhibits absorption bands in the vicinity of 2.7, 1.9, and 1.4 μ. The relative intensities of these bands are approximately 50, 2, and 1. The intense 2.7-μ band is greatly affected by hydrogen bonding, and can only be used with very dilute solutions to overcome this effect with a concomitant loss in sensitivity. The absorbance at 1.9 μ, then, is more useful analytically.

This procedure is unique in that the water content of the sample is determined *vs.* a blank of the same sample which has been dried by a simple technique. It is applicable to the determination of water in alcohols, aldehydes, amines, esters, and ketones.

Procedure. Sample Preparation.—150 ml. of the liquid sample containing 0.02 to 1.00 percent water is mixed with 40–80 g. of Linde Molecular Sieve 4A, 1/16-inch pellets, in a 250-ml., glass-stoppered flask and let stand 12 to 24 hours.

[31] Meeker, R. L., Critchfield, F. E., and Bishop, E. T., Anal. Chem., **34**, 1510, 1962.

An aliquot of the undried sample is placed in a silica cell, 1.00 cm. in thickness.
Absorbance Measurement.—The near-infrared spectrum of the sample is obtained between 1.7 and 2.2 μ with the dried sample in a matched cell in the reference beam. A horizontal baseline is drawn from a selected invariant point on the spectral curve which is unaffected by the water content of the sample. From this baseline the absorbance is measured at the absorption maximum at 1.9 μ.

Calculations.—The absorbance of the sample at 1.9 μ is referred to a calibration curve and the corresponding concentration of water is read from the plot.

A calibration curve is obtained by plotting the absorbance at 1.9 μ of a series of solutions containing 0.1, 0.3, 0.5, 0.7, and 1.0 percent water by weight prepared with the dried sample.

ULTRAVIOLET SPECTROMETRY

The absorption of radiant energy in the 200 to 400-mμ region of the spectrum by organic compounds has been utilized for their qualitative and quantitative determination in one of the earliest of instrumental analytical techniques. Functional group analysis in the ultraviolet region has the advantages of ease of sample preparation, a wide selection of suitable solvents, invariance of cell thickness, and a high sensitivity. It is, however, considerably limited in scope for the direct determination of functional groups since only some of those containing unsaturation exhibit characteristic absorptions of sufficient intensity to be quantitatively useful. Nevertheless the advantages inherent in this technique have led to the development of such a large number of indirect methods that most of the functional groups are amenable to analysis by ultraviolet spectrometry. The literature contains a wealth of material relating to the qualitative and quantitative applications of ultraviolet spectra.[32,33,34] In this section only the highlights of the many typical analyses, illustrating their application to functional group determinations, particularly in micro and trace quantities, are described. In each example it is assumed that the ultraviolet spectrum is obtained with the solvent employed or a blank sample in a matched cell in the reference beam.

HYDROCARBONS—ALKANES (PARAFFINS)

These compounds, by virtue of their single valence bonds, require radiant energy in excess of that found in the near-ultraviolet spectral region to undergo electronic transitions and, therefore, are transparent in the range 200 to 400 mμ. This property makes the saturated aliphatic hydrocarbons useful as solvents in this region.

HYDROCARBONS—ALKENES (OLEFINS)

Characteristic Absorptions

Functional Group	Millimicrons (mμ)
$-C=C-$	$\sim$190
$(-C=C-)_2$ conjugated	225–240
$(-C=C-)_3$ conjugated	255–280
$(-C=C-)_4$ conjugated	305–325
$(-C=C-)_5$ conjugated	335–355
$(-C=C-)_6$ conjugated	365–385

[32] Gillam, A. E., and Stern, E. S., An Introduction to Electronic Absorption Spectroscopy in Organic Chemistry, 2nd Ed., Edward Arnold, London, 1957.
[33] Bauman, R. P., Absorption Spectroscopy, John Wiley, New York, 1962.
[34] Jaffe, H. H., and Orchin, M., Theory and Application of Ultraviolet Spectroscopy, John Wiley, New York, 1962.

Unsaturated aliphatic hydrocarbons contain π electrons, in addition to the σ electrons of the saturated valence bonds, which undergo electronic transitions more readily. Although compounds containing isolated carbon-carbon double bonds absorb at longer wavelengths than those containing only carbon-carbon single bonds, they still do not absorb in the 200–400-mμ region. However, polyunsaturated hydrocarbons, in which two or more of the olefinic groups are conjugated, exhibit characteristic absorptions in this region which increase in intensity with increasing wavelength. The relative ease with which organic compounds containing isolated multiple unsaturated groups can be isomerized to the corresponding compounds in which those groups are conjugated resulted in the development of ingenious methods for the determination of the polyunsaturated constituents of fats and oils.[35,36,37]

EXAMPLE: A MICROMETHOD FOR THE DETERMINATION OF POLYUNSATURATED FATTY ACIDS[38]

Fats and oils contain acid groups with 2 to 5 or more isolated double bonds which do not absorb in the 200 to 400-mμ region of the spectrum. However, by means of a relatively simple procedure, which involves heating the material in a potassium hydroxide-ethylene glycol reagent, the acid groups are isomerized to the corresponding conjugated compounds which exhibit characteristic absorption bands in this region. The method described here is a micromethod employing a 1 to 10 milligram sample of the fat or oil.

Procedure—a. Isomerization. **Apparatus.** *Reaction tube.*—A 1 × 4.5-inch glass tube[35] to which a 5-inch length of $\frac{5}{8}$-inch test tube is sealed.

Temperature bath.—Maintained at 180°C.

Nitrogen tank (oxygen free).

Reagent.—A 21 percent solution of potassium hydroxide in ethylene glycol. Heat 100 g. of ethylene glycol to 190°C. for 10 minutes and allow to cool to 150°C. Add approximately 28 g. of 85 percent potassium hydroxide pellets. Heat this solution to 190°C., under nitrogen, for 10 minutes and allow to cool to room temperature. Standardize the reagent to 21 ± 0.1 percent potassium hydroxide by weight and store under nitrogen in a refrigerator at 40°F.

Method.—Place 5.0 g. of the reagent in the reaction tube. Heat the tube in the bath at 180°C., under nitrogen, for 15 minutes.

Add a 1- to 10-mg. sample to the reagent in the reaction tube. Remove the tube from the bath and shake for a few seconds until a clear homogeneous solution is obtained. Heat the contents of the tube at 180°C., under nitrogen, for exactly 15 minutes measured from the time the sample is added. After this period cool the contents rapidly by immersing the tube in cold water. Treat a duplicate tube, without sample, in the same manner and use as a blank.

Procedure—b. Spectrometry. **Sample Preparation.**—The contents of the reaction tube are quantitatively diluted to 25 ml. with absolute methanol. An aliquot of this solution is placed in a quartz cell 2.5 to 5.0 cm. in thickness depending on the sample size used.

Absorbance Measurement.—The ultraviolet spectrum of the sample solution is obtained between 200 and 400 mμ. The absorbances are measured at the following wave-

[35] Am. Oil Chemists' Soc., "Official and Tentative Methods", 2nd Ed., Chicago, 1946–1964.

[36] Beadle, B. W., and Kraybill, H. R., J. Am. Chem. Soc., **66**, 1232, 1944.

[37] Brice, B. A., Swain, M. L., Herb, S. F., Nichols, P. L., Jr., and Riemenschneider, R. W., J. Am. Oil Chemists' Soc., **29**, 279, 1952.

[38] Herb, S. F., and Riemenschneider, R. W., Anal. Chem., **25**, 953, 1953.

lengths: 233, 268, 315, and 345 mμ. An ultraviolet spectrometric analysis of the sample is made prior to isomerization to determine the presence of interferences (*e.g.*, naturally occurring conjugated unsaturation). Corrections for interferences are made by obtaining the spectra of the isomerized samples against a blank of untreated sample or by calculation.

Calculations.—The following equations are used for the simultaneous determination of linoleic, linolenic, arachidonic, and pentaenoic acids in fats and oils when the exact chain length of the pentaenoic acid is unknown and assumed to be a 50-50 mixture of C_{20} and C_{22} acids:

$$\text{Percent linoleic acid} = 1.092\,a_{233} - 0.573\,a_{268} - 0.259\,a_{315} - 0.126\,a_{346}$$
$$\text{Percent linolenic acid} = 1.105\,a_{268} - 0.879\,a_{315} + 0.190\,a_{346}$$
$$\text{Percent arachidonic acid} = 1.650\,a_{315} - 1.667\,a_{346}$$
$$\text{Percent pentaenoic acid} = 1.449\,a_{346}$$

where a is the absorptivity of each acid at the wavelengths indicated. The absorptivity is equal to the absorbance divided by the product of the concentration of the acid in grams per liter and the sample path length in centimeters.

HYDROCARBONS—ALKYNES (ACETYLENES)

Aliphatic hydrocarbons containing a single carbon-carbon triple bond generally do not absorb in the near-ultraviolet region. Conjugation of multiple triple bonds results in absorptions in this region which are similar to those arising from olefinic conjugation. The acetylenic compounds containing a single triple bond serve as an excellent illustration of the selectivity and sensitivity of the ultraviolet spectrometric technique for the determination of this functional group by an indirect approach.

EXAMPLE: THE DETERMINATION OF ACETYLENIC COMPOUNDS AS MERCURIC ACETATE COMPLEXES[39]

This method is based on the formation of a mercuric acetate addition product with aliphatic compounds containing a triple bond and the measurement of the ultraviolet absorptions of these products. Although mercuric acetate complexes of some acetylenic hydrocarbons absorb strongly in this region they do not exhibit pronounced absorption maxima. In this case absorbance measurements are made at the point of minimum slope. Certain dialkyl substituted acetylenic compounds do not show sufficient absorbance to be determined by this method. The presence of a second functional group in addition to the triple bond generally results in a spectrum with a definite absorption maximum.

Procedure. **Sample Preparation.**—A sample containing 1 to 10 mg. of the acetylenic compound is weighed into a 50-ml. volumetric flask. Then 25 ml. of mercuric acetate reagent (20 g. mercuric acetate per liter acetic acid) is added and the solution is diluted to 50 ml. with acetic acid. The solution is allowed to stand at room temperature for 30 minutes. A similarly prepared solution, without the sample, is used as a blank. Aliquots of these solutions are placed in quartz cells, 1.00 cm. in thickness.

Absorbance Measurement.—After 30 minutes the ultraviolet spectrum of the sample solution is obtained between approximately 260–270 and 350 mμ. The absorbance is measured at the absorption maximum or at the point of minimum slope depending on the nature of the sample.

Calculations.—The absorbance, as measured above, is referred to a calibration curve and the corresponding concentration of the acetylenic compound is read from the plot.

[39] Siggia, S., and Stahl, C. R., Anal. Chem., **35**, 1740, 1963.

A calibration curve is obtained by plotting this absorbance against the concentration of the acetylenic compound in a series of solutions of known concentration over the range 1 to 10 mg. per 50 ml of solution.

HYDROCARBONS—AROMATIC

Characteristic Absorptions

Functional Group	Millimicrons (mμ)
	255
	269
	270
	280
	292
	310
	373

Aromatic hydrocarbons are intense absorbers in the 200 to 400-mμ region of the spectrum because of the inherent conjugated unsaturation of the benzene ring. However, the variation in ultraviolet absorption caused by differences in substitution imposes a limit on this means of functional group analysis. Further, aromatic compounds containing 9 to 10 carbon atoms absorb in the same range and have similar ultraviolet spectra which makes multicomponent analysis of similar compounds of this type difficult. Nevertheless since the aromatic ring is such an excellent chromophore and may be determined with a high sensitivity, there are an enormous number of direct and indirect ultraviolet spectrometric methods available for the analysis of organic compounds containing this group. A few of these are described below.

The characteristic absorptions listed above are those which are most useful for quantitative analytical purposes rather than the most intense of the many bands which these compounds exhibit.

EXAMPLE: THE DETERMINATION OF PHENANTHRENE IN ANTHRACENE

The 292-mμ absorption maximum of phenanthrene coincides with an absorption minimum of anthracene. At this wavelength the contribution by anthracene to the absorbance of phenanthrene is 0.1 times the absorbance of anthracene at 373 mμ.

Procedure. Sample Preparation.—5.0 mg. of anthracene are dissolved in 100 ml. of isopropanol. An aliquot of this solution is placed in a quartz cell 1.00 cm. in thickness.

Absorbance Measurement.—The ultraviolet spectrum of the sample solution is obtained between 255 and 400 mμ. The absorbances are measured at 292 and 373 mμ.

Calculations.—The concentration of phenanthrene in the anthracene sample is calculated by:

$$\text{Phenanthrene (mg./100 ml.)} = \frac{A_{292} - 0.1\ A_{373}}{0.075}$$

EXAMPLE: THE DETERMINATION OF TOLUENE IN POLY(METHYLVINYL ETHER)

The polymerization of methylvinyl ether may be carried out in toluene. The determination of residual toluene in the finished polymer is readily accomplished by means of its absorption at 269 mμ.

Procedure. Sample Preparation.—Dissolve approximately 1 g. of poly(methylvinyl ether) in C.P. methanol, and dilute to 100 ml. An aliquot of this solution is placed in a quartz cell 1.00 cm. in thickness.

Absorbance Measurement.—The ultraviolet spectrum of the sample solution is obtained between 250 and 350 mμ. The difference in absorbance, ΔA_{269}, is measured between the absorption maximum at 269 mμ and the absorption minimum at 267 mμ.

Calculations.—The weight percent of toluene in the polymer is calculated by:

$$\% \text{ Toluene} = \frac{\Delta A_{269} \times 100}{0.018 \times \text{sample wt. (g.)} \times 1000}$$

EXAMPLE: THE DETERMINATION OF BENZENE IN POLY(METHYLVINYL ETHER-MALEIC ANHYDRIDE)

The copolymerization of methylvinyl ether and maleic anhydride may be carried out in benzene. The determination of residual benzene in the finished product is accomplished by an azeotropic distillation and a subsequent spectrometric analysis at the analytical wavelength of 260 mμ.

Procedure. Sample Preparation. *Apparatus.*—A 100-ml., round-bottom flask connected to a 25-ml. Dean-Starke trap fitted with a stopcock and a reflux condenser are required. A piece of glass tubing, flared at one end, and long enough to project above the level of the liquid, is placed in the trap.

Distillation.—A sample of the polymer weighing approximately 10 g. is placed in the round-bottom flask, and 50 ml. of isopropanol are added. The Dean-Starke trap is filled with isopropanol by pouring the alcohol down the condenser tube. The flask is gently heated in a hot water bath and slowly refluxed. The condensed isopropanol drops into the center of the glass tubing in the trap. At half-hour intervals the alcohol in the trap is drained into a volumetric flask. A total of six fractions is required to remove the benzene from the polymer quantitatively. The first 4 fractions are drained into a 100-ml. volumetric flask and the last 2 fractions into a 25-ml. volumetric flask. The volumes are adjusted to 100 ml. and 25 ml. with isopropanol. Aliquots from each volumetric flask are placed in quartz cells 1.00 cm. in thickness.

Absorbance Measurement.—The ultraviolet spectra of the sample solutions are obtained between 220 and 310 $m\mu$. The difference in absorbance, ΔA_{260}, for each solution, is measured between the absorption maximum at 260 $m\mu$ and the absorption minimum at 258 $m\mu$.

Calculations.—The absorbance differences as measured above, ΔA_{260}, are referred to a calibration curve and the corresponding concentration of benzene is read from the plot. The sum of the concentrations of benzene in both volumetric flasks is the concentration of benzene in the polymer sample.

A calibration curve is obtained by plotting the difference in absorbance, ΔA_{260}, against the concentration of benzene in a series of isopropanol solutions of known concentration.

OXYGEN-CONTAINING FUNCTIONAL GROUPS— CARBONYL GROUPS

Characteristic Absorptions

Functional Group	Millimicrons ($m\mu$)
Saturated compounds:	
Acids	200–210
Esters	200–210
Anhydrides	210–220
Ketones	270–285
Aldehydes	280–300

The carbonyl group, possessing π electrons and the n electrons of the oxygen atom, constitutes an isolated chromophore which absorbs weakly in the near-ultraviolet spectral region by virtue of $n \rightarrow \pi^*$ electronic transitions. Although these absorptions occasionally have an analytical utility, saturated acids, aldehydes, anhydrides, esters, and ketones are primarily determined by indirect methods such as those involving the intensification of the absorption band of the parent molecule accompanied by a shift to a longer wavelength in the ultraviolet spectrum of a derivative. The carbonyl group is a more important chromophore in unsaturated aliphatic and aromatic molecules. Those compounds in which the carbonyl group is conjugated with the unsaturated bonds give rise to intense bands in the 200 to 400-$m\mu$ region suitable for quantitative analytical purposes. Ultraviolet spectrometric analysis of these materials is straightforward and requires only the location of a unique absorption band and the correlation of the absorption intensity of this band with the concentration of the compound of interest.

OXYGEN-CONTAINING FUNCTIONAL GROUPS— NONCARBONYL GROUPS

The alcohols and ethers of saturated organic compounds possess only n and σ electrons, and do not absorb in the near-ultraviolet region. Consequently these materials serve as solvents for polar compounds in this region just as the saturated hydrocarbons serve as solvents for nonpolar materials in ultraviolet spectrometry. The hydroxyl group, however, is an important auxochrome as an aromatic substituent. Analysis for this group depends on the existence of an ultraviolet spectrum for the parent molecule. The location and intensity of the bands of the spectrum are altered by the presence of the auxochrome.

EXAMPLE: THE DETERMINATION OF NONYLPHENOL IN NONYLCYCLOHEXANOL

In the reduction of nonylphenol to nonylcyclohexanol, the absorption due to the aromatic nucleus of the residual nonylphenol at 277 mμ is suitable for measuring the extent to which it has been converted to the ultraviolet transparent compound.

Procedure. Sample Preparation.—Dissolve 0.0250 g. of sample in 250 ml. of methanol. An aliquot of this solution is placed in a quartz cell 1.00 cm. in thickness for samples containing 10 to 100 percent nonylphenol or in a quartz cell 10.00 cm. in thickness for samples containing 0 to 10 percent nonylphenol.

Absorbance Measurement.—The ultraviolet spectrum of the sample is obtained between 210 and 400 mμ. The absorbance is measured at 277 mμ.

Calculations.—The absorbance at 277 mμ is referred to a calibration curve and the corresponding concentration of nonylphenol is read from the plot.

Calibration curves are prepared by plotting this absorbance against the concentration of nonylphenol for a series of solutions in methanol containing known amounts of nonylphenol over the two concentration ranges 0 to 10 percent and 10 to 100 percent.

NITROGEN-CONTAINING FUNCTIONAL GROUPS

Saturated organic compounds containing amine, azo, diazo, nitro, nitroso, nitrate, and nitrite groups exhibit only a weak near-ultraviolet absorption. Nitriles and azomethine groups occurring in saturated aliphatic compounds do not absorb in this region.

Aromatic compounds containing these groups are amenable to conventional ultraviolet spectrometric analysis by virtue of the spectral changes, induced by their presence, in the spectra of the parent compounds.

EXAMPLE: THE DETERMINATION OF m-PHENYLENEDIAMINE AND m-NITROANILINE IN HETEROGENEOUS REACTION MIXTURES

The reduction of *m*-nitroaniline to *m*-phenylenediamine is accomplished in an aqueous medium containing a suspended catalyst system. By means of filtration or centrifugation the suspended catalyst is removed from the system leaving a clear aqueous solution suitable for ultraviolet spectrometric analysis. In aqueous solution *m*-phenylenediamine exhibits a sharp absorption maximum at 289 mμ and *m*-nitroaniline a broad maximum at 330 mμ.

Procedure. Sample Preparation.—A sample of the heterogeneous system (containing approximately: 60 percent *m*-phenylenediamine, 40 percent water, 6 percent *m*-nitroaniline and the suspended catalyst), is filtered or centrifuged to remove the suspended materials. An aliquot of the clear solution is diluted 1:1000 with distilled water for the *m*-nitroaniline analysis. Another aliquot of the clear solution is diluted 1:5000 with disilled water for the *m*-phenylenediamine analysis. Aliquots of each of the two diluted samtples are placed in quartz cells 1.00 cm. in thickness.

Absorbance Measurement.—The ultraviolet spectrum of the sample solution diluted 1:1000 is obtained from 300 to 400 mμ. The absorbance is measured at 330 mμ. The ultraviolet spectrum of the sample solution diluted 1:5000 is obtained from 250 to 350 mμ. The absorbance is measured at 289 mμ.

Calculations.—The absorbance at 330 mμ is referred to a calibration curve and the corresponding concentration of *m*-nitroaniline is read from the plot. The absorbance at

289 mμ is referred to a calibration curve and the corresponding concentration of m-phenylenediamine is read from the plot.

Calibration curves are prepared by plotting the absorbances at these wavelengths against the corresponding concentrations of m-nitroaniline and m-phenylenediamine for a series of aqueous solutions containing known amounts of these materials.

EXAMPLE: THE DETERMINATION OF TRACE QUANTITIES OF BASIC NITROGEN IN GASOLINE[40]

The determination of basic nitrogen in gasoline as pyridines and quinolines, with a sensitivity of 0.01 p.p.m., involves their isolation by ion exchange followed by ultraviolet spectrometric analysis. The total basic nitrogen is measured by the absorption at 260 mμ and the ratio of the pyridines to quinolines is measured by the absorption at 300 mμ.

Procedure. Sample Preparation. *Reagents.*—Cation exchange resin: Duolite C-10. (The resin is boiled with an excess of anhydrous methanol for one-half hour before use.)

> Anhydrous ethyl amine, 5 percent (w/v) in methanol.
> Anhydrous ethyl amine, 1 percent (w/v) in methanol.
> Sulfuric acid solution, 5 percent (50 ml. 95 percent/liter methanol).
> Isooctane.

Apparatus.—Ion exchange column including an 8 × 80 mm. section filled with resin.
Sample size.—1 to 500 ml. depending on the concentration of 50 to 0.02 p.p.m.

At a flow rate of 3 to 5 ml. per minute, add successively to the ion exchange column (1) 10 ml. of 5 percent ethyl amine solution, (2) 10 ml. of methanol, (3) 10 ml. of 5 percent sulfuric acid solution, (4) 50 ml. of methanol, (5) sample or blank, (6) 50 ml. of isooctane, (7) 100 ml. of methanol, (8) 25 ml. of 1 percent ethylamine solution and collect a 25-ml. fraction, (9) 10 ml. of 5 percent sulfuric acid solution, (10) 50 ml. of methanol.

An aliquot of the 25-ml. fraction collected in step (8) is placed in a quartz cell 1.00 cm in thickness.

Absorbance Measurement.—The absorbance of this solution is measured at 260 and 300 mμ. The same absorbance measurements are made on 2 blanks run through the ion exchange column and the results are averaged.

Calculations.—The absorbance of the sample solution at 260 mμ is corrected for the absorbance of the blank (average of two determinations) at this wavelength. The parts per million total basic nitrogen is calculated by:

$$\text{p.p.m. Nitrogen} = \frac{150\ A_{260}\ \text{corr.}}{\text{volume of sample (ml.)} \times \text{density of sample}}$$

The ratio of the pyridines' to quinolines' nitrogen is calculated by:

$$p/q = 1.15 \left(\frac{A_{260}\ \text{corr.}}{A_{300}\ \text{corr.}} \right) - 0.87$$

MISCELLANEOUS

Saturated organic compounds which contain sulfur or halogen atoms possess only n and σ electrons and are not expected to absorb in the 200–400 mμ region. The chlorinated aliphatic hydrocarbons, therefore, serve as useful solvents in this region. Some compounds containing the mercapto, sulfide, disulfide, sulfoxide, and iodide groups show a weak absorption in the short wavelength region of the near ultraviolet. The

[40] Snyder, L. R., and Buell, B. E., Anal. Chem., **34**, 689, 1962.

ultraviolet spectrometric method of analysis is again primarily useful for these functional groups when they occur in aromatic compounds.

EXAMPLE: THE DETERMINATION OF MERCAPTOBENZOTHIAZOL IN ANTIFREEZE SOLUTIONS CONTAINING BORAX

In the presence of borax mercaptobenzothiazol (MBT) in methanol solution exhibits absorption maxima at 235, 252, and 315 mμ. In this method the analytical wavelength for the determination is 315 mμ.

Procedure. Sample Preparation.—A sample of antifreeze solution containing approximately 1 mg. of MBT is weighed into a 100-ml. volumetric flask, dissolved in methanol, and diluted to 100 ml. An aliquot of this solution is placed in a quartz cell 1.00 cm. in thickness.

Absorbance Measurement.—The ultraviolet spectrum of the sample solution is obtained between 210 and 350 mμ. The absorbance is measured at 315 mμ.

Calculations.—The percent MBT, in the range 0.0 to 0.5 percent is calculated by:

$$\% \text{ MBT} = \frac{A_{315} \times 100}{1.29 \times \text{sample wt. (mg.)}}$$

EXAMPLE: THE DETERMINATION OF MICROGRAM QUANTITIES OF DIVNYL SULFONE IN AQUEOUS MEDIA[41]

In dilute sodium hydroxide solution, benzenethiol exhibits an absorption maximum at 262 mμ. Although divinyl sulfone does not absorb in the near ultraviolet at these concentrations, the reaction between divinyl sulfone and benzenethiol to form the insoluble bis(phenylthioethyl) sulfone, thereby removing benzenethiol from solution, serves as a sensitive, indirect method for the analysis of divinyl sulfone. The decrease in absorbance at 262 mμ is a measure of the divinyl-sulfone concentration.

Procedure. Sample Preparation.—A sample containing 50 to 200 μg. of divinyl sulfone is dissolved in 5 ml. of distilled water in a 50-ml. volumetric flask. One ml. of benzenethiol solution (60 mg. benzenethiol per 100 ml. 1 N sodium hydroxide) is added. The flask is stoppered and allowed to stand at room temperature for 15 minutes and then diluted to 50 ml. with distilled water. A second 50-ml. volumetric flask containing 1 ml. of the benzenethiol solution (see above) diluted to 50 ml. with distilled water is prepared as a blank. An aliquot of each solution is placed in a quartz cell 1.00 cm in thickness.

Absorbance Measurement.—The ultraviolet spectra of the blank and sample solutions are obtained between 230 and 350 mμ. The absorbances of each solution are measured at 262 and 340 mμ.

Calculations.—The difference in the absorbances at 262 and 340 mμ of the sample solution is subtracted from the difference in the absorbances at 262 and 340 mμ of the blank solution to give ΔA. The micrograms of divinyl sulfone in the sample is calculated by:

$$\mu\text{g. DVS} = \frac{\Delta A}{0.0031 \times \text{sample wt. (g.)}}$$

EXAMPLE: THE DETERMINATION OF TRACES OF CARBON DISULFIDE IN BENZENE[42]

Carbon disulfide in benzene solution exhibits an intense absorption doublet at 314 and 318 mμ. The absorption by benzene is negligible beyond 290 mμ and does not

[41] Stahl, C. R., Anal. Chem., **34**, 980, 1962.
[42] White, R. G., Applied Spectroscopy, **18**, 112, 1964.

interfere with the determination of carbon disulfide at the analytical wavelength of 318 mμ.

Procedure. **Sample Preparation.**—A sample of benzene containing 0.0 to 0.02 percent (w/v) carbon disulfide is placed in a quartz cell 5.00 cm. in thickness.

Absorbance Measurement.—The ultraviolet spectrum of the sample is obtained between 280 and 380 mμ. A baseline is drawn between the following approximate points of minimum absorption: 287 and 353 mμ. From this baseline the absorbance is measured at 318 mμ.

Calculations.—The absorbance at 318 mμ is referred to a calibration curve and the corresponding concentration of carbon disulfide in the benzene sample is read from the plot.

A calibration curve is prepared by plotting the absorbance at 318 mμ against the concentration of carbon disulfide in a series of solutions containing 0.0 to 0.02 percent carbon disulfide (w/v) in pure benzene. Carbon disulfide free benzene is obtained by extracting Reagent Grade benzene with alcoholic sodium hydroxide.

GAS CHROMATOGRAPHY

The relatively recent prominence, both rapid and widespread, achieved by gas chromatography in quantitative analysis attests to the utility of this technique for organic functional group determination. Gas chromatography, in the analytical laboratory, is as widely used as absorption spectrometry. Virtually every functional group in all types of organic materials has been analyzed by some one of the many applications of this technique.

Gas-solid chromatography is comparable in principle to conventional column chromatography with the exception that the moving phase is a gas instead of a liquid. Gas-liquid chromatography is based on the principle of partitioning a material between a moving gas phase and a liquid phase which is immobilized by adsorption on an inert substrate. It is essentially the difference in partition coefficient among the components of a mixture which enables them to be separated in this manner. In both gas-solid and gas-liquid chromatography the separated components in the gas phase are eluted from the column by a carrier gas, detected by a suitable device which produces a signal for each component eluted and displayed on a recorder chart as a series of peaks. The number of peaks displayed is indicative of the number of components in a mixture and the peak area represents the amount of each component. Almost all organic materials are quantitatively analyzed by the gas-liquid chromatographic technique.

The variety of equipment used in gas chromatography is greater than that employed in any other instrumental technique, and new instruments appear with astonishing regularity. Apparatus is available for isothermal and programmed temperature operation. Temperature ranges span those of convenient refrigerants to 500°C. and more. Detectors include devices based on the principles of thermal conductivity employing wire filaments or semiconductors, flame ionization, radioactivity, electron capture, cross section, heat of combustion, and the gas density balance. Mechanical and electronic integration with or without automatic readout are a commonplace feature of recent instruments. Dual column instruments provide a versatility in gas chromatography akin to that enjoyed by double-beam spectrometers. In addition there are dual channel instruments in which a single column is used with two different type detectors. Preparative scale instruments are available. Many sample handling accessories have been devised for the accurate and reproducible introduction of liquid materials in volumes of 0.1 to 10.0 μl. and for gaseous and solid materials. Substances which are not volatile at the temperatures mentioned are amenable to analysis by gas chromatography through the use of pyrolysis techniques. Column tubing, consisting of copper, aluminum, stainless steel, glass, and nylon, ranging in length from several inches to hundreds of feet and from 0.01 inch to 1.0 inch in diameter, is used routinely in gas chromatographic analysis.

Gas chromatographic analysis for the determination of compounds containing specific functional groups depends on the proper selection of such operating parameters as temperature, carrier gas flow rate, detector type, column material, length and diameter, sample size, and column packing, both type and concentration. Of these the nature of the column packing is unquestionably the most important, since it is on the coated substrate that the chromatographic process occurs.[43] The column packing consists of a solid phase which provides a large surface area on which the liquid phase is adsorbed. Variously treated diatomaceous earth supports are most commonly used. Firebrick, glass beads, and fluorinated resins are also employed. These supports generally are used in several mesh ranges between 20 and 200.

The apparently limitless applications of gas chromatography[44,45,46,47,48] to organic functional group analysis stems from the equally unlimited number of materials available and used as the partitioning liquid phase. It is this imposing multiplicity of materials that precludes a comprehensive illustration of the application of gas chromatography to organic functional group analysis in this section. Instead, illustrative gas chromatographic analyses are described to demonstrate some typical procedures in detail. These analyses may be performed with comparable results using different instruments, operating parameters, and column packings. In addition a cross-section is presented of those materials which have been successfully employed as the partitioning liquid phase in the analysis of compounds containing the functional groups listed. While the selection of the appropriate instrumental parameters for a specific application is important in obtaining an optimum analysis, it is the nature of the liquid phase that has the most profound effect on the efficiency of any gas chromatographic analysis.

HYDROCARBONS

Functional Groups	Liquid Phases	Nominal Maximum Operating Temperature °C.
a. Alkanes:	Squalene	30
	n-Hexadecane	50
	Bis[2-(2 methoxy ethoxy) ethyl] ether	50
	Dibenzyl ether	80
	Nujol	100
	Dialkyl phthalates	100–175
	Tri-cresylphosphate	125
	Carbowax 20 M	250
	Apiezons	275–300
b. Alkenes:	Dimethylformamide	20
	Hexamethylphosphoramide	35

[43] Brandt, W. W., Anal. Chem., **33**, 23A, 1961.

[44] Dal Nogare, S., and Juvet, R. S., Jr., Gas-Liquid Chromatography; Theory and Practice., Interscience Publishers, New York, 1962.

[45] Littlewood, A. B., Gas Chromatography, Academic Press, New York, 1962.

[46] Purnell, J. H., Gas Chromatography, John Wiley, New York, 1962.

[47] Knapman, C. E. H., and Scott, C. G., Eds., Gas Chromatography Abstracts, 1958–1961, Butterworth Inc., Washington, D. C., 1958–1961.

[48] Knapman, C. E. H., and Ambrose, D., Eds., Gas Chromatography Abstracts, 1962, Butterworth Inc., Washington, D. C., 1962.

Functional Groups	Liquid Phases	Nominal Maximum Operating Temperature °C.
	Dimethyl sulfolane	50
	Propylene carbonate	50
	β,β' oxydipropionitrile	100
	Dialkyl phthalates	100–175
	Silicone grease	300
c. Alkynes:	Hexamethylphosphoramide	35
	Dialkyl phthalates	100–175
	Transformer oils	200
d. Aromatics:	7,8-Benzoquinoline	100
	Dialkyl phthalates	100–175
	Benzyldiphenyl	120
	Tri-cresylphosphate	125
	Polypropyleneglycol	150
	Bentone 34	200
	Silicone oils	200–225
	Carbowax 20 M	250
	Apiezons	275–300

EXAMPLE: ANALYSIS OF A C_{10}–C_{18} ALIPHATIC HYDROCARBON MIXTURE

Column.—A 6-foot length of 0.25-inch, outside diameter, copper tubing is packed with 5 percent (w/w) Carbowax 20 M on Anachrom ABS 70/80 mesh. The Carbowax 20 M is a polyethylene glycol of molecular weight 20,000. Anachrom ABS is a diatomaceous earth, acid and base treated and silanized.

Preparation.—Dissolve 2.5 g. of Carbowax 20 M in 200 ml. of methylene chloride. Transfer the solution to a glass tray. Add slowly, while stirring, 47.5 g. of Anachrom ABS to the solution in the tray. Place the tray on a steam bath in a hood and stir the slurry gently while allowing the solvent to evaporate. Drying is completed by placing the tray in an oven at a temperature near the boiling point of the solvent. Fill a 6-foot length of copper tubing with the dried packing. The packing is evenly distributed by tapping or vibrating the tubing during the filling process. A glass wool plug, 0.5 inch long, at each end of the column holds the packing in place. The tubing is formed to a convenient size and shape depending on the dimensions of the oven in the instrument. The column is conditioned in the instrument under the conditions of the analysis until a flat baseline is obtained.

Apparatus.—Programmed temperature gas chromatograph with a flame ionization detector.

Operating Conditions.—1. Temperatures:

    a. Column-programmed 100 to 250°C. at 5°C. per minute;

    b. Injection port—310°C.,

    c. Detector block—340°C.

  2. Carrier gas: Helium.

  3. Flow rate: 85 cc./minute.

  4. Sample size: 2 μl.

Under these conditions the hydrocarbons are eluted in the following order at the approximate retention times indicated:

C_{10}, 1.1 minutes;
C_{12}, 2.4 minutes;
C_{14}, 5.2 minutes;
C_{16}, 9.3 minutes,
C_{18}, 13.8 minutes.

The area under the peak of each hydrocarbon is related to its concentration in the mixture. The area under each peak is divided by the sum of the areas of all peaks to obtain the individual concentrations in area percent. The area concentration of each component is related to its weight or mole percent by calibration.

OXYGEN-CONTAINING FUNCTIONAL GROUPS

Diatomaceous earth supports tend to cause tailing with oxygenated compounds. This has been attributed to the presence of metallic impurities and silanol groups. Acid and base washing of the support improves performance by removing the metals and reaction with dimethyldichlorosilane renders the silanol groups relatively inactive.

Functional Groups	Liquid Phases	Nominal Maximum Operating Temperature °C.
a. Carbonyl Groups		
Acids:	Carbowaxes 4M terminated with terephthalic acid	175
	Silicone oils	200–225
	Polyesters (LAC 446)	225
	Apiezons	275–300
Aldehydes:	Quadrol	100
	Dialkyl phthalates	100–175
	Carbowaxes	100–250
	Diglycerol	150
	Cyanosilicones	150
	Apiezons	275–300
Anhydrides:	Cyanosilicones	150
	Silicone gum rubber	400
Esters:	Nujol	100
	Dialkyl phthalates	100–175
	Cyanosilicones	150
	Silicone oils	200–225
	Diethylene glycol adipate	225
	Diethylene glycol succinate	225
Ketones:	Dialkylphthalates	100–175
	Carbowaxes	100–250
	Cyanosilicones	150
Lactones:	Carbowax 20 M	250
	Apiezons	275–300
b. Noncarbonyl Groups		
Alcohols:	Carbowaxes	100–250
	Diglycerol	150
	Cyanosilicones	150
	Castorwax	200
	Ucons(Polar)	225

Functional Groups	Liquid Phases	Nominal Maximum Operating Temperature °C.
Ethers:	β,β' thiodipropionitrile	100
	Carbowaxes	100–250
	Tri-cresylphosphate	125
	Flexol 8N8	200
	Apiezons	275–300
Phenols:	Cyanosilicones	150
	Diglycerol	150
	Carbowax 20M	250
	Apiezons	275–300
	Silicone gum rubber	400

EXAMPLE: ANALYSIS OF A MIXTURE OF OXYGENATED SOLVENTS (METHANOL, ETHANOL, ACETONE, TETRAHYDROFURAN, AND DIOXANE)

Column.—A 12-foot length of 0.25-inch, outside diameter, copper tubing is packed with 20 percent (w/w) Flexol 8N8 on Columnpak 30/60 mesh. The Flexol 8N8 is a plasticizer, 2,2'-(2-ethylhexanamido)-diethyl di 2-ethylhexoate, and the Columnpak is a firebrick.

Preparation.—Dissolve 10.0 g. of Flexol 8N8 in 200 ml. of acetone. Transfer the solution to a glass tray. Add slowly, while stirring, 40.0 g. of Columnpak to the solution in the tray. Place the tray on a steam bath in a hood and stir the slurry gently while allowing the solvent to evaporate. Drying is completed by placing the tray in an oven at a temperature near the boiling point of the solvent. Fill a 12-foot length of copper tubing with the dried packing. The packing is evenly distributed by tapping or vibrating the tubing during the filling process. A glass wool plug, 0.5 inch long, at each end of the column holds the packing in place. The tubing is formed to a convenient size and shape depending on the dimensions of the oven in the instrument. The column is conditioned in the instrument under the conditions of the analysis until a flat baseline is obtained.

Apparatus.—Isothermal gas chromatograph with a thermistor detector.

Operating Conditions.—1. Temperature:
    a. Column—100°C.
2. Carrier gas: Helium.
3. Flow rate: 45 cc./minute.
4. Sample size: 10 μl.

Under these conditions the oxygenated materials are eluted in the following order at the approximate retention times indicated:

Methanol, 4.2 minutes;
Acetone, 5.0 minutes;
Ethanol, 6.3 minutes;
Tetrahydrofuran, 9.7 minutes;
Dioxane, 18.6 minutes.

The area under the peak of each compound is related to its concentration in the mixture. The area under each peak is divided by the sum of the areas of all peaks to obtain the individual concentrations in area percent. The area concentration of each component is related to its weight or mole percent by calibration.

NITROGEN-CONTAINING FUNCTIONAL GROUPS

Diatomaceous earth supports tend to cause severe tailing of amines. The addition of a few percent of strong base or the use of silanized supports aids in the reduction of these adsorptive effects.

Functional Group	Liquid Phases	Nominal Maximum Operating Temperature °C.
Amines:	Carbowaxes	100–250
	Cyanosilicones	150
	4:1-Carbowaxes: potassium hydroxide	150–250
	4:1-Apiezons: potassium hydroxide	300
Nitriles:	Dialkyl phthalates	100–175
	Cyanosilicones	150
	Silicone oils	200–225
	Phenyl diethanolamine-succinate	225
	Apiezons	275–300
	Silicone gum rubber	400
Pyrrolidines:	Carbowax 20 M	250
Piperazines:	Theed	100
	Flexol 8N8	200
	Carbowax 20 M	250

EXAMPLE: ANALYSIS OF A MIXTURE OF NITROGEN-CONTAINING COMPOUNDS (ETHYLENEDIAMINE, DIETHYLENETRIAMINE, GLYCOLONITRILE, AMINOACETONITRILE, AND PIPERAZINE)

Column.—A 3-foot length of 0.25-inch, outside diameter, copper tubing is packed with 2 percent Carbowax 20 M on Tee 6. The carbowax is a polyethyleneglycol of molecular weight 20,000, and Tee 6 is specially processed and screened Teflon 6.

Preparation.—Dissolve 1.0 g. of Carbowax 20 M in 200 ml. of methylene chloride. Transfer the solution to a glass tray. Add slowly, while stirring, 49.0 g. of Tee 6 to the solution in the tray. Place the tray on a steam bath in a hood and stir the slurry gently while allowing the solvent to evaporate. Drying is completed by placing the tray in an oven at a temperature near the boiling point of the solvent. Fill a 3-foot length of copper tubing with the dried packing. The packing is evenly distributed by tapping or vibrating the tubing during the filling process. A glass wool plug, 0.5 inch long, at each end of the column, holds the packing in place. The tubing is formed to a convenient size and shape depending on the dimensions of the oven in the instrument. The column is conditioned in the instrument under the conditions of the analysis until a flat baseline is obtained.

Apparatus.—Programmed gas chromatograph with a hot wire detector.

Operating Conditions.—1. Temperatures:
　　　　　　　　a. Column—maintained at 75°C. for 10 minutes, then programmed to 230°C. at 10°C. per minute.
　　　　　　　　b. Injection port—280°C.
　　　　　　　　c. Detector block—240°C.
　　　　　　2. Carrier gas: Helium.
　　　　　　3. Flow rate: 55 cc./minute.
　　　　　　4. Sample size: 5 μl.

Under these conditions the nitrogen-containing materials are eluted in the following order at the approximate retention times indicated:

Glycolonitrile, 2.1 minutes;
Ethylene diamine, 5.0 minutes;
Piperazine, 10.0 minutes;
Aminoacetonitrile, 18.2 minutes;
Diethylenetriamine, 21.0 minutes.

The area under the peak of each compound is related to its concentration in the mixture. The area under each peak is divided by the sum of the areas of all peaks to obtain the individual concentrations in area percent. The area concentration of each component is related to its weight or mole percent by calibration.

MISCELLANEOUS

Functional Group	Liquid Phases	Nominal Maximum Operating Temperature °C.
Alkyl and Aryl Halides:	Benzyl ether	80
	Dialkyl phthalates	100–175
	Silicone oils	200–225
	Carbowax 20 M	250
	Apiezons	275–300
Mercaptans:	Dialkyl phthalates	100–175
	Tri-cresylphosphate	125
Sulfides:	Squalane	30
	Dialkyl phthalates	100–175
	Silicone oils	200–225
Silanes:	Dialkyl phthalates	100–175
	Silicone oils	200–225

EXAMPLE: ANALYSIS OF 1,4-DICHLORO-2-BUTYNE AND 1,2,4-TRICHLORO-2-BUTENE MIXTURES

Column.—A 12-foot length of 0.25-inch, outside diameter, copper tubing is packed with 20 percent Silicone Oil DC 200 on Chromosorb. Chromosorb is a treated diatomaceous earth.

Preparation.—Dissolve 10.0 g. of Silicone Oil DC 200 in 200 ml. of chloroform. Transfer the solution to a glass tray. Add slowly, while stirring, 40.0 g. of Chromosorb to the solution in the tray. Place the tray on a steam bath in a hood and stir the slurry gently while allowing the solvent to evaporate. Drying is completed by placing the tray in an oven at a temperature near the boiling point of the solvent. Fill a 12-foot length of copper tubing with the dried packing. The packing is evenly distributed by tapping or vibrating the tubing during the filling process. A glass wool plug, 0.5 inch long, at each end of the column, holds the packing in place. The tubing is formed to a convenient size and shape depending on the dimensions of the oven in the instrument. The column is conditioned in the instrument under the conditions of the analysis until a flat baseline is obtained.

Apparatus.—Isothermal gas chromatograph with a hot wire detector.

Operating Conditions.—1. Temperature:
   a. Column—150°C.
2. Carrier gas: Helium.
3. Flow rate: 80 cc./minute.
4. Sample size: 25 μl.

Under these conditions the chlorinated hydrocarbons are eluted in the following order at the approximate retention times indicated:

1,4-Dichloro-2-butyne, 13.4 minutes;
1,2,4-Trichloro-2-butene, 20.0 minutes.

The area under each peak is related to the concentration of that component in the mixture. The area under each peak is divided by the sum of the areas under both peaks to obtain the individual concentrations in area percent. The area concentration of each component is related to its weight or mole percent by calibration.

MASS SPECTROMETRY

The routine application of mass spectrometry to organic analysis began with the quantitative determination of hydrocarbons by the petroleum industry, from which a thorough study of the mass spectral characteristics of the hydrocarbon class resulted.[49] More recently the success enjoyed by this technique in the fields of identification and structure elucidation[10,50] has renewed interest in the application of mass spectrometry to organic functional group analysis.

Mass spectrometry involves the admission of a gaseous sample to the spectrometer wherein electron bombardment ruptures the molecules into ionized fragments as well as molecular ions which are separated according to their mass to charge ratios, detected, and recorded. In the resulting spectrum, the appearance of maxima indicates the presence of ions of a particular mass, and the intensities of these maxima are a measure of their abundance. The relative quantities of these ions depend on the ease with which the particular fragments are cleaved from the molecule, which, in turn, is dependent on its atomic configuration. While mass spectra do not indicate the presence of specific functional groups in a molecule directly, the presence of these groups has a direct effect on the fragmentation pattern of the molecule. Examination of a large number of mass spectra permitted correlations to be made between the presence of a functional group in a molecule and the nature of its degradation under electron bombardment.

Some very brief generalizations concerning the fragmentation of compounds containing various functional groups include: cleavage in paraffinic hydrocarbons occurs most readily at branched carbon atoms. Allylic cleavage is favored in olefins. The presence of an aromatic ring tends to stabilize the molecule and enhances the probability of occurrence of a molecular ion. The mass spectra of compounds containing electron donating functional groups, such as the hydroxyl, amine, and ether, are characterized by the presence of fragment ions resulting from cleavage of the beta carbon-carbon bond adjacent to the functional group. Thus, the mass spectra of aliphatic primary amines show the presence of strong maxima at m/e 30 due to CH_2—NH_2 ions. The mass spectra of compounds containing electron-withdrawing functional groups, such as the carbonyl, are characterized by the appearance of fragment ions resulting from cleavage of the alpha bond. Thus the mass spectra of organic acids show the presence of prominent maxima at m/e 45 due to COOH ions.

The direct determination of functional groups by conventional mass spectrometry is hindered by the appearance of isomeric fragments. The CH_2OH m/e 31 fragment of an aliphatic alcohol is indistinguishable from the CH_3O m/e 31 fragment of an aliphatic ether. However, it is still possible to determine each compound for, although the same fragment occurs, the relative amounts of each may differ. Analyses of this type, as well as those involving complex mixtures, are difficult with conventional spectrometers, but they become possible through the utilization of high resolution instruments. For example,

[49] Catalog of Mass Spectra Data, American Petroleum Institute Res. Project No. 44, Carnegie Institute of Technology, Pittsburgh, Pa.
[50] Budzikiewicz, H., Djerassi, C., and Williams, D. H., Interpretation of Mass Spectra of Organic Compounds, Holden-Day, San Francisco, 1964.

the nominal mass of the molecular ions of butane and acetone are 58. The precise mass for butane, however, is 58.078 and for acetone is 58.042. This difference is resolvable with a high performance instrument. It is not likely that such instrumentation wils routinely be available in the analytical laboratory in the near future and the limitationl of conventional instruments must be overcome by means of special auxiliary techniques.

Mass spectra are employed in qualitative and quantitative analysis in a manner quite similar to the utilization of spectra obtained by other spectrometric techniques.[51,52,53] Likewise, reference spectra are invaluable for qualitative analysis and pure samples for calibration purposes are essential for precise quantitative analysis.

EXAMPLE: ANALYSIS OF METHYL- AND PHENYLCHLOROSILANE SOLUTIONS[54]

Mixtures containing 20 to 60 mole percent dimethyl dichlorosilane [Me_2SiCl_2, (D)], 15 to 45 mole percent diphenyldichlorosilane [ϕ_2SiCl_2, (ϕD)], 5 to 15 mole percent methyltrichlorosilane [$MeSiCl_3$, (T)], and 10 to 30 mole percent phenyltrichlorosilane [$\phi SiCl_3$, (ϕT)] are analyzed.

Procedure.—The analytical peaks for each component are selected from the mass spectra of the pure materials. Since these mixtures contain appreciable quantities of each component, it is not necessary to use the most intense peaks for the analysis. Instead, it is possible to select the analytical peaks on the basis of minimal interference from the fragments of the other components of the mixture as well as from possible contaminants. On this basis, the peaks at the following mass numbers are chosen: 128, the molecular ion of Me_2SiCl_2; 148, the molecular ion of $MeSiCl_3$; 210, the molecular ion of $\phi SiCl_3$; and 217, the $\phi_2 SiCl$ ion. The mass number 217 of the $\phi_2 SiCl$ ion is selected because it is closer to the 210 peak than is the parent 252 peak and thus shortens the time of the spectral scan.

Calibration.—A solution of the 4 chlorosilanes is used for the determination of the sensitivities. The concentrations of the individual components in the solution are: 30 mole percent ϕ_2SiCl_2; 20 mole percent $\phi SiCl_3$; 10 mole percent $MeSiCl_3$; and 40 mole percent Me_2SiCl_2. Since diphenyldichlorosilane contributes to the peaks at mass numbers 128 and 148, the sensitivities at these mass numbers are also determined for this compound. This is accomplished by multiplying the sensitivity of diphenyldichlorosilane at the analytical mass number 217, measured from the solution, by the peak height ratios 128/217 and 148/217 obtained from the mass spectrum of the pure material. The sensitivities determined by this calibration are: $S_{128}^D = 3.25$ divisions/micron; $S_{148}^T = 4.94$ divisions/micron; $S_{210}^{\phi T} = 23.7$ divisions/micron; $S_{128}^{\phi D} = 0.24$ divisions/micron and $S_{148}^{\phi D} = 0.05$ divisions/micron.

Calculations.—The composition of the sample mixture, in mole percent of each component, is determined from the mass spectrum of the unknown mixture by means of the following equations

$$H_{128} = S_{128}^D P^D + S_{128}^{\phi D} P^{\phi D}$$
$$H_{148} = S_{148}^T P^T + S_{148}^{\phi D} P^{\phi D}$$
$$H_{210} = S_{210}^{\phi T} P^{\phi T}$$
$$H_{217} = S_{217}^{\phi D} P^{\phi T}$$

[51] Beynon, J. H., Mass Spectrometry and Its Application to Organic Chemistry, Elsevier, Amsterdam, 1960.

[52] Biemann, K., Mass Spectrometry, McGraw-Hill, New York, 1962.

[53] McLafferty, F. W., Mass Spectral Correlations, American Chemical Society, Washington, D. C., 1963.

[54] Hirt, C. A., Anal. Chem., 33, 1786, 1961.

where: H is the peak height in the mass spectrum of the sample at the mass
numbers indicated;

S is the sensitivity of the component designated at the mass numbers
indicated; and

P is the pressure of the components shown.

The equations are solved for P in terms of H and S. Corrections for changes in instrument sensitivity are made from the known pressure of a sample of diphenyldichlorosilane.

NUCLEAR MAGNETIC RESONANCE SPECTROMETRY

Nuclear magnetic resonance (NMR) is a spectrometric technique which is applied to chemical analysis in a manner very similar to the spectrometric procedures involving ultraviolet, visible, and infrared radiation. It differs from these in that it is restricted to samples containing magnetic nuclei. These are placed under the influence of a magnetic field whereupon a magnetic interaction occurs which gives rise to energy levels between which transitions are induced and observed. NMR spectrometry is restricted to nuclei which possess the property of "spin" and in this section the subject is further restricted to the hydrogen nucleus or the proton.

A proton has a spin number of $\frac{1}{2}$ and, as a consequence, when placed in a magnetic field, may align itself with it (parallel orientation) or against it (antiparallel orientation). The energy levels of these orientations depend on the magnetic moment of the proton and the strength of the applied field. A transition from the lower to the higher energy level is induced by applying energy in the form of electromagnetic radiation. The relationship between the frequency (ν) of the radiation required to induce this transition and the strength of the applied field (H_o) is expressed by $\nu = \gamma H_o 2\pi$, where γ, the ratio of the magnetic moment of the proton to its angular momentum, is a constant characteristic of the hydrogen nucleus. The occurrence of this transition is observed by a signal resulting from absorption of the applied energy. An NMR signal in the form of an absorption peak occurs at a frequency characteristic of the hydrogen nucleus (γ) and the applied magnetic field strength (H_o). The utility of the NMR technique arises from the fact that in an organic molecule the nuclei of the various hydrogen atoms are more or less shielded from the magnetic field, depending on their location in the molecule, and, therefore, do not experience a magnetic field equal in strength to the applied field. Transitions of the individual nuclei, therefore, occur at slightly different frequencies of the applied energy.

An NMR spectrum consists of a plot of the frequencies at which each of these transitions occur $vs.$ the intensities of the absorption peaks. Each peak is characteristic of hydrogen nuclei in a given location in the organic molecule and the area under the peak is a measure of the number of nuclei in this environment. The frequency displacement of hydrogen nuclei, in the different structural environments, from some reference point is called the chemical shift. Chemical shifts are expressed in dimensionless units obtained by dividing the displacement from the reference point in cycles per second by the applied frequency and multiplying by 10^6. This results in a scale 0 to 10.00 from right to left on the abscissa of the spectrum. In this system chemical shifts are expressed in parts per million (δ). Another system frequently used expresses the displacement in τ-values on a scale 0 to 10.00 from left to right on the abscissa of the spectrum. Conversion from one system to the other is made by means of the equation: $\tau = 10.00 - \delta$. At present the most commonly used reference is tetramethylsilane (TMS), which is assigned a value of 0.0 in the δ scale and 10.00 in the τ scale.[55, 56]

[55] Roberts, J. D., Nuclear Magnetic Resonance, McGraw-Hill, New York, 1959.

[56] Pople, J. A., Schneider, W. G., and Bernstein, H. J., High Resolution Nuclear Magnetic Resonance, McGraw-Hill, New York, 1959.

Under high resolution it is observed that the individual peaks often appear as multiplets due to interactions among neighboring nuclei. While complicating the ease of interpretation of NMR spectra, these phenomena extend the usefulness of this technique in the characterization of organic compounds. NMR is well established as a powerful tool for the elucidation of molecular structure.[10,57,58] With the advent of simpler and more stable instrumentation, this form of spectrometry is beginning to fulfill its potential as an analytical quantitative tool. It may be used for the determination of the components of mixtures, often in systems containing stereoisomers not readily measurable by other instrumental methods. It is applicable to the determination of hydrogen-containing functional groups, often without the need for calibration with reference materials. Due to the complexity of the instrumentation and the sensitivity of the measurements, operating parameters must be selected and maintained with somewhat more than the normal care required by the other spectrometric techniques for quantitative analysis.[59,60,61,62,63,64,65]

Data, correlating chemical shifts with structural characteristics, are available,[66] and are used in the same way one uses the spectral correlations in the other spectrometric regions.

As a general illustration, the chemical shifts of the protons in some functional groups are tabulated below:

	Chemical Shift	
Functional Group	δ(*p.p.m.*)	τ
1. Hydrocarbons		
a. Paraffins		
—CH$_3$	0.8–0.9	9.1–9.2
>CH$_2$	1.2–1.5	8.5–8.8
>CH	~1.5	~8.5
b. Olefins		
>CH = CH$_2$	4.5–5.0	5.0–5.5
—CH = CH—	5.0–5.5	4.5–5.0
—CH = CH —(cyclic)	5.5–6.0	4.0–4.5
c. Acetylenes		
—C≡CH	2.0–3.0	7.0–8.0
d. Aromatics		
—CH = CH—	6.5–9.0	1.0–3.5

[57] Jackman, L. M., Applications of Nuclear Magnetic Resonance Spectroscopy in Organic Chemistry, Pergamon, New York, 1959.

[58] Stothers, J. B., "Applications of NMR Spectroscopy," Chapter 4 in Elucidation of Structures by Physical and Chemical Methods, Part I, Bentley, K. W., Ed., Interscience, New York, 1963.

[59] Reilley, C. N., Anal. Chem., 30, 839, 1958.

[60] Paulsen, P. J., and Cooke, W. D., Anal. Chem., 36, 1713, 1964.

[61] Shizuo Fujiwara, and Tohru Wainai, Anal. Chem., 33, 1085, 1961.

[62] Hung Yu Chen, Anal. Chem., 34, 1793, 1962.

[63] Flanagan, P. W., Greff, R. A., and Smith, H. F., Anal. Chem., 35, 1283, 1963.

[64] Jungnickel, J. L., and Forbes, J. W., Anal. Chem., 35, 938, 1963.

[65] White, H. F., Davisson, C. W., and Yarborough, V. A., Anal. Chem., 36, 1659, 1964.

[66] High Resolution NMR Spectra Catalog, Vols. 1 and 2, Varian Associates, Palo Alto, California, 1962, 1963.

| | Chemical Shift | |
| *Functional Group* | $\delta(p.p.m.)$ | τ |

2. Oxygen-containing
   Functional Groups

$$CH_3—\overset{|}{C} = O$$

| | 2.0–3.0 | 7.0–8.0 |

$CH_3—O—$ 3.0–4.0   6.0–7.0

$—CH_2—O—$ 3.5–4.0   6.0–6.5

$$R—\overset{H}{C} = O$$ 9.0–10.0   0.0–1.0

3. Nitrogen-containing
   Functional Groups

$CH_3—N<$ 2.0–3.0   7.0–8.0

$—CH_2—N<$ 2.5–3.5   6.5–7.5

4. Miscellaneous

$R—SH$ 1.0–2.0   8.0–9.0

EXAMPLE: THE DETERMINATION OF THE AVERAGE MOLECULAR WEIGHT AND UNSATURATION OF NATURAL FATS[67]

The organic compounds commonly called natural fats consist of the triglycerides of fatty acids. A generic formula of these materials may be written as:

(6) H_2COCOR

(7) $HCOCOR$

(6) H_2COCOR

where R, a typical unsaturated acid, may be written as:

$$\underset{(4)}{—CH_2—}\underset{(2)}{(CH_2)_n—}\underset{(3)}{CH_2—}\underset{(7)}{CH}=\underset{(7)}{CH—}\underset{(5)}{CH_2—}\underset{(7)}{CH}=\underset{(7)}{CH—}\underset{(3)}{CH_2—}\underset{(2)}{(CH_2)_m—}\underset{(1)}{CH_3}$$

This molecule contains seven types of protons [(1)–(7)] which are amenable to analysis by NMR spectrometry. The NMR spectrum of a natural fat obtained in Spectrographic Grade carbon tetrachloride at a 50 percent (v/v) concentration shows seven groups of bands at the following frequencies in p.p.m. from TMS due to the protons

(1) of the three terminal methyl groups	∼0.9 p.p.m.
(2) of the methylene groups attached to two saturated carbon atoms	∼1.35 p.p.m.
(3) of the methylene groups attached to saturated and unsaturated carbon atoms	∼2.00 p.p.m.
(4) of the three methylene groups alpha to the carboxyl group	∼2.25 p.p.m.
(5) of the methylene groups attached to two unsaturated carbon atoms	∼2.80 p.p.m.
(6) of the two methylene groups of the glyceryl group	∼4.20 p.p.m.

[67] Johnson, L. F., and Shoolery, J. N., Anal. Chem., **34,** 1136, 1962.

(7) directly attached to the unsaturated carbon atoms
(olefinic protons) and of the single methine
hydrogen of the glyceryl group $\sim$5.30 p.p.m.

The area, A, under the band at 5.30 p.p.m. is equivalent to the number of olefinic protons, V, and the methine proton. The area, B, under the band at 4.20 p.p.m. is equivalent to the 4 methylene protons of the glyceryl group. The area per proton, therefore, is equivalent to $B/4$. The sum of the areas under all the bands (total area) is C. From these three area measurements it is possible to calculate:

$$\text{Number of olefinic protons, } V, = \frac{A - B/4}{B/4}, \text{ and} \tag{1}$$

$$\text{Total number of protons, } T, = \frac{C}{B/4} \tag{2}$$

If the generic formula of a natural fat is written as:

$$H_2COCO(CH_2)a(CH = CH)xCH_3$$
$$|$$
$$HCOCO(CH_2)b(CH = CH)yCH_3$$
$$|$$
$$H_2COCO(CH_2)c(CH = CH)zCH_3$$

the molecular weight of the fat may be calculated by:

$$\text{M.W.} = 173.1 + 45.1 + 14.027\,(a + b + c) + 26.038\,(x + y + z) \tag{3}$$

where: $173.1 = C_6H_5O_6$, the glyceryl triester group;
$45.1 = $ three $-CH_3$ groups;
$14.027 = $ the $-CH_2$ group; and
$26.038 = $ the $-CH = CH-$ group.

The total number of protons, T, in the above formula is:

$$T = 5 + 9 + 2\,(a + b + c) + 2\,(x + y + z) \tag{4}$$

The number of olefinic protons, V, is:

$$V = 2\,(x + y + z) \tag{5}$$

Equation (4) may be solved for $(a + b + c)$ in terms of T and V:

$$(a + b + c) = \tfrac{1}{2}\,(T - V - 14) \tag{6}$$

and by substituting Eqs. (5) and (6) in Eq. (3) and summing

$$\text{M.W.} = 218.2 + 7.013(T - V - 14) + 13.019V$$
$$\text{M.W.} = 120.0 + 7.013T + 6.006V \tag{7}$$

Thus, from the area measurements A, B, and C, the average molecular weight can be calculated by Eqs. (1), (2), and (7).

The degree of unsaturation may be expressed as a calculated Iodine Number by:

$$\text{Iodine No.} = \frac{126.91}{\text{Equivalent wt.}} \times \text{No. of olefinic protons} \times 100$$

$$\text{Iodine No.} = \frac{12691V}{\text{M.W.}} \tag{8}$$

EXAMPLE: THE QUANTITATIVE ANALYSIS OF ASPIRIN, PHENACETIN, AND CAFFEINE MIXTURES[68]

The NMR spectra of the components of the APC mixture obtained in deuterated chloroform solution show bands at the following frequencies in p.p.m. from TMS due to the protons

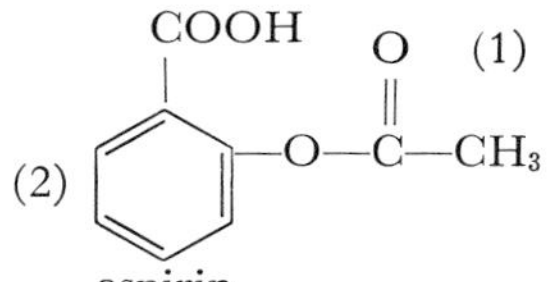

aspirin

(1) of the ester methyl group ∼2.3 p.p.m.
(2) of the aromatic ring ∼7.0–8.2 p.p.m.

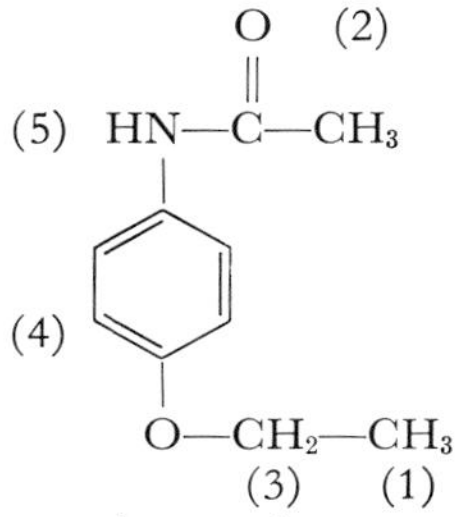

phenacetin

(1) of the ethoxyl methyl group ∼1.3 p.p.m.

(2) of the amide methyl group ∼2.1 p.p.m.

(3) of the ethoxyl methylene group ∼4.0 p.p.m.

(4) of the aromatic ring ∼6.7–7.5 p.p.m.

(5) of the —NH group ∼7.8 p.p.m.

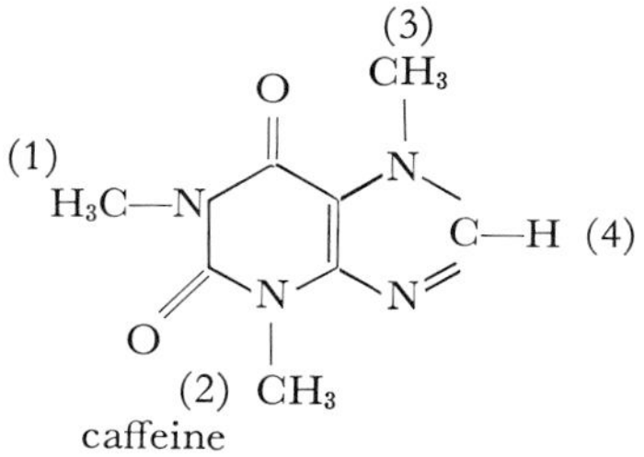

caffeine

(1) of the 1-methyl group ∼3.4 p.p.m.
(2) of the 3-methyl group ∼3.6 p.p.m.
(3) of the 7-methyl group ∼4.0 p.p.m.
(4) of the 8-carbon hydrogen ∼7.5 p.p.m.

The analytical peaks selected are:

Phenacetin—4.0 p.p.m. (A correction is made for the interference at this frequency due to the 7-methyl group band of caffeine by subtracting the area of one of the methyl groups of caffeine at 3.4 and 3.6 p.p.m.
Caffeine—3.4 and 3.6 p.p.m.
Aspirin—2.3 p.p.m.

Spectrometry.—A standard sample containing a known concentration of one of the components (e.g., 50 mg. of caffeine per ml. of deuterated chloroform) is used to determine the absolute integral calibration for the instrument parameters selected for the analysis.

About 60 mg. of the sample is accurately weighed into the sample tube and exactly 0.500 ml. of deuterated chloroform is added by means of a micropipet. The sample

[68] Hollis, D. P., Anal. Chem., **35**, 1682, 1963.

tube is capped, gently warmed, and shaken to dissolve the mixture. Any insoluble components do not interfere with the analysis.

Calculations.—From the NMR spectrum of the sample and the integrated areas under the analytical peaks, the concentrations of the components of the mixture are calculated by the following equations (the absolute integral calibration was made with a standard caffeine solution):

$$A(\text{mg./mg. sample}) = \left[\frac{C}{Ic}\right] \times \left[\frac{\text{M.W.}a}{\text{M.W.}c}\right] \times \left[\frac{\text{MgC}}{\text{ml. soln.}}\right] \text{STND} \times \left[\frac{0.500 \text{ ml.}}{\text{mg. sample}}\right]$$

$$P(\text{mg./mg. sample}) = \left[\frac{A - \frac{1}{2}(B - 0.0055C)}{Ic}\right] \times \frac{3}{2} \times \left[\frac{\text{M.W.}p.}{\text{M.W.}c.}\right] \times \left[\frac{\text{MgC}}{\text{ml. soln.}}\right] \text{STND}$$
$$\times \left[\frac{0.500 \text{ ml.}}{\text{mg. sample}}\right]$$

$$C(\text{mg./mg. sample}) = \left[\frac{\frac{1}{2}(B - 0.0055C)}{Ic}\right] \times \left[\frac{\text{MgC}}{\text{ml. soln.}}\right] \text{STND} \times \left[\frac{0.500 \text{ ml.}}{\text{mg. sample}}\right]$$

where:
A is the area under the peak at 4.0 p.p.m. (phenacetin);
B is the area under the peaks at 3.4 and 3.6 p.p.m. (caffeine);
C is the area under the peak at 2.3 p.p.m. (aspirin);
Ic is the area under the peak of one of the methyl groups of caffeine;
M.W.a, M.W.p, and M.W.c are the molecular weights of aspirin, phenacetin and caffeine respectively; and
$0.0055C$ is a correction factor for the contribution of the C_{13} sideband of the aspirin peak to the area of the 3.4 p.p.m. caffeine peak.

POLAROGRAPHY

The application of polarography to organic analysis has almost overshadowed its original contributions to the inorganic analytical field.[69,70] A tremendous amount of research has been done and is in progress on electrodes, electrode reactions, cells, solvents, systems, and apparatus involved in the polarographic technique.[71]

The dropping mercury electrode is still the most widely used and provides the means of contributing an instrumental technique by which very small amounts of a material may be determined, often in very complex mixtures, and with comparative ease. By observing the precautions necessary to the adaptation of polarography to nonaqueous systems,[72] it is possible to determine organic functional groups which are reducible at the dropping mercury electrode. Some of these include amine oxides, azo and azoxy compounds, conjugated double bonds, carbonyls, diazonium salts, halogens, hydroxyl amines, nitro and nitroso compounds, peroxides, and quinones.

EXAMPLE: THE DETERMINATION OF MALEIC ANHYDRIDE

The half-wave potential of maleic acid in aqueous solution at pH 7.0 occurs at -1.38 volts. The limiting diffusion current at this potential is a measure of the maleic acid concentration.

[69] Zuman, P., and Kolthoff, P. M., Eds., Progress in Polarography, Vols. 1 and 2, Interscience, New York, 1962.
[70] Schmidt, H., von Stackelberg, M., Modern Polarographic Methods, Trans. R.E.W. Maddison, Academic Press, New York, 1963.
[71] Wawzonek, S., and Pietrzyk, D. J., Anal. Chem., 36, 220R, 1964.
[72] Elving, P. J., Komyathy, J. C., Van Atta, R. E., Tang, C. S., and Rosenthal, I., Anal. Chem., 23, 1218, 1951.

Procedure. **Apparatus.**—A polarograph with dropping mercury and saturated calomel electrodes.

Reagents.—Clark and Lubs' buffer pH 7.0 C. P. maleic anhydride.

(1) Residual or Background Current Measurement.—Add 25 ml. of buffer pH 7.0 to a clean, dry, polarographic cell. Remove dissolved oxygen by bubbling nitrogen through the solution for 10 to 15 minutes. Raise the bubbler and allow a stream of nitrogen to pass over the surface of the solution. Record the polarogram over the range −0.8 to −1.8 volts at a sensitivity of about 0.005 μa. per mm. Measure the current between −1.22 and −1.57 volts.

(2) Sample Measurement.—Dissolve the sample containing maleic anhydride in distilled water. The resulting solution should contain 1–10 mg. of maleic acid per ml. Add a 1-ml. aliquot of this solution to the polarographic cell containing the buffer in (1) and purge the oxygen from the cell for 5 minutes. Record the polarogram over the range −0.8 to −1.8 volts at a sensitivity (0.008–0.015 μa. per mm.) which produces a well defined polarographic wave. Measure the limiting diffusion current between −1.22 and −1.57 volts.

(3) Calculations.—Subtract the value of the residual current measured in (1) from the limiting diffusion current measured in (2). Refer the corrected limiting diffusion current to a calibration curve and read the corresponding concentration of maleic anhydride from the plot.

A calibration curve is prepared by plotting the values of the corrected limiting diffusion currents, measured as above, against mg. of maleic anhydride over the range 1–10 mg.

EXAMPLE: THE DETERMINATION OF ANTHRAQUINONE IN COMPLEX MIXTURES

Anthraquinone exhibits two polarographic waves in N,N′-dimethylformamide, (DMF), containing 0.1 M lithium chloride, at half-wave potentials of −0.83 and −1.17 volts. The limiting diffusion currents at these potentials is a measure of the anthraquinone concentration. It is possible to determine anthraquinone polarographically in mixtures containing anthracene, phenanthrene, carbazole, phenanthraquinone, phthalic anhydride, and maleic anhydride. To eliminate interferences by the anhydrides in these mixtures, aqueous lithium hydroxide is added to the polarographic solution to form the lithium salts of the hydrolyzed anhydrides.

Procedure. **Apparatus.**—A polarograph with dropping mercury and saturated calomel electrodes.

Reagents.—N,N′-dimethylformamide. 0.1 M lithium chloride in N,N′-dimethylformamide. 0.5 M aqueous lithium hydroxide.

(1) Residual or Background Current Measurement.—Add 25 ml. of 0.1 M lithium chloride-dimethylformamide solution to a clean, dry, polarographic cell. Add 0.2 ml. of 0.5 M lithium hydroxide solution. Purge the dissolved oxygen from the solution by bubbling nitrogen through it for 10 to 15 minutes. Raise the bubbler and allow a stream of nitrogen to pass over the surface of the solution. Record the polarogram over the range −0.5 to −1.5 volts at a sensitivity of about 0.005 μa. per mm. Measure the current between −0.5 and 1.37 volts.

(2) Sample Measurement.—Weigh 0.0250 g. of sample mixture into a 25-ml. volumetric flask. Add 20 ml. of dimethylformamide, shake to dissolve the sample, and dilute to 25 ml. with dimethylformamide. Add a 2-ml. aliquot of this solution to the polarographic cell containing the DMF-LiCl-LiOH solution in (1) and purge the oxygen from the cell for 5 minutes. Record the polarogram over the range −0.5 to −1.5 volts at a sensitivity (0.008–0.015 μa. per mm.) which produces well defined polarographic waves. Measure the limiting diffusion current between −0.5 and −1.37 volts.

(3) Calculations.—Subtract the value of the residual current measured in (1) from the limiting diffusion current measured in (2). Refer the corrected limiting diffusion current to a calibration curve and read the corresponding concentration of anthraquinone from the plot.

A calibration curve is prepared by plotting the values of the corrected limiting diffusion currents, measured as above, against the milligrams of anthraquinone over the range 1–25 mg.

OPTICAL ROTATORY DISPERSION

A discussion of instrumental methods of organic functional group analysis would not be complete without some mention of polarimetry. Classically it is one of the oldest of instrumental techniques. An asymmetric atom may be considered a functional group. When plane-polarized light passes through a compound containing this group, the plane of vibration of the electrical component of the lightwave is rotated through an angle whose value depends on the thickness of the sample, the temperature, and the wavelength of the light. The sodium D doublet served as the standard wavelength for some time.

The change in the angle of rotation with a change in wavelength is known as the dispersion. As the wavelength of the incident polarized light is decreased, an increase in the angle of rotation usually occurs. However, if the compound containing the asymmetric atom also contains a chromophore which absorbs in the visible or near-ultraviolet regions of the spectrum, an anomalous dispersion curve may be obtained. In this case, rather than observing a gradual increase in angle of rotation with decreasing wavelength, an intense maximum followed by a change in direction to a strong minimum (or vice-versa) with decreasing wavelength is obtained. The wavelength at which this dispersion curve passes through zero angle of rotation in passing from the maximum to the minimum lies in the vicinity of the absorption maximum exhibited in the visible or ultraviolet spectrum of the compound. Not every compound which has a visible or ultraviolet absorbing chromophore displays this effect. Functional groups such as the carbonyl, azide, xanthate, nitrate, dithiocarbamate, conjugated double bonds, and the aromatic rings generally give rise to this effect. Functional groups which do not appreciably absorb in the near-ultraviolet, as the carboxyl, amide, and unconjugated double bond, and those groups which do not absorb at all, as the hydroxyl and amine, fail to show this effect over the ranges scanned by existing instruments.[73]

This technique has been extremely valuable in the study of structures of complex materials and mixtures.[74,75,76] As is usual, the scope of applicability of this technique was dependent on the development of the necessary instrumentation. The photoelectric spectropolarimeter is such a development.[77]

A major application of polarimetry to organic functional group analysis is the determination of the concentration of a compound containing the functional group by relating

[73] Lyle, G. G., and Lyle, R. E., "Optical Rotatory Dispersion," Chapter 1, in Determination of Organic Structures by Physical Methods, Vol. 2, Nachod, F. C., and Phillips, W. D., Eds. Academic Press, New York, 1962.

[74] Djerassi, C., and Ehrlich, R. J., Am. Chem. Soc., **78**, 440, 1956.

[75] Lowry, T. M., Optical Rotatory Power, Longmans, Green, London, 1935.

[76] Djerassi, C., Optical Rotatory Dispersion: Applications to Organic Chemistry. McGraw-Hill, New York, 1960.

[77] Rudolph, H., J. Opt. Soc. Am., **45**, 50, 1955.

its concentration to its optical rotation. The very large optical rotation exhibited by many compounds at wavelengths below those of the sodium D lines concomitantly extends the utility of this method. This can be illustrated by an example taken from the studies on steroidal sapogenins.[74]

In the extraction of hecogenin from yucatan sisal, tigogenin occurs as an impurity. The determination of the relative amounts

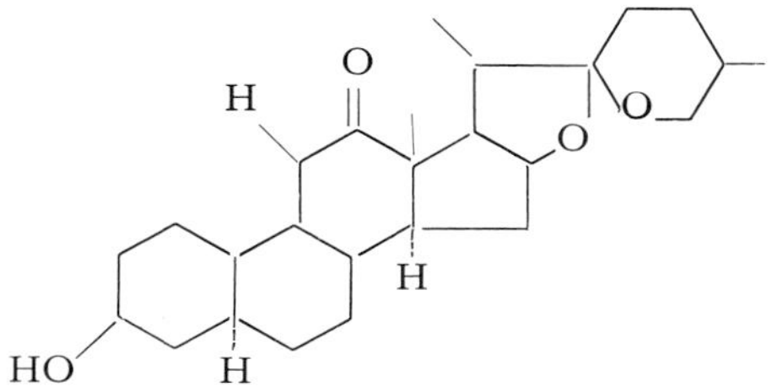

hecogenin

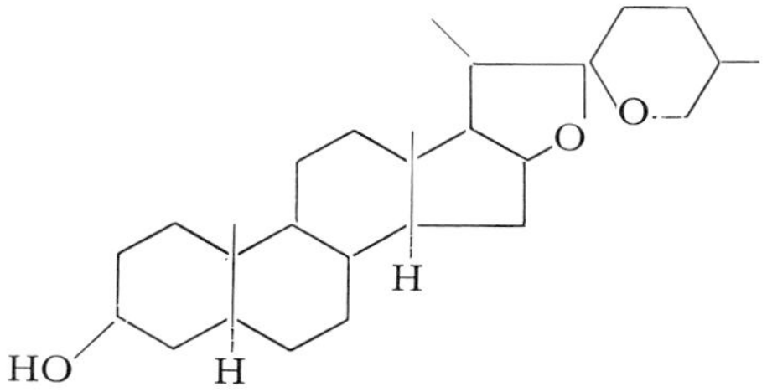

tigogenin

of these materials is a difficult analytical problem by other techniques. In polarimetry the accuracy and precision of analysis of a two-component system is dependent on the magnitude of the difference in optical activity of the components. In a conventional polarimeter utilizing the sodium D lines, the rotations of these sapogenins differ by 53 degrees. In a spectropolarimeter at the analytical wavelength of 312.5 mμ, their rotations differ by 1051 degrees. The considerable enhancement of the analytical method is obvious.

RAMAN SPECTROMETRY

Although the information obtained from infrared and Raman spectrometry is complementary, the latter technique has not been as widely employed by analysts as the former. Undoubtedly, this is partly due to the more rapid advances made in the instrumental development of infrared spectrometers. In addition, infrared spectrometry provides data characteristic of the functional groups of a molecule while Raman spectrometric data are more characteristic of the molecular skeleton. For these reasons, perhaps, Raman spectrometry has advanced to its present state in the hands of molecular spectroscopists rather than in those of analysts. There is a distinct possibility that this situation may change due to the development of the gas laser. The application of the gas laser as a radiant source for Raman spectrometers and the commercial availability of instruments using this source[78] may well herald the advent of analytical research by this instrumental method.

[78] Instrument News, Vol. 15, No. 3, Perkin-Elmer Corp., Norwalk, Conn., Fall 1964.

The experimental difficulties which plagued the advances in Raman spectrometry are primarily attributable to inadequacies in the existing light sources. The gas laser, however, readily provides a very monochromatic light source of high intensity and low background. The lower frequency of the laser beam diminishes photodecomposition of samples and fluorescence excitation. The measurement of the Raman effect becomes possible in more dilute solution and in more intensely colored solutions than heretofore.

This development will undoubtedly increase the importance of Raman spectrometry in the field of organic functional group analysis.

Chapter 52

GASES

By Duane V. Kniebes
Institute of Gas Technology
Chicago, Illinois

Gases have been routinely analyzed for many years by instrumental methods, primarily by mass spectrometry and gas chromatography. The mass spectrometer and the gas chromatograph dominate the field of gas analysis so completely that noninstrumental methods have largely been discarded, with the exception only of a few simple applications such as flue gas analysis. Because of their widespread use, both instrumental methods and relevant chemical methods are described in detail in Chapter 35, of Standard Methods of Chemical Analysis, Volume II, Part B, so will not be repeated here. This chapter will be restricted, therefore, to a brief discussion of instrument applications.

Complete analysis of a gas sample for its major constituents can be accomplished by either the mass spectrometer or the gas chromatograph. Minor and trace constituents can also be determined in many instances, but both accuracy and the lower detection limit for a given component often depend upon the mixture composition, particularly in the case of the mass spectrometer.

The mass spectrometer is particularly well suited for analysis of multicomponent mixtures. Instrument run time varies little whether the samples are simple or complex, and samples of differing types can be run sequentially without changing instrument procedure. Furthermore, calibrations are stable, and instrument response for a component is linear over the entire concentration range. These characteristics make the mass spectrometer an excellent instrument for the laboratory which has a large number of complex gas mixtures to analyze regularly. Under normal conditions the analytical mass spectrometer can detect about 100 p.p.m. of a component, and, with competent interpretation of a sample's mass spectrum, it provides an excellent qualitative as well as quantitative analysis of an unknown mixture. ASTM methods D1137-53[1] for natural gas and D1302-61T[2] for carbureted water gas describe typical mass spectrometer analytical procedures.

The gas chromatograph, which is less costly than the mass spectrometer, also has many attributes which make it an important tool for the analysis of gases. Although complex mixtures usually require complex instrument procedures, including the use of multiple columns and sample runs, many gases can be analyzed quickly and accurately. Also, some components such as the pentane isomers, which in most samples are difficult to determine as individuals by mass spectrometry, can be separated easily by gas chro-

[1] Standard Method for Analysis of Natural Gases and Related Types of Gaseous Mixtures by the Mass Spectrometer, D1137-53, ASTM Standards, Part 19, American Society for Testing and Materials, Philadelphia, 1964, p. 226.
[2] Tentative Method for Analysis of Carbureted Water Gas by the Mass Spectrometer, D1302-61T, ASTM Standards, Part 19, American Society for Testing and Materials, Philadelphia, 1964, p. 295.

matography. Typical analytical methods are described in ASTM Standards D1717-61T[3] for commercial butane-butylene mixtures, D2163-63T[4] for liquefied petroleum gas, D1945-62T[5] for natural gas, and D1946-62T[6] for reformed gas. The natural gas method is also described in Standard Methods of Chemical Analysis, Volume II, Part B, Chapter 35. Most gas mixtures encountered in practice can be analyzed with one of these procedures since the most commonly occurring fixed and hydrocarbon components are determined.

Qualitative analysis with the gas chromatograph is difficult, particularly with complex mixtures. With few exceptions, gas samples in which unsuspected components could occur should also be run by mass spectrometer, or other definitive tests should be made to confirm the identity and number of compounds in the sample.

Although the sensitivity of the thermal conductivity detector commonly employed in a gas chromatograph limits component detection to the same concentration range as the mass spectrometer, other detectors are available to extend instrument sensitivity considerably, into the parts per million and parts per billion range. These include modified thermal conductivity, argon ionization, hydrogen flame ionization, and electron capture detectors. Thus, trace component analysis can often be successfully done with the right combination of column and detector.

Frequently the analyst is required to perform only a partial analysis of a gas sample. In most instances a simplified mass spectrometer or gas chromatograph method will suffice. A more specialized instrument may be of value, however, if very low concentrations of a component must be determined, or if a continuous chart record is required. An instrument often used for single component monitoring is the nondispersive type of infrared analyzer. One important use of this type of instrument is recording carbon monoxide concentration in air or combustion products (see Standard Methods of Chemical Analysis, Vol. II, Part B, Chapter 35). The instrument has many other applications, largely in gas streams containing hydrocarbons, since such compounds as hydrogen, oxygen, nitrogen, and rare gases are not detected by infrared methods.

The determination of sulfur compounds is of special interest in the fields of air pollution and utility gas distribution. An instrument employing bromine titration of the sulfur compounds is in use for the 0.1 to 10 p.p.m. concentration range, which is of most interest. Response of the instrument varies somewhat with the component being detected, so care must be taken in the interpretation of readings for mixtures of sulfur compounds such as commonly occur in odorized natural gas streams. This instrumental procedure is described in ASTM Method D-1355-60[7] for sulfur dioxide content of the atmosphere.

[3] Tentative Method for Analysis of Commerical Butane-Butylene Mixtures by Gas Chromatography, D1717-61T, ASTM Standards, Part 19, American Society for Testing and Materials, Philadelphia, 1964, p. 305.

[4] Tentative Method of Test for Analysis of Liquefied Petroleum (LP) Gases by Gas Chromatography, D2163-63T, ASTM Standards, Part 19, American Society for Testing and Materials, Philadelphia, 1964, p. 395.

[5] Tentative Method for Analysis of Natural Gas by Gas Chromatography, D1945-62T, ASTM Standards, Part 19, American Society for Testing and Materials, Philadelphia, 1964, p. 344.

[6] Tentative Method for Analysis of Reformed Gas by Gas Chromatography, D1946-62T, ASTM Standards, Part 19, American Society for Testing and Materials, Philadelphia, 1964, p. 359.

[7] Methods for Continuous Analysis and Automatic Recording of the Sulfur Dioxide Content of the Atmosphere, D1355-60, ASTM Standards, Part 23, American Society for Testing and Materials, Philadelphia, 1964, p. 1635.

Chapter 53

GLASS

By Stephen H. Laning

Pittsburgh Plate Glass Company
Chemical Division
Barberton, Ohio

Glass making today, far from being just an art, has become a highly developed science. Composition of the glass, or of certain components of it, must often be controlled in order for the glass to meet the desired specifications. With today's production rates, this frequently requires rapid accurate analysis to detect early changes in composition.

Occasionally trouble develops in glass tank operation, with resultant abnormal properties in the glass. Comparative analysis of the abnormal glass with the normal glass can usually point to the cause of the trouble.

The importance of knowing the composition of a glass becomes obvious when, for one reason or another, the product has to be discarded for not meeting specifications.

Chemical methods in glass analysis are often long and tedious, requiring careful separations to avoid interferences. To analyze a glass for the major and minor components and the common trace elements would require many days. Instrumental methods have made it possible to do the same analysis in 2 hr. with conventional equipment, or in a few minutes with some types of automatic equipment designed for production control.

Several instruments in use today contribute to better control of glass products. It is the purpose of this chapter to make the analyst aware of such instruments and, in addition, it is hoped that the procedures presented will be useful to the people concerned with the various instruments.

FLAME AND ATOMIC
ABSORPTION SPECTROMETRY

By P. B. Adams
Research and Development Laboratory
Corning Glass Works
Corning, New York

Spectrochemical methods of analysis that utilize solution techniques are particularly adaptable to the analysis of multicomponent materials, such as glass. Foremost among such spectrochemical methods are flame spectrometry and atomic absorption spectrometry. As applied to glass analysis, the precision and accuracy of both techniques can approach 1 relative percent of the amount measured.

Flame spectrometry is a firmly established technique in most chemical analysis laboratories. It is the most widely used technique for the determination of the alkali elements in a wide range of materials, including glass. Many other elements can be determined when concentrations are large enough and interferences are minimal.

Atomic absorption spectrometry has only recently become a routine laboratory technique. Much of the instrumentation and procedure are similar to those used in flame spectrometry. For about 15 elements, atomic absorption spectrometry is more sensitive than flame spectrometry; for complex matrices, it is potentially more useful because it is subject to fewer spectral interferences.

Flame spectrometry and atomic absorption spectrometry will be discussed as they apply to glass analysis. The following topics will be covered: the principles and instrumentation used in each technique, the elements and concentration levels that can be detected in solutions, the approximate minimum concentration that can be conveniently determined in glass, the advantages and limitations of the two techniques, general procedures for sample preparation and instrument operation, methods of calculating results, analytical procedures found in the literature, a bibliography of selected references, and, finally, a typical procedure for the determination of the alkali elements in glass by flame spectrometry.

PRINCIPLES

Flame and atomic absorption spectrometry both utilize a solution as the analyte. This solution is atomized into a flame, or other energy source, where many of the elements present are dissociated to the atomic state. Flame spectrometry makes use of the radiation emitted from the excited atoms. Atomic absorption spectrometry makes use of the absorbing property of the ground-state atoms; light from a source of radiation, such as a hollow cathode tube, specific for the element to be determined is passed through the flame where it is partially absorbed by these ground-state atoms. In flame spectrometry, radiation from the flame passes through a monochromator. In atomic absorption spectrometry, radiation from a hollow cathode tube containing the element to be determined is attenuated by the flame and passes through a monochromator. The monochromatic radiation is then received by a photodetector, and the signal is amplified and read out. The instrumentation is represented schematically in Fig. 53-1.

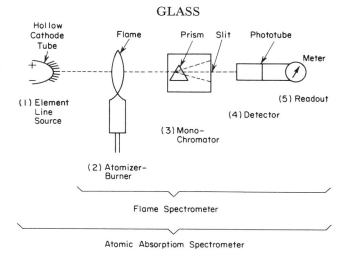

Fig. 53-1.   Schematic Diagram of Flame and Atomic Absorption Spectrometry.

The processes occurring in the atomizer-burner can be represented as follows:

Atomization of solution → evaporation of solvent
→ formation of dried particles → dissociation to

formation of excited atoms (1 percent)

molecules, ions, and atoms

formation of ground-state atoms (99 percent)

Analytical results will be altered by changes which affect any of these processes, such as anions or cations present, flame temperature, mass of material in the flame, and the speed at which this material passes through the flame. Since the equilibrium between excited and ground-state atoms usually favors the ground state very markedly, small shifts in this equilibrium will affect flame spectrometry more than they will affect atomic absorption spectrometry.

INSTRUMENTATION

The complexity and versatility of commercial flame and atomic absorption spectrometers vary widely. Atomizer-burners are of two general types: the premix aerosol type and the total consumption type. Special burners are available for atomic absorption spectrometry. A variety of atomizer-burners is required if a broad range of analytical problems prevails. Monochromators vary from simple glass or interference filters to various combinations of prisms, gratings, and slits. Devices are available for scanning spectra. Photodetectors used include relatively insensitive barrier layer cells and phototubes, as well as extremely sensitive photomultipliers. Amplifier electronics vary from the crude to the refined. Readout devices include simple deflection meters, the Wheatstone bridge type, and recorders. Some instruments employ an internal standard, some are of the double-beam type, but many are single-beam devices.

Criteria in Selection of Instrument.—In selecting an instrument for glass analysis, the following criteria are of extreme importance:

(a) Precision.—The instrument should be stable, capable of repeating determinations to at least ±1 relative percent. Instrument precision is principally a function of the atomizer-burner, the system used to control the atomizer-burner and the electronics.

(b) Sensitivity.—Optimum sensitivity is not only desirable for determining low concentrations of the elements in glass, but also for minimizing chemical interferences which are generally less severe at greater dilutions. Sensitivity depends on all instrument components.

(c) Resolution.—For the analysis of very simple glass systems or when precision and accuracy can be sacrificed, relatively low resolution, such as that obtained with optical filters, will suffice. Interference filters are usually better than glass filters. However, for the analysis of most glass systems, and particularly for the determination of small concentrations, prism or grating instruments capable of resolving lines about 10 A apart are required. For the analysis of very complex glass systems, it may be necessary to resolve lines as close as 1 A.

(d) Source.—The success or failure of a particular analytical method will often depend on the characteristics of the burner-atomizer used. The proper control of the fuel flow system, the proper atomizer-burner, and the proper fuel mixture maximize sensitivity and minimize interferences.

ELEMENTS AND CONCENTRATIONS DETERMINED

About 60 elements have been detected by flame and atomic absorption spectrometry. These are given in column 1, Table 53-1. The reported detection limits for these elements in solution are also shown (columns 2 and 3, Table 53-1). These detection limits pertain to solutions containing only the element to be determined when it is present in the optimum solvent and using the best flame at the most sensitive wavelength. The data for atomic absorption spectrometry are probably less reliable than those for flame spectrometry; they have been obtained from several references in which the best operating conditions may not always have been used.

Minimum working concentrations, expressed as a percent of the element present in a glass, are approximated in columns 4 and 5, Table 53-1. The minimum working concentrations shown assume that (a) a precision of about ±1 relative percent is sought; (b) a typical glass is analyzed that contains, in addition to the element determined, such other elements as the following: silicon, boron, aluminum, titanium, lead, magnesium, calcium, barium, sodium, potassium, and lithium; (c) spectral interferences are more generally present in flame than in atomic absorption spectrometry; (d) the dilution is 1.0 g. of sample per 100 ml. of solution; (e) the best solution technique, flame source, and instrumentation is used in the analysis; and (f) there are no significant chemical interferences.

Although Table 53-1 is a useful guide, it must be recognized that the ease with which a particular element can be determined in different glasses will vary widely. For instance, if interferences dictate that an 0.1 g. sample be diluted to 1000 ml., then the minimum working concentration will be 100 times as great as that shown in Table 53-1. Obviously, the instrumentation employed will greatly affect the ability to attain those minimum working concentrations shown.

ADVANTAGES AND LIMITATIONS

Flame and atomic absorption spectrometry offer several significant advantages in the chemical analysis of glass. Compared to classical methods, the analytical procedures are usually less complex and require fewer chemical manipulations; thus they can be used more readily by nontechnical personnel. The methods are generally quite rapid. Low detection limits for many elements permit the analysis of small samples. Good precision, the order of 1 percent, is readily attained.

TABLE 53-1. ELEMENTS, DETECTION LIMITS IN SOLUTION, AND MINIMUM
WORKING CONCENTRATIONS IN GLASS

Element	Reported Minimum Detection, Limit, p.p.m. in Solution		Approximate Minimum Working Concentration in Glass, percent[c]	
	Flame[a]	Atomic Absorption[b]	Flame	Atomic Absorption
Ag	0.04	0.02	0.4	0.04
Al	0.05	0.5	1.0	1.0
As	2.	1.0	40.	2.0
Au	0.2	0.1	4.0	0.2
B	0.1	250.	2.0	>100.
Ba	0.05	1.0	1.0	2.0
Be	0.1	0.05	2.0	0.1
Bi	2.	0.2	40.	0.4
Ca	0.002	0.01	0.04	0.2
Cd	0.3	0.01	6.0	0.2
Ce	0.2	—	4.0	—
Co	0.1	0.1	2.0	0.2
Cr	0.01	0.01	0.2	0.02
Cs	0.005	0.05	0.1	0.1
Cu	0.02	0.005	0.4	0.01
Dy	0.07	5.	1.4	10.
Er	0.1	2.	2.0	40.
Eu	0.08	12	1.6	24.
Fe	0.06	0.02	1.2	0.04
Ga	0.03	0.5	0.6	1.0
Gd	0.04	—	0.8	—
Ge	5.	—	100.	—
Hg	3.	0.2	60.	0.4

[a] Herrmann, R., and Alkemade, C. T. J., Chemical Analysis by Flame Photometry, 2nd Rev. Ed., Interscience Publishers, Inc., New York, 1963, pp. 260–272, Table 10. (Courtesy of John Wiley and Sons, Inc.)

[b] Analytical Methods for Atomic Absorption Spectrophotometry, Perkin-Elmer Corp., January 1964, and Supplement, May 1964. (Courtesy of Perkin-Elmer Corp.)

Slavin, W., Sprague, S., and Manning, D. C., "Detection Limits in Analytical Absorption Spectrophotometry," Atomic Absorption Newsletter No. 18, Perkin-Elmer Corp., February 1964. (Courtesy of Perkin-Elmer Corp.)

Robinson, J. W., "Recent Advances in Atomic Absorption Spectroscopy," Anal. Chem., **33**, 1068–1069, Table I, July 1961. (Courtesy of Analytical Chemistry.)

[c] The approximate minimum working concentration, MWC, has been defined as follows:

$$\text{MWC} = D \times A \times B \times 100\% \times \frac{V}{W}$$

where MWC = approximate minimum working concentration for the element in glass (percent),

D = detection limit for the element in solution (p.p.m. $\times 10^{-6}$),

A = an estimated factor which, when multiplied by the detection limit, gives an approximate concentration that can be determined to ± 1 relative percent = 200,

B = an estimated factor to account for spectral interferences frequently present with many glasses analyzed even with the best instrumentation: for flame spectrometry, $B = 10$, and for atomic absorption spectrometry, $B = 1$,

V = volume of solution (ml.) = 100 ml., and

W = weight of sample (g.) = 1.0.

TABLE 53-1 (cont.)

Element	Reported Minimum Detection, Limit, p.p.m. in Solution		Approximate Minimum Working Concentration in Glass, percent[c]	
	Flame[a]	Atomic Absorption[b]	Flame	Atomic Absorption
Ho	0.06	—	1.2	—
In	0.02	0.2	0.4	0.4
K	0.0002	0.003	0.004	0.006
La	0.01	—	0.2	—
Li	0.0002	0.005	0.004	0.01
Lu	0.09	—	1.8	—
Mg	0.01	0.003	0.2	0.005
Mn	0.005	0.01	0.1	0.02
Mo	0.4	0.2	8.0	0.4
Na	0.0001	0.005	0.002	0.01
Nb	2.	250.	40.	>100.
Nd	0.02	—	0.4	—
Ni	0.1	0.05	2.0	0.1
Pb	0.1	0.1	2.0	0.2
Pd	0.1	0.3	2.0	0.6
Pr	0.2	—	4.0	—
Pt	1.	0.5	20.	1.0
Rb	0.002	0.02	0.04	0.04
Re	5.	3.	100.	6.0
Rh	0.3	0.3	6.0	0.6
Ru	0.07	0.1	1.4	0.2
Sb	0.4	0.2	8.0	0.4
Sc	0.006	5.	0.1	10.
Se	—	1.	—	2.0
Si	7.	15.	>100.	30.
Sm	0.1	50.	2.0	>100.
Sn	0.5	2.	10.	4.0
Sr	0.005	0.02	0.1	0.04
Tb	0.06	—	1.2	—
Te	3.	0.5	60.	1.0
Ti	0.2	1.	4.0	2.0
Tl	0.06	0.2	1.2	0.4
Tm	0.2	35.	4.0	70.
U	0.7	7.	14.	14.
V	0.1	0.5	2.0	1.0
Yb	0.03	10.	0.6	20.
Y	0.01	—	0.2	—
Zn	0.8	0.005	16.	0.01
Zr	8.	—	>100.	—

Limitations.—The major limitations are chemical and spectral interferences which result from reactions that occur between a species of the element to be determined and some other substance present. Some anions and cations shift the rate at which compounds dissociate to atoms, a type of interference that affects emission and absorption with equal severity. Some substances and conditions shift the equilibrium between the ground- and excited-state atoms, a type of interference that affects emission more markedly than absorption.

Spectral Interferences.—Spectral interferences are caused by overlapping lines and bands from substances present but not determined. In flame spectrometry, the mono-chromator defines the analytical band width: in atomic absorption spectrometry, the emitting atom in the cathode tube essentially defines the analytical band width. Inasmuch as the latter is generally more selective, spectral interferences are usually less severe in atomic absorption spectrometry.

GENERAL SAMPLE PREPARATION PROCEDURE

The ratio of the sample size taken to the final solution volume used for analysis should be appropriate to the sensitivity of the element to be determined. However, this ratio should be as small as possible in order to minimize chemical and spectral interferences. A ratio of 0.1 g. per 500 ml. will maintain the total concentration of glass components at the hundred parts per million level, acceptable for most work. However, optimum ratios for particular analyses may vary from 0.01 g. per 1000 ml. to 1 g. per 10 ml.

Silicate glasses are usually decomposed with a mixture of hydrofluoric acid, to react with the silica, and some other acid which is compatible with the other glass components. (In some instances, it may be necessary to use a high-temperature acid extraction or an alkaline fusion.) After decomposition, silicon tetrafluoride and hydrofluoric acid are usually removed by fuming. The same acid used with the hydrofluoric acid for decomposition is then usually used for solution of the sample. Aqueous solvents are most commonly employed, although organic solvents may provide better sensitivity.

To minimize or eliminate interferences, buffering substances may be added. In some instances, separations may be necessary; precipitation and filtration, solvent extraction, ion exchange, and electrodeposition are commonly employed. If interferences cannot be controlled, a standard is made which closely matches the sample; otherwise, the standard need contain only the element to be determined. The importance of proper solvents and buffers compatible with the correct flame cannot be overemphasized.

GENERAL INSTRUMENT PROCEDURE

The electrical switches are turned on first to allow warm-up time; power is applied to photodetectors, amplifier and readout circuitry, and hollow cathode tubes (for atomic absorption spectrometry). The fuel gases are then turned on, the flame ignited, and any necessary adjustments are made to optimize the fuel mixture. The proper analytical spectral band may be selected either by adjusting a grating (or prism) and a slit, or by inserting an optical filter. The readout scale is nulled and the sensitivity adjusted.

Sample and standard solutions are atomized alternately. Readout response values are obtained by balancing a galvanometer, by noting the deflection of a meter, by recording at the analytical line, or by recording while scanning past the analytical line. Replicate readings are necessary for good precision. For maximum stability, care must be taken to ensure proper operation of the burner-atomizer, including precise control of fuel flow rates and prevention of atomizer clogging. The instrument is generally shut off in the reverse order from which it was turned on.

METHODS OF CALCULATING RESULTS

If working curves are straight lines and interferences can be controlled or compensated with matching standards, the calculation of results is simple. A direct proportion is set up so that the ratio of sample concentration to net sample response is equal to the ratio of standard concentration to net standard response.

If working curves are not straight lines and yet interferences can be controlled or compensated with matching standards, four techniques of calculating results are available: the calibration curve method, the intercept method, the interpolation method, and the internal standard method. The calibration curve technique involves preparing a calibration curve, adjusting the sensitivity of the instrument so that the standard solution response value matches the calibration curve, and then reading sample concentration values directly from it. The intercept method involves preparation of a calibration curve, from which an intercept curve is constructed. This relates any response value from the calibration curve to a value on the response axis that is intercepted by a line tangent to the calibration curve at that response value. Sample concentrations are then calculated from the relationship:

$$\frac{C_{Sm}}{C_{St}} = \frac{R_{Sm} - I}{R_{St} - I}$$

where C_{Sm} = sample concentration,
C_{St} = standard concentration,
R_{Sm} = sample response,
R_{St} = standard response, and
I = response axis intercept value for a line tangent to a point on the calibration curve midway between the points defined by (C_{Sm}, R_{Sm}) and (C_{St}, R_{St}).

The interpolation method involves the use of two standards, the concentrations of which bracket the sample concentration. The unknown sample concentration is determined by direct linear interpolation, either graphically or mathematically. The internal standard method minimizes most physical and some chemical interferences. Intensity ratios are obtained between the determined element line and an internal standard element line. These data are then plotted *vs.* the concentration of the determined element on a log-log scale resulting in a working calibration curve. Of the four methods discussed, the interpolation method is usually the most accurate. Both intercept and interpolation methods assume that the portion of the curve between standards and sample is essentially linear. Therefore, for maximum accuracy, the concentration of the standards and samples must be quite close in concentration. The internal standard method can be very precise, but may be simultaneously very inaccurate.

Two methods of calculation are available which help to compensate for unknown interferences: the method of standard addition and the method of infinite dilution. Standard addition involves the preparation of two or more standards by adding known increments of the element to be determined to aliquots of the sample solution. The responses for standards and sample are then plotted *vs.* concentration added. The curve obtained is extrapolated to the negative side of the concentration axis, and the point at which it intercepts the concentration axis is taken to be the unknown concentration. Infinite dilution techniques depend on the assumption that interferences approach zero as the concentration of interfering elements approaches zero. A series of dilutions of the sample is made. The concentration of each solution in the series is determined by one of the techniques above. The concentrations found, calculated to the same dilution level, are plotted *vs.* the dilution level. The true concentration is then obtained where the extrapolated curve intercepts the concentration axis at infinite dilution.

ANALYTICAL METHODS

ALKALI METALS

There are numerous methods in the literature for the analysis of the alkali metals in glass by flame spectrometry, but only a few atomic absorption methods have appeared to date. There is probably no advantage of atomic absorption over flame spectrometry for these metals. A typical flame method is given below; and other typical flame and atomic absorption methods are referred to in the Selected Bibliography.

The method that follows is used for the spectrochemical analysis of glass for the alkali metals by flame photometry. This method is designated E-2 SM 10–13 by the American Society for Testing and Materials,[1] and is reproduced here with permission. It has been proposed by Williams[2] and Adams.[2]

Scope.—This method covers the flame photometric determination of five elements in glass in the ranges indicated in Table 53-2.

TABLE 53-2. ELEMENTS AND CONCENTRATION RANGES

Element	Concentration Range in which Radiation Measurements are Most Useful, p.p.m.	Concentration Range of Element Oxide in Glass, percent
Lithium	0 to 20	0 to 15
Sodium	0 to 25	0 to 20
Potassium	0 to 25	0 to 20
Rubidium	0 to 20	0 to 15
Cesium	0 to 20	0 to 15

This method is most useful for the routine analysis of glasses. The use of a single calibrating standard shortens the actual working time and eliminates the preparation of analytical curves after they are initially made.

Summary of Method.—The sample is fumed to near dryness with hydrofluoric acid and perchloric acid, and the residue is dissolved, using hydrochloric acid, and followed by dilution to a definite volume.[3] A portion of the solution is atomized into a hydrogen-oxygen flame, and the intensities of analytical lines are measured with a spectrophotometer by comparison with standards. Intensity values for the standard and sample are applied to a specially prepared curve to give an intensity factor, and the concentration of the alkali present is computed by a simple arithmetic relation.

The scope and limitations of this method are, to some degree, dependent on the resolution, the range of the slit width, and the sensitivity of the instrument employed.

Apparatus. Spectrophotometer.—A spectrophotometer is used that is capable of suitably resolving the lines of the alkali elements (Table 53-4) and that has a variable slit-width adjustment.[4]

Excitation Source.—A flame attachment and burner using a hydrogen-oxygen flame is used.[4]

Glassware.—Small 5-ml. beakers are used to hold the solutions during analysis. Stock standard solutions are stored in 96 percent silica-glass containers[5] or polyethylene bottles. Volumetric flasks are necessary to adjust the concentration of sample and standard solutions.

[1] This suggested method has no official status in the Society but is published as information only. The method is based on the experience of the submitters. Comments are solicited.

[2] Corning Glass Works, Corning, N. Y.

[3] Williams, J. P., and Adams, P. B., "Flame Spectrophotometric Analysis of Glasses and Ores," J. Am. Ceram. Soc., **37**, 306–311, 1954.

[4] A spectrophotometer such as the Model DU and the flame attachment No. 9200 with a No. 4020 burner manufactured by Beckman Instruments, Inc., Pasadena, Calif., is a suitable design. A photomultiplier attachment is not necessary.

[5] Vycor brand glass has been found satisfactory for this purpose.

Fuel Tanks and Regulators.—The commercially available hydrogen and oxygen tanks are equipped with suitable two-gauge, two-stage, pressure-reducing regulators in addition to those supplied with the burner attachment.

Platinum Ware.—Platinum dishes are required for decomposition of the glass samples with hydrofluoric acid and perchloric acid.

Miscellaneous.—An agate mortar and pestle are used to brind the glass sample.

Reagents and Materials.—The purity and concentration of the chemical reagents in accordance with requirements specified in the Recommended Practices for Apparatus and Reagents for Chemical Analysis of Metals (ASTM Designation: E 50).[6]

Stock Solutions.—Prepare standard alkali stock solutions as prescribed in Table 53-3 by dissolving individual reagent grade salts in water and diluting to volume. For the lithium solution, dissolve lithium carbonate in dilute hydrochloric acid and evaporate to dryness prior to dilution with water. Distilled or deionized water is used in making all solutions.

Gases.—Tanks of compressed hydrogen and oxygen of commercial grade are used for fuel and for atomizing the solutions into the flame.

Preparation of Standards.—The standard solutions for analysis are prepared by diluting the stock solutions. For example, to prepare a standard solution containing 10 p.p.m. sodium, 5 p.p.m. potassium, and 1 p.p.m. lithium for use in the analysis of a glass (Note 1) containing approximately 3.4 percent Na_2O, 1.5 percent K_2O, and 0.5 percent Li_2O, proceed as follows: First, prepare 100-p.p.m. solutions of each alkali by pipeting 10.0 ml. of each of the 1000-p.p.m. stock solutions shown in Table 53-3 into

TABLE 53-3. STOCK SOLUTIONS

Element	Salt	Weight, g.	Diluted Volume, ml.	Final Element Concentration, p.p.m.
Lithium............	Li_2CO_3	2.6617	500	1000
Sodium............	NaCl	2.5418	1000	1000
Potassium..........	KCl	1.9069	1000	1000
Rubidium..........	Rb_2SO_4	0.7810	1000	500
Cesium............	Cs_2SO_4	0.6807	1000	500

100-ml. volumetric flasks and diluting to 100 ml. Then, pipet 10.0 ml. of the 100-p.p.m. sodium solution, 5.0 ml. of the 100-p.p.m. potassium solution, and 1.00 ml. of the 100-p.p.m. lithium solution into a 100-ml. volumetric flask and dilute to 100 ml. to obtain the desired standard. These diluted standard solutions may be kept in glass-stoppered, volumetric flasks for periods up to three months without appreciable alkali contamination and for longer periods in 96 percent silica-glass[5] or polyethylene containers if proper precautions are taken to prevent evaporation.

Note 1.—A general expression relating the percentage of alkali oxide in a glass sample to parts per million of alkali element in solution is as follows:

$$\text{Alkali element, p.p.m.} = \frac{B \times W \times 10}{F \times V}$$

where B = concentration, in percent, of alkali oxide, known or thought to be present,
  W = weight of sample, in grams,
  F = gravimetric factor to convert alkali to alkali oxide, as given in the section on "Calculations," part (b), and
  V = volume of solution, in liters, in which sample is to be dissolved.

Preparation of Sample.—Decompose 0.100 g. of the sample (Note 2), which has

[6] 1960 Book of ASTM Methods of Chemical Analysis of Metals.

been ground to a fine powder, in a small platinum dish by moistening with about 1 ml. of water and then treating with about 1 ml. of perchloric acid (72 percent) and 5 ml. of hydrofluoric acid (48 percent). A single treatment with hydrofluoric acid is usually sufficient to completely decompose most glasses, but in certain cases a second and even third addition of hydrofluoric acid may be necessary. Evaporate to copious fumes on a steam bath, fume on a low-temperature hot plate about 5 min., cool, wash down the sides of the dish with water, repeat the steam bath evaporation, and finally fume to near dryness on a hot plate. Add 5 drops of hydrochloric acid (1:1) to the cooled residue and quantitatively transfer to a 250-ml. volumetric flask with warm water using more hydrochloric acid (1:1) if necessary. The hydrochloric acid concentration should not exceed 0.02 N in the final solution; i.e., not more than 15 drops of hydrochloric acid (1:1) in 250 ml. When more hydrochloric acid is required for solution of the sample, adjust the hydrochloric acid concentration of the standard solution to approximate that of the sample solution to within ±10 percent.

NOTE 2.—Sample size and treatment may be varied according to composition, but the directions given are satisfactory for most glasses.

Excitation and Exposure.—Adjust the regulators on the tanks of hydrogen and oxygen so that the low-pressure gauges read 10 p.s.i. for hydrogen and 25 p.s.i. for oxygen. Regulate the flame by setting the flow of hydrogen to 5 cu. ft. per hour, and the oxygen flow to 10 cu. ft. per hour, or to meet the specifications of the burner manufacturer.

Turn on the instrument to allow the spectrophotometer to become stabilized by standing for about 15 min. and then bring the meter needle to a null point by adjusting the dark current knob.[7] Set the wavelength drum, the slit width, and the phototube selector of the spectrophotometer to the appropriate positions as shown in Table 53-4.

TABLE 53-4.   ANALYTICAL LINES AND SLIT WIDTHS

Element	Phototube Used	Analytical Line, mμ	Slit Width, mm.	Concentration Range, p.p.m.
Lithium...........	Red	671	0.3	0 to 20
Sodium...........	Blue	589	0.1	5 to 25
Sodium...........	Blue	589	0.2	0 to 8
Potassium.........	Red	767	0.1	5 to 25
Potassium.........	Red	767	0.3	0 to 15
Rubidium.........	Red	795	0.3	0 to 20
Cesium...........	Red	852	0.3	0 to 20

Slight readjustment of the wavelength setting to produce the maximum signal may be necessary. Move the sensitivity control on the spectrophotometer to maximum sensitivity.

Radiation Measurements.—Transfer portions of the standard and sample solutions to 5-ml. beakers, insert the beakers individually into the sample holder, and elevate the holder to atomize the solution into the flame. Obtain the radiation intensity readings from the transmission scale of the spectrophotometer by rotating the transmission knob to zero the null meter. For successive intensity measurements, alternately reverse the order in which the unknown and standard are atomized into the flame. Thus, first read the intensity of the unknown sample solution followed by the standard, and then the standard followed by the unknown. Between successive intensity measurements for any one ion, transfer a fresh aliquot of the sample and the standard to the 5-ml. beakers.

[7] On the Beckman DU instrument the selectro switch is set to 1.0.

Continue intensity measurements until successive readings give ratios of unknown to standard which duplicate each other to a relative difference of less than 2 percent.

At the time of the analysis, regulate and maintain the radiation intensity for known alkali concentrations by minor adjustments of the settings given in the section on "Excitation and Exposure" (above) to ±10 percent relative to the intensities for the same concentrations on the previously prepared analytical curves described in the section on "Analytical Curves" (below). This can readily be done by comparing radiation intensity measurements of the standard solutions with the analytical curves. When small adjustments will not produce intensity readings corresponding to the prepared analytical curves, either the instrument or the burner[8] is not operating correctly, or the standard reference solution is in error.

Since results obtained by flame photometry can be altered by the presence of foreign ions, it is important that some exploratory work be carried out to ascertain whether the particular glass to be analyzed may contain interfering elements. In general, as long as the alkali concentration of a synthetic known sample is ±10 percent relative to the alkali content of the glass solution, satisfactory results can be expected for lithium, sodium, and potassium. Such a generalization may not hold when the ratio of interfering element to determined alkali is of the order of 50 to 1 or more.

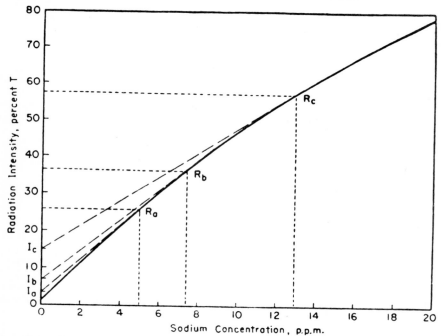

Fig. 53-2. Typical Calibration Curve for Sodium Relating Radiation Intensity (sodium line, 589 mμ and 0.10-mm. slit width) and Sodium Concentration. (Courtesy ASTM.)

For samples of unknown composition, make an exploratory flame analysis of the solution to ascertain the approximate concentration range of the elements to be deter-

---

[8] The oxygen-hydrogen burner requires occasional cleaning and must be replaced by a new burner periodically, depending on use.

mined before preparing a synthetic standard solution. About 8 to 10 p.p.m. is the optimum range of concentration for lithium, sodium, and potassium, but this is not often obtained because of variance in glass composition. Make the composition of the synthetic standard solution ±10 percent relative to any ion determined in the unknown sample solution. Be sure to compensate for the mutual interference of sodium and potassium by adding both alkalies to the standard if they are both present in the unknown.

Analytical Curves.—Draw analytical curves for each alkali and for each oxygen-hydrogen burner by plotting concentration on the abscissa *vs.* intensity on the ordinate of linear coordinate paper. The data for the curves should be obtained when the instrument is receiving the maximum signal that can be obtained using the appropriate instrument settings listed in the section on "Excitation and Exposure" (above). These curves are used in the calculation of results and also to maintain reasonably constant instrument and flame conditions. Figure 53-2 illustrates an analytical curve obtained by measuring the radiation intensities of various concentrations of sodium at 589 mμ with a slit-width setting of 0.10 mm. and then plotting the experimental data.

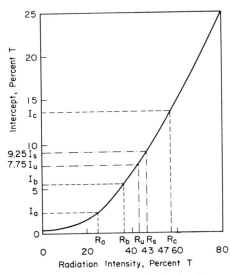

FIG. 53-3. Curve Relating Radiation Intensities to the Intercepts of the Radiation Axis of a Concentration-Radiation Intensity Curve.

For routine work with unknowns of varying composition, the following empirical method of calculations can be adopted. On each of the prepared analytical curves, such as the one illustrated in Fig. 53-2, draw tangents to the curve at a number of points, R_a, R_b, R_c, . . . , along the curve. Then plot the intercepts of the tangents with the intensity axis, I_a, I_b, I_c, . . . , *vs.* the corresponding intensity as shown in Fig. 53-3.

Calculations.—(a) In the calculation of results, two factors must be taken into consideration: (1) radiation intensity measurements are not linear over wide ranges of alkali concentration, and (2) the radiation intensity for a given concentration will not usually fall exactly on a previously prepared analytical curve unless painstaking instrument adjustments are made and constantly checked.

To analyze an unknown, measure the radiation intensities, R_s and R_u, for the standard solution (*s*) and the unknown sample solution (*u*), respectively. From the intensity *vs.* intercept curve, Fig. 53-3, estimate an average intercept, I, for a point midway between between R_s and R_u. From the following relationship, calculate the concentration of the unknown solution:

$$\frac{R_s - I}{R_u - I} = \frac{s}{u}$$

where R_s = radiation intensity for standard solution,
    R_u = radiation intensity for unknown solution,

I = intercept on the intensity axis of a line tangent to an intensity vs. concentration curve at a point midway between R_s and R_u, determined from a curve like Fig. 53-3,

s = concentration of standard solution, in p.p.m., and

u = concentration of unknown solution, in p.p.m.

Two assumptions have been made in the above relationships: (1) the intensity vs. concentration curve is linear between R_s and R_u, and (2) the intensity is essentially the same whether R_s and R_u fall on any one of several similar intensity curves which would result if new analytical curves were prepared at the time of each analysis. These conditions usually prevail when reasonable precautions are taken with instrument setting and burner adjustments and when R_s and R_u do not differ more than 10 percent (Note 3).

NOTE 3.—An example of such readings and calculations is as follows:

$$R_s = 47.0 \text{ percent}$$
$$R_u = 43.0 \text{ percent}$$
$$s = 10.00 \text{ p.p.m. sodium}$$

Average the radiation intensity values, R_s and R_u, to obtain $(47.0 + 43.0)/2$ or 45.0. From the radiation intensity vs. intercept curve (Fig. 53-3) the intercept value of 8.50 percent is found for $(R_s + R_u)/2$ and applied in the equation in Paragraph (a)

$$\frac{47.0 - 8.50}{43.0 - 8.50} = \frac{10.00}{u}$$

$$u = 10.00 \times \frac{34.5}{38.5} = 8.96 \text{ p.p.m. sodium.}$$

(b) The concentrations of the alkalies as parts per million are converted to percentage of alkali oxides as follows:

$$\text{Alkali oxide, percent} = \frac{A \times F \times V}{W \times 10}$$

where A = concentration of alkali in parts per million found by calculation in part (a), above,

F = gravimetric factor to convert alkali to alkali oxide as given in Table 53-5,

V = volume of solution in which sample was dissolved, in liters, and

W = grams of sample used.

TABLE 53-5.   GRAVIMETRIC FACTOR

Element	Ratio of Alkali Oxide to Alkali Element
Lithium	2.1527
Sodium	1.3479
Potassium	1.2046
Rubidium	1.0936
Cesium	1.0602

Accuracy.—An estimate of the accuracy of this method may be gained by comparison of flame photometer analyses with chemical analyses. Typical flame and chemical analyses are illustrated in Table 53-6.[3] The mean difference between flame and chemical results for about 50 widely different glass compositions recorded over the period of about one year was between 0.10 and 0.15 absolute percent and about 3 relative percent

TABLE 53-6. COMPARISONS BETWEEN CHEMICAL AND FLAME ANALYSES

Component	Method	National Bureau of Standards, Standard Glass Samples			Boro-silicate Glass	Lead Glass	Barium Glass
		No. 80	No. 93	No. 91			
Li_2O, percent....	Chemical	—	—	—	0.43	0.54	0.45
	Flame	—	—	—	0.44	0.52	0.40
		—	—	—	0.45	0.52	0.41
Na_2O, percent...	Chemical	16.65	4.16	8.48	5.42	6.91	10.25
	Flame	16.69	4.28	8.48	5.44	6.87	10.30
		16.81	4.36	8.48	5.42	7.10	10.37
K_2O, percent....	Chemical	0.04	0.16	3.25	0.27	6.40	5.28
	Flame	0.05	0.13	3.31	0.27	6.40	5.49
		0.06	0.15	3.35	0.27	6.52	5.50

for each of the three common alkali oxides, lithium oxide, sodium oxide, and potassium oxide. The mean positive and mean negative differences were about equal, indicating that the errors were probably random in nature.[3] The combined alkali-oxide content of these glasses ranged from 0.2 to 20 percent. A study comparing alkali analyses of 25 glass and ore samples by two flame photometers, operated independently, indicated duplication of lithium oxide, sodium oxide, and potassium oxide results to ±0.05 absolute percent.

ALKALINE EARTH METALS

Although not as numerous as the alkali methods, there are many flame spectrometer alkaline earth methods in the literature. Atomic absorption methods are still few in number, although it is probably the better technique, particularly for magnesium. Barium is presently difficult to determine in glass by either technique. Interferences by aluminum, titanium, sulfate, fluoride, and phosphate are a problem for all alkaline earth methods in glass. Buffering systems, such as those containing ethylenediamine-tetracetic acid and/or lanthanum, are to be preferred over techniques employing separations or matching standards. A few typical flame and atomic absorption methods are given in the Selected Bibliography.

OTHER ELEMENTS

Most of those elements having approximate minimum working concentrations that are equal to, or less than, 1 percent as defined in Table 53-1 can be determined in glass with ease. Most of the remaining elements in Table 53-1 can be determined with varying degrees of difficulty in particular glass systems either by flame or atomic absorption spectrometry if the concentration of the element is sufficient. Only a few methods are available in the literature for these other elements in glass. Methods for aluminum, iron, zinc, and manganese are given in the Selected Bibliography. In the author's experience, antimony, boron, cobalt, copper, lead, silver, and niobium have also been determined by flame spectrometry, and chromium and iron by atomic absorption spectrometry. Specific procedures, many of which can be adapted to glass, are available in the literature for most of the elements given in Table 53-1. The proper combination of ratio of sample size to solution volume, sample decomposition process, solvents, buffers (or separations) standards, and flame must be chosen if these methods are to succeed for the analysis of a particular glass.

SELECTED BIBLIOGRAPHY

GENERAL PRINCIPLES, METHODS, APPARATUS

Flame Spectrometry:—(1) "Suggested Practices for Flame Photometric Methods of Spectrochemical Analysis," ASTM E-2 SM 2–5. Methods for Emission Spectrochemical Analysis, 4th Ed., American Society for Testing and Materials, 1964. A brief discussion of principles and practice. (2) Flame Photometry, J. A. Dean, McGraw-Hill Book Co., Inc., New York, 1960. A good general text. (3) "Excitation Processes in Flame Spectrometry," J. H. Gibson, W. E. L. Grossman, and W. D. Cooke, Anal. Chem., 35, 266, 1963. Discusses factors involved in excitation. (4) "Chemiluminescent Flame Spectrophotometry" (College Park, Md., June, 1962), P. T. Gilbert, Proceedings of the Xth Colloquium Spectroscopicum Internationale, 171–215, 1963, E. R. Lippencott and M. Margoshes, eds., Spartan Books, Washington, D. C., 1963. Detailed discussion of the chemiluminescent flame spectrometry. (5) Chemical Analysis by Flame Photometry, R. Herrmann and C. T. J. Alkemade, 2nd Rev. Ed., Interscience Publishers, Inc., New York, 1963, translated by P. T. Gilbert. A good text containing tables of spectra, detection limits, and interferences.

Atomic Absorption Spectrometry:—(6) "The Use of Organic Solvents in Atomic Absorption Spectrophotometry," J. E. Allan, Spectrochimica Acta, 17, 467–473, 1964. (7) Atomic Absorption Spectrophotometry, W. T. Elwell and J. A. F. Gidley, The Macmillan Co., New York, 1962. A brief discussion of principles and early practice. (8) "The Physical Basis of Analytical Atomic Absorption Spectrometry," K. Fuwa and B. L. Vallee, Anal. Chem., 35 (8) 942–946, July 1963. Demonstrates applicability of Beer-Lambert law. (9) "Performance of a Simple Atomic Absorption Spectrophotometer," B. M. Gatehouse and J. B. Willis, Spectrochimica Acta, 17 (7) 710–718, 1961. Discusses important instrument factors and detection limits. (10) Analytical Methods for Atomic Absorption Spectrophotometry and Supplement, Perkin-Elmer Corporation, Norwalk, Conn., January and May, 1964. A cookbook of procedures. (11) "Effect of Organic and Aqueous Solvents on Flame Photometric and Atomic Absorption Spectroscopy," J. W. Robinson, Anal. Chim. Acta, 23, 479–487, 1960. Discusses theory of excitation and absorption in flames. (12) "Recent Advances in Atomic Absorption Spectroscopy," J. W. Robinson, Anal. Chem., 33 (8), 1967–1971, July 1961. Discusses equipment and variables with detection limits in aqueous and organic solvents. (13) "Further Observations in Atomic Absorption Spectroscopy," J. W. Robinson and L. J. Kevan, Anal. Chim. Acta, 28, 70–75, 1963. Discusses mechanisms in various flame. (14) "Detection Limits in Analytical Atomic Absorption Spectrophotometry," W. Slavin, S. Sprague, and D. C. Manning, Atomic Absorption Newsletter No. 18, Perkin-Elmer Corporation, Norwalk, Conn., February, 1964. (15) "The Application of Atomic Absorption Spectra to Chemical Analysis," A. Walsh, Spectrochimica Acta, 7 (2), 108–117, 1956. A fundamental discussion.

SOME TYPICAL METHODS FOR GLASSES AND OTHER SILICATES

Flame-Alkali Elements:—(16) "Rapid Flame Photometric Determination of Alkalies in Glasses and Silicates," P. B. Adams, Anal. Chem., 33 (11), 1602–1605, October 1961. Discusses direct determination in hydrofluoric acid solution. (17) "Flame Spectrophotometry for Determination of Potassium and Lithium in Glass, E. J. Broderick and

P. G. Zach, Anal. Chem., 23 (10), 1455–1458, October 1951. (18) "Flame Photometric Determination of Sodium, Potassium, Calcium, Magnesium and Manganese in Glass and Raw Materials," N. Roy, Anal. Chem., 28 (1), 34–39, January 1956. (19) "A Contribution to the Rapid Analysis of Ceramic Raw Materials and Finished Products," Staufenberger, Sprechsal, 16, 94, 1961. Uses a lithium carbonate–boric acid fusion. (20) "Suggested Method for Spectrochemical Analysis of Glass for Alkali Elements by Flame Photometry," ASTM E-2 SM 10–13, J. P. Williams and P. B. Adams, Methods for Emission Spectrochemical Analysis, 4th Ed., American Society for Testing and Materials, 1964. Detailed procedure for determining the alkali elements.

Flame-Alkaline Earth Elements:—(21) Suggested Method for Spectrochemical Analysis of Glass for Alkaline Earth Elements Using the Flame Photometer Technique," ASTM E-2 SM 10–17, P. B. Adams and J. P. Williams, Methods for Emission Spectrochemical Analysis, 4th Ed., American Society for Testing and Materials, 1964. A standard procedure involving an R_2O_3 precipitation. (22) "The Determination of Calcium in Glass by Flame Photometry," D. Billings, Glass Ind. 36 (5), 255–256, 280, May 1955. Uses matching standards. (23) "The Flame Photometric Analysis of Calcium in Glasses with Particular Consideration of the Influence of Aluminum on the Calcium Emission," Von F. Gobhardt and M. Achilles, Glastech Ber., 36 (6), 225–232, June 1963. (24) 'The Flame Photometric Determination of Calcium in Phosphate, Carbonate and Silicate Rocks," H. Kramer. Anal. chim. Acta, 17 (5), 521, November 1957. Uses buffer. (25) See Reference number 18. (26) "The Use of Lanthanum Chloride to Prevent Interferences in the Flame Photometric Determination of Exchangeable Calcium in Soils," C. H. Williams, Anal. Chim. Acta, 22, 163–171, 1960.

Flame—Aluminum, Iron, Manganese:—(27) "Flame Spectrophotometric Determination of Iron in Siliceous Materials," J. A. Dean and J. C. Burger, Anal. Chem., 27 (7), 1052–1056, July 1955. (28) "The Direct Flame—Spectrometric Determination of Aluminum in silcates," F. Hegemann and O. Osterried, Ber. Deutsch. Keram. (29) "Quantitative Spectrochemical Analysis of Manganese in Mineral Pulps and Rocks by Flame Photometry," R. Ishida. Rept. Gov. Chem. Research Inst., Tokyo, 50, 35–39 (1955). (30) See Reference number 18.

Atomic Absorption—Sodium, Potassium Magnesium, Calcium, Strontium Iron, and Manganese:—(31) "The Determination of Exchangeable Sodium, Potassium, Calcium, and Magnesium in Soils by Atomic-absorption Spectrophotometry," D. J. David, Analyst, 85 (1012), 495–503, July 1960. Uses lanthanum as buffer. (32) "Determination of Strontium and Biological Materials and Exchangeable Strontium in Soils by Atomic-absorption Spectrophotometry," D. J. David, Analyst, 87 (1037), 576–585, July 1962. Uses ion exchange to remove phosphate. (33) "Determination of the Major Metals in Granite and Diabasic Rocks by Atomic Absorption Spectrophotometry," D. Trent and W. Slavin, Atomic Absorption Newsletter No. 19, Perkin-Elmer Corporation, Norwalk, Conn., 1–6 March 1964. A rough method for sodium, potassium, iron, magnesium, manganese, and calcium.

THE ELECTRON MICROPROBE

By William P. Whitney

Corning Glass Works
Technical Staffs Division
Research and Development Laboratory
Corning, New York

Perhaps the most powerful instrument available for analysis of small sample volumes is the electron microprobe. The microprobe is capable of qualitative and quantitative elemental analysis of 2 to 5 cubic μ volumes with a spatial resolution of about 1 μ. This permits the analysis of samples which were previously impossible, or at best impractical, to analyze.

Typical problems encountered in the glass industry where the microprobe can be of value include the following: studies of diffusion profiles at glass-glass or glass-metal seals; analysis of the dielectric material in electronic microcircuits; investigation of surface volatilization phenomena; and analysis of stones and cords to determine their origin. From these few examples, it is apparent that the potential of this instrument to the research scientist is very broad.

FUNDAMENTAL THEORY OF OPERATION

One convenient way to visualize the microprobe is to consider it as a hybrid of an electron microscope and an x-ray fluorescence spectrograph. A beam of electrons is focused to a small spot on the surface of the specimen through a magnetic lens system similar to that found in an electron microscope. The impinging electrons excite atoms in the sample; as these excited atoms return to their ground state, they emit x-rays of a wavelength characteristic of their atomic number. The wavelength of the emitted x-rays is determined by recording the x-rays diffracted from a crystal of known interplanar spacing with an x-ray detector. This is identical to the function of an x-ray fluorescence spectrograph.

Qualitative analysis is accomplished by comparing the wavelength of the emitted x-rays to tabulated values of the characteristic wavelength of each element. Quantitative analysis is accomplished by comparing the intensity of the characteristic radiation from the sample to that from a standard of known composition.

THE MICROPROBE LABORATORY

The electron microprobe laboratory should be an isolated room containing only this instrument. It should be located away from electric arc furnaces and other sources of RF noise and be provided with an RF ground. The temperature must be maintained within $\pm 2°F$. of any comfortable temperature. Facilities should be available to keep the relative humidity below 50 percent. Black window shades are required to block out all daylight. If possible, it is convenient to have a switch controlling the room lights mounted on the microprobe console.

SAMPLE PREPARATION

Criteria of Sample.—Samples which are suitable for microprobe analysis must fulfill three basic criteria: the area of interest must be flat within a tolerance of about 5 μ;

the mounted sample must provide a conductive path for the electrons impinging upon it; and the sample must be able to withstand vacuum.

Procedure.—Isolation of the area of interest reduces the sample bulk which must subsequently be polished and makes the sample size compatible with the instrumental limitations. This may be accomplished with a diamond saw, diamond stylus, or any feasible means. For ease of handling, the samples are mounted in thermosetting plastic. Amber Bakelite is recommended for this purpose because of its low vapor pressure which minimizes contamination of the instrument if the electron beam strikes the mounting material. A typical size limitation of the mounted sample is a cylinder 1 in. in diameter, less than $\frac{1}{4}$ in. thick. Polishing is accomplished by standard metallographic procedures. The samples are ground sequentially on 240-, 320-, 400-, and 600-grit silicon carbide paper with water. If water leaching will alter the sample, kerosene can be used as a lubricant on the silicon carbide papers. After grinding on the 600-grit silicon carbide paper, the samples are polished sequentially with 6-, 1-, and $\frac{1}{4}$-μ diamond paste on cloth laps. Standard lapping oil is used as a lubricant on the diamond laps. All samples which are poor conductors must be coated with a conductive film. Painted films of Aquadag or vacuum evaporated films of carbon, silver, aluminum, or copper may be used. A carbon film 250–300 A thick provides adequate conductance, is nearly transparent, and does not seriously reduce the energy of the electrons striking the sample. For quantitative analysis, samples and standards must all be coated in the same manner.

CAPABILITIES AND LIMITATIONS

Area of Analysis.—The single feature of the electron microprobe which makes it such a powerful tool is the ability to analyze chemically areas a few microns in diameter. Two different spot size parameters are commonly used to define the minimum area a particular microprobe is capable of analyzing. The electron spot size is the diameter on the surface of the sample which the electrons will strike. This is a function of the field strength, stability, and astigmatism of the magnetic lenses and is usually less than 1 μ. The fluorescent spot size is the diameter on the sample surface from which x-rays emerge. This is a function of the x-ray wavelength and the absorption characteristics of the sample. The fluorescent spot size determines the minimum area which can be analyzed by x-ray techniques and ranges from 2 to 5 μ in most glass compositions.

Elements Analyzed.—By using both K-series and L-series x-ray spectra, the microprobe can analyze for any element heavier than neon ($Z = 10$) if it is equipped with a vacuum or helium path spectrometer. If air path x-ray spectrometers are used, only elements heavier than titanium ($Z = 22$) can be analyzed. Special instrumentation has been developed capable of analyzing for elements as light as boron ($Z = 5$), but this equipment has only recently become commercially available.

Limit of Detection.—The limit of detectability for microprobe analysis is a rather nebulous term. In a homogeneous material, the limit of detectability is only about 500 p.p.m.; however, when analyzing a small inclusion in a large mass, the limit of detectability may be far less than 1 p.p.m. The relatively poor limit of detectability is primarily a result of the high background intensity associated with electron excitation.

PRESENTATION OF DATA

Most microprobes are capable of numerous modes of data presentation, each having particular advantages. These modes include image display, strip chart traces, and counting rate measurement. There are no fixed rules for choice of technique, but some general applications can be considered.

Image Display.—Image display is accomplished by sweeping the electron beam across an area on the sample while a synchronized cathode-ray tube displays the signal as a function of light intensity. The signal controlling the cathode-ray tube intensity may be a characteristic x-ray signal, the back-scattered electron intensity, or the current passing through the sample. A characteristic x-ray signal will provide an image display with respect to the concentration of a particular element. A back-scattered electron or sample current signal will provide an image display with respect to the mean atomic weight of the sample. Image displays are particularly useful for distinguishing phases of different atomic weight or for showing the location of specific elements in a sample.

Strip Chart.—Strip chart traces are used for nearly all qualitative analyses. The x-ray spectrometer is driven through various wavelength regions at a known speed, while the pen deflection is governed by the intensity of the x-rays diffracted from the analyzing crystal and entering the detector. This provides a trace of the x-ray intensity as a function of wavelength and permits identification of the characteristic radiation excited in the sample. Strip chart traces are also used for the analysis of diffusion profiles. The pen deflection is governed by the x-ray intensity at a particular wavelength, whereas the sample is driven under the electron beam at a known speed. This provides a trace of x-ray intensity as a function of position on the sample and permits determination of the extent of diffusion.

Counting Methods.—Counting rate measurements are obtained using a scaler and electronic timer. The signal from an x-ray detector is measured for a fixed number of counts or a fixed time and recorded in terms of counts per second. This is the most precise method of measurement and is used primarily for quantitative analyses.

CALCULATIONS

Qualitative Analysis.—Qualitative analysis does not involve calculations. The wavelength of the characteristic x-rays emitted from the sample, as measured with the x-ray spectrometer, is compared with tabulated values of the characteristic x-ray wavelength for the various elements.

Semiquantitative Analysis.—Semiquantitative analysis, which is suitable for most problems encountered in the glass industry, involves only minimum calculations. Since it is nearly impossible to prepare mixtures which are homogeneous on a micron scale, pure elements are usually employed as microprobe standards. In an alternate method, the intensity from several positions on a set of analyzed standards covering the composition range of interest is measured.

If pure elements are used as standards, a linear relationship (passing through the origin) between x-ray intensity and concentration is assumed for all compositions. This relationship may be expressed as:

$$I = mW + B$$

where I = intensity of the characteristic radiation,
     m = slope of the calibration curve,
     W = weight fraction,
     B = background intensity.

The intensity of the characteristic radiation is measured at the same wavelength from the pure element and each sample. The background intensity is measured at the characteristic x-ray wavelength from a blank which does not contain the element of interest or is measured on each sample at a wavelength which does not correspond to the characteristic wavelength of any element in the sample. Knowing the intensity for the pure element and B, the equation can be solved for m. Using this value of m and the measured I from each sample, W can be calculated for each sample.

If analyzed standards covering the range of composition of interest are used, the characteristic x-ray intensity is measured at several positions on each standard. A calibration curve is constructed by plotting the average intensity from each standard against its composition. Knowing the intensity from any sample, its composition can be read from the curve.

Quantitative Analysis.—Quantitative analysis with the microprobe is a very involved procedure. Pure element standards and blanks are used to establish the end points of the calibration curves. Theoretical factors are then applied to correct for any deviations from linearity of the experimental curve. These factors correct for electron absorption, secondary fluorescence, x-ray absorption, detector deadtime, and atomic number effects. Because of the complexity of the calculations, appropriate correction procedures have been developed mainly for binary systems. This seriously limits their application to problems in the glass industry. The various correction factors are discussed at length in the literature. Due to their limited application to glass analysis, they will not be discussed here.

SELECTED BIBLIOGRAPHY

Birks, L. S., Electron Probe Microanalysis, Interscience Publishers, Inc., New York, 1963.
Thomas, P. M., "Outline of a Method for Correcting for Atomic Number Effects in Electron Probe Microanalysis," Brit. J. Appl. Phys., **14,** 397–398, 1963.
Ziebold, T. O., and Ogilvie, R. E., "Quantitative Analysis with the Electron Microanalyzer," Anal. Chem., **35,** 621–627, 1963.

POLAROGRAPHIC AND AMPEROMETRIC TITRATIONS

By Vincent E. Caldwell

Pittsburgh Plate Glass Co.
Glass Research Center
Harmarville, Pennsylvania

Polarographic and amperometric methods have been used for the determination of a number of elements in the analysis of glass. These include aluminum, antimony, barium, cadmium, lead, potassium, selenium, sodium, and zinc. Procedures for these determinations are described in the following sections.

POLAROGRAPHIC METHODS

DETERMINATION OF ANTIMONY (Sb_2O_5) [9]

Reagent. Standard Antimony Solution, approximately 1 mg. Sb_2O_5 per ml.—Dissolve 1.03 g. of antimony potassium tartrate hemihydrate in water and dilute to 500 ml. Standardize the solution volumetrically by titrating with standard iodine solution.

Procedure.—Accurately weigh a ground sample containing 1 to 5 mg. of Sb_2O_5 into a platinum dish. Add 5 ml. of 1:1 sulfuric acid, 5 ml. of concentrated nitric acid, and 15 ml. of 48 percent hydrofluoric acid. Heat the mixture on a hot plate until fumes of sulfuric acid appear.

If the sample contains no lead and less than 1 mg. of TiO_2, add 0.5 g. of hydrazine sulfate to the solution in the platinum dish, cover with a watch glass, and heat over a low flame until the hydrazine sulfate has decomposed. Cool the solution and add about 30 ml. of water. Heat the mixture to dissolve the salts, cool, and transfer to a 50-ml. volumetric flask.

Transfer a portion of the solution to the polarographic cell. Remove dissolved oxygen by bubbling nitrogen through the solution for 10 min. Run a polarogram from 0 to −0.5 volt *vs*. the saturated calomel electrode. Measure the diffusion current due to antimony and obtain the weight of Sb_2O_5 present from a standard curve.

Prepare the standards by pipeting aliquots of the standard antimony solution into 50-ml. volumetric flasks, adding 4 ml. of 1:1 sulfuric acid and diluting to volume. Plot diffusion current *vs*. weight of Sb_2O_5.

$$\text{Percent } Sb_2O_5 = \frac{\text{weight } Sb_2O_5 \times 100}{\text{sample weight}}$$

If the sample contains lead, transfer the sulfuric acid solution from the platinum dish to a 250-ml. beaker and dilute to about 50 ml. Cover the beaker and boil the mixture for 30 min. Add water, if necessary, to maintain the volume at about 50 ml. while boiling. Cool the solution. If more than 1 mg. of TiO_2 is present, add 5 ml. of freshly prepared 4 percent cupferron and stir the mixture. Filter the solution into a 150-ml. beaker. Wash the precipitate with water, adding the washing to the filtrate.

[9] Caldwell, V. E., Pittsburgh Plate Glass Co., unpublished data.

Evaporate the solution to fumes of sulfuric acid. If the cupferron was added, destroy the excess with nitric acid during the latter part of the evaporation. Add 0.5 g. of hydrazine sulfate and proceed as described above.

If titanium is present but lead is not present, proceed as in the preceding paragraph, omitting the boiling step.

DETERMINATION OF SELENIUM AND CADMIUM[10]

Reagents. **Standard Selenium Solution, 0.10 mg. selenium per ml.**—Dissolve 0.1405 g. of pure selenium dioxide (SeO_2) in water and dilute to 1 liter.

Standard Cadmium Solution, 0.10 mg. cadmium per ml.—Dissolve 0.1631 g. of pure, dry cadmium chloride ($CdCl_2$) in water and dilute to 1 liter.

Procedure.—Accurately weigh a ground sample containing 0.1 mg. or more of selenium into a platinum dish. Moisten the sample with water and add 10 ml. of a 1:1 mixture of nitric acid and perchloric acid. Add 15 ml. of hydrofluoric acid and stir the mixture with a platinum rod to dissolve the sample. Heat the mixture on a hot plate until fumes of perchloric acid appear. Rinse down the sides of the dish and again evaporate to fumes of perchloric acid. Dissolve the salts in water and transfer the solution to a 100-ml. beaker. Add 5 ml. of a 10 percent solution of ascorbic acid. Let stand for 15 min. and then filter off the metallic selenium using a Millipore filter. Reserve the filtrate for the cadmium determination. Place the filter containing the selenium precipitate in a 50-ml. beaker. Add 5 ml. of nitric acid and 1.5 ml. of perchloric acid. Heat the mixture on a hot plate to fumes of perchloric acid. Cool the solution and add several ml. of water and 10 ml. of 2.5 M ammonium chloride. Transfer the solution to a 25-ml. volumetric flask. Add 1 ml. of a 0.075 percent solution of gelatin and 1 drop of phenolphthalein indicator. Add ammonium hydroxide dropwise to the first permanent pink color. Dilute the solution to volume and transfer a portion to the polarographic cell. Remove dissolved oxygen by bubbling nitrogen through the solution for 10 min. Run a polarogram from −1.1 to −1.8 volts *vs.* the saturated calomel electrode. Measure the diffusion current and obtain the weight of selenium from a standard curve.

Prepare the standards by pipeting aliquots of the standard selenium solution into 25-ml. volumetric flasks, adding 10 ml. of 2.5 M ammonium chloride, 1 ml. of 0.075 percent gelatin, and ammonium hydroxide to the phenolphthalein end point. Plot diffusion current *vs.* weight of selenium.

$$\text{Percent Se} = \frac{\text{weight Se}}{\text{sample weight}} \times 100$$

Transfer the filtrate from the selenium precipitation to a beaker and add 5 ml. of nitric acid. Evaporate the solution to fumes of perchloric acid. Add more nitric acid, if necessary, to destroy all of the organic matter. Rinse down the sides of the beaker and evaporate the solution to dryness. Dissolve the residue in 4 ml. of 1:1 hydrochloric acid and transfer the solution to a 25-ml. volumetric flask. Add 2 ml. of 0.075 percent gelatin and dilute to volume. Transfer a portion of the solution to the polarographic cell and remove dissolved oxygen by bubbling nitrogen through the solution for 10 min. Run a polarogram from −0.3 to −0.8 volts *vs.* the saturated calomel electrode. Measure the diffusion current and obtain the weight of cadmium from a standard curve.

Prepare the standards by pipeting aliquots of the standard cadmium solution into 25-ml. volumetric flasks, adding 4 ml. of 1:1 hydrochloric acid and 2 ml. of 0.075 percent gelatin. Plot diffusion current *vs.* weight of cadmium.

[10] Caldwell, V. E., Pittsburgh Plate Glass Co., unpublished data.

$$\text{Percent Cd} = \frac{\text{weight Cd}}{\text{sample weight}} \times 100$$

DETERMINATION OF SODIUM + POTASSIUM ($Na_2O + K_2O$), BARIUM (BaO), ALUMINUM (Al_2O_3), ZINC (ZnO), AND LEAD (PbO)[11]

Reagent. Tetraethylammonium Hydroxide, 1 M.[12]—Dissolve 21 g. of pure tetraethylammonium bromide in 100 ml. of water. Add 12 g. of pure silver oxide and stir the mixture for 15 min. Allow the solids to settle and decant the supernatant liquid into a polyethylene bottle. Place the solution in the dark for 8 days, and then filter off the solids that have separated.[13] Solutions prepared in this manner should be stable for several weeks.

Procedure.—Weigh a 0.25-g. sample into a platinum dish. Add 3 ml. of hydrofluoric acid and 1 ml. of perchloric acid. Carefully evaporate the mixture to dryness in such a manner that fusion of the perchlorate residue is avoided; otherwise, aluminum may be lost by volatilization. Add 1 ml. of perchloric acid and again evaporate to dryness, avoiding fusion of the residue. Dissolve the residue in water and add 2 drops of perchloric acid. Transfer the solution to a 50-ml. volumetric flask and dilute to volume.

If barium and sulfate are both present in the glass, treat a 0.15-g. sample with hydrofluoric and perchloric acids and evaporate to dryness. Fuse the residue with 1 g. of sodium carbonate. Dissolve the residue in a minimum amount of hydrochloric acid and dilute to 50 ml. in a volumetric flask. This solution is used exclusively for the determination of barium.

Barium, Sodium, and Potassium.—Pipet 10.0 ml. of the sample solution into a 25-ml. volumetric flask and dilute to volume. Transfer a 4.0-ml. aliquot of this solution into a dry polarographic cell (mercury pool anode) and add 1.0 ml. of 1 M tetraethylammonium hydroxide. Remove oxygen by bubbling nitrogen through the solution for 10 min. Record the barium wave between -1.6 and -2.0 volts.

Add 0.1 ml. of 0.1 M phosphoric acid to precipitate calcium. Bubble nitrogen through the solution for several minutes and record the wave of sodium plus potassium between -1.8 and -2.3 volts.

Lead and Zinc.—Pipet 4.0 ml. of the sample solution into a dry polarographic cell. Add 1.0 ml. of 1 M ammonium hydroxide and 1 drop of 0.1 percent methyl red. Expel oxygen by bubbling nitrogen through the solution for 10 min. Record the lead wave between -0.2 and -0.6 volt. Record the zinc wave between -0.8 and -1.2 volts.

Aluminum.—Pipet 10.0 ml. of the sample solution into a 25-ml. volumetric flask. Add a drop of 0.1 percent dimethyl yellow indicator and carefully neutralize the solution with 1 M sodium hydroxide to a pH of 4. Add 0.4 ml. of 0.05 M hydrochloric acid and 5 ml. of 1 M lithium chloride. Dilute the solution to volume and transfer a portion to the polarographic cell. Remove oxygen by bubbling nitrogen through the solution for 10 min. Record the aluminum wave between -1.4 and -2.0 volts. Since the solution is slightly acidic, the aluminum wave will be preceded by a hydrogen wave. The adjustment of the pH is very critical because the height of the aluminum wave is dependent on the hydrogen ion concentration.

Iron in amounts equal to, or greater than, the amount of aluminum interferes with the aluminum determination; smaller amounts do not interfere.

[11] Vandenbosch, V., Anal. chim. Acta, **2**, 566, 1948; Caldwell, V. E., Pittsburgh Plate Glass Co., unpublished data.
[12] Weaver, J. R., and Lykken, L., Anal. Chem., **19**, 372, 1947.
[13] Zlotowski, I., and Kolthoff, I. M., Ind. Eng. Chem., Anal. Ed., **14**, 473, 1942.

AMPEROMETRIC METHOD

TITRATION OF POTASSIUM (K_2O)[14]

Reagents. **Standard Potassium Solution, 5.00 mg. K_2O per ml.**—Dissolve 7.1950 g. of pure, dry potassium chloride in water and dilute to 1 liter.

Sodium Tetraphenylborate Solution.—Dissolve 17.1 g. of the reagent in about 800 ml. of water and add 5 ml. of 0.5 N sodium hydroxide. Add several grams of freshly precipitated and washed alumina to the solution and stir for 5 min. Let the solution stand for 15 min.; then filter and dilute to 1 liter. Standardize the reagent by titrating aliquots of the standard potassium chloride solution by the procedure described below and calculate the K_2O titer. Since the solution is not stable, it should be restandardized about once a week.

Buffer Solution.—Dissolve 108.8 g. of sodium acetate $(NaC_2H_3O_2 \cdot 3H_2O)$ and 45.7 ml. of glacial acetic acid in water and dilute to 1 liter.

Apparatus. **Saturated Calomel Reference Electrode.**—Use an electrode saturated with sodium chloride instead of potassium chloride. Bridge the electrode to the sample solution through a sodium chloride–agar plug.

Procedure.—Accurately weigh a ground sample containing 6 to 30 mg. of K_2O into a platinum dish. Moisten the sample with water and add 5 ml. of perchloric acid and 15 ml. of hydrofluoric acid. Evaporate the mixture to dryness on a hot plate. Dissolve the residue in hot water and transfer the solution to a 100-ml. beaker. Use a total of about 25 ml. of water for dissolution and rinsing. Add 25 ml. of buffer solution. Place the beaker on a magnetic stirrer and position the saturated calomel electrode (S.C.E.) and the dropping mercury electrode in the solution. Adjust the potential of the dropping mercury electrode to $+0.12$ volt *vs.* S.C.E. It is not necessary to remove dissolved oxygen from the solution. Add sodium tetraphenylborate titrant in 1.0-ml. increments before the end point. Measure the diffusion current after each addition. The stirrer must be turned off and the solution allowed to come to rest before making the measurement. When the current begins to increase near the end point, add the titrant in 0.10-ml. increments. After the end point is passed, the diffusion current increases linearly to a value of about 17 μA. As more titrant is added beyond this point, the current becomes erratic.

Correct the diffusion current measurements for dilution by multiplying each current reading by $(V + v)/V$, where V is the original volume of the sample solution and v is the volume of titrant added. Plot the corrected diffusion current against volume of titrant and extrapolate the straight-line portions of the curve. The point at which the straight lines intersect is the end point.

$$\text{Percent } K_2O = \frac{\text{ml. titrant} \times K_2O \text{ titer}}{\text{sample weight}} \times 100$$

[14] Amos, W. R., and Sympson, R. F., Anal. Chem., **31,** 133, 1959; Caldwell, V. E., Pittsburgh Plate Glass Co., unpublished data.

POTENTIOMETRIC TITRATIONS

By Paul Close

Owens-Illinois Technical Center
Toledo, Ohio

The volumetric end-point determination by potentiometry in glass analysis is of practical use for the estimation of iron(II) and arsenic. Generally, only the determination of the total arsenic is of interest. However, procedures for the differential estimation of arsenic(III) and arsenic(V) are available.[15] Since iron directly colors glass, a knowledge of the amount of each oxidation state, (II) and (III), is frequently necessary. Iron(II) colors glass blue; iron(III), yellow. The result, in the absence of other colorants, is a range of greenish colors or tints from yellow-green to blue-green. The color depends on the ratios of the two oxidation states to each other. Even when other colorants are added, the final effect is usually dependent upon the ratio of iron(II) and (III) to each other. The quality control of glass color, or the apparent lack of color in what is called "flint" glass, frequently depends upon the glassmaker's knowledge of the amount of iron(II) and total iron in his glass. The laboratory determines iron(II) on a separate weighing of the sample and the total iron on another. The total iron is commonly reported as "total Fe as Fe_2O_3" and iron(II) as FeO. When the total iron is higher than a few tenths percent, *e.g.*, a half percent or more, each oxide may be reported separately. When this is done, the analyst should so indicate in his report. Total arsenic is reported as As_2O_3 unless each oxidation state is determined separately.

DETERMINATION OF TOTAL ARSENIC AS As_2O_3

The bromate titration of arsenic proceeds smoothly at room temperature in 2 to 3 M hydrochloric acid. The bimetallic electrode pair, platinum-tungsten, is satisfactory for the titration. The potential change is about 340 millivolts at the end point, Figure 53-4. Student type potentiometers, pH meters with millivolt scales, or vacuum-tube voltmeters are suitable for the end point detection.

The minimum amount of arsenic titratable is about 0.3 to 0.4 mg. The use of a 2-g. sample will enable about 0.015 to 0.020 percent arsenic as trioxide to be determined. For arsenic contents of 0.05 percent and higher, 1-g. samples are sufficient.

Reagents. Potassium Bromate ($KBrO_3$), ACS Analytical Reagent.—Potassium bromate meeting ACS specifications is an acceptable primary standard. If a question remains as to its dryness, proceed as follows: crush 3 g. of bromate in an agate mortar and dry at 180°C. for 1 to 2 hr., cool, transfer to a weighing bottle, and store in a desiccator. To prepare a 0.1 N solution (1/60 M), weigh 2.784 g., dissolve in water, and dilute to exactly 1 liter. Prepare 0.01 N or 0.02 N solutions by appropriate dilutions of the 0.1 N standard. One ml. 0.01 N $KBrO_3$ = 0.00004946 g. As_2O_3.

Other Reagents.—No special considerations.

Apparatus. Arsenic Distillation Flask, Fig. 53-5.—The Scherrer[16] flask is a standard piece of laboratory apparatus. It is sold as specified by ASTM Designation E50–60, Apparatus No. 5. It is listed in Catalog 64, Ace Glass, Inc., as Item 5319; and Catalog LG3, Corning Glass Works, Item 90205.

[15] Close, Paul, Shepherd, H. M., and Drummond, C. H., J. Am. Ceram. Soc., **41** [11], 455–460, 1958.
[16] Scherrer, J. A., J. Research Natl. Bur. Standards, **21** [1], 95–104, 1938; RP 1116.

Procedure.—Weigh 1 or 2 g. of minus 100-mesh sample into a 75-ml. platinum dish. For each gram of sample taken, add 5 ml. water, 5 ml. nitric acid, 5 ml. 1:1 sulfuric acid, or 8 ml. perchloric acid, and 5 ml. hydrofluoric acid; stir the sample with a platinum wire when the hydrofluoric acid is added. Perchloric acid is preferred to sulfuric and is required if the glass contains 2 to 3 or more percent of lead or barium. Evaporate to light fumes of sulfuric or perchloric acid. Usually the fluorides will react vigorously at this point. The best procedure is to cover the dish with a platinum lid, leaving only about an eighth of the top area uncovered so vapors can escape; when the reaction has subsided, cool, and rinse off the cover and down the sides of the dish with cold water. Evaporate to light fuming of acid, add 2 to 3 ml. saturated boric acid (to assure expulsion of fluoride) and again evaporate to light fuming. Fuming for any length of time is to be avoided. Cool, add 5 ml. water and transfer to the distilling apparatus with 50 to 60 ml. hydrochloric acid. Add 0.5 g. hydrazine dihydrochloride dissolved in 2 ml. hot water and 2 to 3 ml. hydrobromic acid to the apparatus. Use a 400-ml. beaker for a receiver; add about 50 to 100 ml. water to the beaker and position it so the end of the condenser dips into the water about $\frac{1}{4}$ to $\frac{1}{2}$ in. The beaker should sit in a pan of ice water or in a cool bath of running water. Start a stream of carbon dioxide through the apparatus and maintain at the rate of 5 to 10 bubbles per second. Heat the flask, preferably with a hemispherical heating mantle and distill until the temperature reaches 108° to 111°C. Then add dropwise, via the dropping funnel, hydrochloric acid at such a rate that the temperature remains constant. When 75 ml. of acid has been added in this way, the distillation is complete for amounts of arsenic usually encountered in glasses.

Remove the receiver, dilute to 300 to 350 ml., and titrate potentiometrically. A buret, readable to 0.01 ml. and capable of delivering individual drops of titrant of approximately 0.01 ml., should be used.[17]

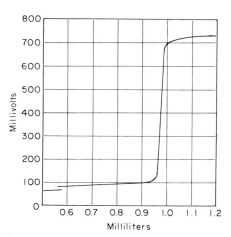

Fig. 53-4. Potentiometric Titration Curve—Oxidation of Arsenic(III) with Potassium Bromate. Arsenic(III) as As_2O_3 taken—0.4946 mg.; found—0.4897 mg. Volume 300 ml. 3 M hydrochloric acid, titrant 0.01 N (1/600 M) potassium bromate.

DETERMINATION OF IRON(II) AS FeO

The determination of iron(II) is preceded by solution of the sample under an inert atmosphere to avoid air oxidation. Two arrangements will be described to accomplish this. The principles of the method are essentially those of Pratt;[18] the techniques to be

[17] Kimble Catalog SC300; Catalog No. 17100-F; Buret, Precision Bore, Micro ($\frac{1}{100}$ ml. drops) with Teflon Plug. 10 ml. cap., 0.02 ml. subdivisions. The same buret but with a three-way stopcock for auto-filling is available as Cat. No. 17105-F. It is particularly useful when many repetitious titrations are to be made.

[18] Hillebrand, W. F., and Lundell, G. E. F., Applied Inorganic Analysis, 2d Ed., John Wiley and Sons, Inc., New York, 1953, pp. 917–919.

described have been developed by the author and coworkers[19] at the Owens-Illinois Technical Center.

Ceric sulfate is used as titrant. Normally iron(II) is the only ionic species present in the sample solution that is oxidizable by cerium(IV). Arsenic(III) or antimony(III) are only oxidized in the presence of a catalyst (osmium tetroxide or iodine monochloride). However, their presence obscures or depresses the potential break expected at the end point. Kolthoff and Bhayia[20] employed a small amount of ferrous-1,10 phenanthroline sulfate to improve the amperometric cerimetric titration of iron(II). Normally employed as a visual oxidation-reduction indicator, the use of this reagent for the detection of the end point potentiometrically is also successful, arsenic(III) and antimony(III) no longer obscuring the potential inflection.

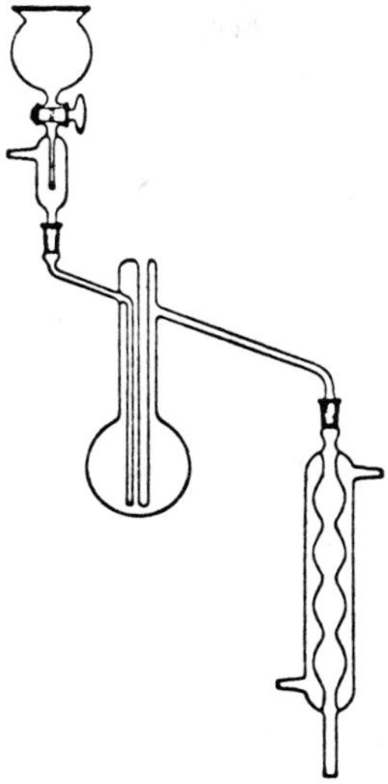

The titrant can be either $\frac{1}{50}$ or $\frac{1}{200}$ M. The stronger solution is suitable for many colored and heat-absorbing glasses containing 0.2 percent or more of total iron. For colorless or lightly colored glasses containing 0.02 to 0.20 percent total iron, the more dilute titrant is required. One ml. $\frac{1}{200}$ M ceric sulfate will oxidize 0.00036 g. iron(II) (as FeO). Starting with a 2-g. sample, 0.005 percent FeO can be readily analyzed with a precision (and accuracy) of ±0.0005 percent FeO. The minimum amount determinable is about 0.004 percent FeO.

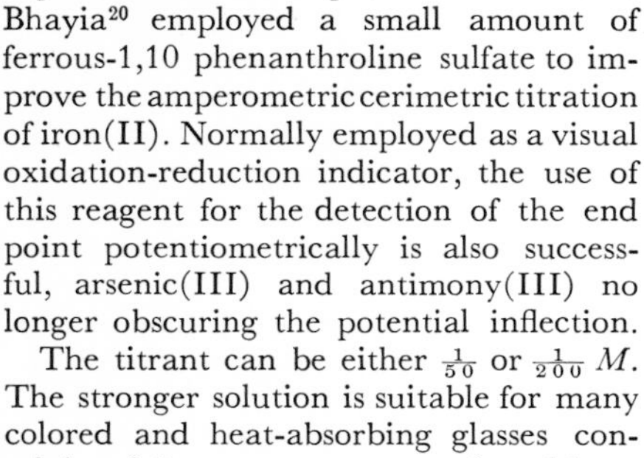

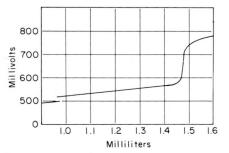

Fig. 53-5. Arsenic Distillation Flask.

The potential change at the end point is about 100 millivolts. The overall change of the system from start to finish is about 350–400 millivolts, Fig. 53-6. A bimetallic electrode system is not suitable; platinum-calomel is used instead. Because of possible contamination, the calomel electrode is connected to the sample solution via a salt bridge. An alternative is a liquid bridge or junction which can be flushed clean with potassium chloride solution between titrations. The end point may be detected with equipment suitable for the titration of arsenic.

Reagents. **Ceric Sulfate,** $Ce(SO_4)_2$. —Prepare approximately $\frac{1}{50}$ and $\frac{1}{200}$ M solutions in $\frac{1}{4}$ to $\frac{1}{2}$ M sulfuric acid. Standardize against freshly prepared $\frac{1}{50}$ or $\frac{1}{200}$ M ferrous ammonium sulfate (ACS Reagent

Fig. 53-6. Potentiometric Titration Curve—Oxidation of Iron(II) Plus "Ferroin" with Ceric Sulfate. Iron(II) as FeO taken—0.493 mg.; found—0.491 mg.; 0.4946 mg. arsenic(III) present as As_2O_3. Actual glass sample carried through procedure. Titrant 0.005 N (1/200 M) ceric sulfate; 0.5 ml. dilute "Ferroin" added at start of titration.

[19] Close, Paul, Shepherd, H. M., and Drummond, C. H., *op. cit.*
[20] Kolthoff, I. M., and Bhayia, B. B., Microchem. J., 4 [4], 451–457, 1960.

Grade) in $\frac{1}{20}$ M sulfuric acid. The standardization is carried out at the same volume and concentration of sulfuric acid as indicated for titration of a sample.

"Ferroin" (Ferrous-1,10 Phenanthroline Sulfate).—Dilute stock 0.025 M solution about 25 times. One milliliter will give a "blank" titer of about 0.15 ml. $\frac{1}{200}$ M ceric sulfate. To standardize, proceed as with the standardization of the ceric sulfate but titrate 2.0 ml. of the diluted indicator instead. The "blank" per 0.10 ml. of indicator will then be accurately known for the subsequent titration of samples. In actual practice, the "blank" is determined before standardization of the ceric sulfate as the amount of indicator solution used with the samples must be used for the standardization.

Hydrofluoric Acid, HF.—Dilute ACS Reagent hydrofluoric acid with an equal volume of water in a large platinum dish (250-ml. capacity or larger). Add $\frac{1}{10}$ M potassium permanganate dropwise until the solution is faintly pink. Heat until the permanganate is reduced. Again add permanganate, but just enough for a very faint pink color; continue heating until any trace of permanganate has disappeared. Cool and store in a very clean, high-density (high-melting) polyethylene laboratory reagent bottle.

Sulfuric Acid, H₂SO₄.—Prepare 1:1 sulfuric acid, ACS Reagent and cool to about 50° to 60°C. Treat similarly to the hydrofluoric acid with permanganate before use. Cool and store in a borosilicate glass reagent bottle.

Boric Acid, H₃BO₃.—Add 100 g. boric acid to 1 liter of water and boil for 5 min. Cool to 60° to 70°C. for use. Cooling to a lower temperature would allow some recrystallization to occur.

Water.—Freshly boiled and cooled water is recommended unless stock distilled or deionized water is known to contain little dissolved oxygen.

***Apparatus.* Platinum Flask.**—Figure 53-7 shows a platinum flask with an inlet tube for the introduction of carbon dioxide, stopper, and funnel for the addition of

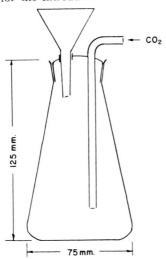

FIG. 53-7.   Platinum Flask.

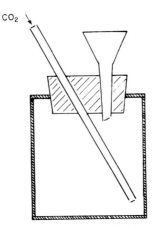

FIG. 53-8.   Plastic Beaker.

reagents. The flask is the same size and shape as a standard 250-ml. glass Erlenmeyer flask. This apparatus permits the boiling of the sample and attendant loss of silica, and also the rapid expulsion of sulfide from amber glasses. Although boiling is a must for many minerals to effect solution, it is not necessary for glasses.

Plastic Beaker.—The plastic beaker shown in Figure 53-8 can serve as well for glasses as the platinum flask. It is preferably made of polystyrene, although any transparent material resistant to cold hydrofluoric and sulfuric acids is suitable. It should have a capacity of about 250 ml. It is fitted with a rubber stopper, through which pass a gas inlet tube and funnel. The inlet tube may be platinum or rigid plastic; the funnel, plastic or wax-coated glass. The gas inlet tube is set at an angle and does not quite touch the bottom of the beaker near the bottom and side joint. Thus, when making a determination of ferrous iron in a sulfide amber glass, it is possible to sweep out the hydrogen sulfide by bubbling carbon dioxide through the sample solution. The tube is retracted so as to be above the solution level for samples not containing sulfide.

Procedure. **Using the Platinum Flask.** —Transfer to the flask a 1.000-g. sample of amber glass and other glasses high in iron, or a 2.000-g. sample for flint glasses, emerald-green glass containing chromium, or other glasses low in iron (less than 0.2 percent). Minus 100-mesh glass is satisfactory. Pass a stream of oxygen-free carbon dioxide[21] through the apparatus for 10 min. to flush out all air (see Fig. 53-9). Add 25 ml. hot water, 7 to 8 ml. 1:1 sulfuric acid, and 8 ml. 1:1 hydrofluoric acid for each gram of sample taken. Quickly bring to a boil and boil gently for $2\frac{1}{2}$ to 3 min. Two or three small pieces of crumpled platinum foil will aid in smooth boiling. Gentle swirling of the flask while adding the reagents will prevent caking and subsequent bumping. When boiling begins, slow the stream of carbon dioxide to about one-half the flushing-out rate. After boiling, remove the flask from the heat, add 60 ml. of 60°C. 10 percent boric acid for 1-g. samples or 100 ml. for 2-g. samples, place the flask in cold water, and cool rapidly.

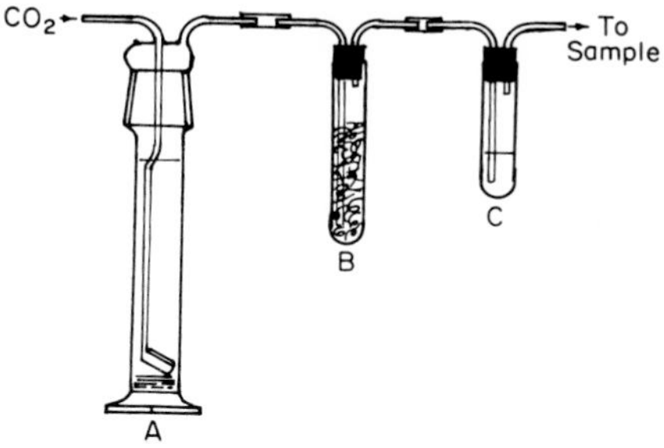

When cool, shut off the carbon dioxide and transfer the solution to a 250-ml. beaker. Add 8 to 10 ml. more of 1:1

Fig. 53-9. Arrangement for Providing Oxygen-free Carbon Dioxide. Part A consists of a gas washing bottle with fritted disc, 250-ml. cap. (Kimble Cat. No. 28215 or Corning Cat. No. 31760). The chromous oxygen absorbing solution is approximately 0.5 M in chromium ion and 0.5 M in sulfuric acid. It may be prepared starting with chromate or bichromate, in which case the chromium(VI) is reduced to chromium(III) with sulfur dioxide, the excess being removed by boiling. The chromium(III) solution is transferred to the gas washing bottle, approximately 50 g. of mercury—2 percent zinc amalgam is added, and the contents shaken vigorously. The chromium(III) is reduced to chromium(II) and is ready for use. It is regenerated by occasionally reshaking with the amalgam, which need not be removed from the bottle. When not in use, the solution is protected from the atmospheric oxygen. Part B is a 25 mm. × 150 mm. test tube $\frac{2}{3}$ filled with glass wool and serves as a splash or carryover trap. Part C is a 25 mm. × mm. test tube with just enough water to enable the flow rate to be counted, usually 10–20 bubbles per second.

sulfuric acid and 0.5 ml. of diluted "Ferroin." Titrate potentiometrically using a semimicroburet as specified for the titration of arsenic. Subtract the "Ferroin blank" and calculate the percent FeO in the sample.

[21] A scrubbing arrangement as shown in Fig. 53-9 is satisfactory for removing traces of oxygen from cylinder carbon dioxide. The mercury-zinc amalgam is used to regenerate the chromous sulfate solution from time to time by shaking the glass cylinder vigorously. The splash trap and bubble counter are simple conveniences to protect the sample and control the gas stream.

Using the Plastic Beaker.—Weigh a suitable size sample (as described for the platinum flask) into the dry beaker and flush out with carbon dioxide. Start the magnetic stirrer moving slowly and add 2 ml. of water, 7 to 8 ml. 1:1 sulfuric acid, and 8 ml. 1:1 hydrofluoric acid for each gram of sample taken; continue to stir for 5 min. Then add 6 g. boric acid crystals for a 1-g. sample or 10 g. for a 2-g. sample and dilute to 100 ml. The stirrer may be speeded up but not so fast as to cause splashing. If the carbon dioxide stream is so fast as to cause splashing, slow it down but do not shut it off entirely. After 5 to 10 min. of additional stirring, the carbon dioxide may be shut off, the tube and stopper rinsed off, "Ferroin" added, and the potentiometric titration carried out without removing the sample from the beaker.

When determining iron(II) in sulfide-containing glasses, it is necessary to sweep out the evolved hydrogen sulfide. After the addition of the decomposing acids, stop the stirrer, tilt the beaker about 15°, and clamp it in this position. Push the gas inlet tube nearly to the bottom of the beaker so that the carbon dioxide bubbles through the sample solution. Allow the gas to "sweep out" the hydrogen sulfide for 20 min. Then proceed as above with the addition of boric acid and the subsequent potentiometric titration.

X-RAY SPECTROGRAPHIC METHODS

By Stephen H. Laning

Pittsburgh Plate Glass Co.
Chemical Division
Barberton, Ohio

The x-ray spectrograph has become a very versatile instrument for elemental analysis covering the elements from sodium through the transuranium elements, and, even at the present time, advances in x-ray instrumentation have brought the elements between sodium and beryllium into the practical analytical picture.[22]

X-ray spectrographic methods offer several advantages over conventional wet methods: they are accurate, give greater speed, and generally are nondestructive to the sample, allowing it to be used for other studies after x-ray analysis.

The procedures to be presented here are limited to the general classification of soda-lime-silica glasses, which include plate, window, and container glasses.

INSTRUMENTATION

Instrument Requirements. Optical Path.—Vacuum, hydrogen, or helium must be employed in the x-ray optical path to analyze for elements below atomic number 22 (Ti), since air completely or nearly completely absorbs their x-radiation before it reaches the detector.

Components of X-ray Spectrograph.—The main components of an x-ray spectrograph are x-ray tube, sample positioning chamber, analyzing crystals, collimators, and detectors. Highly regulated power supplies are required for the x-ray tube and the detector in order that power fluctuations be held to a minimum during the analysis of an element. Undesirable electronic noise and x-radiation are reduced by means of a pulse height analyzer (PHA).

X-ray Tubes.—X-ray tubes commonly employed in x-ray spectrographs have tungsten or chromium targets, although other elements are used in special cases where emission lines from tungsten or chromium may interfere. Tungsten is the general purpose x-ray tube, whereas chromium is used to excite the lighter elements more efficiently than tungsten. For this reason chromium is recommended for glass analysis if only one x-ray tube is available.

Analyzing Crystals.—A variety of analyzing crystals is necessary in order to analyze for the various elements found in glass. Table 53-7 is a list of analyzing crystals and elements determined with each. This list is somewhat arbitrary, depending on circumstances of instrumentation, available intensities, and interferences.

The PET crystal replaces ethylenediamine D-tartrate formerly used, since the new crystal has approximately twice the reflecting power of EDDT. The germanium crystal is used to eliminate second-order interferences making it possible to analyze for phosphorus in the presence of calcium.

Collimation.—Collimation in the x-ray spectrograph is designed to reduce undesirable scattered radiation, thus reducing background and improving resolution. If collimation is too fine, intensities are reduced drastically; and if too broad, the resolution is too poor. Consequently, collimation is a compromise between these factors.

[22] Chem. Eng. News, **41**, No. 47, 40–41, Nov. 25, 1963.

TABLE 53-7. ANALYZING CRYSTALS AND ELEMENTS DETERMINED WITH EACH

Crystal	Element
Gypsum or potassium acid phthalate (KAP)	Na
Ammonium dihydrogen phosphate (ADP)	Mg
Pentaerythritol (PET)	Al, Ca, Cl, Si
Germanium[a]	P
Sodium chloride	S
Lithium fluoride	Sb, As, Ba, Ni, K, Se, Sr, Ti, Zr
Topaz[b]	Cr, Co, Cu, Fe, Mn, Zn

[a] The germanium crystal eliminates second-order reflections and is used whenever such interferences occur.

[b] The topaz crystal has high dispersion and is used whenever adjacent elements interfere.

Detectors.—The one detector suitable for general glass analysis is the gas-flow proportional counter employing P-10 gas, a mixture of 90 percent argon and 10 percent methane. Some instruments are equipped with double detectors, in which case the scintillation counter is used for the shorter wavelength radiations since it is more efficient than the gas-flow proportional counter. Special thin windows of Formvar, or other film-forming materials, can be prepared for the flow-proportional counter making it more sensitive than quarter mil Mylar customarily used for the light element x-ray spectra.

Pulse Height Analyzer.—The pulse height analyzer, PHA, serves to reduce background and thus improves peak to background ratio. This is particularly important for light element analysis and trace elements. There are several ways to operate the PHA.[23,24] In differential operation there are two modes of operation. In one case, the baseline is fixed at as low a voltage as possible without introducing instrument noise while the detector high voltage is changed for each element. The window width may be varied to give the best possible intensity with low to moderate background. Under these conditions, the detector voltage decreases as the wavelength of x-rays decreases.

In the second case, the detector high voltage is held constant while the baseline is changed to bring in the desired radiation of the element of interest.

In both these modes of operation it is best to check the settings using pure elements or compounds which would not introduce interfering elements.

The PHA can be operated in integral position also. This mode eliminates the upper limit on the window and permits higher linear counting rates. Advantage can be taken of this in the calcium and silica determinations to be considered later.

DATA ACQUISITION

There are several modes of operation that can be used to obtain intensity data from the various elements in glass. Generally speaking, no one method is the best for all elements. The choice depends on the available counting rate and the desired precision and accuracy needed for the determination.

Scanning.—Often one is interested in obtaining peak height or intensity above background. The latter measurement is often difficult to obtain in a glass, since it is difficult to find glasses that have the particular element absent, and going to either side of the peak is not always satisfactory since another element line could be present in the wavelength interval of interest. High and low standards for the element make the background measurement unnecessary unless it is variable. The latter situation occurs in the deter-

[23] Miller, D. C., Norelco Reporter, **IV**, No. 2, 37–40, 1957.
[24] Kiley, W. R., Norelco Reporter, **VII**, No. 6, 143–149, 1960.

mination of sulfur where the background changes with the calcium content of the glass.

In the case of minor elements with concentrations below half a percent where a relative error of 2–5 percent is permissible, scanning 1° per minute with a 4-sec. time constant over the peak position, measuring the peak height above background and comparing against standards, which were run previously under the same conditions, give the concentration in a few minutes.

Counting and Charting.—Where greater precision is needed, counting or charting methods are necessary. Fixed count and fixed time operations are familiar to experienced spectrographers, but the charting method has been neglected by many. However, charting offers several advantages over counting methods. Charting the intensity using a time constant of 4, 8, or 16 sec. while the goniometer remains stationary at a wavelength of interest gives a record of intensity fluctuations with time. The record shows any abnormal variations that should be disregarded, drifts in intensity for which correction can be made, and when the intensity has become steady. Counting methods do not compensate for the first two situations.

The main disadvantage of charting is the unknown degree of linearity of the recorder. This problem can be overcome by calibrating the recorder with a standard frequency which is built into the scaling circuits.

COUNTING STATISTICS

The precision desired for a particular analysis is governed by counting statistics, which are related to background, counting rate, and the total count accumulated. The standard deviation, σ (sigma) is defined as the reciprocal of the square root of the total count taken when the number is large.[25] This is the maximum deviation from the true value expected in 68 percent of a large series of counts. Table 53-8 below gives the number of counts, standard deviation in percent, and the confidence limit for 1, 2, and 3 sigma.

TABLE 53-8.

Number	1σ	2σ	3σ
1,000	3.16	6.32	9.48
5,000	1.41	2.83	4.24
10,000	1.00	2.00	3.00
50,000	0.446	0.89	1.34
100,000	0.316	0.63	0.95
500,000	0.141	0.28	0.42
1,000,000	0.100	0.20	0.30
5,000,000	0.045	0.09	0.13
Confidence limit	68%	96%	99%

To illustrate a typical problem, consider the determination of K_2O in glass. Let us assume 1.5 percent K_2O in the sample, that background is negligible, and it is desired to have the error not exceed ± 0.01 percent K_2O. What counts must be accumulated to assure that the error is within the desired limit 96 percent of the time?

$$\frac{0.01}{1.50} \times 100 = 0.67\% \text{ maximum error}$$

$$2\sigma = 0.67\% \text{ or } 1\sigma = 0.33\%$$

$$\frac{100}{\sqrt{N}} = 0.33; \quad N = 91,700 \text{ counts}$$

[25] Zingaro, P. W., Norelco Reporter, **V**, Nos. 5–6, 99–100, 1958.

It is not difficult to attain a counting rate of 5000–10,000 counts per second for this concentration of K_2O, and thus only a few seconds are required to accumulate the count. High and low standards are run similarly to determine the slope of the calibration curve in order to evaluate the unknown.

In like manner, if background count makes a significant contribution to the total count on a peak, the standard deviation, σ, becomes more complex and the total count necessary for the same precision as previously illustrated becomes much greater.

$$\sigma = \frac{1}{P/(B-1)} \sqrt{\frac{P/B[P/(B+1)]}{Np}} \quad \text{or} \quad \frac{1}{R-1} \sqrt{\frac{R(R+1)}{Np}}$$

where R is peak to background ratio, and Np is the total count on the peak.

Calculations for Percent of Element from Intensity Data.—The calibration curve for an element is derived from intensity measurements in terms of counts per second or lines on chart for the high and low standards for that element. Since all elements investigated in this study have linear calibration curves, the easiest way to express the curve is by a linear equation.[26,27] The slope of the curve is obtained by dividing the difference in counting rates or chart lines by the concentration difference between the high and low standards.

To evaluate an unknown it is only necessary to divide the difference in counting rate between the unknown and low standard by the slope of the calibration curve and add the percent of the low standard to this value. Typical examples are given below.

CALCULATION OF PERCENT MgO IN GLASS

Counting Rate Methods		Counts per Second
High standard	(5.50% MgO)	252
Low standard	(0.05% MgO)	14
Unknown	?	163

$$\text{Slope} = \frac{252 - 14}{5.50 - .05} = \frac{238}{5.45} = 43.7 \text{ c/s}^a \text{ for 1\% MgO}$$

[a] c/s = counts per second.

$$\% \text{ MgO in Unknown} = \frac{163 \text{ c/s} - 14 \text{ c/s}}{(43.7 \text{ c/s})/(\% \text{ MgO})} + 0.05\% \text{ MgO}$$

Unknown = 3.41 + 0.05 = 3.46% MgO

Charting Method		Chart Lines
High standard	(5.50% MgO)	63.0
Low standard	(0.05% MgO)	3.5
Unknown	?	40.7

$$\text{Slope} = \frac{63.0 - 3.5}{5.50 - 0.5} = \frac{59.5}{5.45} = 10.9 \text{ lines/\% MgO}$$

$$\% \text{ MgO in Unknown} = \frac{40.7 - 3.5}{10.9} + 0.05 = 3.46\% \text{ MgO}$$

[26] Laning, S. H., Advances in X-Ray Analysis, Vol. 5, William M. Mueller, ed., Plenum Press, New York, 1962, pp. 457–63.
[27] Clark, G. L., Encyclopedia of X-Rays and Gamma Rays, Reinhold Publishing Corp., New York, 1963, pp. 427–430.

SAMPLE PREPARATION

Polishing.—The surface of the glass sample must be reproducible for all samples. A solid plate is preferred to a powder sample when the sample size permits. In one procedure the specimen is cut from the sample by means of a diamond saw or other cutting tool, wet polished with 180-grit silicon carbide or boron carbide abrasives to make plane, washed to remove coarse abrasive, and then finished with a fine abrasive of about 15-μ. diameter to produce a fine matt finish, which is quite satisfactory for all analyses. After the last grinding operation the specimen must be thoroughly cleaned. A 3–5 min. ultrasonic cleaning with a nonionic detergent, rinsing with distilled water, acetone, and air drying produces a clean surface ready for analysis.

Alumina abrasives are not recommended for grinding since they are very difficult to remove from the glass surface and therefore would contribute to the aluminum intensity during analysis.

Fusions.—Another method of sample preparation involves the fusion of about 15 g. of pieces of the glass sample in a flat-bottom, high-purity graphite crucible[28] at a temperature of 1000°C. in a nitrogen atmosphere for about 10 min. The crucible is then removed from the furnace and placed on a block of insulating material. The hot sample surface is pressed moderately with a graphite rod slightly smaller in diameter than the inside diameter of the crucible so that the bottom surface of the molten glass takes the form of the crucible bottom, and the crucible and sample are allowed to cool to room temperature. Upon cooling, the sample separates readily from the graphite crucible and is ready to grind flat, polish, and clean as described earlier.

Precautions.—The latter method of preparation requires some precaution when analyzing container glass. The outside surfaces of some container glasses have been chemically treated, leaving a bonded layer of titanium or tin oxides on the surface which could alter the composition. The bottoms are generally free from such coatings and should be used for sample preparation.

GLASS STANDARDS

There are few commercially available glass standards acceptable as standards for x-ray spectrographic analysis. The NBS glass standards are powders and are not the best type

TABLE 53-9. GLASS STANDARDS

National Bureau of Standards
    No. 80—soda-lime-silica glass
    No. 89—lead-barium-silica glass
    No. 91—opal glass
    No. 93—borosilicate glass
Society of Glass Technology[a]
    Standard Glass No. 1—soda-lime-alumina-magnesia-silica glass
    Standard Glass No. 2—borosilicate glass
    Standard Glass No. 3—potassium-lead-silica glass
    Standard Glass No. 4—opal glass

[a] These standards may be obtained by writing to University of Sheffield, Department of Glass Technology, Elmfield, Northumberland Road, Sheffield 10, England.

for standards. The Society of Glass Technology offers four different type glass standards in plate or rod form which can be prepared in good form for standards. Table 53-9 gives

[28] Ultra Carbon Corp., P. O. Box 747, Bay City, Mich.

a list of available glass standards. Additional standards must be obtained by chemical methods performed by competent analysts.

ELEMENT ANALYSIS

Before beginning the analysis of an unknown glass it is best to give it a general x-ray spectrographic scan using the sodium chloride analyzing crystal covering the angular range from 90° to 10° 2θ at 2° per minute. This range covers all the elements from potassium through the remaining elements of the periodic table. If this is done with standard glasses using a reproducible intensity, it is possible to evaluate the various elements in the angular range covered semiquantitatively to about 10 percent of the amount present.

Order of Element Analysis.—In the analysis of many different glasses, certain element analyses should be deferred until other elements have been run. The ones of concern here are those which have matrix corrections or serious matrix effects, namely, calcium, silica, and sodium.

In order to evaluate calcium, the potassium content of the glass must be known and, therefore, potassium should be determined before calcium.

Silica and sodium should be the last two elements determined, since the matrix has such a significant influence on the intensities of these two elements. Except for these three elements, there is no particular order for the remaining elements.

To facilitate the selection of order of analysis, Table 53-10 gives the recommended instrumental conditions for optimum intensity and resolution for each of the elements. The table is divided into two parts: routine analyses and special analyses. The first group is comprised of the elements usually found in flint or clear glass, and the second group consists of the elements found in colored glasses and specialty ware or infrequently analyzed.

Aluminum.—The determination of aluminum in glass has been found to have no detectable interferences in the concentration range normally found in soda-lime glasses. Only a high and low standard are required to establish the calibration curve. The normal concentration range is from 0.1 percent to about 3.5 percent Al_2O_3.

Data can be obtained by several modes of operation, such as fixed count, fixed time, or charting the peak intensity using an 8- or 16-sec. time constant. The latter method is preferred.

The accuracy of the determination depends on the accuracy of the standards and on the available intensity. It should not be difficult to attain counting rates of 50 to 100 counts per second for 1 percent Al_2O_3, and with this intensity the precision should be about ±0.02 percent Al_2O_3 or less when a counting time of 3 to 4 min. is used. This is usually below the limits of accuracy of the standards. The recommended instrumental conditions are given in Table 53-10.

Calculations.—See section on data acquisition.

Antimony.—The determination of antimony in soda-lime glass offers a little difficulty when using the gas-flow proportional counter. The L-series lines are much more intense than the K-series. However, the potassium $K\beta$ line falls very close to the antimony $L\alpha$ line and, with moderate to high concentrations of potassium, it interferes. The antimony $L\beta_1$ line is free from interference and should be used.

If the scintillation counter is employed, the antimony $K\alpha$ line is used in the determination. No interference has been observed, although background is high.

The concentration of antimony in glass ranges from zero to about 1.0 percent as Sb_2O_5. Counting rates of 1000–2000 counts per second for 1.0 percent Sb_2O_5 can be attained. The precision is about ±0.005 percent, with counting times of 3 to 4 min. The accuracy

TABLE 53-10. INSTRUMENTAL CONDITIONS FOR ANALYSIS

Element	Line	Analyzing Crystal	X-Ray Tube	PHA[a] Window, volts	Mode of Operation	Remarks
			ELEMENTAL ANALYSIS			
Al	Kα	PET	Cr	6	Chart	
As	Kα	LiF	W	6	Chart	PbLα interfers
Ba	Lα	LiF	W	Integral	Scan	
Ca	Kα	PET	Cr	No PHA	Chart	K-matrix effect
Fe	Kα	LiF	W	6	Chart	
Mg	Kα	ADP	Cr	6	Chart	
K	Kα	LiF	Cr	6	Chart	
Si	Kα	PET	Cr	6	Chart	Ca-matrix effect
Na	Kα	KAP	Cr	No PHA	Fixed Time	Matrix effect
Sr	Kα	LiF	W	7.5	Scan	
S	Kα	NaCl	Cr	Integral	Chart	Ca-background effec
Ti	Kα	LiF	W	6	Scan	BaLα may interfer
Zr	Kα	LiF	W	Integral	Scan	
			SPECIAL ANALYSIS			
Sb	Lβ₁	LiF	Cr	6	Chart	
Cl	Kα	PET	Cr	6	Chart	KKβ line interfers
Cr	Kα	Topaz	W	6	Chart	NaCl gives high BG
Co	Kα	Topaz	W	6	Chart	
Cu	Kα	Topaz	W	6	Chart	
Mn	Kα	Topaz	W	6	Chart	
Ni	Kα	LiF	W	6	Chart	
P	Kα	Ge	Cr	7	Scan	
Se	Kα	LiF	Cr	6	Chart	Ca-background effect
Zn	Kα	LiF	W	6	Chart	

a The PHA level control is set at zero or the minimum value short of introducing electronic noise. The detector high voltage is adjusted to give maximum intensity for each element with low background.

depends on the standards, but should be within ±0.02 percent. The recommended instrumental conditions are given in Table 53-10.

Calculations.—See section on data acquisition.

Arsenic.—The determination of total arsenic in the absence of lead is straightforward, requiring only a high and low standard to establish a calibration curve. The normal concentration range is from zero to about 0.3 percent expressed as As_2O_5 and can be determined to about ±0.001 percent.

When lead is present, it interferes with the arsenic determination since the lead $L\alpha$ line coincides with the arsenic $K\alpha$ line. Under these circumstances, the arsenic must be evaluated by the $AsK\beta$ line and the lead by the $L\beta_1$ line. Unless the glass is known not to contain lead, it should be checked by scanning over the wavelength range covering these two elements. Table 53-10 gives the recommended instrumental conditions for this determination.

Calculations.—See section on data acquisition.

Barium and Titanium.—These two elements are determined at the same time by scanning over the angular range from 89° to 84° 2θ with a lithium fluoride analyzing crystal at 1° per minute with a 4-sec. time constant. Such a scan is given in Fig. 53-10,

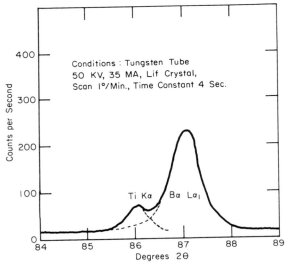

FIG. 53-10. Scanning Technique for the Determination of Barium and Titanium in Glass. The diagram illustrates the procedure for obtaining the background under the titanium line resulting from the tail of the barium line.

which shows the procedure for obtaining the background under the titanium $K\alpha$ peak.[29] Peak height above background is a measure of the concentration and both elements can be evaluated by means of standards run under the same instrumental conditions.

Barium normally ranges from 0.01 to 0.75 percent as BaO, whereas titanium ranges from less than 0.005 percent to 0.5 percent as TiO_2. By this technique barium can be determined to about ±0.01 percent, and titanium can be determined to about ±0.005 percent. The recommended instrumental conditions are given in Table 53-10.

Calculations.—See section on data acquisition.

[29] Laning, S. H., Developments in Applied Spectroscopy, Vol. 2, J. R. Ferraro and J. S. Ziomek, eds., Plenum Press, New York, 1963, pp. 350–359.

Calcium.—The determination of CaO in glass is nearly straightforward covering the range from about 5.0 percent to 12.5 percent CaO. However, the intensity of CaKα radiation is influenced by the potassium content of the sample and, therefore, corrections must be applied to the data. The approach to this difficulty depends on the nature of the analytical problem.

If one is concerned only with the analysis of his company's own glass products where the composition is reasonably constant for a particular tank, the matrix effect cancels out and one is concerned with only the conversion of CaKα intensity to concentration. High and low calcium standards containing the same potassium concentration as that of the tank composition make it possible to evaluate the calcium content of the glass over the small range normally encountered.

If one is concerned with many different glasses, changes in potassium influence the calcium intensity. High and low calcium standards should contain less than 0.1 percent K$_2$O in order to facilitate the analysis of unknown glasses. High and low calcium standards containing low concentrations of K$_2$O are run to establish the slope of the calibration curve. The unknown glass is run and evaluated from the calibration curve as illustrated in the section on data acquisition. To this value is added the potassium correction, which is found by multiplying the K$_2$O content expressed in percent by 0.225 percent CaO. Table 53-11 shows the results of applying the potassium correction to the x-ray data.

TABLE 53-11.   COMPARISON OF CHEMICAL AND X-RAY DATA
FOR CaO IN GLASS

CaO by Wet Anal., %	K$_2$O, %	CaO by X-Ray Uncorrected, %	CaO Corrected for K$_2$O, %
12.51	0.08	12.49	12.51
6.35	0.31	6.27	6.34
6.77	0.50	6.65	6.76
8.49[a]	0.72	8.32	8.48
7.17	1.09	6.96	7.20
7.05	1.12	6.78	7.03
10.87	2.23	10.37	10.87

[a] Society of Glass Technology Standard No. 1.

Illustration: If, from the calibration curve, the value of 8.72% CaO is calculated and if the glass is known to contain 1.24% K$_2$O, the corrected CaO content is 8.72 + 1.24 × 0.225 or 8.72% + 0.28% or 9.00% CaO. The precision of the determination is about ±0.02% CaO, and the accuracy is dependent on the standards used, but ought to be about ±0.05% CaO.

There is one precaution to keep in mind when analyzing for calcium and that is to make sure the intensities encountered stay within the linear range of the detector and the associated electronics, including the pulse height analyzer, if one is used. It is recommended that the PHA be used in integral operation or eliminated entirely in this determination in order to keep the response of the detector linear to 20,000 counts per second or higher. Recommended instrumental conditions are given in Table 53-10.

Chlorine.—No matrix effects have been observed in the analysis for chloride in glass. The normal range is from about 0.005 percent to 0.2 percent as chlorine. The precision is about ±0.002 percent chloride, based on counting rates of 50–80 counts per second for 0.1 percent Cl. The chromium x-ray tube, PET crystal, and PHA are recommended for this determination. The sodium chloride crystal produces a high background and is not recommended. A high and low standard are required for calibration to eliminate any background radiation under the chlorine peak.

Care must be exercised in sample preparation for chloride, since the glass surface is easily contaminated with chloride from the hands. Recommended instrumental conditions are given in Table 53-10.

Calculations.—See section on data acquisition.

Chromium, Manganese, Iron, Cobalt, Nickel, Copper, Zinc.—These seven elements are determined in a similar manner. No matrix effects have been observed for these elements in the concentrations normally found in soda-lime glass and, therefore, only high and low standards are required to establish a calibration curve. These elements are present in concentrations ranging from a few p.p.m. to almost 0.5 percent for some of the elements. If adjacent elements are present in a particular sample, it may be necessary to use an analyzing crystal of high dispersion, such as topaz, to separate the Kβ line of the next lower atomic number element from the Kα line of the element of interest. However, in the absence of such interferences, the lithium fluoride crystal is preferred because intensities are much greater. To illustrate the capabilities of x-ray methods for trace analysis, the determination of cobalt is shown in Fig. 53-11. Recommended instrumental conditions are given in Table 53-10.

Calculations.—See section on data acquisition.

Magnesium.—The normal range for MgO in plate and container glasses is from 0.05 percent to about 5.0 percent, and within this range no matrix effects have been observed.

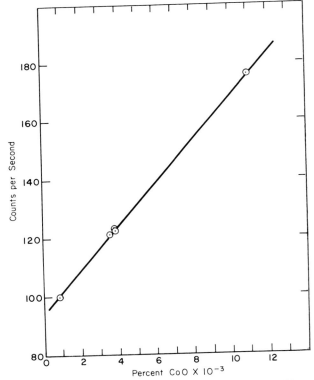

Fig. 53-11.   Calibration Curve for the Determination of Cobalt in Glass. The curve for cobalt illustrates the general sensitivity that the x-ray spectrograph has for this element. Cobalt was analyzed by standard chemical methods.

A high and low standard are adequate for calibration. The greatest difficulty in this analysis is the low intensity normally obtained. Intensities can be greatly improved by using a thin-window chromium target tube, ADP crystal, moderately broad collimation, and an ultra-thin window on the gas-flow proportional counter. It is possible to obtain approximately 40 counts per second above background for 1 percent MgO in glass. The precision ranges from 0.01 percent to 0.03 percent MgO for a 4 to 5 min. counting time for the rate mentioned. Recommended instrumental conditions are given in Table 53-10.

Calculations.—See section on data acquisition.

Phosphorus.—The determination of phosphorus in glass is made somewhat difficult because of the low intensities and the variation of background with calcium content of the glass. The calcium $K\beta$ second-order line interferes with the phosphorus $K\alpha$ line and, in order to overcome this interference, the germanium analyzing crystal must be used.

Peak height above background is linear with concentration in the low levels found in soda-lime glass. Counting rates are low, being only about 100 counts per second above background for 1.0 percent P_2O_5. Normal concentrations range from less than 0.01 percent to about 0.20 percent as P_2O_5. The precision is about 5–10 percent of the amount present when scanning over the peak from 145° to 137° 2θ at 1° per minute with a time constant of 4 sec.

An alternative procedure would be to obtain the counting rates on the peak and background. The recommended instrumental conditions are given in Table 53-10.

Calculations.—See section on data acquisition.

Potassium.—No particular difficulty has been encountered with the determination of K_2O in soda-lime glasses. The normal range of concentration is from about 0.05 percent to 2.5 percent K_2O and is linear over this range; therefore, a high and low standard are sufficient to obtain a calibration curve. A wide range of operating conditions is possible in this determination. Several different crystals can be used, including lithium fluoride, PET, sodium chloride, and germanium in decreasing order of efficiency. The precision of the analysis is ± 0.01 percent or better. Care must be taken not to exceed the linearity of the counting circuits. Recommended instrumental conditions are given in Table 53-10.

Calculations.—See section on data acquisition.

Selenium.—Selenium, though not a common element in soda-lime glasses, does occur in specialty ware in concentrations ranging up to 0.5 percent as Se and gives the glass a ruby color. There are no interferences and, therefore, high and low standards establish the calibration curve. Recommended instrumental conditions are given in Table 53-10.

Calculations.—See section on data acquisition.

Silicon.—The determination of silicon as SiO_2 in glass is quite difficult since the $SiK\alpha$ intensity is dependent on the calcium content of the glass which results in a family of nearly parallel lines.[29] The degree of difficulty depends on the nature of the problem, i.e., whether one analyzes many different glasses or whether one is concerned with glass tank analysis where the composition is nearly constant.

It should not be too difficult to attain counting rates of 10,000 to 15,000 counts per second or more for glass containing about 72 percent SiO_2 by using a thin-window chromium tube, wide collimation, PET crystal, an ultra-thin window on the gas-flow proportional counter, and hydrogen or helium atmosphere. The precision for this determination is dependent on the total count, but it should be about ± 0.05 percent SiO_2 for 5 min. counting time. The pulse height analyzer is used in integral operation or eliminated entirely in this determination. Recommended instrumental conditions are given in Table 53-10. The charting procedure for obtaining the intensity data is shown in Fig. 53-12.

Calculations.—In the general case, three standards are used for best results. In

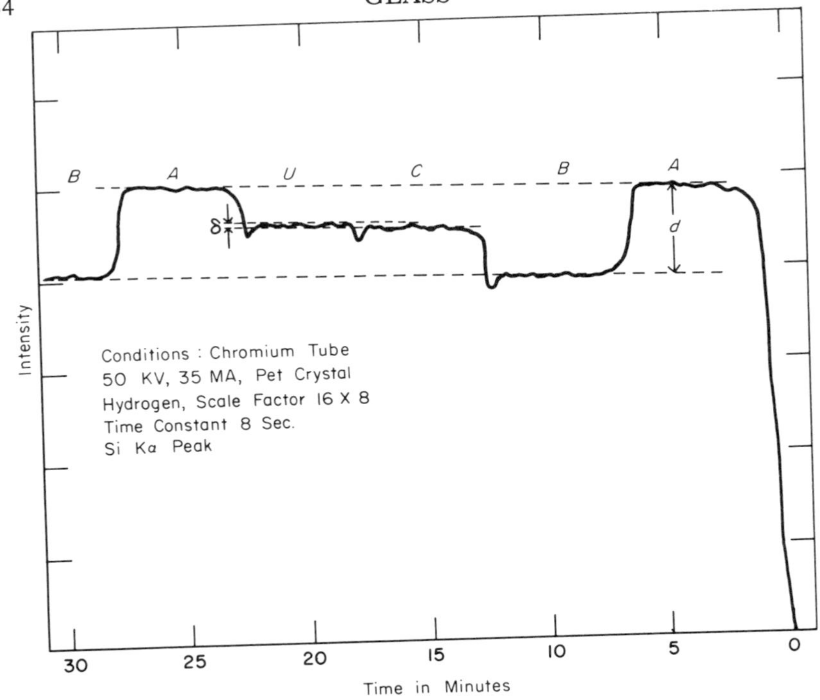

FIG. 53-12. Charting Technique for the Determination of Silica in Glass. A and B are high and low standards; C is a reference standard similar in composition to the unknown U. D is the difference in intensity between the high and low standards which, when divided by the difference in percent silica, gives the slope of the calibration curves. δ is the difference between the unknown and third reference standard.

order to evaluate the slope of the calibration curve, two glass standards are used having the same calcium contents, but which differ by 3 to 5 percent SiO_2. The third standard has the same general composition as the unknown. Difference in intensity between the unknown and the third standard is converted to percent SiO_2 by dividing the intensity difference by the slope. This value is added to or subtracted from the silica value of the third standard to evaluate the unknown.

Example:

High standard	73.83% SiO_2	95.0 lines
Low standard	68.28% SiO_2	80.0 lines
	5.55%	15.0 lines

$$\text{Slope} = 2.70 \text{ lines}/\% \text{ } SiO_2$$

3rd ref. standard	71.48% SiO_2	86.2 lines
Unknown	?	87.1 lines
		+ 0.9 lines

$$\frac{+0.9}{2.7} = +0.33\% \text{ } SiO_2$$

$$\text{Unknown } SiO_2 = 71.48\% + 0.33\% = 71.81\%$$

Sodium.—The determination of sodium in glass is made difficult for two reasons: the very low intensities attainable on most present-day x-ray spectrographs, and the moderately high concentration present in glass. Many things can be done to improve intensities for the light elements down through sodium, such as by employing wide collimation, thin-window chromium x-ray tube, pulse height analyzer, gypsum or potassium acid phthalate analyzing crystal, wide-window gas-flow proportional counter with an ultra-thin window of Formvar or other film making material on the detector, and vacuum, hydrogen, or helium atmosphere. With these modifications it is possible to attain counting rates of 1100 to 1200 counts per second on a specimen of pressed sodium chloride.

This determination has not been studied thoroughly to determine the influence of matrix on the sodium determination. However, there is some influence associated particularly with the silica content. Other elements probably have some influence as well, as shown in Figs. 53-13 and 53-14.

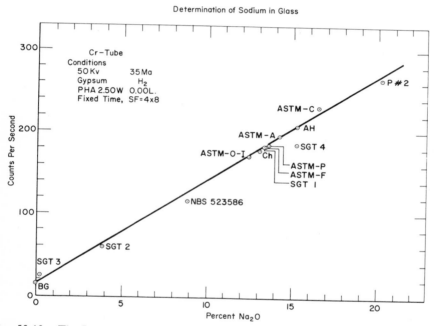

Determination of Sodium in Glass

FIG. 53-13. The Intensity-concentration Curve for Na_2O in Glasses Having a Wide Compositional Range. Included here are Society of Glass Technology Standards, an NBS antimony glass, and 5 glasses from the ASTM.

The procedure for this determination is similar to that for silica in that three standards are required for best results. High and low standards with sodium contents differing by several percent are used to establish the slope of the calibration curve, and the third standard, similar in composition to the unknown, is used to compare with the unknown. Fixed time or fixed count operations are satisfactory. Counting rates between 150 and 250 counts per second for 12 to 16 percent Na_2O can be attained with the previously mentioned rate on sodium chloride. The precision is about 0.5 percent of the amount

GLASS

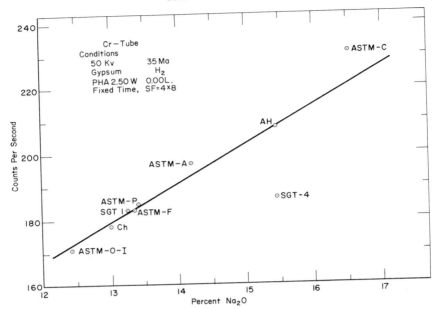

Determination of Sodium in Glass

FIG. 53-14. The Na₂O Concentration Range of Interest in Soda-lime Glasses. Matrix effects are evident.

present with an accuracy of about ±0.12 to 0.16 percent Na₂O for 5–6 min. of counting time. Recommended conditions are given in Table 53-10.

Calculations.—The high and low standards enable one to calculate the slope of the curve. The third standard, similar in composition to the unknown, makes it possible to evaluate the unknown by dividing the difference between the third standard and unknown by the slope and adding this value to or subtracting it from the sodium value of the third standard.

Strontium and Zirconium.—These two elements are determined by a scanning technique similar to barium covering the range from 26° to 21° 2θ using the lithium fluoride analyzing crystal with a scanning speed of 1° per minute and a time constant of 4 sec. Standards are run under the same instrumental conditions. The peak height above background for each is linear with concentration. The upper concentration level is about 0.10 percent as SrO or ZrO₂. The precision is about 0.005 percent for either element. Recommended instrumental conditions are given in Table 53-10.

Calculations.—See section on data acquisition.

Sulfur.—The intensity of sulfur in glass is influenced by the calcium content of the glass, since the background under the sulfur Kα line varies directly as the calcium concentration. Both peak and background must be measured for high and low standards and unknown. The background is measured at 140° when using the sodium chloride analyzing crystal. Figure 53-15 shows the charting technique for obtaining the sulfur concentration.

Peak height above background is linear with concentration in the range up to 0.5 percent SO₃. Counting rates of 200 to 300 counts per second for 0.4 percent SO₃ can

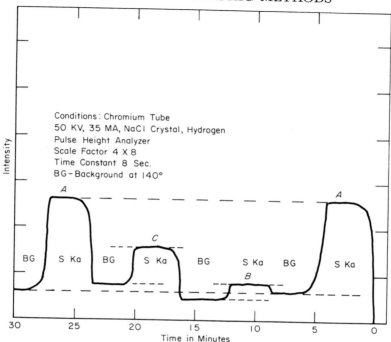

FIG. 53-15. Charting Technique for the Determination of Sulfur in Glass. A and B are high and low sulfur standards, each measured on the sulfur peak and background at 140°. C is the unknown. Peak to background is measured for each glass.

readily be attained and with this rate a precision of better than 0.01 percent SO_3 is possible. The accuracy depends on the standards, but it should be within ±0.02 percent SO_3.

Recommended instrumental conditions are given in Table 53-10.

Calculations.—See section on data acquisition.

Example:

High standard	0.40% SO_3	54.5 lines
Background (140°)		17.0 lines
Low standard	0.02% SO_3	19.0 lines
Background		17.0 lines
Unknown	?	26.8 lines
Background		13.0 lines
High standard diff.	37.5 lines	

Low standard diff. $\dfrac{2.0}{35.5}$ lines $= 0.38\%$ SO_3

Slope $= 93.4$ lines/1% SO_3

Unknown diff. 13.8 lines $- 2.0 = 11.8$ lines

$$\frac{11.8}{93.4} = 0.13\% + 0.02\% = 0.15\% \ SO_3$$

SPECIAL TECHNIQUES IN X-RAY INSTRUMENTATION AND ANALYSIS OF GLASS

By Howard G. Ross

Ford Motor Co.
Glass Technical Center
Lincoln Park, Michigan

It is the unusual sample which offers the greatest challenge to the analyst. The greater the number of techniques and procedures the analyst has at his command, the greater are his chances for finding the answers requested of him.

This section presents some of the more common techniques in instrumentation and sample preparation that are used in glass analysis and the problems associated with glass manufacture.

METHODS OF PREPARATION FOR UNUSUAL SAMPLES

Fusion Methods.—Claisse's[30,31] method for sodium tetraborate fusions is a well known procedure for solving the matrix problem for various materials. However, for glass analysis a dilution of 1:100 is not very practical for light element analysis because the intensities would be much too low. Ratios of glass to flux between 1:2 and 1:9 are much more practical. High-purity, flat-bottom graphite crucibles (Ultra Carbon Corporation, P. O. Box 747, Bay City, Michigan) are recommended for the fusions which are carried out at 1100°C. in an inert atmosphere for 7–10 min. for 10–12 g. of total mix. The fusion releases readily from the graphite crucible after cooling and is ready for polishing and cleaning. The fact that carbon particles adhere to the fusion button presents no problem, since the particles are removed by the polishing step. Platinum crucibles are not recommended for the fusions unless 12 g. or more of total sample is made, because the product is quite viscous and losses are high when pouring. The melt adheres to the platinum even after cooling.

Another flux which is becoming popular for fusions is lithium tetraborate ($Li_2B_4O_7$) (Spex Industries, Metuchen, New Jersey). Materials are generally more soluble in this flux than the sodium tetraborate.

The fusion method allows one to prepare special standards, to reduce matrix effects, to eliminate particle size effects, to make homogeneous samples, or to add an internal standard.

To reduce matrix effects further, barium oxide (BaO) or lanthanum oxide (La_2O_3) is added to the mix before fusion.[32] Borate fusion methods have found wide acceptance in the optical emission field,[33] as well as x-ray.

[30] F. Claisse, Quebec Dept. of Mines, Preliminary Report 327, 1956.
[31] F. Claisse, Norelco Reporter, **IV**, 3–7, 17, 19, 1957.
[32] Rose, H. J., Adler, I., and Flanagan, F. J., "X-Ray Fluorescence Analysis of the Light Elements in Rocks and Minerals," Appl. Spectroscopy, **17**, No. 4, 81, 1963.
[33] Tingbe, W. H., and Matocha, C. K., Anal. Chem., **30**, 495, 1958.

Briquet Methods.—Some glass samples must be analyzed in the form of powders due to the physical nature or size of the sample. Glass should be ground to −200-mesh or finer for normal sample packing methods. Unfortunately, the reproducibility of the method often depends on the operator's skill in preparing pressed samples. Although briqueting may be a rapid method for sample preparation, the intensities are somewhat variable, especially for the lighter elements.

Some materials can be compacted with pressure alone without a binder, *e.g.*, sulfur powder and potassium bromide. However, for consistent results some type of binder should be used. One such binder is Hypalon (granular *n*-butyl-methacrylate, Lucite 2044 acrylic resin manufactured by E. I. duPont) dissolved in toluene to make a 20 percent solution by weight.

Sample Preparation.—Five grams of −200-mesh or finer glass is blended with 20 drops of solution in a mortar for a few minutes. After blending, the mixture is spread out on a clean surface to dry and any lumps broken up with a spatula. The powder is then placed in a suitable die on the bottom of which is placed an aluminum planchet or other stiff material and the sample pressed under 5000 to 20,000 p.s.i. The hard backing prevents the sample from cracking and makes it easier to handle and identify. With reasonable care, such samples last for years.

Physical Concentration Methods.—Some samples, such as stone inclusions, cord, and undesirable areas in glass, may require considerable preparation for valid analysis. Specific gravity methods are useful for separating glass from sand in grinding residues. The same method could be used to separate heavy fractions from sand, lepidolite, or other raw materials, which could cause trouble in glass melting. Stones for x-ray diffraction or x-ray fluorescence analysis can be separated by carefully cutting or sawing out the trouble areas, crushing or lightly grinding in a mortar, spreading out the crushed material onto black glazed paper, and picking out the desired portion with fine tweezers. The separated fragments can be further concentrated by additional careful grinding. The final ground sample can be sprinkled onto a lightly greased (petroleum jelly) microscope slide or preferably on a slab of pure fused silica or Vycor. Another method is to sprinkle the powder onto a slide, dropwise add ethyl alcohol onto it, make a uniform slurry, and let dry. A binocular petrographic or stereo microscope is useful in isolating minute stones, devitrification, or other small inclusions.

Instrumental Methods for Effectively Concentrating the Sample. **Small Area Probes.**—Recently, devices for analyzing small areas have been designed to study sample areas between 1 mm. and 0.1 mm. in diameter using conventional x-ray equipment. Since counting rates are proportional to the areas involved, areas less than 0.1 mm. in diameter are not practical to study by this technique. The Heinrich probe,[34] developed commercially by the General Electric Company for its x-ray equipment, has been in use for several years. It consists of a normal sample drawer, a sample clamping device, a system for producing X-Y micrometer motions, and a tubular collimator that masks the secondary x-ray beam emitted by the sample.

Some means for aligning the emergent sample beam with the desired sample area is necessary. For the 1-mm. collimator, a hypodermic needle ground parallel to the slope of the sample drawer and inserted into the collimator allows one to quickly line up the X direction and gives a fair estimate of the Y direction by just covering over the sample spot desired. The hypodermic needle is removed, the X-Y micrometer read, and the spot area then analyzed. A comparison area, preferably on the same sample, is analyzed by moving the X-Y micrometer away from its previous setting to an adjacent normal area.

Philips Electronic Instruments has recently developed a similar but more refined unit

[34] Heinrich, K. F. J., "X-Ray Probe with Collimation of the Secondary Beam," Advances in X-Ray Analysis, Plenum Press, New York, Vol. 5, 516, 1962.

called the Macroprobe. The Macroprobe works on the same general principle as the Heinrich probe, but uses a curved analyzing crystal which concentrates and focuses the radiation from the sample into a line in front of the detector. A 70× light optical system helps align the sample and observe it during the analysis.

Cord, stones, and other small areas of interest in glass have been analyzed by this means. Figure 53-16 illustrates the probe and sample mounted for study.

Small isolated samples may be mounted in metallurgical Bakelite or Lucite mounts. A very simple and flexible method for small samples is to mount the sample in dental repair acrylic (Tru-Kit Manufacturing Company, Harry J. Bosworth, Chicago, Illinois). This material sets up slowly into a hard plastic that allows 5–10 min. working time to position or build up accurately the general sample area (see Fig. 53-17).

FIG. 53-16.   Heinrich Sample Holder with Sample in Position. Sample is inclusion in glass fragment (x-ray darkened).

FIG. 53-17.   Small Inclusion in Glass Fragment (0.2 mm. in. diameter) which Is Embedded in Dental Repair Acrylic Resin.

For sample areas below 0.1 mm. diameter, the best procedure is to use the electron microprobe discussed in the section under that title.

Small Area Masks.—The small area probe device is not generally needed when various larger sample areas are encountered. The simplest method for intermediate areas is to have masks cut or machined with various shapes and sizes of openings to expose the area of interest. Masks can be prepared from high-purity metals, such as aluminum, copper, silver, tin, and lead. A special adhesive backed lead foil tape (No. 420 made by the Minnesota Mining and Manufacturing Company, St. Paul, Minnesota) can be used to mask areas of any sample. If a comparison area is also to be analyzed, it must be masked to the same area in order for a comparative analysis to be made.

The use of a particular element mask depends on the absence of emission lines that would interfere with the analysis of the sample. Trace impurities in the masking material usually do not interfere with an analysis, because one is concerned generally with relative intensities between an area of interest and the matrix of equal area.

IMPROVEMENTS IN LONG WAVELENGTH ANALYSIS

New X-ray Tubes.—Recently, x-ray tube manufacturers have produced a chromium target x-ray tube in several variations. This tube enhances longer wavelength characteristic radiation (VKα or longer) by a factor of 3–4 times compared to normal intensities from a tungsten target tube. One reason for this advantage of the chromium tube is that the most effective wavelength for exciting an element is the wavelength which is slightly shorter than the absorption edge wavelength for the element.[35] The beryllium window on the tube has also been made thinner, since this permits the transmission of the more desirable wavelengths. For more convenience, the General Electric Company has developed a dual tube with tungsten and chromium targets in the same tube. Either target can be selected at will.

Henke,[36] over a period of time, has developed a whole system for detecting and determining long and extremely long wavelengths. Philips has developed a commercial version of Henke's system. Briefly, a demountable target, very thin-window x-ray tube is used in a vacuum spectrometer. This allows the use of an aluminum, copper, silver, or other target material whose radiations will be most efficient for exciting a particular long wavelength. Even more important is the 6 μ aluminum window which allows high transmission of the long wavelength radiation. Thin-window flow counters are used with special gas mixtures for efficient detection of these elements. Henke also developed high d-value stearate crystals that are capable of dispersing the long wavelength radiation. The ultimate limit appears to be the detection of BKα.

Ultra-thin-window Counter Tubes.—Normally, gas-flow counters have used $\frac{1}{4}$ mil Mylar film to contain the argon-methane gas mixture that is used. However, even this thin window absorbs much of the long wavelength radiation of MgKα and most of NaKα and all of longer wavelengths. Thin windows of collodion, Formvar, and other organic polymer materials can be prepared by using modified electron microscopy film preparation methods. Films of 100 A of carbon can also be prepared by carbon evaporation onto high-quality, freshly cleaved mica, but these strong films tend to rupture while drying on the 100-mesh screen. Suitable film preparation methods are described by Hall.[37] The film can be supported on a high transmission 100-mesh nickel or copper screen (Ernest F. Fullam, P. O. Box 444, Schenectady, New York) attached to a thin metal frame.

When using ultra-thin windows on a flow counter, the plateau has been observed to shift to higher voltages when compared with Mylar windows. This is due to hydrogen, helium, or air leaking into the counter tube. The durability and efficiency of the window are dependent on preparation, counter gas pressure, type of film, method of mounting, and skill of the operator. However, with care a good film may last several weeks to several months. Ultra-thin films do not require a conducting film on them as thicker windows do to dissipate a static charge.

An ultra-thin window gives greatly improved counting rates for wavelengths greater than 5 A. Rates of 2–4 times those for $\frac{1}{4}$-mil Mylar are experienced for silicon, aluminum, and magnesium radiations, whereas sodium radiation increases 5 to 10 times, depending on the thickness of the film. As a consequence, sodium analysis has become practical with the chromium tube and the thin-window counter tube.

New Analyzing Crystals.—In addition to the normal crystals which have been in use for years, a group of recently developed crystals is now available. Most of these new crystals have been specifically designed for long wavelength radiation. Pentaerythritol, PET, is the most practical new crystal for long wavelength radiation through AlKα, increasing counting rates approximately 2 times that of EDDT. Potassium acid phthalate, KAP, has a $2d$ value of 26.4 A which allows one to detect OKα, but it is very useful for NaKα as well as other wavelengths. Ultra-long wavelengths require lead or barium

---

[35] Birks, L. S., X-Ray Spectrochemical Analysis, Interscience Publishers, Inc., New York, Chapter I.

[36] Henke, Eastern Analytical Symposium, New York, 1963.

[37] Hall, C. E., Introduction to Electron Microscopy, McGraw-Hill Book Co., Inc., New York, 1953, Chapter II.

stearate or similar multiple monolayer crystals with $2d$ values approaching 100 Å which have been prepared using old techniques.[38] This type of analyzing crystal can detect $BK\alpha$. Easily cleaved sheets of No. 1 grade India white mica (Precision Mica Company, Peabody, Massachusetts) is also suitable as an inexpensive crystal with a $2d$ value of approximately 19 Å which is useful for analyzing $NaK\alpha$. Gypsum crystals are much less expensive than KAP or other similar crystals in the phthalate family and are suitable for $NaK\alpha$. One can buy large crystals of selenite from mineral supply houses and prepare gypsum crystals very inexpensively. The crystals cleave easily but are quite flexible and have only about half the reflectivity of commercially grown gypsum crystals.

Elimination of Second-Order Interferences.—In addition to the normal use of reverters and pulse height analyzers for removing second-order interference, there are two other methods for solving the problems which may be more efficient in certain situations. Lublin[39] has described the use of single crystals of silicon and germanium cut in the 111 plane so that no second-order reflections are possible, as they are "forbidden" reflections. If one takes the case of second-order $CdK\alpha$ (minor constituent) falling on $SeK\alpha$ (low level) in a typical glass analysis, the KV may be lowered to 25 which does not permit $CdK\alpha$ to be excited but still excites $SeK\alpha$. Pulse height discrimination probably would not have completely eliminated the interference.

Special Uses of Collimators.—The Heinrich probe is furnished with a narrow bladeless type of collimator which is practical due to the fine collimation of the secondary beam with this instrument. The same principle can apply in the case of aluminum, magnesium, or sodium analysis where the counting rate may not be sufficient for useful glass analysis. The blades can be removed or partially removed from the counter collimator and twofold increases in counting rate can be noted. The long wavelength region is best for this method as the elements are widely dispersed. However, higher orders of $CaK\alpha$ or $CaK\beta$ may interfere in certain cases as calcium is a minor or major constituent in many glasses. If greater resolution is needed in normal situations for shorter wavelength radiation, then a finer collimator and/or a low $2d$ value crystal, such as topaz, can be used. The counting rate is lowered by this method, but the signal-to-noise ratio may be improved greatly.

Analyzing Elements from Tin to Cerium.—Normally, one would want to use the $K\alpha$ line of any element that could be excited by 50 kilovolts usually available in the x-ray tube. However, the $K\alpha$ line of the heavier elements have short wavelengths that require scintillation counters or Xenon or Krypton proportional counter tubes for efficient detection. These lines usually have fair sensitivity but can have poor signal-to-noise ratios due to a high background. Dispersion can also be a serious problem. It is usually desirable and practical to use the $L\alpha$ line of tin and heavier elements. The combination of the chromium tube, vacuum, helium or hydrogen path, and thin-window gas-flow counter tube for normal light elemental analysis is very efficient for detecting the $L\alpha$ lines. Using a lithium fluoride analyzing crystal, $InL\alpha$, $SnL\alpha$, and $SbL\alpha$ are very efficiently excited and detected using the above conditions and, in addition, have a low background. $SbL\alpha$ shows a sevenfold increase using chromium radiation and helium or hydrogen compared to tungsten radiation and the $SbK\alpha$ line. The signal-to-noise ratio is also much greater with chromium radiation and the $L\alpha$ line. $BaL\alpha$, $LaL\alpha$, and $CeL\alpha$ are also normally determined with the same conditions. If the sodium chloride analyzing crystal is used, ruthenium, rhodium, palladium, silver, and cadmium are also readily detected; however, the $K\alpha$ lines using the lithium fluoride analyzing crystal are better for these ele-

[38] I. Langmuir, Journal of the Franklin Institute, Vol. 218, p. 153 (1934).
[39] Lublin, P., "A Novel Approach to Discrimination in X-Ray Spectrographic Analysis," Advances in X-Ray Analysis, Vol. 2, Plenum Press, New York, 1959.

ments. The wavelength of the line and the absence of interfering elements are the important criteria which determine the conditions of analysis.

PROCEDURES FOR VARIOUS TYPE SAMPLES

Cord and Ream.—Cord and ream analysis is usually an example of small area analysis which at best is difficult. Cord is generally considered to be an inhomogeneous area in glass that differs in index of refraction from that of the normal glass around it. Variation of index of refraction also implies variation in chemical composition and density. A successful analysis may depend on the size and severity of the inhomogeneity and the skill of the analyst in isolating it for presentation to the x-ray beam since it must be on the surface of the specimen presented to the x-rays.

Detection and isolation of cord is often the major part of the problem. The polariscope is a great aid in locating cord. Other optical means are also available for viewing cord and ream, such as a Schlieren optical system or a simple point source of light. If a sample is immersed in a liquid of matching refractive index, the cord should appear, because it would be higher or lower in refractive index than the surrounding glass. By using polished cross sections of glass, ream or cord can be detected easily after x-irradiating the sample for 5 minutes at 50 kv. and 50 ma., using a Cr target tube. Different types of ream can be classified by their relative color change after irradiation.

Cord analysis usually requires use of the strongest cord of the sample available, careful sample selection, and sometimes long counting times to ascertain small differences in counting rates between the cord and matrix glass. Any of the previously discussed means for increasing counting rates for the light elements are most important in this type of analysis. A number of different samples should be examined in order not to reach erroneous conclusions.

Loffler[40] has stated that ream and cord can be characterized by special etching solutions that have a differential etching action. A high alumina cord will show one type of etch, whereas a high silica or high soda cord will show another type of etch. The difference in etching is subtle and requires an interference microscope in order to observe it.

After a suitable cord or ream area has been located, it must be made into a form suitable to present to the x-ray beam. A section of glass containing the heterogeneity is removed, together with a corresponding area of matrix, and, in the case of container glass, tubing, or other curved glass, flattened by heating if the cord is on the surface. This is done by placing the sections in flat-bottom high-purity graphite crucibles with the cord surface down, placing the crucibles in a muffle furnace at 800°–900°C. in an inert atmosphere for 3–4 min. to soften the glass, removing from the furnace and pressing on the glass with a graphite rod to help flatten the samples, and then allowing them to cool. Any loosely adhering carbon particles can be buffed off before analysis.

If the cord or ream is in the interior of the glass, it is necessary to grind off the matrix glass down to the heterogeneity before the analysis can be made.

The easiest type of cord to detect is one high in zirconium caused by pickup from zirconia refractory. Cord and ream resulting from alumina and silica refractories are generally harder to analyze, since intensities are usually lower than zirconium for the same concentration difference.

One way to detect a sodium cord is to stain the sodium containing glass with the well known copper or silver staining process.[41] This process involves the exchange of copper

[40] Loffler, H., "The Analysis of Cords and Inclusions by Etching and Interference Measurements," (translation) Glas Technische Berichte, October 1954, p. 381.
[41] Weyl, W. A., Coloured Glasses, Dawson's of Pall Mall, London, 1959, Chapters 25 and 27.

or silver for the sodium ions. If the sodium level in one area is greater or lesser than another area, the staining ion will displace the corresponding sodium ions, and an x-ray analysis of the copper or silver ions will identify the cord; or by proper heat treatment the copper or silver ions will color the glass according to the sodium concentration. Recent investigation has shown that the color of the stain may be affected by the iron content of a ream in a soda-lime glass.

Thin Films.—Thin films may be found on glass by accident or by planned process. An unknown film can be analyzed by running a qualitative scan and then comparing the trace to the back side of the sample or a ground-off area.

The thickness of uniform films may also be measured by x-ray spectroscopy. The main element of the film may be counted directly and related to the counting rate of known standard thickness films which have been determined independently by optical or wet chemical means. If the film is organic or composed of too light an element to be detected by x-rays, one must measure the attenuation of a line from the substrate, such as $SiK\alpha$ or $CaK\alpha$.

Chapter 54

PAINT, VARNISH, AND LACQUER

By J. D. McGinness, P. J. Secrest, and D. J. Tessari

Analytical Research Department
Sherwin-Williams Co.
Chicago, Illinois

It is assumed that the reader of this volume has access to Volume II, Part B of this work. In Chapter 37 of Volume II, other authors provide a thorough presentation of the subject, methods for analysis of paint, varnish, and lacquer.[1] Chapter 37 generally serves as a review of all paint analysis with detailed procedures given only for noninstrumental methods. However, in a few instances, rather complete information is also provided for instrumental methods. Consequently, to provide unity and continuity with respect to certain instrumental areas, some material from Volume II is repeated in this volume. Frequent reference to material in Volume II, Chapter 37 will be made or implied.

This chapter, like several others in Volume III, is organized on the basis of technique rather than materials determined. The treatment will be to review briefly the applications of each instrumental area to paint analysis. Procedures will be given only for selected methods which are considered well established or important.

VISIBLE SPECTROMETRY

Almost any material which absorbs visible light or which can be reacted with a reagent to form a product which absorbs visible light theoretically can be determined quantitatively by means of visible spectrometry. The potential applications of visible spectrometry in the paint, varnish, and lacquer industry are many. The number of standard methods, however, is relatively small because of many factors. Adequate instrumentation within the industry is not widespread. Many of the potential determinations can be made more readily and/or more accurately by other means. Absorption of color in many cases is influenced rather drastically by pH and by other constituents which may be present. Time is often required for full color development, and the color is not always stable.

In ASTM Designation E131-63T may be found terms and symbols relating to absorption spectroscopy.[2] ASTM Designation E169-63 contains recommended practices for general techniques of ultraviolet quantitative analysis.[2] For the most part, these practices apply to visible spectrometry also. These two references together with the instruction manual for the specific instrument being used contain general instructions

[1] Lucchesi, C. A., Secrest, P. J., and Hirn, C. F., "Paint, Varnish, and Lacquer," in Vol. II, Part B, Standard Methods of Chemical Analysis, Sixth Ed., F. J. Welcher, Ed., D. Van Nostrand Co., Princeton, N. J., 1963.

[2] American Society for Testing and Materials, Philadelphia, Pa., ASTM Standards, 1965, Part 31, Metallography; Nondestructive Testing; Radioisotopes and Radiation Effects; Industrial Chemicals; Emission, Absorption, and Mass Spectroscopy.

for operating the instrument, making absorbance measurements, and making calculations. These general instructions will not be repeated in the specific methods.

There are many excellent references for colorimetric analysis. Some of the most complete references are those of Snell.[3,4,5] These include many methods potentially applicable to the paint industry. Many details relevant to the specific methods which follow may be found in these references.

IRON IN RAW MATERIALS AND PRODUCTS

In dilute acid solution iron(II) reacts with 1,10-phenanthroline to form a red-colored complex having maximum absorption near 508 mμ. The formation of this complex is the basis of many methods for the determination of iron in various products. In these methods iron is often extracted from the product by ashing the product and dissolving the iron compounds in the ash with acid. A reducing agent, usually hydroquinone or hydroxylamine, is added to convert iron(III) to iron(II). Some type of buffer solution is added to adjust the pH. Other chemicals may be added to precipitate interfering ions or inhibit other color formation. A solution of 1,10-phenanthroline, of course, is always added.

DETERMINATION OF IRON IN ROSIN

ASTM Designation D1064-58 for determining iron in rosin[6] is somewhat typical of the methods for determining iron by use of 1,10-phenanthroline. A summary of this method follows.

Reagents. Hydrochloric Acid (1:19).—Dilute 1 volume of A.C.S. grade hydrochloric acid (sp. gr. 1.18) with 19 volumes of water.

Standard Iron Solution (1 ml. = 0.1 mg. iron).—Dissolve 0.1000 g. of pure iron wire (99.85 percent iron) in 10 ml. of dilute sulfuric acid (1:9) and 3 ml. of concentrated nitric acid (sp. gr. 1.42). Dilute with water to 1 liter in a volumetric flask.

Standard Iron Solution (1 ml. = 0.01 mg. iron).—Pipet 100 ml. of standard iron solution (1 ml. = 0.1 mg. iron) into a 1-liter volumetric flask and dilute to mark with dilute hydrochloric acid (1:19).

Hydroxylamine Hydrochloride Solution.—Dissolve 10 g. of C.P. hydroxylamine hydrochloride in 190 ml. of water.

Hydroquinone Solution.—Dissolve 2.5 g. of hydroquinone, Reagent or Photographic Grade, in 100 ml. of hydrochloric acid (1:200). Keep in refrigerator at about 10°C. when not in use.

1,10-Phenanthroline Solution.—Dissolve 0.5 g. of 1,10-phenanthroline in 500 ml. of water.

Sodium Acetate Solution.—Dissolve 100 g. of A.C.S. grade sodium acetate ($NaC_2H_3O_2 \cdot 3H_2O$) in 400 ml. of water.

Calibration.—Pipet 0.5-, 1.0-, 2.0-, 3.0-, 4.0-, and 5.0-ml. aliquots of standard iron solution (1 ml. = 0.01 mg. iron) into 25-ml. volumetric flasks, and dilute to 10 ml. with dilute hydrochloric acid (1:19) measured with a Mohr-type pipet. Add 10 ml. of dilute hydrochloric acid to another 25-ml. volumetric flask and carry through as a reagent blank.

[3] Snell, F. D., and Snell, C. T., Colorimetric Methods of Analysis, Vols. I–IV, Third Edition, D. Van Nostrand, Princeton, N. J., 1948–1954.
[4] Snell, F. D., Snell, C. T., and Snell, C. A., Colorimetric Methods of Analysis, Vol. IIA, D. Van Nostrand, Princeton, N. J., 1959.
[5] Snell, F. D., Snell, C. T., and Snell, C. A., Colorimetric Methods of Analysis, Vol. IIIA, D. Van Nostrand, Princeton, N. J., 1961.
[6] American Society for Testing and Materials, Philadelphia, Pa., ASTM Standards, 1965, Part 20, Paint, Varnish, Lacquer, and Related Products.

Add 2 ml. of hydroxylamine hydrochloride or hydroquinone solution, 5 ml. of 1,10-phenanthroline solution, and 5 ml. of sodium acetate solution to contents of each flask, using volumetric pipets. Mix thoroughly after each addition.

Measure the absorbance of each iron solution at 503 mμ, using the solution from the flask not containing iron as a reagent blank.

Plot the absorbance of each solution against mg. of iron present.

Procedure.—Weigh 5.00 g. of the sample into a high-silica glass, silica, or porcelain dish. If the iron content is less than 5 p.p.m., use a weight of sample such that the solution on which the spectrophotometer reading is made will contain 0.005 to 0.050 mg. of iron.

Place the dish in an electrically heated muffle furnace and raise the temperature slowly until the sample is completely charred. Then raise the temperature to 500°C. and maintain at 500 to 550°C. until the sample is greyish white. This usually requires 4 to 6 hours, but no harm will be done if the sample is allowed to remain in the furnace overnight.

Remove the dish from the furnace, cool to room temperature, and add 5 ml. of dilute hydrochloric acid (1:1) in such a manner that any ash on the sides of the dish is washed to the bottom. Cover the dish with a watch glass and heat just to boiling.

Transfer the sample to a 50-ml. volumetric flask, using water to wash the last trace from the dish and watch glass. Dilute to the mark with water and mix thoroughly.

Pipet 10 ml. of the solution into a 25-ml. volumetric flask. Develop color in the solution and measure the absorbance as described under "Calibration."

Calculation.—Calculate the iron content of the sample in parts per million as follows:

$$\text{Iron, p.p.m.,} = \frac{M}{B} \times 1000$$

where: M = mg. of iron found; and
B = grams of sample represented in aliquot used.

DETERMINATION OF IRON IN FORMALDEHYDE

ASTM Designation D2087-62T for determining iron in formaldehyde is another method based on the red-colored complex formed between iron(II) and 1,10-phenanthroline. This method is similar to the one described above for the determination of iron in rosin. However, variations in the treatment of the sample and use of reagents exist. Below is a summary of the method.

Reagents. Ammonium Acetate Solution (100 g. per liter).—Dissolve 100 g. of ammonium acetate in 100 ml. of water. Add 200 ml. of acetic acid, dilute to 1 liter with water, and mix.

Ammonium Hydroxide (1:1).—Mix equal volumes of concentrated ammonium hydroxide (sp. gr. 0.90) and water.

Congo Red Paper.

Hydrochloric Acid (1:1).—Mix equal volumes of concentrated hydrochloric acid (sp. gr. 1.19) and water.

Hydroxylamine Hydrochloride Solution (100 g. per liter).—Dissolve 10 g. of hydroxylamine hydrochloride in water and dilute to 100 ml.

Iron, Standard Solution (1 ml. = 0.05 mg. iron).—Dissolve 0.3510 g. of ferrous ammonium sulfate ($FeSO_4 \cdot (NH_4)_2SO_4 \cdot 6H_2O$) in 50 ml. of water and 20 ml. of concentrated sulfuric acid (sp. gr. 1.84). Dilute with water to 1 liter in a volumetric flask and mix.

1,10-Phenanthroline Solution (1 g. per liter).—Dissolve 0.1 g. of 1,10-phenanthroline in 10 ml. of ethyl alcohol (Formula 30 of the U. S. Bureau of Internal Revenue is satisfactory) and dilute to 100 ml. with water.

Calibration.—Pipet 0.2, 0.5, 1.0, 2.0, 3.0, 4.0, and 5.0 ml. of the standard iron solution into 100-ml. volumetric flasks. Add the following reagents in order to each flask and to an empty 100-ml. volumetric flask, mixing after the addition of each: 1 ml. of the hydroxylamine solution, 5 ml. of 1,10-phenanthroline solution, enough ammonium hydroxide solution (1:1) to make the solution just alkaline to Congo red paper, and 5 ml. of ammonium acetate solution. Dilute to mark with water, and mix thoroughly.

Allow to stand for 5 minutes. Determine the absorbance of each iron containing solution at 510 mμ, using the solution not containing iron as a blank.

Prepare a calibration curve by plotting the absorbances of the solutions against the milligrams of iron per 100 ml. of solution.

Procedure.—Clean a high-silica glass evaporating dish as follows: Add 10 ml. of hydrochloric acid (1:1), cover with a watch glass, and digest on a steam bath for about 20 minutes. Then discard the acid solution, rinse the dish with water, and dry.

Weigh 50 g. of sample into the cleaned dish and evaporate to dryness on an electric hot plate in a hood. If any organic matter remains, ignite for 5 minutes over a high-temperature gas burner.

Add 10 ml. of hydrochloric acid (1:1), cover with a watch glass, and digest on the steam bath for 15 minutes. Transfer quantitatively to a 100-ml. volumetric flask.

Develop the color in the solution and measure the absorbance as explained under "*Calibration.*" From the calibration curve, read the milligrams of iron present.

Calculations.—Calculate the parts per million of iron as follows:

$$\text{Iron, p.p.m., } = \frac{W}{S} \times 1000$$

where: W = milligrams of iron found; and
S = grams of sample used.

INHIBITORS IN VINYL MONOMERS

Catechols in alkaline solution absorb oxygen with the formation of highly colored compounds. The colors are very sensitive in the low concentration range. ASTM Designation D2120-62T[6] was developed for the determination of 4-*tert.*-butyl catechol in styrene monomer in the range of 0 to 100 p.p.m. Any other compound known to produce color when contacted with aqueous sodium hydroxide solution will interfere, but may be compensated for by including it in the preparation of the standard. The 4-*tert.*-butyl catechol is extracted from the styrene monomer with aqueous sodium hydroxide. The aqueous layer, containing the 4-*tert.*-butyl catechol as the colored quinone, is separated and the color measured. Below is a summary of the ASTM method.

Reagents. **Sodium Hydroxide, Standard Solution (1.0 M).**—Prepare and standardize a 1.0 M solution of sodium hydroxide.

Styrene Monomer, Inhibitor Free.—Wash the styrene monomer three times with equal volumes of 1.0 M sodium hydroxide solution. Wash the monomer with water until the washings are neutral to litmus. Keep the monomer refrigerated at 0 to 5°C. to prevent polymerization.

4-*Tert.*-Butyl Catechol, Standard Solution (125 p.p.m.).—Dissolve 0.113 g. of 4-*tert.*-butyl catechol in 1000 ml. of inhibitor-free styrene monomer at 20°C. *CAUTION:* 4-*tert.*-butyl catechol, when molten or in a concentrated solution, is very corrosive to the skin. It is also a systemic poison when taken orally or absorbed in quantity through the skin. Styrene monomer itself is flammable and polymerizes exothermally in the presence of peroxides, mineral acids, and aluminum chloride.

Calibration.—Prepare standard solutions containing 5, 10, 15, . . . 100 p.p.m. 4-*tert.*-butyl catechol by adding 2, 4, 6, . . . 40 ml. of standard 4-*tert.*-butyl catechol solution, respectively, to 125-ml. separatory funnels and adding sufficient inhibitor-free styrene monomer to make a total of 50 ml. Add 50 ml. of inhibitor-free styrene monomer to another 125-ml. separatory funnel to serve as a blank.

Add 55 ml. of 1.0 M sodium hydroxide solution to each of the separatory funnels. Shake for 3 minutes, allow to settle, and draw off the lower aqueous layer through a filter paper. Measure the absorbance of each clear filtrate exactly 15 minutes after the addition of the sodium hydroxide solution, at a wavelength of 485 mμ, using 1.0 M sodium hydroxide solution as a reference standard.

Prepare a calibration curve by plotting the absorbances of the clear filtrates against the parts per million of 4-*tert.*-butyl catechol.

Procedure.—Pipet 50 ml. of the sample into a 125-ml. separatory funnel. Proceed as described under *"Calibration."* From the calibration curve, read the p.p.m. of 4-*tert.*-butyl catechol corresponding to the observed absorbance.

Methods have also been developed for determining hydroquinone, benzoquinone, and the monomethyl ether of hydroquinone in acrylic monomers.[7]

UREA CONTENT OF NITROGEN RESINS

In amino resins made with either urea or melamine, the amount of urea or melamine can be calculated from the amount of nitrogen present. In mixtures of urea and melamine resins, the amount of neither the urea nor the melamine can be calculated from the nitrogen content. ASTM Designation D1727-62 is applicable to the determination of urea in butylated urea-formaldehyde resin solutions and in mixtures of such urea and melamine resins.[6]

In this method the resin sample is hydrolyzed in methanolic hydrochloric acid, and the urea is then condensed with *p*-dimethylaminobenzaldehyde (Ehrlich's reagent) to develop a yellow color, the intensity being a measure of the urea content. The determination is sensitive to temperature, pH, and amount and type of solvent present. Volumes and time intervals, specified in the method must be followed carefully. Following is a summary of the ASTM method:

Reagents. **Ehrlich's Reagent.**—Weigh 2.00 g. of *p*-dimethylaminobenzaldehyde (Eastman No. 95) into a 150-ml. beaker. Add approximately 70 ml. of 95 percent ethanol and 10 ml. of hydrochloric acid (sp. gr. 1.19). Stir to dissolve. Filter, if necessary, into a 100-ml. volumetric flask and dilute to the mark with 95 percent ethanol.

Ethanol (95 percent).—Undenatured or conforming to formula No. 3A of the U. S. Bureau of Internal Revenue.

Methanolic Hydrochloric Acid.—Add approximately 200 ml. of absolute methanol to a 500-ml. volumetric flask. Add by pipet 50.0 ml. of hydrochloric acid (sp. gr. 1.19), dilute to the mark with methanol, and mix.

Urea, Standard Solution.—Weigh approximately 0.1 g. of urea to the nearest 0.1 mg. into a 150-ml. beaker. Dissolve in the methanolic hydrochloric acid and transfer to a 200-ml. volumetric flask. Dilute to the mark with the methanolic hydrochloric acid. Prepare this solution fresh daily.

Procedure.—Weigh to the nearest 0.1 mg., 0.10 ± 0.01 g. of urea resin solution (containing approximately 23 to 26 percent urea) into a 100-ml. round-bottom flask having a 24/40 ground-glass joint. For melamine resins expected to contain no urea, increase the sample weight to 0.30 ± 0.03 g. For mixed urea-melamine resins, adjust the sample weight proportionally.

---

[7] Johnson, D. P., and Critchfield, F. E., Anal. Chem., **33,** 910, 1961.

Add from a pipet, 10.0 ml. of methanol and 1 ml. of hydrochloric acid (sp. gr. 1.19). Add a pumice stone or similar boiling chip. Attach a 300-mm. water-cooled condenser with a 24/40 ground-glass joint. Reflux for 2 hours.

Cool, and wash down the condenser with a few milliliters of the methanolic hydrochloric acid. Transfer quantitatively to a 50-ml. volumetric flask, dilute to the mark with the methanolic hydrochloric acid, and mix.

From this point, the sample, a standard, and a blank must be carried along at each step. A double quantity of blank is required.

Arrange in order a 50-ml. flask for the blank, a 25-ml. flask for the standard, and a 25-ml. flask for the sample.

Pipet 20.0 ml. of the methanolic hydrochloric acid into the flask for the blank, 10.0 ml. of the standard urea solution into the flask for the standard, and 10.0 ml. of the hydrolyzed resin sample into the third flask.

Pipet 10.0 ml. of Ehrlich's reagent into the flask for the blank and 5.0 ml. into each of the other flasks. Dilute each flask to the mark with water. Mix and allow to stand for 1 hour. Filter the sample (but not the standard or blank) through a fine-texture, retentive paper. Minimize evaporation by using a receiver that fits snugly around the funnel stem and by covering the funnel with a watch glass. Discard the first 10 ml. of filtrate.

Determine the absorbance of the sample solution and absorbance of the standard solution at 420 mμ, using the blank solution in the reference beam and a slit width of 0.15 mm.

Calculations.—Calculate the percentage of urea as follows:

$$\text{Urea, percent} = \frac{A_s U \times 25}{A_u W}$$

where: A_s = absorbance of sample solution;
  A_u = absorbance of standard solution;
  U = grams of urea in 200 ml. of standard solution; and
  W = original weight of resin solution in grams.

TITANIUM IN PIGMENTS

In the usual chemical method of determining titanium dioxide in pigments by means of the Jones reductor, chromic oxide interferes. Some other pigments, if not dissolved in hydrochloric acid and removed, would interfere.

Colorimetric methods based on the yellow color formed when hydrogen peroxide is added to a titanium sulfate solution have been used to determine titanium. Below is a method used in the authors' laboratory for determining the titanium dioxide content of pigments. In this method, molybdenum in large amounts is the only known serious interference. This method is particularly useful if chromic oxide is present in the pigment. Time may be saved in cases where iron blue is present, particularly if chromates are also present.

Procedure.—Weigh to the nearest 0.1 mg. a sample of pigment which will contain approximately 100 mg. of titanium dioxide into a 250-ml. Pyrex beaker.

Break up any lumps with a stirring rod. Add 20 ml. of concentrated sulfuric acid and 10 g. of ammonium sulfate. Mix well. Cover with Pyrex watch glass and heat on a hot plate. Then heat at full heat on a Meker burner, with constant swirling to prevent bumping, for about 10 minutes. White fumes of sulfur trioxide should be visible outside the beaker. *Observe extreme caution*, as the acid is boiling at a temperature above 600°F.

Allow the solution to cool. Cautiously wash down the watch glass and the sides of the beaker with water. Dilute to about 100 ml. and filter while warm into a 250-ml. volumetric flask. Wash the residue with a little 5 percent sulfuric acid and then with hot water.

Add 10 ml. of concentrated sulfuric acid (some lost by fuming) so that the concentration of sulfuric acid after dilution to 250 ml. will be approximately 10 percent.

Dilute with water up to the neck of the flask but not as far as the volume mark on the neck. Swirl the flask gently to mix the acid-water solution. Cool to room temperature.

Dilute exactly to the 250-ml. volume mark, stopper, and mix thoroughly.

Carefully transfer a 10-ml. aliquot to each of two 100-ml. volumetric flasks.

Add 3 ml. of 3 percent hydrogen peroxide to one flask. Dilute each solution to 100 ml. with 10 percent sulfuric acid and mix thoroughly.

Determine the absorbance of the colored solution at 410 mμ, using the colorless solution as a blank.

Calculations.—Calculate the percentage of TiO$_2$ in the pigment as follows:

$$\% \text{TiO}_2 = \frac{(A - 0.0035) \times 2.5 \times 100}{9.14 \times \text{grams of sample}}$$

where: A = absorbance of colored solution;
      0.0035 = correction factor; and
      9.14 = absorptivity of TiO$_2$.

OTHER APPLICATIONS

Swann and Esposito have published a method for the colorimetric determination of bisphenol-type epoxy resins and their fatty acid esters.[8] It is stated that the method has been applied satisfactorily for measuring epoxy resins in blends with silicone resins, in their fatty acid and rosin acid esters, in alkyd resins, and unmodified as in the "two-package" systems.

A method for the direct colorimetric determination of nitrocellulose in lacquers has been developed by Swann.[9] The method is stated to be directly applicable to the measurement of nitrocellulose in lacquer vehicles without interference from solvents, placticizers, or coating resins, with the exception of some rosin products and phenol condensates. Swann has also developed a colorimetric method for the determination of other cellulosic resins in the absence of nitrocellulose.[10] The color development is influenced only by the cellulose content of the resins; consequently the method is not specific for a particular cellulosic resin, and all cellulose ethers and resins will not yield the same amount of color.

Phosphorus in crude, degummed, and refined vegetable oils may be determined by use of AOCS Official Method Ca 12-55.[11] The sample is ashed in the presence of zinc oxide followed by colorimetric measurement as molybdenum blue. This method is also applicable to some resins and other products.

It would be a mistake to terminate a discussion of visible spectrometry without mentioning reflectance spectrometry. Visible reflectance measurements are indeed probably the most important application of spectrometry in the paint industry. A detailed discussion of the tri-stimulus system for relating reflectance data to human observation of color is beyond the scope of this volume. However, it is appropriate to mention that reflectance spectrophotometry may many times be used for identification and

[8] Swann, M. H., and Esposito, G. G., Anal. Chem., **28,** 1006, 1956.
[9] Swann, M. H., Anal. Chem., **29,** 1504, 1957.
[10] Swann, M. H., Anal. Chem., **29,** 1361, 1957.
[11] American Oil Chemists' Society, Chicago, Ill., Official and Tentative Methods of the American Oil Chemists' Society, Second Edition, 1947–63.

estimation of pigmented compositions.[12] Reflectance spectrophotometry indeed appears to offer the only suitable means of analyzing the color pigmentation in light tints. An extensive library of reflectance data on full strength and quantitative letdowns of pure colors is required. Further, for effective qualitative and quantitative analysis, digitized reflectance curves and a computer program is required.

ULTRAVIOLET SPECTROMETRY

GENERAL

Both aromatic groups and conjugated unsaturated groups absorb ultraviolet light strongly. Since these groups are found in many paints, varnishes, and lacquers, ultraviolet spectrometry has many applications in the coatings industry. However, due to the somewhat limited distribution of satisfactory instruments in the industry, relatively few applications have resulted in standard methods. Standard methods include the determinations of various dibasic acids in alkyd resins, inhibitor contents of vinyl monomers, and composition of unsaturated fatty acids in oils.

Recommended practices for general techniques of ultraviolet quantitative analysis may be found in ASTM Designation E169-63.[13] These instructions plus those given in the instruction manual for the specific instrument being used should be sufficient for general practices and procedures in using the instruments, calibrating, making measurements, and making calculations. Such explanations will not be given in the methods which follow.

PHTHALIC ANHYDRIDE CONTENT OF ALKYD RESINS AND ESTERS CONTAINING OTHER DIBASIC ACIDS

In the usual gravimetric procedure for determining the phthalic anhydride of alkyd resins and esters by means of ASTM Designation D563-52,[14] the phthalic anhydride is separated as the dipotassium salt. Other dibasic acids, if present, also form salts and interfere with the determination. ASTM Designation D1307-56[14] is applicable for the quantitative determination of phthalic anhydride in alkyd resins and esters containing other dibasic acids such as maleic, fumaric, adipic, and sebacic. An abstract of this method is given below.

Calibration of Spectrophotometer.—Weigh to the nearest 0.1 mg. about 0.3 g. of potassium acid phthalate (National Bureau of Standards, standard sample 84D suggested) into a calibrated 1-liter volumetric flask. Dissolve in water, pipet in 10 ml. of hydrochloric acid (sp. gr. 1.19), dilute to the mark with water, and mix. Pipet 50 ml. of this solution into a 250-ml. volumetric flask, dilute to the mark with 0.1 M hydrochloric acid, and mix. Measure the absorbance at 276 mμ, using matched 1-cm. silica or quartz cells and 0.1 M hydrochloric acid as a blank. Repeat the measurement with the blank in the cell position formerly used for the standard, and *vice versa*. Average the measurements to obtain the absorbance, A; record the slit width used. Calculate the absorptivity of phthalic acid, a_p, as follows:

$$a_p = \frac{A}{C_p}$$

[12] Duncan, D. R., J. Oil Colour Chem. Assoc., **45**, 300, 1962.
[13] American Society for Testing and Materials, Philadelphia, Pa., ASTM Standards, 1965, Part 31, Metallography; Nondestructive Testing; Radioisotopes and Radiation Effects; Industrial Chemicals; Emission, Absorption, and Mass Spectroscopy.
[14] American Society for Testing and Materials, Philadelphia, Pa., ASTM Standards, 1965, Part 20, Paint, Varnish, Lacquer, and Related Products.

where: C_p = concentration, expressed as g. per liter, of phthalic acid (not salt) present in the final diluted solution measured.

Repeat the entire calibration procedure on two additional prepared solutions of the potassium acid phthalate standard. Average the three values of a_p, and use the average value in carrying out analyses. The absorptivity of phthalic acid should be approximately 7.80.

Procedure A (***Both Maleic and Fumaric Acids Absent***).—Weigh to the nearest 0.1 mg. a sample sufficient to yield 0.8 to 1.2 g. of potassium alcohol phthalate into a 500-ml. Erlenmeyer flask, with a ground-glass joint. Add 150 ml. of benzene, warming slightly on a steam bath if necessary, to effect solution. Add 60 ml. of anhydrous ethyl alcoholic potassium hydroxide solution containing 66 g. of potassium hydroxide per liter of alcohol. Attach an air condenser to the flask and place flask in a water bath to a depth about equal to that of the contents of the flask. Warm the bath, maintaining a temperature of 40°C. for 1 hour, and then gradually raise the temperature until the alcoholic solution boils gently. Reflux for 1.5 hours.

Remove the flask from the bath and wash down the inside of the condenser with a few milliliters of a solution consisting of one volume of absolute ethyl alcohol and three volumes of benzene. Remove the condenser, cap the flask, and cool.

When cool, filter with vacuum immediately and as rapidly as possible through a tared fritted-glass crucible, using the alcohol-benzene solution for transferring the precipitate and washing the reaction flask. Wash the precipitate with successive portions of the alcohol-benzene solution until a few milliliters of the washings collected in a second suction flask are no longer alkaline to phenolphthalein. Do not allow air to be drawn through the crystals as they are hygroscopic. Finally pour 25 ml. of ethyl ether into the crucible and draw through the precipitate with the aid of suction.

Wipe the outer surface of the crucible with a clean cloth and place in a gravity convection oven at 60°C. for 1 hour. Cool and weigh (Note 1).

Extract the precipitate by passing about 200 ml. of water through the crucible with the aid of suction. To the aqueous extract in the suction flask, add 20 ml. of hydrochloric acid (sp. gr. 1.19). If sebacic or other slightly soluble acidic material is present, a precipitate or cloudiness may appear. If the acidified solution is perfectly clear, transfer with rinsing to a 2-liter volumetric flask, dilute to the mark with water, and mix. If, however, even a slight cloudiness is evident, filter the entire solution (before dilution) with suction through a fine filter paper on a Büchner funnel, wash the residue with 100 ml. of water, transfer the combined filtrate and washings to a 2-liter volumetric flask, dilute to the mark with water, and mix. Pipet 50 ml. of solution from the 2-liter flask into a 250-ml. volumetric flask, dilute to the mark with 0.1 M hydrochloric acid, and mix. Using a spectrophotometer slit-width identical with that used in the calibration procedure, measure the absorbance at 276 mμ against a blank of 0.1 M hydrochloric acid, following the cell-switching practice used in calibrating.

Procedure B (***Maleic or Fumaric Acid, or Both, Present***).—If maleic or fumaric acid is known to be present (Note 2) and it is desired to correct the phthalic acid value for either of these acids, proceed as follows:

(a) Measure the absorbance, A, of a pure sample of the interfering acid at a suitable concentration, C_i, in 0.1 M hydrochloric acid at 276 mμ. Calculate the absorptivity of the acid as follows:

$$a_i = \frac{A}{C_i}$$

(b) Carry out the analysis exactly as described in Procedure A except that the weight of the dried precipitate shall be recorded as B in "Calculations."

Calculations.—For samples tested in accordance with Procedure A, calculate the phthalic acid concentration, C_p, in grams per liter of the final diluted solution as follows:

$$C_p = \frac{A_1}{a_p}$$

where: A_1 = measured absorbance of the final diluted solution; and
$\quad\quad\; a_p$ = absorptivity value for pure phthalic acid.

For samples tested in accordance with Procedure B, calculate the phthalic acid concentration, C_p, of the final diluted solution from the following pair of simultaneous equations:

$$A_2 = a_p C_p + a_i C_i$$
$$B/2f = F_p C_p + F_i C_i$$

where:

$\quad\quad A_2$ = measured absorbance of the final diluted solution;
$\quad\quad a_p$ = absorptivity value for pure phthalic acid;
$\quad\quad a_i$ = absorptivity of the interfering acid;
$\quad\quad C_1$ = concentration of interfering acid in solution measured;
$\quad\quad B$ = grams of dried precipitate;
$\quad\quad f$ = dilution factor used in the final dilution (Note 3); and
F_p and F_i = factors for conversion of phthalic acid and the interfering acid respectively to their potassium salts equivalents as they occur in the precipitate. (For phthalic acid, use $F_p = 1.735$; for maleic or fumaric acid, use $F_i = 1.654$.)

Calculate the percentage of phthalic anhydride in the sample from the C_p value obtained from solving the simultaneous equations, as follows:

$$\text{Phthalic Anhydride, \%,} = \frac{89.16 \times C_p \times 2f}{W}$$

where: f = dilution factor (Note 3); and
$\quad\quad\; W$ = grams of sample used.

Notes.—1. The precipitate is the alcoholate $C_6H_4(COOK)_2 \cdot C_2H_5OH$, and the alcohol of crystallization will be slowly driven off on prolonged heating. It is safe, however, to dry the alcoholate at temperatures up to 60°C. for as long as 1 hour.

2. Work in the authors' laboratory and other published work indicates that maleic and fumaric esters form ethoxysuccinate upon alcoholic saponification.[15,16] If this is true, it is unlikely that the corrections for fumaric or maleic acid obtained by use of this procedure will be exactly correct. However, the absorption of phthalic acid at 276 mμ is high relative to that of any of the other compounds, and the error will be small unless large amounts of fumaric or maleic acid are present.

3. The value of 2 in the equation corrects for 2-liter volume of initial extract.

PHTHALIC ACID ISOMERS AND BENZOIC ACID IN ALKYD RESINS AND ESTERS

Isophthalic acid is sometimes used as a partial or complete replacement for phthalic anhydride in alkyd resins. Isophthalic acid and/or terephthalic acids may be used with phthalic anhydride in other esters. In the usual gravimetric procedure for the determination of phthalic anhydride, ASTM Designation D563-52,[14] these acids interfere. Benzoic acid is used as a partial replacement for fatty acids in many oil modified alkyd

---

[15] Tessari, D. J., unpublished work.
[16] Hanson, N. W., J. Oil and Colour Chemists' Assoc., **41**, 203, 1958.

resins. In the analysis of alkyd resins, the benzoic acid is separated usually with the fatty acids. An ultraviolet method, ASTM Designation D1651-61,[14] is applicable for the quantitative determination of any of the three phthalic acid isomers or benzoic acid if present in excess of one percent in a resin. Following is a summary of this method.

Procedure A (Phthalic Acid Isomers).—Weigh to the nearest 0.1 mg. about 2 to 3 g. of resin or ester solution estimated to contain 0.1 to 0.5 g. of total phthalic acid into a 500-ml. Erlenmeyer flask with a ground-glass joint. Add 10 ml. of benzene, warming if necessary, to effect solution. Add 100 ml. of ethyl alcoholic potassium hydroxide solution containing 33 g. of potassium hydroxide per liter of alcohol. Stopper the flask with a cork and warm in an oven or bath at 45°C. for at least 4 hours. Attach an air condenser and reflux in a water bath for 1 hour. Add 150 ml. of benzene, stopper lightly, and cool in running water.

Filter through a dry Gooch or coarse glass crucible containing asbestos, using benzene for transferring and washing the precipitated salts. Collect the filtrate in a clean suction flask and retain if analysis for benzoic acid is to be made. Give the Erlenmeyer flask and crucible a final wash with ethyl ether.

Dry both Erlenmeyer flask and crucible at 105°C. Dissolve the dried salts from the flask and crucible in water and dilute to 200 ml. in a volumetric flask.

Withdraw by pipet an aliquot (not exceeding 10 ml.) that represents about 5 mg. of phthalic acid, and dilute with 0.1 M hydrochloric acid methanol-water (1:1) solution to 100 ml.

Determine the absorbance of the sample solution at 275, 281, and 287 mμ, using a mechanical slit width of 0.5 mm. and using 0.1 M hydrochloric acid methanol-water (1:1) solution as a blank.

Calculations.—Calculate the concentration of each acid as follows:

Set I:

$$c_{ortho} = \left(+0.3878 \times \frac{A_{275}}{b}\right) - \left(0.1799 \times \frac{A_{281}}{b}\right) - \left(0.1586 \times \frac{A_{287}}{b}\right)$$

$$c_{iso} = \left(-0.9201 \times \frac{A_{275}}{b}\right) + \left(1.778 \times \frac{A_{281}}{b}\right) - \left(0.3015 \times \frac{A_{287}}{b}\right)$$

$$c_{tere} = \left(+0.2272 \times \frac{A_{275}}{b}\right) - \left(0.4219 \times \frac{A_{281}}{b}\right) + \left(0.2927 \times \frac{A_{287}}{b}\right)$$

where: c = concentration in grams per liter;
A = absorbance; and
b = cell length in centimeters.

If the calculations from Set I indicate the presence of only one of the phthalic acids, recalculate as indicated in Set III.

If the above calculations indicate the presence of only two of the phthalic acids, recalculate as indicated below to improve the accuracy of the determination.

Set II:

(1) If only *ortho-* and *iso*phthalic acids are present:

$$c_{ortho} = \left(+0.5109 \times \frac{A_{275}}{b}\right) - \left(0.4085 \times \frac{A_{281}}{b}\right)$$

$$c_{iso} = \left(-0.6861 \times \frac{A_{275}}{b}\right) + \left(0.7435 \times \frac{A_{281}}{b}\right)$$

(2) If only *ortho*- and *tere*phthalic acids are present:

$$c_{ortho} = \left(+0.2473 \times \frac{A_{275}}{b}\right) - \left(0.2047 \times \frac{A_{287}}{b}\right)$$

$$c_{tere} = \left(-0.1023 \times \frac{A_{275}}{b}\right) + \left(0.1848 \times \frac{A_{287}}{b}\right)$$

(3) If only *iso*- and *tere*phthalic acids are present:

$$c_{iso} = \left(+0.7511 \times \frac{A_{281}}{b}\right) - \left(0.6777 \times \frac{A_{287}}{b}\right)$$

$$c_{tere} = \left(-0.3165 \times \frac{A_{281}}{b}\right) + \left(0.3856 \times \frac{A_{287}}{b}\right)$$

Set III:

(1) If only *ortho*phthalic acid is present:

$$c_{ortho} = \frac{A_{275}}{7.465 \times b}$$

(2) If only *iso*phthalic acid is present:

$$c_{iso} = \frac{A_{281}}{5.129 \times b}$$

(3) If only *tere*phthalic acid is present:

$$c_{tere} = \frac{A_{287}}{9.990 \times b}$$

Calculate the percentage of phthalic acid from the concentrations obtained, using Sets I, II, or III, as follows:

$$\text{Phthalic acid, \%,} = \frac{20c}{BV} \times 100$$

where: c = concentration, expressed in grams per liter, of acid (*ortho*, *iso*, and/or *tere*);
V = milliliters of aliquot; and
B = grams of sample used.

Procedure B (Benzoic Acid).—Transfer the filtrate from the separation of phthalic acid salts (Procedure A above) to a large beaker and evaporate the solvents on a water bath, adding water periodically to replace the solvents.

Transfer to a 500-ml. separatory funnel and dilute to 300 ml. with water. Neutralize with hydrochloric acid (sp. gr. 1.19) and add a 5 ml. excess. Cool to room temperature.

Extract the fatty acids with three 50-ml. portions of carbon tetrachloride, making a fourth extract if the third is colored. Combine the solvent extracts and transfer the water layer to a 2-liter volumetric flask.

Wash the carbon tetrachloride extractions in 50-ml. portions through three successive separatory funnels, each containing 300 ml. of water. Combine the 900 ml. of wash water with the first aqueous layer in the 2-liter flask and dilute to the mark. The carbon tetrachloride may be discarded unless it is desired to measure the fatty acids.

Fill a 500-ml. separatory funnel with sample from the 2-liter flask and allow to stand. If any further separation occurs, draw off the lower layer together with some of the

aqueous solution and discard. Filter about 200 ml. of the remaining solution through a
rapid, hardened filter paper and discard the first 50 ml. From the remaining filtered
solution, draw a 100-ml. aliquot by pipet and transfer to a 400-ml. beaker. Neutralize
with a solution containing 13.2 g. of potassium hydroxide in 100 ml. of water and add
an excess of 20 drops. Insert a glass stirring rod and evaporate the sample to dryness in a
bath (oil bath at 110°C. is satisfactory). Finally dry the beaker in an oven at 105°C. for
15 minutes.

Dissolve the residue in 25 ml. of water, cool, neutralize with hydrochloric acid (1:1)
and add 1 ml. of hydrochloric acid (sp. gr. 1.19) in excess. Transfer to a 100-ml. volumetric flask and add 50 ml. of methyl alcohol. Continue rinsing the beaker with water,
adding to the flask until diluted to the mark.

Mix well and determine the absorbance at 273 mμ, with a slit width of 0.6 mm.,
using a 0.1 M hydrochloric acid methanol-water (1:1) as a blank.

Calculations.—Calculate the concentration of benzoic acid in grams per liter, C, as
follows:

$$c = (A/7.72) - (B \times N \times 0.0097)$$

where: A = absorbance at 273 mμ;
B = grams of sample used; and
N = nonvolatile fraction of sample.

Calculate the percentage of benzoic acid as follows:

$$\text{Benzoic acid, } \%, = \frac{c \times 200(\text{based on 100-ml. aliquot})}{B}$$

FATTY ACIDS IN OILS AND OIL MODIFIED ALKYD RESINS

Conjugated double bonds absorb ultraviolet light strongly. The absorption maximum
depends upon the number of double bonds conjugated, two conjugated bonds giving
an absorption maximum at about 233 mμ, three bonds at about 268 mμ, and four bonds
at about 315 mμ. The absorption of conjugated double bonds and the dependence of
absorption maximum upon the number of double bonds conjugated have been the basis
of many methods for determining the compositions of fatty acids in various types of
drying oils and oil modified alkyd resins. Many of the methods have been in use for long
periods of time. The relatively recent and rapid development of gas chromatography has
provided methods by which most of the fatty acids can be more readily identified and
quantitatively determined. However, many of the ultraviolet methods are still used, and
summaries of some of these methods will be given.

SPECTROPHOTOMETRIC DIENE VALUE OF DEHYDRATED CASTOR OIL AND ITS DERIVATIVES

ASTM Designation D1358-58[14] is applicable to the determination of the spectrophotometric diene value as a measure of the content of conjugated dienoic acids in
dehydrated castor oil and its derivatives. Due to the high linoleic acid content in dehydrated castor oil and its derivatives, the absolute conjugated dienoic acid content
cannot be determined by this method. However, the value obtained is useful in evaluating dehydrated castor oil and is part of the ASTM specification for dehydrated castor
acids. A summary of the ASTM procedure follows.

Procedure.—Weigh to the nearest 0.1 mg. 90 to 130 mg. of the sample into a 100-ml.
volumetric flask. Add about 75 ml. of Spectroscopic Grade isooctane.

Rotate the flask and warm the contents, if necessary, to completely dissolve the sample.

Cool to room temperature, and allow to stand at least 15 minutes to attain temperature equilibrium. Dilute to volume with the Spectroscopic Grade isooctane and mix thoroughly.

Make necessary dilutions with the isooctane, in no greater than ten-fold steps, to give a final concentration of about 0.01 g. of the sample per liter.

Measure the absorbance of the solution at 233 mμ, using a matched cell containing the isooctane.

Calculation.—Calculate the percentage of conjugated dienoic acids as follows:

$$C = 0.84 \times \left(\frac{A}{bc} - a\right)$$

where: C = percentage of the conjugated dienoic acid;
  a = 0.07 for esters, = 0.03 for acid;
  A = observed absorbance at 233 mμ;
  b = cell length in centimeters; and
  c = grams of sample per liter of the solution being used for the absorption measurement.

POLYUNSATURATED ACIDS

Two conjugated double bonds exhibit an absorption maximum at 233 mμ, three at 268 mμ, four at 315 mμ, and five at 346 mμ. Acids containing these groups are present in drying oils and in alkyd resins. Nonconjugated polyunsaturated acids may be isomerized to the corresponding conjugated acids by alkali treatment. Procedures applicable to the determination of polyunsaturated acids from dienoic through pentaenoic in fatty acids containing only the natural or *cis*-isomers have been developed. The procedures are not generally applicable to fatty acids containing *trans*-unsaturated fatty acids. Details for these procedures may be found in AOCS Tentative Method Cd 7-48.[17] Generally gas chromatographic analyses may be made more readily than the ultraviolet analyses. Also, the gas chromatographic procedures have much broader application since saturated and *trans*-unsaturated acids may be determined.

p-TERT.-BUTYLBENZOIC ACID

p-tert.-Butylbenzoic acid is used in alkyd resins. In the usual analysis of alkyd resins, *p-tert.*-butylbenzoic acid is separated along with the fatty acids. Separation of *p-tert.*-butylbenzoic acid from fatty acids is difficult. Secrest and Kosciesza have developed an ultraviolet method for the determination of *p-tert.*-butylbenzoic acid in coconut oil-type alkyd resins.[18] The method is applicable only to alkyd resins containing fatty acids which are only slightly unsaturated. However, *p-tert.*-butylbenzoic acid is seldom used with highly unsaturated fatty acids. The method is based on the difference in absorbance exhibited by *p-tert.*-butylbenzoic acid at 282.5 and 300.0 mμ. The difference in absorbance exhibited by the coconut oil-type fatty acids at these two wavelengths is very small. Therefore, the amount of *p-tert.*-butylbenzoic acid in mixtures of the acids may be determined without any separation.

MELAMINE CONTENT OF NITROGEN RESINS

ASTM Designation D1597-60 is applicable to the determination of melamine in butylated or caprylated melamine-formaldehyde resins and in mixtures of such resins

---

[17] American Oil Chemists' Society, Chicago, Ill., Official and Tentative Methods of the American Oil Chemists' Society, Second Edition, 1947–63.
[18] Secrest, P. J., and Kosciesza, B., Anal. Chem., **31**, 1402, 1959.

and urea resins.[14] The method is not applicable to analogous resins made from substituted melamine derivatives. The sample is hydrolyzed by refluxing with dilute hydrochloric acid. The melamine concentration is determined by measuring the absorbance at 237 $m\mu$ and correcting for background absorption at 255 $m\mu$ by an empirically determined factor. Below is a summary of the ASTM method.

Calibration.—Transfer about 0.20 g. of melamine (recrystallized twice from water and dried), weighed to the nearest 0.1 mg., to a 1000-ml. volumetric flask. Dissolve in hydrochloric acid (1 volume of hydrochloric acid, sp. gr. 1.19, and 99 volumes of water), dilute to the mark with the acid, and mix.

Introduce a 3.0-ml. aliquot of the prepared melamine solution (accurately measured from a microburet) into a 100-ml. volumetric flask. Dilute to the mark with the dilute hydrochloric acid (1:99) and mix. Measure the absorbance, A, of the solution at 237 $m\mu$ and at 255 $m\mu$, using matched silica cells, a slit width of 0.8 mm., and the dilute hydrochloric acid (1:99) as a blank. Calculate the absorptivity of melamine, a_{237}, as follows:

$$a_{237} = \frac{A}{bc}$$

where: b = cell light path in cm.; and

$\quad c$ = concentration, in grams per 1000 ml., of melamine in the final solution measured.

Prepare a second solution of the melamine standard and repeat the calibration procedure. Average the values obtained.

If the absorptivity at 237 $m\mu$ falls within the range of 79.1 to 81.1 and the absorbance at 255 $m\mu$ does not exceed 0.020 units, the spectrophotometer is performing properly and the recommended value of 80.1 can be used in the resin analysis.

Procedure.—Weigh to the nearest 0.1 mg. approximately 0.15 g. (approximately 0.10 g. if the resin contains more than 20 percent of melamine) into a 250-ml. Erlenmeyer flask. Pipet exactly 10 ml. of ethanol into the flask and dissolve the sample by gently swirling the contents.

Add 100 ml. of hydrochloric acid (1 ml. hydrochloric acid, sp. gr. 1.19, and 99 ml. of water), attach a water-cooled reflux condenser, and reflux for 1 hour. Cool. Rinse down the condenser with 25 to 30 ml. of the dilute hydrochloric acid (1:99).

Filter the solution through a rapid, ashless paper into a 200-ml. volumetric flask. Rinse the flask and wash the filter paper with hydrochloric acid (1:99), running the washings into the volumetric flask. Dilute to volume with hydrochloric acid (1:99).

Select and dilute further suitable aliquots so that the absorbance measurements at 255 and 237 $m\mu$ will be in the range from 0.3 to 0.5 units. See following table:

Anticipated Melamine Content, percent	Sample Weight g.	Dilution of Initial 200-ml. Solution	
		255 $m\mu$	237 $m\mu$
5	0.15	None	5 ml. to 50 ml.
10	0.15	None	5 ml. to 100 ml.
20	0.15	1:1	5 ml. to 200 ml.
30	0.10	1:1	5 ml. to 200 ml.
40	0.10	1:2	5 ml. to 250 ml.

Scan or measure the absorbance in the spectral region from 260 to below 230 $m\mu$, using a slit width of 0.80 mm. and dilute hydrochloric acid (1:99) as a blank. Take the absorbance readings at 255 mμ and 237 mμ. The absorbance readings should be taken within 2 hours of the completion of the hydrolysis step.

Calculations.—Calculate the percentage of melamine in the resin as follows:

$$\text{Melamine, } \% = \frac{(f_1 A_{237} - 3 f_2 A_{255})}{5 a_{237} b W} \times 100$$

where: f_1 = dilution factor for 237 mμ reading;
f_2 = dilution factor for 255 mμ reading;
A_{237} = absorbance at 237 mμ;
A_{255} = absorbance at 255 mμ;
a_{237} = absorptivity of melamine at 237 mμ;
b = cell light path in cm.; and
W = grams of sample used.

OTHER APPLICATIONS[19]

Ultraviolet spectrometry is very useful for the quantitative analysis of a solution when the solution has only a few known components, and when one or more of the components exhibits ultraviolet absorption. Ultraviolet spectrometry has many applications then in the quality control of highly purified products which are liquid or can be dissolved. It is also useful in determining the amounts of ultraviolet absorbing impurities or additives in nonabsorbing, relatively pure products.

INHIBITORS IN VINYL MONOMERS

Many vinyl type monomers used in making polymers, such as ethyl acrylate, methyl methacrylate, and vinyl acetate have little or no absorption in certain portions of the ultraviolet region. These vinyl monomers are reactive or unstable. Many of the inhibitors, such as hydroquinone and the methyl ether of hydroquinone added to prevent polymerization of the monomers, exhibit very high ultraviolet absorption in the region where the monomers have little or no absorption. Ultraviolet methods are used for determining the contents of such inhibitors in vinyl monomers. In most of these methods a calibration curve is prepared by adding known amounts of the inhibitor to portions of the inhibitor free monomer and then measuring the absorbance of these solutions at a wavelength where the inhibitor exhibits high absorption. The inhibitor free monomer is used as a blank. In some cases the calibration solutions and the blank solution are further diluted with a nonabsorbing solvent. The absorbance of the sample solution is determined by the same procedure used for the calibration of solutions. The amount of inhibitor is then read from the calibration curve. Ultraviolet methods for determining inhibitors in vinyl monomers include determinations of methyl ether of hydroquinone in acrylic monomers, hydroquinone in vinyl acetate, diphenylamine in vinyl acetate, and hydroquinone in acrylic monomers.

SPECIFICATIONS AND QUALITY CONTROL

Most aromatic compounds exhibit two absorption maxima in the ultraviolet region. Absorption minima, of course, fall on each side of each absorption maximum. The absorptivities of a pure compound at these absorption maxima and minima can serve as a basis for quality control and as a specification characteristic. Three absorptivities, one for an absorption maximum and two for the absorption minima on each side of the absorption maximum are usually sufficient. The addition of almost any material to the compound will change one or more of the measured absorptivities. The same technique can be used for the determination of an aromatic impurity in a nonabsorbing compound

[19] Secrest, P. J., Sherwin-Williams Co., private communication.

or of an aromatic impurity which can be extracted into a nonabsorbing solvent. Many nonaromatic compounds also exhibit absorption spectra which can be utilized in much the same manner as the spectra of aromatic compounds.

INFRARED SPECTROMETRY

Throughout Chapter 37 in Volume II, rather extensive use of infrared spectrometry is outlined and recommended for the identification of polymers, resins, oils, plasticizers, solvents, additives, organic pigments, and even inorganic pigments. Certainly for all, except probably the solvents, oils, and pigments, infrared spectrometry as a single technique will remain unsurpassed for some time as "the technique" for qualitative identification of such paint materials. At the time of writing Volume II, 1962, the authors hesitated to represent the infrared procedures as standard. This hesitation will not be necessary much longer as certain qualitative infrared procedures are being seriously considered for designation as "standard" by committees in the American Society for Testing and Materials, Committee D-1 on Paint, Varnish, and Lacquer, included. Infrared spectra also continue to gain legal recognition in the area of chemical patents.

Since the coverage of the applications of infrared spectrometry for qualitative analysis of paint, varnish, and lacquer has been so extensive in Volume II, it will be the objective of the authors only to refer the reader to the previous volume, and to add important new references, to discuss the value of a careful study of the spectra of families of related compounds, to make comments on recent developments in infrared sampling techniques, and finally to outline a few infrared procedures for the quantitative determination of specific chemical groups or compounds in coating formulations.

QUALITATIVE ANALYSIS
RECENT REFERENCES AND COMPILATIONS

For the practicing paint analytical chemist, the 160 page monograph on infrared spectroscopy, prepared in 1960 by the Technical Committee for the Chicago Society for Paint Technology, has apparently found widespread usefulness, and is generally recommended.[20] Since the preparation of that monograph and publication of Volume II of Standard Methods of Chemical Analysis, the Dow Chemical Co. has made available quality reference spectra of 125 plastics and resins[21] and reference spectra of 189 plasticizers and other additives.[22] In addition to the growing commercial or sponsored collections of reference spectra mentioned previously,[23] it may be of interest to note that a major collection of infrared reference spectra is now also being prepared in Japan.[24] Peek-A-Boo data retrieval for infrared spectroscopy has been introduced.[25] Computer programs for searching the infrared literature have also been prepared,[26,27,28] and new

[20] Brown, W. H., Ansel, R. E., Lucchesi, C. A., and McGinness, J. D., Offic. Dig. Federation Soc. Paint Technol., **33**, Part II, March, 1961.

[21] Nyquist, R. A., Infrared Spectra of Plastics and Resins, The Dow Chemical Co., Midland, Michigan, 1960.

[22] DuVall, R. B., Infrared Spectra of Plasticizers and Other Additives, The Dow Chemical Co., Midland, Michigan, 1962.

[23] Brown, W. H., Ansel, R. E., Lucchesi, C. A., and McGinness, J. D., Offic. Dig. Federation Soc. Paint Technol., **33**, Part II, 39, March, 1961.

[24] Infrared Data Committee of Japan.

[25] Schlichter, N. E., and Wallace, E., Appl. Spectroscopy, **17**, 98, 1963.

[26] Sadtler, P., Pittsburgh Conference on Analytical Chemistry and Applied Spectroscopy, March 2–6, 1964, Paper No. 221.

[27] Thomas, D., "Infrared Spectral Data Retrieval by Digital Techniques," 15th Summer Symposium on Analytical Chemistry, Analytical Div., ACS, U. of Maryland, 1962.

[28] Savitzky, A., and Roche, J. M., Pittsburgh Conference on Analytical Chemistry and Applied Spectroscopy, March 2–6, 1964, Paper No. 219.

detailed compilations of group frequency and structure correlations have been made available.[29]

STUDY OF SPECTRA OF FAMILIES OF RELATED COMPOUNDS

In spite of the apparent wealth of infrared data available, there is still plenty of correlation and interpretive work to be done, if not new correlations, certainly revaluation of some of the older ones. An example of the result of a study and revaluation of the spectra of a family of compounds is represented by the recent work of one of the authors of this chapter. Secrest restudied the spectra of a number of phenolic resins and discovered that some earlier assignments in the literature for the important methylol and ether groups were in error.[30] A summary of his subsequent assignments for some of the commoner

TABLE 54-1. INTERPRETATION OF PHENOLIC RESIN SPECTRA[31]

Region of Spectrum, μ	Assignments
2.75–3.3	Phenolic and aliphatic OH groups
About 3.3	Aromatic C—H
3.4–3.5	Aliphatic C—H
5–6	Series of weak bands characteristic of substitution type of ring. Detectable only with p-phenylphenol resins.
6–7	Four bands due to semi-unsaturated carbon-carbon bonds of benzene ring. Two of these bands appear near 6.2 microns—only one band apparent in many resins due to overlapping of bands. 1,4-, 1,2- and 1,2,4-substituted rings absorb at 6.65 microns while 1,2,3,5- and most 1,2,3-substituted rings absorb at 6.75 microns. Fourth band, near 6.9 microns, may be obscured by CH_2 band.
7–7.8	Aliphatic and aromatic hydrocarbon groups.
7.8–8.8	Phenolic hydroxyl groups.
8.8–9.1	Sharp, relatively strong band believed to be due to phenolic hydroxyl group.
9.4	Ether groups
10	Aliphatic hydroxyl groups
11–15	Out-of-plane CH bending of substituted aromatics
11.2–11.7	1,2,3,5-substituted rings.
12.2	Composite of many bands: 1,2,4-substituted rings absorb at 12.3 microns, 1,2,3-substituted rings at 11.9–12.2 microns, 1,4-substituted rings at 12.0–12.2 microns, and 1,2–substituted rings at 11.9–12.4 microns.
12.8	1,2,4-substituted rings
13.3	1,2,3- and 1,2-substituted rings
14.4	1-substituted ring

coating type phenolic resins is reproduced in Table 54-1. Again, this is an example of the value of a systematic and careful review of a given class of materials. Sometimes a

[29] Szymanski, H. A., Infrared Band Handbook, Plenum Press, New York, 1965.
[30] Secrest, P. J., Offic. Dig. of Soc. Paint Technol., **37**, 187, 1965.
[31] Secrest, P. J., Offic. Dig. Federation of Paint Technol., **37**, 201, 1965. Copyright 1965 by the Federation of Societies for Paint Technology and reprinted with permission of copyright owners.

spectrum viewed alone has little meaning. However, when all the bands or inflections in the spectral curves of a family of materials are carefully considered, new and sometimes significant correlations are discovered.

SAMPLING BY INTERNAL REFLECTANCE

Again, since publication of the previously mentioned monograph and Chapter 37 of Volume II, a somewhat revolutionary method for determining the infrared spectra of solid materials, particularly interesting for paint films, has been developed. The sampling technique is variably called attenuated total reflectance, frustrated multiple internal reflectance, or simply multiple internal reflection. It is based upon the variations in internal reflection characteristics of a solid optical component as it is placed against various solid samples. The basic principle of the phenomenon and its significance for sampling were first reported in the United States by Harrick[32] and in Europe by Fahrenfort.[33]

Internal reflection attachments are now available from most infrared instrument and accessory makers. One accessory maker has even gone into building a special infrared spectrophotometer for internal reflectance sampling which he claims optimizes the advantages of this new reflectance method. Single pass reflectance units are good for most solids with a few square millimeters of "infrared" smooth surface. Multiple pass units are found necessary for weakly absorbing solids or solids with irregular surfaces. With reflectance units with a large number of effective passes, the infrared spectra of powders, such as pigments, may be determined. With such units the composition of adsorbed material on catalysts has been studied.[34] In the same manner it would appear that organic surface treatments of pigments could be determined by infrared reflectance techniques. One author has suggested that one might be able to obtain infrared spectra of only the outermost few molecular layers of material on the surface of a paint film by choosing an internal reflectance optical component with a refractive index which will properly limit penetration of the reflected infrared beam.[35]

The fact that the penetration of the infrared beam into a surface is dependent only upon the refractive index and optical arrangement of the particular reflectance unit, is of significant importance for sampling paints and vehicles. It means that one need not be concerned with controlling the film thickness of a coating material to obtain the reproducible spectra desirable for qualitative comparison and necessary for quantitative comparisons. Harris and Svoboda[36] and McGowan[37] have published internal reflectance work on alkyd vehicles which demonstrates this application. Careful control of the size of contact surface and the constancy of the reflectance angle, however, are critical. With some units this control is difficult. A worker in the authors' laboratory has converted a commercial liquid sampling reflectance attachment to a liquid flow type unit. With Irtran II® as the optical material it appears that useful spectra can even be obtained on a flowing stream of hot resin, opening the way for possible on-stream infrared plant control of resin processes.[38] Harrick has proposed an even simpler multiple pass cell in the form of a rod which may simply be immersed in the liquid sample.[39]

[32] Harrick, N. J., Phys. Rev. Letters, **4**, 224, 1960; J. Phys. Chem., **64**, 1110, 1960.
[33] Fahrenfort, J., Spectrochim. Acta, **17**, 698, 1961.
[34] McDonald, R. S., Pittsburgh Conference on Analytical Chemistry and Applied Spectroscopy, March 2–6, 1964, Paper No. 191.
[35] Lucchesi, C. A., Offic. Dig. Federation Soc. Paint Technol., **35**, 982, 1963.
[36] Harris, R. L., and Svoboda, G. R., Anal. Chem., **34**, 1655, 1962.
[37] McGowan, R. J., Anal. Chem., **35**, 1664, 1963.
[38] Scott, R. W., unpublished work.
[39] Harrick, N. J., Anal. Chem., **36**, 188, 1964.

POTASSIUM BROMIDE SAMPLING OF SMALL SAMPLES AND IDENTIFICATION SCHEMES

For strictly qualitative work, it is possible by a relatively simple sampling method to tell a great deal about a paint film. Contrary to the above discussion of internal reflectance, and all the effort expended in Volume II to provide a means for separation and purification of various components for analysis, the potassium bromide pellet method may often be used for simple classification of a paint when only a few milligrams of dry paint chips are available. Information about both the pigment and binder may be gained. This is possible because the binder portion generally exhibits many absorption bands while the inorganic pigment portion exhibits one to two stronger absorption bands. The procedure for handling small samples of dried or cured paint in the authors' laboratory entails the following operations:

(a) Remove a few milligrams of paint or varnish from the coated object by scraping or otherwise abrading with a razor blade or other suitable tool.

(b) Grind the paint chips with a hard mortar and pestle to a fine powder.

(c) Add about 4 mg. of powdered sample to about 500 mg. of Infrared Quality powdered potassium bromide.[40] In cases where the paint chips are not brittle and will not powder, "steps b", and "c" must be combined. The "rubbery" sample is ground together with 50 to 100 mg. of larger particle size potassium bromide in a mortar and pestle to which a few drops of a volatile solvent such as chloroform has been added. After the chips have been disintegrated and mixed with the potassium bromide by grinding, the mixture is gently heated to drive off the solvent and about 400 mg. of the 200 over 325 mesh Infrared Quality potassium bromide is added.

(d) Place the mixture in a Wig-L-Bug vibrator capsule containing one ball pestle and blend on the vibrator for 15 to 20 seconds.[41] Overgrinding results in opaque pellets and is to be avoided.

(e) Transfer the blend to a suitable one half-inch diameter vacuum die and form into a pellet under a twelve ton load in a hydraulic press. Vacuum is usually applied alone for two minutes, followed by two minutes of vacuum and full press load. Relatively clear pellets should result.

(f) Record the infrared spectrum of the pelleted sample. Disregard absorption bands at 2.9 and 6.1 μ due to moisture adsorbed on the potassium bromide before pelleting. Also observe and disregard any residual solvent bands, such as the strongest absorption band due to chloroform at 13.3 μ wavelength. High apparent background absorption is usually observed due to reflection losses due to poor dispersion, in spite of the above steps which were taken to obtain homogeneous dispersion of the paint sample. More presentable spectra can be obtained by compensating for the background by means of reference beam attenuation or by use of the electronic expansions which are available on some double beam spectrophotometers.

(g) Interpret the spectrum according to the "Identification Scheme for Polymers, Resins, and Oils . . ." given on page 1629 of Volume II repeated here as Table 54-2, and a similar scheme for inorganic pigments[42] given here as Table 54-3. For confirmation, reference should then be made to actual spectra of the materials suspected. The short compilation of spectra given in Chapter 37, Volume II may suffice; however, the longer ones given by Brown, et al.[20] or Sadtler[43,44] may instead be required. For pigments,

[40] Harshaw Chemical Co., 1945 East 97th Street, Cleveland 6, Ohio.

[41] Crescent Manufacturing Co., Chicago, Illinois.

[42] Scott, R. W., Sherwin-Williams Co., private communication.

[43] Sadtler Commercial Spectra, Sadtler Research Laboratories, Philadelphia 2, Pa., Pigments and Dyes.

[44] Ibid., Monomers and Polymers.

TABLE 54-2. IDENTIFICATION SCHEME FOR POLYMERS, RESINS, AND OILS BASED ON
INFRARED ABSORPTION BANDS

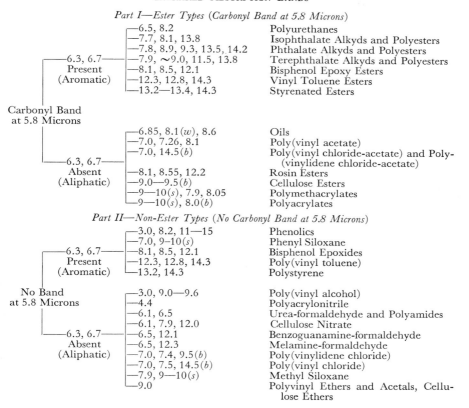

Part I—Ester Types (Carbonyl Band at 5.8 Microns)

	—6.5, 8.2	Polyurethanes
	—7.7, 8.1, 13.8	Isophthalate Alkyds and Polyesters
	—7.8, 8.9, 9.3, 13.5, 14.2	Phthalate Alkyds and Polyesters
6.3, 6.7 —7.9, ~9.0, 11.5, 13.8	Terephthalate Alkyds and Polyesters
Present —8.1, 8.5, 12.1	Bisphenol Epoxy Esters
(Aromatic) —12.3, 12.8, 14.3	Vinyl Toluene Esters
—13.2—13.4, 14.3	Styrenated Esters

Carbonyl Band
at 5.8 Microns

	—6.85, 8.1(w), 8.6	Oils
	—7.0, 7.26, 8.1	Poly(vinyl acetate)
	—7.0, 14.5(b)	Poly(vinyl chloride-acetate) and Poly-
6.3, 6.7		(vinylidene chloride-acetate)
Absent —8.1, 8.55, 12.2	Rosin Esters
(Aliphatic) —9.0—9.5(b)	Cellulose Esters
—9—10(s), 7.9, 8.05	Polymethacrylates
—9—10(s), 8.0(b)	Polyacrylates

Part II—Non-Ester Types (No Carbonyl Band at 5.8 Microns)

	—3.0, 8.2, 11—15	Phenolics
	—7.0, 9–10(s)	Phenyl Siloxane
6.3, 6.7 —8.1, 8.5, 12.1	Bisphenol Epoxides
Present —12.3, 12.8, 14.3	Poly(vinyl toluene)
(Aromatic) —13.2, 14.3	Polystyrene

No Band
at 5.8 Microns

	—3.0, 9.0—9.6	Poly(vinyl alcohol)
	—4.4	Polyacrylonitrile
	—6.1, 6.5	Urea-formaldehyde and Polyamides
	—6.1, 7.9, 12.0	Cellulose Nitrate
6.3, 6.7 —6.5, 12.1	Benzoguanamine-formaldehyde
Absent —6.5, 12.3	Melamine-formaldehyde
(Aliphatic) —7.0, 7.4, 9.5(b)	Poly(vinylidene chloride)
—7.0, 7.5, 14.5(b)	Poly(vinyl chloride)
—7.9, 9—10(s)	Methyl Siloxane
—9.0	Polyvinyl Ethers and Acetals, Cellulose Ethers

Key: (w), weak; (s), strong; (b), broad.

reference to the compilation and remarks of Harkins, Harris, and Shreve[45] may also be beneficial. For polymers, the work of Nyquist[21] would be expected to be of benefit.

One should be able to ascertain whether a paint is primarily based on an oil type binder, a particular type of alkyd (*ortho*-phthalate or isophthalate; plain, vinyl toluenated, or styrenated), or a vinyl, acrylic, styrene-butadiene, epoxy, urea, melamine, cellulose nitrate, silicone, cellulose, or vinyl ether type binder. In whites the broad strong absorption due to titanium dioxide will be apparent starting at 13 or 14 μ wavelength. It will, in fact, usually mask the stronger aromatic absorption bands of phthalate alkyds and styrenated binders.

The type of extender, whether carbonate, sulfate, silica, or silicate, can usually be determined. In pastels there is usually not enough colored pigment present to be apparent in the infrared spectrum. For these, reference should be made to earlier section on visible spectrometry, and specifically the reflectance reference.[12] For the full strength colors the sharp multiple absorption bands so characteristic of the organic pigments may

[45] Harkins, T. R., Harris, J. T., and Shreve, O. D., Anal. Chem., **31**, 541, 1959.

TABLE 54-3. IDENTIFICATION SCHEME FOR INORGANIC* PIGMENTS AND EXTENDERS BASED ON INFRARED ABSORPTION OF STRONGEST BAND

Wavelength of Bands (Microns)		
Major Band	*Other Significant Bands*	*Pigment or Extender*
4.8	7.1(*w*)	Iron blue, Ammonium Ferric Ferrocyanide
7.0	11.45(*w*), 13.94(*w*)	Whiting, Calcium Carbonate
7.0	11.70(*w*), 14.4(*w*)	Barium Carbonate
7.1	14.70(*w*), 14.40(*w*)	Basic Carbonate White Lead, $PbCO_3 \cdot Pb(OH)_2$
8.9	15.0(*w*)	Gypsum, Hydrated Calcium Su ate, and Extended Titanium Dioxide
9.1	12.5(*w*)(*b*)	Amorphous Silica
9.2	12.5–12.9 Doublet(*w*)	Crystalline Silica
9.2	8.40(*w*), 10.30(*w*)	Basic Sulfate White Lead, $2PbSO_4 \cdot PbO$
9.20	8.40, 8.90(*s*), 10.15(*w*)	Barytes, Blanc Fixe, $BaSO_4$
9.7	9.1, 9.9(*s*), 11.0, 14.4	Clay, Hydrated Aluminum Silicate
9.85	15.0	Talc, Hydrated Magnesium Silicate
9.75–10.1	13.4(*w*)	Mica, Hydrated Alkali Aluminum Silicate
11.0	10.8(*s*), 11.85	Strontium Chromate
11.1	12.6(*s*)	Raw Sienna, Hydrated Iron Oxide
11.4	10.5(*s*), 12.5(*s*)(*b*)	Zinc Yellow, Zinc Chromate
11.6	—	Chrome Yellow, Lead Chromate
11.8	10.7(*b*)	Barium Chromate
11.60	9.50(*b*)	Molybdate Orange, Lead Chromate-Lead Molybdate
13.5	—	Antimony Trioxide
13.5–16.0	—	Titanium Dioxide

Key: (*w*) weak; (*s*) strong; (*b*) broad.
* Organic pigments are excluded because of the complexity of their spectra and a general lack of major bands which set one class apart from another. Much of the variation in spectra of organic pigments result from a multitude of variations in aromatic substitution on one of the intermediates.

be evident. Sometimes these will be superimposed on the broader strong inorganic absorptions present when the colors are barium sulfate lakes or when additional color such as chromates or lead molybdates are present. Oxide colors and carbon black do not generally exhibit infrared absorption bands in the 2–15 μ wavelength spectrum.

QUANTITATIVE ANALYSIS

Qualitative identification of a material from its infrared spectrum depends upon the wavelength of absorption by various functional groups. Quantitative analysis depends upon the intensity of the absorption band exhibited by the particular functional group to be determined. Absorption is logarithmic. In systems which obey the Beer-Bouger or Beer-Lambert absorption law, concentration is directly proportional to absorbance. With the proper choice of sample and instrument conditions, quantitative analyses can be performed. Due to the high degree of qualitative specificity of infrared, several components of a mixture may often be determined simultaneously.

For the approximate analysis of mixtures, particularly for mixtures of various types of film formers analyzed as cast films by either transmission or perhaps more conveniently by internal reflection, the ratio absorbance methods suggested by one of the authors in an earlier publication[46] should be considered. However, for more precise determination of specific components, analysis of samples in solution in carefully calibrated sealed cells is more desirable. Quantitative analyses performed on paint or related material prior to 1960 are covered in the bibliography of a previous publication.[47] Summaries of four quantitative procedures regularly used in the authors' laboratory will now be given. Although the specific absorptivities and instrument conditions used by the authors are given, these are offered only as a guide. Other analysts using other instruments should set up their own operating parameters and derive absorptivity values with their own standards. The instrument used for the four procedures given here was a Perkin-Elmer Model 21 spectrophotometer.

POLY(VINYL ACETATE) IN VINYL RESINS

This method may be used to determine the percent of poly(vinyl acetate) present in poly(vinyl chloride)-poly(vinyl acetate) resins. It is based upon measuring the infrared absorbance of the carbonyl group absorption at 5.72 μ wavelength in the spectrum of an ethylene dichloride solution of the sample. Compounds such as aldehydes, ketones, carboxylic acids, and esters would exhibit interfering carbonyl absorption. Some vinyl resins contain small amounts of maleic acid which may be compensated for when the amount is known. However, if it is known that poly(vinyl acetate) is the only source of carbonyl absorption in a sample, there is little reason to believe that the method cannot be extended to many other poly(vinyl acetate) copolymers or blends of homopolymer with other resins.

Standardization.—Prepare a few solutions of poly(vinyl acetate) homopolymer (Bakelite Resin AYAA may be used) in ethylene dichloride. Use sample weights ranging from 0.2 to 0.5 g. diluted to 100 ml.

Set up spectrophotometer for programmed resolution setting corresponding to 102 μ slit reading and 0–100 percent transmission at 5.72 μ wavelength, with gain set for slight recorder pen overshoot following abrupt 20 percent deflection, with slight upscale amplifier drift, response filter in "1" position, and no automatic speed suppression.

Fill 0.25-mm. sealed cell with sample solution and place in sample beam. Fill another 0.25-mm. sealed cell with ethylene dichloride and place in reference beam. Scan between 5 and 6.5 μ at 2 minutes per micron rate.

Measure the baseline absorbance of the absorption band at 5.72 μ with a baseline tangent at about 5.25 μ and intersecting at 6.5 μ. Prepare a graph of absorbance per centimeter path length *vs.* concentration of poly(vinyl acetate) in grams per liter. The calibration should be a straight line passing through the origin. The slope of the calibration curve then represents the absorptivity value of the poly(vinyl acetate) according to the absorption law in the form:

$$a_s = \frac{A}{bc}$$

[46] Brown, W. H., Ansel, R. E., Lucchesi, C. A., and McGinness, J. D., Offic. Dig. Federation of Soc. Paint Technol., **33**, 57, Part II, March, 1961.

[47] *Ibid.*, p. 61.

where: a_s = absorptivity;
     b = path length in centimeters;
     c = concentration in grams per liter; and
     A = baseline absorbance.

Procedure.—Dissolve an accurately weighed sample of dry vinyl resin (in an amount equivalent to about 0.2 g. poly(vinyl acetate)) in about 50 ml. of ethylene dichloride in 250-ml. beaker on magnetic stirrer. When dissolved, quantitatively transfer and dilute to mark in 100-ml. volumetric flask.

Run spectrum and determine baseline absorbance as described under "Standardization."

Calculate the poly(vinyl acetate) content from equation:

$$\text{Percent PVA} = \frac{A(100)}{a_s(b)w}$$

where: A = baseline absorbance;
     a_s = absorptivity (4.72 for Bakelite AYAA);
     b = cell path in centimeters; and
     w = sample concentration in grams per liter.

NOTE.—a_s for maleic acid is about 3.9. Therefore, for low concentrations of maleic acid, subtract about 0.8 percent for each one percent of maleic acid found to be present in the resin on the basis of acid number titration.

OIL CONTENT OF RESIN MODIFIED OIL VARNISHES

This method may be used to estimate the oil content of phenolic resin modified oil varnishes and styrenated or vinyl toluenated oil vehicles. It is based upon measuring the absorption of the carbonyl group at 5.75 μ wavelength in the infrared spectrum of solutions of the varnish or vehicle.

The method is only applicable when it is known that no carbonyl functions other than those due to the oil are present. The method theoretically should be standardized directly with standard varnish or vehicle samples containing known oil contents. However, the resin modifications here considered are not believed to affect the absorptivity of the oil carbonyl group. Consequently, it is considered practical to apply data obtained on pure oil samples directly to modified oil products.

Standardization.—Transfer approximately 5 ml. of pure oil, accurately weighed by difference from a syringe, to a 100-ml. volumetric flask. Dilute to volume with reagent quality chloroform. Place in 0.1-mm. path sealed infrared cell. Fill a matching cell with pure chloroform.

Place the cells in the respective sample and reference beam positions in the infrared spectrophotometer. Scan slowly between 5 and 7 μ with instrument set for quantitative measurement at 5.75 μ. Determine the baseline absorbance of the 5.75 μ absorption band with a baseline tangent to the spectrum at about 5.25 μ and 6.5 μ.

Calculate the absorptivity from the absorption law (See typical a_s data in Table 54-4 from authors' laboratory):[48]

$$a_s = \frac{A}{bc}$$

where: A = baseline absorbance;
     b = cell path in centimeters; and
     c = concentration of oil in grams per liter.

[48] Scott, R. W., and Curtiss, D. M., unpublished work.

TABLE 54-4. ABSORPTIVITY VALUES OF COMMON OILS
AT 5.75 MICRONS

Coconut oil	1.488
Soya bean oil	1.108
Blown linseed oil	1.119
Blown fish oil	0.734
Blown castor oil	1.054
Heat bodied litho oil	1.059
Dehydrated castor oil, bodied	1.242
Dehydrated castor oil	1.022
Safflower oil	1.100
Safflower oil, nonbreak	1.109
Oiticica oil	1.030
Tung oil	1.114
Alkali refined linseed oil	1.114
Raw linseed oil	1.095
Alkali refined soya oil	1.124
Cottonseed oil	1.109
Raw castor oil	1.060

Procedure.—Transfer an accurately weighed sample of varnish by difference from a syringe into a 100-ml. volumetric flask. The size of sample taken should be chosen, based on the expected oil content of the solids, to contain approximately 5 ml. of oil. Dilute the sample to 100 ml. with reagent quality chloroform.

Place solution in 0.1-mm. path sealed cell, pure chloroform in matched reference cell, and scan under conditions used for "Standardization." Determine baseline absorbance as before. Where there is obvious resin interference with the baseline at 6.5 μ (but not at 5.75 μ) consider only the 5.25-μ region background as "baseline."

Calculation.—Calculate the approximate oil content of the varnish or vehicle solids from the absorption law as follows:

$$\text{Percent oil} = \frac{A(100)}{a_s bw}$$

where: A = baseline absorbance;

b = cell path in centimeters;

w = concentration of sample (on nonvolatile basis) in grams per liter; and

a_s = absorptivity determined for oil known or expected to be present. (See Table 54-4.)

CELLULOSE NITRATE CONTENT OF LACQUERS

This method is generally applicable to the determination of cellulose nitrate in coatings in the concentration range of a few percent to 100 percent cellulose nitrate. The primary prerequisite of the method is that the dry film of the clear portion of the coating will redissolve in acetone or tetrahydrofuran. For optimum results, the exact nitrogen content and type of cellulose nitrate involved must be known or samples of it be available for standardization. Also some idea of the total coating composition must be obtained in order that the proper options in the procedure may be chosen to eliminate interferences from other resins.

The method is based upon measuring the absorbance due to the covalent nitrate group. In most cases the 11.9-μ wavelength band suggested first by Rosenberger and

Shoemaker[49] is used. When interferences require it, the 6.05-μ band, used independently by the authors for a few years and later reported by Levitsky and Norwitz,[50] may be used. When the 11.9-μ band is chosen, acetone is used as the "transparent" solvent. When the 6.05-μ band is chosen, tetrahydrofuran is used as the solvent. The procedure based on the 11.9-μ band must be used when urea or polyamides are involved because of interference with the 6.05-μ absorption band. The procedure based on the 6.05-μ band is not required unless interference due to bisphenol epoxy, some phenolics, chlorinated polyphenyl, or large amounts of polyvinyl alcohol, methyl methacrylate, or some acrylates is evident in the 11.9-μ wavelength region.

Standardization.—Following the directions in "Procedure," determine the absorptivity of the various grades of cellulose nitrates at the levels and in the combinations anticipated in later unknowns. This might include samples of various viscosity and nitration grades of RS and SS type cellulose nitrate carefully* dried for several hours at 60°C. in a vacuum oven and stored in a vacuum desiccator. It might include actual synthetic blends of known resins with cellulose nitrate. Or it might include known resins without the cellulose nitrate to allow estimation of blank or correction factors where these other resins are known present and are known to have a slight overlap of their absorption bands with the nitrate absorption band.

Use the following formula for the absorptivity determination:

$$a_s = \frac{A}{bc}$$

where: a_s = absorptivity;
   A = measured baseline absorbance;
   b = cell path in centimeters; and
   c = concentration of cellulose nitrate in grams per liter.

For the most accurate work, prepare a calibration plot of A/b vs. cellulose nitrate concentration. Note that the slope of the line is absorptivity. A separate line or plot

TABLE 54-5.   SAMPLE DATA ON KNOWNS

Type and Grade of Cellulose Nitrate	Nitrogen Content	Absorptivity Data			
		a_s 6.05 μ		a_s 11.9 μ	
		Duplicate	Av.	Duplicate	Av.
RS $\frac{1}{4}$ sec.	12.14%	3.68	3.63	1.75	1.75
		3.59		1.75	
RS 5–6 sec.	12.20	3.68	3.70	1.74	1.75
		3.71		1.76	
RS 500–1000 sec.	11.75	3.46	3.46	1.71	1.65
		3.47		1.59	
SS $\frac{1}{4}$ sec.	10.98	3.37	3.39	1.60	1.59
		3.40		1.57	
SS $\frac{1}{2}$ sec.	10.91	3.43	3.40	1.57	1.56
		3.39		1.55	

should be graphed for each type of cellulose nitrate. See Table 54-5 for typical data from the authors' laboratory.

Procedure.—Decide, based on what standardization data is available and the par-

[49] Rosenberger, H. M., and Shoemaker, G. J., Anal. Chem., **31**, 1315, 1959.
[50] Levitsky, H., and Norwitz, G., Anal. Chem., **34**, 1167, 1962.
* Observe caution stressed in supplier's literature for handling dry cellulose nitrate.

ticular circumstances of composition or interference in the unknown, which nitrate absorption band will be the basis for the determinations. It is sometimes useful to use both for confirmation purposes.

Quantitatively transfer an appropriate (see Table 54-6) dry sample or clear lacquer

TABLE 54-6. RECOMMENDED SAMPLE AND INSTRUMENTAL PARAMETERS

	at 6.05 μ	at 11.9 μ
Sample, approx. 0.6 g. CN per 25 ml.		X
Sample, approx. 0.35 g. CN per 25 ml.	X	
Solvent	THF	Acetone
Slit Program Set 980, approx. width =	112 μ	308 μ
Gain, normal	X	X
Scan speed, 2 min. per micron	X	X
Scan range	5–7 μ	10–14 μ
0–100% T set at analytical band	X	X
Baseline intercepts, wavelength microns	5.5 and 6.5	11.0 and 12.85

sample to a 25-ml. volumetric flask. For the undried samples, evaporate the bulk of the thinners by connecting the flask to a rotary thin film vacuum evaporator, with the flask partially immersed in a hot water bath operated behind a safety shield. If solvents are suspected whose infrared spectra have interfering infrared absorption bands, dry the sample further by placing the flask in a 60°C. vacuum oven for at least one hour. (*CAUTION:* Dry lacquer grade cellulose nitrate has been known to explode under certain conditions. Follow instructions for handling furnished by supplier. *Keep the quantities of dried sample small. Never grind in mortar and pestle or ball mill*).

Allow the flask to cool, add about 15 ml. of acetone (or THF),* insert a small magnetic stirring bar and stir on magnetic stirrer until cellulose nitrate has dissolved. Remove the bar after rinsing with a little solvent; then fill to the 25-ml. mark. If some cloudiness exists, allow the flask to stand or centrifuge some of it until a relatively clear solution is obtained.

Transfer some of the clear solution to a sealed 0.1-mm. absorption cell. Fill matched reference cell with acetone (or dry THF). Set proper instrument controls, place cells in their respective sample and reference positions, and scan through the required wavelength range.

Measure the baseline absorbance (according to Table 54-6) at the appropriate absorption maximum for the nitrate group.

Calculate the concentration of cellulose nitrate from the following equation:

$$\text{Percent cellulose nitrate (NVM)} = \frac{A(100)}{a_s(b)(w)}$$

where: A = measured baseline absorbance (See Note 1)

a_s = absorptivity from "Standardization" corresponding to the appropriate cellulose nitrate type or empirical calibration curve;

b = cell path in centimeters; and

w = concentration of nonvolatile sample in grams per liter.

NOTE 1.—The most common minor interferences will probably occur due to overlap of carbonyl groups from esters with the 6.05-μ nitrate group. There are two simple approaches to correcting for this. A definitely approximate, but fairly practical approach when the ester content is low, is simply to trace in what one would expect the high wavelength side of the

* Only dry, peroxide free, inhibited tetrahydrofuran should be used.

ester absorption band to be if the cellulose nitrate were not present. Then the baseline absorbance of the 6.05-μ point on the imaginary trace is calculated and deducted from the total baseline absorbance measured in the manner specified in the method.

The other approach, a more formal and definite version of the scheme just described, is to inspect a number of ester spectra free of cellulose nitrate, and to calculate the percentage of the carbonyl absorption, the 5.7- or 5.8-μ peak baseline absorbance, that is represented by the overlap at 6.05-μ wavelength. Acrylic polymers appear to exhibit about a 2 percent overlap, phthalate plasticizers and alkyd resins, 2 percent, saturated oils, 1 to 2 percent overlap, and cis-unsaturated drying oils, 3 to 10 percent overlap. Consequently, to correct the baseline absorbance for acrylic ester overlap, one might use the formula:

$$\text{corrected absorbance} = A - A_e \frac{(A_n')}{A_e'}$$

where: A = measured baseline absorbance at 6.05 μ;
A_e = measured baseline absorbance of ester at carbonyl absorption maximum (5.7 or 5.8);
A_n' = measured baseline absorbance of a similar (nitrocellulose free) ester at 6.05 μ; and
A_e' = measured baseline absorbance of the same nitrocellulose free ester at the carbonyl peak absorption maximum.

UNREACTED ISOCYANATE (NCO) IN URETHANE INTERMEDIATES

In the preparation of intermediates for use in urethane foams, it is desirable to know the amounts of unreacted isocyanate groups present at various times during the reaction. Isocyanate groups exhibit an intense absorption band near 4.5 μ. The only common chemicals which absorb near 4.5 μ are compounds with dienoid or triple bond structures such as isocyanates, cyanates, cyanides, nitriles, or alkynes. Below is a method developed in the authors' laboratory for the determination of unreacted NCO in urethane intermediates.

Standardization.—Prepare several standard solutions of isocyanate monomer (of the type used to prepare the product which is to be analyzed) in dry toluene which will have absorbances covering the useful absorbance range, approximately from 0.200 to 0.800 (For toluene diisocyanate in the 0.25-mm. cell, samples over the range of 0.5 to 2.5 g. per liter are recommended). To accurately prepare such dilute solutions, it is recommended that a concentrated stock solution be carefully prepared first. Then appropriate aliquots may be taken and diluted in separate flasks. *CAUTION: Isocyanates are toxic and the NCO functionality is lost by rapid reaction with water or water vapor.*

Establish instrument conditions which will give adequate resolution and reproducibility in the 4- to 5-μ region. The following conditions have been used for the Perkin-Elmer Model 21 spectrophotometer.

Pen Speed	—	3 seconds full scale, setting "11"
Slit	—	Program setting to produce 80 μ slit reading at 4.46-μ wavelength. Approximate resolution setting "980"
Amplifier	—	3 percent upscale drift per 10 seconds
Gain	—	Set at position producing active pen response without overshoot after 20 percent abrupt deflection from 50 percent at 4.5 μ.
Response	—	1
Auto Suppression	—	0
Scale	—	0–100 percent T full scale, at 4.5 μ.
Reference Beam	—	Variable space cell filled with dry toluene and adjusted to compensate for toluene in the standard solution or sample. For example, for a 2 percent concentration of sample (that is 98 percent toluene) in a 0.250-mm. cell, a reference cell of 0.245-mm. light path filled with dry toluene should be used. For concentrations lower than 2 percent, matched cells may be used.

Record the spectrum of each of the standard solutions versus toluene. Scan between 4 and 5 μ in three minutes. Measure the baseline absorbance of the peak near 4.5 μ for each solution. Record these readings on a graph of absorbance per centimeter path length on the ordinate *vs.* concentration of monomer in grams per liter on abscissa. Draw the "best" line for these points.

Calculate the absorptivity from the slope or from the formula for the absorption law in the form:

$$a_s = \frac{(A/b - t)}{c}$$

where: a_s = absorptivity (11.6 for toluene diisocyanate);
    A = baseline absorbance for any point chosen on the straight line of the graph;
    t = absorbance intercept of the line extrapolated to zero concentration;
    c = concentration of monomer in grams per liter; and
    b = cell path in centimeters.

Procedure.—Weigh the urethane intermediate sample by difference from a syringe to the nearest 0.1 mg. into a volumetric flask partially filled with dry toluene. The sample size should be such that absorbances are obtained near 0.500 in the cell chosen. Scan the sample between 4 and 5 μ *vs.* toluene in a properly spaced reference cell under the same conditions which were used in the "Standardization." Measure the baseline absorbance in the same manner as used in the "Standardization."

Calculation.—Calculate the unreacted NCO content as isocyanate monomer from the following formula:

$$P = \frac{(A/b - t)100}{a_s(w)}$$

where: P = percent unreacted NCO calculated as isocyanate monomer by weight (note that NCO is not necessarily present as free monomer);
    A = baseline absorbance;
    t = absorbance intercept from calibration curve for zero concentration;
    w = concentration of sample in grams per liter;
    b = cell path in centimeters; and
    a_s = absorptivity for NCO monomer from standardization (found to be 11.6 for toluene diisocyanate).

Alternate Procedure for Estimation of Low Amounts of Free (Monomeric) Isocyanate in Isocyanate Modified Vehicles.

—Place a few drops of vehicle directly in the cavity of a 1-mm. lead spacer positioned on a polished NaCl window. Quickly place another window over the sample (NCO groups react with moisture in the air) and clamp in a demountable cell mount.

Place cell in the sample beam. Adjust instrument to expand 0 to 20 percent transmission to full scale (or whatever expansion is needed to bring background nearer 100 percent transmission), being sure of adequate gain and pen response, and reasonable resolution. Place cell in the sample beam and scan slowly between 4- and 5-μ wavelength.

Inspect resulting spectrum for evidence of isocyanate group absorption band near 4.4 μ. Comparison with the spectrum of a similar vehicle (one known to be isocyanate free) run under the same conditions should aid in discerning whether a new peak due to isocyanate is present. If still in doubt, make another scan of some of the unknown vehicle to which a trace of monomer has been freshly added. If a significant absorption band is evident in the unknown sample, estimate its baseline absorbance. Any isocyanate monomer present in the vehicle above a few parts per million would be expected to exhibit enough absorption above the other bands to be detected by inspection.

Estimate the maximum level of free isocyanate monomer which could be present from the following formula:

$$\text{Estimated possible free monomer} = \frac{A(100)}{a_s(b)(w)}$$

where: A = estimated baseline absorbance due to NCO group;

b = cell path in centimeter (1 mm. = 0.1 cm.);

a_s = previously determined absorptivity for monomer believed to be present (11.6 found for toluene diisocyanate in toluene, similar value assumed in a vehicle system*); and

w = sample concentration in grams per liter (Specific gravity of vehicle times 1000).

This last procedure for free monomer is approximate, and is intended only as a means to detect and intercept vehicles which appear that they might contain small amounts of free isocyanate monomer approaching the maximum level that is considered safe with regard to toxicity. It does not distinguish NCO groups on difunctional monomers from end NCO groups left on half reacted monomer that is part of a polymer. The only technique known to the authors which appears to determine only the free isocyanate monomer is gas chromatography. Such a gas chromatographic method is given later in this chapter on page 1316.

FLAME EMISSION SPECTROMETRY

A large number of the metals present in paint, varnish, and lacquer materials may be detected and determined by flame spectrometry. The elements extractable from pigments and extenders, or the ash from ignited paint or lacquer, with the exception of zinc and aluminum which are more amenable to determination by absorption flame photometry or other emission methods, are readily detected and determined as major elements in aqueous acid extracts or organic solvent extracts. In Table 54-7 are listed elements found in paints which may be detected by flame spectrometry.

ALKALI METALS

As a group, the compounds formed from alkali metals are considered the most water soluble. The alkali metals, followed by the alkaline earth elements, are the elements more easily detected by flame spectrometry. Flame spectrometry is most readily used when only the elements sought are already in solution or where they may be readily dissolved. Consequently, flame spectrometry for determination of the elements sodium and potassium in raw materials or coatings, or in the water extracts thereof, is of obvious research and development interest where coatings for exterior exposure or water resistance are involved.

Although sodium and potassium are classically determined by flame spectrometry, their determination is ironically one of the more critical ones. The alkali metals exhibit mutual radiation interference, they are subject to self absorption effects at relatively low concentration, and are susceptible to the depressant effect of other elements such as aluminum. Consequently, the choice of specific details of a method for the alkali metals must be considered carefully.

---

* It does not appear feasible to standardize this method directly with additions to isocyanate free vehicles because one would expect active hydrogens in such a vehicle to consume some of any addition of monomer.

TABLE 54-7. MAJOR PAINT ELEMENTS DETERMINED BY FLAME SPECTROMETRY

Element*	Usual Source of Element
Sodium	Surfactants, additives, sodium lithol, traces in most raw materials
Potassium	Surfactants, additives, clay extenders
Lithium	Additives
Calcium	Additives, whiting, gypsum, driers, calcium chromate, calcium lithol, resins
Copper	Phthalocyanines, copper fungicidal pigments, copper maroon pigment
Manganese	Driers, some maroon and red pigments
Strontium	Strontium chromate, strontium lithol
Chromium	Various chromate pigments, chromium oxide pigments
Iron	Red oxide, ferrite yellow, iron blue, black iron oxide, metallic brown pigments, driers, low grade extenders
Barium	Barium carbonate, barium sulfate, barium chromate, barium lithol, and additives
Boron	Additives
Cobalt	Driers, cobalt blue pigment, additives
Tin	Driers, additives
Cadmium	Cadmium lithopones, cadmium reds, cadmium yellows
Lead	White lead carbonate or sulfate, chrome yellow and green, leaded zinc oxide, driers
Aluminum	Aluminum pigments, clay and some talcs, aluminum stearate

* Listed in order of decreasing detectability.[51]

The literature is full of methods for sodium and potassium. However, a standard method for determination of alkali metals in paint, *per se*, is not known to the authors. When determination of alkali metals is necessary, it is recommended that one of the methods found in the literature be investigated. Dean lists references to methods for sodium in 36 classes of materials.[52] The American Society for Testing and Materials furnishes flame spectrometric methods which might be extended or adapted to paint applications, depending on the particular type of paint being examined.[53] The material covered by these methods for alkali metals appropriately include glass, titanium and aluminum oxides, industrial water, polyols, fuel oil, and gasoline.

As previously noted, the alkaline earth group of elements is generally the next most readily detected by flame spectrometry. Compounds of the alkaline earth elements are common paint ingredients. Consequently, if of interest, it may be useful as a starting point to consider another flame method recommended by ASTM for the determination of magnesium, barium, and calcium in glass.[54]

METALS IN VEHICLES

Elements in vehicles separated from paint are often determined when substandard performance brings up a question of drier metals not being present in the proper proportion or where it is suspected that some vehicle constituent has reacted to bring some

[51] Beckman Instruments, Inc.: Instruction Manual-Models DU and B Flame Spectrophotometers, Bull. 334-A, Fullerton, Calif.
[52] Dean, J. A., Flame Photometry, McGraw-Hill, New York, Toronto, London, 1960, p. 166.
[53] Methods for Emission Spectrochemical Analysis, 3rd Ed., American Society for Testing and Materials, Philadelphia, 1960.
[54] *Ibid.*, p. 515.

pigment element into solution. Flame spectrometry is useful for comparing the elemental composition of such vehicles.

Vehicles simply need to be diluted to a low enough viscosity that they may be readily aspirated into the flame. Particulate material must be filtered or centrifuged out completely, otherwise erratic emission due to burner clogging will result. As pointed out by Dean,[55] and by Curtis, Knauer, and Hunter,[56] the organic solvent matrix, inherent in oil or solvent based paint vehicles, usually enhances the emission of elements over that expected for the same elements in aqueous solution. This varies some from one element to another. However, from the standpoint of enhancement, the better solvents for diluting paint vehicles are probably the more volatile oxygenated solvents. The aliphatic hydrocarbons do not seem to enhance emission at all, while aromatics tend to produce such a luminous flame that the signal to noise ratio, and, thus, sensitivity, is greatly reduced.

METAL CONTENT OF PAINT DRIERS

Although complexometric titration methods based on the use of EDTA[57] are probably now more universally used for routine control of metallic paint driers, emission flame spectrometry is a very useful method. The flame method is particularly good for analysis of mixed or contaminated driers where its specificity is a definite advantage over the generally less selective EDTA methods.

Methods for routine control of single element paint driers have been developed and used extensively in the authors' organization.[58] A Beckman DU spectrophotometer equipped with a No. 9200 flame attachment, a No. 4300 photomultiplier attachment, and a No. 14500 battery power regulator was used in development of these methods. Use of other equipment may make minor changes in the methods, such as sample weights, slit width, etc., necessary.

Procedure.—Prepare a solvent blend by mixing 2 volumes of benzene, 1 volume of alcohol, and 1 volume of acetone.

Prepare a standard drier solution, using the weight and dilution indicated in Table 54-8. For driers having metal contents other than the samples listed, adjust the sample

TABLE 54-8. DETAILS OF PROCEDURE

Drier	Emission Line $(m\mu)$	Slit Width (mm.)	Sample Size (g.)	Diluted to (ml.)
24% Lead	405.8	0.07	0.2500	100
6% Cobalt.	341.2	0.07	0.2000	50
6% Manganese	403.3	0.06	0.2500	250
5% Calcium.	422.7	0.0125	0.1250	250

size so that the metal concentration of the solution would be the same as that indicated in the table. For example, if a lead drier containing 23.1 percent lead were to be used in preparing the standard drier solution, the weight of the sample in grams should be $0.2500 \times 24/23.1$ or 0.2597. Alternately, the amount of dilution may be varied. The drier solutions are usually stable for months except for the manganese solution which begins to deteriorate within a few hours.

[55] Dean, J. A., *op. cit.*, Ch. 5.
[56] Curtis, G. W., Knauer, H. E., and Hunter, L. E., "The Effect of Organic Solvents on the Flame Photometric Emission of Certain Elements," ASTM, Spec. Tech. Publ., 116, 67–74, 1951.
[57] Lucchesi, C. A., and Hirn, C. F., Anal. Chem., 30, 1877, 1958.
[58] Secrest, P. J., Offic. Dig. Federation Soc. Paint Technol., 30, 1026, 1958.

Prepare a solution of the drier to be tested, using the weight (approximate to the nearest 0.1 mg.) and dilution indicated in Table 54-8. For a drier known to have a metal content significantly different from that indicated in the table, the weight should be adjusted accordingly. For example, if a lead drier containing approximately 6 percent lead is to be tested, the sample weight should be approximately (in grams) 4×0.2500 or 1.0000.

Compare the emission of the sample solution with the emission of the standard solution as follows: using the slit width and emission line indicated in Table 54-8, adjust the instrument so that a transmittance reading of 50.0 is obtained with the standard or reference solution. With no change in instrument settings, obtain transmittance of sample solution. Still with no change in instrument settings, obtain transmittance of standard solution again. Make 2 more such comparisons. Calculate the average of the 6 transmittance readings of the standard solution and the average of the 3 transmittance readings of the sample solution. The average transmittance of the standard solution should be within ±10 percent of the average transmittance of the standard solution. If this is not the case, another sample solution containing a different weight of drier should be prepared and compared with the standard solution. Usually this is not necessary in routine control of driers because the metal content will nearly always be at least within ±10 percent of the specified metal content.

Calculations.—Calculate the metal content of the drier being tested by use of one of the formulas listed in Table 54-9.

TABLE 54-9. FORMULAS FOR CALCULATING
METAL CONTENTS

$$\%Ca = \frac{0.0171[(\% \text{ T Sample} \times 50.0)/(\% \text{ T Std.}) - 13.3]}{\text{Sample Wt.}}$$

$$\%Pb = \frac{0.16[(\% \text{ T Sample} \times 50.0)/(\% \text{ T Std.}) - 12.5]}{\text{Sample Wt.}}$$

$$\%Co = \frac{0.0335[(\% \text{ T Sample} \times 50.0)/(\% \text{ T Std.}) - 14.2]}{\text{Sample Wt.}}$$

$$\%Mn = \frac{0.0354[(\% \text{ T Sample} \times 50.0)/(\% \text{ T Std.}) - 7.6]}{\text{Sample Wt.}}$$

Discussion.—Of the elements normally found in driers with the exception of phosphorus, which has a very serious depressant effect on calcium, with nominal dilution, there is not believed to be a significant effect of one drier metal on the emissivity of another. Consequently, each drier metal may generally be determined in the presence of any of the others. As mentioned before, this is the primary advantage of the flame method for paint driers over the EDTA method, although even the EDTA methods are being specialized to some extent to provide selectivity.[59]

Because of the selectivity and simplicity of the flame spectrometric method and the relatively low cost of the equipment, paint companies will probably continue to rely upon the flame spectrometer for determination of paint drier metals in mixed driers and vehicles separated from finished paints. This will probably be true even when more sophisticated instrumental methods for the elements are available. However, the natural applicability of the flame method for driers probably makes it an exception. Where

[59] Graske, A., Offic. Dig. Federation Soc. Paint Technol., **33**, 855, 1961.

more universal elemental methods such as light and x-ray emission spectrometry, or neutron activation analysis are available, these will undoubtedly find preference over the flame method for general elemental analysis of paints, varnish, and lacquer materials. For further information on emission flame spectrometry the reader is referred to Chapter 7 in this volume and to recent reviews.[60]

EMISSION SPECTROMETRY

The optical or arc-spark spectrograph, like the x-ray emission spectrograph, is a powerful tool for the determination of elemental composition. Each technique has only slight advantages or disadvantages with respect to the other. Both techniques have been refined during recent years to the point that there is little that one instrument will do that the other will not. Indeed, where once one instrumental technique excelled, the other is now in competition. Nevertheless, there are slight differences, and it is definitely an advantage to have both techniques available.

Optical emission probably still has an edge on x-ray for trace and microsample work and for determination of low concentrations of the lighter elements. X-ray emission is very good for quantitative analysis of major constituents, particularly some of the heavier elements which are difficult or nearly impossible to do by any other method of analysis. The fact that x-ray methods are nondestructive is definitely an advantage. In any case, few paint companies are now equipped with such relatively expensive and specialized equipment. However, many commercial analytical laboratories and the laboratories of major pigment producers are so equipped. As the paint industry continues to become more technically sophisticated, and through calls upon the commercial laboratories or pigment suppliers for spectrographic help, becomes more aware of the value of such analytical data, the need and use of emission techniques in the industry will grow. Less expensive and easier to use emission spectrometers are also appearing. Consequently, the technique of emission spectrometry deserves mention in this chapter.

Within the authors' laboratory only x-ray emission spectrometry is used directly. However, for qualitative detection of low atomic number elements in low amounts, such as lithium, boron, sodium, magnesium, aluminum, and silicon, and for confirmatory checks for other trace elements, samples are regularly submitted to an outside testing laboratory for emission spectrographic analysis. A semiquantitative analysis will typically cost less than $50 per sample. For qualitative analysis, only 10 or 20 mg. of sample is usually required.

It is the general opinion of a number of chemists in this field, that once a pigment mixture has been separated from a paint it is amenable to analysis as a powder by any of the great multitude of standard spectrographic techniques. Emission spectrometry is reportedly very good for the determination of trace elements in pure pigments used in specialty coatings. Two notable examples of this application are zinc oxide and titanium dioxide pigments. Apparently the only warning which is in order when emission spectrometry is to be used for paint analysis is that one should realize the possibility of extreme variations in vaporization rates for some elements. This would be particularly true of elements such as mercury or tin present as organic compounds or surface treatments with the less volatile, even refractory silicas and titanias. To safeguard against this eventuality complete unknowns should be arced as "complete burns."

"Complete burns" are apparently the rule for those who must obtain an elemental analysis of extremely small samples by a "one shot" spectrographic procedure. In the crime laboratory where only a fraction of a milligram of paint, collected at the scene

[60] Scribner, B. F., Margoshes, M., Anal. Chem., **36**, 329R, 1964.

of a crime or on a suspect or victim, is available, this is the situation.[61] The speck of paint is sandwiched between layers of graphite (without grinding) in the cavity of the tip of a carbon electrode. The d.c. arc is carefully struck and the spectrographic film is exposed during the entire "burn" in an effort to pick up every element that is present regardless of its fugitive or transient nature.

For the general principles, applications, and instrumentation of emission spectrometry, the reader is referred to Chapter 8 of this volume. Reference to the latest edition of the publication "Methods for Emission Spectrochemical Analysis" is also recommended.[62]

X-RAY EMISSION SPECTROMETRY

X-ray emission spectrometry, like optical emission spectrometry, is a fundamental technique for determination of elemental composition. Most of the elements in the periodic table, except the very low atomic number elements and some low atomic number elements in low amounts, are determinable by routine procedures. In agreement with Liebhafsky and Melbon,[63] x-ray methods are of particular value for exploratory and semiquantitative work, for determination of elements difficult to do by ordinary methods, and, in favorable cases, for determination of traces. Few paint companies have x-ray emission equipment, and little has been published on applications specific to the paint industry. Nevertheless, one might observe from inspection of a recent review,[64] that the paint industry has many problems very closely related to those in other industries which are regularly solved by x-ray spectrometry.

For strictly qualitative analysis of unknown paints, and for some "go, no go" quality control of finished products, where suitable "bracketing" standards are available, it is convenient to scan paint samples as dry paint films. Samples sent from other laboratories as coatings on aluminum or steel panels, or paint dried in a flat-bottomed disposable aluminum moisture dish, can be cut to fit the sample holder of the x-ray spectrograph by means of a cutting die in a hydraulic press. However, as will be discussed below, normal paint film thicknesses (15 to 100 μ) are not usually suitable for good quantitative, or even semiquantitative, analysis.

Because of its fundamental basis (spectrum associated with inner electrons rather than outer valence electrons), x-ray emission spectrometry should be an analytical technique universally applicable to elemental analysis of any material regardless of its chemical or physical state. For quantitative analysis one should be able to correlate x-ray emission intensity for a particular element directly with the quantity of that element present. With qualification this is the description of x-ray emission spectrometry. However, to the degree that the sample cannot be presented for analysis as a monoatomic or monomolecular layer, one has to cope with deviations from proportionality due to absorption or enhancement effects (sometimes called matrix or interelement effects). There are also absorption effects traceable to physical inhomogeneities in the sample such as surface effects or segregation.

Except for instances where pigment particles may be intentionally surface treated with heavy elements, or there is a very wide range of particle size, the problem of obtaining a homogeneous sample, so much a problem in some other fields, is practically a minor one in the paint industry. All paints are composed of mixtures of compounds in solution or in very finely divided suspension. However, for quantitative work this advan-

[61] Dr. Albert Forslev, City of Chicago Dept. of Police, private communication.
[62] American Society for Testing and Materials, Philadelphia 3, Pa.
[63] Liebhafsky, H. A., Melbon, W. W., Offic. Dig. Federation Soc. Paint Technol., 33, 42, 1961.
[64] Campbell, W. J., Anal. Chem., 36. 312R, 1964.

tage is offset to a considerable extent, relative to other fields, by the fact that the matrix in paint changes drastically from one color or type to another with regard to x-ray absorption and enhancement effects.

Although the binder portion of a paint film is usually composed only of light organic elements, the pigment and extender portion is usually composed of compounds of heavy elements such as lead or barium mixed in a wide range of concentrations with compounds of light elements such as titanium, aluminum, magnesium, silicon, sulfur, oxygen, and carbon. X-ray spectrometry is a very valuable instrumental technique for both qualitative and quantitative elemental analysis in the paint industry, however, the extreme absorption effects operating should not be overlooked from a quantitative standpoint even when only semiquantitative or dependable detection limits are of concern. The data in Table 54-10 from the authors' laboratory serves as a not too unrepresentative example illustrating the seriousness of the problem.[65] These data were obtained on pigment powders (smaller than 325 mesh) at thicknesses well above infinite thickness.

TABLE 54-10. EXTREME ABSORPTION EFFECTS IN SOME PIGMENT PAIRS

Element Measured	Intensity Counts per sec.	Percent w/w	Matrix Substances
Sb Kα	6260	1	Antimony oxide
		99	Magnesium silicate
Sb Kα	630	1	Antimony oxide
		99	Basic lead chromate
Ca Kα	14,260	1	Calcium carbonate
		99	Magnesium silicate
Ca Kα	560	1	Calcium carbonate
		99	Basic lead chromate
Ti Kα	43,900	30	Titanium dioxide
		70	Magnesium silicate
Ti Kα	37,600	30	Titanium dioxide
		70	Basic lead chromate
Fe Kα	22,270	1	Iron oxide
		99	Magnesium silicate
Fe Kα	10,240	1	Iron oxide
		99	Basic lead chromate

QUANTITATIVE PIGMENT ANALYSIS

For dry pigment powders, the matrix dilution technique outlined by Gunn[66] has been useful in reducing the absorption effects represented by the data in Table 54-10. The pigment sample is diluted in a 1:1 mixture of starch: lithium carbonate, mixed by hand in a mortar and pestle, then pressed under a 10-ton load into a $1\frac{1}{4}$ in. diameter pellet or briquet. The usual portion is 0.1 to 1 g. of pigment per 6 g. of diluent. The sample size taken for dilution is chosen on the basis of the apparent concentration of the element sought, estimated after a preliminary scan of the original pigment mixture.

As pointed out by Claisse,[67] dilution with heavy elements may be as effective, if not

[65] Harper, R. L., and Mortensen, J. S., unpublished work.
[66] Gunn, E. L., Anal. Chem., **29,** 184, 1957.
[67] Claisse, F., "Sample Preparation Techniques for X-ray Fluorescence Analysis," Quebec Dept. of Mines, P.R. 402, 1960.

more effective, for leveling the absorption coefficient of the total matrix to a useful constant value. However, it is difficult to choose a heavy element compound as a universal diluent because of the relatively large number of interfering lines encountered due to the heavy elements. When lead is not sought, red lead pigment, Pb_3O_4, is a useful heavy element compound for addition to the starch-lithium carbonate mixture before pelleting. One g. added to the 6 g. of light element matrix will form a suitable pellet. Others working in a related field have reported that adding a few percent of sodium borate to such dilution matrices is helpful as a grinding and dispersing aid when the original sample is composed of large or irregular sized particles.[68]

The above procedures are useful, but a more general approach for paint pigments is still needed. The consensus of current opinion among the x-ray experts would appear to be that the thin-film or thin-layer approach is fundamentally the ideal, with solution techniques running a close second in practice. Work directed at preparing and measuring elements as thin-films is becoming common in the literature. The book by Liebhafsky, et al., provides a good foundation for such an approach.[69] The report of Gunn on measuring elements evaporated from solution onto thin-films is an interesting and useful example of the work going on.[70] Similar approaches to paint pigment analysis should be considered.

Actually, with semiquantitative analysis of pigments in liquid paints or lacquers as the goal, it would appear that x-ray spectrographers in the paint industry may have the solution to the absorption and enhancement problem in the technology of their own industry. Although paint films are applied "thick" in practice by the paint consumer, preliminary investigation indicates that uniform thin paint films of less than a few microns effective thickness (with respect to inorganic pigment elements) may be prepared for purposes of x-ray analysis. Single cation element "tinting bases" may be prepared for direct use as standard addition or internal standard "reagents" for paints. Publication of papers on this application is planned by the authors in the near future. Salmon has reported on an interesting thin-layer, controlled mass system for x-ray analysis of elements in minerals, which appears somewhat analogous to the approach currently being studied in the authors' laboratory.[71]

OTHER APPLICATIONS

The next most important application for quantitative x-ray spectrometry in the paint industry is probably for the determination of drier or catalyst metals in paint vehicles or polymer solutions. Due to self absorption and mutual absorption effects, some sample manipulation is also necessary here for reasonable quantitative results. However, if the concentrations of the elements sought are not too low to begin with, rather simple dilutions with organic solvent or metal free vehicle are all that is required.

For suitable semiquantitative working curves, the concentration of total metal in a vehicle must be somewhat below one percent. Dilutions down to a level just a few hundred x-ray counts per second above background is recommended. The limit of detection observed in the authors' laboratory[72] for such a routine organic dilution method for the common drier elements is given in Table 54-11 (it can usually be extended somewhat lower in specific cases).

[68] Dr. E. R. Scheffer, Titanium Division, National Lead Co., private communication.
[69] Liebhafsky, H. A., Pfeiffer, H. B., Winslow, E. H., and Zemany, P. D., X-Ray Absorption and Emission in Analytical Chemistry, John Wiley and Sons, New York, 1960.
[70] Gunn, E. L., Anal. Chem., 33, 921, 1961.
[71] Salmon, M. L., Advances in X-Ray Analysis, Vol. 5, University of Denver, Plenum Press, New York, 1962, p. 389.
[72] Harper, R. L., and Mortensen, J. S., unpublished work.

TABLE 54-11. TYPICAL* DRIER METAL
DETECTION LIMITS

Element	Detection Limit
Cobalt	10 p.p.m.
Manganese	40
Lead	40
Calcium	40
Zirconium	50
Cerium	200

* 50-kv. Norelco vacuum x-ray spectrograph.

However, even with dilution, perfect straight line calibration curves are not usually observed. One then must use families of working curves as has been reported by Davis and Van Nordstrand.[73] As is shown by data in Table 54-12 from the authors' labora-

TABLE 54-12. LIGHT ELEMENT MATRIX EFFECT ON MANGANESE

Matrix	Absorption Coefficient*	Relative Counts per mg. Mn**
Drying Oil in Mineral Spirits	low	12.9
Hydrogen	0.48	—
High Phthalate Alkyd	medium	11.2
Carbon	9.00	—
Water	higher	6.3
Oxygen	21.5	—

* Mn Kα 1.8964 Angstroms.
** 212 p.p.m.

tory,[74] even slight differences in the light element solvent matrix can make a difference when extreme accuracy is sought. An alternative approach is to use an internal standard as illustrated by recent work of Bartkiewicz and Hammatt.[75] This has been found the more useful approach for general nonroutine analyses.

Another valuable application of quantitative x-ray spectrometry has been the determination of the level of metal treatments. The concentration of zinc phosphate treatment on steel or galvanized steel may be determined directly on circles of the metal cut from panels to fit the spectrograph. The treatments are ideal thin-films, allowing virtually straight line calibration for levels of zinc phosphate from 1 mg. per sq. ft. levels to well over the common government standard of 150 mg. per sq. ft. On steel, zinc emission lines could be used. However, for more universal application, measurement of the phosphorus K alpha (or Kα) line is used in practice.

A similar type of analysis is useful for determining chromium and phosphate treatments on aluminum. Tin thickness on tin plate stock used in the container plant is also conveniently determined by direct x-ray comparison. Only two or three standards are required for this type of analysis.

[73] Davis, E. N., and Van Nordstrand, R. A., Anal. Chem., 26, 973, 1954.
[74] Harper, R. L., unpublished data.
[75] Bartkiewicz, S. A., and Hammatt, Anal. Chem., 36, 833, 1964.

X-RAY DIFFRACTION

X-ray diffraction has become established as one of the more fundamental and important research tools. Numerous applications of the science to problems in the paint industry are routine. X-ray diffraction provides a useful method for quality control of polycrystalline raw materials and for pigmented finished products.

In addition to identification and determination of specific crystalline compound forms, x-ray diffraction provides a means for determining crystallite particle size of pigments. Concern with diffraction line broadening was once only of academic interest.[76] Recent work of Rau,[77,78] however, has demonstrated the general utility of the x-ray diffraction method for crystallite size analysis. Comparison of aggregate or agglomerate particle size with true crystallite size can have significant implications with regard to color strength or stability of some pigments in paint.

Besides being applicable to a wide variety of chemical classes of materials, x-ray diffractometry may be applied to samples in a number of physical states or sizes. Routine analysis, both qualitative and quantitative, may be carried out by scanning methods, directly on paint coated panels or on loosely packed powders. Very small powder samples, only a few milligrams, may be examined by long film exposure when properly mounted in a diffraction camera. The latter method is particularly useful for examination of the minute residues involved in corrosion or paint adhesion studies. Diffraction analysis is also useful in the study of the "chalk face" of weathered paints. For any of this work reference data on known compounds must be available. The ASTM X-Ray Powder Data File and Index in book form is highly recommended for anyone working with x-ray diffraction.[79]

The use of x-ray diffractometry for identifying the rutile and anatase crystalline forms of titanium dioxide is probably one of its oldest applications. It is, nonetheless, a very important one in the paint industry. The rutile form of titanium dioxide (when properly surface treated) produces paints noted for chalk resistance when exposed to sunlight and the weather. Anatase, on the other hand, is noted for its promotion of freely chalking paints.

With growing sophistication in factory coated surfaces designed for long outdoor life, paints with closely controlled chalking rates are required. In some coating formulas, even low amounts of anatase, in what otherwise was intended to be straight rutile pigmentation, have been found to produce poor chalk resistance. Consequently, it has become desirable to establish specifications and appropriate test methods for determining anatase in raw materials and finished products. The detailed method adapted in the authors' laboratory from a literature method designed for analyzing the anatase-rutile ratio in paper coatings, follows.[80]

ANATASE TITANIUM DIOXIDE IN TITANIUM DIOXIDE PIGMENTS

This method is intended for the determination of percent anatase in rutile titanium dioxide. With proper considerations for a few possible interferences and proper counting statistics, the method may be applied to paint systems or pigment mixtures. The sample

[76] Klug, H. P., and Alexander, L. E., X-Ray Diffraction Procedures, John Wiley & Sons, Inc., London, 1954, Chapter 9.

[77] Rau, R. C., Advances in X-Ray Analysis, Vol. 5, University of Denver, Plenum Press, New York, 1962, p. 104.

[78] Ibid., Vol. 6, p. 191, 1963.

[79] American Society for Testing and Materials, Philadelphia 3, Pa.

[80] Harper, R. L., Sherwin-Williams Test Method No. 708.2, 1962.

may be presented to x-ray diffractometer in the form of a paint film on metal or paper or as a dry powder or pellet.

It is known that the x-ray diffraction diagram obtained from a material is characteristic of that material and also that the intensity of a diffraction peak entirely due to one component of a mixture is dependent upon the amount of that substance in the mixture. In this method, then, the intensity of the 101 diffraction maximum of anatase and the 110 diffraction maximum of rutile are measured by x-ray diffractometry. The background of each peak is subtracted; the intensity ratio of the rutile peak to the anatase peak is calculated and then converted to percent anatase with the assumption that the sum of the anatase and rutile is 100 percent.

The method is not applicable to "reduced," titanium-calcium pigments unless the calcium sulfate is first removed chemically. It is desirable to analytically assure that any residual calcium sulfate is considerably less than the level of anatase being sought. The insoluble residue after removal of the calcium sulfate should not be ignited above 700°C. Chrome yellow and the valentinite form of antimony trioxide also interfere if not removed. High amounts of iron oxide render analysis difficult, due to increased background. Additives such as antimony and zinc, and impurities such as niobium and zirconium, are generally present in solid solution and, thus, would not have interfering diffraction peaks. Surface treatments such as silica and alumina are essentially amorphous and, therefore, would not interfere. Extreme differences in particle size between the anatase and rutile portions will affect the results.

In the calculation employed in the method, a ratio is mathematically converted to a percent. It is implicitly assumed that the sum of anatase and rutile is 100 percent, an assumption normally made in titanium dioxide pigment systems. Materials present as distinct crystalline entities would interfere to the extent that they dilute the sample. The third allotropic form of titanium dioxide, brookite, would have such an effect. However, it reportedly does not occur in commercial titanium dioxide pigments.

A Norelco x-ray diffractometer equipped with voltage and current stabilizers, scintillation detector, high intensity copper tube, and sample spinner can be utilized for this method. Other quantum detectors may be used, but variations in counting time must be made.

Calibration and Standardization.—The value of the constant in the equation (see "Calculation") should be determined for each detector with known samples in the concentration range of interest. The value may vary with composition. Known samples should be rerun occasionally. The same scale factors should be used for standards and unknowns. Routine instrument calibration procedures should be followed.

Constant Counting Procedure (below 1 percent anatase).—This procedure is specifically oriented toward the determination of small amounts of anatase in rutile pigments. Slight variations (0.2°max.) in line positions occur due to the surface condition of the prepared specimen, the orientation of the sample holder, and possibly slight variations in the pigments. It is thus necessary to locate the exact maximum for each peak in each determination. The anatase peak and backgrounds are measured at 8000 counts. The rutile peak is measured at 32,000 counts. Backgrounds are taken at 24.50° and 26.00° two theta. The value of the background for the anatase peak is taken as the mean of these two intensities. Since the effect of the background on the rutile peak is much less, only one background reading (at 26.00°) is necessary. The intensities above background are then computed.

Scanning Procedure (0.5 to 100 percent anatase).—A scanning rate of 0.125° two theta per minute is used for maximum precision. If lower precision can be tolerated, faster rates may be used. The sample is first scanned from 28° to 26° two theta using a scale factor of 1 × 32 and then scanned from 26° to 24° two theta using a scale factor of

1 × 2 when the minimum anatase content is expected. Appropriate changes in scale factor settings are necessary depending on the anatase-rutile ratio expected in the sample.

Calculation.—The percent of the titanium dioxide which is anatase is calculated from the intensities above background with the following formula:

$$\text{Percent anatase} = \frac{1}{1 + K(I_R/I_A)} \times 100$$

The literature value of K for anatase content less than 20 percent is 1.47; for anatase content above 20 percent the value for K is given as 1.26.[81]

Precision.—The normal statistical variation of quantum detectors is the greatest contributor to the instrumental error in determining the intensity of the anatase peak. It can be calculated from the fact that quantum counter errors follow Gaussian distribution curves. When the background and anatase peaks are measured at 8000 counts the "3-sigma" value for this variation in the anatase peak is given by:[82]

$$\text{Percent error (3-sigma)} = \frac{[(I_{\text{peak}} \times 0.0336)^2 + (I_{\text{background}} \times 0.0336)^2]^{1/2}}{I_{\text{peak}} - I_{\text{background}}} \times 100$$

This variation is considerably less for the rutile peak. Other variations in precision should be determined experimentally.

Accuracy.—It is desirable to agree upon standards if results are to be correlated with those of another laboratory.

NUCLEAR MAGNETIC RESONANCE SPECTROMETRY

Nuclear magnetic resonance, or more specifically proton resonance for this discussion, is rapidly being recognized as another analytical tool with wide application to analysis of the wide variety of organic materials utilized in the paint industry. Although the instrumentation is currently somewhat more expensive than that used for infrared, there is some evidence that this technique may be substituted some day to do many of the jobs infrared spectrometry is now doing.

Certainly with both infrared spectrometry and nuclear magnetic resonance, there is little about the composition of an unknown organic compound which cannot be determined. Infrared provides the information on what functional groups are present with a high degree of specificity. Nuclear magnetic resonance also provides an indication of what functional groups are present based on the shift of proton resonance with shifts in electron density around the proton caused by the neighboring functional group. Correlation charts for nuclear magnetic resonance of the type commonly used for identifying functional groups by infrared spectrometry are now appearing in the literature.[82a] A very important added attribute of nuclear magnetic resonance is that spin-spin interaction or coupling data provides information on the sequence of different hydrogenic groups in a molecule. It is also very significant that the area of each resonance peak may be converted directly to the relative number of hydrocarbons of each type that is present in a compound.

For the smaller molecules the utilization of nuclear magnetic resonance is quite straightforward. However, in attempting high resolution work with polymers, one may encounter difficulty obtaining good spectra due to low solubility of the polymer or too high viscosity. For polymer work then, particularly for end group analysis where the

[81] Spurr, R. A., and Myers, H., Anal. Chem., **29**, 760, 1957.
[82] Zingaro, P. Wm., Norelco Reporter, **5**, Nos. 5–6, 1958.
[82a] Dietrich, M. W., and Keller, R. E., Anal. Chem., **36**, 258, 1964.

number of hydrogens in the group of interest is small compared to the total number of hydrogens present in the molecule, or where due to insolubility or high viscosity the concentration is low, a computer of average transients accessory (called "CAT") is usually required. The "CAT" sorts out and sums up the real, but weak, resonance signals separate from the noise from a large number of repetitive scans of dilute solutions. Eventually a useful computed spectrum results. Without access to the "CAT" for polymer solutions, some useful high resolution spectra may be obtained as single scans by means of a heated sample probe accessory. This is true when the concentration is high enough to provide an adequate signal-to-noise ratio and yet the viscosity is not so high that elevated temperatures will not reduce the solution to a low enough viscosity to permit "tumbling" the molecules to average out broadening dipole-dipole interactions. The quality and interpretability of such spectra approach those of simpler molecules and may be treated in a similar manner.

The application of nuclear magnetic resonance to the identification of polyester resins is of special interest to those in the coatings field.[83] Samples may sometimes be run directly in monomer solution if the monomer peaks do not interfere. However, more generally for unknowns, it is best to separate the polyester portion from the monomer. After separation the polyester portion may be dissolved in a suitable deuterated solvent, or sometimes simply heated in the sample probe when such an accessory is available. Most of the common polyester ingredients may be identified and semiquantitatively determined. For polyesters at least, nuclear magnetic resonance appears to have significant advantages over the formerly used infrared approaches. Another application of nuclear magnetic resonance of obvious interest is its use for determination of unsaturation and average molecular weight of natural fats.[84] Agreement with other methods, and in the case of tung oil, improvement over the usual Wijs iodine number method for determination of unsaturation in drying oils has been clearly shown.

A general discussion of the application of high resolution nuclear magnetic resonance to polymers has been given by Bovey, Tiers, and Filipovich.[85] As a start for those interested in pursuing this field further, selected recent references to determinations of composition and/or structure of specific polymer types may be cited. A method for analysis of polyisoprene and polybutadiene rubbers has been reported by Chen.[86] The vinyl acetate content of ethylene-vinyl acetate copolymers[87] has been determined. Ethylene polymers and copolymers,[88] vinylidene chloride-vinyl chloride copolymers,[89] and interesting structural features of stereospecific poly(methyl methacrylates)[90,91] have been studied. Much attention is being given the use of nuclear magnetic resonance for sterochemistry assignments on polymers. A recent news feature highlights the success of this activity.[92]

TURBIDIMETRIC TITRATION OF POLYMERS[93]

One of the physical characteristics of the resin component of a coating that is recently coming into prominence is the molecular weight (in some cases, species) distribution.

[83] Percival, D. F., and Stevens, M. P., Anal. Chem., **36**, 1574, 1964.
[84] Johnson, L. F., and Shoolery, J. N., Anal. Chem., **34**, 1136, 1962.
[85] Bovey, F. A., Tiers, G. V. D., Filipovich, G., J. Polymer Sci., **38**, 73, 1959.
[86] Chen, H. Y., Anal. Chem., **34**, 1135, 1962.
[87] Chen, H. Y., Lewis, M. E., Anal. Chem., **36**, 1394, 1964.
[88] Porter, R. S., Nicksic, S. W., Johnson, J. F., Anal. Chem., **35**, 1949, 1963.
[89] Chujo, R., Satoh, S., and Nagai, E., J. Polymer Sci., **2**, 895, 1964.
[90] Bovey, F. A., and Tiers, G. V. D., Advances in Polymer Sci., **3**, 139, 1963.
[91] Harwood, J., Ritchey, W., and Pustinger, J., O.E.A.N.S. Conference, Mellon Institute, 1963; Chem. Eng. News, **41**, 36, April 22, 1963.
[92] Chem. Eng. News, **43**, 321, Feb. 1, 1965.
[93] Bartosiewicz, R. L., Sherwin-Williams Co., private communication.

There have been several methods advanced in recent years[94,95] that are quite well suited to the fractionation of polymers, but few are of an analytical nature yielding distribution directly without further characterization of the fractions obtained.

In the turbidimetric titration[96,97,98] the solvency of the system is varied by adding a compatible nonsolvent to a very dilute solution of the polymer kept at constant temperature. Under conditions that minimize agglomeration, the insoluble portion of the polymer will come out of solution in the form of a semistable micellular phase, making the solution turbid. Measuring the turbidity provides one with the means of estimating the amount of polymer insoluble at that particular solvency point. As the titration continues, a point of maximum turbidity is reached; at this point all of the polymer that will precipitate has done so. By suitable handling of the raw data a differential distribution curve for the polymer can be obtained.

To obtain reproducible results, experimental conditions must be rigorously controlled. Urwin *et al.*,[98] point out that the choice of solvent and nonsolvent (their refractive indexes should be nearly identical, and the micellular phase should exhibit good stability), the concentration (0.4–0.2 mg. per 100 ml.) and rate of addition of solvent (0.01–0.02 ml./min.) are critical.

In the authors' laboratory, turbidimetric titrations of a comparative nature were carried out on bodied oils, alkyd resins, monomer modified alkyd resins, epoxy resins, solution acrylics, and emulsion acrylics. The solvent–nonsolvent systems employed were chosen principally on the basis of their ability to form a stable micellular phase within a reasonable concentration range; the concentrations used generally ran in the 1.0–10.0 mg. per 100 ml. range to insure sufficient turbidity to be measurable in a 5-cm. flow-through cell (a Beckman DK-1 was used as the detecting system). The titration rates were on the order of 0.2–1.0 ml. per min., to cut down on the total time involved.

Although these conditions are not as gentle as those listed by Urwin *et al.*,[98] useful information on the comparison of similar resins was obtained and, in the case of the Epon resins, a simple relationship between the molecular weight, concentration, and turbidity was found. Extensive work along these lines has been temporarily interrupted in deference to determining how well Gel Permeation Chromatography will produce the same desired molecular species distribution data. (See GPC section later in this chapter.)

POLAROGRAPHY

As reported by Berger and Cadoff,[99,100] few papers have appeared in the chemical literature on the applications of polarographic methods of analysis to paint pigments. They review past work and present useful polarographic methods for determining zinc, lead, and titanium in paint pigments. However, the more common application of the polarograph to inorganic analyses is probably for the determination of selected trace elements in various "pure" pigments or vehicles. For example, determinations of lead and

[94] Allen, P. W., Ed., Techniques of Polymer Characterization, Butterworths Scientific Publications, London, 1959.

[95] Robb, J. C., and Peaker, F. W., Eds., Progress in High Polymers 1, Academic Press, New York, 1961.

[96] Peaker, F. W., "Light-Scattering Methods for the Chemical Characterization of Polymers —A Review," Analyst, **85**, No. 1009, 235, 1960.

[97] Stearne, J. M., and Urwin, J. R., "Turbidimetric Titrations—Part I. The Automatic Turbidimeter," Makromolekulare Chem., **56**, 76, 1962.

[98] Urwin, J. R., *et al.*, "Turbidimetric Titrations—Part II. The Titration of Polystyrene in Butanone with Isopropanol," Makromolekulare Chem., **72**, 53, 1964.

[99] Berger, H. W., and Cadoff, B. C., Offic. Dig. Federation of Soc. Paint Technol., **37**, 28, January, 1965.

[100] *Ibid.*, p. 35.

copper in zinc oxide pigment or cobalt, lead, and manganese in vehicles separated from a paint, or vehicle raw materials, are typical.

Polarography may also be used to advantage for analyses of organic compounds of interest to the paint industry. Small amounts of residual free acrylic[101,102] or styrene[103] monomers in polymers may be determined by organic polarography. Additives in rubber chemicals,[104] antioxidants in hydrocarbon thinners,[105] and peroxides in oils[106,107] may be determined.

The polarographic determination of maleic acid has always been a classic experiment. Its application to the determination of maleic acid or anhydride in phthalic anhydride and to the study of isomerization equilibria in the esterification and hydrolysis of maleate and fumarate polyesters is of particular interest. A significant number of references are concerned with the maleate-fumarate study.[108,109,110,111,112,113]

THERMAL ANALYSIS

With the advent of the development of the highly sensitive heat sensors or detectors that are used in the thermal conductivity detectors of so many gas chromatographs today, interest has grown in the use of these same type detectors for differential thermal analysis. DTA is a thermal analysis technique in which a temperature differential developed between a sample and an inert reference is measured as a function of temperature. The temperatures at which a differential develops correspond to temperatures at which some thermodynamic change is taking place in the sample. These changes may be an endotherm or exotherm of reaction, heat of fusion, or vaporization, or other change in physical state such as a crystalline transition. A knowledge of each of these phenomena may be applied to a number of aspects of paint technology.

A review of recent work in the literature should provide the reader with an idea of how DTA may be used in the paint industry or allied fields. One worker has studied the degree of cure of unsaturated polyester by DTA[114] while others have characterized a series of esters and saturated polyesters.[115,116] Burrell[117] and Putti[118] have concluded that DTA provides the simplest routine method for determination of glass transition temperature of polymers. The glass transition temperature of polymers used in paints is considered important because, among other things, it reflects what the flexibility or elasticity of a paint is likely to be at various service temperatures. DTA has been used

101 Lacoste, R. J., Rosenthal, I., Schmittinger, C. H., Anal. Chem., **28**, 983, 1956.
102 Claver, G. C., Murphy, M. E., Anal. Chem., **31**, 1682, 1959.
103 Ayres, W. M., and Whitnack, G. C., Anal. Chem., **32**, 358, 1960.
104 Mocker, F., Rubber Chem. and Technol., Oct.–Nov., 1254, 1959.
105 Gaylor, V. F., Conrad, A. L., and Landerl, J. H., Anal. Chem., **29**, 228, 1957.
106 Silbert, L. S., J. Am. Oil Chemists' Soc., **39**, 480, 1962.
107 Swern, D., Silbert, L. S., Anal. Chem., **35**, 880, 1963.
108 Vancso-Smercsanyi, I., Maros-Greger, K., Makai-Bodi, E., J. Polymer Sci., **53**, 241, 1961.
109 Elving, P. J., Anal. Chem., **32**, 1538, 1960.
110 Garn, P. D., and Gilroy, H. M., Anal. Chem., **30**, 1663, 1958.
111 Feuer, S. S., et al., Ind. Eng. Chem., **46**, 1643, 1954.
112 Hobart, E. W., Anal. Chem., **26**, 1291, 1954.
113 Elving, P. J., Aaron, M. J., and Rosenthal, I., Anal. Chem., **25**, 1082, 1953.
114 Johnson, G. B., Hess, P. H., Miron, R. R., J. Appl. Polymer Sci., **6**, S19, 1962.
115 Anderson, D. A., and Freeman, E. S., Anal. Chem., **31**, 1697, 1959.
116 Ritchie, P. D., J. Oil Colour Chemists, **45**, 659, 1962.
117 Burrell, H., Offic. Dig. Federation Soc. Paint Technol., **34**, 131, 1962.
118 Putti, G., Materie Plastiche, **30**, 190, 1964 (in Italian).

for the qualitative identification of polymers[119] and for the quantitative analysis of epoxy resins and hardeners.[120]

Similarly, with improvements in microbalances, a related technique, thermogravimetric analysis, TGA, is receiving increased attention. TGA is a thermal analysis technique involving the measurement of changes in weight as a function of temperature. Early interest in TGA has been for characterizing decomposition, formation, hydration, dehydration, and related transitions of inorganic compounds.[121] Some more recent activity has been in the area of studying the thermal degradation of polymers.[122,123,124]

GAS CHROMATOGRAPHY

Gas chromatography, with proper calibration and standardization, will yield qualitative and quantitative information on a wide variety of materials. The most important requirement is that the materials to be analyzed may be volatilized at a few hundred degrees centigrade. Of the three classes of material in paint, varnish, and lacquer, the solvent or thinner is the most volatile and, therefore, is most amenable to analysis with gas chromatography. The other two classes of material, the binder and the pigment, are not usually considered volatile. However, to varying degrees, it has been found practical to convert portions of various binders into volatile fractions or derivatives which may be readily determined with gas chromatography. Some binders contain monomeric volatile materials other than solvents which are in some cases intentional and desirable, while in others they are not. Gas chromatography provides a means for determining these. Plasticizers and free residual monomers best represent the materials of this type.

The purpose of this section will be to provide procedures, outlines, or selected references to methods for solvent analysis, free monomer determinations, and for qualitative analysis of alkyd, acrylic resins, and some other coating binders. Some of the more general philosophy of qualitative and quantitative analysis by gas chromatography will appear as part of the "Solvent Analysis" section.

SOLVENT ANALYSIS

SAMPLE PREPARATION

Except for possibly a nonvolatile determination, no sample preparation need be involved when a thinner or solvent is submitted for analysis. However, it is a different matter when a total paint or vehicle is submitted. Some consideration needs to be given to what is the best approach to removing or separating the solvent from the rest of the sample. Four alternate methods are given here for consideration. The choice of method will depend somewhat on the objective of the analysis.

Vacuum Distillation (Rapid Qualitative).—This is a rapid and simple method for removing the solvent from most paints, varnishes, and lacquers. It requires only simple laboratory apparatus, and has been used with much success in the authors' laboratory. The main feature of the method is that the sample distilled is very small compared to

[119] Yamamoto, A., Shimadzu Rev., **18,** 109, 1961.

[120] Arnold, R. J., Barshatky, J. S., Proc. 17th Ann. Tech. Management Conf., SPI, Sect. 3H-1, Chicago, Illinois, February, 1962.

[121] Duval, C., Inorganic Thermogravimetric Analysis, 2nd Ed., Elsevier Publishing Co., Amsterdam, The Netherlands, 1963.

[122] Doyle, C. D., Anal. Chem., **33,** 77, 1961.

[123] Vassallo, D. A., Anal. Chem., **33,** 1823, 1961.

[124] Anderson, H. C., SPE (Soc. Plastics Engrs.) Trans., **2,** 202, 1962.

the size of the distillation flask. This allows rapid flash-off of the solvent without contamination of distillate by products of initial foam-over or later decomposition of residue in the distillation flask. When the solvents present have a wide range of boiling points, perfect quantitative recovery cannot be claimed because of probable loss of a portion of the lower boilers.

Apparatus Assembly.—Assemble a clean, dry, heavy-walled, 1-liter suction or filter flask at a slight angle on a ring stand in such a position that it may be lowered into a glycerol bath. The glycerol bath is simply a large steel beaker on a hot plate. Fit the top of the flask with a stopper containing a capillary-tipped bleeder tube extending a few inches into the flask and controlled by a shut-off clamp at the other end. To the side arm of the flask connect a short length of glass tubing by means of a short length of heavy walled rubber tubing (glass to glass distance should be spaced to allow flexing of the joint, but the inner rubber tubing wall area exposed should be kept to a minimum).

Insert the glass tube from the side arm of the filter flask through a rubber stopper below the neck, but only a quarter of the way into the bulb, of a special 10-ml. distillation flask. The only thing special about the flask is that it has its side arm turned up rather than down, to allow it to be placed in a 250-ml. beaker. This is easily done over a Meker or Fischer burner. Prepare a mount for the 250-ml. beaker in order that the 10-ml. distillation flask (which will be the receiver here) may be lowered into it. The beaker will serve as a dry ice-methylene chloride cold bath. A small sheet of rigid asbestos should be placed between the hot bath and the cold bath. A vacuum hose should be available for connection of vacuum to the side arm of the receiver in the cold trap.

Procedure.—Lower the assembly into the appropriate bath containers and add the glycerol and dry ice-methylene chloride. Transfer 10 ml. of sample to be analyzed into the 1-liter flask by means of a syringe. Immediately stopper flask, close bleeder, and apply vacuum. After 15 minutes, turn on hot plate and adjust heating rate such that the glycerol reaches a temperature of about 150°C. in 1 hour.

When the glycerol bath reaches 150°C., turn off the vacuum pump and carefully release the vacuum by means of the bleeder. If very high boiling point solvents are present, the glycerol bath can be held at 150°C. for an extended period or, the bath temperature can be increased to 180°C. Disconnect and remove the distilling flask and transfer the contents to a small, closed container. If small amounts of water are observed in the distillate, add anhydrous sodium sulfate. The sample is now ready for infrared and/or gas chromatographic analysis.

Vacuum Distillation (Quantitative).—Another technique for removing the solvent from a vehicle under reduced pressure has been reported by Haslam et al.[125] In this method, a special glass H-tube is used as a combination sample holder and distillate receiver. Since the entire operation is done in a closed system, quantitative recoveries are possible. The procedure follows briefly.

Carefully deliver 1 to 5 g. of sample (depending on quantity of solvent expected) into the sample leg of the H-tube by means of a syringe fitted with a long needle. Place this leg in a dry ice-methylene chloride cold bath. After cooling for a few minutes, seal off the large mouth opening at the top of this leg by means of a hand torch. Then apply vacuum to the opening on the other leg of the tube, keeping the sample leg in the cold bath. After about a minute, seal off this other leg with the vacuum still applied.

Remove the sample leg from the coolant. Place the other leg (the receiver) in the cold bath. As the sample leg warms, distillation will begin to occur. Complete the distillation by placing a suitable hot bath around the sample leg. When complete, remove the source of heat and allow the sample leg to cool to room temperature.

Carefully open the tube with protective leather gloves. Keep the tube cool and work

[125] Haslam, J., Jeffs, A. R., and Willis, H. A., JOCCA, **45**, 325, 1962.

behind a safety shield. (There is a chance of some freak reaction resulting in pressure due to noncondensable products.)

Dilution-Polymer Precipitation.—Another method for separating the solvent from the binder involves the precipitation of the binder with a nonsolvent.[126] This method is most helpful when analyzing lacquer solvents where low boiling aliphatic hydrocarbons can be used effectively as precipitants. With alkyd resins and many polyesters, it is not easy to find a nonsolvent which will efficiently precipitate the resin.

Briefly the method consists of precipitating the resin with a nonsolvent, removing the precipitate by filtration or centrifuging, and analyzing the resulting solution. The nonsolvent must be selected such that it does not interfere with the detection of the solvent components. Also, the nonsolvent must be efficient as a precipitant, otherwise a large amount is required to precipitate the resin and the solvent portion becomes too dilute and analysis more difficult.

Direct Injection.—For quantitative (and often qualitative) analysis, direct vehicle injection into the gas chromatograph can be quite successful. With this technique a solvent-diluent is chosen such that it does not interfere with the detection of the solvent components. The solvent-diluent should be of high purity and selected to elute either before or after all of the solvent components. The procedure is briefly outlined below.[127]

Dilution.—Add about 1 ml. of vehicle and 1 ml. of diluent to a stoppered, 10-ml. vial and mix well. If the viscosity of the resulting solution is too high to permit sampling with a syringe, add more solvent until sampling is possible. Take care not to dilute more than necessary.

The internal standard, if one is used, should be added to the diluted sample. Often, it is advantageous to add a diluent which contains a known amount of the internal standard. In such cases, the vehicle is weighed and the diluent is pipetted into the vial.

Analysis.—Inject the sample into the gas chromatograph and analyze, using normal procedures. The only caution is to avoid excessive injection port temperatures; otherwise polymer degradation will take place. Generally, a temperature of 180°C. is a good starting point. The upper temperature limit, however, will be dictated by the type of polymer in the vehicle.

Injection Port Cleaning.—Needless to say, the injection port must be cleaned about every 10 injections. This can be done with a wire brush (such as that used in cleaning small caliber rifle bores) and strong solvents. Another cleaning technique is to remove the column and turn up the injection port temperature to 400–500°C. overnight with the helium flowing at about 20 ml. per min. This will burn out the organic residue and a quick brushing with solvent will finish the job.

CHROMATOGRAPHY

There are several approaches to the use of gas chromatography for the analysis of paint or lacquer solvents or thinners, depending primarily upon the degree of identification which is required. For specification purposes for such hydrocarbon thinners as the naphthas and mineral spirits it will often suffice to simply compare chromatograms of the "unknown" and the standard prepared under identical operating conditions. A well resolved chromatogram may be considered analogous to a fingerprint. More specific approaches will follow.

Boiling Range.—Certainly, for hydrocarbons, it is being demonstrated that the popular, but crude, distillation range methods, such as ASTM D-86, may be replaced by a gas chromatographic method utilizing one of the silicone packed columns which gen-

[126] Esposito, G. G., and Swann, M. H., Offic. Dig. Federation Soc. Paint Technol., **33**, 1122, 1961.
[127] Tessari, D. J., unpublished work.

erally separate hydrocarbons according to their vapor pressures or boiling points. Workers in the petroleum industry recently reviewed this work and reported on a more refined gas chromatographic procedure, simulating, but requiring only 1 percent of the time normally required for a precise analytical distillation.[128] Better definition of the initial and final boiling ranges, and account of the total sample is claimed. Commercial versions of such automatic analyzers for boiling point characterization are reported near completion. For analysis of solvents with a broad range of volatility, programmed temperature operation is often an advantage.[129]

Multiple Columns.—For the more complex mixtures, particularly those containing components of different chemical types, analysis is best done on more than one type of column. In general, following the old saying of "likes like likes," hydrocarbon solvents are retained longer on a paraffin column than on a polyester column, while polar solvents are retained on the polar polyester column and rapidly released from the paraffin column. Peaks of a polar component and a nonpolar component which overlap on one chromatogram will nearly always separate when the column type is changed. Very interesting and diagnostically useful shifts of groups of peaks are observed in an unknown chromatogram as the chemical type of the liquid partitioning agent in the column is changed.

Relative Retention Data.—Relative retention time or volumes (relative to benzene) for a fairly representative list of solvents have been determined on a didecyl phthalate column,[129] a dinonyl phthalate column,[130] a paraffin wax column,[130,131] a tritolyl phosphate column,[131] and a silicone column.[130] The use of two columns and their relative retention time data such as is given in the listed references will then provide a means of identification for the more common mixtures.

Other systems for classifying compounds according to some retention time index are also worth investigating. A system proposed by Kovats[132] uses *n*-paraffin as reference compounds to establish a retention index. A good review article on Kovats' retention index system has recently been written by Ettre.[133]

Another retention system, labeled as *Retention Volume Ratio*, has been proposed by Merritt and Walsh.[134] With this system, compounds of a particular chemical class are indexed on column pairs. The system also has provisions for classifying retention data obtained with programmed temperature gas chromatography.

For special separations special columns are required. A good example of a special column for a special separation (a separation which long challenged early gas chromatographers) is the Bentone 34-diisodecyl phthalate column used for the rapid and complete separation of ethyl benzene and the xylene isomers.[135] Extensive use is made of the Bentone-phthalate ester column in the authors' laboratory, in conjunction with the use of a second column packed with polydiethyleneglycol succinate (DEGS), for the analysis of commercial xylenes.[136] The polyester (DEGS) column is used to check the unknown samples for aliphatic hydrocarbons (those boiling below 150°C.) and for isopropyl benzene, which is only partially resolved from *o*-xylene on the Bentone column. From the

[128] Green, L. E., Schmauch, L. J., Worman, J. C., Anal. Chem., **36**, 1512, 1964.
[129] Esposito, G. G., and Swann, M. H., Offic. Dig. Federation Soc. Technol., **33**, 1122, 1961.
[130] Haken, J. K., and McKay, T. R., JOCCA, **47**, 517, 1964.
[131] Haslam, J., Jeffs, A. R., and Willis, H. A., JOCCA, **45**, 329, 1962.
[132] Kovats, E., Helv. Chim. Acta, **41**, 1915, 1958.
[133] Ettre, L. S., Anal. Chem., **36**, 31A, 1964.
[134] Merritt, C., and Walsh, J. T., Anal. Chem., **34**, 903, 1962.
[135] Spencer, S. F., Anal. Chem., **35**, 592, 1963.
[136] Tessari, D. J., and Payne, S. B., Sherwin-Williams Co., Sherwin-Williams Method 741.0, 1964.

chromatogram obtained with the DEGS column the percent aliphatic hydrocarbon, isopropyl benzene, o-xylene, and combined ethyl benzene, p- and m-xylene can be calculated. By using the Bentone 34-diisodecyl phthalate column, the ratio of ethyl benzene and m- and p-xylene can be obtained, and by combining this information with that from the DEGS column, a complete quantitative analysis is possible.

Quantitation.—Once the peaks are identified in the chromatogram, the areas under each peak may be measured and corrected for relative response. Data necessary to correct peak areas are available in the literature for many common solvent type compounds.[137,138,139,140,141] It is recommended, however, that each worker calibrate his own detector. Then the corrected areas are divided by the total area and multiplied by 100 to provide percentage compositions. Large petroleum firms often make these computations (and identifications) automatically on some sort of computer.

COMPLEMENTARY IDENTIFICATION SCHEMES

When one happens not to have relative retention data available on his unknown or would rather not bother to try to get it, one may resort to chemical or other instrumental techniques for assistance. Two useful complementary schemes follow.

Infrared Spectrometry.—Although the multiple column approach is indeed useful, if compounds are present on which retention time data are not available, one must turn to other means for identifying the peaks. The commonest approach to this is to collect the fractions representing the unidentified peaks for infrared analysis.

Fraction Collection.—There are probably as many methods for collecting fractions

TABLE 54-13. TYPICAL SAMPLING FOR IR IDENTIFICATION OF GC FRACTIONS

Sealed Cells	Optimum Collected Sample Volume	Cell Volume	Practical Concentration, %
Macro 0.025 mm.	100 μl. or 2 drops	0.1 ml.	100
" 0.10	30 μl.	0.15	20
" 0.25	20 μl.	0.2	10
" 1.0	5 μl. or 0.1 drop	0.5	1
Micro 1.0	0.2 μl.	0.02	1
" 2.0	0.15 μl.	0.03	0.5
" 3.0	0.15 μl.	0.05	0.3
KBr pellet*	1 μl. or 0.02 drop		
KBr pellet, micromask	0.3 μl. or 0.006 drop		
10-cm. Gas cell**	Vapor equivalent to about 10 μl. or 0.2 drop of liquid		

* Is conveniently used for high boilers.[142]
** Sometimes necessary for hard-to-collect volatiles. Longer, multiple path cells may be needed.

[137] Jamieson, G. R., J. Chromatog., **3**, 464, 1960.
[138] Ibid., p. 496.
[139] Hoffmann, E. G., Anal. Chem., **34**, 1216, 1962.
[140] Messner, A. E., Rosie, D. M., and Argabright, P. A., Anal. Chem., **31**, 230, 1959.
[141] Rosie, D. M., and Crob, R. L., Anal. Chem., **29**, 1263, 1957.
[142] McGinness, J. D., Wittenbaugh, J. A., Lucchesi, C. A., Tappi, **43**, 1027, 1960.

as there are gas chromatographs, but in the authors' laboratory fractions suitable for infrared identification have been collected by means of a heavy-walled U-tube immersed in dry ice-methylene-chloride and connected to the exhaust port of the chromatograph, while a component representing an unidentified peak is leaving the detector. More than one pass may be required, but with well resolved peaks, somewhat larger samples may be injected for collection purposes.

Analysis.—After condensation and collection of the unknown fraction, the fraction, which may appear only as a haze inside the tube, is rinsed down with a minimum amount of "infrared" solvent (carbon disulfide for all but water and some alcohols which are insoluble), transferred to a sealed infrared liquid cell, and scanned in the sample beam with the infrared solvent in the reference beam for compensation and cancellation of the absorption due to the diluting solvent.

The information given in Table 54-13 may be used as a guide for collecting optimum sized GC fractions and making the proper dilutions and transfers to the infrared sampling equipment. The data given is based on the standard accessories available from the Perkin-Elmer Corp. for a Model 21 Spectrophotometer.

Interpretation.—One familiar with interpretation of infrared spectra may then readily decide whether the fraction is an aromatic or aliphatic hydrocarbon, a ketone, ester, alcohol, or ether, if not specifically what compound it is. A few infrared reference spectra of solvents and a copy of the Colthup correlation chart are given in reference.[143]

Solubility and Functional Group Tests.—Another very useful approach, particularly suited for use by those not possessing infrared instrumentation, is represented by the work of Haken and McKay.[144] The method is based on the sequential application of solubility and functional group tests, as well as fingerprint chromatograms and retention volume data. Their procedure is to subject samples of unknown solvent separately to extraction by a 10 percent brine solution to remove lower alcohols, by water, to remove water soluble alcohols, ketones, and glycol ethers, by 85 percent sulfuric acid to remove all "polar" solvents, and by concentrated sulfuric acid, to remove all but the aliphatics and chlorinated paraffins. The insoluble layer from each extraction is then run on a polyester column under identical conditions, with the effluent gas mixture passing through a stream splitter into microtubes containing functional group test reagents.

Aided by the functional group tests, relative retention data on a few common solvents, and the solubility classifications, one should be able to piece together a good qualitative analysis of a fairly complex mixture. In certain cases, even those with other kinds of instrumental data might benefit from a few quick solubility tests. The extraction of all components except the aliphatics might be particularly useful in simplifying an analysis.

FREE MONOMER

There are a number of reasons for wanting to determine the amount of free monomer in a polymer system. One usually either wants no monomer to be left after a particular stage of polymerization or he wants a specific amount to be present in order to be able to maintain the desired stoichiometry of some further reaction. One of the main reasons for wanting finished polymer products to be free of residual monomer would appear to be the odor or toxicity of certain monomers.

Undoubtedly, many GC methods for monomer analysis are unpublished. For reasons of company security or for lack of uniqueness or general applicability, these methods

[143] Brown, W. H., Ansel, R. E., Lucchesi, C. A., and McGinness, J. D., Offic. Dig. Federation Soc. Technol., **33**, March, 1961.
[144] Haken, J. K., and McKay, T. R., JOCCA, **47**, 517, 1964.

never reach the journals. Often, one may make slight modifications of a published method for the determination of another monomer. In this case, the analyst may not feel justified in publishing his modifications. At any rate, one will often find it necessary to develop his own method for monomer analysis when dealing with unique and/or complex systems.

The method for free styrene currently in use in the authors' laboratory and a method for diisocyanate monomer from the literature which has been found useful, will each be given in detail. Following these, a review of methods from the literature for some other monomers will be presented.

STYRENE-VINYL TOLUENE

At least two gas chromatographic methods for determining styrene monomer in polymers have appeared in the literature.[145,146] Both of these methods, however, have limitations such that the authors feel justified in presenting a method which was developed in their laboratory.[147] The method described here also permits the determination of vinyl toluene either by itself or in combination with styrene.

Instrument Conditions.

  (a) Column, 10-ft. Reoplex 400 (Polypropyleneglycol adipate).
  (b) Column temperature, 140°C.
  (c) Helium flow, 60 ml./min.
  (d) Injection port temperature, 280°C.
  (e) Sample size, 5–15 μl.

Sample Preparation.

  (a) About 5–7 g. of sample are weighed on an analytical balance when approximately 1–2 percent styrene or vinyl toluene is expected.*
  (b) The sample is weighed into small pigment bottles by means of polyethylene syringes.
  (c) The internal standard is composed of 10 g. durene, $C_6H_2(CH_3)_4$, per liter of toluene.
  (d) Ten ml. of the toluene-durene solution are pipetted into the sample and mixed well.

Calculation.—Calculate the free styrene and vinyl toluene as follows:

$$\% S = \frac{P_s\, D\, 100}{P_d W} \qquad\qquad \% V = \frac{P_v\, D\, 100}{P_d W}$$

where: S and V = styrene and vinyl toluene;
     P_s and P_v = peak areas, S and V;
        D = grams of durene; and
        W = grams of sample.

NOTE.—No correction factors are required because styrene, vinyl toluene, and durene have been found to exhibit the same response per gram.

[145] Seifert, W. K., and Percival, D. F., I&EC Product Research and Development, **3**, 222, 1964.
[146] Shapras, P., and Claver, G., Anal. Chem., **36**, 2282, 1964.
[147] Tessari, D. J., unpublished work.
* When more styrene or vinyl toluene is expected, it is wise not to alter the sample size, but to use more internal standard. This allows for a smaller sample on the gas chromatograph.

TOLUENE DIISOCYANATE

The literature is very scant concerning GC methods for the determination of toluene diisocyanate (TDI) monomer in polymers. Analysis of monomers of the mono-, di-, and triisocyanates of toluene, however, has been reported as far back as 1957.[148]

Recently Neubauer, *et al.*,[149] reported on the determination of free TDI in adducts of TDI and trimethylolpropane. When compared with a wet chemical method, the gas chromatographic method displayed greater precision and accuracy in the range of 0.5 to 10 percent free TDI. The rudiments of this method are outlined below.

A column 2 meters in length, of $\frac{1}{4}$-inch stainless steel tubing, is packed with 10 percent by weight of Dow Corning high vacuum silicone grease on Fluoropak 80. The column is maintained at 125°C. with a helium flow of 80 ml. per minute and an injection port temperature of 175°C.

The sample is prepared by weighing out 8 to 10 g. of sample, adding 1 g. of trichlorobenzene as an internal standard, and adding sufficient dry xylene to reduce the sample viscosity to permit sampling with a syringe. This total mixture is then injected into the chromatograph and the amount of TDI is calculated from peak height or area ratios of trichlorobenzene and TDI.

If necessary, the weight ratio of sample to trichlorobenzene can be changed to accommodate various TDI levels. Also, it has been found desirable to prepare a solution of trichlorobenzene in xylene and then, by pipetting in the proper amount of this solution into the sample, the internal standard and diluent are added in one step. Naturally, the amount of trichlorobenzene added to the xylene and the volume of this solution added to the sample will be governed by the amount of TDI in the sample. This modification has its main advantage in the analysis of routine samples.

MISCELLANEOUS MONOMERS

As mentioned previously, it is often possible to adapt published methods for one's needs with only slight modification. Below will be listed a few more references which may provide a starting point. It should be remembered that samples containing appreciable amounts of water are best determined on a chromatograph equipped with a flame ionization type detector which doesn't "see" water, rather than the perhaps commoner thermal conductivity detector which is readily "washed out" by water vapor.

Latex.—A method for determining residual monomers in latex systems has been reported by Tweet and Miller.[150] In this method the monomer is first isolated from the polymer by distillation in the presence of a known amount of toluene, and then the resulting organic layer is chromatographed. The monomer content is calculated by means of peak area ratios of toluene to monomer. This method has been evaluated for the determination of ethyl acrylate, styrene, and acrylonitrile monomer.

Another method for residual monomers in latex was proposed by Wilkinson, *et al.*,[151] in which the latex sample is dissolved in a suitable solvent. The resulting solution is then injected directly into the gas chromatograph. Using a 10-ft. polyethylene glycol E-6000 column, the authors were able to show the applicability of this method for the determination of 13 monomers in latex systems.

Phenol-Formaldehyde Resins.—Stevens and Percival [152] reported a method for free

[148] Felton, H. R., 1957 International Gas Chrom. Symposium, Instrument Society of America, Pittsburgh, Pa., 1957, p. 142.
[149] Neubauer, N., Skreckoski, G., White, R., and Kane, A., Anal. Chem., **35,** 1647, 1963.
[150] Tweet, O., and Miller, W., Anal. Chem., **35,** 852, 1963.
[151] Wilkinson, L., Norman, C., and Buettner, J., Anal. Chem., **36,** 1759, 1964.
[152] Stevens, M., Percival, D., Anal. Chem., **36,** 1023, 1964.

phenol and formaldehyde in phenolic resins. The formaldehyde is determined by diluting the resin solution with water and injecting the resulting solution into the gas chromatograph. An alternative, and preferred, procedure is to first neutralize the resin solution with acid to precipitate the polymer and then inject the resulting water solution into the gas chromatograph. For free phenol the acidified aqueous solution and resin solids mixture from above is extracted with ether. The resulting ether solution is then analyzed for phenol.

This method was developed specifically for analysis of monomer in phenolic plywood adhesives which, in this case, are water soluble. For monomer analysis in phenol-formaldehyde condensates which are not water soluble, it is feasible to dilute the polymer with any other suitable solvent and inject the total solution into the gas chromatograph.

ACRYLIC RESIN ANALYSIS

PYROLYSIS

Probably the most popular gas chromatographic method for characterizing acrylic polymers is by pyrolysis. The polymer is exposed to a high temperature environment such as hot wire, ribbon, or hot tube, and the volatile fragments are swept onto the column by the carrier gas. The components from the pyrolyzate can be identified, or the overall polymer composition can be characterized, by comparing the chromatograms obtained with the chromatograms of the pyrolyzates of known polymers examined under identical conditions. Methacrylates are particularly interesting because most of their homopolymers tend to unzip almost completely to monomer at certain temperatures.

The techniques, apparatus, and polymer combinations used in pyrolysis studies of acrylics are of such a varied and specific nature that a general description is not practical. The best source of information on this subject is the literature where, in most cases, the analyst can find specific references. As a starting point, a number of references may be selected.[153-162]

Reference to pyrolysis-gas chromatography characterization of some other polymers may also be of interest as follows:

Phenolic resins;[163] Polybutene;[164] Polyethylene and Polypropylene;[165] Poly(Vinyl Acetate) and Poly(Vinyl Chloride), Cellulose Acetate and Butyrate, Nylon 6 and 66, Cotton, Wool, Silk, and Polyurethane;[166] Poly(ethylene-ethyl acrylate) and Poly(ethylene-vinyl acetate);[167] Miscellaneous Elastomers;[168] and Methylstyrene.[169]

[153] Rybicka, S., JOCCA, 47, 475, 1964.
[154] Hewitt, G., and Whitham, B., Analyst, 86, 643, 1961.
[155] Ettre, K., and Varadi, P., Anal. Chem., 34, 752, 1962.
[156] Bombaugh, K., Cook, C., and Clampitt, B., Anal. Chem., 35, 1834, 1963.
[157] Strassburger, J., Brauer, G., Tryon, M., Forziati, A., Anal. Chem., 32, 454, 1960.
[158] Guillet, J., Wooten, W., Combs, R., J. of Applied Polymer Science, 3, 61, 1960.
[159] Ettre, K., Varadi, P., Anal. Chem., 35, 69, 1963.
[160] Radell, E., and Strutz, H., Anal. Chem., 31, 1890, 1959.
[161] Lehmann, F., Brauer, G., Anal. Chem., 33, 673, 1961.
[162] Esposito, G., CCL Report No. 157, Office of Technical Services, U. S. Dept. of Commerce, Washington, D. C.
[163] Parriss, W., Holland, P., British Plastics, p. 372, August, 1960.
[164] Porter, R., Hoffman, A., Johnson, J., Anal. Chem., 34, 1179, 1962.
[165] Cox, B., Ellis, B., Anal. Chem., 36, 90, 1964.
[166] Groten, B., Anal. Chem., 36, 1206, 1964.
[167] Barrall, E., Porten, R., Johnson, J., Anal. Chem., 35, 73, 1963.
[168] Hulot, H., and Lebel, P., Rubber Chemistry and Technol., 37, 297, 1964.
[169] Grant, D., Vance, E., and Bywater, S., Trans. Faraday Soc., 56, 1697, 1960.

ALKOXYL

Another approach for analyzing acrylic resins combines the classical Zeisel method for alkoxyl determination with gas chromatography.[170-174] This method can be used for quantitative analysis of acrylic polymer, provided that sufficient qualitative information is available. For example, one can determine the amount of poly(ethyl acrylate) and poly(methylmethacrylate) in a polymer if the polymer has been qualitatively character-ized. The procedure as outlined below has been used successfully in the authors' labora-tory for the analysis of acrylic polymers containing methyl, ethyl, propyl, and butyl acrylate, and methyl, ethyl, and propyl methacrylate.[174] Poly(butyl methacrylate) can be determined qualitatively but low recoveries have been obtained with polymers con-taining more than 20 percent of this monomer. Styrene and acrylonitrile copolymerized with the acrylics do not interfere.

Chemical Procedure.—The reaction assembly[175] is prepared by adding 25 to 30 mg. of dried resin, 2.5 g. of phenol or 2.5 ml. of propionic anhydride, and warming in a glycerol bath at 120°C. for 15 minutes. Then carefully add 5 ml. of 55–58 percent hydriodic acid (sp. gr. 1.7). Immediately attach trapping assembly[175] with 5 ml. of Reagent Grade heptane in the scrubber. (Substitute pentane to check for propyl iodide.) Adjust nitrogen purge rate to 6 ml. per minute (2 bubbles per second) and cool the scrubber by means of a methylene chloride—dry ice bath. Continue heating for 2 hours.

Remove trapping assembly from reaction assembly and quantitatively transfer the heptane from the scrubber to a 10-ml. screw cap vial. Use only a minimum of heptane for the transfer. Pipet 0.5 ml. of a standard solution of carbon tetrachloride in heptane (20 mg. of carbon tetrachloride in 250 ml. heptane) into the vial, mix well, and add a piece of copper wire to retard decomposition. The sample is now ready for gas chro-matographic analysis.

Chromatographic Procedure.—A 10-ft. by $\frac{1}{4}$-inch column packed with 20 percent w/w Silicon 401 gum rubber on 60–80 mesh Chromosorb P is suitable for this analysis. The column temperature is maintained at 90°C., the flow rate at 60 ml./min., and the injection port at 200°C.

Calculation.—After the chromatograms are obtained and the areas calculated, the percent of each acrylic present can be calculated from the following formula.

$$\% \text{ Acrylic} = \frac{A_a \times W_s \times C}{A_s \times W_a} \times 100$$

where: A_a = corrected area of alkyl iodide;
$\quad\quad A_s$ = corrected area of CCl_4;
$\quad\quad W_a$ = weight of sample in milligrams;
$\quad\quad W_s$ = weight of CCl_4 added to sample; and
$\quad\quad C$ = conversion factor for converting alkyl iodide to corresponding acrylic.

A calibration run is necessary to obtain relative response factors for correcting the alkyl iodide areas relative to that of carbon tetrachloride.

[170] Haslam, J., Hamilton, J., Jeffs, A., Analyst, **83,** 66, 1958.
[171] Samsel, E., and Cobler, J., Anal. Chem., **33,** 677, 1961.
[172] Vertalier and Martin, Chimie Analytique, **40,** 80, 1958.
[173] Belcher, R., Bhatty, M., West, T., J. Chem. Soc., Nov., 4480, 1957.
[174] Tessari, D. J., and Payne, S. B., unpublished work.
[175] Quickfit Assembly 11MD, Quickfit and Quartz Ltd., Quickfit Works, Heart of Stone, Staffordshire, England or equivalent apparatus.

Sample Calculation.—The example given below will aid in understanding the calculations when applied to an actual polymer analysis. The sample problem was worked out for a methyl methacrylate-ethyl acrylate-butyl acrylate terpolymer.

Example: A 25.3-mg. sample was digested as outlined in the method. The heptane solution was transferred from the scrubber to a 10-ml. vial and 0.5 ml. of the carbon tetrachloride-heptane solution (23.1 mg. carbon tetrachloride in 250 ml. heptane) was pipetted into the vial. This mixture was chromatographed and the following corrected areas calculated from the resulting chromatogram.

Methyl Iodide..............	350 area units
Ethyl Iodide................	1572 " "
Butyl Iodide...............	444 " "
Carbon Tetrachloride.........	285 " "

$$\text{Percent Methyl methacrylate} = \frac{350 \times 0.046 \times 0.706}{285 \times 25.3} \times 100 = 15.75$$

$$\text{Percent Ethyl acrylate} = \frac{1572 \times 0.046 \times 0.644}{285 \times 25.3} \times 100 = 64.51$$

$$\text{Percent Butyl acrylate} = \frac{444 \times 0.046 \times 0.697}{285 \times 25.3} \times 100 = \frac{19.73}{99.99\%}$$

ALKYDS

DIBASIC ACIDS

The first step in the analysis of an alkyd resin is usually the determination of the phthalic acid content. This is usually done by the Kappelmeir saponification described earlier in this chapter (see Procedure A, p. 1275, or ASTM Method D563-52 or D1398-58).[176] In this procedure the phthalic acid, and any other dibasic acids present, is isolated as the dipotassium salt by filtration. By preparing the methyl esters of these acid salts, it is possible to characterize the acids present with gas chromatography. The esters can be prepared by using diazomethane and characterized on silicone grease or LAC788 columns as described by Luke, *et al.*, for the identification of stable Krebs cycle acids.[177]

Another approach in the characterization of carboxylic acids in alkyd resins involves the direct preparation of methyl esters by transesterification.[178] The procedure eliminates the saponification step and is rapid, but only gives a qualitative picture. The basic steps in the procedure are outlined below.

Chemical Procedure.—Enough resin solution to yield about 0.3 g. of nonvolatile material and 15 ml. of 0.5 *M* lithium methoxide and a boiling stone are added to 125-ml. flask. Reflux mixture with air condenser attached for about 2 minutes after solution is effected. Remove flask from heat source and quickly add 5 ml. of 5 *N* sulfuric acid.

Transfer contents of flask to separatory funnel, add 50 ml. of water and 35 ml. of methylene chloride. Shake vigorously, then transfer the methylene chloride layer to another separatory funnel, and wash with water until washings are free from sulfuric acid. Add washes to main aqueous phase and save. Dry methylene chloride over anhydrous sodium sulfate and transfer to a beaker. Remove solvent on a steam bath. Sample is now ready for chromatographic analysis.

[176] American Society for Testing and Materials, Philadelphia, Pa., ASTM Standards, 1965, Part 20.
[177] Luke, H., Freeman, T., Kier, L., Anal. Chem., **35**, 1916, 1963.
[178] Esposito, G., Swann, M., Anal. Chem., **34**, 1048, 1962.

Chromatographic Procedure.—The prepared esters are chromatographed on a silicone grease column and then on a DEGS—Carbowax 20M column, with triacetin as a relative retention time reference compound. With this technique one will characterize all of the carboxylic acids present including the fatty acids.

FATTY ACIDS

Separation of Fatty Acids.—The fatty acids portion must be isolated from the resin after saponification of the alkyd with ethanolic potassium hydroxide and removal of the dibasic acids as described earlier in this chapter (see Procedure A, p. 1275, or ASTM Method D1398-58 [176]). The fatty acids are separated from the filtrate and combined washings according to ASTM Method D1398-58.[176] Briefly, this involves concentrating the filtrate down to 25 ml. on a steam bath under nitrogen, and transferring the concentrate to a 500-ml. separatory funnel with 300 ml. of water. The unsaponifiables are extracted with diethyl ether and then the resulting water layer is acidified with hydrochloric acid. The fatty acids are then extracted with diethyl ether, and the ether layer is washed with water, dried over anhydrous sodium sulfate, and evaporated to dryness under nitrogen on a steam bath. (If the fatty acids have to be stored prior to analysis, add hydroquinone, amounting to about 0.05 percent of acids, and store in refrigerator.)

The separated fatty acids are now ready to be methylated and analyzed by gas chromatography. The method is basically that of Zielinski,[179] the authors, and others who cooperated on the evaluation and adoption of ASTM Method D2245-64T and D1983-64T.[176] The steps in the method are summarized below.

Preparation of Methyl Esters.—Weigh accurately about 0.340 g. of fatty acids into a 25-ml. Erlenmeyer flask and about 0.05 g. (accurately weighed) of margaric acid. If only qualitative information is required, add only 10 drops of sample to the flask.

Add 3 ml. of boron trifluoride reagent (125 g. boron trifluoride per liter of methanol), heat on steam bath, and boil for about 3 minutes. Wash into a 125-ml. separatory funnel with 30 ml. ether and 20 ml. of water. Shake, allow layers to separate, discard water layer, and wash ether layer twice with 25-ml. portions of water. Dry over anhydrous sodium sulfate and transfer to a 125-ml. flask, add enough hydroquinone to amount to about 0.05 percent of sample, and evaporate to near dryness. Store in a $\frac{1}{2}$-dram vial in the refrigerator until ready for analysis.

Chromatographic Analysis.—The esters are analyzed on a DEGS column, about 7 ft. in length, maintained at about 200°C. The flow rate is adjusted so that methyl linolenate elutes in 30 minutes or less. The retention time of each peak is tabulated

TABLE 54-14. RELATIVE RETENTION AND RELATIVE RESPONSE VALUES
OF SOME OF THE COMMON FATTY ACID METHYL ESTERS

Methyl Ester	Relative Retention	Relative Response
Myristate	0.56	1.03
Palmitate	1.00	1.00
Margarate	1.32	0.99
Stearate	1.70	0.97
Oleate	1.94	0.95
Linoleate	2.31	0.92
Linolenate	3.00	0.90

relative to methyl palmitate and identified by using the information given in Table 54-14. Next the areas of each peak are determined and corrected by using Table 54-14.

[179] Zielinski, W. L., JAOCS, **41**, 249, 1964.

The retention and response data given in the table are presented as a guide. It is recommended that the analyst redetermine these values on his own equipment.

Calculation.—Calculate the percent of each fatty acid with the following formula:

Percent fatty acid

$$= \frac{\text{Corrected area for the fatty acid peak}}{\text{Corrected area of margarate peak}} \times \frac{\text{Weight of margaric acid}}{\text{Weight of fatty acid sample}} \times 100$$

Interpretation.—Based on the amount and type of monomeric fatty acid found and information as given in Table 54-15, one can usually decide what type of oil was the original source of the fatty acids. When a mixture of oil or oil acid types is suspected, one can profit by comparing the content of some key fatty acids. For example, a high oleate content in what otherwise appears to be a soya type composition would suggest soya plus some tall oil. If, however, the palmitate appears a little high, one would conclude that some cottonseed had been added to the soya type acids.

In the event that chromatographic analysis suggests the presence of polymer, it must be known that the polymer composition is due solely to oil polymer if the calculation of polymer content is to be of value in oil identification. In such cases the polymer content of the oil ester sample plus the percentages of the polyunsaturated acids obtained from the chromatogram can be used to determine the total polyunsaturates present in the original oil. Since the value for total polyunsaturates vary with the oil in question, the experimental value obtained is used as additional evidence for oil identification.

The presence of oil polymer composed of reaction products of the oil acids with cyclo- or dicyclopentadiene, maleic anhydride, styrene, vinyltoluene, or other Diels-Alder adducts, or the presence of rosin acids (in the case of tall oil fatty acids with high rosin content), negates the value of percent polymer determination for assistance in oil identification. In most cases, the presence of these modifications can be detected by running infrared spectra on a portion of the separated fatty acids.

Another more direct interference which has not been mentioned is the presence of carboxylic acid esters other than fatty acids. Although the potassium salts of these acids are generally insoluble in alkaline ethanol, acids such as isophthalic and benzoic acid are still expected to find their way into the fatty acid fraction due to the partial solubility of their potassium salts in the saponification medium. When unfamiliar peaks are observed in the chromatogram of fatty acid methyl esters from whole paint, this type of interference should be considered.

POLYOLS

Polyol Acetates (Saponification of Resin).—The aqueous phase remaining from the fatty acids separation contains the polyols. Although there is no standard gas chromatographic method for analysis of polyols in this mixture, the following qualitative method has been used successfully in the authors' laboratory for all except propylene glycol.[180]

Chemical Procedure.—Transfer the aqueous phase remaining from the fatty acids separation into a 1000-ml., round-bottom flask. Add 200 ml. of benzene, attach a water condenser and a 25-ml. Dean-Stark trap fitted with a stopcock. Reflux, and periodically remove the water from the trap until no more water is carried over by the benzene. Remove condenser and trap from flask, place flask on steam bath, and with a gentle stream of air evaporate to near dryness (leave about 10 ml. of benzene in flask).

Transfer to a 125-ml. Erlenmeyer flask and rinse flask with two 15-ml. portions of acetic anhydride. Attach condenser and reflux for 2 hours (as an alternative, a room temperature acetylation can be carried out by cautiously adding 2 drops of concentrated

[180] Tessari, D. J., unpublished work.

TABLE 54-15. FATTY ACID COMPOSITION OF OILS USED IN PAINT PRODUCTS*

CASTOR OIL

Palmitic	2%
Stearic	1
Oleic	7
Ricionoleic	87
Linoleic	3

COCONUT OIL

Caproic	Trace
Caprylic	6%
Capric	6
Lauric	44
Myristic	18
Palmitic	11
Stearic	6
Oleic	7
Linoleic	2
Linolenic	Trace

COTTONSEED OIL

Capric	Trace
Lauric	Trace
Myristic	1%
Myristoleic	Trace
Palmitic	29%
Palmitoleic	2
Stearic	4
Oleic	24
Linoleic	40
Arachidic	Trace

LINSEED OIL

Palmitic	6%
Palmitoleic	Trace
Stearic	4%
Oleic	22
Linoleic	16
Linolenic	52
Arachidic	Trace
Gadoleic	Trace

OITICICA OIL

Palmitic	7%
Stearic	5
Oleic	6
Licanic	78
Hydroxy Acids	4

PERILLA OIL

Palmitic	7%
Stearic	2
Oleic	13
Linoleic	14
Linolenic	64

SAFFLOWER OIL

Myristic	Trace
Myristoleic	Trace
Palmitic	8%
Palmitoleic	Trace
Stearic	3%
Oleic	13
Linoleic	75
Linolenic	1

SOYBEAN OIL

Myristic	Trace
Palmitic	11%
Stearic	4
Oleic	25
Linoleic	51
Linolenic	9
Arachidic	Trace
Gadoleic	Trace

TALL OIL**

Palmitic	5%
Stearic	3
Oleic	46
Linoleic	41
Linolenic	3
Arachidic	2

TUNG OIL

Palmitic	4%
Stearic	1
Oleic	8
Linoleic	4
Linolenic	3
Eleostearic	80

MENHADEN OIL

Lauric	Trace
Myristic	7%
Myristoleic	Trace
Palmitic	16%
Palmitoleic	16
Stearic	2
Oleic	15
Linoleic	7
Linolenic	2
Arachidonic	17
Clupanodonic	11
Nisinic	4
Shibic	1
Unidentified unsaturates	2

* The percentages and acids used in this chart are taken from "COMPOSITION AND CONSTANTS OF FATTY ACIDS" chart and used by permission of the Archer-Daniels-Midland Company.

** The percent Rosin Acids in Tall Oil may vary from 0–42%. The percent Terpenes from 0–13%. Both variations depend on the grade and refining of the oil.

perchloric acid with mixing for 3 minutes). Cool the flask, add 25 ml. of water, and continue to reflux for 15 minutes.

Transfer the contents to a separatory funnel and extract twice with 20-ml. portions of chloroform. Wash the combined chloroform extracts with 50 ml. of a 10 percent sodium bicarbonate solution followed by a wash with 50 ml. of water.

Dry the chloroform layer over anhydrous sodium sulfate, and filter into a 100-ml. Erlenmeyer flask. Place flask on steam bath and reduce volume to about 5 ml. Do not remove all of the chloroform since there is a possibility of losing some of the low boiling polyol acetates.

Chromatographic Procedure.—The polyol acetates are analyzed on a 4-ft. by $\frac{1}{4}$-in. column packed with 10 percent W/W Carbowax 20M on 60–80 mesh Chromasorb P. Either isothermal or temperature programmed operation can be used. The components can be characterized by comparing their retention time with those of known polyol acetates chromatographed under identical conditions.

Polyol Acetates (Aminolysis of Resin).—Another qualitative method which characterizes the polyols via their acetate esters has been reported by Esposito and Swann.[181] With this technique the polyols are liberated from the alkyd by aminolysis and then acetylated in the same flask. The published procedure is abstracted below with slight modifications.

Chemical Procedure.—Weigh enough resin solution to yield 2 to 2.5 g. of nonvolatile into a 125-ml. Erlenmeyer flask, and dry in 105°C. vacuum oven for 2 hours. Add 6 ml. n-butylamine, and reflux under a water-cooled condenser for 1 hour. If 1,4-butanediol is suspected, use benzylamine.[182] Cool and carefully add 25 ml. of acetic anhydride and reflux for 90 minutes. Cool and add 35 ml. of water and boil 5 to 10 minutes. Cool and transfer to a separatory funnel using water sparingly for transfer. Extract with chloroform as outlined under the procedure above.

Chromatographic Procedure.—The polyol acetates are now analyzed on a 4-ft. by $\frac{1}{4}$-in. column packed with 10 percent W/W Carbowax 20M on 60–80 mesh Chromasorb P conditioned at 240°C. until bleeding is minimized. The flow rate is adjusted to 60 ml. per minute, and the column temperature at 50°C. The sample is injected and the column temperature increased to 225°C. at a rate of 7.9°C. per minute. If temperature programming is not available, the optimum isothermal temperature must be selected by trial and error, depending on which polyols are present.

Interpretation.—The retention time of each peak is recorded, relative to the second reagent peak. The identity of the polyols is then achieved by comparing these relative retention times to those shown in Table 54-16. For best results these values should be determined on the analyst's own instrument using known systems. If o-phthalic acid is present in the alkyd, an interfering peak due to it will appear with a relative retention time of 1.53.

GEL PERMEATION CHROMATOGRAPHY

"Gel Permeation Chromatography" is the name coined for a new chromatographic technique which fractionates polymers on the basis of molecular size. With linear polymers the gel permeation chromatograms may be calibrated to provide accurate molecular weight distribution data. With more complex branched chain systems, molecular size data is somewhat more difficult to interpret in an absolute way. However, even qualitative representation of molecular size information has long been needed to round out the

[181] Esposito, G., and Swann, M., Anal. Chem., **33,** 1854, 1961.
[182] Esposito, G., Anal. Chem., **34,** 1173, 1962.

TABLE 54-16.

Polyol Acetate	Relative Retention Time (Second reagent peak = 1)
Propylene glycol	0.68
Ethylene glycol	0.71
Neopentyl glycol	0.84
1,4-Butanediol	0.97
Dipropylene glycol	1.05
Diethylene glycol	1.16
Glycerol	1.24
Trimethylolethane	1.33
Triethylene glycol	1.43
Pentaerythritol	1.81
Mannitol	3.08
Sorbitol	3.24

characterization of paint vehicles or varnishes. Gel permeation chromatography promises to fill this need.

The technique is described by its inventor as a special liquid-solid elution chromatography that uses columns packed with an inert cross-linked polymer gel which may be eluted with a compatible organic solvent.[183] The basis of the separation is the differential migration or permeation of different sized molecules into the "pores" of the gel beads. The usual adsorption and partition effects which are the basis of other chromatographic separations appear to be absent. Consequently, the technique is applicable to polymers of varied chemical types of both high and low molecular weight.[184] With tetrahydrofuran as the eluting solvent, a worker in the authors' laboratory is successfully applying this new technique to the study of molecular size of alkyds, polyesters, bodied oils, solution acrylics, and high polymer emulsion acrylics or vinyls.[185] Reports of applications to other specific polymers are beginning to appear. Examples are the papers on *cis*-1,4-polybutadiene[186] and epoxy resins[187] given at a recent American Chemical Society Meeting.

The instrumentation necessary for gel permeation chromatography is manufactured as a single unit only by one company at this time.[188] The essential parts are a solvent assembly, a 2-ml. sample injection loop, packed gel columns, a reference column, a process differential refractometer detector, and an automatic effluent syphon and volume counter. The solvent assembly includes a storage and pressure ballast tank, a pump, a degasser, filter, and pressure regulator. The sample columns are supplied as 4-ft. lengths of $\frac{3}{8}$-in. stainless steel tubing packed with rigidly cross-linked polystyrene gel of controlled "pore" size. Larger diameter prep columns are expected to be available also. The gels are available to cover the porosity range of 10^1 Angstroms to 10^6 Angstroms in nominal steps of powers of ten. A gel whose nominal porosity is 10^4 Angstroms will allow

[183] Moore, J. C., and Hendrickson, J. G., "Gel Permeation II: The Nature of the Separation," Paper No. 61, Polymer Preprints, Div. of Polymer Chemistry, Sept., 1964.

[184] Maley, L. E., Applications of Gel Permeation Chromatography to High and Low Molecular Weights, Paper No. 63, Polymer Preprints, Div. of Polymer Chem. ACS, Sept., 1964.

[185] Bartosiewicz, R. L., unpublished work.

[186] Harmon, D. J., "A Comparison of the Solution and Gel Permeation Fractionation of Cis-1,4-Polybutadiene," Paper No. 62, Polymer Preprints, Div. of Polymer Chem. ACS, Sept., 1964.

[187] Miles, B. H., "Application of Gel Permeation Chromatography to Characterization of Epoxy Resins," Paper No. 39, Div. of Organic Coatings and Plastics Chem. ACS, Sept., 1964.

[188] Waters Associates, Inc., Framingham, Mass.

all molecules 10^4 Angstroms and lower to permeate into the gel structure. Larger molecules are confined to the interstitial volume between the gel beads and are not resolved. For best resolution several columns of porosity close to the size of the molecules to be separated are used.

For polymers encountered thus far in paint vehicles or varnishes, it has been found suitable to use a fraction of a milliliter of 0.5 percent solutions of the polymers in tetrahydrofuran, with a flow rate of around 1 mm. per minute of tetrahydrofuran as the eluting solvent. With 4 sample columns in series at room temperatures, a pressure of approximately 50 p.s.i. is required. Each column has approximately 20 ml. of interstitial volume, which means that it takes 20 minutes per column or 80 minutes per 4 columns for the first large molecules to arrive at the detector. The analysis time then may vary from about 30 minutes to 2 or 3 hours depending upon the number of columns which are required to provide the desired separation or resolution.

Chapter 55

PAPER, WOOD, AND PULP

By John L. Parsons

Consultant to the Paper and Allied Industries
Rye, New Hampshire

Introduction.—The evaluation and identification of the differences in the properties of wood, pulp, and paper are made by the application of standard test methods. Many of these methods involve instruments which do not measure an absolute property of the material, but give an empirical value which experience has shown is an index of pulp or paper quality. Much depends on the instrument and the technique employed. Thus, both the instrument and the method define the property of the material.

Most of the test methods included in this chapter are considered "standard" by the Technical Association of the Pulp and Paper Industry and the American Society for Testing and Materials, and are reproduced with permission. A few methods are rated as "tentative standard."

SPECIFIC GRAVITY (DENSITY) AND MOISTURE CONTENT OF PULPWOOD

This method is applicable to pulpwood chips and discs from the cross section of logs.

Pulpwood is usually purchased and handled on a volume basis. In processing it, however, it is desirable to know its moisture content and moisture-free weight in order to conduct pulping operations properly and to determine the percentage yield of pulp on a weight basis. The specific gravity or density of pulpwood relates wood volume to its weight.

Specific gravity (sp. gr.) is the ratio of the mass of a quantity of a substance to the mass of an equal volume of water. It is an absolute value and, since it is a ratio of similar quantities, is expressed without units. Density is the ratio of the mass of a quantity of a substance to the volume of that quantity and consequently is expressed in terms of weight per unit volume.

Since wood swells or shrinks, respectively, with absorption or loss of water, it is necessary to express the specific gravity at specified conditions of moisture content and volume. The most usual conditions are the moisture-free weight[1] and the maximum (green) or the minimum (moisture-free) volume. For most purposes, the maximum volume basis is sufficient. In the method described here the specimen is considered to be swelled to its maximum volume when its moisture content exceeds the "fiber-saturation point," which lies between 18 and 26 percent by weight (wet basis) for most species. Procedures for obtaining the volume on both the green and moisture-free bases are described in this method. This method is standardized as TAPPI T 18 m-53.

---

[1] Many wood technologists believe that the specific gravity of wood is truly expressed only on the basis of moisture-free weight and maximum (green) volume.

APPARATUS

Weighing Scales.—A balance with a capacity of 14 to 16 kg. (30 to 35 pounds) and sensitive to 0.5 g., preferably with a sliding-weight beam graduated in grams (or 0.001 pound).

Drying Oven.—A drying oven maintained at $105 \pm 3°C.$ ($220 \pm 5°F.$).

Centrifuge (for chips).—A centrifuge of the basket type, capable of holding a sample of $\frac{3}{4}$ to 1 pound (350 to 500 g.) of chips, operated at a constant speed between 800 and 1200 r.p.m. A satisfactory basket can be made of $\frac{3}{32}$-in. thick brass, from 6 to 8 in. in diameter and about 5 in. deep, and perforated with $\frac{3}{16}$-in. diameter holes on $\frac{1}{2}$-in. centers in the side and bottom.

Chip Holder.—A suitable holder consists of a wire-mesh basket of 8- to 10-mesh heavy-gauge copper or bronze wire, about 6 in. in diameter and 8 in. high, with a wire-mesh hinged lid provided with a clasp and fitted with a wire-loop handle so arranged that the lid may be opened and closed while the basket is hanging by the handle. The holder should be made heavy enough to sink in water when filled with a sample of chips lighter than water. Variations in design of the chip holder are permissible.

Disc Holder.—A suitable holder consists of a $\frac{3}{16}$-in. diameter rod, 8 to 10 in. long, with one end fitted into the center of a brass or bronze disc about 4 in. in diameter and $\frac{1}{4}$ in. thick. The side of the disc opposite the rod is fitted with three prongs about $1\frac{1}{4}$ in. long and $\frac{1}{8}$ in. in diameter. The sharpened points of the prongs are equidistantly spaced about 3 in. Variations in design of the disc holder are permissible.

Auxiliary Apparatus.—Ring stand and clamps. Pans and other containers for use in soaking samples and obtaining their submerged weights. Devices for suspending samples in water while obtaining their submerged weights by Method 2, below. Counterbalance and tare weights.

REAGENTS

Shellac Solution.—Commercial shellac varnish (containing 5 pounds of ordinary orange shellac per gallon of denatured alcohol) diluted with an equal volume of alcohol.

Kerosene.—Ordinary commercial grade.

Paraffin Wax.—Ordinary commercial grade.

TEST SPECIMEN

Discs.—Select a number of sample logs representative of the material being tested. Saw from each log selected for test a disc of solid wood from $\frac{3}{4}$ to 1 in. thick from an undamaged, sound, and knot-free section. If possible, cut the discs from the center or at least a foot from the end of each log so as to avoid end checks, and obtain the disc from the least dry portion. Use a sharp, clean-cutting saw. Remove any bark, adhering splinters, and sawdust from each disc. Saw into smaller sections any discs too large for the can or vessel used for obtaining the submerged weight and mark them for identification. Place the specimen discs in a covered container as soon as cut, to prevent loss of moisture.

Chips.—From 0.60 to 0.75 pound (300 to 350 g.) of chips are required for one determination. Chips shall be tested at least in duplicate. Select the chips so as to be representative of the material being tested. Unless previously screened to the desired size, remove sawdust and undersized chips by shaking on a 3-mesh sieve. Store the chip sample in a closed container until ready for further preparation.

TOLERANCE IN WEIGHING

All weighings shall be made to the nearest gram or 0.002 pound.

MOISTURE CONTENT

Though not required for determining the density or specific gravity, it is convenient to determine the moisture content of the sample at this time. For this purpose obtain the initial weights, A and B, respectively, of the specimen discs and chips as sampled, and calculate the moisture content from the moisture-free weights of the specimens which are obtained subsequently.

SPECIFIC GRAVITY OR DENSITY

Soaking.—Submerge the sample, whether discs or chips, in water at room temperature for at least 1 hour, or longer if necessary.

The purpose of soaking the wood is twofold: first to insure that the specimen is swelled to its green volume, and second to eliminate an error which occurs if the wood absorbs water during the weighing operation for obtaining its volume. Thus it is necessary to insure that the internal cavities be practically filled with water prior to weighing when submerged, so that further absorption during this weighing is negligible. When the moisture content is above the fiber-saturation point, a 1-hour soaking period is usually sufficient to accomplish both these conditions; otherwise the soaking should be prolonged until checks, if any, are closed.

Draining. (a) **Discs.**—Let the free water drain from the soaked discs by standing them on edge for a short time and then patting with a cloth or piece of blotting paper just prior to weighing. While draining, the discs should not be exposed to a draft, fan, or direct heat. Discs whose surfaces show signs of drying out before the weighings can be completed should be returned to the soaking vessel.

(b) **Chips.**—Allow the sample of soaked chips to drain in a wire-mesh basket for a few minutes, then place in the centrifuge basket and centrifuge for a standardized period of time and speed determined as described in the following section.

Standardization of Speed and Time of Centrifuging.—Determine the specific gravity of identified discs sawed from the ends and middle of a number of correspondingly identified pulpwood logs, representative of the species and kind of wood, according to one of the procedures described in this method. Convert the remaining pieces of the logs to chips, and mix and keep the chips from each log separate.

Weigh out the same chosen quantity of several samples of the chips from each log. Soak and drain the chip samples as described above.

Centrifuge the soaked chips at various speeds and times varying from 800 to 1200 r.p.m. and 1 to 4 minutes. Immediately after centrifuging each sample determine its green volume by one of the methods described. Dry and weigh the chip samples and compute their specific gravities.

For each condition of time and speed, calculate the percent difference, plus or minus, of the average specific gravity of the chip samples determined from the average specific gravity of the discs from the same log. Calculate the average percent variation for all the logs for each condition of time and speed. Adopt as the standard conditions a time and a speed for the chosen quantity of chips at which this average percent variation of the chips from the discs is within ±1.

Determination of Green Volume.—In determining the volume of the specimen it is the outside boundary, exclusive of surface depressions, that is required. For this reason the discs or chips should be cleanly cut and all cracks and checks swelled with water until they are closed.

One of the most accurate methods of obtaining the volume of an object is by displacement in a liquid, usually water. The procedures given below may be varied both as to apparatus and operation. Variations are permissible so long as they adhere to the fundamental principle involved. Two procedures are described as Method 1 (On the Balance) and Method 2 (Off the Balance).

Method 1 (On the Balance). (a) *Discs.*—Place a vessel holding enough water at room temperature to completely immerse an 8- or 9-in. diameter disc on the left-hand pan of the scales, and counterbalance the weight of the container and water. Keep the counterbalance on the pan throughout all subsequent operations.

Impinge a drained disc on the three-pronged rod and carefully lower the disc into the vessel so as not to entrap bubbles of air. In a completely submerged position and not touching either sides or bottom of the vessel, clamp it by means of the ringstand and clamp. If not more than $\frac{1}{2}$ in. of the prongs are immersed, the volume of water displaced by them will be negligible. Again balance the scales. The weight added to restore balance is the weight, C, of the volume of water equivalent to the volume of the specimen.

NOTE.—Discs too large for the container should have been cut into two or more pieces and properly identified prior to soaking. The above operations are performed on each piece separately and the weights added to obtain the weight, C, for the whole disc.

Remove the disc and add water to the vessel until it is counterbalanced again before immersing the next specimen.

(b) *Chips.*—Counterbalance on the scales a vessel containing enough water at room temperature to freely submerge the chip holder. Keep the counterbalance on the pan throughout all subsequent operations. Completely submerge the *empty* chip holder, except for its wire handle, which hooks onto a support, on the ringstand. The chip holder must not touch the sides or bottom of the vessel. Obtain the weight, D, of the volume of water equivalent to the volume of the *empty* chip holder, which is that of the weights necessary to add to the right-hand pan to secure a balance.

Transfer the sample of chips from the centrifuge to the chip holder. Slowly lower the chip holder with chips into the counterbalanced vessel of water. Before hooking the handle onto the support, give the holder a quick twist clockwise and then counterclockwise to release any bubbles of air that might have been entrapped. Place a tare weight equivalent to D on the right-hand pan. Obtain the weight, E, of the volume of water equivalent to the volume of chips, which is that of the weights necessary to add to the tare weight on the right-hand pan to secure a balance.

Remove the chip holder from the vessel and remove all weights except the counterbalance from the scale. Add water to the vessel until it is balanced again before immersing the next sample.

Method 2 (Off the Balance). (a) *Discs.*—Prior to removing the discs from the soaking vessel, not and segregate those that sink and those that float.

Set the scales on the right end of a table so constructed that specimens can be suspended from the right-hand pan. Place a vessel of sufficient size containing water at room temperature below the scales directly under the right-hand pan. Hang on the right-hand pan a stirrup and chain or other convenient device with screw clamp for attaching and adjusting the three-pronged disc holder. Counterbalance the stirrup and disc holder and keep the counterbalance on the scale throughout all subsequent weighings.

Obtain the weight, F, of the soaked, drained disc. Immediately impinge the disc on its holder and carefully lower it into the water so as not to entrap air. Adjust and clamp the disc holder in the stirrup with the disc completely immersed and not touching the sides or bottom of the vessel.

Alternative Procedure.—Instead of immersing the disc horizontally, it may be suspended edgewise (vertically) by clipping it to a large battery clamp attached to a light chain or cord which is hung from the right-hand pan of the scales. Another large battery clamp to which is fastened a weight or plummet is clipped to the lower edge of the disc. Since the plummets need only be heavy enough to sink the disc and steady it in a vertical position, two or three different weights for larger and smaller discs are provided. The counterbalance weight is obtained with the plummet and clamps immersed in water.

Case I.—The disc is lighter than water. Obtain the weight, G, required to restore balance by adding weights to the right-hand pan. The weight of the volume of water equivalent to the volume of the disk is $(F + G)$.

Case II.—The disc is heavier than water. Balance the scale by adding weights, H, to the left-hand pan. The weight of the volume of water equivalent to the volume of the disk is $(F - H)$.

After weighing the immersed disc, raise (but do not remove) the holder from the stirrup, and remove the disc from the holder. Remove all weights except the counterbalance from the scales.

(b) *Chips.*—Hang a stirrup, as described for discs, to the right-hand pan of the scales. Immerse the *empty* chip holder in the vessel of water and suspend it from the stirrup. Counterbalance the stirrup and immersed chip holder by adding weights to the left-hand pan. Keep the counterbalance weight on the scale throughout all subsequent weighings.

Obtain the weight, I, of the sample of soaked, centrifuged chips and transfer them immediately to the chip holder. Carefully lower the chip holder with chips into the vessel of water, give the holder a quick twist clockwise and then counterclockwise to release bubbles of air, and suspend it from the stirrup.

Case I.—The chip sample floats in water. Obtain the weight, J, required to restore balance as for a disk lighter than water. The weight of the volume of water equivalent to the volume of the chips is $(I + J)$.

Case II.—The chip samp'e sinks in water. Obtain the weight, K, required to restore balance as for a disc heavier than water. The weight of the volume of water equivalent to the volume of chips is $(I - K)$.

Remove all weights except the counterbalance from the scale before immersing the next sample.

NOTE.—The choice of displacement method will depend largely on the individual analyst and the laboratory facilities available. Method 1 does not require obtaining the weight of the water-soaked specimens but requires adding water to the vessel on the pan to restore balance after each determination. A bottle of water with syphon and pinch clamp will facilitate adding water to the pan. With Method 2 the vessel of water does not have to be rebalanced each time. The water, if spilled, is below the table top and records are not apt to be spoiled thereby. On the other hand, the weight of the soaked specimens is required and a different method of calculation for "floaters" and "sinkers" is necessary.

Determination of Moisture-Free Weight.—Place the discs on the shelves of the drying oven so that they do not touch each other. Spread out the chips in a wire-mesh tray or basket in the oven. Dry the discs and chips to constant weights, L and M, respectively, which will require from 24 to 48 hours.

Determination of Moisture-Free Volume. (a) Discs.—Dip the dried discs, after weighing and while still warm, into hot paraffin wax, which gives a waterproof seal of negligible volume. Scrape, or if hot enough, wipe off surplus paraffin. Determine the weight of water, N, equivalent to the volume of the disc by Method 1 as described for the water-soaked samples. Alternatively, using Method 2, obtain the weight, O, of the paraffined disc in air before obtaining its weight suspended in water. Let the submerged weight of the disc be P for Case I (disc lighter than water) and Q for Case II (disc heavier than water).

(b) Chips.—Because of the proportionately high volume of paraffin coating on a quantity of chips as compared to that on an equal quantity of wood in the form of discs, as well as the difficulty of immersing the basket of paraffined chips in water without entraining air, the determination of the volume of dried chips by this method is not recommended. The volume can, however, be obtained satisfactorily by coating the chips with shellac and immersing them in kerosene.

Immerse the dried chips, after weighing and while still warm, preferably contained in a wire basket, in an alcoholic solution of commercial shellac for a period of 3 to 5 minutes and then spread out to air dry. Determine the weight of kerosene, R, displaced by the chips by Method 1 as described for water-soaked chips. Alternatively, using Method 2, obtain the weight, S, of the shellac-coated chips in air before obtaining the weight suspended in kerosene. Let the submerged weight of the chips be T for Case I (chip sample lighter than kerosene) and U for Case II (chip sample heavier than kerosene).

REPORT

Moisture Content.—Report the results on the "as-received" basis to the nearest 0.1 percent moisture calculated as follows:

$$\text{Discs: } \frac{A - L}{A} \times 100 = \% \text{ moisture}$$

$$\text{Chips: } \frac{B - M}{B} \times 100 = \% \text{ moisture}$$

Specific Gravity.—The specific gravity as determined by the various procedures described is computed by the formulas given in Table 55-1. The calculation shall be made

TABLE 55-1. FORMULAS FOR COMPUTATION OF SPECIFIC GRAVITY

| | Basis of specific gravity determination | | | |
| | Moisture-free weight per green volume | | Moisture-free weight per moisture-free volume | |
Method of volume determination	*Discs*	*Chips*	*Discs*	*Chips*
Method 1	$\dfrac{L}{C}$	$\dfrac{M}{E}$	$\dfrac{L}{N}$	$\dfrac{MV}{R}$
Method 2				
Case I—Specimen lighter than suspension liquid	$\dfrac{L}{F + G}$	$\dfrac{M}{I + J}$	$\dfrac{L}{O + P}$	$\dfrac{MV}{S + T}$
Case II—Specimen heavier than suspension liquid	$\dfrac{L}{F - H}$	$\dfrac{M}{I - K}$	$\dfrac{L}{O - Q}$	$\dfrac{MV}{S - U}$

separately for each disc or sample of chips and the average of all discs or of all samples of chips reported. The calculation for both individual specimens and the average shall be made to three significant figures.

NOTE.—Since the specific gravity of pulpwood is primarily used in estimating the weights of solid volumes, it is important that the average of the discs be representative of the weight per unit volume of the wood under test. Because of the varying diameters of the logs from which the discs are cut and the fact that specific gravity often varies with diameter, it is recommended that a weighted average, based on the volume of the discs, be computed. The formula for this weighted average is $\dfrac{\text{sum of the products } Sd^2t}{\text{sum of the products } d^2t}$ where S, d, and t are, respectively, the specific gravity, diameter measured to the nearest 0.1 in., and thickness measured to the nearest 0.1

in. of each disc. If the thicknesses of the discs do not vary more than $\pm \frac{1}{16}$ or 0.06 in. from the average thickness, t may be eliminated from the equation. The diameter of the discs, which should be measured prior to drying, can be quickly determined with a steel diameter tape or by taking the average of two diameters measured at right angles.

TABLE 55-2. DEFINITIONS OF SYMBOLS

	Discs		Chips	
Definition	*Containing moisture**	*Moisture-free*	*Containing moisture**	*Moisture-free*
Weight of specimens	A	L	B	M
Weight of liquid displaced by green, or dry and coated, specimens according to Method 1	C	N	E	R
Weight of green, or dry and coated, specimen	F	O	I	S
Weight required to restore balance of scales when determining weight of liquid displaced according to Method 2, Case I "floaters"	G	P	J	T
Weight required to restore balance of scales when determining weight of liquid displaced according to Method 2, Case II "sinkers"	H	Q	K	U
Weight, or equivalent weight, of water displaced by specimens lighter than the liquid used in Method 2. V represents the sp. gr. of kerosene	$F + G$	$O + P$	$I + J$	$\dfrac{S + T}{V}$
Weight, or equivalent weight, of water displaced by specimens heavier than the liquid used in Method 2. V represents the sp. gr. of kerosene	$F - H$	$O - Q$	$I - K$	$\dfrac{S - U}{V}$

* A and B represent the weights of specimens as-received. All other weights of specimens in these columns represent wood in the water-soaked or green condition.

Density.—Density expressed as grams per cubic centimeter is numerically equal to the specific gravity. Density expressed as pounds per cubic foot is obtained by multiplying the specific gravity by 62.4.

A report of specific gravity or density is not complete without a statement of the basis of determination, *i.e.*, "Moisture-free weight per green volume" or "Moisture-free weight per moisture-free volume."

LABORATORY PROCESSING OF PULP (BEATER METHOD)

This method concerns the processing of pulp by means of a laboratory beater prior to forming handsheets, for the purpose of determining its behavior when subjected to a definite beating schedule. Only the furnishing and processing of the stock and the withdrawal and distribution of samples are described. The forming of the sheets is covered by

T 205 m (p. 1337) and the physical testing by T 220 m (p. 1359). This method is tentatively standardized as TAPPI T 200 ts-61.

Apparatus. **Disintegrator,** consisting of a vertically driven shaft rotating at approximately 1750 r.p.m., to which is mounted at the lower end either a propeller or a slotted disc $3\frac{1}{2}$ in. in diameter. (*See* Fig. 55-1.) Also required is a suitable container for holding the stock.

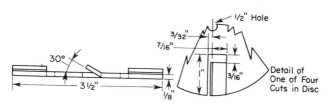

FIG. 55-1. Brass Disc of Disintegrator.

Beater, with Controlled Bedplate.—A dimensioned drawing of the standard $1\frac{1}{2}$-pound beater is shown in Fig. 55-2. The bedplate and roll are made of No. 12 stainless iron (chromium content, 11.5 to 13%). The diameter of the roll is $6\frac{5}{8}$ inches and the diameter of the roll with flybars inserted (32 in number) is $7\frac{5}{8}$ in. The thickness of each flybar is $\frac{3}{16}$ in. and the width of the roll is 6 in. The Brinell hardness of the flybars is 350 to 400 and bedplate bars 325 to 375.

The bedplate has 7 bars, each $\frac{1}{8}$ in. thick and spaced $\frac{3}{32}$ in. apart. These are bent into a V-shaped form, having an angle of 5° with the roll axis, with the apex of the V pointing in the direction of movement of stock over the plate. The grooves between the bedplate bars are filled with strips of kiln-dried white oak. The projected length of the bedplate is $6\frac{1}{4}$ in. and its projected width $1\frac{11}{16}$ in., and is ground in to conform to the bars in the roll. The bedplate fulcrum shaft is located parallel to the axis of the roll.

The lever arms of the controlled bedplate have a ratio of 17.5 to 9, as indicated on Fig. 55-2. The diaphragm is of $\frac{1}{16}$-in. thick live rubber. With 23 liters of water in the beater tub, the lever arm for the controlled bedplate is balanced so that substantially no force is required to cause the bedplate and roll to come into contact. There should be no tension in the rubber diaphragm with the roll and bedplate in contact. When the standard weight of 5500 g. is positioned at the end of the bedplate lever a force of 10,700 ± 100 g. upward on the roll results.

The roll is driven at 500 ± 10 r.p.m. A $\frac{1}{2}$-hp., 1200-r.p.m. motor with belt drive is suitable.

Sampling Cup, to remove the required amount of stock at 1.57 percent (moisture-free) consistency when filled flush with the top for making sheets of standard area and basis weight. This cup should have a height approximately equal to its diameter.

Care of Beater.—It is essential that the bars of the bedplate and beater be kept in good condition. On a new beater, the wood fillers in the bedplate are flush with the surface of the bars, but after the beater has been used for a time the wood may wear down to below the level of the bedplate bars. This does not appear to affect the action of the beater appreciably. Whenever the bedplate is removed from the beater; it is necessary to regrind, since removal and replacement of the bedplate disturbs the smooth fit of the beating surfaces.

In order to grind the beater properly, it is necessary that the bedplate be held in a fixed position relative to the roll, otherwise a truly cylindrical roll will not be obtained. A suitable clamp for this purpose is manufactured by the maker of the beater, the clamp being fastened beneath the beater tub. The position of the bedplate relative to the roll is adjusted by two machine screws, which hold the bedplate lever in a fixed position.

In order to grind the beating surfaces, place 250 g. of 120-mesh emery dust in a charge of stock circulating in the beater tub. The first adjustment should be to bring only the

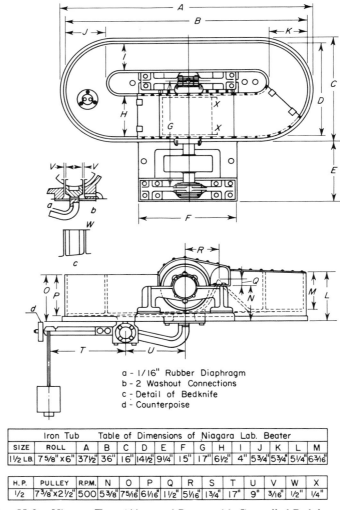

a - 1/16" Rubber Diaphragm
b - 2 Washout Connections
c - Detail of Bedknife
d - Counterpoise

	Iron Tub	Table of Dimensions of Niagara Lab. Beater												
SIZE	ROLL	A	B	C	D	E	F	G	H	I	J	K	L	M
1½ LB.	7 5/8" x 6"	37½"	36"	16"	14½"	9¼"	15"	17"	6½"	4"	5¾"	5¾"	5¼"	6³⁄₁₆"

H.P.	PULLEY	R.P.M.	N	O	P	Q	R	S	T	U	V	W	X
½	7³⁄₈"x2½"	500	5³⁄₈"	7⁵⁄₁₆"	6¹⁄₁₆"	1½"	5⁵⁄₁₆"	1¾"	17"	9"	3⁄₁₆"	½"	¼"

FIG. 55-2.   Niagara Type 1½-pound Beater with Controlled Bedplate.

high points of the roll and bedplate in contact, as indicated by the sound. Proceed with the grinding by gradually adjusting the bedplate up to the roll allowing the highest irregularities to be removed before making another adjustment. When further adjustment of the bedplate fails to produce irregularities in sound, or vibration of the bedplate, indicating that the roll is truly round, dump the charge of stock and abrasive, into a container and wash out the beater. If the roll is well ground, it will run smoothly on the bedplate with the beater containing water only. If the roll and bedplate do not run together smoothly after grinding, empty the water and return the stock and abrasive to the beater and continue grinding until they do. Normally 5 to 15 minutes of grinding will suffice to produce this result. Do not overgrind. Remove the feather edge on the flybars with a piece of emery cloth held in a flat holder or a very smooth flat file, rubbing against and parallel to the top and side surfaces of each bar. Loosen the diaphragm clamp under the beater tub and flush out all the abrasive.

After grinding, and before using the beater for test purposes, beat three successive samples of pulp for 1 hour each, using 5500 g. on the bedplate lever. Note that no play or sideways movement exists in the beater roll or lever bearings, that the bedplate has not tilted, and that no dried stock has accumulated at the sides of the roll.

Provide the bedplate clearance chamber with two $\frac{3}{8}$-in. water inlets. After each test forcibly inject water into this chamber and move the bed plate lever up and down to rid the pockets of accumulated fiber.

Because it is difficult to ensure that the condition of the bars remains constant even after grinding, it is advisable to calibrate the equipment by testing at intervals a sample of pulp from a portion of a bale kept for reference purposes. If the beater does not give reasonable check results and grinding in does not correct it, the bedplate or flybars may need replacing. There is some evidence to indicate that the height the bedplate projects above the base of the tub has an influence on the results. Normally this should be about $\frac{1}{16}$ in.

Sampling.—When dealing with mill consignments, take a sample of pulp of about 4 square inches in area from the interior of every bale included in the official test for moisture (discs bored for the moisture test but *not* dried may be used); or, in the case of a shipment of chemical pulp where the cook numbers are known, take samples in proportion to the number of bales representing each cook, provided no fewer than 3 samples from each cook are obtained. When neither of these methods is possible, select enough samples to be representative of the whole consignment. For a single run the weight of the sample required is at least 360 and preferably 450 g. of moisture-free fiber.

Storage of Pulp Samples.—Store moist pulp samples under water with a few drops of formaldehyde and keep in a cool place away from direct sunlight. Store dry pulp samples in suitable packages away from heat or light.

Test Sample.—Weigh out, to the nearest 5 g., a representative sample of the pulp, obtained by tearing (do not cut the pulp or use cut edges) approximately equal portions from all samples collected, equivalent to 360 g. of moisture-free fiber. If the sample is dry, wet it with cold water, tear into pieces about one inch square and soak in water for 4 hours. Moist pulps may be disintegrated immediately.

NOTE.—As far as is known, soaking a pulp for a longer time (for example, overnight) does not appreciably affect the results.

All water used during the entire processing should be at approximate room temperature as unduly hot or cold water may adversely affect the results.

Procedure.—During the procedure for processing and sheet making, for precise work keep the temperature of both the thick and the dilute stock and the sheets and blotter in the press between 20 and 25°C.

Disintegration.—Make up the 360-g. sample in the disintegrator container to 10 liters and disintegrate until the fibers are separated, as indicated by the lack of undefibered portions of pulp having a core of over $\frac{1}{16}$ in. in diameter. About 10 minutes normally suffices.

Furnishing the Beater.—With the bedplate and lever in balance, start the roll and add about 10 liters of water to the tub to get circulation. Add the pulp to the beater and enough additional water at the necessary temperature to give a total volume of 23 liters in the beater (1.57 percent consistency) at 23 ± 2°C. Let the pulp circulate for 5 minutes without pressure between the roll and the bedplate.

Removing Samples and Beating.—Withdraw an 800-ml. sample (12.5 g. of moisture-free fiber) for the unbeaten test sheets, and add a 5500-g. weight to the bedplate lever arm. Note the time the weight is added as the commencement of the beating operation. Withdraw additional 800-ml. samples at successive time intervals which may be taken from the following suggested schedule:

	Minutes					
Weak bleached coniferous sulfite or deciduous alkaline pulps	5	10	15	20	25	30
Unbleached coniferous sulfite or bleached coniferous alkaline pulps	10	20	30	40	50	60
Strong unbleached coniferous alkaline and other very strong pulps	15	30	45	60	75	90

Even though the quantity of pulp withdrawn be not all used for the test sheets, it is desirable, particularly if it is desired to compare the results with other tests, to withdraw the stated quantity of pulp at the periods suggested or adopted, so as to maintain a uniform rate of beating.

Clearing.—Dilute each 800-ml. sample to 2 liters (0.62 percent consistency) and disintegrate each sample, including that of the unbeaten pulp, for 15,000 revolutions (5 minutes) in the standard disintegrator described in Appendix A of TAPPI Standard T 205 m (p. 1337).

Dilution and Sheetmaking.—Dilute the stock to $8\frac{1}{3}$ liters (0.15 percent consistency) and make and test sets of sheets according to TAPPI Standards T 205 m and T 220 m (pp. 1337 and 1359).

Report.—Report the test results in accordance with TAPPI Standard T 220 m. State the intervals at which samples were taken and note any departures from the standard procedure. Curves are usually desirable, showing the development of the density of the test sheets and the various strength factors plotted against beating times or preferably the logarithm of the beating times.

Precision.—The precision of the results of a beater test are dependent upon many factors such as the time of beating, the type of pulp, and the sharpness and roughness of the beater bars. In addition, the results are affected by the making of the handsheets and their testing. Interlaboratory tests made on the TAPPI Reference Pulp show that no valid comparison between tests made with different beaters can be made unless they have first been calibrated with a reference pulp. With two calibrated beaters, 95 percent of the time, the burst and tear factors from tests on the same pulp, using carefully standardized sheet making and testing equipment, should differ by no more than 20 percent of the mean value.

This statement of reproducibility is approximate only. A special study has been undertaken.[2]

Additional Information.—1. In some mill laboratories, pulps are compared after beating to a maximum burst development. However, the zero-span test is a better measure of ultimate strength. In other laboratories, usually European, pulps are compared after beating to a definite slowness, 50° to 80° Schopper-Riegler, or sometimes to 300 or 500 Canadian standard freeness. Comparison at equal test sheet densities may be a better basis.

In other cases, it is considered to be more desirable to ascertain the approximate

[2] Brandon, C. E., Tappi, **41**, No. 9, 129–130A, Sept., 1958.

equivalent amount of beating to be given the pulp by the mill for the grade of paper into which it is to be made, and to use this degree of beating for comparing or specifying the pulp. The equivalent degree of beating may be established by taking a sample of the unbeaten stock furnish in the mill, and drawing curves showing the development of its density, burst, tear, breaking length, and freeness (or drainage time or drainage factor) against the time of beating. A sample of the fully prepared mill stock, which preferably should be secured from one of the wet presses on the machine, is lightly disintegrated and made into a set of sheets, the physical tests of which are marked on the corresponding development curves of the unbeaten furnish and the nearest equivalent time for the more important test sheet properties selected. Stock from the machine headbox or elsewhere, used for comparisons in this way, is mixed with fine material normally circulating in the machine and stock preparation systems and may give misleading results.

2. Related Method: Canadian CPPA C2.

REFERENCES

Rothchild, H. A., Ely, A., and Poppe, E., "The Beater Method of Evaluating Pulp," Paper Trade J., **89**, No. 14, 72–73, Oct. 3, 1929.

Rothchild, H. A., Lundbeck, I., and Cable, D. E., "Strength Testing of Wood Pulp," Paper Trade J., **90**, No. 8, 264–265, Feb. 20, 1930; Tech. Assoc. Papers **13**, 143–144, 1930.

Moore, F. W., and Willets, W. R., "The Evaluation of Unbleached Pulps," Paper Trade J., **92**, No. 18, 39–42, April 30, 1931; Tech. Assoc. Papers, **14**, 190–193, 1931.

FORMING HANDSHEETS FOR PHYSICAL TESTS OF PULP

This procedure deals with a precision method of forming test sheets from pulps, before or after beating, for testing their physical properties. The testing methods are described in TAPPI Standard T 220 m (p. 1359). The forming of test sheets for determining the optical properties of pulp is given in TAPPI Standard T 218 m (p. 1357). In TAPPI Standard T 221 m (p. 1363) is described a companion method for determining the drainage time and drainage factor of pulps which for many purposes may replace the freeness test.

This method has been drafted with the object of providing a precise standard method giving results having an international significance; also one to which any other pulp-strength-testing method may be compared to obtain accurate conversion factors.

The apparatus and method described are practically identical with the standard method adopted by the Paper Makers' Association of Great Britain and Ireland and by the Technical Section of the Canadian Pulp and Paper Association. For further particulars of the original method, together with complete experimental data, reference is made to the "Interim Report of the Pulp Evaluation Committee to the Technical Section of Paper Makers' Association," and to the Second Report of the same committee. This method is standardized as TAPPI T 205 m-58.

Apparatus. Standard Disintegrator.

Standard 6½ in. diameter. Sheet Machine with Stirrer.

Note.—Sheet machines having a larger or smaller diameter are not in accordance with this standard and may be expected to give significantly different results.

Standard Couch Roll.

Standard Couch Plate.

Standard Pump and Press with Pressure Gauge.

Press Template, for centering the sheets and plates in the press.

Discs.—Seven or more mirror-polished discs, 6¼ in. in diameter.

Drying Rings.—Eight or more drying rings with rubber seatings for holding the sheets to the polished discs during drying.

NOTE.—Specifications for the above equipment, with illustrations, are in Appendix A.

Blotting Paper.[3]—A quantity of sheets of standard blotting paper, 8 in. square, 0.0195 to 0.0205 in. thick, weighing 245 to 255 g. per sq. m. and having an absorbency of not less than 9 nor more than 20 seconds when tested with 0.1 ml. of water according to TAPPI Standard T 432 m (p. 1422).

Cup, wide-mouth, plastic-ware, tea cup.

Bucket, with mark at 16 liters.

Graduated Cylinder, 1000-ml.

Sampling.—When dealing with mill consignments, draw a sample of pulp the equivalent of about 4 square inches in area from the interior of every bale included in the official test for moisture (discs bored for the moisture test but *not* dried may be used); or in the case of a shipment of chemical pulp where the cook numbers are known, take samples in proportion to the number of bales representing each cook, provided no fewer than 3 samples from each cook are obtained. When neither of these methods is possible, take a sufficient number of samples in such a way as to be representative of the whole consignment. At least 50, preferably 100 g. of pulp (moisture-free basis), are required.

Storage of Pulp Samples.—Store pulp samples under water with a few drops of formaldehyde and keep in a cool place away from direct sunlight. Store dry pulp samples in suitable packages away from heat or light.

Test Specimen.—Weigh out to the nearest 0.5 g. a representative specimen of the pulp obtained by *tearing* equal portions from all the samples collected, equivalent to 24 g. of moisture-free fiber. Do not cut the pulp or use cut edges. If the pulp is dry, wet it in cold water, tear into pieces about 1 in. square, and soak in water for 4 hours; or in the case of a dried sample of mechanical pulp which is to be furnished in the moist form, allow it to soak for 24 hours.

NOTE.—As far as is known, soaking pulp for a longer time, for example over night, does not appreciably affect the results.

Procedure. **Disintegration.**—Make the mixture up to 2000 ml. (1.2 percent consistency) with water at 23 ± 2°C. and disintegrate for 75,000 revolutions (3000 on the 25:1 counter) in the standard disintegrator with the propeller running at 3000 r.p.m. in the stock. After disintegration, dilute the stock to 16 liters (0.15 percent consistency) with water at 23 ± 2°C.

NOTE.—For beaten pulps, the amount of pulp taken, the dilution and the disintegration period depend largely upon requirements. In general, however, 8 to 10 g. of beaten pulp, diluted to 1500 ml. and disintegrated for 7500 revolutions, will satisfactorily disperse any clots that may be present. If it is necessary to use other conditions, these should be stated in the report.

Sheetmaking.—Partially fill the sheet-machine container with water. Then let out the water until its level is just above the wire, so as to ensure driving out all the air from beneath the wire. Accurately measure out and pour into the container 800 ml. of the well mixed, dilute stock at 0.15 percent consistency, the water supply being simultaneously turned on until the depth of the dilute suspension is 35 cm. above the wire surface.

---

[3] If the absorbency of the blotting paper is much greater than stated, difficulty may be experienced in couching certain treated, or finely ground pulps. The Sorg Paper Co., Middletown, Ohio, The Standard Paper Manufacturing Co., Richmond, Va., and the Rochester Paper Co., Rochester, Mich., offer such blotters. Compliance with all the specifications given, should be confirmed.

NOTE.—The ultimate requirements are sheets each weighing between 1.14 and 1.26 g. moisture-free, corresponding to a basis weight of 60 g. per sq. m. with a tolerance of 5 percent. Consequently for a finely divided pulp, slightly more than 800 ml. should be added—*e.g.,* 840 ml. for an average groundwood pulp, to allow for a 5 percent fiber loss through the wire. (See also Appendix B.)

Insert the perforated stirrer and in 6 seconds move it steadily down and up 6 times, keeping the disc beneath the level of the liquid. Repeat this double movement very slowly, once in 10 seconds, and gently withdraw the stirrer. After a pause of 10 seconds, during which time the surface of the liquid should have become almost motionless, fully open the drain cock of the machine with a rapid movement and let all the water drain from the sheet under suction. Immediately after the water has drained from the sheet, tilt the container, and couch the sheet off the wire. If the machine is of the old pattern without an air-inlet groove at the side of the grid plate, open the needle valve before couching.

Couching.—Lay two pieces of standard blotting paper centrally on the pulp sheet on the wire. Now lay the flat brass couch plate centrally on the blotters and place the brass couch roll gently on the middle of the plate. Move the roll backward, no other pressure being applied, to within less than $\frac{1}{4}$ in. of the edge of the plate, which is maintained horizontally by placing the fingers on the opposite edge; then forward to within less than $\frac{1}{4}$ in. of the front edge; then back and forth four times; and finally to the middle; then lift off the roll. Take about 20 seconds to perform the five complete rolls.

Remove the pulp sheet and blotters and covering brass plate from the wire in a manner similar to that of opening the cover of a book, when the sheet will be found adhering to the blotter next to it (the couch blotter). Immediately detach the couch blotter and sheet from the other blotter (couch filler) and plate, and by means of the press template, lay it centrally, test sheet uppermost, on one dry blotter (the press filler) which has been previously placed in the press. Place a mirror-polished plate on the test sheet and cover with another press filler, ready to receive the next couch blotter and sheet.

Wash the wire in the sheet machine in position by turning on the water, and make the next test sheet in precisely the same way. Make a minimum of seven sheets in all so that the stack in the press when complete will consist of press filler, couch blotter, sheet and plate, repeated seven times. Finally lay a single blotter on the uppermost plate to avoid possible damage to the press cover.

NOTE.—For some pulps it has been found convenient to couch the sheets from the wire by a vacuum couching procedure with $7\frac{1}{2}$-in. diameter, die-cut, round blotters, instead of using the couch plate and couch roll. Such a method has been described by Clark.[4] Results when using this procedure are substantially the same as those obtained when using the standard procedure; in case of dispute, however, the standard procedure shall apply.

First Pressing.—Put on the cover of the press and screw the wing nuts down hand-tight. Raise the pressure, as indicated by the gauge, to 50 p.s.i.[5] in $\frac{1}{2}$ minute from the time the needle begins to move, and maintain it there for 5 minutes. At the end of that time release the pressure and remove the press cover.

NOTE.—For this pressure only two diagonally opposite nuts need to be used for the press cover.

Second Pressing.—After the first pressing, remove the polished plates with test sheets attached from the stack of moist blotters. Using the press template, lay the plate that was on top of the stack during the first pressing centrally on a dry blotter, test sheet

---

[4] Clark, J. d'A., "Improvements in the Couching and Pressing of Sheets for Pulp Testing," Paper Industry, **29,** No. 7, 992–4, Oct., 1947.
[5] This is equivalent to approximately 60 p.s.i. on the sheet.

uppermost, and cover the sheet with one new blotter. This blotter also serves as a base for the next plate and test sheet. The stack so built on a foundation blotter will comprise plate, sheet, and press filler, repeated seven times. The order of the sheets is thus reversed in the second pressing. Place the cover in position as before and raise the pressure rapidly to 50 p.s.i. as indicated by the gauge and keep it there for 2 minutes. (There is no necessity to fix a time period for attaining the stipulated pressure in the second pressing, because the tendency for the pressure to fall off is very much less than before.)

During couching and pressing, the felt sides of the blotters and not the wire sides shall be in contact with the sheets; and, for precise work, it is desirable that those in contact with the sheet be new blotters.

NOTE. *Alternate Procedure.*—For the first and second pressing, although a controlled hand-operated hydraulic system has been described for the official standard procedure, any equivalent system of pressure application can be used, provided the idea of the floating plate, actuated by either liquid or gas, is maintained, and provided also that the time and pressure cycles specified in the method are maintained. Automatic pressing equipment which complies, is available from the makers of the standard sheet-making equipment in U. S. A.

Drying.—Remove the stack from the press and fit the plates with the attached test sheets into a set of drying rings, each test sheet uppermost and in contact with the rubber of the next ring, and place a heavy weight or a clamp on the pile of rings. Do not allow the sheets to dry below the normal moisture content reached by drying under standard conditions specified in TAPPI Standard T 402 m (Vol. 2, Part B, p. 1795). It is advisable to place the pile of rings in the constant humidity room and there dry and condition them concurrently. Allow the sheets to become fully dried in position in the rings before removing them.

NOTE.—If there is a shortage of drying rings when making sheets from relatively free stock, it is permissible to clamp two sheets, with their plates back to back, between each pair of drying rings.

Testing.—Test the sheets, especially if of groundwood, within a day after their being made, and according to the procedures described in TAPPI Standard T 220 m (p. 1359).

APPENDIX A

SPECIFICATIONS OF APPARATUS

Disintegrator.—The disintegrator shown in Fig. 55-3 consists of a removable container, *A*, and brass propeller and phosphor-bronze shaft, *B*, driven at 3000 r.p.m. by a leather belt from an electric motor.

The inside dimensions of the container are 6 in. diameter by 7.5 in. high, and the inside is provided with four spiral baffles made of 0.25 in. square copper rod with rounded ends. The center of the 0.125 in. radiused end of each baffle commences 1.25 in. from the bottom and ends 2.25 in. from the top, having gone exactly halfway round the circumference. The edges of the baffles are rounded with a 0.016 in. radius. Around the bottom of the container is a filet with a 0.5 in. radius. The outside edge of the container base is beveled and when in position, fits into two beveled lugs fixed on the base of the disintegrator. It is secured by a third lug in the form of a sliding clamp, *K*. A pin in the side of the base prevents rotation.

The propeller is 9 cm. (3.55 in.) diameter and is built up of three 1.6-mm. (0.062 in.) thick, hard brass blades set at 120° apart and sweated into milled slots in a hub. The hub is fitted to the end of the propeller shaft by means of a standard conical seating, nut, and washer. The blades are sloped 2° upwards from the horizontal and thus arrange to throw the stock downwards. The dimensions of each blade are 18.2 mm. (0.72 in.)

wide at its junction with the hub, and 22.5 mm. (0.89 in.) wide just before the edges of the tip are radiused 4.0 mm. (0.16 in.). The edges around the blade are rounded to a 0.032 in. radius.

The shaft B is arranged to slide up out of the chuck, C, which grips the shaft to the driven pulley. The driven pulley is mounted on a hollow shaft which runs in ball bearings

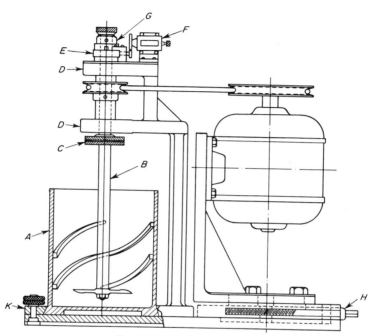

Fɪɢ. 55-3.   Disintegrator.

in the housings, D, and at the upper end of the shaft is a worm wheel, E, fixed to the shaft by means of a grub screw, and geared to the revolution counter, F, by a 25:1 worm wheel. The thickness of the spacer washer, G, is such that when the propeller is pushed right down, the bottom edges of the blades are 1 in. from the bottom of the container. The upper portion of the clamp K is made 1 in. wide and may conveniently be used for checking this height.

An alternative construction for holding the shaft has been found desirable in some instances. The spacer washer G is replaced with one made of steel about 1.25 in. outside diameter and 0.5 in. thick, having a pair of dogs integral with the body of the washer, 0.125 in. or more deep, which fit into corresponding slots cut in the upper end of the shaft sleeve. This washer contains a $\frac{3}{16}$-in. or $\frac{1}{4}$-in. headless set screw, which engages in one of two depressions cut in the propeller shaft so as to locate the propeller either 1.0 or 2.0 in. above the bottom of the container.

The $\frac{1}{4}$-hp. motor may be arranged for either a.c. or d.c., the former being preferable as the drop in speed when the propeller is immersed in the stock is only about 1 percent, whereas with a d.c. motor the drop may be as much as 8 percent. The speed of the propeller may be altered appreciably by means of the belt tension. Take care to check the speed if the belt is replaced by a new one, because a variation in the diameter of the belt also affects the propeller speed.

The tension of the round leather driving belt is adjusted by means of the screw at H, which moves the motor support.

Keep the worm wheel and eccentric for the counter arm greased, otherwise the counter arm is liable to wear, and after a time the counter ceases to function correctly. If wear takes place, the trouble can be remedied by loosening the clamping screw on the boss of the arm and resetting it.

Take care not to bend the propeller blades when removing the propeller from the shaft. It is best detached by fitting the jaws of an adjustable spanner over the hub of the propeller and tapping the top of the spanner.

A propeller gauge, furnished with the disintegrator, is used to check the blades if they are suspected of being bent.

NOTE.—The vital parts of the above specifications are: (a) details of the container; (b) propeller design and position; and (c) propeller speed.

If gummy with pitch, the propeller shaft and sleeve may be cleaned by loosening the chuck, holding the propeller firmly with one hand, starting the motor, and applying a few drops of light lubricating oil to the shaft while moving it up and down while the sleeve is rotated by the motor.

Sheet Machine.—The complete sheet machine is shown in Fig. 55-4. The main parts of the machine consist of a base, B, connected by a drainage pipe, P, and cock, G, to the sump; a wire-covered grid plate, C, on which the sheet is formed, and which rests in the top of the base; and a cylindrical container, A, which is preferably provided with a hinge and which fits over the plate and the base.

The outer trough for overflow water is connected to the sump by means of two brass drain pipes, J. Around the top of the funnel of the base is machined a recess on which the grid plate rests. In the new hinged model an air vent is cut in this recess which is closed by the rubber gasket in the base of the cylinder when in position. The inside of the funnel is carefully machined and a removable 4-fin baffle, L, made of $\frac{1}{16}$-in. brass sheet, rests in it. The function of the baffle is to prevent any possible swirling. A horizontal disc is fitted in the baffle over the drainage pipe to distribute the suction uniformly over the grid plate.

NOTE.—On machines made prior to 1947 this disc was $1\frac{1}{4}$ in. in diameter. However, with the larger bore of the $1\frac{3}{8}$ in. drainage pipe standard in the U. S., it is desirable to increase the diameter of the disc to $1\frac{5}{8}$ in. This may be done by soldering to the edges four quarter-circle pieces of flattened $\frac{3}{32}$-in. diameter copper wire. This will eliminate the small but detectable extra thickness of the center portions of test sheets made from free, unbeaten pulp.

The grid plate, which is 6.812 in. in diameter and 0.359 in. thick, is perforated all over (except for a $\frac{1}{4}$ in. wide ring around the edge) with $\frac{3}{8}$-in. square holes, spaced 0.486 inch, the ribs so formed, which are about $\frac{1}{8}$ in. thick at the base, are tapered and then beveled to an edge $\frac{1}{32}$ in. thick at the top, and the top corners formed by the intersection of the edges of the ribs, are removed by a V cut, so that in effect the wire laid upon it, is supported by the equivalent of a $\frac{1}{2}$-in. mesh wire.

The screen on which the sheet is formed is 150 mesh (diameter of wires 0.0026 to 0.0028 in.) and is backed by a 20-mesh screen (wire diameter 0.0148 to 0.0150 in.), both being stretched flat and fixed around the edge by soldering, or in the new model by means of a clamping ring, to the surface of the plate.

The top part of the apparatus, the container A, is 0.187 in. thick, 15.75 in. high and exactly 6.25 in. (15.88 cm.) inside diameter. A groove is cut 350 mm. (13.75 in.) from the surface of the wire. The bottom of the cylinder is stepped out to fit over the base of the instrument and carries a soft rubber ring, which makes contact around the edge of the grid plate. The cylinder is made either to lift on and off, or in the new model is provided with a hinge and clamp, so that a water-tight joint is made between the cylinder, the upper edge of the top face of the plate and the upper edge of the base.

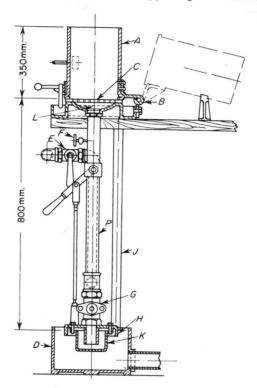

FIG. 55-4.   Sheet Machine.

A needle valve, F, which is desirable but not essential if the air inlet-groove at the side of the grid plate is cut, is placed in the drainage tube 6 in. down from the surface of the wire. The drainage valve, G, is operated by a lever mechanism as shown in the figure.

The sump consists of a cylinder, D, with an outlet hole threaded for a 2-in. pipe either in the side as shown or in the center of the bottom if required. Three lugs are provided for screwing the sump to the floor.

A cross bar, H, carries a circular apron to prevent splashing, and bolted to the underside of the bar with distance pieces is an overflow vessel, K. The distance from the surface of this vessel to the top of the wire is adjusted to be exactly 800 mm. (31.5 in.). This is the suction head on the wire.

The drainage pipe, the bore of which is actually 1.375 in., is connected by means of a $1\frac{1}{4}$- to $1\frac{1}{2}$-in. T-piece and $\frac{1}{2}$-in. elbows to the water supply valve, E.

The perforated stirrer (not shown) has a disc 6.125 in. diameter, perforated with sixty $\frac{7}{16}$-in. diameter holes countersunk smoothly at the surfaces of the disc. To the central rod of the stirrer are fixed four baffles 0.032 in. thick, 2.75 in. wide and 6 in. deep, with their lower edges 1 in. from the disc. These prevent swirling. All edges are carefully rounded and smoothed so as not to collect fibers when the stirrer is used.

The couch plate is of hard sheet brass, 6.75 in. diameter by 0.020 in. thick.

The couch roll (not shown) is made of brass, 4 in. diameter with a 7-in. face, and weighs 13 kg. (28.67 lb.).

NOTE.—Owing to the accuracy required in the construction and dimensions of the sheet machine and grid plates, it is advisable to use a machine approved by and bearing the official serial number of the British Paper and Board Makers' Association, Inc. Approved machines are now being manufactured in several countries; for use in U.S.A., by the Hermann Manufacturing Co., Lancaster, Ohio; for use in Canada, by The Robert Mitchell Co., Ltd., Montreal 9, Que., and inspected by the Pulp and Paper Research Institute of Canada, for use elsewhere, through the British Paper and Board Makers' Association, St. Winifred's, Welcomes Rd., Kenley, Surrey, England.

Press.—A side elevation of the press is shown in Fig. 55-5. The cover, A, is of cast aluminum so that it can be easily lifted and the base, B, is of close-grained cast iron.

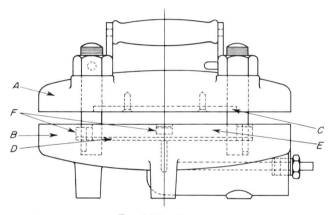

FIG. 55-5. Press.

A hard brass disc, C, 6.875 in. diameter, is properly bedded and fixed in the lid. The cover is provided with a handle and is held down by means of four 1-in. diameter phosphor-bronze studs and chromium-plated hard-brass wing nuts. Two diagonally opposite nuts only need be used for normal pressures (not exceeding 60 p.s.i.). The base is recessed to contain a heavy rubber diaphragm, D, held down around the edges by a brass ring with brass countersunk screws. A flat platen, E, 6.875 in. diameter, is loosely fitted inside the ring to rest on the diaphragm, and the platen is prevented from coming out by four lugs, F, which work in four shaped slots around its edge. The upper and lower surfaces of the brass plates are carefully machined flat. The working fluid (glycerine) is forced under the rubber diaphragm and the maximum distance through which the platen can rise is $\frac{3}{8}$ in. The machined surfaces of the cast-iron base are well covered with aluminum paint to prevent rust.

NOTE.—From the construction of the press it will be noticed that the platen is free to float on the rubber diaphragm. This ensures that an even pressure is applied over the entire surface of the pile of sheets and blotters, and in this respect is superior to plunger-type presses. The press should never be used for small pieces of paper, etc., as by virtue of the feature just mentioned, if a high pressure is employed, the platen is liable to bend round the object pressed.

Pump.—The hand operated pump is shown in Fig. 55-6. The body is made of gun-metal and has a bore of 1.75 in. in a 4-in. stroke. The pressure is applied by means of a gunmetal plunger, *D*, which is actuated by a steel left-hand screw, *R*, through a bronze

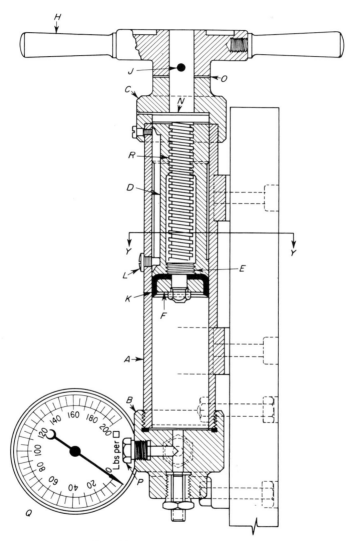

Fig. 55-6. Hand-operated Pump.

thrust washer, *N*, and nickeled or chromium-plated brass handwheel, *H*. A cup leather, *K*, held in position by a brass washer and nut, *F*, prevents leakage. This leather washer assembly is screwed into the plunger, *E*, and the plunger is prevented from rotating by means of a hardened steel screw, *L*, working in a slot, *D*, cut in it. Both press and pump are mounted together on a heavy base.

The pump is usually shipped filled with glycerine. If ever necessary to refill the pump and press with fluid, remove the gauge and screw in its place the special filler cup supplied. Turn the handwheel clockwise till the plunger is farthest in, and then fill the cup with pure glycerine while the handwheel is slowly turned to draw the liquid into the body of the pump. When the pump itself is full, unscrew the filler cup and replace the gauge. Loosen the screws around the ring holding down the press diaphragm several turns with a screwdriver, and remove the four screws and lugs holding down the platen. Turn the handwheel to force the glycerine into the press, whereupon the air escapes round the edges of the diaphragm, the platen being prevented from rising by hand pressure. As soon as glycerine begins to exude, wipe off the diaphragm and platen with a moist rag, replace the platen and lugs, and by tightening each screw in the ring in turn a small amount at a time, clamp the diaphragm in position. If the screws are not tightened uniformly, the diaphragm will not be flat. It is undesirable to tighten the screws any more than is necessary to prevent leakage. Put on the cover and screw the wing nuts handtight. Again remove the gauge, screw in the filler cup and fill with glycerine. Turn the handwheel forward (this eliminates a few air bubbles) and then backwards, until it comes to the stop, meanwhile keeping the filler cup supplied with glycerine.

Withdraw the filler cup and replace the pressure gauge. Remove the press cover and turn the handwheel forward to its farthest extent. If the platen is felt to touch the lugs before the handwheel is fully screwed in, remove the gauge temporarily and turn the handwheel fully home so as to express the superfluous glycerine.

NOTE.—The above press and pump specifications are not vital, provided that the apparatus used is capable of providing a uniformly distributed pressure of the same magnitude. This is equivalent to an actual pressure of about 60 p.s.i. on the test sheets. A template for centering the stack of sheets in the press is necessary.

Press Template.—The press template for centering the sheets (not shown) is of 0.125 in. thick aluminum plate. The guide slots fit over any two adjacent studs in the press, and when in position, the 6.25 in. diameter semicircle which is cut in it, is concentric with the platens of the press.

Drying Plates.—The mirror-polished stainless steel or chromium-plated brass plates (not shown) are 6.25 in. in diameter and about 0.020 in. thick. They should be free from bulges or uneven edges and if any are damaged in this way and not capable of being repaired, they should be discarded. When not in use, they should be kept in a saw-slotted wooden block, made to hold them stacked vertically in a horizontal row.

Drying Rings.—The drying rings (not shown) are made of hard brass and arranged to fit into each other, clamping each polished plate and test sheet around the edges. The circumference of the sheet is gripped by the rubber seating and the plate pressed against this by the extended portion of the ring below. For many purposes, however, the rubber seating is unnecessary and two plates, back to back, with the sheets on the outside, may be placed in a single pair of drying rings, thus doubling their capacity. The air for drying circulates through eighteen $\frac{3}{4}$-in. diameter holes.

APPENDIX B

TESTING OF BOARD STOCK

Pulp suitable for paperboard manufacture is as a rule relatively weak and relatively free, and often contains quantities of shives; consequently, it is suggested to use 150 g.

per sq. m. as a standard basis weight for testing this class of stock, employing 1000 ml. of stock at 0.3 percent consistency for each sheet and determining the drainage corrected to 150 g. per sq. m. and 20°C. Two pieces of blotter are employed for couching, as for normal lightweight sheets, but 2 dry blotters are used in place of the single blotter normally required in both first and second pressings, the rest of the procedure for disintegrating and testing remaining the same as for papermaking stock.

APPENDIX C

MODIFICATION FOR ROUTINE CONTROL WORK

A speedy and simple method suited for groundwood mill control has been described for use with the 5-in. diameter prototype sheet-making equipment, by Clark[6] in which the drainage time and the bursting strength of the pulp may be obtained in about 15 minutes.

Between such a rapid method and the complete standard method, a suitable routine method can be devised to meet any required conditions. Where substantially unbeaten stocks are being tested, the double pressing may be dispensed with and the sheets given a single pressing for 5 min. at 50 p.s.i. gauge pressure, without using the plates, then separated from the blotters and dried in a current of air in the humidity room for testing. Results with some pulps will be nearly the same as with the standard method.

If departures are made from the standard method as described, or different apparatus is used, it is essential that conversion factors be obtained for each particular type of pulp being tested and with their aid, the results may be approximated to standard.

APPENDIX D

RAPID METHODS OF DRYING AND CONDITIONING

An excellent method of drying and conditioning the sheets has been developed by the Forest Products Laboratories of Canada which shortens the time required for both to less than an hour, while still conforming to the standard procedure. The apparatus consists of a closed box provided with one or more 6-in. wide vertical slots in its sides, inside and against which the drying rings are stacked. An electric fan exhausts air from the box through a suitable opening, the air passing in through the holes in the drying rings and over the sheets. The whole apparatus is kept in the constant-humidity room.

NOTE.—If a fan is used to *blow* air into the box, the fan motor will become heated and, being in the path of the air, may cause the relative humidity of the air passing over the sheets to be appreciably lower than that of the air in the room.

Alternatively, for rapidly drying the sheets in a constant-humidity room, it is sometimes more convenient to lead part of the conditioned air through a slotted duct in one of the walls or in a corner of the room, the duct having slides and clamps to hold the rings. The conditioned air is thus blown through the rings and over the sheets and dries and conditions them effectively. This obviates the need for an additional fan and makes a particularly neat piece of equipment.

Another modification for obtaining results quickly, including a good design for a rapid air drier, has been described by Bradshaw.[7]

[6] Clark, J. d'A., "Pulp and Paper Manufacture in North America," Proc. Tech. Sect., Paper Makers' Assoc., Gt. Britain and Ireland, VII, Part 2, pp. 242–246, March, 1927.
[7] Bradshaw, F. W., "Routine Control Testing," Pulp Paper Mag. Canada, 33, No. 10, 481–484, 518, Dec., 1932.

APPENDIX E

SHEET SHRINKAGE

The shrinkage during drying may be determined as follows: After pressing make two marks on the sheet 15.0 cm. apart, preferably with a gauge made from two chisel-pointed pins set in a suitable metal holder, after inking the points with a moistened indelible pencil. Pull the sheet off the plate in a direction perpendicular to the marks, then allow to dry without restraint and measure the shrinkage between the marks. This shrinkage, expressed as a percentage, is a useful indication of the degree of hydration of the pulp.

ADDITIONAL INFORMATION

1. At the annual meeting of the Canadian Pulp and Paper Association in 1931 was presented the result of an investigation[8] into the method by the Forest Products Laboratories of Canada, employing free and slow groundwood, sulphite, kraft, and soda pulps. A close relationship between the resulting strength of the pulps and those obtained by the Canadian method then existing, a slightly modified Genberg-Laymon method, was indicated, with reproducibility in favor of the British apparatus and method. A further report[9] of comparative tests on several sheetmaking machines and methods, presented at the annual meeting in 1932, definitely confirmed the superiority of the method described. A concurrent independent investigation by Laymon[10] between the Genberg-Laymon method (previous TAPPI method) and this method gave similar indications. Some experimental conversion ratios for the two methods are also given in that paper. An independent investigation[11] by the U. S. Forest Products Laboratory in Madison, Wis. in 1933 has also confirmed the superiority of this method. Reference is also made to a discussion of the differences between the two methods at the 1930 TAPPI fall meeting in Erie, Pa., when the apparatus was first demonstrated in this country.

2. An informative paper by Harrison[12] contains much experimental data on the operation of this apparatus and method with pulps beaten in a Lampen mill.

3. A companion precision method for evaluating the beating characteristics of pulps, using a laboratory kollergang, is described in TAPPI Method T 225 sm.

4. A method for simultaneously measuring the drainage times of stock when being formed into standard test sheets, and which for most purposes may serve in place of freeness tests, is described in TAPPI Standard T 221 m (p. 1363).

SPECTRAL REFLECTIVITY AND COLOR OF PULP

This method measures the spectral reflectivity and color of pulp relative to magnesium oxide. Spectral reflectivity is usually expressed in the form of a curve giving reflectivity as a function of wavelength over the range 400 to 700 mμ. Reflectivity is the ratio, for the

[8] Adlington, W. E., Jones, Douglas, Alexander, C., and Legendre, J. R. A., "Comparison of the Canadian and British Methods of Preparing Test Sheets," Pulp Paper Mag. Canada **31**, No. 26, 766–767, 780, 782, June 25, 1931; C.P.P.A. Proc. Tech. Sect. 1932, pp. 9–15.

[9] Report of the Canadian Committee of Chemical and Physical Standards, C.P.P.A. Tech. Sect. Proc. 1931, pp. 7–11.

[10] Laymon, H. W., "American and British Pulp Testing Methods," Paper Trade J., **92**, No. 26, 43–46, June 25, 1931; Tech. Assoc. Papers, **14**, 254–257; discussion, 104–106, May, 1931.

[11] Doughty, R. H., and Curran, C. E., "A Comparison of Sheet Machines for Pulp Evaluation," Paper Trade J., **97**, No. 23, 38–44, Dec. 21, 1933; Tech. Assoc. Papers, **17**, 463–469, 1934.

[12] Harrison, H. A., "The Beating of Wood Pulp in the Laboratory and Mill," World's Paper Trade Rev. (Dec. 5, 1930); Proc. Tech. Sect. Paper Makers' Assoc. Gt. Britain and Ireland 11, Part 2, 272–333, March, 1931.

same geometry and wavelength of monochromatic light, of the amount of light reflected by the sample to that reflected from a pure and properly prepared surface of magnesium oxide. It is thus a relative quantity and is correctly termed *apparent reflectivity*, although in common usage it is simply referred to as *reflectivity* or *reflectance*. Color is specified according to the standard observer and colorimetric coördinate system recommended in 1931 by the International Commission on Illumination. The appearance of a pulp is not completely defined by these specifications; it may also be influenced by other properties, such as texture. This method is standardized as TAPPI T 216 m-47.

Apparatus. Instrument.—The instrument shall consist of a spectrophotometer, either visual or photoelectric type, which can adequately measure the spectral reflectivity of a sample relative to a standard over the wavelength range of 400 to 700 mμ. Provision must be made for the elimination of stray energy, such as by stray-energy filters or by the use of two dispersing prisms.

Reflectance Standards.—The standard of reflectivity shall be a layer (at least 0.5 mm. thick) or magnesium oxide freshly prepared according to TAPPI Standard T 633 m (p. 1460) by collecting the smoke from burning magnesium ribbon or turnings on a suitable surface. If any other material is employed as standard, its spectral reflectivity shall be specified.

Illumination and Viewing.—The standard and sample shall be illuminated under identical conditions.

The manner of illumination shall be specified, stating whether the illumination is diffuse or unidirectional. If diffuse, the geometry of the illumination shall be specified, including the nature of the reflecting surface within the integrating sphere, the solid angle subtended, at the sample surface, by the illuminating beam of light, and the area of the sample illuminated.

The manner and angle of viewing shall be specified together with the solid angle subtended, at the sample, by the viewing rays of light, and the area of the sample viewed.

NOTE.—This method (measurement of spectral reflectivity) serves to specify the optical properties of pulp which are responsible for its color, subject to the limitation that the color may depend upon the manner of illumination and viewing. It is important to specify the geometry of the illumination and viewing, and the most important single characteristic is whether or not the specular component of reflected energy is included in the measurement. In every case it shall be definitely stated whether or not the reflected light measured includes light reflected specularly from the surface of the sample.

Calibration.—The calibration of the photometer scale or other intensity measuring unit shall be carefully checked for accuracy at reasonable intervals.

The accuracy of the wavelength calibrations shall be checked at reasonable intervals by a sodium flame and other sources of monochromatic light at several wavelengths from 400 to 700 mμ.

The slit-width or filter bands of the monochromatizing system shall be kept sufficiently narrow to insure good approximation to monochromatic light.

The spectral reflectivity of secondary standards (working standards) shall be measured against magnesium oxide at reasonable intervals.

Test Specimen.—Tests shall be made on handsheets prepared according to TAPPI Standard T 218 m, Forming Handsheets for Optical Tests of Pulp (p. 1357).

Procedure.—The test sheets shall be handled carefully to avoid discoloration and care must be taken not to touch the part tested. The condition of the sample before and after analysis shall be carefully noted and any change in the appearance of the surface shall be recorded.

Readings shall be made at each of the various wavelengths from 400 to 700 mμ to establish a reliable indication of the percentage of light reflected by the sample at each

of these wavelengths, the number of wavelengths at which the measurements are made
to be sufficient to represent accurately, graphically or numerically, the characteristic
reflectivity of the sample.

NOTE.—Typical spectral reflectance curves of pulps are shown in Fig. 55-7.

A sufficient number of thicknesses of the sample shall be employed to the extent that
a doubling of the number of thicknesses will not cause appreciable change in the reflectance at any wavelength.

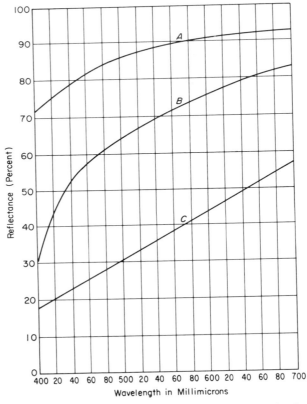

FIG. 55-7.   Pulps. *A*, Bleached sulfite. *B*, Groundwood. *C*, Unbleached kraft.

Report.—The report of the spectral reflectivity and color of a pulp sample shall
consist of the following:

1. The characteristic spectral reflectivity of the sample relative to that for magnesium
oxide.

2. The nature of and special reflectivity of any other material than magnesium oxide
employed as a standard.

3. The manner of illumination and manner of viewing, as specified above, or as an
alternative, a statement of the model number and the name of the instrument, without
modifications, employed for the measurement.

4. The tristimulus specification of the color computed from the spectral reflectivity according to the standard observed and colorimetric coördinate system recommended in 1931 by the International Commission on Illumination and for I.C.I. Illuminant C (representative of average daylight).

Note.—A report of the spectral reflectivity and color of the pulps in Fig. 55-7 is given as follows:

(a) The spectral reflectivity is shown in the figure.

(b) No standard other than magnesium oxide was employed.

(c) *Either:* The illumination was undirectional at 90° to the sample, the solid angle subtended by the said illumination varying from about 0.00013 steradian in the red to 0.00035 in the blue. The viewing was approximately diffuse, the important differences being (1) light specularly reflected (as well as some diffuse near to the specular position) passes out of the sphere through an aperture subtending about 0.00895 steradian, and (2) the viewing photocell sees light once reflected from the sample at about 41° through a solid angle of 0.0854 steradian. The size of sample illuminated was equal to that viewed, a circular area of 22 mm. diameter.

Or: The illumination and viewing of the sample is defined by the construction of the General Electric recording spectrophotometer, catalog number 4980125 GL, serial number 716175.

(d) Tristimulus specification:

Trichomatic Coefficients	(A) Bleached Sulphite	Pulps (Fig. 55-7) (B) Groundwood	(C) Unbleached Kraft
x	0.3198	0.3381	0.3627
y	0.3288	0.3457	0.3604
z	0.3514	0.3162	0.2768
Dominant wavelength in mμ	573.5	577.0	580.0
Excitation purity, %	6.0	15.5	25.8
Visual efficiency, %	89.1	70.8	38.3

These data were calculated by the 30 selected ordinate method described in Chapter 6, "Handbook of Colorimetry," by A. C. Hardy and Staff of M.I.T. Color Measurement Laboratory, Technology Press, 1936. For those who desire to practice this calculation the simple curve for unbleached kraft pulp, a straight line connecting $R_{400} = 17.8$ and $R_{700} = 57.0$, is recommended.

BRIGHTNESS OF PULP

The term "brightness," as applied to white and near-white papers, has come to be associated with the numerical value of the reflectance of those papers to light in the blue and violet portions of the spectrum, the measurement being made using an instrument known to be in calibration with a master instrument of particular type and design as described in Appendix A. This special use of the term was derived from long use of the word as descriptive of the "whiteness" of papers in the pulp and paper industry and from the fact that the results from brightness measurements on each of two "white" papers will usually correlate well with subjective estimates of the relative whiteness of the two samples. If this correlation does not obtain, it will usually be found that a subjectively whiter paper can be produced from the materials used in the making of the sheet having the higher brightness test value. The above use of the term "brightness" is also applicable to all naturally colored pulps.

It is highly important to assure as far as possible (1) that all brightness tests be on a single scale, that scale being the one to which the presently used instruments conform; (2) that means be provided for checking the calibration of every instrument used for brightness testing so that the user may rely upon the test results; and (3) that criteria be provided by which one may judge whether or not any instrument differing in optical, geometrical and photometrical characteristics from those now generally used may safely be employed in performing the brightness test.

This test procedure divides logically into three parts in the sequence given below:

1. A detailed description of the significant spectral, geometrical, and photometrical characteristics of a master instrument to be maintained in a central standardizing laboratory with a statement of the tolerances which must be maintained in its construction, maintenance, and use. This includes also a description of a method of preparation of a primary reflectance standard and of a system of secondary reflectance standards against which variations in the brightness scale with the passage of time can be checked.

2. Description of a system of preparation, distribution and use of reflectance standards by which the instrument can be maintained in continuous agreement, to within specified tolerances, with the master instrument.

3. Test procedures for use of the instrument itself in measuring the brightness of samples of pulp test sheets.

Only the third part will usually be of interest to one desiring to make a brightness determination of pulp. This being the case, the discussion of the master instrument and of the standardizing system is given in Appendices A and B.

Appendix A furnishes sufficient basic information for one to determine whether or not a particular instrument differing in constructional details from the master instrument is likely to give results in satisfactory agreement with the master instrument. The system of calibrated secondary standards (see Appendix B) should enable one to check, by actual measurement, whether or not such an instrument gives and continues to give sufficiently accurate results.[13,14,15,16] This method is standardized as TAPPI T 217 m-48.

Apparatus. **Instrument.**—The instrument shall be a reflection meter of such design and in such adjustment that its calibration is correct to within the tolerances specified in the following section on Calibration.

NOTE.—Identity of reading with that of the master instrument on one or two of the secondary standards is not sufficient proof that readings on the test instrument and on the master instrument will be identical on all samples even though the latter have brightness values very close to that of the secondary standard in question. If the instrument reads properly on all the secondary standards, it will usually be in proper calibration.

Brightness Standards.—The secondary standards of brightness shall comprise, in each set, at least 5 pads of paper tabs and two working standards, all of brightness accurately established by measurement on the master instrument.

The ultimate standard of reflectance, magnesium oxide (MgO), shall be prepared in accordance with TAPPI Standard T 633 m (p. 1460). The magnesium oxide shall preferably be deposited on a block of magnesium carbonate. Split the block in two and, with a clean straight-edge, scrape an inner surface so as to render it plane. Deposit the magnesium oxide on this surface. Prepare at least 6 such blocks.

Calibration.—When in use, check the instrument readings against the assigned values of all the secondary standards at least daily. If the instrument is found to be appreciably in error (the largest discrepancies being greater than about 0.3 point), adjust the instrument (frequently the focus of the lamp image) so that the readings of the paper brightness standards against those of the working standards agree with the assigned values.

Obtain brightness standards set by the master instrument at monthly intervals and calibrate the instrument with their aid as soon as they are received. (See Appendix B.)

[13] Instrumentation Studies. XIII, Paper Trade J., **104**, No. 18, 47–53; No. 19, 51–63; No. 20, 45–49, May 6, 13, 20, 1937. XX, Paper Trade J., **105**, No. 18, 135–141; No. 19, 27–39, Oct. 28, Nov. 4, 1937. XXI, Paper Trade J., **105**, No. 25, 46–50, Dec. 16, 1937. XXII, Paper Trade J., **105**, No. 27, 42–46, Dec. 30, 1937. XXVIII, Paper Trade J., **107**, No. 20, 33–37, Nov. 17, 1938. XXIX, Paper Trade J., **107**, No. 25, 29–40, Dec. 22, 1938. XXXVII, Paper Trade J., **112**, No. 1, 13–22, Jan. 2, 1941.

[14] Davis, M. N., Paper Trade J., **101**, No. 1, 36–44, July 4, 1935.

[15] Hunter, J. Optical Soc. Am., **30**, 536, 1940.

[16] Michaelson, J. L., Gen. Elec. Rev., **38**, No. 4, 194–196, April, 1935.

At intervals of 1 to 3 years, depending upon the conditions of use, the instrument should be disassembled and carefully inspected, tested and adjusted to insure that its geometrical and spectral variables fall within proper limits, and that its photometric system is accurate.

Tests shall be made on handsheets prepared according to TAPPI Standard T 218 m (p. 1357), Forming Handsheets for Optical Tests of Pulp.

Test Specimens.—Cut the test sheet into tabs 2 by $1\frac{1}{2}$ in. ($\pm\frac{1}{16}$ in.), the number of sheets being such that when arranged in a pad, the brightness of the pad is not changed by doubling its thickness. Assemble the tabs in a pad, with the sides next to the filter paper uppermost, and mark the top tab near the edge to indicate the top side. Do not use the cover tabe for brightness measurements.

Do not include in that portion of the area of the test specimens used for the measurement of brightness watermarks, large dirt specks, blemishes or anything that might influence the accuracy of the result. Protect the test specimens from contact with the fingers or contaminating agents and from the destructive influences of elevated temperature, light and time.

Procedure.—Without contaminating the test areas of the specimens with the fingers or other objects, remove the protective cover tab, placing it on the *back* of the pad, then place the pad of handsheet tabs over the sample aperture of the instrument with the felt or top side facing the instrument. Make one half of the determinations using one orientation of the tabs, and the other half with the samples turned through 90°.

Place a 1-kg. weight having a plane base upon the pad. Measure and record the brightness reading to 0.1 unit. Move the lower tab to the back of the pad and make another brightness determination. Repeat this procedure until 6 different tabs have been tested.

Report.—The report shall state the average percentage brightness of the sample (based on magnesium oxide = 100.0), to one decimal place, together with the minimum and maximum readings. It shall also state clearly and conspicuously any deviations from the standard procedure and note any unusual features or characteristics of the sample handsheets.

APPENDIX A

MASTER INSTRUMENT

In order to evaluate the brightness of the standards employed in the adjustment and calibration of all instruments used for the measurement of brightness as set forth in this method, a master instrument shall be maintained so that it will, as all times, correctly measure the brightness of pulp handsheets relative to that of freshly prepared magnesium oxide, which latter is taken equal to 100.0 percent.

The master instrument is defined by characteristics which are classified as *spectral, geometrical,* and *photometrical.*

Spectral Characteristics.—(a) The effective wavelength of the instrument when used with the filter required for the determination of brightness shall be 457.0 ± 0.5 mμ. The effective wavelength is that wavelength of monochromatic light for which the transmittance of a filter having spectral transmittance given by $T = a + b\lambda$ is equal to that determined with the master instrument, after proper account or correction is made for effects associated with refraction and reflection, angular spread of rays through the filter, photometric error, and wavelength error in the spectrophotometer employed to determine the spectral transmittance. In the foregoing equation, which need hold only for that wavelength range encompassed by a brightness filter, T is transmittance, a and b are constants, and λ is wavelength. The effective wavelength of the master instrument shall be determined by the method associated with the foregoing definition (see "Additional Information 1"). If the filter having a linear spectral transmittance consists of a film or plate, its transmittance shall be measured relative to a clear, nonabsorbing film or plate of equal thickness and similar index of refraction; if it be a liquid filter, the transmittance shall be measured relative to a clear, nonabsorbing liquid filter comprised of an identical filter cell containing the pure solvent used for the solution in the absorbing liquid filter. The spectral transmittance shall be so measured in both the master instrument and the spectrophotometer, and the cells shall be so disposed with respect to apertures as to minimize error due to scattering of light in the filters between the sample aperture and the light scattering the same in the master instrument and the spectrophotometer (see "Additional Information 2").

(b) The area under the curve, which represents the product for all wavelengths greater than 700 mµ of the spectral sensitivity of the photoelectric cell and the spectral transmittance of all filters between the sample aperture and the photoelectric cell, shall be so small compared with the similar area for the wavelength range 360 to 510 mµ that no detectable part of the photoelectric current may be ascribed to infrared fluorescent light arising in the test specimen.

(c) The spectral energy distribution of the light incident upon the test specimen shall be of such nature that (1) the rate of absorption of energy in the test specimen shall be insufficient to cause an appreciable elevation of temperature, and (2) the intensity of ultraviolet light shall be insufficient to modify the reflectivity of the test specimen through photochemical reaction during the course of measurement.

(d) The effective wavelength, 457.0 ± 0.5 mµ, shall be arrived at by the combination of (1) lamp, glass optics and filters, for which the mathematical product of relative spectral energy distribution and spectral transmission is $F(\lambda)$; and (2) a photoelectric cell chosen to make the effective wavelength 457.0 ± 0.5 mµ, and where $F(\lambda)$ is that function of wavelength given in Table 55-3.

TABLE 55-3. PRODUCT OF RELATIVE SPECTRAL ENERGY DISTRIBUTION, SPECTRAL TRANSMISSION OF GLASS OPTICS AND SPECTRAL TRANSMISSIONS OF ALL FILTERS

Wavelength, mµ	$F(\lambda)$ (arbitrary units)	Wavelength, mµ	$F(\lambda)$ (arbitrary units)
360	0.0	440	58.6
370	0.1	450	90.5
380	0.8	460	99.8
390	1.9	470	83.5
400	4.4	480	52.0
410	8.3	490	23.1
420	16.2	500	8.0
430	32.1	510	0.0

NOTE.—The foregoing may be illustrated with information regarding the master instrument with which the existing scale of brightness has been established. The function $F(\lambda)$ is the product of the relative spectral energy distribution of the light from a concentrated filament lamp operated at a color temperature of 3100° K; the spectral transmission of four aspheric lenses (two between light source and sample aperture and two between sample aperture and photoelectric cell); the spectral transmission of a filter cell containing a 1-cm. thickness of a 10 percent copper sulphate solution containing 1 percent concentrated sulphuric acid (placed between light source and sample aperture to remove heat from incident rays); the spectral transmission of a particular Wratten 49 filter, the measured spectral transmission of which has arbitrarily been taken as standard (this filter between sample aperture and photoelectric cell) and the spectral transmission of a Jena BG-18, melt S1152, filter ground to a thickness of 0.020 in., which is placed between the sample aperture and the photoelectric cell to remove any infrared fluorescent light arising in the test specimen.

The photoelectric cell used shall be regarded as satisfactory if, and only if, its use results in the instrument having the proper effective wavelength, as determined by the method given in (*a*) above.

The permissible range of variation from the values given in Table 55-3 shall be that corresponding to the wavelength range, ± 1.5 mμ; independently of this restriction upon $F(\lambda)$, the effective wavelength shall be maintained between 456.5 and 457.5 mμ.

(*e*) The minimum value of the spectral sensitivity of the photoelectric cell or combination of filter and photoelectric cell in the range 400 to 500 mμ shall be not less than one third the maximum value in that range. This restriction precludes the use of a combination of filter and photoelectric cell or photoelectric cell alone which gives rise to proper effective wavelength, but is responsive to a wavelength range less than that encompassed by the data of Table 55-3. Preferably the spectral sensitivity curve shall be free of strong curvature in the range 400 to 500 mμ.

Geometrical Characteristics.—(*a*) The mean angle of incidence of rays upon the test specimen shall be $45 \pm 1°$.

(*b*) The incident rays upon a point of the test specimen shall be confined within a cone having a half angle of $11.5 \pm 2°$. This cone shall be filled with light, and have its vertex in the sample aperture and base at the emergent aperture of the condensing lenses.

(*c*) The sample aperture shall be circular and have a diameter of between 0.460 and 0.500 in.; however, the exit aperture of the optical system which accepts reflected rays for measurement shall be coincident with the image of the disc concentric and coplanar with the sample aperture, and have a diameter of 0.375 ± 0.02 in., so that light reflected from the rim of the sample aperture shall not arrive at the photoelectric cell.

(*d*) The mean angle of rays reflected by the test specimen and accepted by the receiving optical system for measurement shall be between 0 and 1° with the normal to the plane of the sample aperture.

(*e*) The accepted reflected rays shall be confined within a cone having a half angle of $22.5 \pm 2°$.

Photometrical Characteristics.—(*a*) A null photometric method shall be employed. Light intensity shall be regulated by means of a sector diaphragm, in the following manner: With the test specimen over the sample aperture, the sectors of the photometer shall be opened to the angle corresponding to the reflectance of the standard, and the photoelectric current shall be noted; then, with the standard over the sample aperture, the sectors shall be so adjusted that the photoelectric current returns to the previously noted value, and the reflectance of the sample shall be read from the reflectance scale.

(*b*) The sector diaphragm shall be placed between the pair of lenses of the receiving optical system with its center on the optic axis, and shall be comprised of (1) a pair of sectors in a fixed plate, each bounded by radii separated by 93° and circles of radii respectively 0.188 and 1.125 in., each radius being constant to within ± 0.001 in., the two members of the pair being separated by 180° and centered upon a line which is perpendicular to the plane containing the axes of the incident and reflected rays of light; and (2) a rotatable pair of sectors, geared to a reflectance dial, each sector bounded by radii separated by 90° and circles of radii respectively 0.188 ± 0.001 in. and approximately 1.2 in., the two members of the pair being separated by 180°, and the nature of the gear train being such that, when the reflectance dial is set at 100, the openings formed by the two pairs of sectors are each approximately 83°, and when the reflectance dial is set at zero, the openings are $0.0 \pm 0.1°$.

(*c*) The defining edges of the sector diaphragm shall be thin and so beveled and blackened as to be nonreflecting. The plane of the sharp edges of the fixed sectors shall be in contact with that of the rotatable sectors, and the two pairs of sectors shall be concentric to within 0.001 in.

(*d*) The reflectance dial and the train of gears linking this dial with the sector diaphragm shall be of such accuracy that the total area of opening of the sector diaphragm shall be directly proportional to the dial reading to within 0.1 percent of the full opening.

Calibration of Working Standards for Use with Master Instrument.—The ultimate standard of reflectance, magnesium oxide (MgO), shall be prepared in accordance with TAPPI Standard T 633 m (p. 1460). The magnesium oxide shall preferably be deposited on a block of magnesium carbonate. Split the block in two, and, with a clean straight-edge, scrape an inner surface so as to render it plane. Deposit the magnesium oxide on this surface. Prepare at least 6 such blocks.

In turn place each block over the sample aperture of the master instrument upon shims which have been previously placed in position to hold the blocks so that the easily compressed layer of magnesium oxide will only just touch the surface. This may be judged by sighting beneath the magnesium oxide block. If shims are not used, a small disc of the magnesium oxide will be extruded into the sample opening, and an erroneously high instrumental reading will result. Compare the reflectance of each of the prepared surfaces with each other and discard any obviously inferior surfaces. Measure the reflectances of a master working standard by assigning a reflectance of 100.0 percent to each magnesium oxide surface, and average the results to arrive at the assigned reflectance of the master working standard. Repeat this procedure for at least 15 different master working standards, 8 of which exhibit a reasonably flat spectral reflectance curve, and 7 of which are buff colored (having spectral reflectances somewhat similar to that of typical pulps).

APPENDIX B

Calibration Service.—The central laboratory to which is delegated the responsibility of maintaining and operating the master instrument will, upon arrangement, distribute secondary standards for the calibration service. A set of secondary standards usually will comprise at least 5 pads of paper tabs and 2 working standards of brightness accurately established by measurement on the master instrument.

The paper standards will cover a range from about 60 to 85 percent brightness. The paper from which these standards are prepared will have the following properties: (1) its brightness shall not change over a reasonable period of time; (2) it shall be white; (3) it shall be clean; (4) it shall be uniform in brightness; and (5) it shall have a relatively smooth surface but shall not be supercalendered.

The working standards will satisfy the following requirements: (1) the surface shall not deviate from a true plane by more than 0.0015 in. in a central circle of diameter $\frac{5}{8}$ in. and shall not be concave; (2) the nature of the surface polish and hardness, and the optical stability of the material shall be such that the brightness during 1 month of intensive but careful use shall not vary more than 0.3 point; (3) the nature of the surface and of the material shall be such that the standards may be easily and effectively cleansed, and sufficiently resistant to withstand several cleanings per day; and (4) the color of the working standards shall be white or cream, but the maximum spectral reflectivity shall not be more than twice the minimum in the wavelength range, 400 to 500 mμ.

The standards for calibration of instruments which have spectral, geometrical or photometrical characteristics differing from those of the master instrument require special consideration. They will comprise only paper standards similar to those described above except for a possible difference in size, and the standard scale of brightness shall be transferred to such an instrument only through the use of such paper standards. The readings from such an instrument and the master instrument may not agree for both the paper and working standards because of differences between these standards in translucency, surface, spectral, or other characteristics. For this reason special working standards for such an instrument shall be evaluated by that instrument in terms of the brightness values assigned by the master instrument to paper standards only. The following requirements also shall be satisfied: after having evaluated the average reflectance of any such special working standard by means of the several paper standards, the individual reflectance readings for the special working standard shall not deviate from the average reflectance by more than 0.3 point.

A set of calibrated paper and working standards will be distributed at monthly intervals. Upon their receipt the working standards in use shall be returned to the central laboratory for restandardization.

Additional Information.—1. A solution in a filter cell having a linear spectral transmittance over the range 400 to 500 mμ may conveniently comprise a dilution in distilled water of "Coca-Cola" which has been warmed to remove the dissolved gases, the concentration being in the neighborhood of about 40 percent Coca-Cola and 60 percent distilled water, the exact concentration being arrived at by test of linearity of the spectral transmittance. The spectral transmittance must be measured relative to an exactly similar filter cell containing distilled water.

2. In the master instrument the filter cells are placed just above the aperture which admits light to the photoelectric cell, so that the ratio of diameter of aperture to distance between the filter cell and aperture is not small. When the filter cells are placed in the spectrophotometer, they are so positioned that a similar ratio of aperture diameter to filter cell-aperture distance obtains.

REFERENCES

"Instrumentation Studies. XIII," Paper Trade J., **104**, No. 18, 47–53; No. 19, 51–63; No. 20, 45–49, May 6, 13, 20, 1937.

Natl. Bur. Standards Letter Circular L.C. 547 "Preparation and Colorimetric Properties of a Magnesium Oxide Reflectance Standard."

FORMING HANDSHEETS FOR OPTICAL TESTS OF PULP

This procedure is not intended for making test sheets for optical tests of pulp other than by those test methods adopted by the Technical Association of the Pulp and Paper Industry. It is designed for all unbleached and bleached pulps, provided that their individual fibrous elements are, or can easily be, separated. The method comprises a technique which permits the preparation of a reasonably smooth and reproducible surface for optical measurements with a minimum of washing and contamination of the sample. This precludes the use of the sheet mold as specified in TAPPI Standard T 205 m (p. 1337), because of the large volume of dilution water, its uncertain purity, and the possible contamination of certain unbleached pulps with copper. This method is standardized as TAPPI T 218 m-59.

Apparatus.—The following equipment as specified in TAPPI Standard T 205 m is required:

Disintegrator.—Chromium plated, to avoid possible discoloration of the pulp.

Pump and Press.—With pressure gauge.

Press Template, for centering the sheets in the press.

Drying Press.—Three or more drying rings with rubber seatings for holding the sheets during drying.

Blotting Paper.—A quantity of sheets of standard white blotting paper, 8 in. square, 0.0195 to 0.0205 in. thick, weighing 245 to 255 g. per sq. m., and having an absorbency of not less than 9 nor more than 20 seconds when tested with 0.1 ml. of water according to TAPPI Standard T 432 m (p. 1422).[17]

The following additional equipment also is required:

Büchner Funnel, porcelain, 16 cm. inside diameter.

Suction Flask, capacity 1500 ml. or more.

Filter Paper.—A supply of rapid-draining white filter paper, 15 cm. in diameter and free of soluble impurities.

Filter Paper.—A supply of uncreped white filter paper, 18.5 cm. in diameter and free of soluble impurities.

Graduated Cylinders, two 1-liter.

Sampling.—Select a sample accurately representing the pulp as a whole, equivalent to at least 20 g. of dry fiber.

Storage of Pulp Samples.—The optical properties of many pulps may change significantly during the first few hours after manufacture. As a control test, therefore, optical readings are sometimes of little value unless taken at a definite interval after processing. This interval should be stated in the report. In any event, the pulp samples should be stored in such a manner that they are not subject to contamination, to change in moisture content, nor to the undue influence of heat or light.

If the sample is dry, dilute 20 to 30 g. with distilled water to 2 liters in the disintegrator and stir until the fibers are well separated.

Test Specimen.—Weigh to the nearest 0.1 g., a representative specimen equivalent to 4 g. of moisture-free fiber.

Procedure. **Dilution.**—Dilute the specimen to 2000 ml. with *distilled* water at room temperature and disintegrate for 15,000 revolutions (5 min.) in the standard disintegrator. Immediately divide the contents of the disintegrator equally between the two 1-liter graduated cylinders.

Sheetmaking.—Insert the Büchner funnel in the neck of the suction flask and set the flask upon a level surface. Place a sheet of the 15-cm. filter paper in the funnel and wet it with distilled water from a wash bottle. Apply suction momentarily in order to seat the filter paper properly in the funnel. Ascertain that the funnel is level by pouring a few milliliters of distilled water on the filter paper and sucking this water slowly through the paper. The water layer should disappear simultaneously over the entire area of the filter.

Apply suction, then rapidly pour in 1 liter of the disintegrated stock. Continue the application of suction to the filter flask until the excess water has been removed, then turn off the suction line, and remove the funnel immediately, in order to avoid drawing an appreciable quantity of air through the pulp mat.

Pressing.—Lay 2 new pieces of standard blotting paper on the press, felt side uppermost. Upon these, lay one sheet of the 18.5-cm. filter paper with its felt side uppermost. Invert the Büchner funnel over the press and, by blowing, deposit the handsheet, with its filter paper, centrally upon the surface thus prepared. Center the sheet by means of the press template. Cover with 2 more new pieces of standard blotting paper, felt side uppermost.

Using the other liter of disintegrated stock make a duplicate test sheet and deposit it in the press. The stock will then consist of a repetition of the following series: 2 blotters, 18.5-cm. filter paper, brightness handsheet, and 15-cm. filter paper. Finally, lay 2 blotters on the uppermost sheet. If required, as many as 5 pairs of handsheets may be

---

[17] These are the same as used for TAPPI Standard T 205 m. The Sorg Paper Co., Middletown, Ohio, Standard Paper Manufacturing Co., Richmond, Virginia, and the Rochester Paper Co., Rochester, Mich., offer such blotters. Compliance with these specifications should be confirmed.

pressed simultaneously in this manner, provided that they are formed successively from previously prepared and diluted specimens.

Put on the cover of the press and screw 2 of the diagonally opposite, or the 4, wing nuts down hand-tight. Raise the pressure, as indicated by the gauge, to 50 p.s.i.[18] in 0.5 minute from the time the needle begins to move, and maintain it there for 5 minutes. At the end of that time, release the pressure and remove the press cover.

Drying.—Remove the stack from the press and fit the test sheets, still covered with filter papers, into a set of drying rings in such a manner that the 18.5-cm. filter paper supports the sheet. Place a heavy weight on top of the pile.

Dry the test sheets with the attached filter papers in the drying rings at room temperature in an atmosphere with relative humidity not over 65 percent. To accelerate the drying operation, circulate the air through the drying rings by means of a fan, but do not use hot air.

Testing of Sheets.—After the sheets are thoroughly air dry, remove them from the drying rings with the filter papers attached. Do not remove the latter until the sheets are cut into tabs for the optical readings. The surface to be tested is the one next to the 18.5-cm. filter paper. This was the top surface of the sheet when made in the Büchner funnel.

Test the sheets not less than 2.0 nor more than 4.0 hours after making them, as in some instances the optical properties of the sheets change with time.

Additional Information.—This method is adapted from Method 412 of The Institute of Paper Chemistry.

REFERENCE

Koon, Charles M., and Niemeyer, Donald E., "The Influence of Certain Variables in Forming Brightness Handsheets," Paper Trade J., **114**, No. 5, 30, Jan. 29, 1942.

PHYSICAL TESTING OF PULP HANDSHEETS

This procedure deals with the testing of pulp handsheets, prepared in accordance with TAPPI Standard T 205 m (p. 1337), for strength and other physical properties excepting optical properties, for which see T 218 m (p. 1357).

Five sheets are generally enough for all the usual tests. It is well, however, to prepare 6 sheets and attach one to the report for future reference. This method is revised tentative standard TAPPI T 220 m-60.

Procedure.—Dry the sheets to constant weight and also test them in an atmosphere maintained at 50 ± 2 percent R.H. and a temperature of 23 ± 2°C. (73 ± 3.5°F.).

Test the sheets for each characteristic according to the appropriate standard paper testing method, with deviations as specified below.

A convenient method of dividing and using 5 test sheets for making the usual tests is shown in Fig. 55-8.

Basis Weight.—Determine the average basis weight of the conditioned sheets by weighing them together on a balance sensitive to 0.01 g.

The area of each sheet ($6\frac{9}{32}$ in. diameter) is taken to be 200 sq. cm. Hence if n is the number of sheets in a group weighint w grams, the basis weight is 50 w/n g.s.m., conditioned basis. The moisture-free basis weight is obtained by multiplying this value by the dryness factor z/y (see "Moisture" below).

Thickness.—Before cutting the test sheets, obtain their average thickness by placing 5 sheets in a pile with their glazed surfaces in the same direction and measuring the thickness of the 5 sheets together. Use a micrometer having a pressure foot 14.3 to

---

[18] This is equivalent to approximately 60 p.s.i. on the sheet.

16.5 mm. diameter, and a closing pressure of 0.52 ± 0.03 kg. per sq. cm. If a motor-driven micrometer is not available, apply the pressure slowly and gently, then rap the gauge very gently with the tips of the fingers and take the reading after the needle ceases to move. Take 5 readings to the nearest 0.0001 in., one from the center of the

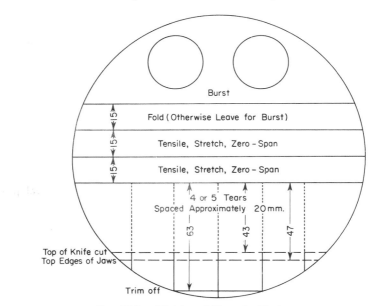

Fig. 55-8.   Division of Sheet for Testing.

pile, and 4 symmetrically around the sheets, halfway between the center and the edge. Calculate the average thickness of a single sheet to 3 significant figures.

NOTE.—To obtain an accurate figure for average sheet thickness from which to calculate the property of Standard Test Sheet Density (or Bulk), which may be used as a basis for plotting results, the described procedure should be carefully and systematically followed. It is not the same as described in T 426 m (p. 1419), but conforms with the original specification for testing pulp sheets given here in T 220 m-42.

Tensile Strength and Stretch.—Use at least 10 strips from 5 test sheets, each strip cut 15 mm. wide. Set the jaws of the tensile tester (see TAPPI Standard T 404 m (p. 1395), 90 to 100 mm. apart and increase the load uniformly at the rate of 1 ± 0.3 lb. (0.45 ± 0.15 kg.) per second until fracture occurs. If the breaking load is less than 4 pounds (1.8 kg.), decrease the rate of loading so that fracture occurs in 5 ± 1 second.

NOTE.—This is a rate different from that specified in T 404 m and conforms with the original specification for testing pulp test sheets.

If the stretch is measured, watch the indicator continuously during the test, and if it jumps when the specimen breaks, record the reading immediately before the jump.

NOTE.—It is convenient to align and clamp the ends of all the strips together in the upper jaws of the tensile tester and successively insert and clamp the lower ends, one at a time, in the lower jaws to break them individually.

Bursting Strength.—Determine the bursting strength one at a time by making at least 10 bursts on the segments of 5 test sheets, the glazed side of each sheet being clamped toward the diaphragm; otherwise, in accordance with TAPPI T 403 m-62.

Tearing Strength.—Determine the tearing strength on a 16-sheet standard tearing tester as described in T 414 m except that, if the readings fall outside of the usual limits, the instrument should be carefully calibrated accordingly. Clamp the sheets so that their smooth sides face the axis of the instrument and the greater part of the specimen is held in the fixed, not the moving, jaw. With chemical pulps, divide portions from 5 test sheets in the manner shown in Fig. 55-8 and test the 5 portions together, making 4 or 5 tears, each being through a total tearing distance of 21.5 cm. (5 × 4.3). Multiply the average reading on the standard tear tester by 3.2 (*i.e.*, $\frac{16}{5}$) to obtain the force in grams required to tear a single sheet.

NOTE.—Accuracy and convenience will be enhanced, especially if the segment of sheets was cut somewhat narrow, if a template is made to draw a pencil line 47.0 mm. from the centrally cut edges of the pack of specimens. When they are clamped in the jaws of the instrument, align the pack so that the scribed line coincides with the top edges of the jaws. The knife should be checked to cut 4.0 mm. above these edges, to give a tearing distance of 43.0 mm.

For groundwood pulps, use 10 quadrant-shaped pieces from 5 test sheets, each piece half the area used for the tear; test as shown in Fig. 55-8. Make 3, possibly 4, tears, each through a total tearing distance of 43 cm. (10 × 4.3). Multiply the reading of the instrument by 1.6 (*i.e.*, $\frac{16}{10}$) to obtain the force in grams required to tear a single sheet. If 10 sheets are used for weak pulps other than groundwood, state this in the report.

If the specimens should be such that 5 sheets together give too high a reading, reduce the number of sheets torn together to 2 and multiply the observed reading by 8 to give the force in grams to tear a single sheet.

Folding Endurance.—Determine the folding strength of the 15-mm. wide strip of paper as shown in Fig. 55-8. Unless otherwise stated, it will be assumed that an MIT tester is used in accordance with T 423 m (p. 1407). With the MIT tester, only a centimeter or so of the strip needs to be clamped in the lower (moving) jaw and by taking care, the exact tension of 1 kg. may be applied, leaving the extra length of the strip projecting through the upper jaw. Since the upper part of the strip is not appreciably affected by the test, after the specimen breaks along the edge of the lower jaw when the test is completed, the broken end of the upper strip can be reclamped in the lower jaw, the correct tension again applied, and another test made. At least two folding endurance tests can then be made on each strip. For a referee test, make 20 tests in this way and report their average; for ordinary work 10 tests are usually sufficient and if the readings are consistent, 5 tests may be enough.

NOTE.—The folding test is very sensitive to the tensile breaking strength of the test strip and to the tension applied during the test. Accordingly, a kilogram weight should be used frequently to check the applied tension with the MIT tester and the basis weight of the test sheets should be kept as near to 60 g.s.m. as possible. Correction factors for varying basis weights have not been established; they probably vary with different pulps and degrees of beating.

Moisture.—When the tests are completed, collect about 2 g. of the scraps of any of the test sheets, weigh them (y g.), place in an oven at 105 ± 3°C. in an uncovered weighing bottle which has been previously dried and weighed with its cover, and dry until no further loss of weight occurs. Between weighings, place the covered bottle in a desiccator without removing the stopper, let it cool, open momentarily to let in the air, close it immediately, and weigh to determine the dry weight of the scraps (z g.).

NOTE.—The cover is used while cooling since the desiccating effect of the pulp may be greater than that of the desiccant used.

The percentage moisture content of the sheets under standard atmospheric condition is then: $(y - z)/y$. The moisture-free basis weight, in g.s.m., is: 50 wz/ny. (See under "Basis Weight," above.)

NOTE.—For the same kinds of pulp, if the humidity room is kept constant, the moisture contents will not vary appreciably and once established, for routine control work, these need be checked only occasionally. Air-dried chemical pulps normally contain less moisture than groundwood, and rag or purified pulps, still less.

Other Tests.—If desired, other tests, such as zero-span tensile, porosity (air pressure applied to the glazed side of the sheets), stiffness, etc., may be made according to standard procedures.

Report.—Report results in terms of their derived units to the nearest third significant figure. If the direct test results, *i.e.*, the actual instrument readings are reported, either (1) metric or (2) English units may be used as is common practice, the unit being stated in each case. For derived units, however, such as the various strength factors, only the metric system is standard. Calculate and report all the results, except the percentage of moisture, on the moisture-free basis weight of the test sheets.

The calculations of the various items reported are shown below by formulas in which:

r = basis weight in grams per square meter (moisture-free basis);
t = single sheet thickness in thousandths of a millimeter (μ);
T = single sheet thickness in thousandths of an inch;
b = bursting strength in grams per square centimeter;
B = bursting strength in pounds per square inch;
p = tensile break load in kilograms on a 15-mm. strip;
P = tensile break load in pounds on a 15-mm. strip; and
e = force in grams to tear a single sheet.

NOTE.—$t = 25.4T$; $b = 70.3B$.

Basis Weight.—In grams per square meter (moisture-free basis).
Moisture.—As a percentage of the air-dried (conditioned) weight.
Bulk (specific volume).—Calculated as cubic centimeters per gram from t/r or $25.4T/r$.
Density (specific gravity).—The reciprocal of bulk.

NOTE.—The result compares the density or bulk of the test sheets (measured under the prescribed pressure) to water, which has a bulk or density of 1.0.

Burst Factor.—From the formula b/r, or $70.3B/r$.

NOTE.—This factor, which has been called the "bursting area," is equivalent to the number of square meters of paper, the weight of which, if applied to each square centimeter of the test sheet clamped in the instrument, would cause a burst.

Breaking Length.—In meters, calculated from the formula

$$\frac{200,000\,p}{3r} \quad \text{or} \quad \frac{30,240\,P}{r}$$

NOTE.—This is equivalent to the length in meters of a uniformly wide strip of paper which, if held at one end (*e.g.*, freely suspending a coil of that paper by its tab end), would just cause the strip to break under its own weight.

Stretch.—As a percentage.
Tear Factor.—From the formula $100e/r$.

NOTE.—This factor, which has been called the "tearing area," is equivalent to the number of square decimeters (100 sq. dm. = 1 sq. m.) of paper, the weight of which, if applied to a single sheet, would cause a tear to progress.

Precision. Repeatability.—If the average basis weight of the test sheet is kept within 57 to 63 g.s.m. as specified, on a complete duplicate test for a set of handsheets made from one sample of pulp by one operator, the repeatability of the average burst factor may be expected to be within 2 percent or less, depending on the precision of the instrument.

Reproducibility.—In tests on a given shipment by different laboratories, if the paper testing instruments are standardized, the following maximum differences may be expected in the averages: burst factor, 5 percent; breaking length, 7 percent; tear factor, 10 percent; bulk, 5 percent. These are about the same as for paper testing.

NOTE.—These percentages have not been checked by a comprehensive statistical analysis. Much wider discrepancies may be introduced if the test sheets are made from pulp samples which have been separately beaten, especially if not with the same equipment. Furthermore, accuracy may be expected only if all the testing equipment is carefully standardized and the procedures meticulously followed.

Additional Information.—This revision of T 220 m-53 clarifies the drying and conditioning of the test sheets, specifies the measurement of their thickness and tear in greater detail, gives directions for folding endurance, and emphasizes that the derived test results are reported in metric units only and on a moisture-free basis, in accordance with now almost worldwide practice.

DRAINAGE TIME AND DRAINAGE FACTOR OF PULP

This method relates to determining numerically a measure of the slowness of stock and may conveniently replace the freeness test in many instances. The tests are carried out with the same sheetmaking and other equipment as specified in TAPPI Standard T 205 m (p. 1337) and the standard drainage time is obtained when preparing the standard test sheets according to the procedure there described by measuring the time required to form a sheet at 20°C. weighing 60 g. per square meter (moisture-free).

In general the drainage time is better suited for groundwood or beaten stock, as the test is insensitive for "free" pulps. The drainage factor,[19] on the other hand, which may be defined as the drainage time in seconds per gram of pulp used in the standard sheet machine at 20°C., may be applied satisfactorily to both very free and very slow pulps. For free pulps a substantial quantity of pulp (30 g. or more) is necessary for each determination of the drainage factor. Consequently, in some cases it may be inconvenient for pulp-testing work. It is, however, an excellent test for mill control work on stock preparation where as a rule plenty of pulp is available for test purposes. This method is standardized as TAPPI T 221 m-51.

Apparatus. **Standard Disintegrator.**—For pulp not in slush form.
Standard Sheet Machine and Stirrer.
The above equipment is as specified in T 205 m.
Stop Watch.—Graduated in 0.2 second or less.
Container, for pulp.
Dipper or enameled cup.
Graduated Cylinder, 1-liter.
Calibration.—Fill the container of the sheet machine to the mark 350 mm. from the wire with clean water and adjust the temperature to 20 ± 1°C. Quickly open the drain valve of the sheet machine and start the stop watch. Stop the watch as soon as the water leaves the wire.

[19] Campbell, W. B., "Measuring the Drainage Time with the British Sheet Machine," Convention No. Pulp Paper Mag. Canada, Feb., 1933; C.P.P.A. Tech. Sect. Proc., 1933, pp. 39–43.

NOTE.—Water from a high-pressure main is sometimes aerated. In such case it should be allowed to become degassed in an open container before pouring into the cylinder, as the presence of air bubbles in the drainage pipe may reduce the drainage time.

The drainage time with the clean grid plate in position should be 3.5 seconds. If over 4.0 seconds, and the wire is clean, it is an indication that the drain valve is either dirty or else through wear its effective opening has become reduced, in which case the plug is easily removed and the hole suitably enlarged with a file.

The spare grid plate supplied with the apparatus should be used to check the cleanliness of the grid plate in use, using some slow stock, and if the drainage time with the new plate is reduced, the grid plate in use should be cleaned by a steam jet, by scouring with weak acid after a weak alkali wash, or by quickly dipping the plate in concentrated sulphuric acid, followed by prompt washing in water. This check should be made at least weekly if the stock contains sizing and filler material. The concentrated acid is effective in dissolving or removing any cellulosic material.

The wire may also be cleaned in certain cases by inverting the plate over a Bunsen burner and carefully burning out the dirt. With this treatment, the wires will bulge out and care is necessary not to burn the fine wire. When the plate is cooled, the wires will return to their normal tautness and a very weak acid wash will complete the process. If none of these treatments is effective, the spare grid plate should be put into use and the old plate returned to the manufacturer for recovering.

Procedure. Drainage Time.—The standard drainage time may be obtained at the same time the standard sheets are formed. The procedure is the same as for sheet making except that the finally diluted stock mixture in the cylinder should have a temperature within 5° of 20°C. (effected by adding some hot or cold water to the stock), and, after a preliminary stirring, the temperature of the stock is taken to the nearest 0.5°C.

After the standard stirring and pause of 10 seconds, open the drain valve and note the time taken in seconds for the formation of each sheet while draining from the 350-mm. mark to the wire. The couching of the sheet follows. Mark the sheets on which the drainage times are determined (a minimum of 3 sheets) with an indelible pencil and determine their average basis weight, separately for especial accuracy; otherwise it may be taken as that of the complete set of sheets.

If the cylinder is not provided with the new hinge and clamp, the use of a seal ring is desirable for very precise work, especially for very wet, beaten pulp, or pulps containing much loading material, having drainage times of upwards of 20 seconds. The method of using the seal ring is described in detail in *Tech. Assoc. Papers* 15, 197, 1932, and *Paper Trade J.*, March 24, 1932, p. 40.

Calculation of Drainage Time.—If d is the average drainage time obtained in seconds, t°C. the average temperature of the mixture in the cylinder, and r the average basis weight (g. per sq. m., moisture-free) of the resulting sheets, then the standard drainage time in seconds for the standard conditions of 20°C. and 60 g. per sq. m. (dry basis) is approximately:

$$\frac{d(60 - K)}{r - K} + \left(\frac{1}{V_t} - 1\right)(d - 4)$$

In this formula, K is a constant for a given type of pulp, usually about 25, the exact figure for which is preferably determined by experiment by plotting the observed drainage time d against a series of values of r over a range of say 50 to 70 g. per square meter at 20°C. and taking the value of K from the point where an extrapolated straight line from the plotted points cuts the r axis; V_t is 100 times the viscosity of water in C.G.S. units at temperature t.

NOTE.—The above formula was worked out empirically by J. d'A. Clark, after a large number of observations, and gives more accurate results than previous formulas which greatly overemphasized the temperature-correction effect for low drainage times.

To facilitate calculation, the following table gives the values of $(1/V_t - 1)$ for different temperatures:

Temperature °C.	$\dfrac{1}{V_t} - 1$	Temperature °C.	$\dfrac{1}{V_t} - 1$	Temperature °C.	$\dfrac{1}{V_t} - 1$
5	−0.34	16	−0.10	27	+0.18
6	−.32	17	−.07	28	+.20
7	−.30	18	−.05	29	+.23
8	−.28	19	−.02	30	+.25
9	−.25	20	0.00	31	+.28
10	−.23	21	+.02	32	+.31
11	−.21	22	+.05	33	+.33
12	−.19	23	+.07	34	+.36
13	−.16	24	+.10	35	+.39
14	−.14	25	+.12		
15	−.12	26	+.15		

Drainage Factor.—Add a sufficient quantity of dispersed stock to the sheet machine to give a drainage time, after the standard dilution, stirring and pause of 10 seconds, of preferably 7 to 15 seconds and, subsequently, a greater quantity of stock to give a drainage time of a much longer period, preferably 20 to 40 seconds. After each has drained, couch each pad off the wire with blotters, dry at 100 to 105°C. and weigh to the nearest 0.05 g. It is advisable to make duplicate determinations.

The amount of stock lost through the wire is almost exactly the same quantity in both cases, so the difference between the moisture-free weights of the pads formed at the long and short periods quite accurately corresponds to the increment of stock for a determined increase in the drainage time.

Calculation of Drainage Factor.—The drainage factor, calculated in seconds per gram of dry pulp at 20°C., is given by:

$$\frac{\{D + [(1/V_{t_1}) - 1](D - 4)\} - \{d + [(1/V_{t_2}) - 1](d - 4)\}}{W - w}$$

In the formula D is the observed drainage time in seconds for a pad weighing W g. to form at temperature t, and d is the observed drainage time in seconds for a pad weighing w g. to form at temperature t_2, the factors $(1/V_{t_1} - 1)$ and $(1/V_{t_2} - 1)$ being taken from the preceding table of values.

The method is not appreciably influenced by the cleanliness of the wire, the size of mesh, the construction of the grid plate, or details of the drainage system, provided the initial effective head on the stock is 1150 mm. and the final head 800 mm.

Modified Method for Drainage Factor.—For mill control or routine purposes, if a graph is drawn of the drainage time (at 20°C.) against weight of stock added, the curve becomes straight. If this straight line is extrapolated, it will cut the weight axis somewhere between 0.2 and 0.8 g., depending on the amount of fine material in the stock. The drainage factor is the slope of this line when plotted for stock at 20°C.

For temperatures other than 20°C. the slope of this line may be calculated from the formula

$$\frac{D + \{[(1/V) - 1](D - 4)\}}{W - w}$$

where D is the observed drainage time (about 20 to 40 seconds) for a sheet weighing W g. to form, and w is the weight at which the extrapolated graph has been found experimentally to cut the weight axis. For approximate work, w may be assumed to be 0.3 g. for a free chemical pulp, 0.5 for slow groundwood, and 0.7 for a slow headbox stock.

Report.—The drainage time shall be reported as the average time in seconds to form sheets of 60 g. per sq. m. moisture-free basis weight at 20°C., to the nearest 0.1 second.

The drainage factor shall be reported as the average number of seconds required per g. of pulp to drain under standard conditions at 20°C. Results shall be reported to the nearest 0.01, if less than 1.0, and to the nearest 0.1, if 1.0 or over.

REFERENCES

"Interim Report of the Pulp Evaluation Committees to the Technical Section of the Paper Makers' Association, London," Paper Makers' Assoc. Gt. Britain and Ireland, Vol. 1, 1929, 120 p. (especially p. 53); and Vol. 2, 1936, 167 p. (especially Chap. V).

Campbell, W. Boyd, and Lodge, Wm. C., "Drainage Characteristics: Laboratory Studies," Pulp Paper Mag. Canada, **38**, No. 2, 189, Feb., 1937.

Hisey, W. O., and Heigl, C. H., "The Drainage Resistance of Papermaking Pulps," Paper Trade J., **110**, No. 6, 34, Feb. 8, 1940; Tech. Assoc. Papers, **23**, 640, 1940.

FREENESS OF PULP

The freeness test is a wholly empirical procedure which gives an arbitrary measure of the rate at which a suspension of 3 g. of pulp in 1 liter of water may be drained. The result depends mainly upon the quantity of debris present,[20] and to a lesser extent, the degree of fibrillation of the fibers, their flexibility, and their fineness. Besides these factors, the result is dependent also on conditions under which the test is carried out, such as pressure head, stock concentration, temperature, character of the draining surfaces, and construction of the drainage orifices.

The instrument and conditions here described[21] were designed to yield results primarily suited to the control of the manufacture of groundwood pulp. They have been used also by some for following the apparent change in the draining quality of various pulps during beating and for the control of beaters and refiners (see also T 221m, p. 1363, Drainage Time and Drainage Factor of Pulp). However, the readings do not necessarily correlate with the drainage quality of a stock on a paper machine. This method is standardized as TAPPI T 227 m-58.

Apparatus. **Freeness Tester.**[22]—The tester, shown in Fig. 55-9, consists of a drainage chamber and a rate-measuring funnel, mounted on a suitable support so that both are held exactly level.

The chamber is a bronze cylinder, the bottom of which is covered with a perforated brass plate and closed with a heavy bronze bottom lid, hinged on one side of the cylinder and latched at the other. The inner side of this lid is covered with a thick, soft, rubber gasket which fits against the flange around the lower side of the perforated plate (screen plate) when the lid is closed. The upper end of the cylinder is closed by a similar lid

[20] Thode, E. F., and Ingmanson, W. L., Tappi, **2**, No. 1, 74–83, Jan., 1959. Especially p. 82.

[21] Technical Section, Canadian Pulp and Paper Association, Official Standard Testing Method C.1.

[22] The instrument, which is the Canadian standard, is obtainable from the Robert Mitchell Co., Ltd., Montreal, Que., or from their United States agents, Testing Machines, Inc., 72 Jericho Turnpike, Mineola, Long Island, N. Y. Instruments and parts supplied by these companies are inspected by the Pulp & Paper Research Institute of Canada before shipment. The perforated plate used in the cylinder should be compared frequently with the plate certified by the Pulp & Paper Research Institute of Canada, Montreal 2, Que.

attached to the shelf bracket in which the cylinder is held when in use. The hinge and latching mechanism are designed to provide an airtight closure, the gasket being put under pressure when the lid is latched shut. An air-cock is provided for the upper lid, by which air can be admitted to the cylinder at the start of the test.

The inside dimensions of the cylinder are 4.00 in. diameter by 5.00 in. high from the upper surface of the screen plate to the rim. The diameter is a critical dimension. The specified height gives the cylinder a capacity of slightly over 1000 ml. above the screen plate. The air-cock bore is $\frac{3}{16} \pm \frac{1}{32}$ in. The screen plate is 0.020 in. thick and has perforations of 0.020 in. diameter, spaced 625 per sq. in. of surface. The plate is held in position with the burrs of the punched perforations downwards. It has not been found possible to duplicate these plates by specifying their physical dimensions, so all plates are standardized against master plates using two different pulps.

NOTE.—It is well to procure two extra plates for reference (see note under "Care of Instrument.") Stainless steel plates have some advantages; they also keep cleaner in use.

The rate-measuring conical funnel is of heavy bronze construction with an open cylindrical top, 8.00 in. inside diameter and the funnel has an over-all depth of $10\frac{15}{16}$ in., neither dimension being critical. The bottom of the conical part is machined on the inside to a 30° slope which

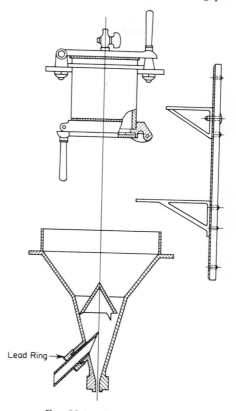

Lead Ring

FIG. 55-9.   Freeness Tester.

flares out to the top cylindrical portion. The bottom of the funnel terminates with a carefully-machined, removable, orifice-piece. The lower part of the funnel is also provided with a side discharge orifice, in the form of a tube.

The diameter of the opening in the bottom orifice is 0.1200 ± 0.0005 in. It is designed so as to deliver 530 ± 5 ml. of 20°C. water per minute, when the funnel is fed with slightly more than this quantity (700 to 750 ml. per minute) so that there is a moderate overflow of the excess through the side orifice. The small bottom orifice is flared outwards.

NOTE.—The bottom orifice can be kept clean by using a moistened pipe cleaner or a moist, soft, cotton string.

The side orifice tube is 0.50 in. inside diameter (not critical) and extends into the funnel. The inside end of the tube is cut at such an angle that the top side of the tube slightly overhangs the lower. The tube is so inserted that the volume between the top of the bottom orifice piece and the overflow level of the tube is 23.5 ± 0.2 ml. This volume is not easily measured because of the effects of surface tension. Its influence on the test is secondary to the rate of flow out of the bottom orifice. The height of the overflow level can be adjusted to some extent by the insertion or removal of lead washers under the shoulder holding the side orifice tube in place.

A detachable spreader cone is supported on three legs inside the funnel to prevent splash from directly entering the side orifice tube. The cylinder and the drainage cone are each supported by flanges in the openings of two machined shelves supported by a slate wall panel. The apparatus is correctly mounted when these shelves are level.

Graduated Cylinders.—1000 ml. and one of the same or lesser capacity with 10 ml. or smaller divisions, to suit the pulp being tested.

Standard Disintegrator.—Required only when the pulp is not in slush form, described in Appendix A of TAPPI Standard T 205 m (p. 1340).

Bucket.—At least 10-liter capacity to hold the stock.

Dipper.—A shallow plastic-ware tea cup with a thick, smooth lip is recommended.

Büchner Funnel and flask.

Weighing Bottle.—Preferably shallow type, to accommodate a folded pad of pulp from the Büchner funnel.

Care of Instrument.—Keep the instrument clean and free from stock accumulations, pitch, oil or grease. Normally, it is well to keep the 1-liter chamber filled with clean water.

NOTE.—Continual use with a sulfite pulp or a sized paper stock will cause the surfaces inside the cone to become water-repellent. Wash with a solution of a synthetic detergent and hot water to make this surface wettable, then thoroughly rinse with clean water.

After each test, rinse the chamber with clean water. It is particularly necessary to see that no pulp is left in the holes of the screen plate. If the instrument is to be left out of use, preferably keep the chamber full of water, otherwise carefully and thoroughly wash away any pulp that might dry on it, and leave both top and bottom lids of the cylinder open. Before making a test, thoroughly wet all the inside surfaces of the instrument with clean water, using a detergent if necessary. If a detergent is used, rinse well with clean hot water to remove *all traces* of the detergent. This is most important.

NOTE.—It is strongly recommended that 1 or preferably 2, spare standard screen plates be kept for reference. The screen plate in current use may then be checked from time to time against one of these, which in turn is checked against the second, or ultimate reference screen plate, once or twice a year, and after use the reference plate should be cleaned, dried, and carefully stored away. With careful use, a screen plate has a long life but under usual mill conditions it soon may become dirty with an accumulation of resin. Resin may be removed with xylene followed by thorough washing with hot water and a detergent. Under *no circumstances should acid be used to clean the plate.* Bent or damaged screen plates should be discarded. When replacing the screen plate, care should be taken to avoid any pressure that will squeeze the chamber out of round. If necessary, use a strap wrench, not a vise, to grip it.

Make sure that both the cylinder and funnel are level. Check the rate of flow from the bottom orifice occasionally by flowing a stream of water on to the apex of the protecting cone in the funnel, at the rate of 700 to 750 ml. per minute and measuring the discharge from the bottom orifice. The latter should be 530 ± 5 ml. per minute. If the flow is less than this, clean the orifice with water or a detergent as described above using a pipe cleaner or soft cotton string. Attempts to clean the orifice by more drastic means may enlarge it too much. If the rate of flow is too great, a new orifice piece is needed.

The side orifice tube can be assumed to have been properly adjusted by the makers with the insertion of lead washers before the instrument is sent to the purchaser. Do not disturb the adjustment unless it is evident that this tube has become displaced.

Sampling.—When dealing with a mill consignment, take a sample of pulp, about 4 sq. in. in area, from the interior of every bale included in the official test for moisture.

(Portions of specimens taken for the moisture test, but not dried, may be used.) The weight of the sample should be at least 50 g., and preferably 100 g. or more, of dry fiber, for duplicate tests.

For slush pulps, take a representative specimen equivalent to at least 18 g. of dry fiber.

Test Specimen.—Unless the pulp sampled is in slush form, disintegrate in water as follows: Weigh to the nearest 0.5 g. a representative specimen by tearing equal portions from all the samples collected, equivalent to 24 g. of moisture-free fiber. If the sample is dry, wet it thoroughly with cold water, tear into pieces about 1 in. square and soak in water for 4 hours; or in the case of a dried sample of mechanical pulp which is to be furnished in the moist form, allow it to soak for 24 hours.

NOTE.—As far as is known, soaking pulp for a longer time than 4 hours, for example overnight, does not appreciably affect the results.

Disintegration.—Make the mixture up to 2000 ml. (1.2 percent consistency) with cold water at 20 ± 2°C. and disintegrate for 75,000 revolutions (25 min.) in the standard disintegrator with the propeller running at 3000 r.p.m. in the stock.

NOTE.—In view of the possible effect of dissolved material on the freeness test, it may be desirable to use distilled water for dilution of the stock for precise work in checking data between laboratories.

It is essential to have the pulp sample completely defibered before making a freeness test, and after disintegration, the pulp should be examined by diluting a small portion to see that the fibers are completely dispersed. If not, and if the pulp has been adequately soaked previously, continue to disintegrate for another 7500 revolutions (2.5 minutes). If not dispersed, continue the disintegration in steps until the stock is completely defibered. If other than the 25-minute defibering time in the standard disintegrator has to be used, be sure to make a prominent note of the stock preparation employed, in the report (see "Additional Information"). Take the temperatures of the stock and the water to be used for diluting. Dilute the defibered pulp to 0.3 ± 0.02 percent (moisture-free) consistency after adjusting the temperature of the diluting water so that the temperature of the stock in the bucket is 20 ± 2°C.

NOTE.—It is necessary that the water used for diluting the sample be sufficiently free from dissolved air so that small bubbles are not liberated from the water in the pulp mixture. Water taken from high-pressure mains may require to be left standing for several hours, or else subjected to a vacuum before use.

Determine the consistency to three significant figures, by stirring well and filtering a representative specimen of the stock through a tared filter paper in the Büchner funnel. Dry the pad at 105 ± 3°C., place in a tared weighing bottle, cool in a desiccator, open the cover to equalize the air pressure and weigh.

NOTE.—For most purposes it is not necessary to have the specimen at exactly 0.3 percent consistency or 20°C., as the appended Tables 55-4 and 55-5 enable corrections to be made. Corrections outside the 0.02 percent and 2°C. limits may give questionable results. The tables are based primarily on tests made with groundwood and the freer corrections with sulfite pulps. Consequently their application to various other pulps may be questionable, and in the case of unusual pulps or for particular purposes, it is advisable to adjust the temperature and concentration to be as near the standard conditions as possible.

Procedure.—Thoroughly clean and wet the freeness tester with clean water at about 20°C. Place the drainage chamber on the upper supporting bracket with its lower lid secured and the air-cock in the upper lid open. Place the graduated cylinder in position to receive the discharge from the side orifice.

Using the cup, thoroughly stir the stock in the bucket and accurately measure 1000

TABLE 55-4. FREENESS CORRECTIONS TO 20°C.*

Freeness read	Temperature of stock at test, °C.																					Freeness read
	10	11	12	13	14	15	16	17	18	19	20	21	22	23	24	25	26	27	28	29	30	
	Points freeness to be added											Points freeness to be subtracted										
30	11	9	8	7	6	5	4	3	2	1	0	1	2	3	4	5	6	7	8	9	11	30
40	12	10	9	8	7	6	5	3	2	1	0	1	2	3	5	6	7	8	9	10	12	40
50	14	12	11	10	8	7	6	4	3	1	0	1	3	4	6	7	8	10	11	12	14	50
60	15	14	12	11	9	8	6	4	3	1	0	2	3	4	6	8	9	11	12	14	15	60
70	17	15	13	12	10	8	7	5	3	2	0	2	3	5	7	8	10	12	13	15	17	70
80	19	17	15	13	11	9	8	6	4	2	0	2	4	6	8	9	11	13	15	17	19	80
90	20	18	16	14	12	10	8	6	4	2	0	2	4	6	8	10	12	14	16	18	20	90
100	21	19	17	15	13	10	8	6	4	2	0	2	4	6	8	10	13	15	17	19	21	100
110	23	21	18	16	14	11	9	7	5	2	0	3	5	7	10	11	14	16	18	21	23	110
120	25	22	20	17	15	12	10	7	5	2	0	3	5	7	11	12	15	17	20	22	25	120
130	26	23	21	18	16	13	11	8	5	3	0	3	5	8	11	13	16	18	21	23	26	130
140	27	24	22	19	16	14	11	8	5	3	0	3	5	8	11	14	16	19	22	24	27	140
150	29	26	23	20	17	14	11	9	6	3	0	3	6	9	12	14	17	20	23	26	29	150
160	30	27	24	21	18	15	12	9	6	3	0	3	6	9	12	15	18	21	24	27	30	160
170	31	28	25	22	18	15	12	9	6	3	0	3	6	9	13	15	18	22	25	28	31	170
180	32	29	26	22	19	16	13	10	6	3	0	3	6	10	13	16	19	22	26	29	32	180
190	33	30	26	23	20	16	13	10	7	3	0	3	6	10	13	16	20	23	26	30	33	190
200	34	31	27	24	20	17	13	10	7	3	0	3	7	10	14	17	20	24	27	31	34	200
210	35	31	28	24	21	18	14	11	7	3	0	4	7	10	14	18	21	24	28	31	35	210
220	36	32	29	25	22	18	14	11	7	4	0	4	7	11	15	18	22	25	29	32	36	220
230	37	33	30	26	22	19	15	11	8	4	0	4	8	11	16	19	23	26	30	33	37	230
240	38	34	31	27	23	19	15	12	8	4	0	4	8	12	16	20	23	27	31	34	38	240
250	39	35	31	27	23	20	16	12	8	4	0	4	8	12	16	20	24	27	31	35	39	250
260	40	36	32	28	24	20	16	12	8	4	0	4	8	12		20	24	28	32	36	40	260
270	41	37	33	29	24	20	16	12	8	4	0	4	8					29	33	37	41	270

280	42	38	34	29	25	21	17	13	8	4	0	4	8	13	17	21	25	29	34	38	42	280
290	42	38	34	29	25	21	17	13	8	4	0	4	8	13	17	21	25	29	34	38	42	290
300	43	39	34	30	25	21	17	13	8	4	0	4	8	13	17	21	25	30	34	39	43	300
310	43	39	34	30	25	21	17	13	8	4	0	4	8	13	17	21	25	30	34	39	43	310
320	43	39	34	30	25	21	17	13	8	4	0	4	8	13	17	21	25	30	34	39	43	320
330	44	40	35	31	26	22	18	13	9	4	0	4	9	13	18	22	26	31	35	40	44	330
340	44	40	35	31	26	22	18	13	9	4	0	4	9	13	18	22	26	31	35	40	44	340
350	44	40	35	31	26	22	18	13	9	4	0	4	9	13	18	22	26	31	35	40	44	350
360	44	40	35	31	26	22	18	13	9	4	0	4	9	13	18	22	26	31	35	40	44	360
370	45	41	36	31	26	22	18	13	9	4	0	4	9	13	18	22	26	31	36	41	45	370
380	45	41	36	31	27	22	18	13	9	4	0	4	9	13	18	22	27	31	36	41	45	380
390	45	41	36	31	27	23	18	14	9	4	0	4	9	14	18	23	27	31	36	41	45	390
400	45	41	37	32	28	23	18	14	9	4	0	4	9	14	18	23	28	32	37	41	45	400
420	45	41	37	32	28	23	18	14	9	4	0	4	9	14	18	23	28	32	37	41	45	420
440	45	41	36	31	27	22	18	13	9	4	0	4	9	13	18	22	27	31	36	41	45	440
460	44	40	36	31	27	22	17	13	8	4	0	4	8	13	17	22	27	31	36	40	44	460
480	43	39	35	30	25	21	17	13	8	4	0	4	8	13	17	21	25	30	35	39	43	480
500	42	38	34	30	25	21	16	12	8	4	0	4	8	12	16	21	25	30	34	38	42	500
520	42	38	34	29	25	21	16	12	8	4	0	4	8	12	16	21	25	29	34	38	42	520
540	41	37	33	29	24	20	16	12	8	4	0	4	8	12	16	20	24	29	33	37	41	540
560	40	36	33	28	24	20	16	12	8	4	0	4	8	12	16	20	24	28	33	36	40	560
580	39	36	32	28	24	20	16	12	8	4	0	4	8	12	16	20	24	28	32	36	39	580
600	37	35	32	28	24	20	14	11	8	4	0	4	8	11	14	20	24	28	32	35	37	600
620	37	33	31	27	23	19	14	10	7	4	0	4	7	10	14	19	23	27	31	33	37	620
640	36	33	29	25	21	18	13	10	7	3	0	3	7	10	13	18	21	25	29	33	36	640
660	35	32	28	25	21	17	13	10	6	3	0	3	6	10	13	17	21	25	28	32	35	660
680	33	31	27	24	20	17	13	9	6	3	0	3	6	9	13	17	20	24	27	31	33	680
700	33	30	26	23	20	16	13	9	6	3	0	3	6	9	13	16	20	23	26	30	33	700

* Prepared by the Pulp and Paper Research Institute of Canada.

TABLE 55-5. FREENESS CORRECTIONS TO 0.30 PERCENT CONSISTENCY*

Freeness read	Consistency of stock at test, percent																					Freeness read
	0.20	0.21	0.22	0.23	0.24	0.25	0.26	0.27	0.28	0.29	0.30	0.31	0.32	0.33	0.34	0.35	0.36	0.37	0.38	0.39	0.40	
	Points freeness to be subtracted											Points freeness to be added										
20	·	·	·	·	·	·	·	·	·	·	0	2	3	5	7	9	11	13	15	17	19	20
30	·	·	·	·	·	10	8	6	4	2	0	2	4	6	8	10	13	15	17	19	21	30
40	22	20	18	16	13	11	9	7	6	2	0	3	5	7	9	12	14	17	19	21	23	40
50	25	23	20	18	15	13	10	8	6	3	0	3	6	8	10	13	16	18	21	23	25	50
60	28	25	22	19	17	14	11	9	6	3	0	3	6	9	11	14	17	19	22	25	27	60
70	31	27	23	20	18	15	12	9	5	3	0	3	6	9	12	15	18	21	24	27	29	70
80	33	29	25	22	19	16	13	10	6	3	0	4	7	10	13	16	19	22	25	28	31	80
90	36	31	27	24	21	17	13	10	7	3	0	4	7	10	13	16	20	23	26	29	32	90
100	38	33	29	26	22	18	14	11	7	3	0	4	7	11	14	17	21	24	27	30	34	100
110	40	35	31	27	23	19	15	11	7	3	0	4	8	11	14	18	22	25	28	31	35	110
120	42	37	33	29	24	19	15	12	8	3	0	4	8	11	15	19	23	26	29	33	36	120
130	44	39	35	30	25	20	16	12	8	4	0	4	8	12	15	20	24	27	31	35	38	130
140	46	41	36	31	26	21	17	12	8	4	0	4	8	12	16	20	24	28	32	36	40	140
150	48	42	37	32	27	22	17	13	8	4	0	4	8	12	16	21	25	30	34	38	42	150
160	50	44	39	33	28	23	18	14	8	4	0	4	8	13	17	22	26	31	35	39	43	160
170	52	46	40	34	29	24	19	15	10	5	0	4	9	13	18	23	27	32	36	41	45	170
180	54	48	42	36	30	25	20	15	10	5	0	5	9	14	19	24	28	33	37	42	46	180
190	56	49	43	37	31	26	20	15	10	5	0	5	10	15	19	24	28	33	38	43	47	190
200	58	51	45	38	32	26	21	16	10	5	0	5	10	15	20	25	29	34	39	44	48	200
210	60	53	46	39	33	27	21	17	10	5	0	5	10	15	21	26	30	35	40	45	49	210
220	61	54	47	40	34	28	22	17	11	5	0	5	10	16	21	26	31	36	41	46	50	220
230	62	55	48	41	35	28	22	17	11	5	0	5	11	16	22	27	32	37	42	47	51	230
240	63	56	49	42	36	29	23	18	11	5	0	6	12	17	23	28	33	38	43	48	53	240
250	64	57	50	43	37	30	23	18	11	5	0	6	12	18	23	29	34	39	44	49	54	250
260	65	58	51	44	37	30	24	18	12	6	0	7	13	19	24	30	35	40	45	50	55	260

270	56	51	46	41	36	31	25	19	13	7	0	6	12	19	25	31	38	45	52	59	67	270
280	57	52	47	41	36	31	25	19	13	7	0	6	12	19	25	32	39	46	53	60	68	280
290	57	52	47	42	36	31	25	19	13	7	0	6	13	19	26	33	40	47	54	62	70	290
300	58	53	48	42	36	31	25	19	13	7	0	6	13	20	27	34	41	48	56	64	72	300
310	58	53	48	43	37	31	25	19	13	7	0	7	13	20	27	34	41	49	57	65	73	310
320	58	53	48	43	37	31	25	19	13	7	0	7	13	20	27	35	42	50	58	66	75	320
330	58	53	48	43	38	32	25	19	13	7	0	7	13	20	27	35	43	51	59	68	77	330
340	59	54	49	44	38	32	26	20	14	7	0	7	14	20	27	35	43	52	60	69	78	340
350	59	54	49	44	38	32	26	20	14	7	0	7	14	21	27	35	43	52	61	70	79	350
360	59	54	49	44	38	32	26	20	14	7	0	7	14	21	28	36	44	52	61	70	80	360
370	59	54	49	44	38	32	26	20	14	7	0	7	14	21	28	36	44	52	61	71	81	370
380	59	54	49	44	38	32	26	20	14	7	0	7	14	21	29	37	45	53	62	71	81	380
390	59	54	49	44	38	32	26	20	14	7	0	7	14	21	29	37	45	53	62	72	82	390
400	59	54	49	44	38	32	26	20	14	7	0	7	14	21	29	37	45	54	63	72	82	400
420	59	54	49	44	38	32	26	20	14	7	0	7	14	21	29	37	45	54	63	73	83	420
440	59	54	49	44	38	32	26	20	14	7	0	7	14	21	29	37	45	54	63	73	83	440
460	59	53	49	44	38	32	26	20	14	7	0	7	14	21	29	37	46	54	63	73	83	460
480	58	52	47	42	38	32	26	19	13	7	0	7	14	21	29	37	46	54	63	73	83	480
500	57	51	46	41	36	30	25	18	12	6	0	6	13	20	29	36	44	53	62	72	82	500
520	56	50	45	40	35	29	24	17	12	6	0	6	13	20	28	36	44	53	62	71	80	520
540	55	49	44	39	34	27	22	16	12	6	0	6	12	19	27	35	43	51	60	69	78	540
560	54	47	42	37	32	27	22	16	11	6	0	6	12	18	26	34	42	50	58	67	76	560
580	52	46	42	37	32	26	21	15	10	5	0	6	11	17	25	33	41	49	57	66	75	580
600	50	44	40	36	31	25	20	15	10	5	0	5	11	16	24	32	40	48	56	65	74	600
620	48	42	38	34	30	25	20	14	9	4	0	5	11	16	24	31	39	47	55	64	73	620
640	47	41	37	33	29	24	19	13	9	4	0	5	11	16	23	31	39	46	55	63	71	640
660	46	39	35	31	28	23	18	13	8	4	0	5	11	16	24	30	38	46	54	63	70	660
680	45	38	34	30	27	22	18	13	8	4	0	5	11	16	23	30	38	46	54	62	69	680
700	44	37	33	29	26	22	18	13	8	4	0	5	11	16	23	30	38	46	54	62	69	700

* Prepared by the Pulp and Paper Research Institute of Canada.

ml. into a clean 1-liter cylinder. Take its temperature to the nearest 0.5°C. Immediately pour the contents of the cylinder gently into the chamber; close the top lid; close the air-cock; open the bottom lid and, after an interval of 5 seconds from the time that the addition of the stock is completed, open the air-cock to start the flow.

When the side discharge has ceased, record the volume discharged from the side orifice. If less than 100 ml., make readings to the nearest ml., from 100 to 250 ml. to the nearest 2 ml. and over 250 ml., to the nearest 5 ml. When necessary, adjust the observed volume to the standard consistency of 0.3 percent and temperature of 20°C., by means of corrections given in Tables 55-4 and 55-5.

NOTE.—It is immaterial which correction be applied first, the second correction being made to the volume adjusted by the first correction.

Make at least two determinations and supplement them by additional tests if they differ by more than 1.5 percent.

Report.—Report the average freeness reading corrected to 0.3 percent consistency and 20°C., to the nearest 1 ml. on readings less than 100 ml., 2 ml. on readings from 100 to 250 ml., and the nearest 5 ml. on readings over 250 ml. Unless the sample was in slush form or the standard defibering time and conditions were used, state also the procedure and time employed for defibering the pulp.

Additional Information.—The test was originally designed for use with groundwood slush pulp, and did not include, as part of the method, any preliminary disintegration. Any disintegration reduces the freeness of a pulp to an extent depending on the freeness of the original stock, the degree of pressing or drying of the laps, and the time kept in the pressed condition.

In general, with slush stock for control purposes, or when measuring the freeness of beaten or prepared stock, disintegration should be avoided unless the fibers are not thoroughly dispersed. However, where pulps are taken for test from a shipment, even if from moist laps or bales, the standard disintegration procedure with 24 g. in 2 liters of stock for 75,000 revolutions should be followed. This not only usually insures complete dispersion of the fibers but also simulates to some degree the defibering treatment that the stock will receive in the mill before use.

The principal changes made in this revision are:

(a) Increased emphasis that freeness is primarily a measure of the quantity of debris in a pulp and not its drainage quality on a paper machine.

(b) Prescribing the use of a detergent to clean the interior surfaces of the instrument before use. This may substantially increase the observed readings.

(c) The disintegration procedure for difficult pulps is modified to insure dispersion.

(d) Restriction of the permissible range of consistency of the specimens to 0.02 percent and the temperature to 2°C.

BACTERIOLOGICAL EXAMINATION OF PULP

The following procedure is recommended for the bacteriological examination of wet and dry pulp in sheet form. The procedure for examination of slush pulp is included in T 631 m. Because of the exacting technique required in bacteriological procedures, reproducible results can be secured only by a well-trained technician. This method is standardized as TAPPI T 228 m-57.

Apparatus and Materials. **Alcohol.**—Methyl, isopropyl, or 95 percent denatured ethyl alcohol for sterilizing instruments.

Balance.—Sensitive to 0.1 g. with a pan large enough to hold the Petri dishes.

Corkborers and Containers.—Standard corkborers 15 to 25 mm. in diameter, for taking samples from rolls or sheets. Enclose them singly in screw cap bottles for sterilization.

Bottles for Dilution.—Several 8-oz., narrow-mouthed, square-sectioned glass bottles fitted either with screw caps or with Escher rubber stoppers.

Bottles for Wet Samples.—Several 4- to 8-oz., wide-mouthed, glass-stoppered bottles for collecting wet-lap stock samples. The type of bottle selected should be able to withstand sterilization. Prior to sterilization, cover the stoppers and the necks of the bottles with metal foil or heavy kraft paper to protect the lips of the bottles from contamination. A strip of paper may be inserted into the mouth of each bottle to prevent sticking of the stopper during sterilization.

Colony Counter.—Any one of several types, the Quebec, Buck, and Wolffheugel colony counters are satisfactory. A hand tally for recording the count is recommended.

Containers for Dry Samples.—When the sampling and testing are done at the same mill, use a single envelope for each; otherwise, use two single envelopes, one placed inside the other. The larger one may be 9 by 12 in. and the smaller 6.5 by 9.5 in. They should be made of a heavy kraft paper that will withstand sterilization in the hot-air oven without undue embrittlement. After sterilization, seal the flap on the outer envelope with pressure-sensitive tape.

Alternatively, make a folder of suitable size from heavy kraft paper and sterilize it in the oven. After the pulp sample has been placed inside the sterile folder, seal the latter with the tape.

Plugs.—Nonabsorbent cotton.

Disintegrators.—Metal jar with a high-speed impeller near the bottom and fitted with a metal cap. Place a kraft paper hood over the cap of each disintegrator jar prior to steam sterilization.

Flaming Equipment.—An alcohol lamp, a gasoline blow torch or a Bunsen burner, to flame tongs, scissors, knives, and the mouths of sterile containers.

Flasks.—Erlenmeyer flasks or bottles, preferably Pyrex, for holding sterile media.

Incubator.—Capable of maintaining a temperature of 36 ± 1°C. (96.8 ± 1.8°F.)

Knife.—Preferably, a type with an inserted blade of adjustable length, to cut pulp.

Petri Dishes.—Pyrex, 100 by 15 mm., are recommended.

Pipets and Containers.—Two sizes: 1.1-ml. milk-dilution type and graduated 10-ml. type. Mohr 10-ml. pipets, with tips cut off to give an opening about 3 mm. in diameter at the delivery end, are best for pipetting pulp suspensions. Special Mohr pipets calibrated from the large end, are available and are preferable to the usual Mohr pipet. Enclose them singly in metal boxes or heavy kraft paper wrappers for sterilization.

Scissors.—Preferably with 4-in. cutting edges.

Nutrient Substrate.—Dehydrated standard tryptone glucose extract agar. That obtained from Difco Laboratories or from the Baltimore Biological Laboratories has been found suitable. It may also be prepared from its ingredients.[23]

Sterilizing Equipment.—Two types of suitable size:

(a) A steam sterilizer for 15 p.s.i. steam, such as an autoclave or a pressure cooker.

(b) A hot-air oven at 165°C., with thermometer. For most laboratories, electrically heated ovens are more satisfactory than those heated by gas, but the latter may be used if desired.

Tongs.—Suitable for handling samples of pulp.

Sterilization of Equipment and Media.—Depending upon the nature of the equipment to be sterilized, use one of three methods.

[23] American Public Health Association, "Standard Methods for the Examination of Water and Sewage," pp. 186, 9th Ed., 1946.

Steam Heat (Autoclave or Pressure Cooker).—Sterilize the following by heating for 20 minutes at a minimum of 121°C. (250°F.), corresponding to 15 p.s.i. steam pressure: (a) caps with hoods and the jars for disintegrators, (b) media (unless other conditions are specified by the manufacturer of the medium), (c) sample bottles, (d) corkborers, and (e) water blanks for dilution.

Dry Heat (Electrically or Gas-Heated Oven).—Sterilize the following by heating for at least 2 hours at a minimum temperature of 165°C. (329°F.): (a) heavy kraft envelopes and folders, (b) tongs, (c) knives, (d) Petri dishes, (e) pipets, and (f) scissors.

Take care to dry glassware completely before heating and avoid scorching any paper containers or wrappers used for the instruments being sterilized.

Alcohol.—Immerse scissors, tongs, knives, and similar instruments in alcohol. When needed for cutting or handling samples, remove, allow to drain for a few moments, then burn off the excess alcohol.

Sampling.—Sample a sufficient number of bales or rolls so that the composite sample taken is representative of the pulp being tested.

Dry Pulp. *Method A.*—Use either a single envelope or two sterile envelopes, one within the other for each sample. Cut away several layers of the pulp surrounding the area to be sampled with a knife and discard them to eliminate any surface contamination. In the exposed area, make a vertical cut with a sterile knife through several thicknesses near the center and parallel to the edge of the bale or roll; a second vertical cut parallel to the first and about 5 in. from the first cut; and a horizontal cut across the bottom of the first two cuts. Tear off and discard the top sheet of the flap, then carefully open the sterilized envelope and slip the end of the adjacent cut flap of pulp into the inner envelope. Then make a horizontal cut across the top of the flap about 6 in. from the bottom cut. The pulp sample will then drop into the inner envelope; after which seal the outer envelope by means of a pressure-sensitive tape. The specimen will be approximately 5 by 6 in. Take samples at different sections of successive bales or rolls.

Method B.—Remove several layers of pulp by cutting with a knife. Take the corkborer from the sterile bottle and cut about $\frac{1}{2}$ in. deep into the exposed area. Replace the borer with its sample in the bottle.

Wet Pulp.—Sample by discarding the outer layers as for dry pulp. Transfer the samples to sterile wide-mouthed bottles with the sterile tongs.

Slush Pulp.—Sample slush stock as for process water described in T 631 m (p. 1458). Take a composite sample of the pulp to determine its moisture content, if its moisture-free weight is not known to within 5 percent.

Procedure. Preparation of Specimen. Dry Pulp.—Method A: Place a closed, sterile Petri dish on the pan of a balance and determine its tare weight. Cut the envelope in which the sample is received along the flap with a sterile knife or scissors. Open the envelope by pressing the sides in without touching the inner surface, and remove the dry lap with sterile tongs. Hold the edge of the sheet of pulp in one hand, trim with sterile scissors, and discard the outer edges. Make a series of cuts about $\frac{1}{4}$ to $\frac{1}{2}$ in. apart, parallel to the side of the sheet, and opposite the edge held in the hand. Partially remove the cover of the tared Petri dish, but retain the cover on the pan of the balance. Cut squares of pulp directly into the dish by making a series of cuts perpendicular to those made previously.

Cut enough pulp to give a 5.0-g. moisture-free specimen and aseptically adjust the amount to within 0.1 g. Replace the cover.

Method B: Remove the corkborer containing the sample discs from its container. With a sterile glass rod, eject the discs into a tared Petri dish on the pan of the balance and aseptically adjust the weight of the specimen to 5.0 ± 0.1 g. Replace the cover.

Wet Pulp.—Remove the sample from the bottle by means of sterile tongs. Hold the edge of the sheet in one hand, trim with sterile scissors and discard the outer edges. Weigh out a 5.0-g. specimen as for dry pulp.

Disintegration.—With sterile tongs, remove the specimen from each dish and place in a disintegrator jar with enough sterile water to give a pulp consistency of 1 percent. In adding material to the jar, do not touch the metal cap with the hands, but lift it by grasping the paper hood placed over the cup before sterilizing. Lift both hood and metal cap only enough to permit access to the jar. If the pulp requires much disintegration, cool the water blanks to prevent the temperature of the disintegrated specimen from exceeding 45°C. (113°F.). Let the paper hood remain on the cap at all times to prevent possible contamination through any opening in the metal cap or around the top of the jar.

Place the jar containing the pulp and water on the electric driving stand and operate until disintegration is complete.

Plating.—As soon as possible after disintegration, plate the specimen. The room in which the specimens are plated should be relatively free from air currents and dust. Also, about $\frac{1}{2}$ hour before plating, sponge the surface of the work table with a solution of a suitable toxicant, such as 5 percent phenol or 0.05 percent phenyl mercuric acetate, further to eliminate extraneous microorganisms.

With a sterile pipet distribute a total of 10 ml. of the 1 percent suspension, equal to 0.1 g., in approximately equal proportions between 5 Petri dishes. Plate additional higher dilutions if it is suspected that the pulp has a high bacterial population. Add to each plate, 15 to 20 ml. of standard tryptone glucose extract agar cooled to about 45°C. (113°F.), then agitate the plates individually to disintegrate clumps of pulp and obtain even distribution of the fibers in the medium, using a quick, short reciprocating motion. It is important that all lumps of pulp be broken up in order that the plates may be examined easily and accurately. Pour one control plate (without pulp) from each container of nutrient medium used to check its sterility.

If a higher dilution is required, add 10 ml. of the 1 percent suspension to a sterile 90-ml. water blank and distribute 10 ml. of this suspension equally between 5 Petri dishes, which together will then contain 0.01 g. of the original pulp specimen.

If possible, the dilution should be adjusted to give from 30 to 300 colonies per plate.

Note.—The amount of fibrous material distributed over a given area of plate surface has been found to be an important factor in the number of colonies observed in a given sample of pulp. It is therefore important to follow carefully directions regarding the pulp consistency, the volume of sample used for plating (10 ml.), and the number and size of plates used.

Incubation.—After the plates have been agitated, place them on a level surface until the medium solidifies; then invert and incubate the plated specimens at 36 ± 1°C. (96.8 ± 1.8°F.) for 48 hours. Do not stack the plates too closely in the incubator.

Note.—The amount of fibrous material distributed over a given area of plate surface has organisms such as "pink slime" for which a lower temperature, of say 30°C., may be better suited, at least for the first half of the 48-hour incubation period. This, or another incubating condition, renders the method nonstandard and the results should be qualified and reported accordingly.

Counting Plate Cultures.—After incubation, examine the cultures for the presence and number of bacterial colonies with a plate counter or by holding the plates against a dark background, indirectly lighted.

If the pulp has been separated into individual fibers and well mixed with the medium, the colonies can be easily counted. If any particles are observed in the culture which cannot be definitely identified as colonies, they should be examined microscopically. Plates with spreading colonies should be counted if possible, otherwise they should be reported as spreading colonies. Examine and make a record of the number of colonies found on each control plate.

Report.—Report the result as colonies per gram of moisture-free pulp examined.

In all cases record the count to no more than two significant figures. For example, record a colony count of 144 as 140, and one of 145 as 150. Report the moisture content or consistency of the pulp as sampled.

FIBER ANALYSIS OF PAPER AND PAPERBOARD

This method relates to the identification of the kinds of fibers present in a sample of paper or paperboard and their quantitative estimation. For accurate results considerable training and experience are necessary. The analyst should make frequent use of standard samples of known composition or of authentic fiber samples and should become thoroughly familiar with the appearance of the different fibers and their behavior when treated with the various stains. A knowledge of morphological characteristics of the different fibers is helpful and, in some cases, essential for their identification. Some information on this subject is given in Appendix A. This method is a revised tentative standard of TAPPI T 401 m-60.

Apparatus and Materials. **Microscope.**—Compound, preferably equipped with a mechanical stage and Abbé condenser. A magnification of 70 to 100 diameters is recommended for observation of fiber colors, although a higher magnification may be desirable for studying morphological characteristics. If an apochromatic objective is used, it is desirable to have a compensating eyepiece and an achromatic condenser.

The eyepiece is provided with a cross hair, pointer, or dot for counting the fibers passing under it. Such an eyepiece can be supplied by the manufacturers, or it may be prepared by the technician, positioning the point in the eyepiece so as to obtain its image in focus.

Slides and Cover Glasses.—Standard slides (1 by 3 inches) of clear, colorless glass, and No. 2 cover glasses (22 mm. square).

Dropper.—A glass tube about 10 cm. long and 8 mm. internal diameter, with one end carefully smoothed, but not constricted, and the other end fitted with a rubber bulb. The tube is graduated to deliver 0.5 ml.

Warm Plate.—A plate with a plane, level top made of solid metal having a black mat finish, and provided with a control to keep the temperature of the surface between 50 and 60°C.[24]

Dissecting Needles.—Two needles mounted in suitable handles. Steel needles may be used but are subject to corrosion by some of the stains used. Needles made from an alloy of platinum and iridium are preferred.

Glass-Marking Equipment.—Either a glass-marking pencil or an aluminum stearate solution (*see* Appendix G) for marking lines on the slide.

Light Source.—A 15-watt "daylight" fluorescent tube or equivalent daylight source.

Camel's Hair Brush, small.

Other Apparatus and Materials.—50- or 100-ml. beaker, test tube, glass beads, and, depending on the specimen, stains, reagents, and apparatus as described in the appropriate section of the procedure.

Test Sample.—Approximately 0.2 g. of paper or paperboard, torn from different portions of the test sample so as to be representative of it.

Disintegration of Sample. **I. Ordinary Papers.**—(a) Tear the sample into small pieces and place in a small beaker. Cover with distilled water, bring to a boil on a hot

[24] Graff, John H.. Paper Trade J., **101**, No. 21, 36–51, 1935; Tech. Assoc. Papers, **18**, 197–211, 1935.

plate, decant the water, roll the individual pieces into small pellets between the fingers, and place in a large test tube. Add a little water and shake vigorously until the water is thoroughly absorbed by the paper. Add a little more water, shake well, and again add some water and shake. Continue in this way until the paper has been thoroughly disintegrated. After the paper has been completely defibered, dilute the suspension by discarding part of it and adding water to the remainder until the suspension has a final consistency of about 0.05 percent. If the sample is difficult to disintegrate, glass beads may be used in the test tube, but if this is done, it should be so stated in the report. Glass beads should not be used if the fibers are to be examined for degree of beating.

(b) If the paper cannot be disintegrated by shaking in water, return the sample to the beaker and cover it with 1 percent sodium hydroxide solution, bring to a boil, decant the alkaline solution, and wash twice with water. Cover the sample with approximately 0.05 N hydrochloric acid, let stand several minutes, decant the acid, and wash several times with water. Roll into pellets and proceed as in method (a).

NOTE.—If it is known that the sample will not disintegrate by method (a), the analyst may start with method (b). Roofing papers and papers containing wool fibers, however, must not be so treated, since the alkali may dissolve the wool.

(c) If the sample cannot be disintegrated by either method (a) or (b), use one of the special methods given below.

2. Specially Treated Papers.—Standardized methods cannot be specified for the disintegration of papers containing tar, asphalt, rubber, viscose, etc., or parchment papers, because the procedure needs to be varied according to the material, the amount present, and the nature of the treatment. The following methods are given as guides.

Tar and Asphalt-Treated Papers.

Method 1.—Place the sample in a dish, cover with kerosene and digest on a steam bath for 1 hour. After this, remove and press the sample between blotters; treat it again on the steam bath and again press between blotters. Then extract with cold benzene until the solution is clear. No sodium hydroxide should be used in the final disintegration of these papers because of the possible presence of wool fibers.[25]

Method 2.—Fill several convenient containers (250-ml. beakers) about half full with carbon tetrachloride. Cut the sample into convenient squares and immerse in the first container. The squares should be moved about and the liquid kept agitated. After several minutes in the first container, transfer the squares to the next container, using forceps. Do not allow the squares to dry. In the case of laminated papers, the sheets may be separated easily after the first or second soaking and this should be done, removing any fabric scrim which can be treated separately, if desired. Continue moving the sample into fresh carbon tetrachloride until the liquid remains clear after the sample has been agitated in it for several minutes, then remove the sample and allow to air dry. After drying, disintegrate the sample in the usual manner.

Method 3.—Place the specimen in a Soxhlet or similar extractor and extract with a chloroform, carbon tetrachloride, dioxane or similar solvent.

Rubber-Treated Papers.—Extract the paper for 6 hours in a Soxhlet extractor with cumene (isopropyl benzene), dry, and then boil in water to which a little wetting agent has been added. In very rare cases, a 1 percent sodium hydroxide solution may be necessary. With most samples, the cumene will take out about 98 percent of the rubber.[26]

Parchment Papers.

Method 1.—To 252 ml. of water, add 25 ml. of concentrated sulfuric acid and cool to

[25] Herzberg, W., "Papierprüfing," 7th Ed., Springer, Berlin, 1932.
[26] Burningham, F., private communication.

50 to 60°C. Place the paper in the acid and when the paper begins to disintegrate, stir quickly and empty into a 1-liter beaker two-thirds full of water.[27]

Method 2.—Soak the sample for about 5 minutes in concentrated hydrochloric acid, wash, boil in 0.5 percent sodium hydroxide solution, and repeat this sequence if necessary. Then wash, acidify with dilute hydrochloric acid, again wash, and then boil in a little water and a wetting agent, and disintegrate.[27]

Pyroxylin-Treated Papers.—Extract or remove the pyroxylin with cellosolve (ethylene-glycol monoethyl ether), ethyl acetate, or amyl acetate.[26]

Wet-Strength Papers.

Method 1.—Tear the paper into small pieces and place in a beaker; cover with 5 percent aluminum sulfate solution and boil from 5 to 20 minutes, depending upon the amount of wet strength present. Decant the alum solution, wash, and proceed as in section 1 (b), for ordinary papers.

Method 2.—When an estimation of the degree of beating of the fibers is not required, the sample may be disintegrated in water in a high-speed electric mixer.

Highly Colored Papers.—If the paper is highly colored, remove the dye by one of the following methods and then disintegrate by the usual procedure. (The treatment selected depends on the characteristics of the dyes.) (1) By solution: Use alcohol, ammonium hydroxide, acetic acid, or hydrochloric acid. (2) By oxidation: Use nitric acid or bleach liquor. (3) By reduction: Use hydrosulfite, stannous chloride, or hydrochloric acid and zinc.[25]

Preparation of Slides.—It is desirable to keep the slides and cover glasses in 50 percent alcohol. After a slide has been dried and polished, draw lines 1 in. from each end, using the glass-marking pencil or aluminum stearate solution. This will keep the fiber suspensions inside the 1-in. square at each end of the slide. Remove any dust or lint from the slide with a small camel's hair brush. Place the slide on the warm plate, shake the test tube containing the defibered sample, and withdraw a portion of the fibers by inserting the dropper and expelling 2 or 3 bubbles of air. Deposit 0.5 ml. of the fiber suspension on the square on one end of the slide. Withdraw another 0.5-ml. portion from the test tube and deposit it on the other end of the slide. Allow the water on the slide to evaporate until there is just sufficient left to float the fibers, then gently tap the suspension with a dissecting needle to distribute the fibers evenly inside the squares. Leave the slides on the warm plate until completely dry.[24]

Stains.—The Graff "C" stain is suggested for general analysis but when desirable, other stains should be used for specific purposes or to confirm results obtained with the "C" stain. Thus, the Herzberg stain is especially useful to differentiate between rag, groundwood, and chemical wood pulps. Either Selleger's stain or Alexander's stain may be used to differentiate between coniferous and deciduous wood pulp and Selleger's stain is also helpful in differentiating between bleached coniferous sulfite and bleached coniferous sulfate. Wilson's stain may be used in place of, or to confirm results with, the "C" stain.

Morphological characteristics identify special fibers such as straw, flax, esparto, and certain types of wood, such as southern pine, Douglas fir, and deciduous woods, so that the correct weight factors may be applied.

Directions for preparing these stains are given in Appendix D, and the directions for preparing and using other stains are given in Appendices E and F.

Staining.—To use the "C" stain, Herzberg stain, Selleger's stain, or Wilson's stain, apply 3 drops of the stain to the fiber field on the slide, then place a cover glass over it in such a way as to avoid air bubbles. Allow the slide to stand for 1 or 2 minutes, then

---

[27] Bartsch, C., J. Soc. Chem. Ind., **30**, 414, 1911; Papier-Fabr., **16**, 171, 1918.

drain off the surplus stain, preferably by tilting the long edge of the slide into contact with a blotter.

NOTE.—Take care not to touch the unstained fibers on the slide with the fingers, since the fingers usually have various metallic salts on them which will be absorbed and later may give rise to puzzling stain reactions.

The colors developed by the stains vary according to the raw materials and the processes used for preparing them. The following discusses the colors to be expected, but the analyst should check known samples to become familiar with their appearance.

"C" Stain.[24]—When lignin is present, a yellow color is developed with the "C" stain. Groundwood gives a very vivid yellow with a tendency toward orange; unbleached jute stains much the same color, but the two fibers can easily be distinguished by their structural appearance. Unbleached pulps of all kinds tend toward the yellow, with the depth of yellow determined by the degree of cooking and the type of cook. Thus, a raw unbleached sulfite will stain a vivid yellow, but as the degree of cooking increases, it tends towards a greenish yellow. Unbleached sulfate tends toward yellowish brown, while an unbleached alpha is more brown than yellow. The hardwood[28] pulps have a tendency to appear bluish and greenish even in their unbleached state. Manila, straw, bamboo, sugar cane, flax hurds, and esparto also give yellow colors with raw, unbleached cooks.

When any pulp is bleached, it has a tendency to give a reddish hue with the "C" stain. In some cases this tendency is very slight, but any hint of red can generally be taken as an indication of some degree of bleaching. The shade of red usually indicates the type of bleached pulp. Thus, rag, which is the purest form of cellulose, gives the purest red, followed by bleached softwood alpha, bleached softwood sulfite, and bleached softwood sulfate in that order. The sulfite is weak enough in red so that it frequently appears purplish-gray. Alkali cooking tends to give a bluish color to wood pulp, so that with bleached softwood kraft pulp the blue coloration nearly overshadows the red and a bluish-gray is seen. Hardwood pulps have a tendency to be bluer than softwood pulps; therefore hardwood alkaline pulps, even though bleached, show almost no red when stained. Unbleached hardwood alkaline pulps cannot be easily distinguished from the bleached pulps, nor can hardwood kraft pulp be distinguished from hardwood soda pulp.

Some special fibers lend their own colors to the system. Thus, manila in the bleached state has a tendency toward purplish gray; bleached jute is a light yellow green; straw, bamboo, sugar cane, flax hurds, and esparto tend toward bluish gray, and sometimes give colors like hardwood alkaline pulps. In these cases, the pulps must be distinguished by their structural appearance. A color chart showing the colors obtained with "C" stain has been published.[29]

Herzberg Stain.[25]—Being an iodine stain, the general color trends discussed under "C" stain apply also to the Herzberg stain. However, in general, it gives much bluer colors than the "C" stain, so that all chemical wood pulps, whether bleached or unbleached, acquire a blue tint. Rag pulp stains pink and can be easily distinguished from chemical wood pulps. Groundwood is a vivid yellow and easily distinguished. Unbleached jute and raw cooks of manila, straw, bamboo, sugar cane, flax hurds, and esparto also give a yellowish coloration; however, except for jute and manila, their bleached pulps stain blue, as do chemical wood pulps. Bleached jute gives a strong greenish yellow color. Manila varies from purple to pink. The raw, unbleached wood pulps will also tend toward greenish yellow if enough lignin is present.

[28] "Hardwood" pulps are those from deciduous or broadleaved trees. "Softwood" pulps are those from the conifers.
[29] Graff, John H., "Color Atlas for Fiber Identification," Inst. of Paper Chemistry, Appleton, Wis., 1940.

The chief value in the Herzberg stain is the fact that all chemical pulps from wood and most grasses stain blue; therefore, a much sharper distinction is made between rag, groundwood, and chemical pulps. If the only interest is in the percentage of rag or of groundwood, the counting is much easier with the Herzberg than with the "C" stain.

Selleger's Stain.—Its reactions also follow the general pattern for iodine stains but, in general, it gives redder colors than either the "C" or the Herzberg stain. Lignin-containing pulps, such as groundwood and unbleached softwood wood pulp, give yellow colors. The depth of the yellow again depends upon the amount of lignin present. Esparto, straw, and alkaline-cooked hardwood woods give a purple or blue coloration which is easily distinguished from the colors given by other pulps.

Softwood alkaline pulps give a much lighter blue, and these pulps can usually be differentiated from the softwood sulfite pulps which tend more to the pink. Rag pulp will stain a little redder than bleached sulfite. Bleached manila and hemp give a wine red. Generally, no attempt is made to differentiate rag with Selleger's stain, but if rag is present, it is counted along with the bleached sulfite, and a correction is made based on the rag determination using Herzberg stain.

Wilson's Stain.[30]—In an effort to obtain more distinctive colors with less overlapping, the commonly used potassium iodide is replaced in this stain with cadmium iodide and the hydroscopic zinc chloride is eliminated. In general, the colors obtained from the Wilson stain are similar to those of the "C" stain. A list of the colors obtained is given in Appendix H.

Alexander's Stain.—This is a modification of the Herzberg stain which is sometimes useful for differentiating bleached sulfite, bleached sulfate, and bleached soda fibers. To use the stain, apply 2 drops of solution A and allow to remain for 1 minute, after which carefully blot off the excess dye and allow the specimen to dry. Add 3 drops of solution B and allow to remain 1 minute; then, thoroughly mix 1 drop of solution C with the solution on the side. Apply a cover glass in the usual manner. Bleached sulfite stains red, bleached soda pulp stains blue, and bleached sulfate gives a bluish red.

Qualitative Identification.—For the proper differentiation of the colors in fiber analysis, and also to become accustomed to the colors developed, it is recommended that the daylight fluorescent tube be always used, placed 10 to 12 in. from the mirror of the microscope.[31]

Place the stained slide in position, center the light, and examine the slide for the different fibers, paying attention also to morphological characteristics. In cases of doubt, make slides of authentic pulps for comparison with the specimen.

NOTE.—These may be obtained from the TAPPI Librarian, Institute of Paper Chemistry, Appleton, Wis.

Quantitative Determination.—With the mechanical stage, move the field so that the pointer is 2 or 3 mm. from a top corner of the cover glass, then slowly move it in a horizontal direction and count and record the fibers of each kind as they pass the pointer. A multiple tally counter, such as is frequently used for blood counting, is most convenient. Alternatively, if care is taken and the slide is not moved vertically, repeated passes may be made for each type of fiber counted.

If part of a fiber passes the center of the pointer more than once, count it each time; but if it follows the center for some time, count it only once. With fiber bundles, as are often present in groundwood, count every fiber in the bundle as it passes under the pointer. Ignore very fine fragments, but count the larger fragments as fractions so that

[30] Wilson, Norval F., "A New Stain for Identifying Paper-making Fibers," Paper Ind., **27,** No. 2, 215–216, May, 1945.
[31] Graff, John H., Paper Trade J., **112,** No. 2, 39, Jan. 9, 1941.

when two or three of the same kind of fiber fractions are observed in the same field, mentally they can be added together to give a whole number.

When all the fibers in a line have been counted, move the stage 5 mm. vertically to a new line and count the fibers in the same way. Continue until the fibers in four separate lines, each 5 mm. apart, have been examined. If the slide has been properly prepared, a total fiber count of between 200 and 300 will have been made.

Multiply the total number of each kind of fiber by its respective weight factor (Table 55-6) to obtain the equivalent weights, and calculate their percentages by weight of the total fiber composition.

TABLE 55-6. WEIGHT FACTORS

Fibers	Factors
Rag	1.00
Cotton linters	1.25
Bleached flax and ramie	0.50
Softwood fibers	
Unbleached and bleached sulfite and kraft	
(except hemlock, Douglas fir, and southern kraft)	0.90
Western hemlock	1.20
Douglas fir	1.50
Southern kraft	1.55
Alpha (northern)	0.70
Hardwood fibers	
Soda, sulfate, or sulfite (except gum and alpha)	0.60
Gum	1.00
Alpha	0.55
Groundwood (depends on its fineness)	1.30
Unbleached bagasse fibers as prepared for boards	0.90
Bleached and unbleached bagasse fibers as prepared for papers	0.80
Esparto	0.50
Manila and jute	0.55
Sisal	0.60
Straw for board	0.65
Bleached straw	0.35

Examine both square-inch fields. If the results for the two fields vary for any type of fiber present by more than the amount stated later under Precision, then prepare and examine one or more additional fields and include the results from all the fields in the reported average.

Weight Factors.—Most of the weight factors given in Table 55-6 were determined by Graff[32] for the species of pulp wood commonly used at that time for making these grades of pulp. To a great extent they depend on the size of the elements included in the count; consequently, each analyst should determine his own values for each kind of pulp he is likely to encounter.

Weight factors depend more upon the species than on the pulping process used and will vary considerably with the different species. This is particularly important in hardwoods, where the weight factors have been found to vary from as low as 0.40 for maple to as high as 1.00 for gum. Likewise, a variation between 0.95 and 2.00 has been reported

[32] Graff, John H., Paper Trade J., **110**, No. 2, 37–40, Jan. 11, 1940.

for cotton linters, depending on the source of the linter and the degree of beating.[33] Therefore, the table should be used only as a guide when no better factors are available.

Whenever possible, the factors should be determined for the actual pulps used in the sample being analyzed. When this is impossible, the width of the fibers can be used by an experienced analyst as a guide in determining the correct weight factor to use.[34] Weight factors are related directly to the coarseness or decigrex of the pulp as determined with TAPPI method T 234 sm.

Report.—Report the proportions of the various fibers found in terms of percentages by weight of the total fiber composition to the nearest whole number, followed by an expression of the accuracy of the given figure. Thus, if the calculated percentage was 22.8 and from several observations the analyst concludes that the accuracy is $\pm 3\%$, the report would read $23 \pm 3\%$. Report percentages less than 2% as "traces." In case of dispute, include the weight factors used.

Precision.—The precision depends upon the skill and experience of the operator and on the selection of the weight factors. Competent workers may be expected to be able to check the composition of a furnish that is not too complex within the following tolerances; provided that the weight factors employed are reliable.

Percentage of Given Fiber in Total Furnish	Tolerance
Less than 20	± 2
20 to 30	± 3
30 to 40	± 4
40 to 60	± 5
60 to 70	± 4
70 to 80	± 3
Over 80	± 2

It is emphasized that to achieve this precision, authentic pulp mixtures should be examined from time to time to insure that sound judgment is exercised when including or rejecting debris in the count. Under ideal conditions with weight factors determined on the pulps examined, it is possible for experienced analysts to check the composition of a furnish to within half the stated limits.

APPENDIX

A. Morphological Characteristics.—These may be obscured by the action of swelling agents in the stains or modifications during refining.[35] The characteristics of common pulpwood fibers are discussed in TAPPI Method T 8 sm, and those of other vegetable fibers in T 10 sm.

The cells in a pulp may be imperfectly or well separated, depending on the type of pulping process used. Groundwood consists chiefly of torn fibers and fiber bundles. Occasionally, fiber bundles show undisturbed groups of wood ray cells at right angles to the longitudinal cells.

The most characteristic cells of pulps from *coniferous* trees are the long, thin-walled springwood tracheids ("fibers") marked on their radial walls by one or more rows of large, irregularly spaced bordered pits and by areas of smaller pits. These large bordered pits allow for intercommunication between adjacent tracheids and the areas of smaller pits are contact regions with the cells of the radially oriented wood rays. Also present

[33] Isenberg, Irving H., and Peckham, Charles L., Tappi, **33**, No. 10, 527–528, Oct., 1950.
[34] Clark, James d'A., Tappi, **34**, No. 7, 317–318, July, 1951.
[35] Harrar, Ellwood S., and Lodewick, J. Elton, Paper Ind., Feb., May, Aug., 1934.

are the summerwood tracheids which have thicker walls, narrower cell cavities, and less pronounced pitting. The ray cells are relatively short, small, flat cells, with tiny pits. The broad springwood tracheids serve best to study ray contact areas when attempting to identify the various softwood pulp species.

Pulps from the *deciduous* trees or hardwoods have a greater diversity of cell types than softwood. The fibers (libriform fibers and fiber tracheids) are narrow, cylindrical cells with small, scattered pits which are not usually helpful in identifying the species. This is readily done by examining the vessel segments, when located. These vessel segments are characteristic of hardwoods and are considerably wider than the fibers and, because of their longitudinal linkage into long tubes or vessels, they show openings or perforations at either end and pits of various sizes and shapes on the side walls. The details of the pits and perforations, cell size, and shape, serve to differentiate the various deciduous pulps. Sometimes vessel segments are scarce because they are lost by washing during pulping.

Groundwood is characterized by the bundles of fibers present. Some of these show undisturbed groups of wood ray cells at right angles to the tracheids. Groundwood is usually produced from nonresinous conifers, but wood from deciduous trees is sometimes used.

Because different weight factors are recommended for chemical pulps of different species, the analyst should endeavor to identify these pulps so that a more exact estimate of the composition may be reported. Douglas fir is readily identified because all the springwood tracheids and nearly all its summerwood tracheids exhibit spiral thickening on the inner surface of the cell wall adjacent to the lumen or cell cavity. Tracheids from the various species of southern yellow pines can be separated with certainty from all American softwoods except jack, ponderosa, and lodgepole pines, because of the irregularly shaped and spaced ray-crossing pits, evident especially on the springwood fibers. Because the tracheids of southern pines have a greater diameter than the other pines listed above, they often may be segregated. The separation of western hemlock from other hemlocks, spruces, and larches is not easy and at times, impossible. The color differentiation of western sulfite pulp with the "C" stain and the tendency toward greater fiber width than the eastern species may be useful. The identification of the black gums and tupelos from other hardwoods except sweet gum (red gum) is accomplished by observing the presence of scalariform perforations containing a relatively large number of bars in the vessel segments. The tips of sweet gum vessel segments have spiral thickening and the black gums do not. If in doubt, authentic pulp specimens should be examined or T 8 sm consulted; otherwise use the general weight factor of 0.60 for hardwoods.

Jute and manila usually constitute the majority of the "rope fibers" found in papers. It is sometimes desirable to differentiate them. Manila fibers are usually longer and have a well-defined, quite uniform, uninterrupted central lumen. Jute fibers have a variable central lumen, changing in the same fiber from broad to narrow and even being entirely interrupted at certain places. The cell walls of jute have longitudinal striations. Manila pulps sometimes have small cells (staining brown with Herzberg stain) which occur singly or in groups. These are infrequent but they do denote the presence of manila if they can be found. Manila and jute can sometimes, but not always, be differentiated by the observation that jute stains yellow and manila wine-red with the Herzberg stain. Unbleached jute stains a strong yellow with Herzberg stain; jute that has been cooked moderately and then bleached gives a lighter yellow color; after drastic cooking and bleaching, the color is a steel blue or gray. Manila hemp may vary from dark blue to light red (not so deep as for rag), depending on the degree of cooking.

Rag pulp consists of cotton and linen fibers. As rags usually undergo considerable pretreatment, it is not always easy to distinguish the twists of cotton and the nodes of linen.

Usually they are not reported separately, but grouped under the general designation of "rag." Pulp produced from cotton linters is also reported as rag. This pulp is composed of a mixture of lint fibers which are similar to rag and fibers which are shorter and coarser. These are more nearly cylindrical than lint cotton or rag fibers and have thicker walls and narrower central canals, and, therefore, a higher weight factor. At their distal ends they taper to a point. At their basal ends the fibers are either open as a result of breaking away from the seed coat during delinting, or they have the mother epidermal cell attached to the fiber. Where the epidermal cell remains attached to the elongated fiber, the latter is found to be narrower than the epidermal cell of which it is an outgrowth, and to be separated from it by a constricted region.[36] Some of these fibers show a decided twisted appearance at the base. The color of these linters with Herzberg stain is red, although the red is darker and tends to give a bluish tinge. This is especially true of the base which is always darker in color.

Esparto, the *straws*, *cornstalks*, and *bagasse* (sugar cane) contain the widest variety of cells. Esparto is encountered in some printing papers, especially those made in Great Britain; unbleached straw is found in many container boards, and bleached straw may occasionally occur in better grades of papers, particularly those from Holland. Cornstalk and bagasse occur mostly in fiberboard used for building purposes.

The majority of the elements found in these pulps are the fibers, which are fine, slender, and without distinctive structure. Serrated cells, pith cells (rings from annual vessels), and vessels are present in all. Most characteristic of esparto are comma-shaped cells known as trichomes; but unless care is exercised, and especially if the pulp has been well washed, they may be overlooked.

Semichemical pulps are cooked by a variety of procedures and thus give various color reactions. Because of the high lignin content, all tend toward the yellow with the "C" stain or Wilson's stain. If the cook is alkaline, the tendency is toward the blue; while if the neutral sulfite cook has been used, the tendency is toward the red. The behavior of these pulps with the stains listed has not yet been established.

B. Synthetic Fibers.—Because of the widespread use of artificial or synthetic fibers in textiles, these are often found in rags and occasionally get into finished paper. The color reactions of these fibers, either before or after a conventional rag cook, are not established, although it is known that the common iodine stains when used on uncooked fibers give blue colors only with the regenerated cellulose fibers such as viscose and Bemberg. The other synthetics give various shades of yellow to reddish tan or do not stain at all, the colors obtained varying considerably with time of contact with the stain and with variations in the manufacture of the fiber.

A comprehensive report on the characteristics of synthetic fibers has been prepared by a committee of the British Textile Institute[37] and schemes for their differentiations have been given by Houghton.[38]

C. Wool.—Varying amounts of wool are often found in building papers and sometimes in mulching papers. The fibers may be easily identified by the epidermal scales covering their surfaces. If undyed, they stain a pale yellow with zinc-iodine stains. Blaisdell and Minor[39] have suggested a weight factor of 22.0 for a coarse wool (basis, cotton = 1.0).

D. Preparation of Stains. "C" Stain.—Prepared "C" stain can be purchased from The Institute of Paper Chemistry, or it may be prepared from the following solutions using reagent grade chemicals and distilled water.[24,40]

[36] Hock, Charles W., Textile Research J., **17**, No. 8, 423–430, Aug., 1947.
[37] Preston, J. M., and Robert, O. D., J. Text. Inst., **32**, No. 6, S22–30, Sept., 1941.
[38] Houghton, F. D., Tappi, **34**, No. 8, 353–356, Aug., 1951.
[39] Blaisdell and Minor, Paper Ind., **15**, 625, 1934.
[40] Graff, John H., Paper Trade J., **109**, No. 11, 65, 73, Sept. 14, 1939.

A. Aluminum chloride solution of 1.15 sp. gr. at 28°C., made by adding about 40 g. of $AlCl_3 \cdot 6H_2O$ to 100 ml. of water.

B. Calcium chloride solution of 1.36 sp. gr. at 28°C., made by adding about 100 g. of $CaCl_2$ to 150 ml. of water.

C. Zinc chloride solution of 1.80 sp. gr. at 28°C., made by adding approximately 25 ml. of water to 50 g. of dry $ZnCl_2$ (fused reagent grade sticks in sealed bottles, or crystals). Do not use $ZnCl_2$ from a previously opened bottle.

D. Iodide-iodine solution, made by dissolving 0.90 g. of dry KI and 0.65 g. of dry iodine in 50 ml. of water. Dissolve the KI and iodine by first thoroughly intermixing and crushing together, then adding the required amount of water drop by drop with constant stirring.

Mix well together 20 ml. of solution A, 10 ml. of solution B, and 10 ml. of solution C; add 12.5 ml. of solution D and again mix well. Pour into a tall, narrow vessel and place in the dark. After 12 to 24 hours, when the precipitate has settled, pipet off the clear portion of the solution into a dark bottle and add a leaf of iodine. Keep in the dark when not in use.

NOTE.—The "C" stain is very sensitive to slight differences, and extreme caution must be exercised in its preparation and use. The solutions used for preparing all iodine stains should be of the exact specific gravity specified and accurately measured with graduated pipets. Dark-colored, glass-stoppered dropping bottles, preferably wrapped with black paper, should be used as containers. Fresh stain should be made every 2 or 3 months.

Herzberg Stain.[25] A. *Zinc chloride solution* of 1.80 sp. gr. at 28°C., made by adding approximately 25 ml. of water to 50 g. of dry $ZnCl_2$ (fused sticks in sealed bottles, or crystals).

B. Iodine Solution. Dissolve 0.25 g. of iodine and 5.25 g. of potassium iodide in 12.5 ml. of water.

Mix 25 ml. of solution A with the entire solution B. Pour into a narrow cylinder and let stand until clear (12 to 24 hours). Decant the supernatant liquid into an amber-colored, glass-stoppered bottle and add a leaf of iodine to the solution. Avoid undue exposure to light and air.

NOTE.—For special tests, the Herzberg stain is sometimes modified by adding more zinc chloride to accentuate the blue, or more iodine to accentuate the red. However, modification is not recommended for normal use.

Selleger's Stain.—Prepare by either of the following methods:

A. Dissolve 100 g. of calcium nitrate, $Ca(NO_3)_2 \cdot 4H_2O$, in 50 ml. of water. Add 3 ml. of a solution made by dissolving 8 g. of KI in 90 ml. of water. Finally, add 1 g. of iodine and let stand for 1 week. The stain is then ready for use.

B. Dissolve 0.267 g. of KI in 53 ml. of water; add 1 g. of iodine, and let stand for 2 weeks, shaking each day to saturate the solution with iodine. Then dissolve in this solution 100 g. of $Ca(NO_3)_2 \cdot 4H_2O$, and the stain is ready for use. (By saturating with iodine a solution containing 1 g. of KI to each 198 ml. of water, a saturated stock solution may be made to which it is only necessary to add $Ca(NO_3)_2 \cdot 4H_2O$ in the proportion of 100 g. to 53 ml. of the stock solution.)

If the stain does not give the colors desired (*see* Appendix G), it may be modified by adding more $Ca(NO_3)_2$ to make it bluer, or more KI to make it redder. A flake of iodine should be kept in the bottle at all times to maintain the proper iodine concentration.

Wilson's Stain.[30]—Dissolve 1.5 g. of iodine and 70.0 g. of cadmium iodide in 100.0 ml. of water. Heat to 110°F. and break the iodine crystals with the end of a stirring rod. When all the solids are dissolved, add 180 ml. of water, 15 ml. of 37 percent formaldehyde, 140 g. of $Ca(NO_3)_2 \cdot 4H_2O$, and 40 g. of cadmium chloride ($CdCl_2 \cdot 2.5H_2O$).

Store the finished solution in an amber stock bottle. Titrate a portion of the stain with 0.01 N sodium thiosulfate (2.482 g. of $Na_2S_2O_3 \cdot 5H_2O$ per liter), adding starch indicator near the end point. Ten ml. of stain solution should be equivalent to 12.0 ± 2.0 ml. of 0.01 N thiosulfate solution.

If the stain is too strong, withdraw 100 ml. for use and heat at 110°F. until titration shows the proper strength. With freshly prepared stain, about 20 to 30 minutes heating is needed to give the proper concentration of iodine. Store the remaining stain in the concentrated form for future use. Check the stain solution in use from time to time by titration to determine whether the solution has become too weak and should be discarded.

Alexander's Stain.—Prepare the following solutions:

A. Dissolve 0.2 g. of Congo Red dye in 300 ml. water.

B. Dissolve 100 g. of $Ca(NO_3)_2 \cdot 4H_2O$ in 50 ml. of water.

C. Herzberg stain, as previously described.

E. Special Stains. Kantrowitz-Simmons Stain (Modified Bright Stain).[41]—Prepare the following solutions:

A. Dissolve 2.7 g. of ferric chloride, $FeCl_3 \cdot 5H_2O$, in 100 ml. of water.

B. Dissolve 3.29 g. of potassium ferricyanide, $K_3Fe(CN)_6$, in 100 ml. of water.

C. Dissolve 0.5 g. of benzopurpurin (Du Pont Purpurin 4B Conc. or its equivalent) in 100 ml. of 50 percent ethyl alcohol. Warm the solution until the dye is completely dissolved. (Some of the dye will precipitate on cooling.)

Keep solutions A and B in separate bottles. These solutions should be renewed frequently. Solution C may be used indefinitely. When the solution becomes cloudy, warm until it becomes clear again.

This stain either may be applied to fibers on the slide, or 1.5 g. of the fibers may be stained in 50 ml. of the solution in a beaker. In either case, mix equal parts of solutions A and B just before using; apply for 1 minute at room temperature, thoroughly wash the stain mixture from the fibers, and then stain them for 2 minutes with solution C. After staining, again thoroughly wash the fibers before observation.

This stain indicates the amount of lignin present and is therefore affected both by the degree of bleaching and of cooking. A well cooked, well bleached pulp will stain red, while a poorly cooked, unbleached pulp will stain blue. All stages between will be found with different degrees of cooking and bleaching; the same pulp will frequently contain both red and blue fibers, or fibers in which one end stains red and one end stains blue. It is evident that care must be exercised in drawing conclusions from the use of this stain.

Lofton-Merritt Stain.[42]—Prepare the following solutions:

A. Dissolve 2 g. of malachite green in 100 ml. of water.

B. Dissolve 1 g. of basic fuchsin in 100 ml. of water.

As in the case of the Kantrowitz-Simmons stain, the Lofton-Merritt stain may be applied either to the fibers on a slide or in a beaker. When staining in a beaker, add 1.5 g. of fibers to a mixture of 15 ml. of solution A, 20 ml. of solution B, and 0.09 ml. of concentrated hydrochloric acid. After 2 minutes at room temperature, pour the dye off the fibers and wash them. If the staining is done on the slide, add a mixture of the dyes first and after 2 minutes remove the excess dye by blotting with a hard filter paper. Add a few drops of 0.1 percent hydrochloric acid and after 30 seconds remove the excess hydrochloric acid by blotting. Finally, add a few drops of water and remove the excess with a cover glass.

[41] Kantrowitz, M. S., and Simmons, R. H., Paper Trade J., **98**, No. 10, 46–48, March 8, 1934.

[42] Lofton, B. E., and Merritt, M. F., Technologic Paper No. 189, U. S. Bureau of Standards, 1921.

This stain is affected also by the amount of lignin present. If the pulp is free of lignin, the fibers will be colorless; if the pulp is highly lignified, they will stain blue. All stages between will be found, depending upon the degree of delignification. Unbleached sulfite pulp has a tendency to give a redder color than unbleached kraft; so, this stain has some value for their differentiation. However, any special treatment given to the pulp, may interfere with the test, and hence it should be used only as an indication of the presence of unbleached kraft or unbleached sulfite, and not as a conclusive test.

F. Spot Stains for Groundwood.—To detect the presence of groundwood, one of the following stains is merely applied to the paper and the resulting color observed. Standards, containing varying percentages of groundwood and other pulps may be prepared and used for comparisons.

NOTE.—When applying a spot stain to the surface of a colored paper, the dyes used may be sensitive to acids and the color change, while apparently showing the presence of groundwood, may be caused by the action of the acid on the dyestuff. In case of doubt, apply a little dilute acid. Some types of safety check papers require particular care in this respect.

Phloroglucinol.[43]—Dissolve 1 g. of phloroglucinol in a mixture of 50 ml. of methyl alcohol, 50 ml. of concentrated hydrochloric acid and 50 ml. of water. This formula gives a water-clear solution that turns yellowish slowly with age. If a stronger stain is desired, the water may be omitted. The life of the solution will be prolonged if it is protected from light.

This stain produces a bright red or magenta color with groundwood. The depth of color being an indication of the amount present. A very light color, however, does not necessarily prove its presence, as partly cooked jute, partly cooked unbleached chemical pulp, and some other ligneous fibers also become slightly colored. Jute papers often show a deep coloration with this stain, so that in the case of strong papers especially, an indication of groundwood should be confirmed microscopically.

Aniline Sulfate (9).[44]—Dissolve 1 g. of aniline sulfate in 50 ml. of water and add a drop of concentrated sulfuric acid. This produces a yellow color on papers containing a considerable percentage of groundwood. It is not quite as sensitive as phloroglucinol, but it is easy to prepare and is less costly.

G. Preparation of Aluminum Stearate Solution.—(a) To 600 ml. of water, add 15 g. of shavings from a good grade of plain soap and stir until the soap is completely dissolved. To the solution add 10 g. of aluminum sulfate, $Al_2(SO_4)_3 \cdot 18H_2O$. A white precipitate of aluminum stearate immediately forms. Stir with a glass rod until the precipitate coagulates into a wax-like mass. With the stirring rod, lift out the precipitated aluminum stearate and place in a desiccator for 48 hours. Store in a well-stoppered bottle to be used as needed.

(b) To 50 ml. of benzene in a glass-stoppered bottle, add 0.7 g. of the desiccated aluminum stearate. Shake well each day until completely dissolved. This usually requires about 10 days. The solution is then ready for use.

NOTE.—If after several weeks it should be found that the solution has lost some of its capacity as a water repellent, add a small piece of aluminum stearate to the solution. This will correct the condition within a few hours.[24]

H. Color Chart for Iodine Stains.—Highly purified pulps (such as alpha) are characteristically kinky in appearance. The word *raw* refers to unbleached pulp, raw or very lightly cooked. *Unbleached* and *bleached* refer to medium and well cooked pulps.

[43] v. Wiesner, J., S.-B. Bais, Akad. Wiss., No. 77, 1876.

[44] v. Wiesner, J., Dinglers Polytechn. J., No. 202, p. 156, Karsten; Bot. Unters. No. 1, 1867, p. 120.

I. *"C" Stain*
  A. Groundwood: *Vivid yellowish orange*
  B. Softwood pulps
    1. Sulfite
      (a) Raw: *Vivid yellow*
      (b) Medium cooked: *Light greenish yellow*
      (c) Well cooked: *Pinkish gray*
      (d) Bleached: *Light purplish gray to weak red purple*
    2. High alpha
      (a) Unbleached: *Very pale brown to brownish gray*
      (b) Bleached: *Moderate reddish orange to dusky red*
    3. Sulfate
      (a) Raw: *Weak greenish yellow*
      (b) Medium and well cooked: *Strong yellowish brown to moderate yellowish green and dark greenish gray*
      (c) Bleached: *Dark bluish gray to dusky purple*
  C. Hardwood pulps
    1. Sulfite
      (a) Unbleached: *Pale yellow green*
      (b) Bleached: *Weak purplish blue to light purplish gray*
    2. High alpha
      (a) Bleached: *Moderate reddish orange to dusky red*
    3. Soda and sulfate
      (a) Unbleached: *Weak blue green to dusky blue green and dark reddish gray*
      (b) Bleached: *Dusky blue to dusky purple*
  D. Rag: *Moderate reddish orange*
  E. Manila
    1. Raw: *Light greenish yellow*
    2. Unbleached and bleached: *Yellowish gray to weak blue and medium gray*
  F. Jute
    1. Unbleached: *Vivid yellowish orange*
    2. Bleached: *Light yellow green*
  G. Straw, bamboo, cane, flax hurds, and esparto
    1. Raw: *Light yellow to weak greenish yellow*
    2. Unbleached and bleached: *Light greenish gray to dark bluish gray and medium purplish gray*
  H. Japanese fibers
    1. Gampi and mitsumata: *Light greenish yellow to light bluish green*
    2. Kozo: *Pinkish gray*
II. *Herzberg Stain*
  A. Groundwood: *Brilliant yellow*
  B. Softwood chemical pulps
    1. Raw: *Light olive gray to olive gray*
    2. Unbleached: *Dark bluish gray to weak purplish blue*
    3. Bleached: *Dark purplish gray to dark reddish purple*
  C. Hardwood chemical pulps
    1. Raw: *Weak olive to dusky blue green*
    2. Unbleached and bleached: *Dark purplish gray to deep reddish purple*
  D. Rag: *Brilliant purplish pink to vivid red purple*
  E. Manila
    1. Raw: *Moderate yellow*

      2. Unbleached and bleached: *Dark purplish gray to moderate purplish pink*

   F. Jute
      1. Unbleached: *Moderate yellowish orange*
      2. Bleached: *Strong greenish yellow*

   G. Straw, bamboo, cane, flax hurds, and esparto
      1. Raw: *Light yellow*
      2. Unbleached and bleached: *Light bluish gray to pale purplish blue and strong purplish pink*

   H. Japanese fibers
      1. Gampi and mitsumata: *Light greenish yellow*
      2. Kozo: *Pinkish gray*

III. *Selleger's Stain*
   A. Groundwood: *Yellow*
   B. Softwood pulps
      1. Sulfite
         (a) Unbleached: *Yellow*
         (b) Bleached: *Red*
      2. High alpha
         (a) Bleached: *Red*
      3. Sulfate
         (a) Unbleached: *Yellow*
         (b) Bleached: *Blue gray*
   C. Hardwood pulps
      1. Sulfite
         (a) Bleached: *Bluish red*
      2. Soda and sulfate
         (a) Unbleached: *Blue*
         (b) Bleached: *Blue*
   D. Rag: *Red*
   E. Manila
      1. Bleached: *Claret red*
   F. Straw and esparto
      1. Bleached: *Blue*

IV. *Wilson's Stain*
   A. Groundwood
      1. Unbleached: *Bright yellow*
      2. Bleached: *Greenish yellow*
   B. Softwood pulps
      1. Sulfite
         (a) Raw cooked: *Very pale yellow*
         (b) Medium cooked: *Colorless*
         (c) Well cooked: *Very pale gray*
         (d) Bleached: *Pinkish lavender*
      2. Alpha
         (a) Unbleached: *Orange red*
         (b) Bleached: *Pale violet*
      3. Sulfate
         (a) Raw cooked: *Dull brown*
         (b) Medium and well cooked: *Gray*
         (c) Bleached: *Blue; some blue with reddish spots*
   C. Hardwood pulps

1. Sulfite
    (a) Raw cooked: *Very pale yellow*
    (b) Medium cooked: *Colorless*
    (c) Well cooked: *Very pale gray*
    (d) Bleached: *Lavender*
2. Alpha
    (a) Unbleached: *Greenish gray*
    (b) Bleached: *Dark blue*
3. Soda
    (a) Unbleached: *Bright purple*
    (b) Bleached: *Pale purple*
  D. Straw
    1. Raw cooked: *Green*
    2. Well cooked: *Blue*
    3. Bleached: *Dark blue*
  E. Cotton: *Red*
  F. Linen: *Pink*

BURSTING STRENGTH OF PAPER

The method is designed to measure the bursting strength of paper and paper products having a bursting strength of not over 200 p.s.i. and in the form of flat sheets not over 0.025 in. thick. It is not intended for use in testing corrugated boxboard, liner board, or hardboards that tend to cut the thin rubber diaphragm.

Bursting strength is defined as the hydrostatic pressure in pounds per square inch (p.s.i.) required to produce rupture of the material when the pressure is applied at a controlled increasing rate, through a rubber diaphragm to a circular area, 1.20 in. in diameter, the area of the material under test being initially flat and held rigidly at the circumference but free to bulge under the increasing pressure during test.

This method is standardized (tentatively) as TAPPI T 403 m-62.

Apparatus.—Bursting tester having the following:

(a) A clamp for firmly and uniformly securing the test specimen, without slippage during the test, between two annular, plane, parallel, and preferably, stainless steel surfaces.

The upper clamping surface (the clamping ring) has a circular opening 1.200 ± 0.001 in. diameter. The surface which is in contact with the paper during testing has a continuous, spiral, 60° V-groove, not less than 0.010 in. deep and of $\frac{1}{32}$ in. pitch, the groove starting at $\frac{1}{8}$ in. from the edge of the opening. The circular edge of the opening which is in contact with the paper during testing, is merely relieved of sharpness, by means of a very fine abrasive cloth (such as crocus cloth), but not rounded off enough to alter effectively the diameter of the opening.

The lower clamping surface (the diaphragm plate) has a thickness of 0.128 in., and an opening 1.302 ± 0.003 in. diameter. Its surface has a series of concentric 60° V-grooves 0.01 in. deep, $\frac{1}{32}$ in. apart, the center of the first groove being $\frac{1}{8}$ in. from the edge of the opening. The thickness of the plate *at the opening* is 0.025 in. The lower edge which is in contact with the rubber diaphragm is rounded by means of an arc of 0.25 in. radius, to prevent cutting of the diaphragm when pressure is applied.

The clamping ring is connected to a clamping mechanism through a swivel-type joint or other means to insure an even clamping pressure. During tests, the circular edges of the openings in the two clamping plates are required to be concentric to within 0.01 in.

Note.—Since the clamping mechanism and clamping surfaces are subject to considerable wear or distortion, they should be examined periodically and repaired or replaced when necessary.

(b) A diaphragm of pure rubber, 0.034 ± 0.002 in. thick, is clamped between the lower clamping plate and the rest of the apparatus, so that, before the diaphragm is stretched by pressure underneath it, the center of its upper surface is below the plane of the clamping surface. The pressure required to raise the free surface of the diaphragm $\frac{3}{8}$ in. above the top surface of the diaphragm plate is required to be 4.3 ± 0.8 p.s.i. In testing this, a bridge gauge may be used, the test being carried out with the clamping ring removed. The diaphragm should be inspected frequently for permanent distortion and renewed when necessary.

(c) Means for applying controlled, increasing, hydrostatic pressure to the underside of the diaphragm until the specimen bursts, by a fluid displaced at the rate of 95 ± 5 ml. per minute. The recommended fluid is U.S.P. chemically pure (96 percent) glycerine. Purified ethylene glycol (permanent types of radiator antifreeze with an additive are not necessary) may be substituted if desired. The hydraulic system, including the gages, is required to be mounted so as to be free from externally induced vibrations.

Note.—Since the bursting resistance of paper increases with the increased rate of loading, the rate of strain must be maintained effectively constant to obtain reproducible results. Air present in the hydraulic system of the tester will lower the rate of distortion of the sample, and must be substantially removed. Air is most commonly trapped under the rubber diaphragm and in the tubes of the gauges. A simple method of testing for the presence of allowable quantities of air is given in a later section.

(d) A maximum-reading pressure gauge of the bourdon type, of appropriate capacity and with a graduated circular scale $3\frac{3}{4}$ in. or more in diameter. The choice and characteristics of the gauge are given in Table 55-7.

TABLE 55-7. GAUGES

Range of Bursting Pressure, p.s.i.	Range of Gauge, p.s.i.	Scale of Graduation Intervals, p.s.i.	Expansibility of Gauge, ml./p.s.i.
5–25	0–30	0.2	0.011
25–110	0–120	0.5	0.004
110–200	0–300	1.0	0.001

Notes.—(1) The 0–120 range gauge may be used for any test within its capacity, if so noted in the report.

(2) The expansibility of a gauge is defined as the volume of liquid entering the gauge tube per unit increase in pressure, when air is absent. It can be determined conveniently by means of a dilatometer device described in the literature cited.[45] The gauge expansibility is required to be within 15 percent of the specified value.

(3) An appreciable flow of liquid into the gauge occurs from the start of the test to the instant of burst. The gauge, therefore, reduces the rate of distension of the sample by an amount depending upon the expansibility of the gauge. When a number of gauges are mounted on a single apparatus, care must be taken that only the gauge on which the measurement is being made is open to the hydraulic system, as otherwise erroneously low burst pressures will be recorded.

(4) To avoid overloading and possible damage to the gauge, a preliminary bursting test should be made with a high-capacity gauge.

Calibration of Gauge.—Calibrate the gauge, while inclined at the same angle at which it is used, by means of a dead-weight tester of the piston type, or by means of a

[45] Tuck, N. G. M., and Mason, S. G., Pulp Paper Mag. Canada, 50, No. 11, 132 Convention Issue 1949.

column of mercury. Such calibration is preferably carried out with the gauge in its normal position in the instrument.

Gauges in frequent use should be calibrated at least once a month. If a gauge is accidentally used beyond its capacity, it needs to be recalibrated before it is used again.

NOTES.—(1) Maximum-reading pressure gauges are subject to dynamic errors in addition to the ordinary static calibration errors. A suitable method of dynamic calibration, for greater precision, has been described.[46]

(2) For rough checking purposes, bursting strengths on aluminum foil may be used. Standardized foils for this purpose, bursting over the range of 15 to 110 p.s.i. may be obtained from the Pulp and Paper Research Institute of Canada, 3420 University Street, Montreal, Que.; also from Testing Foil Service, 304 N. Stevens St., Rhinelander, Wis. An alternative procedure is to carry out comparison bursts with a standardized gauge.

Checking for Air in the System.—When first assembled or subsequent to changing gauge or diaphragms or adding liquid, the instrument is checked as follows: fill the opening from the rubber diaphragm to the level of the clamping surface with water and clamp a rigid metal plate, with a sheet of thin rubber to prevent leakage, in the position normally occupied by the sample. Turn the shaft of the pump by hand until a pressure is just registered on the gauge. Then turn the shaft so that 0.4 ml. of fluid is displaced. (In the Mullen tester where a pump shaft rotates at 115 r.p.m., a displacement of 0.4 ml. corresponds to a half turn (180°) of the shaft.) Observe the pressure developed. Pressures less than the following indicate the presence of excessive quantities of air in the system or erroneous gage expansibilities.

Gauge Range	Pressure Developed, p.s.i.
0–30	12
0–120	35
0–300	90

A gradual loss in the pressure obtained indicates a leak in the system which should be corrected.

Test Specimen.—At least 10 and preferably 20 specimens, at least 2.5 by 2.5 in., and representative of a sample obtained according to the standard method for "Sampling Paper for Testing" (Vol. 2, Part B, page 1794).

Procedure.—Condition and test the paper in an atmosphere in accordance with T 402 m (Vol. 2, Part B, p. 1795).

Clamp the specimen securely in position, apply the hydrostatic pressure as specified until the specimen ruptures, and record the maximum registered by the pressure gauge. Watch carefully for any movement of the unclamped margin of the specimen. If slippage is indicated, discard the test and increase the clamping pressure for subsequent tests. Make at least ten tests, applying an equal number to each side of the paper.

Make no tests on areas containing watermarks, creases, imperfections, or visible damage. After each test, return the indicator needle of the gauge gently to zero.

Report.—Report the bursting strength in pounds per square inch (p.s.i.) as the arithmetical mean of the test results, corrected for any gauge error, to three significant figures. Include the number of tests and either the standard deviation or alternatively, the maximum and minimum values.

The term "points" is frequently used in place of pounds per square inch in connection with bursting strength of paper and the results may be so reported if desired.

Additional Information.—The principal changes in this revision as compared with the previous method are:

[46] Tuck, N. G. M., Faichney, L. M., and Mason, S. G., "The Dynamic Calibration of Maximum-Reading Pressure Gages" (to be published).

1. The scope is reduced from a maximum of 250 to a maximum of 200 p.s.i.

2. The following changes have been made in the instrument. (a) The thickness of the lower clamping plate has been increased from 0.100 to 0.128 in. in order to prevent it from bending under the higher pressures, but without altering the diameter of the hole or the thickness of the edges at the opening. (b) The pressure to inflate the diaphragm has been reduced from 5 to 6.5 p.s.i. to 4.3 ± 0.8 to conform with the new plate. (c) Glycerine is preferred hydraulic fluid because its high viscosity better resists leaking or the intrusion of air. However, once the air is in the liquid, it is easier to remove from ethylene glycol.

3. Related Methods ASTM, D 774; British B.P. & B.M.A., PT8; Canadian C.P.P.A., D8; Swedish PCA 8 Australian APPITA, P403.

REFERENCES

Carson, F. T., and Worthington, F. V., "A Critical Study of the Bursting Strength Test for Paper," Natl. Bur. Standards J. Research 6, 339, Research Paper RP 278, 1931.

Carson, F. T., "Some Notes on the Revision of Methods for Measuring the Strength of Paper," Paper Trade J., 102, TS 253, 1936.

Clark, James d'A., "Determining the Bursting Strength of Paper," Technical Assoc. Papers, 4, 367–370, 1932.

Oliver, C. V., "Variability in Results Met with in Paper Strength Testing," Proc. Tech. Sec. B.P.M.A., 11, Part 1, 53, 1930.

Underhay, C. F., "Bursting Tester Standardization," Proc. Tech. Sect. P.M.A. 11, Part 2, 247, 1931.

Carson, F. T., and Worthington, F. V., "Diaphragm Error and Testing Rate in the Paper Bursting Test," Tappi, 35, 539–544, Dec., 1952.

Thompson, G., "Some Factors Affecting the Bursting Test," Proc. Tech. Sect. B.P. & B.M.A. 38, Part 2, 293, 1957.

Aldrich, Lyman C., "Standardization of Model C Mullen Testers in a Multi-Mill Company," Tappi, 43, No. 5, 221A, 1960.

TENSILE BREAKING STRENGTH OF PAPER AND PAPERBOARD

This method is for determining the tensile breaking strength of papers and paperboards. This method is standardized as TAPPI 404 os-61.

Apparatus. **Tensile Testing Machine.**—The machine should have the following:

1. Two clamps from 0.5 to 2.0 in. wide (see section "Test Specimen" for preferred widths) with clamping surfaces in the same plane parallel to the direction of motion of the applied stress and so aligned that they hold the test specimen in that plane throughout the test without slippage. At the start of the test the edges of the jaws of the clamps are set apart at 180 ± 5 mm. (7.1 ± 0.2 in.).

NOTE.—Many instruments are arranged for an 8-in. jaw separation distance, especially for paperboard and coarse papers; however, the preferred jaw separation at start of test is 180 mm. in all cases. It is usually not difficult to have the instrument changed accordingly.

2. Means for applying a smoothly increasing load to the test specimen until it breaks, the increase being such that additional load applied each second is not different by more than 10 percent from the additional load applied in the previous second.

NOTE.—This condition is fulfilled by most motor driven, tensile breaking strength testers, including the incline plane testers, temperature-compensated spring testers, the usual pendulum type of apparatus, and the constant-rate-of-elongation testers or other instruments, provided that the slope of the stress-strain curve does not change abruptly.

3. Means of indicating the applied load at the instant of rupture, to within ±1 percent.

Calibration.—Check the apparatus for cleanliness. Then level it accurately in each of the principal directions. Check all the moving parts to ensure that they move freely. Apply various deadweights to the clamp actuating the indicating mechanism and note the scale readings when the weights and mechanism come gently into an equilibrium position from the direction and at the speed somewhat slower than that used in an actual test.

Note 1.—The speed is specified to be slower than in use so as to minimize the effect of the extra inertia of the added dead weight.

Note 2.—When calibrating the pendulum type of tester, determine the effect of the friction of the pawls as follows: I. With the pawls engaged as in normal use, allow the calibration weight to exert its force by gently lowering it by hand at a speed somewhat slower than that used in an actual test. II. With pawls wedged up with a small piece of paper bent double, gently apply the same calibration weight at a speed to be used and allow the pendulum to come to equilibrium from the same direction as in an actual test. If the reading by I is measurably less than by II, then the friction of the pawls is the more important; therefore, if this friction cannot be reduced, calibrate the scale by method I. If the reading by I is greater than by II, the friction is less significant than the inertia, therefore calibrate by method II.

Note 3.—With other types of testers, follow the manufacturer's, and the general instructions given above.

Verify the instrument over the range to be used at three or four widely spaced points within 1 month prior to any test. If errors greater than 1 percent are found, construct a correction curve.

Test Specimen.—Obtain the samples in accordance with TAPPI Standard T 400 m (vol. 2, part B, p. 1794), and condition them in accordance with TAPPI Standard T 402 m (vol. 2, part B, p. 1795). For each principal direction to be tested, cut at least ten specimen strips with clean and parallel edges to a width within 0.1 mm. of the nominal width, and over 200 mm., preferably 250 mm. (9.9 in.) long. Avoid abnormalities, watermarks, creases, and wrinkles.

For paper, cut the strips preferably 15.0 mm. (0.59 in.) wide. For coarse papers, such as building papers and paperboards over 0.12 in. thick, cut them preferably 1.00 in. (25.4 mm.) wide. In either case, do not cut the test strips less than 0.5 in. nor more than 2.0 in. wide.

Note.—Varying the width of the test specimen between 0.5 and 2 in. does not, in general, make much difference in the proportionate test results except for unbeaten long-fiber papers, when the difference may be appreciable. Accordingly a minimum strip width of 15 mm. should then be used.

Procedure.—Make the test in an atmosphere conditioned according to TAPPI Standard T 402 m.

Avoid touching the portions of the strips that will be between the jaws. Tightly clamp one end of a test strip in one jaw after placing the strip loosely in the other jaw and checking its alignment. Then tightly clamp the lower end of the specimen and apply the load.

Note.—Except for a referee test, time may be saved by aligning and clamping the ends of the ten specimen strips together in one jaw and breaking them one at a time, after clamping the other end of each in the other jaw.

Operate the tester so that the *average* time for the completion of the test will be within 10 ± 5 seconds. The appropriate setting of the tester may be determined from a trial test strip, or a table may be prepared giving the approximate settings for a particular type of tester for the width of the specimen and its expected breaking strength and elongation.

NOTE.—In cases of dispute, the average time to fracture should be 10 ± 2 seconds. Normally the rate of loading is not a very important factor; doubling it usually results in an increase of only about 2 percent.

Reject readings from individual strips if the strip slips or breaks in or at the edge of the clamps or during the test shows evidence of uneven stressing across its width.

Record the result of each individual breaking load to the nearest 2 or to 3 significant figures.

Test at least 10 strips cut in each principal direction of the paper, unless the strength in one direction only is required.

Compute the average breaking load and, preferably also the standard deviation, for each direction tested.

Report.—Report results obtained on strips cut in the machine direction as the tensile strength, machine direction, and on strips cut in the cross direction as the tensile strength, cross direction.

Report the average value of the breaking load calculated either to kg. per 15 mm. or, less desirably, to pounds per inch to three significant figures (kg. per 15 mm. × 3.71 = lb. per in.).

A complete report requires in addition, statements of:

(a) The width of the test specimen.
(b) The distance between the jaws at the start of the test.
(c) The average value of the "time to break" for each principal direction tested.
(d) The number of strips tested in each direction.
(e) The standard deviation for each direction tested.
(f) The type of instrument and speed of operation of the driven head.

NOTE.—In a pendulum tester, the speed depends on the scale used and the leverage of the pendulum as well as the rate of movement of the stressing jaw. The speed of operation may be expressed as the average time to break, or, as the average increase of load per second; preferably however, if available, the average extension per second.

Reproducibility.—Duplicate determinations of the tensile breaking strength from samples from the same shipment but on different instruments, are expected to agree within 5 percent.

Additional Information.—If a lesser distance between the clamps is employed, a higher test is usual. For papers which have a poor formation, the difference between 100 mm. and the standard distance of 180 mm., may amount to over 10 percent. Where a length of strip of 180 mm. is not possible, the machine may be adapted to 150 mm. (6 in.), 100 mm. (4 in.), or 50 mm. (2 in.). If the specimen strips are too short for the tester, they may be extended by means of strips of strong gummed kraft. In any of these deviations from standard, however, the fact should be recorded in a prominent position in the report.

The jaw separation distance of 100 mm. is standard for pulp test sheets. The results are calculated to breaking length in meters, based on the moisture-free basis weight of the test sheets in accordance with the formula $B.L. = 20,000\ P3/R$ meters; where P is the load in kilograms to break a 15-mm.-wide test strip, and R is the moisture-free basis weight in grams per square meter. See TAPPI Standard T 220 m (p. 1359).

The main change in this revision is to replace the requirement for the rate of loading from a rather complicated specification to the same time of 10 ± 5 seconds for all papers and paperboards.

Related Methods: Canadian CPPA., D-6; British BPBMA, PT12; German VZPCI, V12; French AFNOR, Q03-001.

REFERENCES

1. Carson, F. T., "Some notes on revision of methods for measuring the strength of paper," Paper Trade J., **102**, No. 19, 39–42, May 7, 1936; Tech. Assoc. Papers, **19**, 172–175, June, 1936.
2. Clark, J. d'A., "Some observations on burst, tensile, and stretch tests," Paper Trade J., **102**, No. 2, 40-a, Jan. 9, 1936; Tech. Assoc. Papers, **19**, 264–266, June, 1936; discussion 19, 90–94, June, 1936.
3. Griffin, R. C., and McKinley, R. W., "Studies of tensile and bursting tests," Paper Trade J., **102**, No. 2, 34–35, Jan. 9, 1936; Tech. Assoc. Papers, **19**, 222–223, June, 1936.
4. The Institute of Paper Chemistry, "Instrumentation Studies XL. Measurement of the Tensile Strength of Paper. XLI. The Scott Serigraph, Model J-3. XLII. The Amthor Universal Tensile Strength Tester. XLIII. The Schopper electrically driven strength tester," Paper Trade J., **115**, No. 5, 12–18; No. 7, 13–22; No. 19, 18–22; No. 26, 14–21; 116, No. 6, 10–12; No. 23, 13–14, July 30, Aug. 13, Nov. 5, Dec. 24, 1942: Feb. 11, June 10, 1943.
5. Oliver, C. V., "Variability of results met with in paper strength testing," Proc. Tech. Section, Paper Makers' Assoc. Gt. Britain and Ireland 11, 53–84, Oct., 1930.
6. Paper Makers' Assoc. Gt. Britain and Ireland, Tech. Section, Paper Testing Committee., First Report, London, the Association, 1937, 85 pages: Proc. Tech. Section 18, part 1A, June, 1937; World's Paper Trade Review, Technical Convention Number: 4–72, March, 1937.
7. Hindman, H., and Burr, G. S., "The Instron tensile tester," Trans. A.S.M.E., 798–796, Oct., 1949; Burr, G. S., "Servo-controlled tensile strength tester," Electronics, May, 1949.
8. Van den Akker, J. A., and Hardacker, K. W., "Instrument Studies. LXXXI. The Automatic Recording of the Load Elongation Characteristic of Paper. III. The Table Model Instron (Universal Testing Instrument)," Tappi, **41**, No. 8, 224A–231A, Aug., 1958.

BASIS WEIGHT OF PAPER AND PAPERBOARD

The commercial standard for expression of the basis weight of paper in most English-speaking countries has been the weight in pounds of a ream, usually of 500 sheets of a given size but occasionally 480 sheets. The metric system used elsewhere expresses the basis weight in grams per square meter. For convenience, this is now abbreviated to g.s.m.

The basis weight of paperboards is also expressed in g.s.m. or as the weight in pounds per 1000 sq. ft. Generally, all heavy, stiff sheets over 0.012 in. thick, other than blotting paper, are considered to be paperboards. However, the term also includes materials of lesser thickness, such as liner and corrugating board. This method is standardized as TAPPI T 410 os-61.

Apparatus. **Balance** with a sensitivity of 0.25 percent, or better, of the applied load and such that readings of this degree of accuracy can be made. The balance may be a specially constructed sheet-weighing device that indicates the equivalent weight in g.s.m., when one sheet of a given size of at least 500 sq. cm. is weighed; or the equivalent weight of 1000 sq. ft. of paperboard in pounds when one sheet 1 sq. ft. in size is weighed. For small specimens an analytical balance is essential to obtain the required accuracy.

Cutter.—When a template is used for preparing specimen sheets, the paper should be cut to exact size with a sharp knife on a hardwood board. A paper cutter having an attachment for ensuring parallelism of the opposite edges is recommended.

Calibration.—Calibrate the balance not more than 7 days prior to the test, both with increasing and decreasing loads by applying accurate weights. Take care that after calibration, the level of the balance is not disturbed.

Test Specimen.—In accordance with TAPPI Standard T 400 m (vol. 2, part B, p. 1794) select not less than 10 sheets representative of the shipment, each at least 500 sq. cm. (80 sq. in.) in area, and for paperboard, not less than 5 representative sheets each at least 1 sq. ft. in area.

Procedure.—Condition and test the specimens in an atmosphere in accordance with T 402 m (vol. 2, part B, p. 1795). Determine the area of each specimen to the nearest 0.5 percent of its total area, *i.e.*, measure the dimensions of each to within 0.25 percent. Determine the weight of the specimens to the nearest 0.25 percent of their total weight. Calculate the average weight in grams per square meter from the measured area of the specimens and their weight.

Report.—For paper, express the weight in grams per square meter to three significant figures and if desired, the equivalent weight for the ream size used by the paper industry for the particular kind of paper.

For paperboard, report the basis weight in grams per square meter or in pounds per 1000 sq. ft. or both, to three significant figures.

If the total area of the test specimen unavoidably is less than that specified, state the actual area and number of specimens tested.

Additional Information.—1. For weighing specimen sheets on a gram balance or on a paper scale:

If a = length of sample in inches,
or y = length of sample in centimeters;
   b = width of sample in inches,
or z = width of sample in centimeters;
   g = weight in grams of sheets weighed,
or p = indicated weight on scale for 500-sheet ream;
and
   n = number of sheets weighed;

then the weight in grams per square meter is given by:

$$\frac{1550\,g}{abn} \quad \text{or} \quad \frac{10{,}000\,g}{yzn} \quad \text{or} \quad \frac{1406\,p}{abn} \quad \text{or} \quad \frac{9070\,p}{yzn}$$

2. In Table 55-8 conversion factors are given for converting the weights of some customary trade sizes of 500-sheet reams (t) and grams per square meter (m):

TABLE 55-8.   REAM WEIGHT CONVERSION FACTORS

Kind of paper	t in. Trade size	A (m to t)	B (t to m)
Writing & printing.................	17 × 22	0.266	3.760
(Demy size)......................	17½ × 22½	0.280	3.571
Blotting.........................	19 × 24	0.324	3.083
Cover...........................	20 × 26	0.370	2.704
Tissue (Double Crown size).........	20 × 30	0.427	2.343
Cardboard.......................	22 × 28	0.438	2.282
Bristol & tag....................	22½ × 28½	0.456	2.195
News & wrapping.................	24 × 36	0.614	1.627
Book...........................	25 × 38	0.675	1.480
(Former TAPPI Standard size)......	25 × 40	0.711	1.406
Paperboard......................	1000 sq. ft.	0.205	4.881

In Table 55-8:

A = 0.711 × (area of trade size sheet in square inches ÷ 1000)
B = 1406 ÷ (area of trade size sheet in square inches)

If the given trade size is in 480 sheets, then the above factor A is multiplied by 48/50 (or 0.960) and B by 50/48 (or 1.042) for conversion.

Examples.—Grams per square meter $\times A$ = pounds weight of given trade size: e.g., 60 g.s.m. $\times$ 0.614 = 36.8 lb. (24 $\times$ 36—500).

Pounds weight of given trade size $\times B$ = grams per square meter: e.g., 50 lb. (25 $\times$ 38—500) $\times$ 1.480 = 74 g.s.m.

3. To within less than 0.5 percent, grams per square meter is numerically equivalent to pounds (35 $\times$ 40—500), so that by adjusting the size of the template to suit, most ream weight scales may be used to read directly in g.s.m.

4. This revision withdraws the former TAPPI Standard size of (25 $\times$ 40—500) and in its place substitutes grams per square meter (g.s.m.) as the sole TAPPI Standard unit for the basis weight of paper and also recommends it as an alternative for paperboard. It is, of course, permissible to state the basis weight of paper in any desired form in parentheses following its statement in grams per square meter.

The tolerance for the determination of the area of the specimen also has been broadened.

5. Related Methods: Canadian CPPA Tech. Sect., D-3; Australian APPITA, P 405 m; British BPBMA, PT4; German VZ & PCI, V/11; Swedish PCA 5. All recognize grams per square meter as a standard unit of basis weight.

THICKNESS AND DENSITY OF PAPER

Definitions.—The *thickness* of paper or paperboard is the thickness (in thousandths of an inch) of a single sheet when placed under a steady pressure of 7 to 9 pounds per square inch, between two circular and parallel plane surfaces, the smaller of which has an area of approximately 0.25 sq. in. (160 sq. mm.).

The *density* of paper or paperboard is the weight per unit volume or the apparent specific gravity.

The *specific volume* is the volume in cc. of 1 g. of paper or paperboard. This is the reciprocal of the density.

Scope.—The method for determining thickness shall be used for finding the thickness of a single sheet as it would measure when placed between plane surfaces and to determine variations in thickness among the sheets of a sample, especially for paper or paperboards which are to be used singly.

The density and specific volume of paper shall be used for expressing the bulkiness of the structure of paper. This method is standardized as TAPPI T 411 m-44.

Apparatus.—The micrometer used shall be in accordance with the following requirements:

1. It shall have two plane faces, the smaller of which is circular and 0.25 to 0.33 sq. in. (160 to 215 sq. mm.) in area, corresponding to a diameter of 0.56 to 0.65 in. (14.3 to 16.5 mm.). The faces shall be parallel to within 0.0002 in. (0.005 mm.) and constrained to move apart in an axis perpendicular to themselves.

2. When the specimen is clamped between the faces, it shall be under a steady pressure of 7.0 to 9.0 p.s.i. (0.49 to 0.63 kg. per sq. cm.).

3. The distance between the graduations on the dial shall be such as to permit estimating the thickness to at least 0.0001 in.

4. The micrometer shall be such as to repeat its readings to within 0.0001 in. at zero setting or on a steel gauge block.

5. Measurements made on standard steel thickness gauges shall be within the following tolerances of permissible deviation of the reading from the actual thickness of the standard steel gauge:

Intervals		Tolerance	
mm.	*inch*	*mm.*	*inch*
0 to 0.25	0 to 0.01	0.0025	0.0001
Over 0.25 to 1.02	0.01 to 0.04	0.0051	0.0002
Over 1.02 to 3.05	0.04 to 0.12	0.0102	0.0004

Calibration. **Parallelism of the Faces.**—A hard steel ball about $\frac{1}{16}$ in. in diameter, fixed firmly in a thinner flat piece of metal to serve as a handle, shall be placed at different points on the anvil and the readings noted.

Accuracy of the Readings.—The instrument shall be set to zero and standard gauges shall be placed between the plane faces and the corresponding dial readings observed over the range to be used. For thickness measurements, standard steel gauge blocks having an accuracy of 0.00001 in. shall be used.

Pressure Between the Faces.—The force required to just prevent the movement of the plunger foot, from a reading corresponding to about the average paper thickness tested to a lower reading, shall be determined with a suitable balance, and the contact pressure determined with this force. For example, where the pressure foot projects through the top of the apparatus, a fine copper wire is attached to it and by means of a coarse balance or a calibrated spring, the force necessary to prevent the closing of the foot is measured.

Alternately, a stirrup may be used, made of a flat metal plate having a hole larger than the diameter of the micrometer foot, covered at the bottom of the plate by a thin metal disc of about the average thickness of the paper to be measured. The stirrup is suspended from a suitable balance.

Test Specimen.—The test specimen shall consist of not less than 10 sheets and shall have a minimum dimension, if possible, of not less than 2 in. Any necessary noncompliance with this requirement shall be noted in the test report as a minor deviation. They shall be taken from the test sample in such a way as to be thoroughly representative of it, and shall be free from creases. They shall have been conditioned according to TAPPI Standard T 402 m (vol. 2, part B, p. 1795).

Procedure.—The test shall be made in an atmosphere conditioned according to TAPPI Standard T 402 m.

Place the specimen between the jaws of the micrometer and lower the pressure foot as gently as possible upon the surface of the paper with its edge at least 0.25 in. (0.6 mm.) from the edge of the paper. Each of 10 different sheets shall be tested in not less than two different places.

Report.—The thickness shall be reported in decimals of an inch to the nearest 0.0001 (0.002 mm.), together with the maximum and minimum readings and number and size of the specimen sheets.

When desired, the specific volume or the density shall be reported to the nearest third significant figure. The specific volume and density are calculated as follows:

Let SV = specific volume,
D = density,
T_1 = thickness in mils (0.001 inch),
T_2 = thickness in microns (0.001 mm.),
W_1 = basis weight in pounds, 25×40—500,
and W_2 = basis weight in grams per sq. meter.

$$\text{Then} \qquad SV = \frac{T_2}{W_2} = \frac{T_1}{W_1} \times 18.08$$

$$\text{and} \qquad D = \frac{1}{SV}$$

Reproducibility of Results.—Duplicate determinations from different sets of samples from the same shipment and on different instruments are expected to agree to within 0.0002 in. for thickness and to within 3 percent for the specific volume or density.

Additional Information.—Depending upon the type of paper, a variation in pressure of from 5 to 10 p.s.i. causes a corresponding decrease in the results by about 3 percent. Halving the area of the pressure foot while maintaining the unit pressure constant results in an increase of from 1 to 3 percent.

REFERENCES

Houston, P. L., and Miller, D. R., "A Study of Commercial Dial Micrometers for Measuring the Thickness of Paper," Bureau of Standards Technologic Paper, No. 226.

Carson, F. T., "Critical Study of Methods of Measuring the Bulk of Paper," Bureau of Standards Research Paper, No. 69.

"Standard Method for Determining the Thickness and Bulk of Paper," British Paper Makers' Association Committee on Bulk and Thickness. (Contains method and considerable new data which justify the restrictions in the foregoing method.)

Strachan, James, "Piezo Micrometer and its Applications," P.M.A. Proc., Vol. III, Part I, October, 1922.

Strachan, James, "Notes on Paper Testing," P.M.A. Proc., Vol. I, Part I, March, 1921.

INTERNAL TEARING RESISTANCE OF PAPER

Scope.—This method covers the determination of the average force in grams required to tear a single sheet of paper after the tear has been started. This method is not suitable for determining the cross-directional tearing strength of highly-directional boards and papers.

This method is standardized as ASTM D 689-62.

Summary of Method.—A pendulum is permitted to make one swing and thereby cause the tearing of one or more sheets together through a fixed distance. The work done in tearing is measured by the loss in potential energy of the pendulum. The scale is calibrated to indicate average force (work done divided by tearing distance).

Instrumental and Procedural Variables.—Several Elmendorf-type tearing strength testers are available and in use throughout the world, representing principally those of Australian, Swedish, German, and United States manufacture. These may differ in at least two major respects: (1) design of the Pendulum Sector—the older models permitted the specimen to come in contact with the sector during the test, whereas the newer models eliminate this undesirable specimen contact. Differences in test values of the order of 10 percent or more have been observed[47] as a direct result of differences in sector design, higher values being obtained with the older sector. (2) Design of Specimen Clamps—the specimen clamps may be different for instruments of each manufacturer, and more than one design may be chosen from those of one manufacturer. Differences in clamp design, together with the structure of the paper (that is, the structural characteristics that govern the nature of the tear with respect to its splitting tendencies in this test), can have a pronounced influence on the mode of tear and introduce differences in the result of the order of 10 percent or more.[48] It should be recognized that the foregoing, together with other differences in design details between instruments precludes the writing of a single tearing strength method that would give essentially the same test values when using Elmendorf instruments of different models and from various manufacturers. Even for one specific model, some procedural variables, such as the

[47] W. E. Cohen, and A. J. Watson, "The Measurement of Internal Tearing Resistance," Proceedings Australian Pulp and Paper Ind. Tech. Assn., Vol. 3, 1949.

[48] W. A. Wink, and Roger H. van Eperen, "Does the Elmendorf Tester Measure Tearing Strength?" Tappi, **46**, No. 5, May, 1963, pp. 323–325.

number of plies torn, may alter the test values as much as 100 percent.[48] Hence, the method by necessity must be arbitrary and limited to a particular make and model of Elmendorf.

Evaluation and standardization of this method were performed with the Elmendorf-type instrument, Model 60–100, capacity 1600 g., as manufactured by the Thwing-Albert Instrument Co. The instrumental and procedural details and the statement on precision were determined in a series of studies involving the older and newer models of the Thwing tester.[49] It is not known to what extent those details are applicable to other Elmendorf testers.

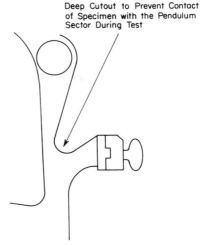

Deep Cutout to Prevent Contact of Specimen with the Pendulum Sector During Test

Apparatus. **Elmendorf Tearing-Strength Tester,** with a cutout as shown in Fig. 55-10, in order not to permit the specimen to come in contact with the pendulum sector during the test (Note 1). Other features are as follows: (*1*) a stationary clamp; (*2*) a movable clamp carried on a pendulum formed by a sector of a circle free to swing on a ball bearing; (*3*) a cutter (knife) mounted on a stationary post for starting the tear; (*4*) means for leveling the instrument; (*5*) means for holding the pendulum in a raised position, and means for releasing it instantaneously; and (*6*) means for registering the maximum arc through which the pendulum swings when released. This consists of a graduated scale mounted on the pendulum, a pointer mounted on the same axis as the pendulum with constant friction just sufficient to stop the pointer at the highest point reached by the swing of the sector, and an adjustable pointer stop for setting the zero of the instrument.

Fig. 55-10. Cutout in Tearing-strength Tester.

Note 1.—*Old Model Instruments.*—Some of the older ·models of the Elmendorf tearing-strength tester, which permit the specimen to come in contact with the pendulum sector during the test or which *do not have* a cutout as shown in Fig. 55-10, yield tearing-strength results significantly higher than those obtained with the newer models, which are designed to eliminate specimen contact. Differences up to 10 percent are not uncommon, but the relationship between the results of the two models may vary considerably with different types and basis weights of paper. For this reason, it is preferable that newly prepared product specifications specifically reference this test method. For *referee-type* testing required to determine conformance with product specifications that do not clearly require the "new" instrument, the testing should be performed in accordance with the provisions of this method, except that the "old" model tester (without cutout) is to be used. Product specifications that do not specify which tester is to be used should be reconsidered in the light of this standard method. At the earliest possible date, all product specifications should be revised to reference this method and the "new" instrument.

With the pendulum in its initial position ready for a test, the two clamps are separated by an interval of 2.8 ± 0.3 mm., and are so aligned that the specimen clamped in them lies in a plane parallel to the axis of the pendulum, the plane making an angle of 27.5 ± 0.5° with the perpendicular line joining the axis and the horizontal line formed

[49] T. W. Lashof, "APPA-TAPPI Reference Material Program. I. Interlaboratory Investigation of TAPPI Standard T 414 m-49, Internal Tearing Resistance of Paper," Tappi, **45**, p. 656, 1962.

by the top edges of the clamping jaws. The distance between the axis and the top edges of the clamping jaws is 104 ± 1 mm.

Jaws, having a clamping surface in each jaw 36 ± 1.0 mm. wide and 15.9 ± 0.08 mm. deep.

Pendulum Scale, graduated so as to indicate a constant, K, times the work done in gram-centimeters by the pendulum when tearing a specimen of paper. The scale graduations and the constant K are as follows:

(1) Elmendorf tearing tester, capacity 1600 g.: 0 to 100 by units, $K = 1/137.6$.

(2) Elmendorf tearing tester as in Item (1), but with augmenting weight, capacity 3200 g.: 0 to 100 by units, $K = 1/275.2$ (see footnote 48 and the manufacturer's instructions).

NOTE 2.—The scale of the Elmendorf tearing tester indicates the ratio of the work done (in gram-centimeters) when 16 sheets are torn together to the total tearing distance. This distance is 16 (sheets) × 4.3 cm. (tearing length per sheet) × 2 = 137.6 cm., the factor 2 being included because in order to tear a given length of sheet the tearing force has to be applied twice that distance. The scale for the Elmendorf tearing tester with an augmenting weight is based on the tearing length of 32 sheets.

Cutting Knife, centered between the clamps and adjusted in height so that the tearing distance is 43.0 ± 0.15 mm.; that is, the distance between the end of the slit made by the knife and the upper edge of the specimen shall be 43.0 ± 0.15 mm. when the lower edge of the 63.0-mm. wide specimen rests against the bottom of the clamp.

Pendulum Sector, having a cutout in the region adjacent to the clamp so that the specimen does not rub against the sector during the test (Fig. 55-10).

Precision Sample Cutter to ensure a parallel strip 63.0 ± 0.15 mm. wide with sharp and clean edges (that is, two hardened and ground base shears, twin knives tensioned against the base shears, and a hold-down mechanism).

Sampling.—Obtain the sample to be tested in accordance with the Method of Sampling Paper and Paperboard (vol. 2, part B, p. 1794).

Conditioning.—Precondition the sample on the dry side and condition in accordance with the Method of Conditioning Paper and Paper Products for Testing (vol. 2, part B, p. 1795).

Test Specimens.—Cut each ply of the test specimen 76 ± 2.0 mm. long by 63.0 ± 0.15 mm. wide.

Determine from the product specification how many plies make up a specimen, and how the plies for each specimen are to be selected from the units of the sample. Unless otherwise stated in the product specification, (1) take all of the plies to be torn together from a single sheet, or, if this does not provide sufficient material, from adjacent sheets of a unit, and (2) adjust the number of plies to be torn together to give an instrument scale reading nearest 40. If one ply would give a scale reading higher than 60, use the Elmendorf tearing tester with augmenting weight and a one-ply specimen. However, in making comparisons between two or more sets of papers of the same grade and basis weight, use the same number of plies.

NOTE 3.—*Factors Affecting Results.*—The work done in tearing a number of sheets of paper includes a certain amount of work to bend the paper continuously as it is torn, to provide for the rubbing of the torn edges of the specimen together, and to lift the sample of paper. The number of plies torn at one time and their size can strongly affect the result in the testing of some papers. Empirical requirements for both the apparatus and the method are necessary to keep the additional work not used for tearing to approximately a definite quantity.

Prepare for each unit of the sample ten specimens in each principal direction of the paper, unless tests in only one direction are required by the product specification. For each specimen keep the wire sides of all plies facing the same way. It has been found from round-robin studies[49] that generally there is no advantage in testing more than ten specimens of a homogeneous sample.

Preparation of Apparatus.—Sometimes, as a result of frequent use, a notch is worn in the pendulum sector at the point of contact with the sector stop, giving a jerky release of the pendulum. If this happens, either repair the sector by cutting out and replacing the worn edge or adjust the height of the stop to the very lowest point of the sector edge.

Rest the pendulum sector against its stop, and check the alignment of the clamps. Adjust the pendulum stop if necessary. Verify by visual check that the knife is centered between the clamps, and adjust if necessary. Check the sharpness of the knife. A dull knife will result in a V-notch near the top of the cut and will push the paper out. If necessary, sharpen the knife with a rough stone. (A rough edge is better than a razor edge.) Check the tearing distance and adjust the height of the knife if necessary. Do *not* change the dimensions of the specimen to adjust the tearing distance.

Level the instrument so that, with the sector free, the line on the sector indicating the vertical from the point of suspension is bisected by the edge of the pendulum stop mechanism. Movement of the instrument during the swinging of the pendulum is a significant source of error. Therefore, securely anchor the instrument to a heavy table or bench. Use a table so rigid that there will be no perceptible movement of the table or instrument during the swing of the pendulum.

NOTE 4.—*Securing Instrument.* Threaded bolt holes are usually provided in the base of the instrument and may be used to secure the instrument to the table. An alternative procedure is to place the instrument on a guide which ensures that the instrument always has the same position on the table. (Such a guide is available from the manufacturer of the instrument.)

Draw a pencil line on the stop mechanism 1 in. to the right of the edge of the sector stop. With the sector raised to its initial position and the pointer set against its stop, on releasing the sector and holding the sector stop down, the sector should make at least 20 complete oscillations before the edge of the sector that engages the stop no longer passes to the left of the pencil line. Otherwise, clean, oil, and adjust the bearing.

Operate the leveled instrument several times with nothing in the jaws, the movable jaw being closed. If zero is not registered, the pointer stop should be adjusted until the zero reading is obtained. Do *not* change the level to adjust the zero.

Set the pointer at the zero reading on the scale before releasing the sector, and after release see that the pointer is not pushed *more than three scale divisions (4 mm.) nor less than two scale divisions (2½ mm.)* beyond the zero. If the pointer friction does not lie between two and three divisions, remove the pointer, wipe the bearing clean, and apply a trace of good clock oil to the groove of the bearing. Reassemble and check pointer friction. Recheck the zero and readjust the pointer stop if necessary.

Verification. **Scale.**—(*1*) Once the scale has been verified, it is unnecessary to repeat this step provided the tester is kept in adjustment and no parts become changed or worn.

(*2*) Anchor and level the tester as described under "Preparation of Apparatus" (above). Clamp a known weight in grams, W, to the radial edge of the sector beneath the jaws, the center of gravity of the weight (including means of attaching) having been previously marked by a punched dot on the face of the weight that is to be to the front of the instrument.

(*3*) Raise and set the sector as for tearing a sheet and, by means of a surface gauge or cathetometer, measure in centimeters to the nearest 0.01 cm. the height, H, of the center of gravity of the weight above a fixed horizontal surface. Then release the sector, allow it to swing, and note the pointer reading. Without touching the pointer, raise the sector until the edge of the pointer just meets with its stop, in which position again determine the height, h, of the center of gravity of the weight above the fixed surface.

(4) The work done is $W(h - H)$ gram-centimeters. The pointer reading should be $KW(h - H)$, where the constant K is as given in the section on Apparatus, Pendulum Scale (page 1404).

(5) One or more weights may be clamped on the edge of the sector in different positions, the work done in raising each being calculated and added together.

(6) If the deviations of the indicated readings are greater than one-half division, the instrument should be returned to the manufacturer for repair and adjustment.

Tearing Distance.—To check the 43.0-mm. tearing distance, it is helpful to apply a small amount of graphite to the cutting knife (from an ordinary pencil), so that when the cut is made some of the graphite transfers to the paper; this serves to contrast the cut from the uncut portion of the paper and facilitates the measurement. As a very minimum, this measurement should be made with a good quality rule, preferably a steel rule graduated in 0.2 mm. or better, and under magnification. An alternative procedure is to use a "go, no-go" gauge, which may be available from the manufacturer of the instrument.

Procedure.—Level and adjust the testing apparatus, if necessary, before each set of tests.

Make all tests under standard atmospheric conditions in accordance with Method D 685 (vol. 2, part B, p. 1795).

Raise the pendulum sector to its initial position and set the pointer against its stop. Center the specimen in the clamps with the bottom edge carefully set against the stops. Securely clamp the specimen, using approximately the same pressure on both clamps, and make the initial slit. Depress the pendulum stop as far as it will go, thus releasing the pendulum. Hold down the stop until after the tear is completed and catch the pendulum on the return swing without disturbing the position of the pointer.

Make only one test per specimen, each specimen consisting of the specified number of plies. For each specimen keep the wire sides of all plies facing the same way. Make tests alternately with the wire sides of all plies toward the pendulum and with the wire sides of all plies away from the pendulum. Make certain that the specimen leans toward and not away from the pendulum by gently creasing the specimen at the clamp if necessary, but in doing so avoid affecting the relative humidity of the test area.

Record the number of plies and the scale reading to the nearest half division.

If the line of tear fails to pass through the top edge of the specimen but deviates to one side, note and report this fact. Do not use the reading obtained. If more than one third of the tests exhibit this behavior, this method should not be used for the material concerned.

Calculation.—Make the calculations for each principal direction as follows:

(a) Compute the average of the ten scale readings. Determine in accordance with the Recommended Practice for Dealing with Outlying Observations or by other suitable statistical test, whether a value that appears to be excessively high or low should be included in the average.

(b) Compute the average force in grams required to tear a single ply as follows:

$$\text{Average force} = \frac{16 \times A}{B}$$

$$\text{Average force (for tester with augmenting weight)} = \frac{32 \times A}{B}$$

where:

A = average scale reading, and
B = number of plies.

(c) Using similar relationships, also compute the maximum and minimum tear values from the maximum and minimum scale readings.

(d) When standard reference material is used, correct the values given in Paragraph (b) in accordance with the instructions accompanying the reference material. Standard reference material (NBS Standard Sample No. 704), as an aid in standardizing the method, is obtainable from the National Bureau of Standards, Washington 25, D. C.

Report.—The report shall include the following:

(1) Number and value of test values rejected and reasons for rejection,

(2) For each principal direction, the average, maximum, and minimum of accepted test values of the force required to tear a single ply. Report to the nearest 0.1 g. for values up to 100 g. and to the nearest 1 g. for values above 100 g.,

(3) Number of plies torn at one time,

(4) Whether augmenting weight has been used, and

(5) Make and model number of instrument used.

Report results with the tear parallel with the machine direction as resistance to internal tearing in the machine direction, and those with the tear perpendicular to the machine direction, as resistance to internal tearing in the cross direction.

Precision.—On the basis of studies made in accordance with the Recommended Practice for Interlaboratory Evaluation of Test Methods Used with Paper and Paper Products,[49, 50] the standard deviation of a test result, representing the average of ten readings, has been found to be:

(1) 1.5 percent of the test for the same material tested within the same laboratory.

(2) 2.5 percent for different materials tested within the same laboratory.

(3) 4.5 percent between laboratories.

The last figure may be reduced to 3.0 percent by using a reference material for standardizing the instruments.

In each of the above situations, two test results, each representing an average of ten readings, may be considered alike with a probability of 95 percent when the two results agree within 2.77 times the appropriate standard deviation.

REFERENCES

A. Elmendorf, "Strength Test for Paper," Paper, **26**, April 21, 1920, p. 302.

F. T. Carson, and L. W. Snyder, "Increasing the Capacity of the Elmendorf Tearing Tester," Paper Trade Journal, **86**, No. 13, March 29, 1928, p. 57.

J. d'A. Clark, "Calibration of the Elmendorf Tearing Tester," Technical Association Papers, Tech. Assn. Pulp and Paper Industry, Series XV, **1**, 1932, p. 262; Paper Trade Journal, **94**, No. 1, Jan. 7, 1932, p. 33.

J. d'A. Clark, Proceedings Technical Section, Canadian Pulp and Paper Assn., **29**, Jan., 1943, p. 61; Pulp and Paper Magazine of Canada, **44**, No. 2, Feb., 1943, p. 91.

"Tearing Strength of Paper, Part I," Instrumentation Studies XLVI, Inst. of Paper Chem., Paper Trade Journal, **118**, No. 5, Feb. 3, 1944, p. 13.

FOLDING ENDURANCE OF PAPER

This method provides for use of two different forms of apparatus: the Schopper type and the M.I.T. (Massachusetts Institute of Technology) type. The Schopper tester specified is for papers having a thickness of not more than 0.01 in. The M.I.T. tester

[50] T. W. Lashof, "APPA-TAPPI Reference Material Program. II. Effectiveness of a Reference Material in Reducing the Between-Laboratory Variability of TAPPI Standard T 414 m-49 for Internal Tearing Resistance of Paper," Tappi, **46**, No. 3, March, 1963, pp. 145–150.

can be adjusted for papers of any thickness. There is no constant relation between the test values obtained with the two types of testers. This method is standardized as TAPPI T 423 m-50.

SCHOPPER FOLDING ENDURANCE

Apparatus.—The testing instrument shall consist of:

(1) Two horizontally opposed clamps, approximately 10 cm. apart, provided with spring tension that varies during the folding cycle as a slotted folding blade, sliding back and forth between creasing rollers, folds the paper. The clamps while in motion are freely suspended between the tension springs, except that they are supported from below by rollers. The folding blade is 0.50 mm. (0.02 in.) thick, and the edges of the vertical folding slot are cylindrical and extend somewhat above and below the normal position of the test specimen. The four creasing rollers, each approximately 6 mm. in diameter and 18 mm. long, are arranged symmetrically about the midposition of the folding slot, and are preferably provided with jewel bearings.

(2) A means of imparting harmonic motion of constant period to the reciprocating blade. A power-driven apparatus is preferable.

(3) A device to register the number of double folds, which stops automatically when the specimen breaks.

Adjustment and Calibration.—Test the clamps by fastening a specimen in place in the manner described under "Procedure" and alternately applying and releasing the tension a number of times. Then, with tension released, note whether the specimen remains smooth and straight as originally inserted. Buckling or waviness indicates a faulty clamp, allowing the specimen to slip.

Inspect all rollers for worn surfaces and for bearing friction, and make necessary corrections. Adjust the supporting rollers so that they do not bind against the clamps in any position. With leaf gauges inspect the four creasing rollers for parallelism and clearances. Also make sure that the two edges of the folding slot are parallel with each other and with the creasing rollers. The distance between the folding blade and the two creasing rollers on each side of it should be 0.38 mm. (0.015 in.), and the width between rollers of the space occupied by the unbent specimen should be approximately 0.5 mm. As a final test of alignment, fold a specimen somewhat short of failure and inspect it for uniformity of wear along the crease. If the specimen seems weaker at one end of the crease than at the other, faulty alignment of the rollers or the folding slot is indicated (if the clamps are free of suspicion) which may be suspected of leading to low folding results.

Adjust the tension springs attached to the clamps against dead-weight load so that the tension on the specimen during a test is 790 g. when the clamps are farthest apart (when the specimen is straight and free) and approximately 1 kg. when they are nearest together. The adjustments are preferably made *in situ* with the aid of a suitable weighing device, such as a balanced bell-crank lever with knife-edge fulcrum at the center of gravity, capable of balancing the tension of a horizontal spring against the weight of a known mass. Fasten a strip of strong paper or celluloid, about 0.005 in. thick, in the clamps and apply the tension. Set a pair of bow dividers (by spanning the distance between two suitably placed fiducial marks, such as small punch marks) to show the displacement of each clamp. With a load of 790 g. acting on one clamp and spring, adjust the spring until this displacement is reproduced. Repeat for the other spring. To verify the tension at maximum displacement, set a pair of dividers to show the displacement of each clamp when the folding blade has pushed the crease in the specimen to the end of its stroke each side of the midposition (four measurements). With the aid of the weighing device, load each clamp until this displacement is reproduced in each case. The load required in each case should be approximately 1 kg.

The roller friction can also be measured by means of the bell-crank lever weighing device. First, set a pair of bow dividers to show the displacement of each clamp when loaded directly with 1 kg. Then, shift the weighing device 90° so as to load a clamp through a ribbon passed around one of the creasing rollers. Add weights in excess of 1 kg. until the direct 1-kg. displacement is reproduced. This excess weight is a measure of the roller friction in terms of the increased tension it will produce. Repeat for the other 3 rollers. The excess weight required shall in no case exceed 100 g.

Folding testers in steady use shall be adjusted and calibrated at intervals of not more than 1 month.

Test Specimen.—Specimens to be tested shall be cut accurately in each principal direction of the paper with a width of 15 mm. (0.59 in.) and 10 cm. (4 in.) in length. They shall initially be free from folds, wrinkles or blemishes not inherent in the paper and the area where the flexing takes place shall not contain any portion of a watermark. The edges of the specimens must be clean-cut and parallel to the opposite edge. The specimens shall be so selected from the sample secured by the standard sampling method as to be representative of the sample. At least 10 specimens cut from each principal direction of the paper shall be tested.

Procedure.—Folding endurance tests shall be made on paper conditioned according to the standard method for conditioning and in the atmospheric conditions therein specified (vol. 2, part B, p. 1795).

With the vertical slot of the reciprocating blade in its central position, place the specimen in the slot and fasten the ends firmly and squarely in the clamps with the surface of the specimen lying wholly within one plane. Handle the specimen by the ends and do not touch it with the hands in the region which is to be folded. Then apply the specified tension and fold the specimen at a uniform rate of approximately 120 double folds per minute until it is severed at the crease. Record the number of double folds required to sever the specimen.

Report.—Results shall be reported as Schopper Folding Endurance (double folds) and shall include the number of tests, and the average, the maximum, and the minimum results for each of the principal directions of the paper. Tests run on strips having their length cut in the machine direction shall be designated as those of "machine direction." Tests run on strips cut at right angles to the machine direction shall be designated as those of "cross direction." In reporting average results all digits after the first two shall be rounded to zero.

M.I.T. FOLDING ENDURANCE

Apparatus.—The testing instrument shall consist of:

(1) A loading clamp constrained to move without rotation in a direction perpendicular to the axis of rotation of the folding head specified below and having its clamping surfaces in the plane of this axis. The load is applied through a spring attached to the loading clamp which is easily adjustable to provide any desired tension on the specimen from 0 to 1.5 kg. The deflection of the spring when loaded shall not be less than 17 mm. (0.67 in.) per kg.

(2) An oscillating folding head supporting two smooth, cylindrical folding surfaces parallel to, and symmetrically placed with respect to, the axis of rotation. The position of the axis of rotation should be approximately in the common tangent plane to the

two folding surfaces in the conventional design and midway between them. The folding head is provided with a clamping device back of the axis of rotation and so designed that no clamping pressure is exerted nearer than 0.375 in. to the bending axis. The rotary oscillating movement of the folding clamp shall be such as to fold the paper through an angle of 135 ± 5° to both right and left of the position of zero fold.

Each of the two folding surfaces has a radius of curvature of 0.38 ± 0.015 mm. (0.015 ± 0.001 in.) and a length of not less than 19 mm. (0.75 in.). The distance separating the folding surfaces shall be greater than the uncompressed thickness of the paper being tested but shall not exceed it by more than 0.25 mm. (0.01 in.).

(3) A power-driven device for imparting a rotary oscillating motion of constant period to the folding clamp.

(4) A device for registering the number of double folds required to sever the specimen.

Adjustment and Calibration.—All working parts shall be in good condition, well oiled, and in proper adjustment. Particular care shall be given to make certain that the folding edges are free from rust or dirt.

The plunger friction shall be measured by determining the additional load required to move the plunger perceptibly when displaced under a load of 1.0 kg. or the load tension used in testing. The additional load required shall not be greater than 25 g.

The change in tension due to eccentricity of rotation of folding edges shall be measured as follows: Place a test strip of strong paper, cut in the machine direction, of the proper thickness in the tester in the same manner in which a folding test would be made, and apply a tension of 1 kg. or that used in the testing. Rotate the folding head slowly throughout the entire folding cycle and measure the maximum change in displacement of the plunger to an accuracy of 0.1 mm. (0.004 in.). The amount of load required to produce the same displacement shall not be greater than 35 g. The curvature of the folding edges can conveniently be measured by means of suitable casts magnified in profile and compared to standard circles. Folding testers in steady use shall be adjusted and calibrated at intervals of not more than 1 month.

Test Specimen.—All of the provisions given under Schopper Folding Endurance shall apply, except that test specimens of definite length are not required. They are cut of such length as to ensure a firm grip in the clamps without buckling.

Procedure.—Tests shall be made on paper conditioned according to T 402 m (vol. 2, part B, p. 1795) and in the atmospheric conditions therein specified.

Place the oscillating folding head in the position of zero fold. Place on top of the plunger a weight equivalent to the tension desired on the specimen and clamp the plunger in position when depressed under this load. Then clamp the specimen firmly and squarely in the jaws with the surface of the specimen lying wholly within one plane and not touching the jaw mounting-plate. Handle the specimen by the ends and do not touch it with the hands in the region which is to be folded. Then apply the specified tension to the test strip by releasing the plunger. If the reading of the load indicator has changed, reset it by means of the adjusting screw to agree with the reading obtained when the weight was applied. Whenever possible a tension of 1 kg. shall be used, but if this does not afford practical test results, a greater or a lesser tension may be used. Fold the strip at a uniform rate of 175 (±25) double folds per minute until it is severed at the crease. Record the number of double folds required to sever the specimen.

Report.—Results shall be reported as M.I.T. Folding Endurance (double folds) and shall include the number of tests, and the average, the maximum, and the minimum results for each of the principal directions of the paper. Tests run on strips having their length in the machine direction shall be designated as those of "machine direction." Tests run on strips cut at right angles to the machine direction shall be designated as those of "cross direction." In reporting average results all digits after the first two shall be rounded to zero.

REFERENCES

(a) Schopper folding endurance:

Veitch, F. P., Sammet, C. F., and Reed, E. O., "Folding Endurance of Paper," Paper, **20**, No. 12, 13–19, May 30, 1917.

Herzberg, W., "Resistance to Folding," Chem. Abstracts, **14**, 2262, July 20, 1920.

Carson, F. T., and Snyder, L. W., "Calibration and Adjustment of Schopper Folding Tester," Bureau of Standards Technologic Paper No. 357, 1929.

Anon., "The Schopper Bending Endurance Tester, Instrumentation Report No. 23," Paper Trade J., **109**, No. 5, 35, Aug. 3, 1939.

(b) M.I.T. folding endurance:

Snyder, L. W., and Carson, F. T., "A Study of the M. I. T. Paper Folding Tester," Paper Trade J., **96, No. 22,** 40–44, June 1, 1933.

CONTRAST GLOSS OF PAPER AT 57.5°

Gloss is the geometrically selective reflectance of a surface responsible for its shiny or lustrous appearance. (Surface reflectance is commonly at a maximum in or near the geometric directions in which a mirror would reflect light.) The following contrast-gloss method, based on the Ingersoll Glarimeter, is intended primarily for white and nearly white papers, such as newsprint, writing, and ledger, having a low gloss. It is recommended for measurements of the tendency of these papers to glare when observed under improperly distributed light. It is not recommended for measurements of the shininess of supercalendered book, waxed, glassine, or other shiny papers measuring more than 75 percent gloss by this method; nor is it recommended for colored papers. This method is standardized as TAPPI T 424 m-52.

Apparatus.—The testing instrument shall consist of:

(1) A photometer so fixed in relation to the test specimen at an angle of 57.5° that the amount of polarized light reflected from the test specimen relative to the total amount reflected from the test specimen at an angle of 57.5° may be measured.

(2) A source of diffused illumination consisting of a frosted B lamp, G 18½ bulb, 110 volts, 25 watts, so fixed in relation to the test specimen that the light subtends an angle of 11.25° and falls on the test specimen at an angle of 57.5°.

(3) An opal glass diffusing screen between the source of light and the specimen aperture.

(4) A metal box having the photometer housed in one end, the source of illumination housed in the other end, and an aperture in one side over which the specimen is clamped in a fixed position. The box shall be so made as to exclude all outside light and shall have all of its interior surfaces blackened.

Test Specimen.—The specimens for test shall consist of not less than 5 pieces of paper cut from different portions of the test sample, secured by the official sampling method so as to be representative of it. These shall be of sufficient size to extend beyond all sides of the aperture of the metal box. The test specimens shall be clean, free from wrinkles and folds, shall not be exposed for any considerable length of time to extreme atmospheric conditions, and the areas actually tested shall not have been touched with the fingers.

Procedure.—The test specimen shall be firmly clamped in position so that its sides extend beyond all sides of the aperture of the metal box. If the paper is translucent, a sufficient number of test specimens shall be stacked one upon another so that no incident light can penetrate entirely through them. Two tests shall be made on each side of not less than 5 specimens, one test in the machine direction of the paper and one in the cross direction. The test results shall be recorded in degrees to the nearest $\frac{1}{5}°$. The average degrees of gloss shall be computed and converted to percent gloss by the formula:

$$\text{Percent gloss} = \cos 2 (60° - \text{degrees gloss}) \times 100$$

Duplicate determinations shall agree within 0.5 percent gloss.

Report.—The results shall be reported in percentage gloss to the nearest 0.1 percent. The average, maximum, and minimum gloss shall be reported. Where required, in order to show the difference in finish between the two sides of the paper, the gloss of each side shall be reported separately.

REFERENCES

Ingersoll, R. L., "The Glarimeter, An Instrument for Measuring the Gloss of Paper," J. Opt. Soc. Am., May, 1921.

Ingersoll, R. L., "An Improved Form of Glarimeter," Paper, **27**, No. 23, 18, Feb. 9, 1921.

Ingersoll, R. L., "A Means to Measure the Glaze of Paper," Electrical World, **63**, 645, March 21, 1914; Pulp Paper Mag. Canada, **12**, 233, April 15, 1924.

Ingersoll, R. L., "Determination of Glare," Electrical World, **64**, 35.

Ingersoll, R. L., "An Improved Form of Pickering Polarimeter for Gloss Measurements (by the Polarization Method)." A paper presented before the Fifth Meeting (Dec. 27–29, 1920) of the Optical Society of America (at the University of Chicago).

"The Ingersoll Glarimeter," Bull. 100, Chicago, Ill., Central Scientific Co.

Lofton, R. E., "The Glarimeter and the Measurement of the Finish of Paper," Paper Trade J., **80**, No. 7, 47–49, Feb. 12, 1925.

For a description of the Pickering Polarimeter, see Proc. Am. Acad. Arts and Sciences, **9**, 1, 1873; also **21**, 294, 1885.

OPACITY OF PAPER

The essential principle of this contrast-ratio method for determining the opacity of paper is as follows: the reflectance of paper when combined with a white backing is higher than that of paper when combined with a black backing because, in the former case, light transmitted through the imperfectly opaque sheet is largely reflected by the white backing, and a portion of the light thus reflected is transmitted through the paper a second time. Contrast ratio, $C_{0.89}$, is defined as 100 times the ratio of the diffuse reflectance, R_B, of a specimen backed with black of not more than 0.005 reflectance, to the diffuse reflectance, R_W, of the same specimen backed with a white body having an absolute reflectance of 0.89; $C_{0.89} = 100 (R_B/R_W)$. These reflectances are absolute; the absolute diffuse reflectance for magnesium oxide being very nearly 0.98. Accordingly, the contrast ratio is 100 percent for perfectly opaque paper, and is only a few percent for a perfectly transparent sheet. This method is standardized as TAPPI T 425 m-60.

Apparatus. **Opacity Meter,** equipped with an accurately linear or a corrected photometric system. The reflectances involved in the determination of contrast ratio should be either for normal illumination and diffuse viewing, or the equivalent converse, *i.e.*, diffuse illumination and normal viewing.

NOTE.—The direction of illumination or, alternatively, the direction of viewing, should not be more than 20° from the normal.

The instrument may be designed directly to measure the ratio of reflectances of paper backed by black and white, or alternatively, the instrument may be adjusted to indicate a cardinal value such as 100.0 with the white backing in place and then the ratio of reflectances obtained by replacing the white body with the black body. The photometric system must be sufficiently stable that the instrument will not fluctuate by more than approximately 0.2 percent of its full-scale deflection while the contrast ratio is being measured.

The more important requirements of the apparatus are as follows:

(a) *Standard Black Backing*, consisting of a cavity lined with black velvet or other material which will cause the reflectance of the cavity to be less than 0.005.

(b) *Standard White Backing*, having an absolute reflectance equal to 0.89 when illuminated under the conditions of actual testing with a sheet of paper in place.[51] This backing consists either of a permanent diffusing surface of this apparent reflectance in contact with the sample, or of an equivalent cavity such as that provided by a diffusing surface separated from the sample by a cover glass.

(c) *Incandescent Light Source*, with a color temperature of between 2400 and 2800°K. In a single-photocell instrument, this implies that the voltage must not change by more than approximately 0.1 percent.

(d) *Photoelectric Cell*, corrected with an optical filter to have a relative spectral sensitivity closely approximating that of the human eye.

(e) *Specimen Holder*, so constructed that the specimen may be viewed or illuminated through a round window not less than 14.3 mm. in diameter and to hold the specimen flat to within 0.15 mm.

Calibration.—Calibrate the instrument at frequent intervals as follows:

1. Adjust the *area of specimen to be assessed* so that it is centrally situated within its window and has a uniformly illuminated or viewed diameter 2 to 3 mm. less than the window.

NOTE.—The assessed area needs to be smaller than the window as specified, otherwise the calibration of the instrument with the opal-glass opacity standards[52] may be inaccurate because of edge error.

2. Establish that the *photometric scale is linear* or prepare a calibration chart to correct for nonlinearity, for example as described in Appendix I.

3. Adjust the *effective reflectance of the white backing* so that the instrument gives correct readings of opacity with one or more opal-glass standards (which must be perfectly clean when used), or with some temporary opacity standards prepared from uncoated paper. When using the latter, employ the reflectance and opacity chart[53] shown in Fig. 55-11, which is based on the Kubelka and Munk theory[51,54,55] and follow the procedure described in Appendix I. *SX* on the original chart has been changed to *sW* to conform with nomenclature now preferred in the paper industry.[56]

The appendix gives detailed instructions for calibrating one type of opacimeter for these three steps.[57,58]

[51] Report No. 22, Part II, to the American Paper Association; Instrumentation Studies XLVIII, Part II, Calibration of the Bausch and Lomb Opacimeter. Paper Trade J., **119**, No. 17, 27–30, Oct. 26, 1944.

[52] Judd, D. B., "Opacity Standards," J. Research Natl. Bur. Standards, **13**, 381, 1934; Research Paper 709.

[53] Judd, D. B., "Optical Specification of Light-Scattering Materials," Paper Trade J., **106**, No. 1, 39–46; T. S. 5–12, Jan. 6, 1938.

[54] Kubelka, P., and Munk, F., "Ein Beitrag zur Optik der Farbanstriche," Z. tech. Physik, **12**, 593–601, 1931.

[55] Steele, F. A., "The Optical Characteristics of Paper. I. The Mathematical Relationships Between Basis Weight, Reflectance, Contrast Ratio, and Other Optical Properties," Paper Trade J., **100**, No. 12, 37–42, March 21, 1935; Tech. Assoc. Papers, **18**, 299–304, June, 1934.

[56] Van den Akker, J. A., Scattering and Absorption of Light in Paper and Other Diffusing Media, Tappi, **32**, No. 11, 498–501, Nov., 1949.

[57] Davis, M. N., "A Simple and Reliable Photoelectric Opacity Tester," Tech. Assoc. Papers, **16**, 277, 1933.

[58] "The Bausch and Lomb Opacimeter," Service Bulletin No. II (D-236, 400 VI, 36). Rochester, N. Y., The Bausch and Lomb Optical Co.

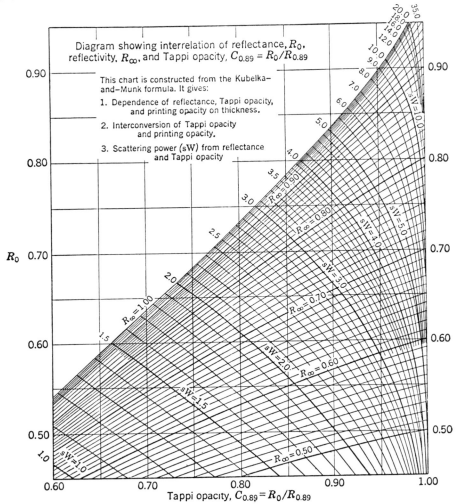

Diagram showing interrelation of reflectance, R_0, reflectivity, R_∞, and Tappi opacity, $C_{0.89} = R_0/R_{0.89}$

This chart is constructed from the Kubelka-and-Munk formula. It gives:

1. Dependence of reflectance, Tappi opacity, and printing opacity on thickness.

2. Interconversion of Tappi opacity and printing opacity.

3. Scattering power (sW) from reflectance and Tappi opacity

Tappi opacity, $C_{0.89} = R_0/R_{0.89}$

FIG. 55-11.   Opacity Chart. (From D. B. Judd, Color in Business, Service, and Industry; courtesy John Wiley and Sons, Inc.)

Test Specimen.—Select at least 5 representative specimens for each test (see TAPPI Standard T 400 m, vol. 2, part B, p. 1794) free from watermarks or blemishes and of sufficient size to fit the specimen holder, and completely cover the standard backings. Do not touch the test areas with the fingers, and keep these areas perfectly clean and free from folds and wrinkles.

Procedure.—Condition the specimens according to TAPPI Standard T 402 m (vol. 2, part B, p. 1795). Measure the contrast ratio as follows: Set the meter at zero, then, with the specimen backed by the standard white backing, set the instrument to read 100.0. Replace the white backing with the black body, and read the meter to obtain the contrast ratio. Record the individual results to 3 significant figures. Average the values obtained for the 5 or more specimens.

NOTE 1.—The mechanical zero of the instrument should be checked and adjusted if necessary. Then with the apparatus turned on and the specimen aperture covered with the black body, the scale reading should not exceed 0.5 divisions.

NOTE 2.—If it is impossible to set the instrument at 100.0 for the normal range of white papers, when backed by the white body, the integrating cavity of the instrument should be resmoked or the photocell and/or lamp bulb should be replaced. If, because of low reflectance of the paper, the adjustment to 100.0 with the specimen backed with the white body is impossible, set the instrument at 90.0, 80.0, or other cardinal value; the contrast ratio is then obtained from the readings with the black and the white bodies respectively over the specimen.

NOTE 3.—Usually neither the side nor direction of the grain of the paper makes any significant difference. If either effect is appreciable, place the specimen with the selected side toward the instrument and in the selected orientation, and state the conditions used in the report.

Compute the contrast ratio range, R (largest minus smallest value), and if five specimens were tested for a sample, multiply by 0.51 to obtain the 95 percent confidence limits of the mean.[59] If more than 5 specimens are tested, replace the factor 0.51 with an appropriate factor from the following table:

Number of Specimens	Factor
6	0.40
7	0.33
8	0.29
9	0.26
10	0.23

Report.—Report the mean value of contrast ratio for each test sample to the nearest 0.1 percent together with the 95 percent confidence limits, $C_{0.89} \pm 0.51R$ (or other appropriate factor for R).

APPENDIX

Calibration of the Bausch and Lomb Opacimeter. **Optical Adjustment.**—Arrange the instrument to permit the beam of light to fall on the surface of a wall about 10 ft. away from the instrument, and adjust the variable aperture to its full opening. Two images of the filament situated approximately in the center of the projected spot of light and reversed with respect to each other should be seen. One of the images is formed by rays which have been reflected by the mirror behind the source. The two lenses and the lamp should be adjusted to obtain the following results: (1) the two images of the filament projected on the wall should be in focus; (2) when a sheet of paper is laid over the specimen aperture to inspect the distribution of light in the aperture, the circular light spot should be (a) centered in the aperture, (b) nearly fill the aperture, but should not be in contact with the edge of the aperture—there should be a clearance of about 1 mm. between the edge and the boundary of the light spot, and (c) the boundary of the light spot should be as sharp and free of color as possible. After the tube and lenses have been adjusted, usually it is necessary to adjust the lamp only for subsequent checks of the optical system. The alignment and state of focus of the lamp should be checked before each standardization of the instrument. The lenses should be cleaned to minimize the light scattered into the integrating cube. Cleanliness of the optical system may be tested by comparing the mechanical zero of the meter with the

[59] Dixon, W. J., and Massey, F. J., Jr., Introduction to Statistical Analysis, Table VIII, p. 316, McGraw-Hill, New York, 1951.

reading when the instrument is in operation with a black body placed over the specimen aperture. There should be very little difference.

Photometric Linearity.—The current output of the photoelectric cell used for the opacimeter varies with the radiation on it and with the resistance of the external circuit employed to measure the photocurrent. When the resistance of the external circuit is low or zero, the total current generated within the cell is essentially a linear function of the illumination. The departure from linearity of response increases as the external resistance of the current-measuring circuit increases. Since the circuit employed for measuring a photocurrent has an external resistance somewhat greater than 200 ohms, a small departure from linearity may be expected so it is desirable to check it.

Figure 55-12 shows a diagram of the circuits employed for this purpose. The opacimeter circuit is shown at the right and its integrating cube is shown schematically by

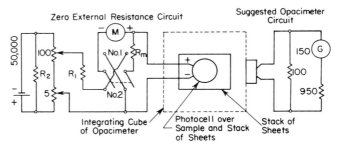

FIG. 55-12.   Circuit for Checking Linearity of Opacimeter.

the dotted lines forming the square. The zero-external-resistance circuit, which is used as a standard in this method, is shown at the left, with a new photocell mounted over a diffusing screen and the specimen aperture in the integrating tube.

The diffusing screen consists of one or more thicknesses of white paper, the number of thicknesses being selected with regard to their total transmission so that an approximately full-scale deflection is obtained on the meter M (galvanometer or very sensitive microammeter). It is essential that this meter be calibrated so that corrections may be made for any departure from linearity.

It will be seen that with this arrangement, the photocells in both circuits receive their energy from the same light source—namely, the lamp in the opacimeter. The light viewed by the photocell in the opacimeter depends, in part, upon the amount of light reflected by the paper over the specimen aperture, whereas the light viewed by the photocell in the zero-external-resistance circuit is that transmitted by the paper. For a given change in the incident light, the relative change in the amount of light reaching the two photocells is the same. To obtain values over the full range of the meter scale, the intensity of the incident light is changed in appropriate steps by interposing neutral wire screens (several wire screens having different transmission values) between the lamp and the lens system of the opacimeter. Neutral screens may be made by lightly sooting wire screens over burning camphor.

The zero-resistance circuit contains three resistances of undesignated value: R_M is a simple combination of wire-wound resistance which, *by actual test*, has a resistance very nearly the same as that of meter M. R_1 is any stable resistor whose value, obtained by trial, results in a condition of critical damping of M (preferably, the meter should overshoot slightly). R_2 depends on the sensitivity of M; it should be such that nearly full-scale deflection is obtained when one or more sheets of paper (serving as a diffuser) are over the specimen aperture, and the light beam is at full intensity. The cell indicated in the diagram is any single cell, 1.2 to 2 volts.

The following procedure is recommended: (1) With the D.P.D.T. switch open, set the mechanical zero of M to zero on the scale (or, if desired, read and record the mechanical zero). (2) Reduce the illumination of the photocells to zero by interposing a piece of black paper in the light beam between the lamp and the lens system. Then move the 5- and 100-ohm rheostats to obtain zero potential difference (on the diagram, toward each other, to the common point of connection), and put the switch in its no. 1 position. M should read zero. Put the switch in its no. 2 position; M should continue to read zero. The deflection of the opacimeter meter G should be zero; if it is not, make the mechanical adjustment of meter G to obtain zero deflection. (3) Remove the black paper screen and adjust the diaphragm to obtain exactly 100 divisions on G. Then move the switch to its no. 1 position and adjust the 5- and 100-ohm rheostats to obtain zero deflection of M. Then move the switch to its no. 2 position and read M. After *correcting* the reading of M by means of the calibration chart provided for this meter, the proper photocurrent is obtained. (4) Place the neutral screen of highest transmission in the light beam in such manner that it cannot shift or move in any way. Read and record the deflection of G. With the switch in the no. 1 position adjust the 5- and 100-ohm rheostats to obtain zero deflection of M. Put the switch in the no. 2 position, read M, correct the reading, and record the corrected reading. (5) Remove the screen and readjust the diaphragm to obtain 100 divisions on G. Place the next screen in the light beam and proceed as under step 4. (6) Continue with the remaining screens and, at adequately frequent intervals, check the zeros of both meters. The work with all screens should be repeated to yield a final correction curve having good accuracy.

Plot the difference between the corrected readings of M and that of G as the correction chart for the opacimeter.

NOTE.—Whenever the level of illumination is changed as when a screen is changed or a screen is removed, the 5- and 100-ohm rheostats must be adjusted with the switch in the no. 1 position to obtain zero deflection of M. The current read with the switch in the no. 2 position will be accurate *only* after this adjustment has been made. If the instrument is quite nonlinear, improvement may result from installation of a new Weston Photronic 594RR or 594YR cell with a Viscor filter.

Adjustment of White Backing.—The adjustment of the white backing to conform to the requirement that it have an absolute reflectance of 0.89 (under the conditions of actual test with a test specimen or standard in place), may be carried out either (A) by means of opal-glass standards, or (B) by means of paper and the Kubelka-Munk theory.

Adjustment by Means of Opal-Glass Standards.—I. Clean the opal glass standard by brushing it with a mild soap solution, rinsing it with water, and drying it with a clean towel.

II. Read the opacity of the calibrated area (indicated by four engraved lines pointed toward center of the area) of the opal-glass standard. If this opacity reading conforms to the value of opacity certified for the standard within 0.4 percent, the white backing may be regarded as correctly adjusted.

III. If the reading departs from the certified value of opacity by more than 0.4 percent, adjust the distance between the magnesium carbonate surface and the cover glass. Too high an opacity reading means that the distance must be decreased; too low a reading means that it must be increased.

IV. Check the adjustment by means of opal-glass standards of different opacities, if available. It is usually possible to adjust the white backing so that the opacimeter will read within 0.4 percent of the correct opacities of specimens of any opacity from 60 to 95 percent, but sometimes discrepancies as high as 1 percent may have to be tolerated for opacities near 50 percent.

Adjustment by Means of Kubelka-Munk Theory.—A basic procedure for adjusting the white body rests upon an application of the Kubelka-Munk theory[51,54,55] which is most conveniently employed in this connection in the form of the reflectance-opacity charts prepared by the Photometry and Colorimetry Section of the National Bureau of Standards; see Fig. 55-11. In addition to this chart, the following materials are required:

Uncoated paper samples, covering the working range of opacity and having good formation, preferably with no filler content and of a neutral white color and a dull but smooth finish;

A magnesium carbonate block coated with magnesium oxide according to TAPPI Standard T 633 m (p. 1460), using magnesium ribbon for smoking with magnesium oxide;

NOTE.—The reflectance of magnesium oxide and magnesium carbonate is fugitive and, hence, the magnesium oxide layers should be used soon after preparation and then be removed from the blocks of magnesia when the calibration is completed, and the blocks stored for further use.

A working standard of reflectances, to be evaluated in absolute units, and to be used for the various settings of the instrument after the standardization with the magnesium oxide; and

Adhesive cellophane tape, for holding a single sheet of paper over the sample opening.

NOTE.—A working standard (c) is suggested for checking the reflectance scale, in view of the fragile nature of the magnesium oxide.

Procedure.—Carefully place the magnesium oxide surface over the specimen opening of the instrument, taking care not to press it against the opening since the oxide layer is easily compressed and appreciable error might result if the reflecting portion of the layer is pushed a little way in. Adjust the instrument to obtain a reading of 98.0 on a 100 division meter. Evaluate a working standard at this time, and record its absolute reflectance (for example, 0.734).

Reflectance readings obtained with paper should now be close approximations to their proper absolute values if the calibration chart (prepared with the zero-resistance circuit) is used.

With the instrument adjusted to read correctly on the absolute scale, place a specimen of one of the several samples to be used in the calibration over the specimen opening. Put a hinge of adhesive cellophane tape to the top edge of the specimen, so that the sheet may be lifted for checking the reflectance scale and subsequently let down to occupy exactly its previous position. *It is most important that the sheet in contact with the specimen opening be fixed into position for the measurement of the reflectances involved in the calibration.*

Back the specimen with the black body, and read and record the reflectance R_0. Then back the specimen with the white body, and read reflectance R_W. R_W is the reflectance influenced by the effective reflectance of the white backing body. Finally, back the specimen with an opaque pad of exactly similar paper, and read and record the reflectance R_∞.

For example, suppose that the following reflectances are obtained: $R_0 = 0.600$; $R_W = 0.831$; $R_\infty = 0.800$. Considering the reflectance-opacity chart (Fig. 55-11), it will be seen that the $R_0 = 0.600$ ordinate intersects the $R_\infty = 0.800$ line, at a contrast ratio $C_{0.89} = 0.7075$. Since $C_{0.89} = R_0/R_W$, the calculated value of R_W is 0.848. Alternatively, the value of R_W may be computed quite precisely without reference to the reflectance-opacity chart, by the following formula.[60] For the above sample, the computation is:

$$Rw = (0.600 - 0.89[(1/0.800 + 0.800)(0.600) - 1])[1 - 0.89(0.600)] = 0.848.$$

Actually, a value somewhat lower than this was obtained—namely, 0.831. This means that the effective reflectance of the white body is less than the ideal value, 0.89. In this event remove the white body from the instrument, and adjust it to increase its reflectance. This body usually consists of a metal cylinder containing a solid cylinder of magnesium carbonate and capped with a cover glass.[58] On removing the threaded base of this container, it will be found possible, after loosening a small set screw in the wall of the container, to remove or rotate an inner threaded sleeve which holds the magnesium carbonate, and thus vary the separation between the cover glass and the reflecting surface of the magnesium carbonate. If a sufficiently high reflectance cannot be obtained even with the reflecting surface in contact with the cover glass, remove the magnesium carbonate block and take off a surface layer to expose a fresh surface with a higher reflectance. Take care that after removal, the surface remains flat and parallel to the cover glass.

After this preliminary adjustment, obtain the corrected values for the 3 reflectances R_0, R_W, and $R\infty$, for the several samples of paper, and determine the corresponding correct values of R_W from the reflectance-opacity chart, as described above. By comparison of these chart values with the directly determined values of R_W, refining adjustments of the white body may be made. After performing the final adjustments, the directly determined contrast ratios for white paper should agree with the chart values rather well, typical discrepancies being about 0.3 percent, with occasional differences of the order of 1 percent, the larger discrepancies usually occurring at the lower opacities. Until the contrary is definitely demonstrated, it is believed it is not possible visually to distinguish between contrast ratios differing by less than about 1.5 percent[61] and hence, that the above-described method will serve to satisfactorily maintain an instrument in a state of calibration better than required for visual purposes and sufficiently accurate for most technical purposes.

REFERENCES

Sammet, C. F., "A Measure of the Translucency of Paper," U. S. Bur. Chem. Circular 96 1912.
"Specification of the Transparency of Paper and Tracing Cloth," Natl. Bur. Standards Circular 63, Ed. 1, 1917.
Clark, J. d'A., "The Measurement of the Contrast Ratio of Opaque and Translucent Papers," Paper Trade J., **89**, TS210, Nov. 14, 1929.
Davis, M. N., "Methods and Instruments for Opacity Measurements," Tech. Assoc. Papers, **15**, 347, 1932.
Judd, D. B., "Sources of Error in Measuring the Opacity of Paper by the Contrast Ratio Method," J. Research Natl. Bur. Standards, **12**, 345, 1934; Research Paper 660.
"Standards for Checking Opacity Meters," Natl. Bur. Standards Letter Circular 418, 1934.

BULKING THICKNESS OF PAPER AND PAPERBOARD

The bulking thickness of paper or paperboard is the average single-sheet thickness in thousandths of an inch when a pile of several sheets is placed under a steady pressure

[60] Kubelka, P., New Contributions to the Optics of Intensely Light-Scattering Materials, J. Opt. Soc. Amer., **38**, No. 5, 448–457, May, 1948 and No. 12, 1067, Dec., 1948.
[61] Report No. 22, Part I, to the American Paper and Pulp Association; Instrumentation Studies XXX, Part I, Paper Trade J., **109**, No. 4, 29–34, July 27, 1949.

of 7 to 9 p.s.i. between two circular and parallel plane surfaces, the smaller of which has an area of approximately 0.25 sq. in. (160 sq. mm.).

The method for determining the bulking thickness shall be used for finding the average thickness of paper when placed in a pile, as for use in books. This method is standardized as TAPPI T 426 m-46.

Apparatus.—The micrometer used shall be in accordance with the following requirements:

It shall have two plane faces, the smaller of which is circular and 0.25 to 0.33 sq. in. (160 to 215 sq. mm.) in area, corresponding to a diameter of 0.56 to 0.65 inch (14.3 to 16.5 mm.). The faces shall be parallel to within 0.0002 inch (0.005 mm.) and constrained to move apart in an axis perpendicular to themselves.

When the specimen is clamped between the faces, it shall be under a steady pressure of 7.0 to 9.0 p.s.i. (0.40 to 0.63 kg. per sq. cm.).

The distance between the graduations on the dial shall be such as to permit of estimating the thickness to 0.0001 in. or less.

The micrometer shall be such as to repeat its readings to within 0.0001 in. at zero setting or on a steel gauge block.

Measurements made on standard steel thickness gauges shall be within the following tolerances of permissible deviation of the reading from the actual thickness of the standard gauge.

Intervals		Tolerance	
mm.	*inch*	*mm.*	*inch*
0 to 25	0 to 0.01	0.0025	0.0001
Over 25 to 1.02	0.01 to 0.04	0.0051	0.0002
Over 1.02 to 3.05	0.04 to 0.12	0.0102	0.0004

Calibration. **Parallelism of the Faces.**—A hard steel ball about $\frac{1}{16}$ in. in diameter, fixed firmly in a thinner flat piece of metal to serve as a handle, shall be placed at different points on the anvil and the readings noted.

Accuracy of the Readings.—The instrument shall be set to zero and standard gauges shall be placed between the plane faces and the corresponding dial readings observed over the range to be used. For precision measurements, standard steel gauge blocks having an accuracy of 0.00001 in. shall be used. For bulking thickness measurements the commercial feeler gauges may be used, but the accuracy of these must be determined to the nearest 0.0001 in. by means of a screw micrometer of known accuracy.

Pressure between the Faces.—The force required to just prevent the movement of the plunger foot, from a reading corresponding to about the average paper thickness tested to a lower reading, shall be determined with a suitable balance, and the contact pressure determined with this force. For example, where the pressure foot projects through the top of the apparatus, a fine copper wire is attached to it and by means of a coarse balance or a calibrated spring, the force necessary to prevent the closing of the foot is measured.

Alternatively, a stirrup may be used, made of a flat metal plate having a hole larger than the diameter of the micrometer foot, covered at the bottom of the plate by a thin metal disc of about the average thickness of the paper to be measured. The stirrup is suspended from a suitable balance.

Test Specimen.—The test specimen shall consist of not less than 10 sheets and shall have a minimum dimension, if possible, of not less than 2 in. Any necessary noncompliance with this requirement shall be noted in the test report as a minor deviation. The sheets shall be taken from the test sample in such a way as to be thoroughly representative of it, and shall be free from creases. They shall have been conditioned according to TAPPI Standard T 402 m (Vol. 2, Part B, p. 1795).

Procedure.—The test shall be made in an atmosphere conditioned according to TAPPI Standard T 402 m.

A pack not less than 0.1 in. thick shall be tested in not less than 10 different places evenly distributed over the pack. Place the pack between the jaws of the micrometer and lower the pressure foot as gently as possible upon the surface of the paper with its edge at least ¼ in. (6 mm.) from the edge of the paper.

Report.—The bulking thickness shall be reported in decimals of an inch, being the average thickness of the pack divided by the number of sheets in it, and shall be expressed to the nearest 0.00005 in. (0.001 mm.).

Reproducibility of Results.—Duplicate determinations from different sets of samples from the same shipment and on different instruments are expected to agree within 3 percent.

Additional Information.—In general for ordinary papers, the average bulking thickness is approximately the same as the single-sheet thickness but usually from about 2 to 6 percent lower. Also depending on the type of paper, a variation in pressure of from 5 to 10 p.s.i. causes a corresponding decrease in the results by about 3 percent. Halving the area of the pressure foot while maintaining the unit pressure constant results in an increase of from 1 to 3 percent.

REFERENCES

Houston, P. L., and Miller, D. R., "A Study of Commercial Dial Micrometers for Measuring the Thickness of Paper," Natl. Bur. Standards Technologic Paper No. 226.

Carson, F. T., "Critical Study of Methods of Measuring the Bulk of Paper," Natl. Bur. Standards Research Paper No. 69.

"Standard Method for Determining the Thickness and Bulk of Paper," British Paper Makers' Association Committee on Bulk and Thickness (contains method and considerable new data which justify the restrictions in the foregoing method).

Strachan, James, "Piezo Micrometer and its Applications," Proc. Tech. Section, Paper Makers' Assoc. Gt. Britain Ireland, Vol. III, Part 1, Oct., 1922.

Strachan, James, "Notes on Paper Testing," Proc. Tech. Section, Paper Makers' Assoc. Gt. Britain and Ireland, Vol. I, Part 1, March, 1921.

INK ABSORPTION OF BLOTTING PAPER

This method is standardized as TAPPI T 431 m-45.

Reagent. **Standard Ink.**—The ink used for this test is in accordance with the following formula:

	grams
Tannic acid	11.7
Gallic acid crystals	3.8
Ferrous sulphate	15.0
Hydrochloric acid, dilute, U.S.P.	12.5
Carbolic acid (phenol)	1.0
Soluble blue (Schultz No. 539, C.I. 707)	3.5
Distilled water to make a volume of 1000 ml. at 20°C. (68°F.)	

All chemicals shall be of C.P. quality. Some blue dyes react with carbolic acid to cause a film having a metallic appearance and such dyes should not be used. The ink is made as follows:

Dissolve the tannic acid and gallic acid in about 400 ml. of water at about 50°C.

(122°F.). In a separate vessel dissolve the ferrous sulphate in about 200 ml. of water which contains the HCl. In a third vessel dissolve the dye in about 200 ml. of water. Mix the 3 solutions in a 1-liter volumetric flask, rinse the vessels with small portions of water and add the rinsings to the flask. Add the carbolic acid and dilute with water to 1 liter at 20°C. (68°F.).

Test Specimen.—Each test specimen shall consist of a single sheet of the paper, approximately 4 by 4 in. The test specimens shall be cut from the sample in such a way as to be thoroughly representative of it.

Procedure.—The tests shall be made on paper conditioned according to the standard method for conditioning, T 402 m (Vol. 2, Part B, p. 1795), and in the atmospheric conditions therein specified.

Place the test specimen on a 4-mesh wire screen, which is slightly dished and supported by the edges so that the ink remains in a pool in the center. Flow 1 ml. of the ink, at a temperature of 21°C., on the specimen near its center from a pipet, the tip of which is held $\frac{1}{2}$ in. from the specimen. The time of delivery of the ink must not be less than 4 nor more than 6 seconds. Measure the time of absorption in seconds with a stop watch, from the start of flow of ink from the pipet until the 1 ml. of ink is completely absorbed, as indicated by no further reflection of light from the ink when it is viewed at an angle. An equal number of tests shall be made on each side of the paper and not less than 10 specimens shall be tested.

Report.—The report shall give the minimum, maximum, and average time of ink absorption in seconds.

Precision.—The reproducibility of average test results secured by this method is usually within 5 percent.

REFERENCE

Reed, "Determining the Absorbency of Paper," Paper, **21**, No. 19, 14, Jan. 16, 1918.

WATER ABSORPTION OF BIBULOUS PAPER

This method is applicable to paper having a fairly rapid rate of water absorption, such as paper toweling. This method is standardized as TAPPI T 432 m-45.

Test Specimen.—Each test specimen shall consist of a single sheet of the paper approximately 4 by 4 in. The test specimens shall be taken from different rolls or packages selected from different units of the lot of paper in such a way as to be thoroughly representative of the entire lot.

Procedure.—The test shall be made on paper conditioned according to TAPPI Standard T 402 m (Vol. 2, Part B, p. 1795), and in the atmospheric conditions therein specified.

Place the specimen on a 4-mesh wire screen. Fill a 1-ml. measuring pipet, graduated in hundredths of a ml., with distilled water at a temperature of 23 ± 2°C. Hold the pipet at an angle of about 30° with the horizontal, with the tip nearly in contact with the paper, and allow 0.1 ml. of water to flow on the specimen near its center. While the water is flowing, keep the tip of the pipet in the drop of water until delivery of the water is completed. If the time of absorption is more than 2 minutes, cover the water on the paper with a watch glass. Measure with a stopwatch the rate of absorption in seconds from the start of flow of water until the drop of water is completely absorbed as indicated by no further reflection of light from it when viewed at an angle. An equal number of tests shall be made on each side of the paper and not less than ten specimens shall be tested.

Report.—The report shall state the amount of water absorbed and the minimum, maximum, and average absorption time in seconds.

Precision.—The reproducibility of average test results secured by this method is usually within 5 percent.

REFERENCES

Reese and Youtz, "A Water Absorbency Tester Using 0.1 cc. of Water," Paper Trade J., **100**, No. 7, 33, Feb. 14, 1935.

Carson and Worthington, "New Types of Equipment for Testing Paper," Paper Trade J., **95**, No. 16, 34–36, Oct. 20, 1932. For thin tissue products, the use of as little as 0.01 ml. of water has been found desirable. A pipet has been devised for accurate delivery of an extremely small amount of water at the desired angle in making absorption tests.

Carson, F. T., "Testing Paper for Permeability to Liquid," Paper Trade J., **80**, No. 10, 59, March 5, 1925.

Scribner, B. W., "Standards for Paper Towels," Natl. Bur. Standards Circular No. 407, 1935.

WATER RESISTANCE OF PAPER AND PAPERBOARD (DRY-INDICATOR METHOD)

This method is based on the dry-indicator method of Carson[62,63,64,65] and modifications of it developed by the TAPPI Paper Testing Subcommittee on Water Resistance under the direction of Abrams[66] and Codwise.[67,68,69] It consists in bringing one side of the test specimen in contact with water and finding the time required for the water to pass through the specimen, as indicated by the development of color in an indicator powder consisting of a mixture of water-soluble dye, sugar, and starch. The sugar serves the two-fold purpose of masking the color of the particles of dye as long as they are dry, and of absorbing the transuded moisture and holding it in close proximity to the dye. The starch increases the stability of the mixture. This method is standardized as TAPPI T 433 m-44.

Apparatus.—Any form of apparatus for applying the test may be used which fulfills the following conditions: (1) one surface of the specimen is wetted uniformly at the moment the count of time is begun; (2) the indicator on the opposite surface is continuously visible; (3) no moisture reaches the indicator except that which passes through the specimen from the wetted surface; (4) no moisture which does so reach the indicator escapes from contact with it. The following apparatus has been found suitable for testing paper and paperboards:

(*a*) For specimens having a high degree of water resistance, a vessel of water of sufficient area for floating several specimens simultaneously, immersed in a water bath with which the temperature of the water in the vessel can be maintained at 23 ± 0.5°C.;

[62] Carson, F. T., Tech. Assoc. Papers, **8**, 91, 1925; Paper Trade J., **80**, No. 10, 59–62; TS 85–88, March 5, 1925.

[63] Carson, F. T., U. S. Bureau of Standards Technologic Paper No. 326, Sept., 1926.

[64] Carson, F. T., and Worthington, V., Paper Trade J., **95**, No. 16, 34–36; TS 188–190, Oct. 20, 1932.

[65] Carson, F. T., Tech. Assoc. Papers, **8**, 91, 1925; 264–266, May 24, 1934.

[66] Abrams, A., Tech. Assoc. Papers, **12**, 49, 1929; Paper Trade J., **88**, No. 9, 40–42; TS 147–149, Feb. 28, 1929.

[67] Codwise, P. W., Tech. Assoc. Papers, **14**, 175, 1931; Paper Trade J., **92**, No. 10, 55–57; TS 138–140, March 5, 1931.

[68] Codwise, P. W., Tech. Assoc. Papers, **15**, 234, 1932; Paper Trade J., **94**, No. 5, 42–45; TS 46–49, Feb. 4, 1932.

[69] Codwise, P. W., Tech. Assoc. Papers, **17**, 143–145, 1934; Paper Trade J., **98**, No. 10, 43–45; TS 123–125, March 8, 1934.

a sealing medium prepared by melting together and mixing thoroughly equal parts of beeswax and rosin; a medicine dropper.

(*b*) For specimens that require a very short time to test, such that an edge seal is not required, the float arrangement[64] shown in Fig. 55-13 will facilitate the test. It is made

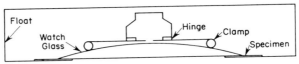

FIG. 55-13.   Cross Section of Float.

of a thin-walled aluminum pan about 5 in. in diameter and 1 in. high with a hole 2 in. in diameter cut in the bottom. The surface is coated with paraffin or beeswax to make it more water-repellent. The watch glass is clamped over the specimen by means of a wire-frame clamp hinged at one side and fastened under a spring at the opposite side. In the absence of the float such papers can be supported by a hollow cylinder having the upper end barely submerged under the surface of the water in a suitable vessel, while the watch glass is placed over the indicator. Such a cylinder may also be found useful in supporting an occasional paper whose surface is so easily wetted that it would be difficult to float it unsupported when prepared as shown in Fig. 55-13.

Shaker and desiccator for the indicator as shown in Fig. 55-14. The shaker is prepared from a 10-ml. screw-top vial by cutting away most of the metal of the flat portion

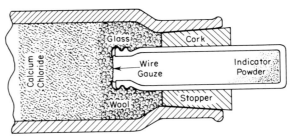

FIG. 55-14.   Longitudinal Section Showing Construction of Dessicator and Shaker.

of the top, fitting a 70-mesh wire screen inside the top, and screwing it back in place. The desiccator is made of a small wide-mouthed bottle containing anhydrous calcium chloride covered with a layer of glass wool. A hole is bored in the cork stopper just large enough to admit the shaker. The bottle remains on its side and the vial is inserted through the hole with the screened end inside. The assembly is kept in the usual type of laboratory desiccator when not in use.

Watch glasses, 2 in. in diameter.

Stop watch.

Reagents. Indicator.—The water-transudation indicator is composed of pure, powdered cane sugar, pure soluble starch, and methyl violet dye (Du Pont N. E. methyl violet, National Aniline and Chemical Co. 2 B. P. methyl violet, or equivalent). Pass each ingredient separately through a No. 100 screen, and completely dry it in a desiccator over anhydrous calcium chloride before making the mixture. When dry, weigh and mix the following proportions by weight:

Sugar	45
Soluble starch	5
Dye	1

Mix the ingredients by screening repeatedly through a No. 60 screen until the mixture is uniform. Keep the indicator in a desiccator when it is not being used. (The prepared indicator may be obtained from the M. Ames Chemical Works, Inc., 21 Rogers Street, Glens Falls, N. Y.

NOTE.—The powdered sugar may be prepared by grinding granulated or "domino" sugar. Confectioners' sugar must not be used, as it contains starch.

Water.—Water of fair purity, such as the usual drinking water, is suitable.

Test Specimen.—The test specimens shall be cut from different portions of the test sample in such a way as to be thoroughly representative of it. They shall be free from folds, wrinkles, or other blemishes not commonly inherent in the material. A convenient size is about 2.5 in. square. The specimens shall be conditioned for testing according to TAPPI Standard T 402 m (Vol. 2, part B, p. 1795).

Procedure.—The tests shall be made in the atmospheric conditions specified in TAPPI Standard T 402 m. During the tests the water used for testing shall be maintained at $23 \pm 0.5°C$.

Place the test specimen on a level, smooth surface, and sprinkle the indicator on the specimen by gently tapping the inverted shaker until a thin, even layer is formed, avoiding either a very sparse covering or one in which the powder is piled up. In the former case, the color change produced by too few dye particles may be insufficient to attract attention, unless they are exposed for a longer time than the proper end point. When the powder is placed on too thickly, the upper layer may obscure changes in that in contact with the paper. Also the greater total quantity of powder may require more time to change since it would necessitate more moisture to affect all the dye. Handle the test specimen with care once the powder is applied, for jarring or excessive tipping may cause rearrangement of the particles of powder, which then tend to form in clusters, thus destroying the intimate contact and uniform thin layer that is desirable. As soon as the application of the layer of the indicator powder is completed, cover it with a 2-in. watch glass and keep it covered during the test.

In testing material having a high degree of water resistance, use the apparatus designated for the purpose. First seal the edges of the specimen to prevent water from entering through the edges and reaching the indicator without going entirely through the material. Grasp the specimen with thumb and forefinger as a pivot and dip into melted beeswax-rosin mixture to a depth of $\frac{1}{8}$ in.; rotate 90° and dip the next edge; and repeat until all four edges are saturated and sealed. When the wax is hardened, add the indicator powder as described, seal the watch glass over it with melted beeswax-rosin, using a medicine dropper as illustrated in Fig. 55-15, then float the specimen on the water. For papers having a short testing period it is generally not necessary to seal the cover glass; the float shown in Fig. 55-13 may be used or the specimen and cover glass may be supported by a submerged cylinder.

In placing the specimen in the water, make contact with the water at a slight angle to avoid trapping air bubbles that might cause uneven wetting of the specimen. When testing materials having uneven surfaces, wet with water the surface to be in contact with water, using a soft brush, immediately before placing the specimen in the water. Examine each specimen after the test, and if there is evidence of uneven wetting, discard the test result.

Measure the time interval from the instant of contact of the test specimen with water until the rate of change in the color of the indicator is at a maximum. In testing materials having a low degree of water resistance, this time interval is conveniently determined as the mean of the values corresponding to the development of pronounced color in one-fourth and in three-fourths of the area covered by the indicator. For materials of this kind on which the color develops uniformly over the whole area, it may be necessary to tabulate the values of the time interval against the intensity of the color to determine the maximum rate of change. In judging the end point on specimens requiring considerable time to reach the end point, it may be helpful to note the following three general color phases: The powder as it is first sprinkled on the test area often shows a slight tinge of color other than the predominant white. This first color may appear slightly different on surfaces of different color. After the test has been in progress for such a time that the end point is reached, a more intense color is present and is a somewhat reddish purple. Finally, if the sample is left for a longer time than the proper end point, the reddish cast tends to disappear and the powder appears a

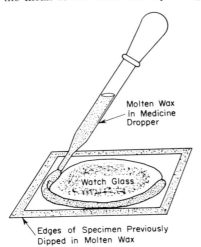

Molten Wax in Medicine Dropper

Watch Glass

Edges of Specimen Previously Dipped in Molten Wax

FIG. 55-15. Method of Preparing the Specimen Showing the Watch Glass Being Sealed Over the Indicator Powder.

dark purple; also, the particles often appear as if quite moist. Sometimes when the specimens are unevenly resistant, there may be hints of two or possibly all three phases at once, but it should be easily ascertainable which is predominant. In any case, taking the first hint of change from the white should be avoided; allow enough change to take place to be positive. On the other hand, do not wait for the last purple phase, for once it is attained there is little further change to note with the passage of time. Artificial light, when used for viewing the test specimen, should be reasonably brilliant but completely shaded from the eyes. The light should be applied to one side of the specimen (thus avoiding reflection from the cover glass) and the eye should view from the side next to the illuminant, to avoid interference of shadows cast by the indicator particles with the judgment of the color.

Make at least 5 tests from each side of the material, except that asphalted fabric-lined papers shall be tested with the fabric side only in contact with the water.

Report.—The report shall give the average, the minimum, and the maximum values of the time of transudation in minutes or hours from each of the two sides of the material. For ordinary papers designate the sides as wire side and felt side when they can be differentiated; otherwise, use a suitable code designation such as Side I and Side II, or when there is an obvious difference between the sides, such as Side I, coated, and Side II, uncoated. The side designated shall be that which was in contact with the water.

Precision.—The reproducibility of the average test results by experienced operators is within 10 to 15 percent.

Additional Information.—This method is sometimes not applicable to materials containing large amounts of water-soluble components.

Penescope.[70]—This device can be used for the dry-indicator test. It consists of a cast

[70] Abrams, A., Paper Trade J., **84**, No. 3, 44–47; TS 38–41, Jan. 20, 1927.

brass chamber which is filled with water; a hollow screw cap, with an opening for observation of the test specimen, in which the test specimen is inserted and then screwed tightly against the chamber; and pipe connections at top and bottom of the chamber by means of which the water can be introduced, maintained at a desired level, and removed. The suitability of this device for a given purpose should be determined by comparing the results obtained with it with those obtained by the standard method.

Related TAPPI Methods.—T 431 m-45, Ink Absorption of Blotting Paper (p. 1421); T 432 m-45, Water Absorption of Bibulous Paper (p. 1422); T 441 m-58, Water Absorptiveness of Nonbibulous Paper and Paperboard, immediately below.

Investigations of the use of high temperatures (up to the boiling point of water) in the dry-indicator test have shown that, in general, there is good correlation between transudation time and temperature. For products that show such relation, the use of hot water is of value in shortening the test period, and in some instances in making the end point more distinct.[71,72]

WATER ABSORPTIVENESS OF NONBIBULOUS PAPER AND PAPERBOARD (COBB TEST)

This method is based upon the method of Cobb and Lowe[73] and Cobb[74] and has been investigated by the TAPPI Paper Testing Subcommittee on Water Resistance.[75] It is suitable for determining the penetration of water into paper and paperboard 0.004 in. and over in thickness. It may be generally employed satisfactorily except to measure the resistance of the surface of a sheet to minute quantities of water, such as from writing with a pen. It is not recommended as a sizing test for writing papers. This method is standardized as TAPPI T 441 m-60.

Apparatus and Materials.—Any form of apparatus may be used which permits the following:

A predetermined area of one side of the specimen to be wetted uniformly at the moment the soaking period begins.

The absorption of water to be stopped at the end of the test period by removal of all free surface water.

An accurate weight of the specimen to be obtained both before and immediately after exposure to water.

Specimen Holder.—One form[76] is shown in Fig. 55-16. It comprises a metal ring with a machined lower face, 10 cm. inside diameter,[77] 2.5 cm. high and about 0.6 cm. thick, clamped to a flat base plate about 15 by 15 cm. with a metal cross bar 17 × 2.5 × 0.6 cm. and two wing nuts on a pair of studs. The cross bar has a hole at one end and a slot at the other to permit speedy operation. One or more rubber mats, larger than the outside dimensions of the ring are provided, on which the specimen is clamped.

Stopwatch or stop clock.

Blotter.—Soft absorbent cloth or blotting paper.

[71] Codwise, P. W., Tech. Assoc. Papers, **26,** 165, 1943; Paper Trade J., **116,** No. 9, 30–33; TS 90–93, March 4, 1943.
[72] Mullen, E. G., Paper Trade J., **119,** No. 2, 41–42; TS 11–12, July 13, 1944.
[73] Cobb, R. M., and Lowe, D. V., "A Sizing Test and Sizing Theory," Tech. Assoc. Papers, **17,** 213–216, 1934; Paper Trade J., **98,** No. 12, 43–46 March 22, 1934.
[74] Cobb, R. M., "What I Do Not Know About Sizing and Capillary Flow," Tech. Assoc. Papers, **18,** 290–293, 1935; Paper Trade J., **100,** No. 16, 42–45, April 18, 1935.
[75] Codwise, P. W., "Water Resistance of Paper," Tech. Assoc. Papers, **19,** 231–235, 1936; Paper Trade J., **102,** No. 3, 39–43, Jan. 16, 1936.
[76] Egy, W. L., "The Cobb Sizing Test," Pulp Paper Mag. Canada, 499, June, 1937.
[77] For many purposes it would be more convenient to make the inside character 11.2 cm. to give a test area of 100 sq. cm.

Water.—Of reasonable purity, such as ordinary drinking water.

Test Specimens.—If soft-sized, cut 10 representative test specimens free from folds, wrinkles, or other blemishes not commonly inherent in the paper and of such a size as to fit the apparatus employed. If hard-sized, 5 specimens are sufficient.

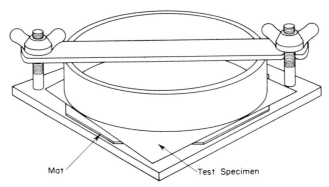

Mat   Test Specimen

FIG. 55-16. Water Absorption Apparatus.

Procedure.—Make the test on specimens conditioned according to TAPPI Standard T 402 m (Vol. 2, part B, p. 1795), and in the atmospheric conditions therein specified. Maintain the temperature of the water and apparatus at $23 \pm 1°C$.

Using the metal ring and clamp as shown in Fig. 55-16, cut the test specimens into squares which just easily fit between the studs, in this case $12\frac{1}{2} \times 12\frac{1}{2}$ cm. Weigh each to an accuracy of 0.01 g. Place a dry rubber mat (or felt) on the metal plate and lay a weighed specimen on it with the surface to be tested uppermost. After wiping perfectly dry, place the metal ring upon the sample, and fasten it firmly enough in place with the crossbar to prevent any leakage between the ring and the specimen. Pour water into the ring to a depth of 0.5 to 1.0 cm., and start the stopwatch at the same time. Fifteen to 20 seconds before the expiration of the predetermined test period, pour the water quickly from the ring taking great care not to drop any water upon the untested portion of the specimen. Without delay, loosen the wing nuts, swing the crossbar out of the way and hold the ring in its former position by pressing it down with one hand.

At the end of the test period, quickly mop the water from the paper surface with a soft rag or absorbent paper; immediately remove the ring taking care not to get any drops of water on the unwetted part of the specimen and remove any traces of liquid water from the paper, checking that the wetted surface is dull by reflected light.

Unless it is wished to examine the specimen visually, fold the sample with the wetted area inside. Immediately reweigh to an accuracy of 0.01 g. Measure the average inside diameter of the ring to the nearest 0.1 cm., and calculate its area in sq. cm. Subtract the conditioned weight of the specimen from its final weight, and calculate the weight of water absorbed per sq. m. of ring area.

Unless otherwise stated on the report, it will be assumed that a standard exposure period of 120 seconds was employed. This is suitable for most well sized papers. If any liquid has passed through the sheet to the backing mat, the test is not acceptable, and either the time should be shortened to 60 seconds, or two or more specimen sheets should be stapled together. In such a case, the calculated test area will remain that of the inside of the ring. For hard-sized papers, a longer period, *e.g.*, 5 minutes, may be found advisable. Any deviation from a 2-minute exposure period and a single-sheet specimen should be prominently stated in the report.

Report.—Give the test period (usually 2 minutes) and the absorptiveness calculated as the average weight of water absorbed in grams per square meter, for the wire and the felt sides of the paper separately. State the maximum and minimum values for each side also, if desired.

Precision.—This test has not been statistically examined. However, the reproducibility of the average test results by experienced different operators may be expected to be within 10 percent.

Additional Information.—Another instrument which may be used for this test is the penescope.[78] This is a device which consists of a cast brass chamber which may be partly filled with water, and a hollow screw cap, with an opening for observation of the test specimen if desired. The test specimen is inserted and then screwed tightly against the chamber. The method of using this instrument for this test is as follows.

Cut the test specimen to circular form fitting the instrument and weigh it accurately. Place the specimen in the penescope which has been previously filled to a definite level with water at the standard temperature. Then invert the penescope so that the water comes in contact with the sample and start the stopwatch simultaneously. Let the water remain in contact with the sample until 10 seconds before the expiration of the predetermined test period and then again invert the penescope, unscrew the cap, remove the specimen and, at the exact expiration of the test period, blot off the surface water and reweigh.

This test was designed for nonbibulous papers and paperboards, but satisfactory results have been obtained with up to about 20 sheets of highly absorbent paper stapled together and tested for 60 instead of 120 seconds.

For very hard-sized or specially treated papers, the test may be extended to periods up to 18 hours to increase the sensitivity.

For layers of absorbent papers, the quantity of water absorbed is almost proportional to the time of exposure. For well sized papers, the quantity is approximately proportional to the square root of this time.

This test is similar to British PBMA Test Method PT 15, and Swedish PCA. 13.

SPECTRAL REFLECTIVITY AND COLOR OF PAPER

This method measures the spectral reflectivity and color of paper relative to magnesium oxide. Spectral reflectivity is usually expressed in the form a curve giving reflectivity as a function of wavelength over the range 400 to 700 mμ. Reflectivity is the ratio, for the same geometry and wavelength of monochromatic light, of the amount of light reflected by the sample to that reflected from a pure and properly prepared surface of magnesium oxide. It is thus a relative quantity and is correctly termed *apparent reflectivity*, although in common usage it is simply referred to as *reflectivity* or *reflectance*. Color is specified according to the standard observer and colorimetric coordinate system recommended in 1931 by the International Commission on Illumination. The appearance of a paper is not completely defined by these specifications; it may also be influenced by other properties, such as texture and gloss. This method is standardized as TAPPI T 442 m-47.

Apparatus. **Instrument.**—The instrument shall consist of a spectrophotometer, either visual or photoelectric type, which can adequately measure the spectral reflectivity of a sample relative to a standard over the wavelength range of 400 to 700 mμ.

[78] Abrams, A., Paper Trade J., **84**, No. 3, 44–47, Jan. 20, 1927.

Provision must be made for the elimination of stray energy, such as by stray-energy filters or by the use of two dispersing prisms.

Reflectance Standards.—The standard of reflectivity shall be a layer (at least 0.5 mm. thick) of magnesium oxide freshly prepared according to the standard method (p. 1460) by collecting the smoke from burning magnesium ribbon or turnings on a suitable surface. If any other material is employed as standard, its spectral reflectivity shall be specified.

Illumination and Viewing.—The standard and sample shall be illuminated under identical conditions.

The manner of illumination shall be specified, stating whether the illumination is diffuse or uni-directional. If diffuse, the geometry of the illumination shall be specified, including the nature of the reflecting surface within the integrating sphere, the solid angle subtended, at the sample surface, by the illuminating beam of light, and the area of the sample illuminated.

The manner and angle of viewing shall be specified together with the solid angle subtended, at the sample, by the viewing rays of light, and the area of the sample viewed.

Note.—This method (measurement of spectral reflectivity) serves to specify the optical properties of paper which are responsible for its color, subject to the limitation that the color may depend upon the manner of illumination and viewing. It is important to specify the geometry of the illumination and viewing, and the most important single characteristic is whether or not the specular component of reflected energy is included in the measurement. In every case it shall be definitely stated whether or not the reflected light measured includes light reflected specularly, from the surface of the sample. The appearance of paper requires for its specification in addition to the above measurements some measure of its gloss. Such a measure is beyond the intended scope of the present method.

Calibration.—The calibration of the photometer scale or other intensity-measuring unit shall be carefully checked for accuracy at reasonable intervals.

The accuracy of the wavelength calibrations shall be checked at reasonable intervals by a sodium flame and other sources of monochromatic light at several wavelengths from 400 to 700 mμ.

The slit-width or filter bands of the monochromatizing system shall be kept sufficiently narrow to insure good approximation to monochromatic light.

The spectral reflectivity of secondary standards (working standards) shall be measured against magnesium oxide at reasonable intervals.

Procedure.—The sample shall be handled carefully to avoid discoloration and care must be taken not to touch the part tested. The condition of the sample before and after analysis shall be carefully noted and any change in the appearance of the surface shall be recorded.

Readings shall be made at each of the various wavelengths from 400 to 700 mμ. to establish a reliable indication of the percentage of light reflected by the sample at each of these wavelengths, the number of wavelengths at which the measurements are made to be sufficient to represent accurately, graphically or numerically, the characteristic reflectivity of the sample.

Note.—Typical spectral reflectance curves of papers are shown in Fig. 55-17.

A sufficient number of thicknesses of the sample shall be employed to the extent that a doubling of the number of thicknesses will not cause appreciable change in the reflectance at any wavelength.

Report.—The report of the spectral reflectivity and color of a paper sample shall consist of the following:

(*a*) the characteristic spectral reflectivity of the sample relative to that for magnesium oxide;

(*b*) the nature of and spectral reflectivity of any other material than magnesium oxide employed as a standard;

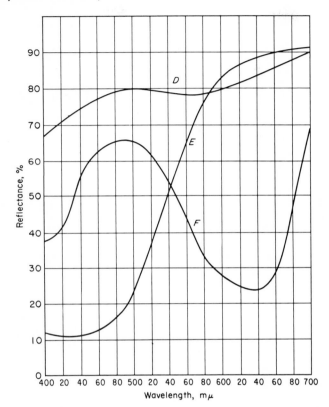

Fig. 55-17. Spectral Reflectance Curves. D, Magazine paper. Paper and Ink. E, Goldenrod Bond Paper. F, Ink (Paper Trade Journal, outside front cover, 1937–8).

(*c*) the manner of illumination and manner of viewing, as specified above, or, as an alternative, a statement of the model number and name of the instrument, without modifications, employed for the measurement;

(*d*) the tristimulus specification of the color computed from the spectral reflectivity according to the standard observer and colorimetric coordinate system recommended in 1931 by the International Commission on Illumination and for I.C.I. Illuminant C (representative of average daylight).

Note.—A report of the spectral reflectivity and color of the papers in Fig. 55-17 is given as follows:

(*a*) The spectral reflectivity is shown in the figure.

(*b*) No standard other than magnesium oxide was employed.

(*c*) *Either:* The illumination was unidirectional at 90° to the sample, the solid angle subtended by the said illumination varying from about 0.00013 steradians in the red to 0.00035 in the blue. The viewing was approximately diffuse, the important differences being (1) light specularly reflected (as well as some diffuse near to the specular position) passes out of the sphere through an aperture subtending about 0.00895 steradians, and (2) the viewing photocell sees light once reflected from the sample at about 41° through a solid angle of 0.0854 steradians. The size of sample illuminated was equal to that viewed, a circular area of 22 mm. diameter.

Or: The illumination and viewing of the sample is defined by the construction of the General Electric recording spectrophotometer, catalog number 4980125 GL, serial number 716175.

(*d*) Tristimulus specification:

	Papers and Ink (Fig. 55-17)		
	(D) Magazine Paper	(E) Goldenrod Bond Paper	(F) Outside Front Cover of Paper Trade Journal (Ink) 1937–38
Trichromatic Coefficients....			
x.....................	0.3150	0.4565	0.2453
y.....................	0.3212	0.4304	0.2984
z.....................	0.3639	0.1132	0.4562
Dominant wave length in millimicrons.............	577.5	581.0	487.5
Excitation purity, %........	2.6	69.7	35.6
Visual efficiency, %........	79.1	59.3	45.2

These data were calculated by the 30 selected ordinate method described in Chapter 6, Handbook of Colorimetry, by A. C. Hardy and Staff of M.I.T. Color Measurement Laboratory, Technology Press, 1936.

SILVER-TARNISHING TEST OF PAPER

This method is designed to determine the presence or absence of materials which will tarnish or stain silver in paper used for wrapping silverware. It is chiefly intended for testing tissue papers which, in use, are in direct contact with silverware. Certain types of paper, such as parchmentized, water-repellent types and metal-coated papers, may require modification of the test procedure. (See Note 3.) The test results indicate the type of tarnish or stain, and the relative distribution of the materials causing such tarnishing or staining. This method is standardized as TAPPI T 444 m-47.

Apparatus.—The special apparatus consists of:

Metal Plates.—Flat plates 6 by 6 in., cut from commercial rolled sheet brass 0.25 in. thick. One 6 by 6 in. flat surface of each plate should be buffed smooth and as free as possible from tool marks and then plated with pure silver to a thickness of about 0.005 in., buffed again, and plated with another 0.005 in. of silver. In this way a smooth, continuous layer of pure silver about 0.010 in. thick will be obtained which can be cleaned and polished repeatedly. It is advisable to check the amount of silver by weighing the brass plates before and after plating. A layer of silver 0.010 in. thick should weigh 0.056 oz. Troy (1.73 g.) per sq. in.

If the brass plates are plated with pure silver on both sides, one side of each plate will serve as a "blank" during the test and will indicate whether the air in the oven will tarnish silver or not. The use of plates coated on both sides with silver will obviate the use of the extra strips of silver foil called for in Note 1.

Two plates as described above are needed for each test and are probably sufficient for occasional tests of paper. Several sets are necessary where frequent routine testing is desired.

Silver Polish.—A good grade of silver-polishing powder or paste which will not scratch pure silver and contains no cyanides. A paste made up of the finest grade of Tripoli powder, such as used for polishing metals for metallographic work, and distilled water containing a small amount of ammonium hydroxide will clean silver completely.

Oven.—A temperature-controlled air oven or cabinet, protected from access to laboratory fumes.

Test Specimen.—Sufficient test specimens, each 6.5 in. square, shall be cut from the paper being evaluated so as to be representative of it. Five specimens are recommended wherever possible.

The sample for test and the cut specimens should be protected at all times from contamination. They should not be handled with bare hands. Use metal forceps.

Procedure.—Thoroughly clean the silver surface of each plate and polish it to a high luster, free from grease, then rinse the plate with alcohol followed by ether and dry. Holding one of the 6.5 in. square test pieces by means of paper clips or forceps, wet it with distilled water as uniformly as possible, so that the paper is saturated but not dripping wet. This can be readily done by means of an all-glass atomizer operated by compressed air (not a rubber bulb) or by steaming over the outlet of a wash bottle containing boiling distilled water. As soon as the test piece of paper is saturated with water, place it on the polished silver surface of one brass plate, taking care to have as few wrinkles or air bubbles as possible. Then lay the other brass plate, silver surface down upon the paper. Place the test assembly in the air oven or cabinet and adjust the temperature so that the paper will dry completely in not less than 3 hours (150° to 170°F. is usually sufficient. See Note 1). When the paper is dry, examine the silvered surface of each plate for evidence of tarnishing or staining. Note the color, and character of any stains found. If isolated spotting occurs, estimate the approximate size of the spots and count their number on each plate.

Report.—The report shall state:

1. The number of specimens tested.

2. The color and character of tarnishing or staining, if any (whether spots, large areas, etc.).

3. The number of tarnished or stained areas as maximum and minimum number found in any one test piece and the total number found in all pieces tested.

NOTE 1.—Wherever doubt regarding the presence of sulfur compounds in the air in the oven exists, it is advisable to hang one or more small strips of clean, highly polished, pure silver foil, in the oven while the test specimens are there. If tarnishing or staining of these strips occurs, the air entering the oven should be purified, or the oven should be set up where the air causes no tarnishing of the silver.

NOTE 2.—Cardboard and papers other than tissue require a rather long time to dry throughout in this test. Cardboard $\frac{1}{8}$ to $\frac{1}{4}$ in. thick may require 48 hours or more. Therefore, these types should not be too wet when placed between the test plates. If cardboard is dried too rapidly, it frequently buckles sufficiently to lift the test plates out of contact with most of the test specimen. Therefore, when testing cardboard it may be necessary to clamp the test plates together with C clamps after inserting the wetted test specimen between them.

NOTE 3.—Parchmentized, glassine, and other water-repellent papers, and metal-coated papers will require certain modifications of the test procedure. In most cases they may be tested without wetting the test specimen and by prolonging the time in contact with the silver to at least 24 hours. When such types of paper are tested, the report should state any modification in the procedure which is used.

NOTE 4.—The principles of this test method are also suggested for use where wrapping paper is to be tested for its staining or corrosion properties with respect to other metals, as steel, copper, nickel, etc. In such cases it is necessary to use plates or forms of the particular metal or alloy in question, and to make such modifications as may be required for the particular purpose. For example, in the case of a metal that would rust, such as steel, the paper obviously could not be wetted; it would be necessary instead to heat in an atmosphere of high humidity.

NOTE 5.—A permanent record may be obtained for future reference by placing tracing paper over the plate after the test and tracing the spots or stained areas.

See also T 406 m., Reducible Sulphur in Paper (Vol. 2, Part B, p. 1797).

WATER VAPOR PERMEABILITY OF PAPER AND PAPERBOARD

This method is for the determination of the water vapor permeability of paper and paperboard under normal atmospheric conditions. It is considered generally suitable also for other sheet materials up to 1 in. in thickness.

Water vapor permeability is defined for this test as the weight of water transmitted per unit of time, per unit area, measured while the specimen separates an atmosphere below 5 percent R. H. on one face from the standard atmosphere of 50 percent R. H. and 73°F. on the other face. This method is standardized as TAPPI T 448 m-49.

Apparatus. **Test Dish.**—An open-mouthed cup or dish or such size and shape that it can be accommodated readily on the pan of an analytical balance. The opening should be as large as practical, an area of at least 50 sq. cm. being preferred. (This is equivalent to a circle about 3 in. in diameter.) The test dish shall be of such design that a wax seal can be made which will be impervious to leakage of water vapor and will define clearly the test area. Suitable designs for the dish with supporting rings and flanges are shown in Fig. 55-18. Other modifications of these designs may be made,

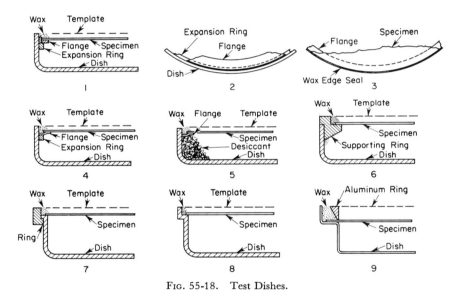

Fig. 55-18. Test Dishes.

provided the principle of preventing edge leakage by means of a complete wax seal is retained.

Template, for use in defining the test area and effecting the wax seal, consisting of a circular metal disc 0 to $\frac{1}{4}$ in. thick, with the edge bevelled to an angle of about 45°. The diameter of the bottom (smaller) face of the template shall be approximately equal to and not greater than the diameter of the effective opening of the cell in contact with the specimen. A small hole through the template to admit air will facilitate its removal after the wax solidifies.

Analytical balance, of 200-g. capacity, sensitive to 0.001 g., with pans large enough to hold the test dishes.

Testing room or cabinet provided with conditioned air maintained at 50 ± 2 percent R. H. and 73°F. according to TAPPI Standard T 402 m (Vol. 2, Part B, p. 1795), and continuously circulated at a rate not less than 500 feet per minute over the exposed surfaces of the specimens under test.

Grill or Reticulated Rack in the testing room or cabinet, capable of supporting the inverted specimens in a manner to afford free access of the circulating air.

Materials. **Desiccant,** with a powerful affinity for water vapor and a high drying efficiency—that is, a low vapor pressure after absorbing a large amount of water. The desiccant shall remain essentially unchanged in physical condition and exert, while dry, no chemical or physical action other than dehydration effects on membrane materials with which it is in contact. The desiccant used shall be in the form of small lumps, free from fines that will pass a No. 30 sieve. (Anhydrous magnesium perchlorate made by the G. Frederick Smith Co., Columbus, Ohio, is recommended. This substance may be explosive at elevated temperature and should not be regenerated. Anhydrous calcium chloride is also suitable.)

Wax, for sealing the specimen to the testing dish, made of a mixture of 60 percent of a suitable refined amorphous wax (for example, Socony Vacuum Grade Nos. 2300, 2305, or 2310) and 40 percent of refined crystalline paraffin wax. The wax mixture shall cling tenaciously to the surfaces and not be brittle at ordinary room temperatures. Care shall be taken to prevent contamination of the wax with particles of calcium chloride or other salts when it is salvaged for reuse. The wax in use should be replaced frequently with new material. The stability and water absorption of the mixture shall be tested by applying a heavy film of the wax about 10 sq. in. in area to a glass plate, exposing to an atmosphere of high temperature and humidity (about 90 percent R. H. at 100°F.) and determining whether any significant change occurs in the weight of the film and plate—for example, more than 0.001 g. per day. Ordinary rosin as used in beeswax-resin mixtures will absorb a significant amount of moisture when so tested.

Petrolatum, for application to the bevelled edge of the template in order to facilitate removal of the latter after sealing the test sheet to the dish. The petroleum jelly commonly used by druggists is suitable.

Test Specimen.—A suitable code designation should be used to distinguish between the 2 sides of the material, such as Side I and Side II; or when there is an obvious difference between the 2 sides, such as Side I, waxed, and Side II, unwaxed.

The test specimens shall be representative of the material. At least 2 specimens shall be prepared for each type of test required.

The different types of test include: (1) Flat samples with Side I exposed to the higher humidity; (2) Flat samples with Side II exposed to the higher humidity; (3) and (4) Creased samples exposed as in (1) and (2).

Procedure.—Place sufficient desiccant inside the dish to cover the sheet area evenly to a depth of about 15 mm.

The following method of affixing the test specimen to the dish is for paper and for paperboards not over $\frac{1}{8}$ in. thick: Cut the test specimen so that its diameter is equal to that of the larger diameter of the template. Place the sheet over the aperture of the dish and center it as closely as possible on the supporting ring or flange. With the tip of the finger apply a thin film of petrolatum to the bevelled edge of the template. Wipe off any petrolatum which may have been deposited on the smaller surface of the template. Center the template with the smaller surface down, exactly over the specimen and dish opening. Flow molten wax into the annular space surrounding the bevelled edge of the template, using a medicine dropper to dispense the molten wax. Remove the template from the sheet surface as soon as the wax has cooled and solidified.

For paperboards over $\frac{1}{8}$ in. thick, the method of preparing the test assembly is modified as follows: to prevent edge leakage, rotate the edge of the test specimen in molten wax of such fluidity that it does not penetrate into the edge more than $\frac{1}{16}$ in., suspend it inside the dish to a distance of about half the thickness of the specimen, and run molten wax, by means of a medicine dropper, around the edge of the specimen to seal it to the dish.

Weigh the assembly on the analytical balance to 0.001 g. Place the dish on the rack inside the testing room or cabinet in an inverted position so that the layer of desiccant is in direct contact and evenly distributed over the inner face of the test sheet and so that free access of the conditioned circulating air is provided on the exposed surface of the sheet.

Make successive weighings of the assembly at suitable intervals until a constant rate of gain is attained. For papers that are relatively pervious, the weighings should be frequent enough to complete the test before drops of liquid agglomerate are formed in the desiccant or caking of the desiccant occurs. These conditions will be indicated by a drift from the constant rate of gain, after which no readings should be recorded. Plot the weight gain against time. The slope of the resulting curve will furnish a measure of the water vapor permeability.

Report.—The water vapor permeability shall be reported to 2 significant figures as grams per square meter or ounces per 100 square yards per 24 hours at 73°F. and for a moisture gradient defined in the preceding section. The calculation should be made for the period of constant rate of gain. For example, in a test run for 190 hours on an exposed area of 55 square centimeters (0.0055 sq. m.), assume that the rate of gain was substantially constant after 18 hours, and that during the subsequent 172 hours the moisture absorbed by the desiccant was 67 mg.; the water vapor permeability is then

$$\frac{0.067 \times 24}{0.0055 \times 172} = 1.7 \text{ g. of moisture passing through 1 square meter of the material every}$$

24 hours at 73°F. from 50 percent R. H. on one face to desiccant in contact with the other.

NOTE.—For conversion purposes, grams per square meter $\times$ 2.95 = ounces per 100 square yards.

The report shall contain the average, maximum, and minimum values for each type of test made.

The report shall state what desiccant was used.

Reproducibility of Results.—Duplicate determinations should check within 10 percent, depending largely on the variation in the sheet material itself. As the spread between very permeable sheets and those having a low permeability is at least a thousand fold, a precision of 10 percent on a given material will establish it quite definitely in the scale of permeabilities normally encountered in sheet materials.

REFERENCES

Abrams, Allen, and Chilson, W. A., Paper Trade J., **91**, No. 18, 175–180, Oct. 30, 1930; Tech. Assoc. Papers, **14**, 379–384, May, 1931.

Abrams, Allen, and Brabender, G. J., Paper Trade J., **102**, No. 15, 32, April 9, 1936; Tech. Assoc. Papers, **19**, 121–130, June, 1936.

Brabender, G. J., Paper Trade J., **108**, No. 4, 39, Jan. 26, 1939; Tech. Assoc. Papers, **22**, 95 and 251, June, 1939.

Carson, F. T., National Bureau of Standards, Miscellaneous Publication M127, Washington, D. C., Aug. 5, 1937.

Carson, F. T., Paper Trade J., **107**, No. 18, 59, Nov. 3, 1938.

Water Vapor Permeability Symposium, Tech. Assoc. Papers, **20**, 90–102, 1937.

Brabender, G. J., Paper Trade J., **110**, No. 18, 27, May 2, 1940; Tech. Assoc. Papers, **23**, 358–361, June, 1940.

BACTERIOLOGICAL EXAMINATION OF PAPER AND PAPERBOARD

The following procedure is recommended for the bacteriological examination of paper and paperboard. Because of the exacting technique required in bacteriological procedures, reproducible results can be secured only by a well trained technician. This method is standardized as TAPPI T 449 m-57.

Apparatus and Materials. **Alcohol.**—Methyl, isopropyl, or 95 percent denatured ethyl alcohol, for sterilizing instruments.

Balance.—Sensitive to 0.1 g., with a pan large enough to hold the Petri Dishes.

Corkborers and Containers.—Standard corkborers 15 to 25 mm. in diameter, for taking samples from rolls or sheets. Enclose them singly in screwcap bottles for sterilization.

Bottles for Dilution.—Several 8-oz., narrow-mouthed, squared-sectioned glass bottles, fitted either with screw caps or with Escher rubber stoppers. (Either tap or distilled water is satisfactory for dilution.)

Colony Counter.—Any one of several types, the Quebec, the Buck, and Wolffhuegel colony counters are satisfactory. A hand tally for recording the count is recommended.

Containers for Dry Samples.—When the sampling and testing are done at the same mill, use a single envelope for each; otherwise, use two single envelopes, one placed inside the other. The larger one may be 9 by 12 in. and the smaller 6.5 by 9.5 in. They should be made of heavy kraft paper that will withstand sterilization in the hot-air oven without undue enbrittlement. After sterilization, seal the flap on the outer envelope with pressure-sensitive tape.

Alternatively, make a folder of suitable size from heavy kraft paper and sterilize it in the oven. After the paper sample has been placed inside the sterile folder, seal the latter with the tape.

Plugs.—Nonabsorbent cotton.

Disintegrators.—Metal jar with a high-speed impeller near the bottom and fitted with a cap. Place kraft paper hood over the cap of each disintegrator jar prior to steam sterilization.

Flaming Equipment.—An alcohol lamp, a gasoline blowtorch, or a Bunsen burner, to flame tongs, scissors, knives, and the mouths of sterile containers.

Flasks.—Erlenmeyer flasks or bottles, preferably Pyrex, for holding sterile media.

Incubator.—Capable of maintaining a temperature of $36 \pm 1°C.$ ($96.8 \pm 1.8°F.$).

Knife.—Preferably the type with an inserted blade of adjustable length to cut paper and board.

Petri Dishes.—Pyrex, 100 by 15 mm., are recommended.

Pipets and Containers.—Two sizes: 1.1 ml. milk-dilution types and graduated 10-ml. type. Mohr 10-ml. pipets, with tips cut off to give an opening of about 3 mm. in diameter at the delivery end, are best for pipetting fiber suspensions. Special Mohr pipets calibrated from the large end, are available and preferable to the usual Mohr pipet. Enclose them singly in metal boxes or heavy kraft paper wrappers for sterilization.

Scissors.—Preferably with 4-in. cutting edges.

Nutrient Substrate.—Dehydrated standard tryptone glucose extract agar. That obtained either from Difco Laboratories or from the Baltimore Biological Laboratories has been found suitable. It may also be prepared from its ingredients.[79]

[79] American Public Health Association, Standard Methods for the Examination of Water and Sewage, p. 186, 9th Ed. (1946).

Sterilizing Equipment.—Two types of suitable size:

(a) A steam sterilizer for 15 p.s.i. steam, such as an autoclave or a pressure cooker.

(b) A hot-air oven at 165°C., with thermometer. For most laboratories, electrically heated ovens are more satisfactory than those heated by gas, but the latter may be used if desired.

Tongs.—Suitable for handling samples of paper.

Sterilization of Equipment and Media.—Depending upon the nature of the equipment to be sterilized, use one of three methods as follows.

Steam Heat (Autoclave or Pressure Cooker).—Sterilize the following by heating for 20 minutes at a minimum of 121°C. (250°F.), corresponding to 15 p.s.i. steam pressure: (a) caps with hoods and the jars for disintegrators, (b) media (unless other conditions are specified by the manufacturer of the medium), (c) sample bottles, (d) corkborers, and (e) water blanks for dilution.

Dry Heat (Electrically or Gas-Heated Oven).—Sterilize the following by heating for at least 2 hours at a minimum temperature of 165°C. (329°F.): (a) heavy kraft envelopes and folders, (b) tongs, (c) knives, (d) Petri dishes, (e) pipets, and (f) scissors.

Take care to dry glassware completely before heating and avoid scorching any paper containers or wrapper used for the instruments being sterilized.

Alcohol.—Immerse scissors, tongs, knives, and similar instruments in alcohol. When needed for cutting or handling samples, remove, allow to drain for a few moments, then burn off the excess alcohol.

Sampling.—Sample a sufficient number of rolls or bundles, so that the sample is representative of the lot of paper being tested.

At the same time take a sample of the paper or paperboard to determine its moisture content, if not known to within 2 percent.

Method A.—Use either a single envelope or two sterile envelopes, one within another, for each sample. With a knife, cut away several layers of paper or paperboard surrounding the area to be sampled on a roll and discard them to eliminate any surface contamination. In the exposed area then make a vertical cut with a sterile knife through several thicknesses near the center and parallel to the edge of the roll; a second vertical cut parallel to the first and about 5 in. from the first cut; and a horizontal cut across the bottom of the first two cuts, thus allowing the cut flap to spring out from the surface of the roll. Cut off and discard the top two sheets of the flap, then carefully open the sterilized envelope and slip the end of the adjacent cut flap of the sample into the envelope. Then make a horizontal cut across the top of the flap and about 6 in. from the bottom cut. The sample will then drop into the inner envelope; after which seal the outer envelope by means of a pressure-sensitive tape. The sample will be approximately 5 by 6 in. Take samples at different sections of successive rolls.

This procedure can be adapted for sampling paper from bales or skids, using flamed tongs for handling the samples of cut paper.

Method B.—Remove several layers of paper or paperboard by cutting with a knife. Take the corkborer from the sterile bottle and cut about $\frac{1}{2}$ in. deep into the exposed area. Replace the borer with its pulp in the bottle.

Procedure. **Preparation of Specimen.** *Method A.*—Place a closed, sterile Petri dish on the pan of the balance and determine its tared weight. Cut the envelope in which the sample is received along the flap with a sterile knife or scissors. Open the envelope by pressing the sides in without touching the inner surface, and remove the sample with sterile tongs. Hold the edge of the sample sheet in one hand, trim with sterile scissors and discard the outer edges. Make a series of cuts about $\frac{1}{4}$ to $\frac{1}{2}$ in. apart, parallel to the side of the sheet and opposite the edge held in the hand. Partially remove the cover on the tared Petri dish on the balance but retain the cover on the pan. Cut squares of the sample directly into the dish by making a series of cuts perpendicular to those made previously.

Cut enough paper to give a 5.0-g. moisture-free specimen and aseptically adjust the amount to within 0.1 g. Replace the cover.

Method B.—Remove the corkborer containing the sample discs from the container. With a sterile glass rod, eject the sample into a tared Petri dish on the pan of the balance and aseptically adjust the weight of the specimen to 5.0 ± 0.1 g. Replace the cover of the Petri dish.

Disintegration.—With sterile tongs, remove the specimen from the dish and place in the disintegrator jar with enough sterile water to give a fiber consistency of 1 percent. In adding material to the jar, do not touch the metal cap with the hands, but lift it by grasping the paper hood placed over the cap before sterilizing. Lift both hood and metal cap only enough to permit access to the jar. If the specimen of paper or board requires disintegration, cool the water to prevent the temperature from exceeding 45°C. (113°F.) during disintegration. Let the paper hood remain on the cap at all times to prevent possible contamination through any opening in the metal cap or around the top of the jar.

Place the jar containing the weighted specimen and sterile water on the electric driving stand and operate until disintegration is complete.

Plating.—As soon as possible after disintegration, plate the specimen. The room in which the specimens are plated should be relatively free of air currents and dust. Also, about ½ hours before plating, sponge the surface of the work table with a solution of a suitable toxicant, such as 5 percent phenol or 0.05 percent phenyl mercuric acetate, further to eliminate extraneous microorganisms.

With a sterile pipet, distribute a total of 10 ml. of the 1 percent suspension, equal to 0.1 g., in approximately equal proportions between 5 Petri dishes. Plate additional higher dilutions if it is suspected that the sample has a high bacterial population. Add to each plate 15 to 20 ml. of standard tryptone glucose extract agar, cooled to about 45°C. (113°F.), then agitate the plates individually to disintegrate clumps of fibers and obtain an equal distribution of the fibers in the medium, using a quick, short reciprocating motion. It is important that all lumps be broken up in order that the plates may be examined easily and accurately. Pour one control plate (without paper pulp) from each container of nutrical medium used, to check its sterility.

If a higher dilution is required, add 10 ml. of the 1 percent suspension to a sterile, 90-ml. water blank and distribute 10 ml. of this suspension equally between 5 Petri dishes, which together will then contain 0.01 g. of the original pulp specimen.

If possible, the dilution should be adjusted to give from 30 to 300 colonies per plate.

NOTE.—The amount of fibrous material distributed over a given area of plate surface, has been found to be an important factor in the number of colonies observed in a given sample of paper or board. It is therefore important to follow carefully directions regarding the fiber consistency, the volume of sample used for plating, and the number and size of plates used.

Incubation.—After the plates have been agitated, place them on a level surface until the medium solidifies; then invert and incubate the plated specimens at 36 ± 1°C. (96.8 ± 1.8°F.) for 48 hours. Do not stack the plates too closely in the incubator.

NOTE.—A temperature as high as 36°C. may be unfavorable for the growth of certain organisms for which a lower temperature, of say 30°C., may be better suited. However, this or another incubating condition, renders the method nonstandard and the results should be qualified and reported accordingly.

Counting Plate Cultures.—After incubation, examine the cultures for the presence and number of bacterial colonies with the plate counter or by holding the plates against a dark back-ground, indirectly lighted.

If the specimen has been separated into individual fibers and well mixed with the medium, the colonies can be easily counted. If any particles are observed in the culture which cannot be definitely identified as colonies, they should be examined microscopically. Plates with spreading colonies should be counted if at all possible, otherwise they should be reported as spreading colonies. Examine control plates also and make a record of the number of colonies found on each control plate.

Report.—Report the results for paper or paperboard as the number of colonies per gram of moisture-free sample examined.

In all cases record the count to not more than two significant figures. For example, record a colony count of 144 as 140 and one of 145 as 150.

BRIGHTNESS OF PAPER AND PAPERBOARD

The term "brightness," as applied to white and near-white papers and paperboards, has come to be associated with the numerical value of their reflectance to light in the blue and violet portions of the spectrum, the measurement being made with an instrument known to be in calibration with a master instrument of the particular type and design described in Appendix A. This special use of the term was derived from long use of the word as descriptive of the "whiteness" of papers in the pulp and paper industry, and from the fact that the results from a brightness measurement on each of two "white" papers will usually correlate well with subjective estimates of the relative whiteness of the two samples. If this correlation does not obtain, it will usually be found that a subjectively whiter paper or paperboard can be produced from the materials used in the making of the sheet having the higher brightness test value.

This use of the term brightness is applicable to all naturally colored pulps and to papers and boards made therefrom. A measurement of brightness, *per se*, is not of great significance when the paper or paperboard contains added coloring matter (such as yellow or green dyestuff) which appreciably absorbs light in that part of the spectrum extending from about 400 to 500 mμ. Such a measurement may have significance if it be one of several reflectivities measured at various effective wavelengths for the purpose of establishing spectral reflectivity.

It is important to ensure as far as possible; (1) that all brightness tests be on a single scale, this being the one to which the presently used instruments conform; (2) that means be provided for checking the calibration of every instrument used for brightness testing so that the user may rely upon the test results; and (3) that criteria be provided by which one may judge whether or not any instrument differing in optical, geometrical, and photometrical characteristics from those now generally used, may safely be employed in performing the brightness test.

In this method there is given:

1. A detailed description (in the Appendix) of the significant spectral, geometrical, and photometrical characteristics of a master instrument to be maintained in a central standardizing laboratory, with a statement of the tolerances which must be maintained in its construction, maintenance, and use. This includes also a description of a method for the preparation of a primary reflectance standard, and of a system of secondary reflectance standards against which variations in the brightness scale with the passage of time, can be checked.

2. A description of a system of preparing, distributing and using reflectance standards by which the instrument can be maintained in continuous agreement, to within specified tolerances, with the master instrument.

3. The test procedure for using the instrument to measure the brightness of a sample of paper or paperboard.

Appendix A furnishes sufficient basic information to determine if a particular instrument which differs in constructional details from the master instrument, is likely to give results in satisfactory agreement with the master instrument. The system of calibrated secondary standards (see Appendix B) enables a check to be made by actual measurement, as to whether or not an instrument gives and continues to give, sufficiently accurate results.[80,81,82,83] This method is standardized as TAPPI T 452 m-58.

Apparatus. **Brightness instrument,** a reflection meter of such design and in such adjustment that its calibration is correct to within the tolerances specified in the section on calibration.

NOTE.—Identity of reading with that of the master instrument on one or two of the secondary standards, is not sufficient proof that readings on the test instrument and on the master instrument will be identical on all samples, even though the latter have brightness values very close to that of the secondary standard in question. If the instrument reads properly on all the secondary standards, usually it will be in proper calibration.

Ultimate standard of reflectance; magnesium oxide (MgO), prepared and deposited on a block of magnesium carbonate in accordance with TAPPI Standard T 633 m (p. 1460) (see also Appendix A, last section.)

Secondary standards, comprising at least five pads of paper tabs, and two working standards in each set, each having a brightness value accurately established by the master instrument.

Calibration.—When in use, check the instrument readings against the assigned values of all the secondary standards at least daily. If the instrument is found to be appreciably in error (the largest discrepancies being greater than about 0.3 point), adjust the instrument (frequently the focus of the lamp image) so that the readings do agree with the assigned values.

Obtain brightness standards set by the master instrument at monthly intervals, and calibrate the instrument with their aid as soon as they are received (see Appendix B).

At intervals of 1 to 3 years, depending upon the conditions of use, the instrument should be disassembled and carefully inspected, tested, and adjusted to insure that its geometrical and spectral variables fall within proper limits, and that its photometric system is accurate.

Test Specimen.—Cut a representative sample of the paper or board into 7 or more tabs 2 in. by $1\frac{1}{2}$ in. (51 by 38 mm.), to within $\frac{1}{16}$ in., the short dimension being in the machine direction, avoiding any watermark, dirt, or blemish. Assemble the tabs in a pad with the felt (or topliner) side up. Use the top tab only as a cover; mark it near one corner to identify the sample and the felt side. More than seven specimen tabs may be required for thin or transparent samples to prevent show-through of the backing weight. If show-through occurs, increase the number of tabs for the pad until the measured brightness is not changed by doubling its thickness.

Do not touch the test areas of the specimens with the fingers, and protect them from contamination, excessive heat or intense light.

Procedure.—Without touching the test areas of the specimens with the fingers, remove the protective cover tab, placing it on the back of the pad, then place the pad

[80] Instrumentation Studies XIII, Paper Trade J., **104,** No. 18, 47–53; No. 19, 51–63; No. 20, 45–49, May 6, 13, 20, 1937. XX, Paper Trade J., **105,** No. 18, 135–141; No. 19, 27–39, Oct. 28, Nov. 4, 1937; XXI, Paper Trade J., **105,** No. 25, 46–50, Dec. 16, 1937; XXII, Paper Trade J., **105,** No. 27, 42–46, Dec. 30, 1937; XXVIII, Paper Trade J., **107,** No. 20, 33–37, Nov. 17, 1938; XXIX, Paper Trade J., **107,** No. 25, 29–40, Dec. 22, 1938; XXVII, Paper Trade J., **112,** No. 1, 13–22, Jan. 2, 1941.

[81] Davis, M. N., Paper Trade J., **101,** No. 1, 36–44, July 4, 1935.

[82] Hunter, R. S., J. Optical Soc. Am., **30,** 536, 1940.

[83] Michaelson, J. L., Gen. Elec. Rev., **38,** No. 4, 194–196, April, 1935.

over the specimen aperture of the instrument with the machine direction of the paper parallel to the plane determined by the axes of the incident and reflected rays of light, and with the felt or topliner side, facing the instrument. If it is considered desirable (as in the testing of creped or embossed specimens) to orient the test specimen in some other direction or to average the readings in both principal directions, clearly and conspicuously state this in the report.

Place a 1-kg. weight having a flat base, upon the pad. Measure and record the brightness reading to 0.1 unit.

NOTE.—Detailed instructions for measuring the brightness will be found in Appendix A under "Photometric Characteristics."

Move the lower tab to the back of the pad and take another reading. Repeat this procedure until six different tabs have been tested.

Report.—Report the average percentage brightness of the sample (based on magnesium oxide = 100.00) to one decimal place, together with the minimum and maximum readings. State clearly and conspicuously any deviations from the standard procedure, and note any unusual features or characteristics of the sample.

APPENDIX A—MASTER INSTRUMENT

In order to evaluate the brightness of the standards employed for the adjustment and calibration of instruments used for measuring brightness as described in this method, a master instrument is maintained to measure correctly the brightness of paper relative to that of a freshly prepared magnesium oxide standard, which is taken equal to 100.0 percent.

The master instrument is defined by spectral, geometrical, and photometrical characteristics, which are described as follows:

Spectral Characteristics.—(a) The effective wavelength of the instrument, used with the filter required for the determination of brightness, is 457.0 ± 0.5 mμ.

The effective wavelength is that wavelength of monochromatic light for which the transmittance of a filter having a spectral transmittance given by $T = a + b\gamma$, is equal to that determined with the master instrument; after a correction is made for effects associated with refraction and reflection, angular spread of rays through the filter, photometric error, and the wavelength error in the spectrophotometer employed to determine the spectral transmittance. In the foregoing equation, which need hold only for that wavelength range encompassed by the brightness filter, T is transmittance, a and b are constants, and λ is the wavelength.

If the filter having a linear spectral transmittance consists of a film or plate, its transmittance is measured relative to a clear, nonabsorbing film or plate of equal thickness and similar index of refraction; if it be a liquid filter, the transmittance is measured relative to a clear, nonabsorbing liquid filter comprised of an identical filter cell containing the pure solvent used for the solution in the absorbing liquid filter.

NOTE.—A solution in a filter cell having a linear spectral transmittance over the range 400 to 500 mμ may conveniently comprise a dilution in distilled or clear water, of "Coca-Cola" which has been warmed to remove the dissolved gases, the concentration being in the neighborhood of about 40 percent Coca-Cola and 60 percent water, the exact concentration being arrived at by a test of the linearity of the spectral transmittance. The spectral transmittance must be measured relative to an exactly similar filter cell containing distilled water.

The spectral transmittance is so measured in both the master instrument and the spectrophotometer, and the cells are so disposed with respect to apertures, as to minimize error due to scattering of light in the filters and to make such error as may be due to light scattering the same in the master instrument and the spectrophotometer.

Note.—In the master instrument the filter cells are placed just above the aperture which admits light to the photoelectric cell, so that the ratio of diameter of aperture to a distance between the filter cell and aperture, is not small. When the filter cells are placed in the spectro-photometer, they are so positioned that a similar ratio of aperture diameter to filter cell-aperture distance, obtains.

(b) The area under the curve, which represents the product for all wavelengths greater than 700 mμ of the spectral sensitivity of the photoelectric cell, and the spectral transmittance of all filters between the sample aperture and the photoelectric cell, are so small compared with the similar area for the wavelength range 360 to 510 mμ that no detachable part of the photoelectric current may be ascribed to infrared fluorescent light arising in the test specimen.

(c) The spectral energy distribution of the light incident upon the test specimen is such that it will not appreciably heat or fade the specimens during the course of meas-urement.

(d) The effective wavelength, 457.0 ± 0.5 mμ, is obtained by the combination of (1) lamp, glass optics, and filters, for which the mathematical product of relative spec-tral energy distribution and spectral transmission is $F(\lambda)$ and (2) a photoelectric cell chosen to make the effective wavelength 457.0 ± 0.5 mμ where $F(\lambda)$ is the function of the wavelength as given in Table 55-9.

TABLE 55-9. PRODUCT OF RELATIVE SPECTRAL ENERGY DISTRIBUTION, SPECTRAL TRANSMISSION OF GLASS OPTICS AND SPECTRAL TRANSMISSIONS OF ALL FILTERS

Wavelength mμ	$F(\lambda)$ (arbitrary units)	Wavelength mμ	$F(\lambda)$ (arbitrary units)
360	0.0	440	58.6
370	0.1	450	90.5
380	0.8	460	99.8
390	1.9	470	83.5
400	4.4	480	52.0
410	8.3	490	23.1
420	16.2	500	8.0
430	32.1	510	0.0

Note.—The foregoing may be illustrated with information regarding the master instrument with which the existing scale of brightness has been established. The function $F(\lambda)$ is the product of the relative spectral energy distribution of the light from a concentrated filament lamp operated at a color temperature of 3199°K; the spectral transmission of four aspheric lenses (two between light source and sample aperture and two between sample aperture and photoelectric cell); the spectral transmission of a filter cell with a 1-cm. thickness of a 10 percent copper sulphate solution containing 1 percent concentrated H$_2$SO$_4$ (placed between light source and sample aperture to remove heat from incident rays); the spectral transmission of a particular Wratten 49 filter, the measured spectral transmission of which has arbitrarily been taken as standard (this filter being placed between the sample aperture and photoelectric cell); and the spectral transmission of a Jena BG-18 melt, S1152 filter, ground to a thickness of 0.020 in., which is placed between the sample aperture and the photoelectric cell, to remove any infrared fluorescent light arising in the test specimen.

The photoelectric cell used is satisfactory if, and only if, its use results in the instru-ment having the proper effective wavelength, as described in (a) above.

The permissible range of variation from the values in Table 55-9 is that corresponding to the wavelength range there given, ±1.5 mμ. Independent of this restriction upon $F(\lambda)$, the effective wavelength is required to be between 456.5 and 457.5 mμ.

(e) The minimum value of the spectral sensitivity of the photoelectric cell or combination of filter and photoelectric cell in the range 400 to 500 mμ, is not less than one-third the maximum value in that range.

This restriction precludes the use of a combination of filter and photoelectric cell or photoelectric cell alone, which gives rise to proper effective wavelength, but is responsive to a wavelength range less than that encompassed by the data of Table 55-9. The spectral sensitivity curve should not have a pronounced curvature in the range 400 to 500 mμ.

Geometrical Characteristics.—(a) The mean angle of incidence of rays upon the test specimen is 45 ± 1°.

(b) The incident rays upon a point of the test specimen is confined within a cone having a half angle of 11.5 ± 2°. This cone is filled with light, has its vertex in the sample aperture, and has its base at the emergent aperture of the condensing lenses.

(c) The specimen aperture is circular with a diameter of 0.480 ± 0.020 in. (12.2 ± 0.5 mm.). The exit aperture of the optical system which accepts reflected rays for measurement, is coincident with the image of the disc, concentric and coplanar with the sample aperture, and has a diameter of 0.375 ± 0.020 in. (9.0 ± 0.5 mm.) so that light reflected from the rim of the sample aperture does not reach the photoelectric cell.

(d) The mean angle of rays reflected by the test specimen and accepted by the receiving optical system for measurement, is between 0 and 1° with the normal to the plane of the sample aperture.

(e) The accepted reflected rays are confined to a cone having a half angle of 22.5 ± 2°.

Photometrical Characteristics.—(a) The null photometric method is employed, the light intensity being regulated by means of sector diaphragms. A test made as follows: with the test specimen over its aperture, the sectors of the photometer are opened to a reflectance reading corresponding to the reflectance of the standard and the photoelectric current is noted; then, with the standard over the aperture, the sectors are adjusted so that the photoelectric current returns to the previously noted value and the reflectance of the sample is read from the reflectance scale.

(b) The sector diaphragm is located between the pair of lenses of the receiving optical system with its center on the optical axis, and consists of: (1) a pair of sectors in a fixed plate, each bounded by radii separated by 93°, and circles of radii which are respectively 0.188 and 1.125 in. (4.67 and 28.57 mm.) each radius being constant to within ±0.001 in. (0.025 mm.); the two members of the pair being separated by 180° and centered upon a line which is perpendicular to the plane containing the axes of the incident and reflected rays of light; and (2) a rotatable pair of sectors, geared to a reflectance dial, each sector being bounded by radii separated by 90° and circles of radii respectively 0.188 ± 0.001 in. (4.67 ± 0.2 mm.) and approximately 1.2 in. (31 mm.), the two members of the pair being separated by 180°; the nature of the gear train being such that when the reflectance dial is set at 100, the openings formed by the two sectors are each approximately 83°, and when the reflectance dial is set at zero, the openings are 0.0 ± 0.1°.

(c) The defining edges of the sector diaphragm are thin, beveled, and blackened as to be nonreflecting; The plane of the sharp edges of the fixed sectors is in contact with that of the rotatable sectors, and the two pairs of sectors are concentric to within 0.001 in. (0.025 mm).

(d) The reflectance dial and the train of gears linking this dial with the sector diaphragm, are of such accuracy that the total area of opening of the sector diaphragm is directly proportional to the dial reading, to within 0.1 percent of the full opening.

Calibration of Working Standards for Use with Master Instrument.—The ultimate standard of reflectance is prepared in accordance with TAPPI Standard T 633 m with the magnesium carbonate deposited on a block of magnesium carbonate. The block is split in two and, with a clean straight-edge, an inner surface is scraped so as to make it plane. The magnesium carbonate is deposited on this surface and at least six such blocks are prepared.

In turn, each block is placed over the specimen aperture of the master instrument upon shims which have been previously placed in position to hold the blocks so that the easily compressed layer of magnesium carbonate will only just touch the surface. This may be judged by sighting beneath the magnesium carbonate block. If shims are not used, a small disc of the magnesium carbonate will be extruded into the sample opening, and an erroneously high instrument reading will result. The reflectances of each of the prepared surfaces are compared with each other, and any obviously inferior surface is discarded. The reflectances of a master working standard are measured by assigning a reflectance of 100.0 percent to each magnesium carbonate surface and the results are averaged to arrive at the assigned reflectance of the master working standard. This procedure is repeated for at least 15 different master working standards, eight of which exhibit a reasonably flat spectral reflectance curve, and seven of which are buff colored (having spectral reflectances somewhat similar to that of typical pulps).

APPENDIX B—CALIBRATION SERVICE

The central laboratory to which is delegated the responsibility of maintaining and operating the master instrument will, upon arrangement, distribute secondary standards for the calibration service. A set of secondary standards, usually will comprise at least 5 pads of paper tabs and 2 working standards of brightness accurately established by measurement on the master instrument.

The paper standards will cover a range from about 60 to 85 percent brightness. The paper from which these standards are prepared will be white, have a fairly stable brightness, be uniform in brightness, and have a relatively smooth, but not a super-calendered, surface.

The working standards will have a surface not deviating from a true plane by more than 0.0015 in. (0.038 mm.) in a central circle $\frac{5}{8}$ in. (16 mm.) diameter. The nature of the surface polish and hardness, and the optical stability of the material will be such that the brightness during one month of intensive but careful use will not vary more than 0.3 point; be such that it may easily and effectively cleaned, and be sufficiently resistant to withstand several cleanings per day. The color of the working standards will be white or cream, with the maximum spectral reflectivity not more than twice the minimum, over the wavelength range of 400 to 500 mμ.

The standards for the calibration of instruments which have spectral, geometrical, or photometrical characteristics differing from those of the master instrument require special consideration. They will comprise only paper standards similar to those described above, except for a possible difference in size, and the standard scale of brightness should be transferred to such an instrument only through the use of such paper standards. The readings from such an instrument and the master instrument may not agree for both the paper and the working standards because of differences between these standards in translucency, surface, spectral or other characteristics. For this reason, special working standards for such an instrument are to be evaluated by that instrument in terms of the brightness values assigned by the master instrument to the paper standards furnished. After having evaluated the average reflectance of any such special working standard by means of the several paper standards, the individual reflectance readings should not deviate from the average reflectance by more than 0.3 point.

A set of calibrated paper and working standards will be distributed at monthly intervals. Upon their receipt, the working standards in use should be returned to the central laboratory for restandardization.

NOTE.—Secondary standards used for the calibration service will be paper regardless of whether the instrument is used for paper or paperboard.

This method in all essential details, is the same as TAPPI Standard T 217 m, Brightness of Pulp (p. 1351).

This revision changes the title and method to include paperboard and makes a number of editorial changes without altering the previous equipment or procedure.

REFERENCE

Natl. Bur. Standards Letter Circular L.C. 547 "Preparation and Colorimetric Properties of a Magnesium Oxide Reflectance Standard."

STRETCH OF PAPER AND PAPERBOARD

The stretch of a paper is important whenever a web is handled under tension because, together with its tensile breaking strength, the stretch is closely related to the initial tearing strength. A satisfactory stretch is necessary for a sheet to fold well and to resist local stress, as when used for packaging. It is also important in twisting papers, cable papers, corrugating board, toweling and tissues. Stretch is also a factor in the bursting strength test—a sheet of high stretch has a greater bursting strength than a sheet of the same tensile strength but possessing a lower stretch.

The numerical result includes not only both the elastic and the inelastic stretch of the paper up to failure but also the small distance through which the broken strip will elongate during the test while being held together by protruding fibers, as this factor prevents the indicating mechanism from being released at the reading when the break starts. For this reason the test may be termed more correctly "the percentage elongation of a strip of paper up to, and partly including, rupture under tension." This method is standardized as TAPPI T 457 m-46.

Apparatus.—(The following requirements, except Items 2 and 4, are the same as for the tensile breaking strength apparatus in TAPPI Standard T 404 m, p. 1395).

The instrument used shall have: 1. Two clamps whose centers shall be in the same plane parallel with the direction of motion of the applied stress and so aligned that they will hold the test specimen in one plane throughout the test without slippage. At the start of the test the edges of the jaws of the clamps shall be 180 ± 10 mm. (7.09 ± 0.04 in.) apart, except that for coarse papers, such as building papers, and for paperboards over 0.012 in. thick, the distance may be from 152 mm. (6.0 in.) to 203 mm. (8.0 in.).

2. Means of applying a predetermined initial tension to the test specimen while it is being clamped.

3. Means of applying a gradually increasing load to the test specimen until it breaks, the increase being such that the additional load applied each second is not different by more than 5 percent from the additional load applied in the previous second. (This condition is fulfilled by the usual pendulum type of apparatus.)

4. Means of indicating the elongation of the test specimen up to the instant of complete fracture to an accuracy of within 0.5 mm. (0.02 in.).

Calibration.—With the pendulum type of tester, clamp the pendulum at zero, set the lower clamp near the upper clamp and set the stretch indicator at zero, with the trigger mechanism operating the stretch indicator adjusted to and engaged with the lower clamp. With inside vernier calipers measure the distance between the clamps to the nearest 0.01 in. (0.2 mm.). Move the lower clamp down a little distance and again measure the distance between the clamps. The indicated reading should correspond with the difference between the two vernier readings. Repeat the same procedure for various points along the elongation scale.

An alternative method of calibration is as follows: grip a heavy rubber strip between the clamps of the tester and compare the changes in the indicated readings with the distances between the clamps, as measured with vernier calipers, using a rule with squared ends to extend the range of the calipers if required.

If necessary, prepare a calibration table or chart for applying any corrections.

To ensure that the stretch-indicating mechanism is stable, place the pendulum in position about halfway up the scale, set the stretch indicator at some intermediate position, and then jar the instrument slightly and note whether the stretch indicator moves. If it does move, either the stretch mechanism must be counterbalanced or the spring friction holding it in position must be increased. Otherwise a serious error may be caused in the reading by the jar that occurs, especially when a strong specimen breaks under test.

If necessary, adjust the overhang on the trigger-release mechanism so that, immediately after the strip breaks, the indicator no longer is actuated.

Unless the apparatus is altered in any vital way, there is no need to repeat the calibration once it has been established; but if the stretch-indicating mechanism is not counterbalanced, it should be tested for stability to jarring from time to time.

Test Specimen.—The requirements for the test specimens are the same as for the tensile breaking strength method, TAPPI Standard T 404 m. They shall be strips cut accurately and parallel to within 0.1 mm. and with clean edges, in each principal direction of the paper, and over 200 mm., preferably 250 mm. (9.9 in.) long. The width shall be 12.7 mm. (0.5 in.), 15.0 mm. (0.59 in.) or 15.9 mm. (0.625 in.), except that for coarse papers, such as building papers, or for paperboards over 0.012 inch thick, the width may be 1 in. or 2 in. The specimens shall be conditioned according to TAPPI Standard T 402 m (Vol. 2, Part B, p. 1795). They shall be free from abnormalities, watermarks, creases and wrinkles.

Procedure.—The test shall be made in an atmosphere condition according to TAPPI Standard T 402 m.

Load each specimen in the following manner[84] until it breaks.

1. For weak papers such as tissues, paper towels, newsprint, etc., requiring a breaking load of 5 pounds (2.3 kg.) or less, have the machine speed so adjusted that fracture occurs in not less than 5 nor more than 15 seconds.

2. For other papers, and paperboards, requiring a breaking load of not more than 30 pounds (13.6 kg.) use a constant rate of loading of about 1 ± 0.32 pound (0.45 $\pm$ 0.15 kg.) per second.

3. For papers and paperboards requiring a breaking load of more than 30 pounds (13.6 kg.), adjust the machine speed so that fracture occurs in not less than 30 nor more than 45 seconds.

The appropriate rate of loading may be determined from a trial test strip.

Tightly grip one end of each strip in the upper clamp after placing the strip loosely in the lower clamp and checking its alignment. Then apply an initial stress of 0.5 pound (0.23 kg.) to each strip before clamping, except for papers having a tensile strength of less than 5.0 pounds (2.3 kg.). In the latter case, subject 2 or 3 test specimens from the same sample of paper to a preliminary tensile test and apply an initial tension equal to 10 ± 2.5 percent of the average break load so determined, to each strip while

[84] Items 1, 2 and 3 are the same as for TAPPI Standard T 404 m.

being clamped (see Notes). With apparatus in which the test specimen is clamped vertically, this is conveniently done by temporarily clipping a suitable weight to the lower protruding end of the strip, before tightening the lower clamp. Tightly clamp both ends of the strip and apply the load.

Reject readings from individual strips if the strip slips or breaks in or at the edge of the clamps. Record the result of each individual reading to two significant figures.

Test at least 10, and preferably 20, strips cut in each principal direction of the paper. If the mean value of the lowest and the highest reading differs from the average of all the readings by more than 5 percent, test more specimens until there is agreement within this limit. In the case of an irregular sheet of paper, it therefore may be necessary to conduct a much larger number of tests than 10. An isolated very high or low result, which is not repeated in duplicate, shall be discarded when a consistent average is obtained without the abnormal reading.

Creped Paper.—In testing creped paper follow the same procedure except, if necessary, reduce the length of the specimen to enable the elongation to be within the range of the indicating mechanism, and apply no more initial tension to the test strip before clamping than is required to straighten it.

Report.—Results obtained on strips cut in the machine direction shall be reported as stretch, machine direction, and results obtained on strips cut in the cross direction shall be reported as stretch, cross direction. The average value of the results on the individual strips shall be reported as a percentage of the length between the clamps, to one decimal place.

A complete report requires in addition:

1. Maximum and minimum results and number of strips tested.
2. The length of the test specimen—*i.e.*, the distance between clamps at the start of the test.
3. The width of the test specimen.
4. A statement of the rate of loading used.

Reproducibility of Results.—Duplicate determinations on different sets of samples from the same shipment, and on different testing instruments, are expected to agree to within 0.2 for results of 2.0 or less, and within 5 percent for higher results.

NOTE 1.—The initial load on the strips specified in the procedure is to remove any cockles or waviness which might be present. With most papers this small initial load will not cause any sensible extension beyond removing the defects mentioned. The value of the initial tension is not critical for flat papers; hence, except for very precise work, it is sufficient to remove the waviness or cockles by application of a slight tension to the strip with the fingers before tightening the clamp in the tester.

NOTE 2.—The stretch test for some papers is not appreciably influenced by the rate of loading, while for others, especially creped papers, doubling the rate of loading may increase the result by as much as 5 percent of the recorded amount.

NOTE 3.—If a smaller distance between the clamps is employed, a higher test may be expected, since the elongation after the initial fracture has been made is appreciable and is independent of the length of the strip used. Like the tensile breaking strength test, the effect of the length of strip on the stretch is also somewhat dependent upon the formation of the sheet. In addition, the accurate indication of stretch for strips much less than 180 mm. is open to question unless unusually good apparatus is employed. Varying the width of the test specimen between 12 mm. and 25 mm., with a proportionate rate of loading, does not in general make much difference in the test results, except for unbeaten long-fibered papers, where the differences may be appreciable—perhaps 10 percent of the recorded amount.

NOTE 4.—The test is designed to be carried out, if desirable, at the same time as the standard method for determing the tensile strength. For precise work or for papers having a relatively low stretch (less than 2 percent), the stretch attachment to the usual pendulum tester is not very accurate, because deficiencies in the release mechanism tend to give unduly high results. An instrument especially designed for measuring stretch according to this method is available, in which the sample is clamped under a predetermined tension in a horizontal plane and the load is applied transversely to the center of the strip by a plunger moving vertically. The stretch of the strip before breaking is indicated by a scale on the plunger or computed from the vernier, showing the distance which the plunger traveled before the strip broke.

REFERENCES

Houston, Paul L., "Effect of Length and Width of Test Specimen on the Breaking Strength and Elongation of Paper," Paper Trade J., **76**, No. 12, 54–55, March 22, 1923; Technical Association Papers, **6**, 72–73, 1923.

Clark, James d'A., "Some Observations on Burst, Tensile, and Stretch Tests," Paper Trade J., **102**, No. 2, 40–42, Jan. 9, 1936; Technical Association Papers, **19**, 264–266, 1936.

Instrumentation Studies—Report No. 36, "The Measurement of the Stretch of Paper," American Paper and Pulp Association, New York, Feb. 10, 1942.

SURFACE WETTABILITY OF PAPER
(ANGLE-OF-CONTACT METHOD)

This method is for a quantitative measurement of the resistance of paper surfaces to wetting. It is useful for determining the writing and ruling qualities of papers, also investigating problems related to the resistance which the surface of paper offers to water or an aqueous ink. The procedure recommended is that of Lafontaine[85] for measuring the angle of contact. A method proposed by Codwise[86,87] which depends on the spreading of a drop of water, is described as a supplementary test.

It is well-known that the advancing angle of contact between a liquid and a smooth solid surface is a measure of the wettability of the latter by the former and the following procedure has been evolved around this fact. This method is standardized as TAPPI T 458 m-59.

Apparatus. **Projection Apparatus.**—A preferred form, a side elevation of which is shown in Fig. 55-19, consists of:

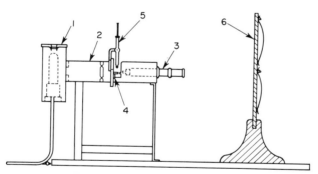

FIG. 55-19. Projection Apparatus.

(a) Ventilated lamp housing, 1, containing a 250-watt projection lamp.

(b) Tube, 2, containing a lens to concentrate the beam of light.

(c) Microscope draw-tube, 3, fitted with a 25-mm. objective and a 5X ocular, mounted horizontally beside the stage.

(d) Horizontal stage, 4, to hold the specimen under test, the stage being vertically adjustable.

[85] Lafontaine, G. H., Paper Trade J., **113**, No. 6, 29, Aug. 7, 1941.
[86] Codwise, P. W., Tech. Assoc. Papers, **13**, 200, 1930.
[87] Codwise, P. W., Tech. Assoc. Papers, **22**, 246, 1939.

(e) Syringe, 5, such as a 1-ml. hypodermic, equipped with a No. 27 stainless steel needle. (This gives 150 to 200 drops per ml.)

(f) Frosted glass screen, 6, with clamps to hold a sheet of transparent paper on its far side.

(g) A cell containing copper sulphate solution inserted between the lens which concentrates the light rays and the stage on which the sample is placed, to reduce the heat on the specimen and drop.

If the above equipment is not available, a suitable microscope can be arranged to project the image of the drop on the glass screen. Small projection microscopes are available with a magnification of about 30X, suitable for the purpose. A small buret or pipet adjusted to deliver 0.05 to 0.06 ml. may be substituted for the hypodermic syringe if desired.

Solutions.—For determining the sizing quantity for writing with common ink, use the standard writing ink specified in TAPPI Standard T 431 m (p. 1421).

For determining the sizing quality of paper for ruling and similar inks, use a solution of 0.01 g. of a pure water-soluble, blue dye dissolved in 100 ml. of distilled water.

Test Specimen.—Take representative samples of the paper, and if possible identify and mark the wire and felt sides. If not possible, mark all the sheets on one side of the paper as "A." Without touching the areas to be tested, cut at least five 4 by ½-in. clean specimen strips which are free from blemishes or watermarks. Mark one side of each strip "W," "F," or "A" to identify the side.

Procedure.—Condition and test the specimens in an atmosphere in accordance with TAPPI Standard T 402 m (Vol. 2, Part B, p. 1795).

Place a test strip on a slide on the stage and hold it in close contact with the surface of the slide by means of small weights placed close enough on each side of the syringe located above the stage to prevent distortion of the paper when it is wetted by the drop of ink or water.

Set the tip of the hypodermic needle 2.5 mm. from the surface of the strip and deposit a drop of about 0.05 ml., on the paper. Project the image of the drop, enlarged 25 to 30 times, on the glass screen, at the back of which is clamped a sheet of transparent onionskin paper. Draw a horizontal line on the transparent paper coinciding with the image of the base of the drop, and as soon as the specified time of contact of the drop with the paper has elapsed, quickly draw two tangents to the curve at the two points of contact with the base line. The interior angle between the base line and each tangent, is designated as the angle of contact. Measure the angles with a protractor.

For initial wettability, used as a measure of ruling quality, measure the angle after the drop has been in contact with the paper for 5 seconds. For rate of change in wettability, used as a measure of writing quality, make two measurements, one after 5 seconds and the other after 60 seconds.

During the test, turn off the lamp when not needed, to avoid heating the specimens on the stage any more than is necessary.

Calculate the Rate of Change of Wettability as follows:

$$R = (A - a)/55,$$

where: R is the rate at which the angle of wetting changes, in degrees per second;

A is the average angle of contact after 5 seconds; and

a is the average angle of contact after 60 seconds.

Test at least 5 specimens on each side of the paper. Move the transparent paper behind the screen to a new position between successive tests.

Report.—State the liquid used for the test.

Report the average, the minimum and the maximum contact angles separately for each side of the paper, to the nearest degree, as the Initial Wettability.

Report the average Rate of Wettability Change, for each side of the paper in degrees per second, to 2 significant figures.

Precision.—While variations between individual drops on one side of a single strip of paper may be as great as 5°, the average of 10 measurements will usually not vary by more than 2° between two strips cut from the same sheet of paper, when tested on the same side of the sheet, provided the variations in finish between the two strips cut from different parts of the sheet are not too pronounced.

Interpretation of Results.—In considering the results of the angle-of-contact test, the following factors should be borne in mind. These affect the results in different degrees: (a) the wetting power of the solution used; (b) the wettability of the sizing agent used in sizing the paper; and (c) the surface texture or finish of the paper.

For instance, the standard ink will show smaller angles of contact than will water, since ink wets the paper more readily than water. Papers surface-sized with starch, will generally show smaller angles than papers of about the same finish surface-sized with glue. A machine-finished paper with a grainy surface will show a greater angle of contact than a plated or calendered paper sized to the same degree.

In practice, ruling results will depend on both the surface wettability and the finish of the paper; the angle of contact gives a good idea of what may be expected. It has been found that excellent ruling will result when the average angle of contact with water lies between 100° and 90°; when the angle of contact is greater than 110°, breaks are likely to occur in the ruled lines; when the angle is smaller than 90°, the ruling ink is likely to feather.

In judging the writing qualities of paper, the tendency of a writing paper to feather will be indicated by the decrease in the angle of contact between the 5- and 60-second measurements. In hard-sized papers, the angle of contact will not change perceptibly between the 5- and 60-second readings. If the initial wettability is less than 90°, it is quite likely the paper will feather as soon as it is written upon. Medium-sized papers will show feathering occasionally when the ink has only partly penetrated the paper.

The range of contact angles for specific conditions is small, consequently careful testing technique is required as is indicated by the above examples.

Additional Information.—In cases where the above equipment is not available, or to supplement the test described above, there is another method: the manner of a spreading of a larger drop of water on the paper surface. A drop of distilled water, about 0.2 ml., is applied from a pipet by holding the tip just above the surface, in such a way that the tip remains in the drop as it is being formed. Upon coming into contact with the paper, the drop tends to form a spherical shape and, when the surface is sized, the surface of contact between the paper and the drop assumes a clear, bright appearance which gradually darkens as the water penetrates the surface.

When the drop of water is first placed upon a sized surface, the appearance of the paper around it is unchanged. However, as the wetting of the surface proceeds, a feathering around the drop commences. The period of time from the application of the drop to the surface, until the water commences to creep outwards from the drop, is recorded as the numerical result of this test. The range of results is wide, and when the test is made at standard temperature and humidity, it is quite reproducible. An unsized surface will feather immediately; a poorly sized writing paper, which will feather with pen and ink, may give only a 10-minute test; a satisfactory writing surface, 10 hours; and a hard-sized board surface, over 24 hours. If the test extends over a long period, the drop of water should be covered with a watch glass to prevent evaporation.

Similar methods: Canadian C.P.P.A., F.3.

AIR RESISTANCE OF PAPER

This method of test is applicable to papers and paper products which permit the passage of 100 ml. of air in 2 to 1800 seconds, except those which cannot be clamped securely against surface and edge leakage, such as crepe and corrugated papers. This method is standardized as TAPPI T 460 m-49.

Apparatus. **Instrument.**—The instrument shall consist of an outer cylinder which is partly filled with oil, and an inner cylinder, having an open or closed top, sliding freely in the outer cylinder. Air pressure for the test shall be provided by the weight of the inner cylinder. The instrument shall be arranged to furnish air pressure to the specimen held between clamping plates having a circular orifice with an area of 1.00 sq. in. The clamping plates may form the top of the inner cylinder, or may be mounted in the base of the apparatus, the latter construction being preferable. An elastic gasket shall be attached to the clamping plate on the side exposed to air pressure, and the paper specimen shall be held in contact with the gasket when clamped for test. The purpose of the gasket is to prevent leakage of air between the surface of the paper and the clamping plate.

The gasket shall consist of a thin, elastic, oil-resistant, nonoxidizing material, having a smooth surface. Thiokol, grade ST, polished plate molded, $\frac{1}{32}$ in. thick, 50 to 60 durometer hardness, is a satisfactory material. The inside diameter of the gasket shall be 1.125 in. and the outside diameter shall be 1.375 in. The aperture in the gasket shall be accurately aligned with the aperture in the clamping plates and the gasket shall be securely attached to the clamping plate. To align and protect the gasket in use, it shall be cemented with shellac into a groove machined in the clamping plate. This groove shall be concentric with the aperture in the opposing orifice plate. It shall be 1.128 in. inside diameter and 0.020 in. deep. Its outside diameter may be 1.385 in. for convenience in inserting and attaching the gasket.

The outer cylinder shall be 10 in. high and shall have an internal diameter of 3.25 in. It shall be equipped with four bars, each 7.5 in. long, 0.094 in. wide, and 0.094 in. thick, mounted vertically and equidistantly on the inner surface of the outer cylinder to act as guide tracks for the movable cylinder. The movable inner cylinder shall be graduated in units of 50 ml. and shall have a total range of 350 ml. It shall be 10 in. high, and shall have an external diameter of 3.00 in., and an internal diameter of 2.916 in. It shall weigh 567 ± 1.0 g.

NOTE.—Some inner cylinders are also graduated in units of 25 ml. for the first 100 ml., and have a graduation at the 400-ml. interval.

Oil.—The oil used with the instrument shall be a lubricating oil having a viscosity of 60 to 70 seconds Saybolt Universal at 100°F. (37.8°C.) and a flash point of not less than 275°F. (135°C.).

NOTE.—A light spindle oil is suitable for this purpose. Oil is used in preference to water because it does not affect the moisture content of the sample, nor deteriorate the aluminum inner cylinder. The oil should not contain any essential oil, or other easily volatile oil, and for that reason, a minimum flash point is specified.

Calibration.—The apparatus shall be tested for air leakage by clamping a thin piece of smooth, hard-surfaced, airtight material, such as metal foil or cellophane, between the orifice plates, and testing by the standard method described under "Procedure." The leakage shall not exceed 50 ml. in 5 hours.

Test Specimen.—The test specimen shall be approximately $1\frac{7}{8}$ in. wide, and 5 in. long, except that specimens of any size larger than $1\frac{7}{8}$ in. in both directions may be used in the apparatus having the clamp in the base. The test specimens shall be conditioned for testing according to TAPPI Standard T 402 m (Vol. 2, Part B, p. 1795).

Procedure.—Make the test in an atmosphere conditioned according to TAPPI Standard T 402 m. Place the instrument on a level surface so that the cylinders are vertical. Fill the outer cylinder with oil to a depth of approximately 5 in., as indicated by a ring marked on the inner surface of the cylinder.

For the instrument having the clamp in the top of the inner cylinder, raise the inner cylinder and hold in a raised position with one hand, clamp the specimen between the clamping plates, then lower the inner cylinder and allow it to float in the oil. Alternatively, the inner cylinder may be removed, the specimen clamped, and the cylinder replaced in the outer cylinder, lowering gently until it floats in the oil.

Note.—The proper procedure for clamping the specimen is to hold the inner cylinder in a raised position with one hand, and alternately tighten the knurled nuts so that the clamping pressure will be equal on both sides; or, the inner cylinder may be removed and replaced in the outer cylinder after the paper has been clamped. If only one nut at a time is turned down, the clamp will not bear evenly on the specimen, and air leakage will occur between the surfaces of the clamp and the specimen.

For the instrument having the clamp in the base, first raise the inner cylinder until its top rim is supported by the catch, and then clamp the specimen between the clamping plates. Then lower the inner cylinder gently until it floats.

When a steady movement has been attained, measure with a stopwatch, or other timing device, the number of seconds required for the first two consecutive 50-ml. intervals to pass the rim of the outer cylinder, starting at the zero mark. With very resistant papers the reading may be taken at the end of the first 50-ml. interval and the results doubled. With very open or porous papers a larger volume of air may be read on the inner cylinder and converted to the 100-ml. standard quantity. In cases where it is not possible to obtain a steady movement of the inner cylinder before the zero mark is reached, the test may be started at the 50-ml. mark.

Note.—Precautions should be taken to avoid subjecting the apparatus to vibration, as this increases the rate of air displacement.

Test at least 5 samples with the felt side up and 5 samples with the wire side up, and average the results. If the mean value of the highest and lowest reading differs from the average of all the readings by more than 10 percent, additional samples shall be tested until there is agreement within these limits. An irregular sheet of paper may, therefore, require more than 10 tests. An isolated very high or very low reading, which is not repeated in duplicate, shall be discarded when a consistent average is obtained without the abnormal reading

Report.—The average number of seconds required for the displacement of 100 ml. of air through an area of 1 sq. in. of the paper shall be reported as the air resistance.

Reproducibility of Results.—The agreement to be expected between duplicate series of independent tests is approximately as follows:

Air Resistance, seconds	Reproducibility, %
40	5
100	6
200	8
300	10

Additional Information.—American Society for Testing and Materials Designation D 202-38T, Air Resistance, describes the instrument having an open-top inner cylinder.

REFERENCE

"First Report of the Paper Testing Committee to the Technical Section of the Paper-makers' Association of Great Britain and Ireland," pp. 62–66, 1937.

FLAMMABILITY OF TREATED PAPER AND PAPERBOARD

This method is applicable to papers and paperboards of all types, not over $\frac{1}{16}$ in. thick, that have been treated to prevent the spread of flame when ignited. Such papers are commonly designated in the trade as "flameproofed," but in reality they are merely flame resistant to a more or less degree. This method is standardized as TAPPI T 461 m-48.

Apparatus. **Stopwatch.**

Metal frame designed to hold a specimen of paper 2.75 in. wide and 8.25 in. long by gripping $\frac{3}{8}$ in. of each long edge in a clamp. The specimen with an area 2 by 8.25 in. thus exposed is held with the long axis in a vertical position.

Test flame is supplied by a Bunsen or Tirrill gas burner having a tube of $\frac{3}{8}$ in. inside diameter.

Test Specimen.—The test specimen shall consist of a piece of the sample 2.75 in. wide and 8.25 in. long. Specimens shall be cut in both principal directions of the sheet.

Procedure.—Clamp the test specimen in the metal frame with the long axis in a vertical position. Adjust the test flame to a height of 1.5 in. with the air supply closed. Apply the test flame to the center of the lower edge of the test specimen, taking precaution to protect it from cross drafts, at a level that will make the distance from the top of the burner tube to the edge of the specimen 0.75 in. Apply the test flame for 12 seconds and then withdraw. Record with a stopwatch the time of glow after withdrawal of the flame, and measure the height that is charred to the extent that it will separate readily when crumpled between the thumb and forefinger. Not less than three specimens shall be tested in each principal direction of the sheet.

Report.—Results shall be reported as *char length*, which is the average maximum height of the charred or burned areas in inches, measured from the bottom edge of the piece to the nearest $\frac{1}{8}$ or 0.1 in.; and as *after glow*, which is the average time in seconds that the specimens continue to glow after the burner flame is removed.

Additional Information.—In general, papers which show a char length of over 4.5 in., with the maximum char length of any one specimen over 5.5 in., would not be considered sufficiently flame resistant to be effective. This statement, however, is not intended to set up a specification for flame-resistant papers *per se.*

The after-glow test often provides valuable additional information regarding the efficacy of the flame-resisting treatment.

DEGREE OF CURL AND SIZING OF PAPER

This method applies the principle of wetting one side of the paper and determining (a) the maximum curvature developed, or (b) the time required to reach maximum curvature. The maximum curvature is an indication of the relative tendency of certain papers, especially printing papers, to curl under normal conditions of usage.[88],[89] The time required to reach maximum curvature is a measure of relative degree of sizing such as secured with rosin.[90] This method is standardized as TAPPI T 466 m-52.

[88] Carson, F. T., and Worthington, V., Paper Ind., **22,** 246, June 1940.

[89] Carson, F. T., and Worthington, V., Natl. Bur. Standards J. Research, **30,** 113, Research Paper RP1522, 1943.

[90] Carson, F. T., Paper Trade J., **79,** No. 17, 44, Oct. 23, 1924.

Apparatus. **Curl Tester.**—The apparatus, shown in Fig. 55-20, consists of a float having near the center a rectangular wetting aperture about 2 in. long (perpendicular to the plane of the figure) and a width, *L*, which is adjustable from zero to about 1 in. A stop, *H*, is provided to hold one end of the curling specimen at a fixed angle, *F*, with

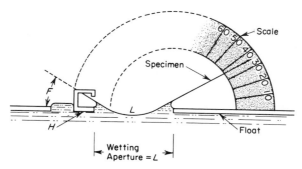

Fig. 55-20.   Curl Tester.

respect to the horizontal. A scale with stippled surface, graduated in degrees, is fastened to the float to indicate the movement of the pointed end of the curling specimen.

A stopwatch or other suitable timing device is required for testing degree of sizing.

A vessel of water at 23 ± 2°C. Distilled water is preferable but drinking water of reasonable purity may be used.

Test Specimen.—Cut the specimens in the shape of a right trapezoid having an altitude of 1.5 in. in the machine direction and bases of 1.5 and 2.75 in. extending in the cross direction.[88] Condition them before testing according to TAPPI Standard T 402 m (vol. 2, Part B, p. 1795).

Procedure.—The tests shall be made in an atmosphere conditioned according to TAPPI Standard T 402 m.

Degree of Curl.—Put the float on the water, place the square end of the trapezoidal specimen under the stop with the longest, pointed side next to the scale, and allow the specimen to fall across the aperture and become wet over that area. Read the scale angle reached by the point of the specimen at the instant the direction of curling reverses. If this angle is less than 30 or more than 60°, adjust the width of the aperture until the angle lies within the desired range. In general, if the curve of the specimen departs noticeably from a circular cylindrical surface, reduce the width, in the cross direction, of the wetted portion of the specimen until the curve is substantially circular. Test in this way at least 5 specimens from each side of the paper, making sure that the top of the float is dry before each test. Add the average scale angle to the fixed angle (about 30°) which the square end of the specimen makes with the horizontal. Divide this sum by the width in centimeters of the aperture used (length of arc of wetted, curled portion of specimen in cross direction). The result is the maximum curvature in degrees per centimeter of arc.

Degree of Sizing.—Affix the specimen in the apparatus as described under "Degree of Curl." Determine the time from contact of the specimen with the water until the maximum curvature is reached; that is, until the point of the specimen reverses its direction of movement. For this test it is preferable to adjust the width of the aperture so that maximum curvature is reached near the middle of the scale. Test at least five specimens for each side of the paper.

Report.—(*a*) Report as degree of curl the average value and the range of maximum curvature, in degrees per centimeter of aperture width.

(*b*) Report as degree of sizing (curl test) the average value and the range of time in seconds to reach maximum curvature.

Additional Information.—The factors out of which curling troubles grow are many and complex. It is, therefore, necessary to use caution in interpreting curling data obtained by this test in connection with certain types of curling troubles. A high curl test does not necessarily mean that the paper will, in every case, curl in practice.

A somewhat more precise measurement of curling tendency can be made by using a narrow rectangular specimen and measuring the displacement of the chord by means of a suitably mounted lens and index line.[89] A fairly good estimate of curling tendency can also be made by floating rectangular specimens of known width (cross direction) on water and estimating the maximum height of rise of the edges above the center, from which the minimum radius of curvature can be found by a graphical solution. Or, 2 fine wires may be stuck with wax to the edges perpendicular to the paper so that as the specimen curls they cross at the center of curvature. The minimum radius of curvature can then be estimated. The maximum curvature in degrees per centimeter is 57.3 divided by the minimum radius of curvature in centimeters. In either case the specimen should be narrow enough (in the cross section) so that all of the under side will remain in contact with the water at maximum curl.

An approximate comparison of the degree of sizing of papers of different thicknesses can be calculated by dividing the time of curl by the square of the thickness of the papers.

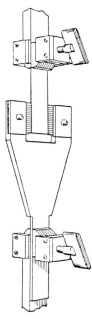

FIG. 55-21. Finch Edge-tear Stirrup.

The Curl Sizing Tester is available for testing both the degree of curl and the degree of sizing.[88,90] For the latter purpose, the apparatus contains a built-in stopwatch which starts automatically when the specimen is lowered to the water.

EDGE TEARING RESISTANCE OF PAPER (FINCH METHOD)

In this method a strip of paper 15.0 to 25.4 mm. (0.59 to 1.00 in.) wide is simultaneously torn at opposite points at the edges of the strip by means of a thin V-notched beam held in a stirrup which is fastened in one of the clamps of a paper tensile tester.

The use of this test shall be limited to papers which will fold evenly over the V-notched beam. This method is standardized as TAPPI T 470 m-54.

Apparatus. **Finch Edge-tear Stirrup** (Fig. 55-21).—This shall be used attached to a suitable pendulum-type tensile strength testing machine. The stirrup consists of a thin steel plate which forms a horizontal beam supported on edge by the ends of a stirrup-shaped frame. The thin metal tang of the stirrup frame is fastened in the lower clamp of the tensile tester so that the vertical center line of the stirrup coincides with the line connecting the midpoints of the upper and lower clamps. The horizontal beam is removable from the stirrup frame and two beams of different thicknesses are furnished for use with papers of different thickness ranges. The edge of the beam forms a shallow V-notch, the side of which subtend an angle of $150 \pm 1°$. The sides of the V-notch are semicircular in cross-section and are formed either by filing and scraping with a semicircular shaped scraper or by soldering a drill rod of a diameter equal to the thickness of the beam to the edges of the V-notch. In either case the edges of the V-notch shall be smooth and straight.

Tensile Tester.—This shall be pendulum type, preferably equipped with 2 or 3 different pendulum weights and corresponding scales of different capacities, including scales with capacities of 0 to 1 kg. (0 to 2.2 pounds) and 0 to 5 kg. (0 to 11 pounds). It shall conform to the requirements specified in TAPPI Standard T 404 m (p. 1395).

Test Specimen.—The specimens for test shall be strips cut with edges clean, straight, and parallel, in the two principal directions of the paper. The specimens shall be not more than 25.4 mm. (1.0 in.) nor less than 15.0 mm. (0.59 in.) wide and not less than 25.4 cm. (10 in.) long, preferably somewhat longer. The specimens shall be conditioned for testing according to TAPPI Standard T 402 m (vol. 2, Part B, p. 1795).

NOTE.—A conventional type of photo paper cutter especially designed for accurately cutting narrow test specimens is preferred. It is particularly important that its cutting edges be smooth and sharp.

Procedure.—The test shall be made in an atmosphere conditioned according to TAPPI Standard T 402 m.

Attach a beam of the proper thickness to the stirrup frame. The beam thickness shall be selected with reference to the paper thickness as follows:

Range of Paper Thickness, inch	Beam Thickness, inch
0.030 and less	0.050 ± 0.002
Over 0.030	0.100 ± 0.002

Fasten the thin tang of the stirrup in the lower clamp of the tensile tester so that the vertical center line of the stirrup coincides with the line connecting the midpoints of the upper and lower clamps of the testing machine, and so that the sides of the V-notch are symmetrically located with the line through the midpoints of the clamps.

NOTE.—The stirrup may be fastened in the upper clamp, if desired. This procedure will require rebalancing the tensile tester to compensate for the weight of the stirrup.

Place the lower clamp of the machine so that the lower edge of the upper clamp is about 9 cm. (3.5 in.) above the V-notched beam. Thread the test specimen through the stirrup, under the beam, bring the two ends together and fasten them in the upper clamp. In this operation, most of the slack in the test specimen is taken up, but care must be exercised not to apply sufficient stress to start tearing the specimen. Apply the load to the test specimen at a rate such that the specimen shall be torn through in not less than 5 nor more than 15 seconds. The application of the first increments of load to the specimen should be made as slowly as possible to minimize abnormal strains due to inertia effects. Record the maximum load required to tear each specimen.

At least 10 and preferably 20 strips cut in each principal direction of the paper shall be tested.

Report.—Report results obtained on strips torn in the machine direction as edge tearing resistance, machine direction, and results obtained on strips torn across the machine direction as edge tearing resistance, cross direction.

The average maximum and minimum results shall be reported in grams for each principal direction of the paper, to 2 significant figures.

Reproducibility of Results.—Duplicate determinations from different sets of samples from the same shipment and on different instruments are expected to agree within 5 percent.

BACTERIOLOGICAL EXAMINATION OF PROCESS WATER AND SLUSH PULP

The following procedure is recommended primarily for the bacteriological examination of process water. It is also applicable to pulp slush stock. Because of the exacting technique required in bacteriological procedures, reproducible results can be secured only by a well trained technician. This method is standardized as TAPPI T 631 m-57.

Apparatus and Materials. **Alcohol.**—Methyl, isopropyl, or 95 percent denatured ethyl alcohol for sterilizing instruments.

Balance.—Sensitive to 0.1 g. with a pan large enough to hold a dilution bottle.

Bottles for Dilution.—Several 8-oz., narrow-mouthed, square-sectioned, glass bottles fitted either with screw caps or with Escher rubber stoppers.

Bottles for Samples.—Several 4 to 8-oz., wide-mouthed, glass-stoppered bottles for collecting samples. The type of bottle selected should be able to withstand sterilization. Prior to sterilization, cover the stoppers and the necks of the bottles with metal foil or heavy kraft paper to protect the lip of the bottle from contamination. A strip of paper may be inserted in the mouth of each bottle to prevent sticking of the stopper during sterilization.

Colony Counter.—Any one of several types, the Quebec, Buck, and Wolffhuegel colony counters are satisfactory. A hand tally for recording the count is recommended.

Plugs.—Nonabsorbent cotton.

Flaming Equipment.—An alcohol lamp, a gasoline blow torch, or a Bunsen burner to flame tongs, forceps, or the mouths of sterile containers.

Flasks.—Erlenmeyer flasks or bottles, preferably Pyrex, for holding sterile media.

Incubator.—Capable of maintaining a temperature of $36 \pm 1°C.$ ($96.8 \pm 1.8°F.$).

Petri Dishes.—Pyrex dishes, 100 by 15 mm., are recommended.

Pipets and Containers.—Two sizes: 1.1-ml. milk-dilution type and graduated 10-ml. type. Mohr 10-ml. pipets, with tips cut off to give an opening about 3 mm. in diameter at the delivery end, are best for pipetting thick suspensions. Special Mohr pipets calibrated from the large end, are available and preferable to the usual Mohr pipets. Enclose them singly in metal boxes or heavy kraft paper, for sterilization.

Sampling Equipment. (a) *Scoops* made from tinned iron sheet. The diameter of the scoop will depend upon the opening of the sample bottle; the length is about 10 in. Wrap the scoops individually in heavy kraft paper and secure with either string or a rubber band, prior to sterilization.

(b) *Spoons.*—Large spoons may be substituted for the scoops.

Nutrient Substrate.—Dehydrated standard tryptone glucose extract agar. That obtained from Difco Laboratories or from the Baltimore Biological Laboratories has been found suitable. It may also be prepared from its ingredients.[91]

Sterilizing Equipment.—Two types, of suitable size:

(a) A steam sterilizer for 15 p.s.i. steam such as an autoclave or a pressure cooker.

(b) A hot-air oven at 165°C. with thermometer. For most laboratories, electrically heated ovens are more satisfactory than those heated by gas, but the latter may be used if desired.

Sterilization of Equipment and Media.—Depending upon the nature of the equipment to be sterilized, use one of three methods as follows.

Steam Heat (Autoclaves or Pressure Cookers).—Sterilize the following by heating for 20 minutes at a minimum of 121°C. (250°F.), corresponding to 15 p.s.i. steam

[91] American Public Health Association, "Standard Methods for the Examination of Water and Sewage," p. 186, 9th Ed., 1946.

pressure: (a) media (unless other conditions are specified by the manufacturer), (b) sample bottles, (c) scoops or spoons, and (d) water blanks for dilution.

Dry Heat (Electrically or Gas-Heated Oven).—Sterilize the following by heating for at least 2 hours at a temperature of about 165°C. (329°F.): (a) Petri dishes, (b) pipets, and (c) forceps.

Take care to dry glassware completely before heating and avoid scorching any paper container or wrapper used for instruments being sterilized.

Alcohol.—Immerse forceps and spoons in alcohol. When needed for handling samples, remove, allow to drain for a few moments, then burn off the excess alcohol.

Sampling. **Frequency of Sampling.**—Occasional single samples are usually inadequate, since the analysis reflects only the conditions which prevailed when such samples were taken. The number and frequency of samples depend largely on the purpose of the analysis.

Method of Sampling.—Use the sterile metal scoop or spoon. Dip a sample from the vat, chest or trough, using caution to avoid contaminating the sample by the hands coming in contact with the stock, or from material adhering to the edges of the system. Transfer the sample to a sterile, wide-mouthed bottle, and immediately replace the stopper or plug.

Alternatively, for sampling water or dilute stock, run directly into the bottle from a valve, faucet or pulp outlet, after proper flushing. Take care that the sample or bottle is not contaminated by the hands during the sampling. When there is a sufficient flow to prevent contamination, hold the bottle by means of sterile tongs or near the bottom with the hand, insert its mouth into the flow of liquid, allow it to fill, remove the bottle and immediately replace its stopper.

With slush stock, take a composite sample, not necessarily under aseptic conditions, to determine its consistency.

Procedure.—Proceed with the examination of the samples as soon as possible after they are taken. If the samples cannot be plated within 1 hour of taking them, refrigerate them at 5 to 10°C. (40 to 50°F.), until they can be plated. Record the times of sampling and of plating and measure and record the temperature of the samples before they are diluted for plating. Record also any other pertinent data with respect to sampling or circumstances that might affect the results.

Preparation of Specimens. *Process Water or Low-Consistency Stock.*—Measure 1 ml. of the sample into a sterile 99-ml. water blank and shake the mixture thoroughly. Use a sterile 1.1-ml. pipet to transfer 1.0 ml. from the first water blank into a second water blank and agitate. Repeat this procedure until the desired dilutions have been made. It may be necessary to plate dilutions as high as 1:1,000,000; experience within a particular mill system will determine what dilution to use to obtain counts in the range of 30 to 300 colonies per plate.

High-Consistency Stock.—Weigh 10 g. of the slush into a tared water blank containing 90 ml. of sterile water. Shake vigorously with at least 20 complete strokes and dilute further if needed.

Plating.—Plate the specimens as soon as possible after diluting. The room in which the specimens are plated should be relatively free of air currents and dust. About $\frac{1}{2}$ hour before plating, sponge the surface of the worktable with a solution of a suitable toxicant, such as 5 percent phenol or 0.05 percent phenyl mercuric acetate further to eliminate extraneous microorganisms.

With a sterile pipet, transfer known volumes of the diluted process water or slush stock to several Petri dishes. Add approximately 15 to 20 ml. of standard tryptone glucose extract agar, cooled to about 45°C. (113°F.) to each dish. Agitate the plates with a quick, short reciprocating motion to obtain even distribution of the pulp fibers or the water. Pour one control plate (without a specimen) from each container of nutrient medium used, to check its sterility.

Incubation.—After the plates have been agitated, place them on a level surface until the medium solidifies; then invert and incubate the plated samples at 36 ± 1°C. (96.8 ± 1.8°F.) for 48 hours. Do not stack the plates too closely in the incubator.

NOTE.—A temperature as high as 36°C. may be unfavorable for the growth of certain organisms such as "pink slime," for which a lower temperature, say 30°C., may be better suited, at least during the first half of the 48-hour incubation period. This or another condition for incubation renders the method nonstandard and the results should be reported accordingly.

Counting Plate Cultures.—After incubation, examine the cultures for the presence and number of bacterial colonies with a plate counter or by holding the plates against a dark background, indirectly lighted.

If, in the case of slush stock, the individual fibers have been well mixed in the medium, the colonies can be easily counted. If any particles are observed which cannot be definitely identified as colonies, they should be examined microscopically. Plates with spreading colonies should be counted if possible, otherwise they should be reported as spreading colonies. Examine and make a record of the number of colonies found on each control plate.

Report.—For both process water and low-consistency stock, express the results as the number of colonies per milliliter of sample examined. Express the results for slush stock of high consistency as the number of colonies per gram of moisture-free stock examined. Report also its consistency. In all cases record the count to no more than 2 significant figures. For example, record a colony count of 144 as 140, and one of 145 as 150.

Unless the samples were plated immediately after taking, report all pertinent data as to times and temperatures that might affect the results.

PREPARATION OF MAGNESIUM-OXIDE STANDARD FOR SPECTRAL REFLECTIVITY

The smoke from magnesium freely burning in air, deposited on a satisfactory base, forms a uniform, fine-grained, diffusing surface of high reflectance. This surface of magnesium oxide may be made reproducible; hence, it serves as a convenient and reliable primary standard for measuring spectral reflectivity. Magnesium oxide is a good diffuser and its light reflectance is 97 to 98 percent. The apparent reflectance for 45° incidence and normal viewing (standard conditions adopted by the International Commission of Illumination, Cambridge, 1931) is 1.00. The reflectance varies with wave length in the visible spectrum by less than 1 percent when the oxide is first prepared. Although the reflectance is apparently constant with time between 550 and 750 mμ., it decreases at wave lengths less than 550 mμ.; this may amount to as much as 3 percent in the violet, and causes the oxide to become slightly yellower with time. A magnesium oxide standard should therefore be discarded after a few hours of use. This method is standardized as TAPPI T 633 m-50.

NOTE.—For Spectral Reflectivity of Paper, see page 1429; for Spectral Reflectivity of Pulp, see page 1348.

Materials. Magnesium.—The magnesium should have high purity and be either in the form of turnings approximately 0.02 in. thick and $\frac{1}{8}$ in. wide, preferably of spiral shape, and containing a minimum of magnesium dust; or in the form of magnesium ribbon 0.006 in. thick and $\frac{1}{8}$ in. wide. "Radio grade" magnesium is recommended as having the highest purity.

Base Surface.—The magnesium oxide must be deposited on a base surface not affected in air by the heat from the burning magnesium. A satisfactory base may be made of depolished aluminum or block porcelain, or a block of magnesium carbonate. A hollow tray-like structure is recommended, with a flat surface and a rim 1 to 1.5 mm. high. The rim prevents the edges of the magnesium oxide coating from chipping off.

NOTE.—Depolished surfaces are better than polished because the oxide adheres better; for the same reason, metallic surfaces are usually to be preferred to nonmetallic. Surfaces of reflectance high and uniform throughout the spectrum are better than dark or chromatic surfaces because with the former a thinner layer of magnesium oxide is trustworthy. The thinner layer is desirable, apart from speed of preparation, because it does not chip off so readily.

Combustion Disc (for use with magnesium turnings).—A refractory disc to hold the burning magnesium, about 4 in. in diameter and 1 in. thick with a recess in the top face and, if desired, vent holes through the disc. Zirconium silicate and magnesium carbonate (magnesite) are suitable refractories from which to make the disc.

Procedure.—Coat the base surface by exposing it to fumes of burning magnesium. Place the base surface to be coated about 8 to 10 cm. (3 to 4 in.) above the flame and tilted about 30° from the horizontal. Use of smaller distances results in a coarse-grained deposit and risks contamination by possible impurities in the magnesium. The flame of the burning magnesium should not be allowed to "lick" the oxide surface.

Move either the combustion disc or the surface base being coated from side to side in order to obtain a uniform deposit.

Repeat the operation several times until a sufficient deposit is obtained. The layer should be so thick that further increase produces no sensible change in reflectance; the critical thickness is about 0.5 mm. Repeated deposits of thin coatings, rather than the full half-millimeter deposit at one time, are recommended. Do not attempt to burn a large charge of magnesium at one time; rather, build up the required thickness by a large number of small charges. In cases where it is inconvenient to measure the thickness of the coating, place a small dot of India ink on the original surface near the edge, then deposit oxide until the spot cannot be seen in good illumination. If the original surface is dark, put on one coat of magnesium oxide first; a deposit of black smoke (from a candle or smoky gas flame), in a small spot near the edge, supplies a similar test.

The operation should be carried out under a well ventilated hood in order to dispose of the excess oxide. However, the current of air should not be sufficiently great to disturb either the flame or the stream of smoke arising from the flame. The air of the room in which the coating is done should be as free as possible of dust and vapors.

The operator's eyes should be protected from the high intensities of visible and ultraviolet radiant energy by suitable goggles or other means.

Magnesium ribbon is preferred for small surfaces employed in standardization; however, where large surfaces are to be coated, magnesium turnings are preferred. The burning is accomplished as follows.

Ribbon.—Cut the magnesium ribbon in a number of 10-in. lengths. Holding one end of a length of ribbon in pliers, wipe the ribbon with a freshly laundered cloth to remove surface impurities. Ignite the free end with a Bunsen burner, and hold the ribbon in an approximately horizontal position under the surface to be coated, moving it or the ribbon so as to get an even coating. When the ribbon has burned to a point within about 1 in. of the pliers, drop it upon a metal or refractory surface below the work. Burn additional lengths of ribbon until the coating process is completed.

Turnings.—Place about 5 g. of the turnings on the refractory disc and ignite them with a hand blow torch or Bunsen burner. Work the unignited turnings beneath the flame until a slowly burning ball or clinker is formed; this gives a steady stream of smoke. When the stream of smoke is steady, introduce into it the base surface to be coated and complete the coating as previously described. When the clinker has to be turned over or broken, in order to permit the magnesium to burn completely, the surface being coated should be temporarily removed, since the burst of flame is likely to carry up large dust particles.

Additional Information.—It is often desirable to use secondary working standards of reflectance calibrated in terms of the freshly prepared magnesium oxide. White enameled-iron panels, blocks of opaque structural glass, glazed tiles, and other ceramic bodies have proved useful as rugged and reasonably permanent working standards of diffuse reflectance.

Although magnesium oxide is almost universally cited as the primary standard of directional reflectance, it is known to be subject to some variation from one preparation to another. It is not certainly known what causes this variation. Between different panels prepared in as close accord as possible with the standard procedure, there are differences which are small, but nevertheless measurable. They are apparently not attributable to impurities in the magnesium, because differences may frequently be found between two panels prepared with the same magnesium.

Chief suspicion has been directed to compounds of magnesium and nitrogen in the magnesium oxide. Where insufficient oxygen has access to the magnesium at the time of burning, some of the magnesium apparently combines with nitrogen to form compounds that are somewhat yellowish. The burning of large chunks of magnesium should therefore be avoided. Yellowing is found to be greater with rapid burning of magnesium than with slow burning.

Because of this variability of magnesium oxide, it is recommended that a number of freshly deposited surfaces be evaluated against a working standard such as a polished block of white Vitrolite structural glass. Thus, faulty panels will be readily detected by comparison and discarded. Furthermore, if the working standard is carefully preserved, its calibration relation to freshly prepared magnesium oxide will gradually increase in reliability until it will serve as a direct check on the preparation of the magnesium oxide standard.

REFERENCE

"Preparation and Colorimetric Properties of a Magnesium Oxide Reflectance Standard," National Bureau of Standards Letter Circular LC547.

Chapter 56

PESTICIDE RESIDUE ANALYSIS

By J. William Cook and Sidney Williams

Division of Food Chemistry
Food and Drug Administration
Department of Health, Education, and Welfare
Washington, D. C.

Introduction.—Historically, chemists who developed methods of analysis for pesticide chemicals made use of those instruments available to them at the time. Instrumentation was relatively simple and few toxic chemicals were in use. With the development of the highly toxic organic pesticidal materials, the need for an increase in sensitivity of methodology has arisen. Standard wet chemical methods have been largely outmoded in most instances so it has been necessary to resort to highly sophisticated methods of analysis in order to achieve desired sensitivity, rapidity, and specificity. The characteristics of much of the current instrumentation are uniquely useful for pesticide work.

One of the great advantages of instrumental techniques for pesticide residue analysis has been the development of complete methods of analysis, that is, extraction, purification, and determination, both quantitatively and qualitatively, for as many as 30 to 40 chemicals in a single operation. This is highly significant because there are several hundred pesticide chemicals registered for use on food products in the United States, and it is frequently necessary to determine pesticide residues in samples of unknown history where any of a large number of compounds may be present. Many can be detected when present at the level of a few parts per billion.

Instrumentation generally is useful primarily as the determinative step in a procedure; the extraction and purification or cleanup steps are important prerequisites to the determinative instrumental step. The methods in this chapter describe, in detail, the techniques for extraction, purification, and determination of a number of groups of related pesticide chemicals. Generally the methods are useful for a number of different food products.

Some of the newer highly sophisticated instruments have been developed specifically for pesticide analysis. An example of this is a gas chromatograph which utilizes a micro-coulometric titration detector.[1] The success in this field led to investigations of the utility of that instrument in other fields. The converse of this, of course, is also true; instruments developed for other purposes have proven to be very useful in the pesticide field—sometimes with little modification. Therefore, the necessity for methods of analysis for these compounds and the development of instruments have gone hand in hand and have been mutually beneficial. The great adaptability of a number of these instruments to this field and the present-day necessity to run numerous analyses have encouraged many of the instrument companies to investigate intensively the development of instrumental techniques. Development has been rapid; it is therefore anticipated that the methods

---

[1] Coulson, D. M., Cavanagh, L. A., DeVries, J. E., and Walther, B., J. Agr. Food Chem., **8**, 399, 1960.

presented in this chapter may soon be modified and improved. This, of course, is always the case in any field of endeavor but it is especially true in this field.

The procedures which are presented have been proven to be very useful as described. A modern analyst should be alert to the new materials being presented regularly in current literature. Caution should be exercised in making alterations in any portion of the schemes presented until work is done to prove that the modification does not invalidate some other portion. This caution is particularly important in procedures in which 20 to 30 chemicals are determined at the same time, for an improvement in the determination of one chemical may invalidate the method for others.

CAUTION.—Many of the pesticide chemicals are highly toxic compounds. Some are readily absorbed through the skin as well as the digestive and respiratory systems. Great care should be exercised in handling the concentrated material.

EXTRACTION AND CLEANUP (PURIFICATION)

Instrumental analysis for any chemical is dependent, in part, on presenting the chemical in the proper state of purity to the instrument. Some published reports suggest use of "crude" extracts and, under certain limited circumstances, valid results are possible. However, to obtain reliable results routinely for a number of chemicals, purification or cleanup procedures are a necessity in the preparation of food samples for most instrumental methods currently in use in pesticide residue analysis.

A large number of procedures may be useful in preparing samples for instrumental analysis, but for the sake of simplicity for this chapter, only one procedure will be presented for each class of pesticides. The procedures presented permit the simultaneous extraction and cleanup of a large number of the significant pesticide chemicals in each class from a variety of food products.

CHLORINATED ORGANIC PESTICIDES

The following chlorinated organic pesticide chemicals are quantitatively extracted (85 to 100 percent recovery) and cleaned up by the extraction procedure described in this chapter. They can then be determined quantitatively by the gas chromatographic procedures and semiquantitatively by the thin-layer and paper chromatographic procedures described.

DDT	Dieldrin	Heptachlor epoxide
DDD (TDE)	Endrin	Kelthane
DDE	Toxaphene	Chlorbenside
Lindane	Strobane	PCNB
BHC	Perthane	TCNB
Methoxychlor	Chlordane	Thiodan I
Aldrin	Heptachlor	

Many more chlorinated pesticides can be determined by the determinative steps but the efficiency of the extraction and cleanup procedures have not been established for others not listed. (See Table 56-1 for others that chromatograph.)

METHOD[2]

Reagents. Acetonitrile.—Burdick and Jackson* or Sohio product, AR Grade, or Technical Grade may be used. Purify Sohio products by the following procedure: To

[2] Mills, P. A., Onley, J. H., and Gaither, R. A., J. Assoc. Offic. Agr. Chemists, **46,** 186, 1963.
* Burdick and Jackson (B and J), Muskegan, Mich., produce "distilled-in-glass solvents suitable for pesticide residue analysis without further purification."

1 gal. (4 liters) add 1 ml. 85 percent phosphoric acid, 30 g. phosphorus pentoxide, and boiling chips, and distill at 81°–82°C. Do not exceed 82°C.

Petroleum Ether.—B and J* or AR Grade. AR Grade must be redistilled between 30° and 60°C.

Ethyl Ether.—AR, U.S.P., or anhydrous grades. Purify as follows (in quantity sufficient for 1–2 days): Transfer a suitable volume to a separatory funnel and wash twice with portions of water equal to about one-half the volume of ether. Shake the washed ether with 50–100 ml. saturated sodium chloride solution and discard all aqueous layers. Draw the washed ether into a ꟷ flask, add a large excess of anhydrous sodium sulfate, and shake vigorously to remove water (15–30 min. on a mechanical shaker.) Add 2 percent v/v ethanol.

Eluting Solvent #1 (6 + 94).—Dilute 60 ml. purified ethyl ether to 1 liter with redistilled petroleum ether (B and J* or AR Grade, see above). Add 10–25 g. anhydrous sodium sulfate to remove moisture.

Eluting Solvent #2 (15 + 85).—Dilute 150 ml. purified ethyl ether to 1 liter with redistilled petroleum ether. Add 10–25 g. anhydrous sodium sulfate to remove moisture.

Activated Florisil, 60–100 mesh.—Floridin Company, Tallahassee, Florida. Florisil is available in three activation grades: 230°F. (110°C.), 500°F. (260°C.), and 1200°F. (650°C.). The 650°C. material activated not less than 1 nor more than 3 hours is the product useful for pesticide work. It must be reheated at 130°C. not less than 5 hr. and cooled and held in a desiccator, if not used within 2 days. Florisil that has been overheated at 650°C. cannot be treated in any way to restore adsorbent properties for this work. For test to determine proper activity, see J. Assoc. Offic. Agr. Chemists, **44,** 142, 1961.

Celite 545.—Johns-Manville Company.

Magnesium Oxide.—Sea Sorb #43 (Food Machinery Company, Westvaco Division). Treat as follows: Slurry about 500 g. with distilled water, heat on steam bath about 30 min., and filter with suction. Dry overnight at 105°–130°C. and pulverize to pass 60-mesh. Store in closed jar.

Magnesium Oxide-Celite Mixture.—Mix treated magnesium oxide with Celite 545, 1 + 1 by weight.

Alcoholic NaOH, 2 percent w/v.—Dissolve 2 g. sodium hydroxide in anhydrous ethanol and dilute to 100 ml.

Apparatus. **Graduated Cylinders,** 100 ml., ꟷ glass-stoppered.

Erlenmeyer Flasks, 500 ml., 1 liter.; ꟷ glass-stoppered.

Separatory Funnels, Teflon Stopcocks, 1 liter.

Chromatographic Columns with Coarse Discs and Teflon Stopcocks, 25 mm. outside diameter × 300 or 400 mm.

Chromatographic Columns without Stopcocks, 25 × 300 or 400 mm.

Kuderna-Danish Concentrators, 500 ml. with graduated tubes (Kolmer or Mills type, Kontes Glass Company, No. K-57005, Vineland, New Jersey).

Preparation of Sample and Extraction.[2] **Leafy Vegetables, Firm Fruits, Roots.**—Chop into small pieces and mix thoroughly.

Soft Fruits (Tomatoes, Peaches, Etc.).—Blend a representative quantity.

Isolation of Pesticides.[2]—Weigh 100 g. chopped or blended sample into a Waring Blendor jar, and add 200 ml. acetonitrile and about 10 g. Celite. Mix at high speed for 1–2 min., and filter with suction through a 12-cm. Büchner funnel into a 500-ml. suction flask. Transfer filtrate to a 250-ml. graduated cylinder and record volume. Transfer measured filtrate to a 1-liter seperatory funnel. Carefully measure 100 ml. petroleum ether into the same graduate used for the filtrate, and pour into the separatory funnel. Shake vigorously (1–2 min.), add about 10 ml. saturated sodium chloride solution and about 600 ml. water, and mix gently, but thoroughly. Allow to separate, discard the aqueous (lower) layer, and wash (gently) the solvent layer with two successive 100-ml. portions of water. Discard washings, transfer solvent layer to a 100-ml. stoppered graduate, and record volume. Add about 15 g. anhydrous sodium sulfate and shake vigorously.

NOTE.—This solution may be transferred directly to a Florisil column or it may be concentrated to 5–10 ml. in a Kuderna-Danish concentrator before it is placed on the column.

Preparation of Sample and Extraction[3]—**Dairy Products. (a) Butter.**—Warm at about 50°C. until fat separates and decant fat through dry filter.

(b) Cheese.—Place 100 g. diced cheese, 2 g. sodium or potassium oxalate, and 100 ml. ethanol in Waring Blendor and blend 2–3 min. Pour into 500-ml. centrifuge bottle, and add 50 ml. ethyl ether and 50 ml. petroleum ether, shaking vigorously after addition of each. Centrifuge at about 1500 r.p.m. for 5 min. Blow off solvent layer with wash-bottle device into beaker and re-extract twice with 50-ml. portions of mixed ethers (1 + 1). Evaporate combined extracts at low temperature to obtain fat.

(c) Milk.—To 100 g. fluid milk in centrifuge bottle, add 100 ml. ethanol and about 1 g. sodium or potassium oxalate, and mix. Add 50 ml. ethyl ether and shake vigorously; then add 50 ml. petroleum ether and shake vigorously. Centrifuge at 1500 r.p.m. and blow off solvent layer with wash-bottle device[3a] into a 1-liter separator containing 500–600 ml. water. Re-extract by centrifuging twice with 50-ml. portions of mixed ethers (1 + 1). Mix combined extracts and water cautiously. Drain and discard water. Rewash twice with additional 100-ml. portions of water, discarding the water each time. Pass ether residue through column of anhydrous sodium sulfate, 2 in. deep, and collect eluate in a Kuderna-Danish concentrator. Wash the column with small portions of petroleum ether and evaporate (boiling chip) the combined extracts to about 10 ml. Transfer to a weighed 100-ml. beaker, using small portions of petroleum ether, and continue evaporation at low temperature under current of air to obtain fat. Reweigh to obtain weight of fat.

Isolation of Pesticides.—Transfer a weighed amount of fat (not more than 4 g.) to a 125-ml. separator, using small portions of petroleum ether. Rinse container with small protions of petroleum ether and add rinsings to separator to a total volume of 25 ml. Add 50 ml. acetonitrile saturated with petroleum ether and shake vigorously for at least 1 min. Allow to separate and transfer the acetonitrile (lower) layer to a 1-liter separatory funnel containing 700 ml. 2 percent sodium chloride solution and 100 ml. petroleum ether. Re-extract the fat solution with 2 additional 50-ml. portions of acetonitrile saturated with petroleum ether, each time shaking vigorously for 1 min. Combine the acetonitrile extracts in the 1-liter separatory funnel. Mix thoroughly but gently and allow to separate. Transfer the aqueous layer to a second 1-liter separator and extract with 100 ml. petroleum ether, shaking vigorously for 15 sec. Allow to separate and discard the aqueous layer. Combine the petroleum ether layers in the first separator and wash gently with three 100-ml. portions of water. Drain off as much of the water as possible and filter the petroleum ether through a 25 × 50 mm. column of anhydrous sodium sulfate into a 500-ml. Kuderna-Danish concentrator. Add boiling chip and concentrate to 5–10 ml. for Florisil column cleanup.

Cleanup of Sample[2]—Prepare a chromatographic column, with stopcock, that con-

---

[3] Mills, P. A., J. Assoc. Offic. Agr. Chemists, **44,** 171, 1961.
[3a] Use tube similar to delivery tube of ordinary wash bottle but with intake end bent up into a U shape in opposite direction to outlet end, with opening about $\frac{3}{8}$ in. higher than bottom of U, cut off horizontally. Set delivery tube loosely enough in stopper so that it can be raised or lowered. In operating, adjust opening of U bend to about $\frac{1}{8}$ in. above surface of aqueous layer and blow ether layer off gently by blowing through mouthpiece tube inserted in adjacent hole in stopper.

tains 4 in. (after settling) of activated Florisil topped with about $\frac{1}{2}$ in. of anhydrous sodium sulfate. Pre-wet the column with 35–40 ml. petroleum ether, and place a receiver (Kuderna-Danish concentrator) under it. Transfer the petroleum ether extract from "Isolation of Pesticides" (vegetables, fruit, etc.) (page 1465) contained in the 100-ml. graduate or the 5–10 ml. concentrate from dairy products above to the column, letting it pass through at a rate of about 5 ml. per minute. Finally rinse graduate and the sodium sulfate in it or the container with the 5–10 ml. with 2 successive portions of about 5 ml. each of petroleum ether, pour rinsings onto column, rinse walls of chromatographic tube with an additional small quantity of petroleum ether, and elute column with 200 ml. Eluting Solvent #1 at a rate of 5 ml./min.

Change receivers and elute column at 5 ml./min. with 200 ml. Eluting Solvent #2. Concentrate each eluate to a suitable definite volume.

For fruits and vegetables calculate sample represented by eluates as follows: Sample represented by eluates = $S \times (F/T) \times (P/100)$, where S is g. sample taken; F is volume of filtrate; T is total volume (ml. water contained in sample plus ml. acetonitrile added minus correction in ml. for volume contraction); and P is ml. petroleum ether extract.

EXAMPLE.—Sample contains 85 ml. water; 200 ml. acetonitrile is added; volume contraction is 5 ml. Then total volume (T) is 280 ml. If volume of filtrate is 235 ml., and volume of petroleum ether extract is 85 ml., then $100 \times (235/280) \times (85/100) = 71$ g. represented in concentrated eluate. For many fruits and vegetables "$T = 280$ ml." is a good approximation. This assumes a moisture content of 85 percent.

Gas Chromatography.—The concentrated eluates of the 6 + 94 and the 15 + 85 elutions from nonfatty foods (less than 2 percent fat) are suitable for microcoulometric gas chromatography without further preparation, but the 15 + 85 eluates from butterfat need additional cleanup about half of the time.

The 15 + 85 eluates of many materials can be analyzed by electron capture gas chromatography without additional cleanup; however, certain products (carrots and many fatty foods) need additional cleanup as described under paper chromatography. The 6 + 94 eluates are usually satisfactory for electron capture.

Paper Chromatography.—The concentrated eluate from the 6 + 94 elution is usually suitable for paper chromatography. If further cleanup is necessary, transfer the concentrate to a new Florisil column, elute as before, and concentrate to a suitable volume.

The eluate from the 15 + 85 elution may require an additional cleanup step, as follows:[2] Transfer approximately 10 g. magnesium oxide-Celite (1 + 1) mixture, to a chromatographic column without stopcock, using vacuum to pack. Prewash with about 40 ml. petroleum ether, discard prewash, and place a receiver under column. Transfer concentrate from Florisil cleanup to column, using small portions of petroleum ether. When sample and washings have been forced into magnesium oxide-Celite mixture (slight pressure or vacuum), elute column with about 100 ml. petroleum ether. Concentrate to a suitable volume.

Some eluates may still not be sufficiently free from oily materials. In those cases transfer concentrated eluate from magnesium oxide column to a $\mathbf{\mathfrak{F}}$ flask (125 ml.) with petroleum either, evaporate just to dryness, add 20 ml. 2 percent alcoholic sodium hydroxide, and reflux 30 min. under an air condenser. Transfer to a 125-ml. separatory funnel and rinse flask with three successive 10-ml. portions of petroleum ether, pouring each into the separatory funnel. Add 20 ml. water and shake vigorously. Separate and draw the aqueous layer into a second separatory funnel containing 20 ml. petroleum ether, shake this mixture vigorously, separate, discard aqueous layer, and add petroleum ether layer to first funnel. Wash combined petroleum ether extracts with three successive 20-ml. portions of 50 percent v/v aqueous alcohol solution. Discard washings, dry the solvent layer through a column of anhydrous sodium sulfate, concentrate and chromatograph on magnesium oxide-Celite as before. Concentrate eluate and make to definite volume. Take the whole eluate or an aliquot for paper chromatography.

This treatment is suitable for dieldrin and endrin, but will destroy Thiodan and Tedion.

ORGANOPHOSPHATES

The development of adequate extraction, cleanup, and determinative procedures for the simultaneous determination of residues of a number of organophosphate pesticide residues has been a difficult task. In contrast to the chloro-organics, most of which are nonpolar compounds, the organophosphates vary through a wide spectrum of polarities from those with limited solubility in water to those infinitely soluble in water. Many of the nonpolar parent pesticides convert to a series of more polar compounds in or on the plant or animal treated.

The following extraction and cleanup procedures have not been studied as extensivley as the procedures presented for the chlorinated compounds, but the data so far developed indicated that the major known compounds will be extracted and cleaned up adequately for determination by gas, thin layer, and paper chromatography. It is known that a large number of significant organophosphates are extracted by the extraction procedures, and it is also known that many of them pass through the gas chromatography system or can be chromatographed by thin layer. Less is known about the number of compounds, particularly the more polar metabolites, that are efficiently cleaned up; however, it is known that some of the polar metabolites are adequately recovered.

METHOD[4]

Reagents and Materials.—**Benzene,** B and J* or ACS. Redistill latter with a Vigreux or Snyder column. Discard first 100 ml. and leave the last 300 ml. when distilling 5 liters.

Ethyl Acetate, B and J* or ACS. Redistill latter through a Vigreux or Snyder column.

Acetonitrile.—B and J* or redistill from phosphorus pentoxide and phosphoric acid as in Acetonitrile, page 1464.

Acetone, B and J* or ACS. Redistill ACS over permanganate.

Standard Chromatographic Column.—25 × 400 mm. with coarse disc and Teflon stopcock.

Celite 545.

Norit SG-Extra.—An acid washed Norit from the American Norit Company.

Magnesium Oxide.—Sea Sorb #43. See magnesium oxide, page 1465.

Glass Wool, Pyrex.

S & S "Sharkskin" Filter Paper, 15 cm.

Rubber Stoppers, #4, with bore to fit tip end of columns.

Side-arm Adapter for Vacuum, ⊥ 24/40.

Rotary Evaporator.

Water Bath, 45°–50°C.

Mills Concentration Tube, Kontes Glass Company No. K-57005.

Adsorbent Mixture.—In a ⊥ flask, 5 g. Norit SG-Extra, 4 g. magnesium oxide, and 8 g. Celite 545 are mixed by shaking. This may be prepared in batch quantities; 17 g. is used.

Extraction.—To a 100-g. sample of chopped up crop in a Waring Blendor add 10–15

---

[4] Storherr, R. W., Getz, M. E., Watts, R. R., Friedman, S. J., Erwin, F., Giuffrida, L., and Ives, F., J. Assoc. Offic. Agr. Chemists, **47,** 1087, 1964.
   * See asterisk footnote on page 1464.

g. Celite 545 and 250 ml. acetonitrile. Blend the mixture vigorously for 5–7 min. and filter through a Büchner funnel (about 6 in. in diameter) containing two "sharkskin" papers. Disconnect the vacuum, rinse Blendor with 100 ml. acetonitrile and use this to rinse filter cake. Connect the vacuum and collect the rinse with the original filtrate.

Transfer filtrate to a 1-liter round-bottom flask and connect to a rotary vacuum evaporator. Concentrate to the aqueous phase, as evidenced by water droplet formation, in a 45°–50°C. water bath. Transfer contents to a 250-ml. separatory funnel. Rinse flask with four 25-ml. portions of ethyl acetate, collecting rinses with the aqueous layer, shake funnel vigorously, and set aside a few minutes until phases completely separate. (With crops other than fruits, solid sodium chloride is usually added to hasten the separation of phases.) Withdraw the aqueous (lower) layer into another 250-ml. separatory funnel and shake with 50 ml. ethyl acetate. Discard the aqueous layer and combine the ethyl acetate extracts. Filter through a glass wool plug into a 1-liter round-bottom flask. Rinse separatory funnel and plug with three 25-ml. portions of ethyl acetate. Concentrate the combined extract and rinses to 10–20 ml., using the rotary evaporator with vacuum. Transfer contents quantitatively to a 100-ml. volumetric flask and make to volume with ethyl acetate. Twenty-five ml. of this extract is used for the column cleanup step. This extract should be stored in a freezer if it is to be held for any length of time.

Cleanup.—To a chromatographic column fitted with stopcock and a one-hole #4 stopper, add the side-arm vacuum adapter and a 1-liter round-bottom flask. Connect to vacuum line and open vacuum. Add $\frac{1}{2}$–1 in. of Celite and tamp solidly. Add 17 g. adsorbent mixture and tamp. Add a glass wool plug to hold down adsorbent. Prewash the column with 15 ml. ethyl acetate, 20 ml. benzene, and finally 40–50 ml. ethyl acetate. Close stopcock when ethyl acetate is about 1 in. above glass wool and maintain this ethyl acetate head to ensure a clean column. Disconnect vacuum, discard prewash eluate, insert a clean 1-liter round-bottom flask and connect to open vacuum line.

With column stopcock closed, add 25 ml. extract (equivalent to 25 g. sample) to column. Adjust stopcock to maintain a moderate flow rate (about 10 ml. per minute). When last of extract reaches glass wool plug, rinse sides of column twice with 5–10 ml. ethyl acetate. Elute pesticides with 200 ml. 25 percent ethyl acetate in benzene; column may be taken to dryness. Disconnect vacuum line, and rinse off column and side-arm vacuum adapter with ethyl acetate. Collect rinses in the flask and concentrate flask contents on rotary vacuum evaporator to 10–15 ml. Quantitatively transfer the concentrated eluate to a 100-ml. beaker, using four 10–15 ml. ethyl acetate rinses. Concentrate again to a small volume (5 ml.) by means of an air jet and a hot plate set on the lowest setting. Quantitatively transfer the solution to a 10-ml. Mills tube and concentrate volume to 0.5- or 1.0-ml. volume, using an air jet. It is advisable to place the Mills tube in a beaker of water at room temperature during this final concentration step to inhibit water condensation inside the tube.

This final solution is ready for gas, paper, and thin-layer chromatography.

HERBICIDES—CHLOROPHENOXY ACIDS AND THEIR ESTERS

The chlorophenoxy acid type of herbicide, such as 2,4-D, is frequently applied in the form of an ester on an amine salt. However, plants convert these compounds, in large part, to the free acid. The rate of conversion in many plants has not been studied, so analysis for the esters must also be made. Some commercial processes, such as the manufacture of edible vegetable oils, also tend to hydrolyze the esters to free acids.

Procedures described here are capable of determining the free acids in vegetable oil and both the acid and ester in green crops and wheat with a sensitivity of 0.01–0.02 p.p.m. Because the free acids do not come through the commonly used GLC columns they are converted to the methyl esters before chromatographing. This step is included under this section of extraction and cleanup.

The compounds determinable by this procedure are 2,4-D, 2,3,6-TBA, MCPA, PCP, 2,4-DB, 2,4,5-T, 2,4,5-TP and their esters.

METHOD[5,6,7]

Reagents. Sodium Bicarbonate Solution.—4 percent (w/v).

Sulfuric Acid Solution.—(1) 10 percent (v/v) in water (1 + 9); (2) 10 percent in ethanol (1 + 9).

Petroleum Ether.—B and J* or redistilled at 30°–60°C.

Chloroform.—B and J* or redistilled 61°–62°C.

Diazomethane.—In ether. Made from "Diazald" (N-methyl-N-nitroso-p-toluene-sulfonamide) according to directions of manufacturer (Aldrich Chemical Company, Inc., 2369 N. 29th St., Milwaukee, Wisconsin). Keep diazomethane in freezer when not in use.

Cotton, Absorbent.—Chloroform washed, then dried.

Stock Standard Solutions.—Dissolve 100 mg. of each herbicide in 60 ml. ethyl ether, then make to 100 ml. with redistilled n-hexane.

Working Standard.—Using a 1:1 mixture of ethyl ether and hexane as diluting solvent, prepare a 10 μg. per ml. solution for each herbicide. Also prepare a mixture containing each herbicide at a concentration of 10 μg. per ml. Similar solutions should be prepared for any esters present.

Florisil.—Activated at 650°C. by manufacturer; 60–100 mesh (Floridin Company, Pittsburgh, Pa.). Elution pattern of each batch should be checked with mixture of standards before use.

Acetonitrile.—80 percent in water (v/v).

Sodium Sulfate.—ACS anhydrous, large crystals.

Ethyl Ether (ACS) Solutions.—3 percent, 10 percent, and 15 percent solutions in petroleum ether.

Procedure for Vegetable Oils.—Transfer 50 g. oil to a 500-ml. separatory funnel with 125 ml. petroleum ether. Add 35 ml. ethanol and 50 ml. sodium bicarbonate solution, and carefully shake mixture. After releasing the pressure in the funnel several times, shake vigorously for 1 min. Allow the layers to separate. Both layers may be turbid. Drain the bottom aqueous layer into another 500-ml. separatory funnel. Repeat the extraction 2 more times, using 15 ml. ethanol and 40 ml. sodium bicarbonate each time. Combine the aqueous phases and discard the organic phase.

Extract the bicarbonate extract twice with 25 ml. chloroform each time. Drain off the chloroform and discard. Carefully acidify the aqueous solution with 25 ml. 10 percent sulfuric acid. Extract the acidified solution 3 times with 30 ml. chloroform each time. Drain each chloroform extract through a cotton plug in a small glass funnel into a Phillips beaker. Rinse the cotton plug with chloroform after the third chloroform extract has filtered through. Remove the cotton and replace the funnel in the mouth of the Phillips beaker. Add boiling chips (carborundum), and evaporate just to dryness on the steam bath. Remove the final traces of chloroform with the aid of ether and an air jet.

Working in the hood, away from the steam bath, rinse the walls of the beaker with about 4 ml. ethyl ether. Add 2 ml. diazomethane solution. Let stand for 10 min. with occasional shaking. Evaporate the solvent on the steam bath and transfer the sample to a

[5] Yip, G., J. Assoc. Offic. Agr. Chemists, **45**, 367, 1962.
[6] Yip, G., J. Assoc. Offic. Agr. Chemists, **47**, 343, 1964.
[7] Yip, G., J. Assoc. Offic. Agr. Chemists, **47**, 1116, 1964.
* See asterisk footnote on page 1464.

glass-stoppered test tube (12-ml. size) with petroleum ether. Evaporate just to dryness by placing the tube in a warm water bath at 50°C. Add a measured volume (100–200 μl.) of isooctane to dissolve residue. This solution is ready for chromatography.

Prepare standards by placing 1-ml. aliquots of the working standard in glass-stoppered test tubes. Evaporate just to dryness and esterify the residue with 2 ml. diazomethane. After the reaction, remove solvent, and then dissolve the residue in 200 μl. isooctane.

Determination may be made on these solutions by microcoulometric or electron capture gas chromatography, or by paper chromatography as described for the chlorinated hydrocarbon pesticides, pages 1472, 1481, and 1500.

Procedure for Wheat.[6]—Grind wheat kernels in a mill to pass a 30-mesh sieve. Place 100 g. of sample in an Omni-mixer cup (Ivan Sorvall, Inc., Norwalk, Connecticut), and blend 3 min. with a mixture of 100 ml. petroleum ether, 100 ml. ethyl ether, and 20 ml. of 10 percent sulfuric acid in ethanol. Keep the cup cooled by immersing it in an ice water bath. Centrifuge 10 min. at 1500 r.p.m. Decant ethers through a layer of glass wool (contained in a glass funnel) into a 500-ml. separatory funnel. Resuspend the wheat in 50 ml. petroleum ether and 50 ml. ethyl ether. Centrifuge, and add extract to the separatory funnel. Rinse glass wool with 10 ml. ethyl ether and 30 ml. petroleum ether.

Add 100 ml. sodium bicarbonate solution and 35 ml. ethanol; shake vigorously for 1 min. Let layers separate. If aqueous layer does not separate in 10 min., add 5 ml. ethanol and shake again; repeat until separation occurs.

Draw off the aqueous layer into a 250-ml. separatory funnel. Filter the ether layer through a bed of sodium sulfate (contained in a glass funnel) into a 500-ml. glass-stoppered Erlenmeyer flask. Wash the separatory funnel twice with 5–10 ml. petroleum ether into the Erlenmeyer flask. Add 50 ml. petroleum ether to the aqueous solution, shake, and separate. Return the aqueous layer (containing acid form) to the original 500-ml. separatory funnel. Add the petroleum ether through sodium sulfate into the Erlenmeyer flask containing the esters.

Analyze for the free acids as described above under "Vegetable Oils" beginning with "Extract the bicarbonate extract twice with 25 ml. chloroform. . . ."

Concentrate the ester fraction to an oily residue on a steam bath with the aid of a Snyder column. Add 10 ml. *n*-hexane to the concentrate, replace the Snyder column with a small glass funnel, and evaporate the solvent. Use an air jet to remove final traces of solvent. Prepare a column (23 × 400 mm.) containing 7 cm. Florisil topped with 1 in. sodium sulfate. Place a 250-ml. Phillips beaker under the column as receiver. Transfer sample to column with several portions of petroleum ether, letting each portion sink into the column. Finally, elute column with 100 ml. 15 percent solution ether in petroleum ether.

Concentrate the eluate to small volume on steam bath, using a funnel reflux. Quantitatively transfer the concentrate with petroleum ether to a 125-ml. separatory funnel previously marked at the 25-ml. level. Wash the Phillips beaker 3–4 times, and add washings to separatory funnel until the 25-ml. mark is reached. Extract vigorously with 25 ml. 80 percent acetonitrile in water three times, combining the acetonitrile layer in a 1-liter separatory funnel. Add 750 ml. water, 30 g. sodium chloride, and 80 ml. petroleum ether, and shake vigorously. Let layers separate, discard the aqueous layer, and reshake with 100 ml. water. Discard water.

Prepare a short column containing 3 cm. Florisil topped with sodium sulfate. Let the petroluem ether extract percolate through the column. Rinse the separatory funnel 2–3 times with 10-ml. portions petroleum ether, then with 40 ml. 3 percent ethyl ether solution in petroleum ether. Place the original Phillips beaker under the column, and elute the esters from the column with 100 ml. 10 percent ethyl ether solution in petroleum ether. (The butoxyethanol ester does not behave like the rest of the esters. Instead of eluting from the short Florisil column with the 10 percent ether, it requires the use of 15 percent ether solution. This step provides a means of separating the butoxyethanol ester from the others.) Evaporate the eluate just to dryness and transfer the residue to a glass-stoppered test tube with petroleum ether. Evaporate to dryness on a warm water bath with the aid of an air jet. Dissolve the residue in hexane to take an aliquot for analysis by gas or paper chromatography as described for chlorinated organic pesticides.

Procedure for Green Crops.[5]—Place 100 g. finely chopped greens in a 560-ml. Omni-mixer cup. Add 10 ml. 10 percent sulfuric acid in ethanol, 25 ml. ethanol, 50 ml. petroleum ether, and 150 ml. ethyl ether to the cup and blend for 3 min. at high speed. Centrifuge 10 min. at 1500 r.p.m. Decant ethers through glass wool into a 500-ml. separatory funnel. Resuspend the chopped greens in 50 ml. petroleum ether and 50 ml. ethyl ether. Centrifuge and add extract to the separatory funnel. Repeat extraction once more. Rinse glass wool with 10 ml. ethyl ether and 30 ml. petroleum ether.

Proceed as under "Procedure for Wheat" beginning with "Add 100 ml. sodium bicarbonate solution. . . ."

GAS-LIQUID CHROMATOGRAPHY (GLC)[8–13]

The instrumental procedure most frequently used for pesticide residue analysis is that of gas-liquid chromatography. Since the cleanup procedures and the gas chromatographic columns are not efficient enough to eliminate all extraneous materials completely, some discrimination between pesticide and residual plant material must be made by the detector system of the gas chromatograph before chromatograms can be obtained which can be interpreted with any degree of certainty.

The detectors most used for pesticide analysis are electron capture and halogen-sensitive microcoulometric titration for the halogenated compounds and a sulfur-sensitive microcoulometric titration for sulfur-containing organophosphates. A new detector, the sodium thermionic detector, appears to show great promise as a specific and quantitative detector for the organophosphates. The electron capture detector responds to electrophores—compounds which have an affinity for electrons. It appears that most chlorinated compounds are electrophores; however, not all electrophores are halogenated compounds. The halogen-sensitive microcoulometric detector is quite specific for halogenated compounds (except fluorine), and the sulfur microcoulometric detector is quite specific for sulfur-containing compounds.

Even though gas chromatographic systems and detectors have a high degree of specificity, none are completely specific; therefore, in order to facilitate interpretation of chromatograms, it is well to have a highly controlled and unified system of columns and detectors which complement each other. For example, when a peak appears from an unknown at a given time on a given column using an electron capture detector, there is assurance that an electrophore is present. If the peak response coincides with the retention time for a chlorinated pesticide chemical, there is presumptive but equivocal evidence that it is that pesticide. Much more certainty can be attached to the identity of the compound if the retention time and response to the electron capture detector is supplemented by a similar response to the halogen-sensitive microcoulometric system. Likewise, the sulfur cell of the microcoulometric system can be useful to substantiate the presence of compounds containing sulfur and either phosphorus or halogen or both. To

[8] Burke, J., and Giuffrida, L., J. Assoc. Offic. Agr. Chemists, **47**, 326, 1964.
[9] Shuman, H., and Collie, J. R., Sr., J. Assoc. Offic. Agr. Chemists, **46**, 992, 1963.
[10] Burke, J., and Johnson, L., J. Assoc. Offic. Agr. Chemists, **45**, 348, 1962.
[11] Burke, J., and Holswade, W., J. Assoc. Offic. Agr. Chemists, **47**, 845, 1964.
[12] Giuffrida, L., J. Assoc. Offic. Agr. Chemists, **47**, 293, 1964.
[13] Giuffrida, L., and Ives, F., J. Assoc. Offic. Agr. Chemists, **47**, 1112, 1964.

compare quantitative responses to a given compound by the electron capture and microcoulometric detectors, the efficiency of the columns and detectors must be known. Factors which affect efficiency of columns and detectors are discussed on the following pages.

There are many gas chromatographic column packings suitable for specific purposes. However, one column packing has been found to give superior resolution for all types of pesticides covered in this chapter and to work equally well with all detectors.

The following columns and packing are recommended:

Column. (a) **Electron Capture and Sodium Thermionic Detectors.**—Pyrex glass, 6 ft. long; 4 to 6 mm. inside diameter. These glass columns can be used straight, coiled, or bent as a U or a W to fit the instrument available.

(b) **Microcoulometric Detector.**—Aluminum tubing, 6 ft. long, 4.5 mm. inside diameter. If oven permits, use in W shape rather than coil. Care should be exercised in coiling or bending the column after packing to avoid crushing or fracturing the packing material. Crushing results in exposing untreated packing support particles which may ruin the column for recovery of certain pesticide chemicals.

Column Packing.[8, 9]—Anakrom ABS, 80/90 mesh coated with 10 percent Dow Corning (DC) 200 (12,500 centistokes (cst.)).

Prepare the column packing material in 20-g. batches by slurrying 18 g. Anakrom ABS with 2 g. DC 200 silicone fluid dissolved in about 100 ml. chloroform in a 300-ml. Morton flask. Remove the solvent by a flash evaporator at about 50°C. with vacuum and mix the slurry intermittently by occasionally switching on the rotator.

Plug the exit end of the column with about 2 in. of glass wool and fill the column with the coated packing. Keep vibration of the column to a minimum to avoid fracturing the packing particles. The columns will require about 25 to 30 ml. of packing. After filling, loosely plug the injection end with about 3 in. of glass wool.

Column Conditioning.[8]—Condition columns as follows: Heat in oven at 250°C. for 4 or more days with a continuous nitrogen gas flow of about 120 cc. per minute.*

Columns must be conditioned for relatively long periods of time at temperatures well above operating conditions. The purpose of the conditioning is twofold. First, it materially improves chromatography; and second, it reduces the amount of "bleed" of silicones from the columns during use. Silicones which do bleed off during operation damage both the electron capture and the sodium thermionic detectors.

The best way to obtain a "well conditioned" column has not been fully developed. Even with the above recommended conditioning, columns continue to improve under proper use. Chromatographing cleaned-up crop extracts improves the column. Chromatographing 1–10 nanograms (ng.) of pesticide standards for 1–2 weeks does not in general improve it; however, chromatography of milligram quantities (a large overload) usually improves the column as illustrated in Fig. 56-1.

Curve A of Fig. 56-1 shows the first electron capture chromatogram obtained from a new column after conditioning 40 hr. at 250°C. One ng. each of lindane, heptachlor, aldrin, and heptachlor epoxide and 5 ng. of DDT were injected; electrometer setting was 1×10^{-9} AFS. Heptachlor and DDT are proportionately much lower than they should be and the DDT peaks are not well formed.

Curve B of Fig. 56-1 represents the same quantity of the 5 pesticides 1–2 hr. after a total of 1 mg. of the mixture had been injected. Recovery from the column is better for all 5 compounds, especially heptachlor. DDT is a little low but the peak shape is improved, and recovery will be better after the column has been used a day or two. This simple treatment is usually enough for the first 4 compounds, and only slight improve-

* Recent work has shown that a new column conditioned at 250°C. with nitrogen flow of 120 ml. per minute for 4 weeks gave satisfactory endrin peaks.

ment in their chromatography will be noticed as the column is used. However, some pesticides, including endrin, Perthane, methoxychlor, Kelthane, and Tedion, do not chromatograph well until the column is even more thoroughly conditioned.

On the Anakrom ABS column endrin generally appears as a single peak with a long

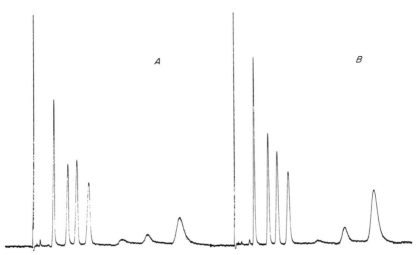

Fig. 56-1.   *A.* First Chromatogram from New Column (10 percent d.c. 200 on 80/90 Anakrom ABS) after 40-hr. conditioning. *B.* Second Chromatogram 1–2 Hr. Later Following 1-mg. Injection of Mixed Pesticide Standard. Pesticides, from left to right, 1 ng. each: lindane, heptachlor, aldrin, heptachlor epoxide, and 5 ng. technical DDT. Column temp., 200°C. Electrometer, 1×10^{-9} AFS. (Reproduced with permission from Burke, J., and Giuffrida, L., J. Assoc. Offic., Agr. Chemists, **47,** 326, 1964.)

tailing section or as a single peak with a shoulder on the back side. The size and time relationship between the peak and tailing portion does not change when the column temperature is varied between 175° and 220°C. Chromatographic peaks obtained from endrin are affected by the solid support.

The chromatography of endrin on the Anakrom ABS column improves with column use. It requires more column "conditioning" than the other compounds to obtain satisfactory chromatograms.

Effect of Uncleaned Extracts on Columns.[8]—A good column that is well conditioned can be used for hundreds of quantitative determinations if it is properly handled, but may be ruined by one determination if it is mishandled.

In order to continue to obtain reliable results from a good column, it is imperative that the sample extracts that are injected be adequately cleaned up. Many analysts attempt to short cut the cleanup, but there are many inherent dangers in so doing.

The following example illustrates one hazard to a column from inadequate cleanup. A vegetable extract which had little prior cleanup was merely transferred from the diluted acetonitrile extract into petroleum ether and injected into a column. Electron capture GLC of a sample representing 30 mg. of spinach gave upper curve A shown in Fig. 56-2. The only apparent abnormality is the failure of the recorder pen to return to the original zero baseline. However, a standard solution injected *after* the spinach sample shows a marked change, particularly DDT (curve B, Fig. 56-2). The *p,p'*-DDT peak is decreased and a peak with the same retention time as DDE also appears. With further "contamination" of the column this process continues until the p,p'-DDT peak disappears and the "DDD" and "DDE" peaks become larger. A third peak appears just before the "DDE" peak. (The compounds which are formed in the chromatographic system as indicated by these peak changes have not been definitely identified.) Loss of heptachlor on the GLC column is also observed.

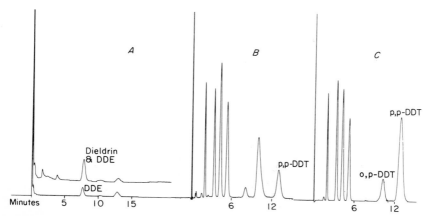

Fig. 56-2.   A. Lower Curve Obtained from 30 mg. Cleaned-up Spinach Extract, Fraction 1. Upper Curve Obtained from 30 mg. Crude Spinach Extract. B. Standard Solution: lindane, heptachlor, aldrin, heptachlor epoxide, and technical DDT chromatographed following crude extract. C. Same Standard Solution Chromatographed Before Crude Extract. Column: 10 percent d.c. 200 on 80/90 Anakrom ABS; temp. 200°C. Electrometer, 3×10^{-9} AFS. (Reproduced with permission from Burke, J., and Giuffrida, L., J. Assoc. Offic. Agr. Chemists, 47, 326, 1964.)

Various methods used in column conditioning (injection of large quantities of insecticides, acetic anhydride, and tris (2-biphenyl) phosphate; high temperature heating and outgassing; and changing the glass wool in the injection end of the column) failed to overcome the effect of the spinach sample and the column had to be discarded.

Besides losses and degradation on the column, unclean samples cause changes in detector sensitivity which must be avoided for quantitative work (see discussion under electron capture detector. In Fig. 56-2 a comparison of curve B (standard solution chromatographed after the spinach sample) with curve C (standard chromatographed before the spinach) shows an increase in sensitivity for some compounds. After the detector was cleaned, the sensitivity returned to normal. In the analysis of the uncleaned sample (curve A) DDE and dieldrin cannot be differentiated. They can be separated by column chromatography in the cleanup step.

Injecting uncleaned samples representing 10 mg. of kale, carrots, and potatoes apparently did not harm another GLC column. However, the chromatograms exhibited several peaks that were not due to insecticides, so that the curves were difficult to interpret.

Column Temperature.—For isothermal chromatography of mixed pesticides—200°C.

Gas Flow.[8]—Operate column with a flow of 100–120 ml. prepurified nitrogen per minute. This flow rate is most effective if both resolution and total retention time are considered when using the GLC system as a "multiple detection" technique for the common chlorinated pesticides. These conditions are also recommended because of the following experiment.

A mixture of 6 compounds was chromatographed at several flow rates. The column temperature was adjusted at each rate to nearly constant elution times. The response of all compounds decreased as the gas flow increased (Fig. 56-3). The response depends less on flow at the higher rates. This is, of course, a detector effect.

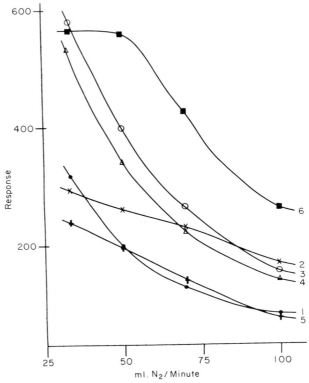

Fig. 56-3.   Response with Change in Flow Rate. 1, lindane, 0.5 ng. 2, heptachlor, 1 ng. 3. aldrin, 1 ng. 4, heptachlor epoxide, 1 ng. 5, o,p'-DDT. 6, p,p'-DDT, 5 ng. technical DDT. Electrometer, 1×10^{-9} AFS. (Reproduced with permission from Burke, J., and Giuffrida, L., J. Assoc. Offic. Agr. Chemists, **47,** 326, 1964.)

A second effect is due to the stability of individual compounds on the column itself. Heptachlor, o,p'-DDT, and p,p'-DDT show marked losses at the lower flow rates, and sections of raised baseline on chromatograms indicate that these compounds are degraded on the column. Lindane, aldrin, and heptachlor epoxide appear to be stable at all flow rates. These results were verified by experiments with another GLC system utilizing a coulometric detector and both isothermal and temperature programming conditions.

The combinations of these two effects (lower response of the electron capture detector and less dependence on flow, and greater stability of sensitive compounds at higher flow rate) has led to choice of the 120 ml. per minute flow rate. Gas flow rate should be checked at least once daily by a system that is known to be accurate. A rising soap film technique utilizing a 100-ml. buret is recommended for checking flow rates.

CAUTION.—Plastic containers must not be used to store solvents because extractables may give electron capture or other detector responses.

QUALITATIVE ANALYSIS

All cautions should be exercised to be certain that artifacts as were discussed under "Effect of Uncleaned Extracts on Columns" are not formed since they may interfere materially with qualitative interpretation of the chromatogram. A single analysis by gas chromatography does not unequivocally identify the material under study. The retention time (time from injection until the chromatographic band enters the detector) is the basis for gas chromatographic identification. It is readily seen that 2 or more compounds, with any given column and conditions, could have retention times which are the same or so nearly the same that their respective chromatographic bands overlap. In such cases identification is difficult.

Various techniques may be employed to reduce conflicting responses in any given GLC analysis—for example, use of a detector that is specific for the compounds or type of compound being investigated. Column chromatography prior to GLC can be used to separate compounds with conflicting retention times. Chemical methods may be used to differentiate between compounds with conflicting retention times—for example, by decomposing one, changing them chemically, or making derivatives.

Since the number of chlorinated pesticides that could conceivably be present as residues is quite large, the analyst should have access to retention data on the materials he is likely to encounter. Actual retention times vary with slight changes in column temperature and gas flow rate. They are not precisely reproducible from one column to another, even with the same type of packing. Relative retention times, that is, retention times relative to the retention time of a reference compound and expressed as a relative value, are reproducible from column to column (with the same type of packing) and do not change markedly with slight variations in column temperature and flow rate. Table 56-1 lists relative retention times for 68 compounds. Although this is not a complete listing of chlorinated pesticide chemicals, it should aid the analyst in making a tentative identification.

QUANTITATIVE ANALYSIS

Quantitation can be made by comparing the area under the residue peak to the area under the peak obtained from a known quantity of the proper standard. Ideally, an amount of standard equal to the amount of the unknown should be chromatographed after the unknown; however, this is difficult and time consuming in routine multiple detection analysis. Often two or more compounds may be found, so that a standard equivalent to each would have to be run. To avoid as much of this extra standard injection as possible all precautions given so far should be exercised to keep the detectors and columns performing ideally. Also, the operational parameters which yield linearity of response over a wide range should be carefully controlled. (See procedure to obtain optimal linearity under "Electron Capture Detector" later.)

It is suggested that a familiar mixed standard (lindane, heptachlor, aldrin, heptachlor epoxide, and DDT) be chromatographed about 3 times daily to show any change in sensitivity, column degradation, leaks, etc., to obtain the best quantitation.

Peak area can be determined by two methods: triangulation [(base $\times$ peak height)/2] and by use of automatic integration. The baseline must be steady in order to make good

TABLE 56-1. RELATIVE RETENTION TIMES OF CHLORINATED PESTICIDES
BY ISOTHERMAL ELECTRON CAPTURE GLC; APPROXIMATE
RESPONSE OF SYSTEM TO PESTICIDES

Column: 6 ft. $\times$ 4 mm. i.d. 10 percent DC 200 (12,500 cst.) on 80/90 mesh Anakrom
ABS—well conditioned
Column temperature: 200°C.
Injection temperature: 225°C.
Carrier gas flow rate: 120 ml. per minute N_2
Detector: Tritium source; concentric type
Detector voltage: 50 v d.c.
Recorder: 5 millivolt
Electrometer sensitivity: 1×10^{-9} AFS

Pesticide	Retention Times Relative to Aldrin Ratio	Response[a] Ng. for $\frac{1}{2}$ FSD 1×10^{-9} AFS
Monuron	<0.1	30
Diuron	0.11	10–15
Neburon	0.11	10–15
TCNB	0.28	0.5–0.6
Methyl ester 2,4-D	0.29	10
CIPC	0.31	1000–2000
Vegadex	0.37	3
BHC	*0.38*, 0.47[b]	1–2
Isopropyl ester 2,4-D	0.41	10
Hexachlorobenzene	0.43	0.3–0.4
Lindane	0.47	0.5
PCNB	0.50	0.3–0.4
Dichlone	0.54	3–4
Tetraiodoethylene[c]	0.54	4
Isobutyl ester 2,4-D	0.61	5
Isopropyl ester 2,4,5-T	0.66	2
n-Butyl ester 2,4-D	0.71	40
Ronnel	0.78	1
Heptachlor	0.79	0.75–1
Parathion[c]	0.98	15
Aldrin[d]	1.00	0.75–1
Kelthane	1.01	2–3
Chlorthion	1.05	60–70

Chlorinated phenoxyacetic acids and their salts do not chromatograph on this column.
The approximate response of the electron capture detector to chlorinated pesticide
chemicals may vary among individual detectors. All detectors may not have the same
response characteristics at given operational parameters, *i.e.*, detector voltage and
temperature and carrier gas flow rate.

[a] Quantity (nanograms) of pesticide required to cause $\frac{1}{2}$ full scale recorder deflection at an
electrometer sensitivity of 1×10^{-9} AFS.
[b] When more than one peak is present, the major peak(s) is italicized.
[c] Not chlorinated.
[d] Aldrin reference-retention time approximately 4.25 min.

TABLE 56-1 (cont.)

Pesticide	Retention Times Relative to Aldrin Ratio	Response[a] Ng. for ½ FSD 1 × 10⁻⁹ AFS
n-Butyl ester 2,4,5-T	1.08	2
Telodrin	1.10	1
o,p'-DDD olefin	1.17	16
Dyrene	1.21	75
Captan	1.22	40–50
Sulphenone	1.24	4
Heptachlor epoxide	1.24	1
Chlorbenside	1.36	2
p,p'-DDD olefin	1.42	2–3
α-Chlordane	1.43	1
Perthane olefin	1.47	40
o,p'-DDE	1.48	2
Propylene glycol butylether ester 2,4-D	1.51	20
Thiodan	1.58, 2.16	1–2
Ovex	1.58	3
β-Chlordane	1.60	1
Butoxy ethanol ester 2,4-D	1.78	12
DDT (tech.)	1.81, 2.44, *3.03*[b]	5
p,p'-DDE	1.81	1
Dieldrin	1.83	1–1.5
o,p'-DDD	1.86	2
Iso-octyl ester 2,4-D	2.00, 2.37	30
Endrin	2.05, 2.29	2
Ethyl hexyl ester 2,4-D	2.07	8
Perthane	2.11	50–150
p,p'-DDD	2.33	1.5
Chlorobenzilate	2.43	10
o,p'-DDT	2.44	4
Kepone	2.70	4–5
Iso-octyl ester 2,4,5-T	2.73, *3.14, 3.73*[b]	10
Trithion	2.83	10
Prolan	2.83	5
Dilan	2.83, *3.37*[b]	5–10
Butoxy ethanol ester 2,4,5-T	2.85	4
p,p'-Methoxychlor olefin	2.91	8
p,p'-DDT	3.03	4
Bulan	3.35	40
Methoxychlor	4.5	8–10
Tedion	5.4	5–7
BEP ester 2,4,5-T	0.16, 0.67, 1.06, *2.79,*[b] 3.24, 5.15, 6.9	35
Chlordane (tech.)	0.44, 0.62, 0.70, 0.79, 0.95, 1.14, *1.42*, 1.59, 2.56[b]	1–2

TABLE 56-1 (cont.)

Pesticide	Retention Times Relative to Aldrin Ratio	Response[a] Ng. for $\frac{1}{2}$ FSD 1×10^{-9} AFS
BEP ester 2,4-D (tech.).................	0.73, 1.84, 2.10, 3.33,· *4.89*[b]	50
Strobane............................	1.07, 1.29, 1.50, 1.76, 1.90, 2.05, *2.28*, 2.64, 3.04, 3.55[b]	25
Toxaphene...........................	1.18, 1.51, 1.76, *2.34*, 2.63, *3.06*, *3.61*, 4.31, 4.51, 4.97[b]	20
Co-Ral..............................	9.5	100–150

interpretation from either system. At chart speed of $\frac{1}{3}$ in. per minute, peaks with retention times less than about 4 or 5 min. are so sharp that triangulation is difficult. Measurement of peak areas by either method is more accurate at somewhat faster chart speed ($\frac{1}{2}$ in. per minute).

Occasionally, chromatograms contain overlapping peaks, or unexplained interference, etc., so that measurement of peak area is not clear-cut. In such cases the analyst must exercise judgment in obtaining a quantitative estimation.

GAS CHROMATOGRAPHY

ELECTRON CAPTURE DETECTOR

There are many different manufacturers of gas chromatographic equipment in which the electron capture detector can be used. Each has some features which differ from others; however, any equipment which permits the use of column, detectors, and operating conditions as outlined should be useful for the efficient analysis of pesticide residues.

Detector.—The following type of cell and operating conditions have been found to be optimal for routine pesticide residue analysis, because with the operating conditions suggested there is (1) much better linearity of response, (2) greater latitude between the smallest and largest amount that can be measured quantitatively, (3) less change in response from small voltage changes than when the cell is operated at its highest sensitivity, and (4) good overall stability (steady baseline, etc.).

The cell should have an internal diameter of $\frac{1}{2}$ in. and the opening should be $\frac{3}{4}$ in. deep. It should be the concentric loaded, adjustable probe type, charged with tritiated foil $\frac{1}{2}$ in. wide and long enough to extend around the inside circumference of the lower $\frac{1}{2}$ in. of the internal wall of the cell. The anode should be adjustable and should project through the center of the top of the cell. It should project $\frac{1}{4}$ in. within the cell so that the end of the probe is even with the top of the tritiated foil. The response of the cell is dependent on the position of the end of the probe with respect to the foil as well as the voltage applied.

With such a cell, measure the response to 1 ng. of heptachlor epoxide repeatedly while the voltage is varied. These values can be plotted as a voltage *vs.* response curve as shown in Fig. 56-4. Observe the curve and choose a voltage for that cell which yields a response at the early part of the flattened portion of the curve as indicated by the arrow

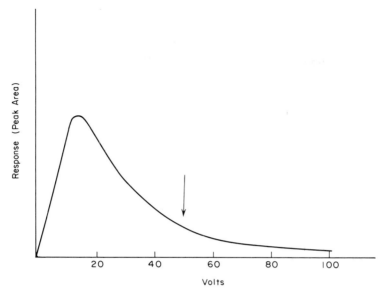

Fɪɢ. 56-4.   Response Obtained from Repeated Injections of 1 ng. Heptachlor Epoxide while Voltage on Electron Capture Cell Was Varied from 0 to 100 Volts.

in Fig. 56-4. At 10^{-9} AFS, 1 ng. of heptachlor epoxide should give a deflection of about $\frac{1}{2}$ full scale. For many cells this value is about 50 volts.

   Conditions of Operation.—Columns (see "Column" under "Gas-Liquid Chromatography" for discussion and details of preparation).

   Glass—6 ft. long, 4–6 mm. inside diameter.

   Column packing—Anakrom ABS 80/90 mesh.

   Column coating—10 percent DC-200 (12,500 cst).

   Temperatures

       Flash heater—225°–230°C.

       Column—200°C.

       Detector—200°C.

   Volume to inject—5 to 10 μl.

       Sample equivalency—up to 100 mg. This will permit the determination of 0.01 p.p.m. of most of the common chlorinated organic pesticides.

   Table 56-1 shows the approximate amounts of many pesticides that are required to give one-half full scale response after passing through the above column and detector system.

MICROCOULOMETRIC DETECTOR[10,11]

   Much of the work done on the analysis of pesticide residues by gas chromatography has been done with the microcoulometric detector device,[1] which became available in 1961. The selectivity of the earlier detectors for gas chromatography, such as thermistors and argon ionization, was not adequate, when combined with the state of purity obtainable with current cleanup procedures, to yield meaningful and interpretable results for general residue analysis. The microcoulometric detector was the first to add the specificity needed for an adequate analytical system.

There is, at present, only one type of commercially available microcoulometric gas chromatograph (MCGC). It consists of a Micro Tek gas chromatograph unit combined with Dohrmann combustion and detection units. Two types of titration cells are available, one specific for halogens, the other specific for sulfur.

The microcoulometric halogen detector responds only to chlorine, bromine, or iodine from compounds which pass through the gas chromatographic column. The detector is about 1000 times less sensitive to certain pesticide chemicals than the electron capture detectors, yet its sensitivity is adequate for pesticide residue analysis. This is due in part to its high selectivity in response which permits injection of much larger samples than is possible with electron capture detectors.

Instrument Operating Conditions

Cells—T-200-S (halogen), T-200-P (sulfur).

Column—(see "Column" under "Gas Liquid Chromatography").

Gas flow—(check flow rate at least daily) 120 ml. prepurified N_2 per minute.

Injection port—240°C.

Transfer line—250°C.

Combustion inlet block—250°C.

Furnace—800°C.

Chart speed—$\frac{1}{2}$ in. per minute.

Sensitivity—usually operate at 64 or 128 ohms.

Standard solutions of 10 to 100 μg. pesticide per ml. in isooctane are convenient for most work.

Occasionally nonhalogenated solvents contain materials that cause a response, e.g., a small peak at the beginning of the chromatogram. This may be eliminated by venting during the first minute after injection. Redistilled (or B and J*) petroleum ether and acetonitrile only are used in the extraction and cleanup methods to keep solvent peaks to a minimum.

The detector response (peak area) to a given quantity of a chlorinated or thio pesticide depends on the amount of chlorine or sulfur in the molecule and on the efficiency with which the compound passes through the chromatographic system. Response cannot always be predicted on the basis of chlorine or sulfur content alone, primarily due to the column efficiency. Efficient chromatography of several compounds may not be achieved until the column is well conditioned. Table 56-2 shows the relative retention time (relative to retention time of aldrin) for 87 halogenated pesticide chemicals and the approximate quantity of pesticide necessary to give a one-half scale recorder deflection at a sensitivity setting of 64 ohms. These data were obtained from a well-conditioned column operating at high efficiency. Detector sensitivity can be doubled (128 ohms) without an appreciable increase in the noise level; the 256-ohm sensitivity (4 times as sensitive as 64 ohms) can frequently be used, depending on the stability of the individual MCGC system. Rarely can the 512-ohm sensitivity be effectively utilized. The 128-ohm sensitivity is most useful in residue analyses.

It is difficult to assign a maximum sensitivity to the microcoulometric technique in terms of p.p.m. pesticide residue. This varies with the individual pesticide, the amount of sample injected, the product from which the pesticide was extracted, the degree to which the sample has been cleaned up, and the operating efficiency and stability of the. individual MCGC system. The injection system is designed to receive large-volume injection; injection volumes of 50–100 μl. are common. This volume may represent the equivalent of 10–25 g. of the original sample. Certain pesticides that cause a high chloride response and are eluted in narrow chromatographic bands can be determined

* See asterisk footnote on p. 1464.

TABLE 56-2. RELATIVE RETENTION TIMES AND APPROXIMATE RESPONSE
OF MICROCOULOMETRIC GLC SYSTEM TO CHLORINATED AND THIO PESTICIDES

Column: 10 percent DC 200 (12,500 cst) on 80/90 Anakrom ABS, 6 ft. $\times$ 4.5 mm. i.d.
Column temperature, 210°C.; flow rate, 120 ml. per minute
Injection temperature, 240°C.
Detectors: T-200-S (halogen); T-200-P (sulfur)
Detector sensitivity: 64 ohms[a]

Pesticide	Relative Retention Time	Approximate Quantity (μg.) for $\frac{1}{2}$ FSD[b]
HALOGEN DETECTION (Retention time relative to retention time of aldrin)		
Dichloral urea..........................	0.15	1.5
Trithion, thiol-sulfoxide.................	0.15, 1.78, 1.89	150
Ethylene dichloride.....................	0.16	1
Chloropicrin...........................	0.17	1
Trithion, sulfoxide......................	0.17, 1.78, 2.46, *4.54*[c]	60
Ethylene dibromide.....................	0.18	0.75
p-Dichlorobenzene......................	0.18	0.75
Monuron..............................	0.18	1.5
Diuron...............................	0.19	2
Neburon.............................	0.19	2
Ethide...............................	0.19	1.5
DDT (tech.)...........................	0.35, 1.69, 2.21, *2.70*[c]	4
TCNB................................	0.36	1
Methyl ester 2,4-D.....................	0.36	4
CIPC.................................	0.37	3.5
Vegadex..............................	0.44	4
BHC (tech.)...........................	*0.44*, 0.52[c]	1.25
Isopropyl ester 2,4-D...................	0.44	1.5
Simazine.............................	0.45	4
α-BHC................................	0.46	0.75
Propazine............................	0.47	5
Hexachlorobenzene.....................	0.49	0.4
β-BHC................................	0.50	0.75
Methoxychlor (tech.)...................	0.50, 2.87, *3.90*[c]	7.5
Lindane..............................	0.52	0.75
PCNB................................	0.54	0.75
δ-BHC................................	0.55	0.75
Dichlone.............................	0.57	2.25

[a] Sensitivity can be doubled (128 ohms) without appreciable increase in noise level.
[b] Approximate quantity necessary to cause a $\frac{1}{2}$ full-scale recorder deflection.
[c] When more than one peak is present, the major peak(s) is italicized.
[d] Not chlorinated.
[e] Aldrin reference: retention time approximately 5.5 min.
[f] Sulphenone reference: retention, approximately 5.9 min.
[g] Large response immediately after injection.

Table 56-2 (cont.)

Pesticide	Relative Retention Time	Approximate Quantity (μg.) for ½ FSD[b]
Pentachlorophenol	0.60	7.5
Tetraiodoethylene[d]	0.63	8
Isobutyl ester 2,4-D	0.63	2
Isopropyl ester 2,4,5-T	0.65	2
n-Butyl ester 2,4-D	0.69	2.5
Ronnel	0.77	2.5
Heptachlor	0.81	1
Chlorthion	0.99	2
Kelthane (tech.)	0.99, 3.82[c]	15
Aldrin[e]	1.00	1
n-Butyl ester 2,4,5-T	1.05	2
Telodrin	1.09	1
o,p'-DDD olefin	1.12	5
Dyrene	1.15, 1.38, 1.61, 1.87, 2.23[c]	25
Captan	1.16	3.5
Sulphenone	1.19	8
Heptachlor epoxide	1.20	1
Chlorbenside	1.25	3.5
p,p'-DDD olefin	1.34	2
Propylene glycol butyl ether ester 2,4-D	1.34, 3.12	6
γ-Chlordane	1.35	1.5
Perthane olefin	1.35	6
o,p'-DDE	1.37	2
Thiodan	1.44, 1.91[c]	3
Ovex	1.46	5
β-Chlordane	1.46	1
Methyl ester p,p'-DDA	1.48	7
Butoxy ethanol ester 2,4-D	1.50	5
p,p'-DDE	1.69	2.5
Iso-octyl ester 2,4-D	1.70, 1.98[c]	9
Dieldrin	1.72	1.75
o,p'-DDD	1.72	2
Aramite	1.76, 1.84	15
Ethyl hexyl ester 2,4-D	1.77	10
Trithion, thiol	1.89	24
Trithion, thiol-sulfone	1.89, 2.54, 3.23[c]	150
Perthane	1.91	4.5
Endrin	1.90, 2.09[c]	3
Chlorobenzilate	2.07	7
Dilan	2.05, 2.40, 2.86[c]	15
p,p'-DDD	2.12	2.5
o,p'-DDT	2.21	3.5
Iso-octyl ester 2,4,5-T	2.28, 2.62, 3.08, 3.60[c]	10

Table 56-2 (cont.)

Pesticide	Relative Retention Time	Approximate Quantity (μg.) for $\frac{1}{2}$ FSD[b]
Butoxy ethanol ester 2,4,5-T	2.32	5
Kepone	2.35	3
Prolan	2.40	11
Bulan	2.40, *2.89*[c]	10
Trithion	2.44	8
p,p'-Methoxychlor olefin	2.52	8
p,p'-DDT	2.70	3.5
p,p'-Methoxychlor	3.90	7
Tedion	4.22	8
Trithion, sulfone	4.30	30
Chlordane (tech.)	0.52, 0.66, 0.74, 0.82, 0.96, 1.14, *1.36*, 1.50, 2.3[c]	10
Strobane	0.91, 1.07, 1.24, 1.44, 1.63, *2.07*, 2.35, 2.66, 3.17, 3.77[c]	18
Toxaphene	1.29, 1.45, 1.55, 1.87, 2.17, 2.45, *2.85*, *3.36*, 4.03, 4.52[c]	22
BEP ester 2,4,5-T (tech.)	0.66, 1.06, 2.32, 2.72, 3.85, *5.23*[c]	30
BEP ester 2,4-D (tech.)	0.71, 1.21, 1.53, 1.81, *3.51*, 8.5[c]	18
Co-Ral	7.6	25

Chlorinated phenoxy acids and their salts do not chromatograph.

SULFUR DETECTION
(Retention time relative to retention time of sulphenone)

Trithion, sulfoxide	0.13, 1.52, 1.61, 2.10, *3.90*[c]	16
Trithion, thiol	0.13, *1.61*[c]	4
Ethion	0.16, *1.83*[c]	1
Thiono Systox	0.27	1
Systox	0.27, *0.37*[c]	0.75
Delnav	*0.41*, 0.67[c]	4
Diazinon	0.44	1
Dimethoate	0.51	0.75
Methyl parathion	0.60	2
Ronnel	0.65	2.5
Malathion	0.71	0.75
Trithion, thiol-sulfone	0.72, 1.61, *2.77*[c,g]	60
Parathion	0.78	1.5
Chlorthion	0.81	1

TABLE 56-2 (cont.)

Pesticide	Relative Retention Time	Approximate Quantity (μg.) for $\frac{1}{2}$ FSD[b]
Captan	0.95	6
Sulphenone[f]	1.00	2.5
Ovex	1.23	3.5
Thiodan	1.23, 1.64[c]	10
Aramite	1.48, 1.58	10
Trithion, thiol-sulfoxide	1.53, 1.62, 2.03[g]	60
Trithion	2.10	3
EPN	3.15	17
Trithion, sulfone	3.62	6
Tedion	3.67	20
Guthion	3.75	20
Co-Ral	6.55	6

at the 0.005 p.p.m. level. Generally speaking, however, at levels below 0.01 p.p.m. the determination is not made routinely.

Because a large sample injection is necessary for detection of low-level residues in food products, the purified extract must be concentrated to a small volume, generally 0.2 to 0.5 ml. Quite commonly the final step of the concentration is the evaporation of the solvent (to a small volume or to dryness) in a gentle stream of clean dry air or nitrogen. Experiments indicate that significant losses of pesticide can occur in this step, particularly at volumes below 1 ml., and that large losses occur if the solution is taken to dryness.

One method that allows rapid concentration to volumes of 0.2–0.5 ml. with good recovery of pesticide makes use of a micro Snyder column, as follows: Using a Kuderna-Danish concentrator, concentrate the cleaned up sample to a volume of 5–10 ml. Cool and fit a micro Snyder column* onto the calibrated collection tube and evaporate until the desired volume is reached. Allow the apparatus to cool and permit the solvent vapor condensate to drain back into the tube before removing the column. Accurately measure the volume and inject an aliquot representing the desired sample size into the MCGC.

Immediately after the sample chromatogram is obtained, inject a similar volume of the appropriate standard pesticide solution. Use a standard solution of a concentration such that the peaks of the standards will be approximately the same size as the sample peaks for the compounds of interest.

The coulometric titration of halogen (Cl^-, Br^-, or I^-) and sulfur dioxide proceeds according to Faraday's law, which allows for the calculation of the quantity of halogen or sulfur being titrated. Knowing the quantity of the particular compound injected, its halogen or sulfur content, instrument sensitivity, recorder sensitivity, chart speed, and peak area, it is possible to determine the theoretical recovery of the material through the MCGC system. Not all pesticides pass through the MCGC system with a high percentage of theoretical chloride or sulfur recovery. However, the recoveries are usually constant (the system is linear) when the pesticide is present above some minimum quantity. A plot of theoretical recovery as the ordinate vs. quantity injected as the abscissa

* Micro Snyder column, No. K-56900; Kontes Glass Co., Vineland, N. J.

will show the linear range of the instrument and the recovery level for the compound in question.

Table 56-3 gives the average theoretical recovery obtained from 14 chlorinated pesticides and 3 sulfur-containing pesticides. The lower quantity of the range is the level below which negative deviation from linearity occurs.[11]

TABLE 56-3. RECOVERY OF PESTICIDES THROUGH MCGG SYSTEM[a]

Column: 10 percent DC 200 (12,500 cst.) on 80/90 mesh Anakrom ABS
Column temperature, 210°C.; flow rate, 120 ml. per minute

Pesticide	Average Percent Theoretical Recovery		Range (μg.)[b]	
	128 ohms	64 ohms	128 ohms	64 ohms
CHLORIDE DETECTION[c]				
Lindane	88	87	0.3–0.7	0.6–1.2
BHC	78	80	0.4–1.5	0.4–3.0
Heptachlor	88	92·	0.3–0.7	0.6–1.2
Aldrin	98	97	0.3–0.7	0.4–1.2
Heptachlor epoxide	97	97	0.1–0.7	0.4–1.2
p,p'-DDT	86	88	1.5–3.5	2.0–6.0
p,p'-DDD	89	91	0.4–2.0	0.8–4.0
p,p'-DDE	88	90	0.4–2.0	0.8–4.0
p,p'-Methoxychlor	78	81	1.5–5.0	3.0–10.0
Dieldrin	95	95	0.4–1.5	0.8–3.0
Endrin	83	88	0.2–1.5	1.2–3.0
Thiodan	93	94	0.1–2.0	0.2–4.0
Tedion	90	88	0.2–5.0	0.4–10.0
Toxaphene	90	95	4.0–20.0	8.0–40.0
SULFUR DETECTION[d]				
Thiodan	76	70	0.6–3.0	0.8–6.0
Tedion	90	88	0.5–5.0	1.0–10.0
Parathion	74	71	0.4–2.0	0.4–4.0

[a] Reproduced with permission from Burke, J., and Holswade, W., J. Assoc. Offic. Agr. Chemists, **47**, 845, 1964.
[b] Average determined in this region of constant recovery. Lower quantity indicates level below which negative deviation from linearity occurs.
[c] T-200-S titration cell.
[d] T-200-P titration cell.

Generally speaking, a linear response is obtained when quantities of pesticide present are above about 0.5 μg. Below this level there is a negative deviation from linearity which varies with the compound; heptachlor epoxide shows a linear response down to 0.1 μg., but p,p'-DDT shows a deviation from linearity at about 1.5 μg. The linear region is extended to lower quantities by use of the 128-ohm sensitivity. The system is linear between these two sensitivity settings; the same quantity of pesticide causes twice the response at 128 ohms that it does at 64 ohms.

There may be a number of causes for the negative deviation from linearity. However, if the analyst is aware of this fact and compares peaks to be measured with standard peaks of approximately the same size frequently enough, good quantitative results will be obtained down to minimum detectable quantities.

Injection volumes of less than 10 μl. should not be used with this instrument in quantitative work.

Cleanup.—Since this system takes larger sample equivalents for low-level analysis, some special precautions may be necessary.

It is sometimes difficult to clean up thoroughly extracts of materials containing large amounts of fats or oils, *e.g.*, dairy products, animal tissue, cottonseed meal, fish oils, etc. The oily material that may remain when such an extract is concentrated to a fraction of a milliliter will almost always cause irreversible damage if injected into a GLC column.

Waxy or colored coextracted materials may also damage the GLC column; however, their effect is not so readily apparent as is that from oily material. Small amounts of colored matter (presumably carotenes) do not seem to harm the column; however, the injection of any extract that is not well cleaned up should be avoided. The user of the MCGC must determine if individual samples are suitable for analysis. In some instances, it will be necessary to reject or perform further cleanup on some samples prior to analysis.

The injection system of the Micro Tek-Dohrmann equipment is designed so that a Vycor tube may be inserted into the injection block. This tube, in which nonvolatile material accumulates, can be periodically removed for replacement or cleaning. The tube is easily cleaned by flaming off the accumulated material. This insert protects both the injection block area and the column from the damaging deposits and eliminates the troublesome need for cleaning the block. Retention of oily material is better, and protection of the GLC column is increased if a cylinder of platinum gauze, 2 in. long, is placed inside the Vycor tube. The use of the Vycor tube at all times is recommended.

If "unclean" extracts and those which contain oily material are not injected, a single column can be used for hundreds of analyses.

Small amounts of coextracted material do not cause a detector response to either halogen or sulfur, except from a few crops. A small halogen response at the beginning of the chromatography may be obtained from injection of large quantities of cabbage and radish extract. A very large sulfur response may be obtained from injections of large quantities of cabbage and onion extract. A response is usually obtained at the beginning of the chromatogram when extracts of fish oil or animal tissue are injected. However, to avoid this detector response, it is general practice to vent the column effluent to atmosphere during the first 1–2 min. of the chromatography via the system provided on the instrument.

GAS CHROMATOGRAPHY FOR ORGANOPHOSPHATES

SODIUM THERMIONIC DETECTOR[12,13]

One of the great difficulties which has impeded the development of any type of adequate methods for the organophosphates has been the lack of a sensitive, selective, and simple determinative procedure. Recently a new detector highly sensitive and selective to phosphorus compounds has been developed which gives every promise of fulfilling this serious lack.

In the usual flame ionization detector, when an organic compound is burned in a hydrogen flame, the conductivity is increased. This response, which is believed to be directly related to the thermally generated carbon ions in the compound burned, varies with the number of carbon atoms present. Halogen and phosphorus atoms do not affect the response; therefore, there is no selective response to compounds containing these elements. It has been found that when sodium ions are present in the flame, the response from phosphorus is greatly enhanced, the halogen response increased to a lesser extent, and the carbon response is unchanged.

A detector based on this phenomenon and the optimal operation parameters for its use in gas chromatography of some organophosphate pesticide chemicals has been developed.[12,13] This detector has been termed a sodium thermionic detector. The response of the sodium thermionic detector to an organic compound containing 10 carbon atoms and one phosphorus atom is about 600 times greater than the response obtained from the same compound by using a conventional flame ionization detector. For a compound containing 6 chlorine atoms, the increased response is about 20 times that shown by the flame ionization detector for the same compound. Carbon compounds that do not contain phosphorus or halogen respond to the same degree with the sodium thermionic detector as with the flame ionization detector. Organophosphates containing no sulfur respond as well as those containing sulfur. Therefore, phosphorus compounds can be determined with minimal interference from other organic compounds.

The device consists of a conventional flame detector except that a coat of a sodium salt, such as sodium sulfate, has been fused onto the electrode.

One advantage of this modification of a hydrogen flame ionization detector is that the conversion to the sodium thermionic detector is simple—*i.e.*, the regular electrode is interchanged with an electrode coated with a fused sodium salt. The conventional hydrogen flame detector acts as a mass detector, whereas the sodium thermionic detector acts as a highly selective one.

The sodium thermionic detector[12,13] is an adaptation of a standard flame ionization detector as shown in Figs. 56-5 and 56-6. The positive electrode is replaced by a length

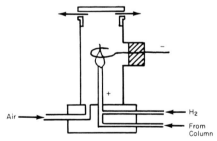

Fig. 56-5. A Schematic Drawing of a Hydrogen Flame Detector of Basic Design. (Reproduced with permission from Giuffrida, L., J. Assoc. Offic. Agr. Chemists, **47**, 297, 1964.)

of wire extending as a coil above the flame. The wire, 0.016-in. platinum-iridium, is wound with a mandrel as shown in Fig. 56-6. The mandrel is made from a short piece of $\frac{10}{32}$-in. threaded rod fitted with a $\frac{1}{16}$-in. rod.

The five-turn helical electrode formed by the threaded rod is coated with sodium sulfate by putting a drop of saturated aqueous sodium sulfate solution on the electrode and heating gently in a Bunsen burner. This is repeated about 3 times. At red heat the salt fuses and distributes over the electrode spirals. The electrode is then assembled in the detector and positioned with the bottom of the electrode about 2 mm. above the jet. The sodium sulfate coating on the electrode is effective for about 2 months of use of 8 hr. per day.

Use a hydrogen flame detector of a basic design that is fitted with an electrode assembly which allows electrodes to be interchanged and easily adjusted. Apply a potential from a 300-volt battery. Supply air to the burner at the rate of 300 ml. per minute.

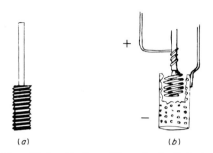

(a)   (b)

Fig. 56-6. Sodium Thermionic Detector. (Reproduced with permission from Giuffrida, L., and Ives, F., J. Assoc. Offic. Agr. Chemists, **47,** 1112, 1964.)

Detector jets of #18 stainless-steel tubing are most suitable. Flame "blow-outs" caused by solvent volumes are rare. Retention times of compounds through the gas chromatograph are not affected by increases in hydrogen to the detector. Trials with jets of about #22 tubing produced longer retention times at higher hydrogen flows, indicating pressure in the detector that affected the gas flow in the column. The shape of the flame itself is undoubtedly less distorted with changes in flame gas mixtures when a larger diameter jet is used.

Sensitivity is directly related to the temperature of the sodium salt and varies directly as the concentration of hydrogen in the flame when all other variables are held constant. A constant, careful measurement of hydrogen flow is difficult to achieve.

The difficulty of measuring the hydrogen supplied is eliminated by introducing another relationship—a direct relationship between hydrogen concentration in the flame and flame conductivity. Flame conductivity is referred to as baseline current (BLC). Changes in hydrogen concentration produce a corresponding change in BLC which can be directly measured accurately and easily. Thus, sensitivity to phosphorus-containing compounds varies directly with the BLC.

In addition to hydrogen, there are two gas supplies to a hydrogen flame burner.

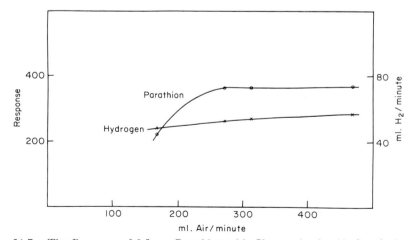

Fig. 56-7. The Response of 0.5 μg. Parathion with Changes in the Air Supplied to the Detector. The Baseline Current Was Held Constant at 6×10^{-9} Amp. by Varying the Hydrogen Flow. (Reproduced with permission from Giuffrida, L., J. Assoc. Offic. Agr. Chemists, **47,** 293, 1964.)

Changes in both air and carrier gas have a marked effect on the temperature of the flame, and concurrent adjustments in hydrogen are necessary.

The effect on detector response of changes in air supplied can be observed at several air-flow rates. The BLC is adjusted by hydrogen supply to 6×10^{-9} amp. The effect of changes in the air supply is shown in Fig. 56-7. At low air flows, sensitivity is suppressed, an effect that indicates an insufficient oxygen supply. As air is increased from 250 to 500 ml. per minute, small increases in hydrogen are required to maintain BLC. The effect of changes in air above 500 ml. is slight. The 300-ml. per minute air rate is chosen for routine operation of the detector.

The effect of changes in carrier gas-flow rates can also be observed. Changes in this parameter are critical because the size and composition of the flame is affected. Figure 56-8 shows the response of parathion as the carrier gas-flow rates are increased while

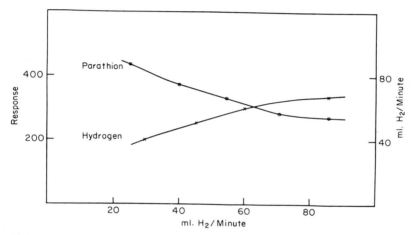

FIG. 56-8. The Response of 0.5 μg. Parathion at Constant Baseline Current (6×10^{-9} Amp.) with Changes in Column Flow Rates. The carrier gas was nitrogen. (Reproduced with permission from Giuffrida, L., J. Assoc. Offic. Agr. Chemists, **47**, 293, 1964.

the BLC is held constant at 6×10^{-9} amp. by varying the hydrogen flow. A rate of 60 ml. nitrogen per minute was found to be good for chromatography and detector operation.

Column.—Prepare the column as described on page 1473.

    Glass—5 ft. long by 4 mm. inside diameter.

    Packing—10 percent Dow Corning 200 on 80/90 mesh Anakrom ABS.

    Gas—nitrogen at 60 ml. per minute.

Instrument Temperature

    Inlet—225°C.

    Column—205°C.

    Detector oven—190°C.

Electrometer Setting

    For 0.025–0.125 μg. pesticide use 3×10^{-8} AFS

        0.125–0.4 μg. pesticide use 1×10^{-7} AFS

        0.4–1.5 μg. pesticide use 3×10^{-7} AFS

Detector Voltage—300

Sample Injection.—With properly cleaned-up sample extracts, injections equivalent to 500 mg. or more of sample may be made routinely. The volume injected may range from 5 to 50 μl.

Quantitation of the pesticide residue is made by comparison with chromatographs of known amounts of standard pesticides. The retention time is useful for identification and comparison of peak areas for quantitation. Table 56-4 shows relative retention times with the recommended column and the sodium thermionic detector.

TABLE 56-4. RELATIVE RETENTION TIMES OF ORGANOPHOSPHATE PESTICIDES WITH SODIUM THERMIONIC DETECTOR[a]

Column: 10 percent DC 200 on 80/90 mesh Anakrom ABS, 5 ft. $\times$ 4 mm. i.d.
Temperatures: Column, 205°C.; inlet, 225°C.
Carrier gas: 60 ml. nitrogen per minute

Compound[b]	Relative Retention Time[c]
Phosdrin	0.14
Thiono Systox	0.28
Sulfotepp	0.30
Dibrom	0.34
Thimet	0.38
Thiol Systox	0.42
Rogor	0.42
Diazinon	0.52
Di-Syston	0.57
Methyl parathion	0.72
Paraoxon	0.81
Ronnel	0.83
Malathion	0.91
Parathion	1.00
Merphos	1.31, 1.88
Ethion	2.57
Trithion	2.89
Imidan	3.93
EPN	4.37
Co-Ral	9.25
Dipterex, DDVP, TEPP	<0.1

[a] Reproduced with permission from Giuffrida, L., J. Assoc. Offic. Agr. Chemists, **47**, 293, 1964.
[b] Delnav, Schradan, Ruelene do not chromatograph well on this column.
[c] Relative to parathion with an elution time of about 4.25 min.

THIN-LAYER CHROMATOGRAPHY (TLC)[14,15]

Thin-layer chromatography has fairly recently been proven to be a very effective technique for the detection and estimation of many pesticide residues, including a large number of chlorinated and organophosphate compounds. It has certain advantages over paper chromatography. The migrating spots generally remain more compact and

[14] Kovacs, M. F., Jr., J. Assoc. Offic. Agr. Chemists, **46**, 884, 1963.
[15] Kovacs, M. F., Jr., J. Assoc. Offic. Agr. Chemists, **47**, 1097, 1964.

thus are more easily separated in a short migration range. Partly because the spots are compact, there is greater contrast between spot and background so that smaller quantities of chemical can be detected; therefore, the system can be considered to be more sensitive. A greater range of solvents and chromatographic reagents can be utilized so that certain separations and color reactions can be performed which are impossible on paper chromatograms.

CHLORINATED PESTICIDES

Many chlorinated pesticide residues can be identified at about 0.01 p.p.m. in many food products.

METHOD[14]

Apparatus. Desaga/Brinkmann Standard Model Applicator.
Desaga/Brinkmann Standard Mounting Board.
Window Glass.—8 × 8 in. double strength (Pittsburgh Plate Glass Company).
Desaga/Brinkmann Drying Rack.—Accommodates ten 8 × 8 in. plates.
Desaga/Brinkmann Desiccator Box.
Chromatographic Tank and Accessories.—As described in J. Assoc. Offic. Agr. Chemists, **36,** 1187, 1953; **40,** 999, 1957; Arthur H. Thomas Company Cat. No. 3106-FO5, or equivalent. *Note:* Use metal instead of glass troughs.
Dipping Tank and Accessories.—As described in J. Assoc. Offic. Agr. Chemists, **41,** 481 and 781, 1958.
Spotting Pipets.—1 μl. (Kontes Glass Company, Vineland, New Jersey).
Spray Bottle.—8-oz. Arthur H. Thomas Company, No. 9186-R2.
Tank Liners.—Two pieces, $12\frac{1}{4}$ × $8\frac{3}{4}$ in., cut from desk blotters, and bent into an L-shape to fit the tank.
Light.—Four G.E. germicide tubes, 15 watt, 18 in. long, mounted in a housing about 5 in. above the chromatograms and shielded to protect the operator. The shield may be of reflecting material to concentrate the light on the specimen (General Electric Company, G15T8, G30T8).
Reagents. Adsorbent.—Aluminum oxide G (neutral) with calcium sulfate: Manufactured by E. Merck, Darmstadt, West Germany. Distributed by Brinkmann Instruments, Inc., Westbury, New York.
Developing Solvents.—(1) n-Heptane: Commercial Grade (Phillips Petroleum Company, Bartlesville, Oklahoma) is satisfactory. (2) n-Heptane plus 1 percent or 2 percent acetone (Merck, Reagent Grade).
Chromogenic Agent.—Dissolve 0.100 g. silver nitrate in 1 ml. water, add 20 ml. 2-phenoxyethanol (Practical, Eastman Organic Chemicals), dilute to 200 ml. with acetone, Reagent Grade, add a very small drop of 30 percent hydrogen peroxide, and mix.
Standard Solutions.—(*1*) *Stock Solution A (10 and 5 mg./ml.):* Mixture of aldrin, heptachlor, Perthane, lindane, heptachlor epoxide, methoxychlor. Into one 10-ml. glass-stoppered flask, weigh 0.1 g. of each pesticide; into a second flask, 0.05 g. of each. Dissolve in ethyl acetate, dilute to 10 ml. with ethyl acetate and mix. 1 μl. = 10 μg. and 5 μg., respectively, of each pesticide.
(*2*) *Stock Solution B (10 and 5 mg./ml.):* Mixture of DDE, DDT, DDD, dieldrin, endrin, and Kelthane. Prepare as in Stock Solution A.
Stock Solutions of Individual Pesticides.—Prepare 10 and 5 mg. per ml. separate stock solutions of toxaphene, chlordane, and BHC.
Diluted Stock Solutions.—Dilute each stock solution with ethyl acetate to contain 2, 1, 0.5, 0.2, 0.1, 0.05, 0.02, 0.01, 0.005, and 0.001 mg. per ml. for each pesticide or mixture of pesticides present.

Procedure. (a) **Preparation of Adsorbent Layer.**—Select 8 × 8 in. double-strength window-glass plates of uniform width and thickness, and smooth off the corners and edges with a file or other suitable instrument. Wash the plates in hot soapy water and thoroughly rinse with distilled water; then press snugly into position on the plastic board (above) mounted so that the long side of the board with raised ledge faces the operator while the short side with ledge is to his right. Before coating, wipe the surface of the plates with a few ml. of 95 percent ethanol on a tissue to remove fingerprints or other adhering material. Position the applicator, trough open, with the left edge $\frac{1}{4}$ in. in from the edge of the first plate to be coated.

To coat 5 plates, weigh 30 g. aluminum oxide into a 250-ml. $ Erlenmeyer flask. Add 60 ml. distilled water to aluminum oxide, stopper flask, and shake moderately for 15 sec. (*Caution:* Violent shaking produces bubbles and results in a "pock-marked" layer.)

NOTE.—Suspensions which contain adsorbents with binders set rapidly, and the entire procedure from the preparation of the slurry to the final coating must be completed within 2 min. Otherwise, the adsorbent hardens and the mixture is wasted.

After shaking, immediately pour the slurry into the applicator chamber. Rotate the chamber by turning the large lever handle through 180°. After a few seconds, the slurry begins to flow out of the exit slit. Grasp the applicator with both hands and pull it with a steady motion across the series of plates (takes about 5 sec.); immediately tap the edge of the mounting board or shake the entire board gently to smooth out slight ripples or imperfections in the wet coating.

Let plates coated with aluminum oxide dry in position on the mounting board for 15 min. Remove plates from mounting board, slide into the drying rack, and dry at 80°C. for 30 min. in a forced draft oven; remove and cool. Examine the plates carefully in transmitted and reflected light for imperfections or irregularities in the coating; discard if the layer is extensively rippled or mottled.

(Five more 8 × 8 in. plates may be prepared while the first set is drying. The applicator must be thoroughly cleaned and dried before reusing. The 10 coated and dried plates may be prewashed immediately.)

(b) **Prewashing of Adsorbent Layer.**—Prewashing must be done parallel to the direction of layer application and must begin on the side of the plate to be spotted or the side coated last by the applicator, so that minor imperfections in the quality of the layer on the side where coating began, due to variations in glass thickness, can be ignored.

Scrape $\frac{1}{2}$ in. of adsorbent off the edge of the plate with a razor blade; then pour 10 ml. of 50 percent aqueous acetone into a metal trough inside the chromatographic tank. Cut out a $\frac{1}{2}$ × 8 in. strip of Whatman No. 1 filter paper, wet with 50 percent acetone, and place over the scraped-off portion, slightly overlapping the adsorbent layer.

Place the plate in a covered tank and develop to within 1 in. from the top of the plate (about 75 min.). Remove the plate from the tank, remove the filter paper wick, invert the plate, and dry in the hood 5 min. Dry the plate at 80°C. for 45 min.

(After the washing and drying, the plates may be used immediately or stored in the desiccator until needed. The prepared and washed plates may be stored in the desiccator for as long as 2 weeks without deterioration of the coating.)

(c) **Sample Spotting.**—The following is a convenient means for spacing the spots: make a pencil mark $1\frac{1}{2}$ in. from the bottom edge of the plate on both sides. An imaginary line between the two points indicates the sample spotting or origin "line." Draw a line (which removes the coating) completely across the plate $5\frac{1}{2}$ in. from the bottom edge, to represent the solvent front after development. On the lower edge of the adsorbent, starting $\frac{3}{4}$ in. in from the left edge of the plate, make 18 marks with a pencil at $\frac{6}{16}$-in. intervals, to serve as horizontal guides for sample application. The identity of samples and standards may be drawn directly into the adsorbent layer above these marks.

(The imaginary spotting "line" is actually a shadow line cast by a strong light source from a wooden ruler supported 1 in. above the plate and aligned on the two $1\frac{1}{2}$-in. marks on either edge of the plate. The shadow line and 18 marks, respectively, serve as vertical and horizontal guides for sample application.)

Transfer a suitable aliquot of purified sample solution (containing 0.01–0.2 μg. of each pesticide sought) to a conical centrifuge tube. (With proper cleanup, aliquots equivalent to as much as 60 g. of sample may be spotted.) Evaporate the extract in a gentle stream of air at room temperature to about 0.05 ml. Transfer the sample repeatedly with a micropipet to one of the origin points on the plate, drying after each application to restrict spot size. After all the sample has been spotted, rinse down the sides of the tube with 0.05 ml. petroleum ether (a 100-μl. Hamilton syringe is convenient) and transfer to the same spot. Repeat the rinsing operation. Spot all 6 + 94 eluates from the Florisil cleanup column on one plate and the 15 + 85 eluates on another plate.

Transfer standard solutions of pesticides (mixtures A and B or single compounds) to other spots on the same plate with a 1-μl. pipet. Choose the pesticides used for identification according to the residues expected to be present in the crop examined. For semiquantitative estimation, varying amounts of knowns may be chromatographed from spots adjacent to samples.

(d) Development of Plates.—Prepare the chromatography tank after the samples and standards are spotted on the plate. Place the liners and metal trough in the tank.

For plates spotted with 6 + 94 eluates, first pour 50 ml. n-heptane into the trough, then 50 ml. into the bottom of the tank. Immediately put the plate into the metal trough with the top portion of the plate leaning against the side of the tank. Place the glass cover plate on the tank and seal with masking tape.

For plates spotted with the 15 + 85 eluates, use 2 + 98 acetone-heptane as developing solvent.

When the solvent front *just* reaches the pencil line 10 cm. above the spotting "line" (about 15 min.), remove the plate and allow to air-dry in the hood for 5 min.

(e) Spraying of Plates.—Support the plate on one side and spray with chromogenic reagent, using lateral motions of the spray bottle perpendicular to the direction of solvent flow and holding it far enough away to prevent droplets from disturbing the coating. The entire chromatographed portion of the plate must be uniformly covered with chromogenic reagent for optimum results. After spraying, dry the plate in the hood for 10 min.

(f) Exposure.—Expose the plate to ultraviolet light until the spot for the standard of lowest concentration appears (up to 30 min.).

General.—For best results, prewashing the prepared coatings with 50 percent acetone to remove chlorides prior to analytical use is recommended. On unwashed plates of aluminum oxide-G, the maximum sensitivity that can be attained is about 0.05 μg. for all compounds examined except chlordane, Perthane, Strobane, and toxaphene (0.1 μg.). Not only is sensitivity reduced, but the spots take longer to develop and the background darkens after exposure.

The spotting technique for thin-layer chromatography, in general, is similar to that for paper chromatography. An 8 × 8 in. plate can accommodate as many as 18 samples. In no case should a sample be spotted nearer than $\frac{3}{4}$ in. to either edge of the plate. Spots are distorted if too near the edge of the plate.

The solvents used travel rapidly through the aluminum oxide coating (13–15 min.).

It must be emphasized that the plate should be removed from the tank *just* as the solvent front reaches the 10-cm. line; otherwise, compounds with high R_f values will "pile up" at this point.

Ultraviolet light exposure times for prewashed plates of aluminum oxide are not critical because backgrounds do not darken after a prolonged period of exposure (3–4 hrs.) nor on subsequent standing. Thus, plates should be exposed as long as necessary to fully delineate spots of the lowest concentration sought.

The location, size, and intensity of spots obtained from the unknowns compared to spots from the knowns serve to identify chlorinated residues and to give an estimate of their quantity.

The R_f value for a specific compound may vary from plate to plate and is affected by slight changes in temperature, plate thickness, solvent composition, etc. A more constant value is the R_{DDD}—the ratio of the distance traveled by a compound to the distance traveled by a spot of DDD. Table 56-5 presents R_{DDD} values of compounds developed on aluminum oxide with n-heptane as developing solvent.[14]

TABLE 56-5. R_{DDD} VALUES OF CHLORINATED PESTICIDES ON Al_2O_3-G PLATES WITH n-HEPTANE AS DEVELOPING SOLVENT[a]

Pesticide	R_{DDD}
Aldrin	1.67
DDE	1.62
Heptachlor	1.59
DDT	1.41
Perthane	1.17
Lindane	1.03
DDD	1.00
Heptachlor epoxide	0.74
Endrin	0.54
Dieldrin	0.53
Methoxychlor	0.34
Kelthane	0.06

[a] Reproduced with permission from Kovacs, M. F., Jr., J. Assoc. Offic. Agr. Chemists, **46,** 884, 1963.

On aluminum oxide with n-heptane as developing solvent, toxaphene and Strobane produce streaks, chlordane gives two distinct spots and many indefinite spots, and BHC produces four spots whose R_{DDD} values are close to Perthane, lindane, methoxychlor, and Kelthane. Heptachlor and DDE do not completely resolve with n-heptane; neither do dieldrin and endrin. Heptane + 2 percent acetone will resolve dieldrin and endrin, with endrin having the higher R_{DDD} value.

Maximum sensitivities achieved for all compounds examined were 0.005 μg., with the exception of Perthane and BHC (0.01 μg.), toxaphene (0.05 μg.), and chlordane (0.02 μg.).

For this method, as with paper chromatography, rigorous cleanup of sample extracts is required. The 15 + 85 eluates should be further purified before chromatographing. For the layer thickness used (250 μ.), it does not appear that thin-layer chromatography can tolerate any more interfering substances in the sample extract than paper. However, because thin-layer chromatography is approximately 10–100 times more sensitive than paper chromatography for chlorinated pesticide residue analysis, smaller amounts of sample may be chromatographed, so interfering substances are less troublesome. Thicker layers may be suitable for chromatographing larger amounts of sample, but sensitivity is proportionately decreased.

ORGANOTHIOPHOSPHATE PESTICIDES[15]

The chromogenic reagents used for the organophosphorothioates are not as sensitive as those for the chloro-organics, but they are sufficiently sensitive for the identification and estimation of significant residue quantities of many of the organophosphorothioates.

METHOD[15]

Apparatus.—Same as under "Chlorinated Pesticides" except for the addition of:
Chromatography Spray Flask, 250-ml. (Microchemical Specialties Company, No. 5-4530).

Reagents. Adsorbents.

Aluminum Oxide G (Research Specialties Company, Richmond, California).

Aluminum Oxide G (neutral) with calcium sulfate. (Manufactured by E. Merck, Darmstadt, West Germany; distributed by Brinkmann Instruments, Inc., Westbury, N. Y.)

Solvent System.

(*1*) *Immobile.*—Dilute 75 ml. (15 percent) or 100 ml. (20 percent) N,N-dimethylformamide (DMF) (Fisher Certified Reagent) to 500 ml. with ethyl ether A.C.S. and mix.

(*2*) *Mobile.*—Methylcyclohexane (practical b.p. 100.5°–101.5°C., Matheson, Coleman and Bell).

Chromogenic Agents.

(*1*) *Stock Dye Solution.*—Dissolve 1 g. tetrabromophenolphthalein ethyl ester (Eastman Organic Chemicals #6810) in 100 ml. acetone (A.C.S.).

(*2*) *Dye Solution.*—Dilute 10 ml. Stock Dye Solution (1) to 50 ml. with acetone.

(*3*) *Silver Nitrate Solution.*—Dissolve 0.5 g. silver nitrate (A.C.S. Reagent) in 25 ml. distilled water and dilute to 100 ml. with acetone.

(*4*) *Citric Acid Solution.*—Dissolve 5 g. citric acid (Granular A.R.) in 50 ml. distilled water and dilute to 100 ml. with acetone.

Standard Solutions.

(*1*) *Stock Solution A (10 and 5 mg. per ml.).*—Mixture of Guthion, methyl parathion, Co-Ral, Delnav, EPN, and Ronnel. Into one 10-ml. glass-stoppered volumetric flask weigh 0.1 g. of each pesticide; into a second volumetric flask, 0.05 g. of each. Dissolve in ethyl acetate, dilute to 10 ml., and mix. 1 μl. = 10 μg. and 5 μg., respectively, of each pesticide.

(*2*) *Stock Solution B (10 and 5 mg. per ml.).*—Mixture of malathion, parathion, Systox, Trithion, and Diazinon. Prepare as in Stock Solution A.

(*3*) *Stock Solution C (10 and 5 mg. per ml.).*—Mixture of sulfotepp and ethion. Prepare as in Stock Solution A.

Diluted Stock Solutions.—Dilute each stock solution to contain 2, 1, 0.5, 0.2, 0.1 and 0.05 mg. per ml. for each mixture of pesticides present.

Procedure. **(a) Preparation of adsorbent layer, (b) prewashing of adsorbent layer,** and **(c) sample spotting** are the same as under organic "Chlorinated Pesticides." For optimum semiquantitative estimates choose an aliquot of crop extract to be spotted which will give a spot within the range of 0.05 to 1 μg. pesticide. Spot 0.05, 0.1, 0.2, 0.5, and 1 μg. of standard mixtures A, B, and C alternately with crop extracts on the same plate.

(d) Development of Plates.—Prepare the chromatography tank after the samples and standards have been spotted on the plate. Place the liners and metal trough in the tank, and pour 50 ml. methylcyclohexane into the trough and 75 ml. into the bottom of the tank.

Quickly fill the dipping tank to within $1\frac{1}{2}$–2 in. from the top with immobile solvent system. Invert the plate and dip with the uncoated side touching the back wall of the tank in order to prevent scraping off the adsorbent layer by the front wall of the tank during the dipping operation. Dip the plate just to the spotting line, remove, and place immediately in the metal trough with the top portion of plate leaning against the side of the tank. Place the glass cover plate on the tank and seal with masking tape.

When the solvent front just reaches the pencil line 10 cm. above the spotting "line" (about 25–30 min.), remove the plate and allow to air dry in the hood for 2 min.

(e) Spraying of Plates.—Immediately spray plate moderately heavily and uniformly with dye solution ((2) above), using lateral motions of the spray flask perpendicular to the direction of solvent flow. The color of the plate should be vivid blue after spraying.

Using the spray bottle, overspray plate lightly but uniformly with the silver nitrate solution. At this point, the plate should be bluish-purple and spots should become just visible.

After 2 min., overspray the plate moderately but uniformly with citric acid solution, using the spray bottle. After spraying, the thiophosphate pesticides should immediately appear as vivid blue or purple spots against a yellow background. The color of the spots reaches maximum intensity about 5–10 min. after the citric acid spraying. After approximately 10 min. the background begins to change from yellow to greenish-blue, masking the spots. At this point, respraying the plate with citric acid changes the background back to yellow and makes the spots stand out as well as, or better than, originally. Evaluation of the chromatogram should be made within 10 min. of respraying, since the blue spots will fade completely and irreversibly after approximately 30-40 min. from the time of the original citric acid spraying.

General.—Aluminum Oxide G (Research Specialities Company) does not normally require prewashing with distilled water for chloride removal for organophosphate work. If, however, the maximum compound sensitivities of 0.05 μg. cannot be achieved with unwashed Aluminum Oxide G (Research Specialities Company) coating, prewashing with distilled water is recommended. In all cases, the Merck Aluminum Oxide G coatings must be prewashed with distilled water. Chloride in the adsorbent layer reacts with the silver nitrate and prevents coupling with the dye and pesticide to form the characteristic blue or purple color.

Of the compounds tested, the chromogenic spray reacts only with the sulfur-containing phosphate esters. The following compounds so not react: paraoxon, DDVP, Dibrom, Phosdrin, Phosphamidon, and Dipterex. The following amounts of sulfur-containing phosphate esters can be detected: 0.05 μg. Diazinon, Systox (thiono), Trithion, parathion, malathion, Ronnel, Delnav, EPN, Co-Ral, sulfotepp, and ethion; 0.1 μg. Guthion, methyl parathion, and Systox (thiol). The lower limits of detectability of Rogor, Imidan, Methyl Trithion, Thimet, and Di-Syston were not determined.

At 0.5 μg. or greater the thiophosphate esters vary as to color produced with the chromogenic reagents. Trithion, parathion, EPN, Co-Ral, and Diazinon appear vivid blue. Ethion, Guthion, sulfotepp, Delnav, and malathion appear purple. Ronnel and methyl parathion appear dull blue, and Systox (thiol) and (thiono) appear bluish-purple. The color of the spot should not be used as a criterion of identity, but the location, size, and intensity of spots obtained from the unknowns compared to spots from the knowns will help to identify thiophosphate residues and give an estimate of their quantity.

Table 56-6 presents the absolute R_f values of compounds developed on Aluminum Oxide G (Merck) with methylcyclohexane as developing solvent and either 15 or 20 percent DMF in ethyl ether as immobile solvent.[15] Fifteen percent DMF as immobile solvent resolves low R_f compounds better, whereas 20 percent DMF resolves the higher R_f compounds better. The choice of concentration of immobile solvent used will depend upon the compounds under investigation.

TABLE 56-6. R_f VALUES OF THIOPHOSPHATE PESTICIDES BY TLC[a]
ADSORBENT—Al_2O_3-G (MERCK) MOBILE SOLVENT—METHYLCYCLOHEXANE

Pesticide	Immobile Solvent	
	15% DMF	20% DMF
Rogor	0.01	0.01
Guthion	0.09	0.06
Imidan	0.09	0.07
Me Parathion	0.17	0.11
Co-Ral	0.23	0.15
Malathion	0.34	0.22
Delnav	0.37	0.24
Parathion	0.41	0.27
Systox (thiol)	0.44	0.32
EPN	0.49	0.33
Me Trithion	0.50	0.36
Sulfotepp	0.69	0.55
Trithion	0.74	0.59
Ronnel	0.76	0.62
Ethion	0.77	0.63
Systox (thiono)	0.79	0.67
Thimet	0.81	0.71
Di Syston	0.82	0.72
Diazinon	0.86	0.78

[a] Reproduced with permission from Kovacs, M. F., Jr., J. Assoc. Offic. Agr. Chemists, **47,** 1097, 1964.

PAPER CHROMATOGRAPHY[16,17]

Paper chromatography has for years been one of the most valuable tools of the residue chemists. Recently, gas chromatography and thin-layer chromatography with their greater speed and sensitivity, and in the case of gas-liquid chromatography, greater ease in quantitation, have to some extent replaced paper chromatography. However, paper chromatography is a useful technique and, in some applications, the best available.

As used in pesticide residue analyses, the equipment and procedure have been fairly well standardized for all types of compounds. Only the developing solvents and chromogenic agents differ for the different classes of compounds.

[16] Mills, P. A., J. Assoc. Offic. Agr. Chemists, **42,** 734, 1959.
[17] Mitchell, L. C., J. Assoc. Offic. Agr. Chemists, **40,** 999, 1957.

The equipment is, in general, similar to that described in the section on "Thin-Layer Chromatography" and will not be listed here. Readers wishing more detail should consult articles by Mills[16] and Mitchell.[17]

Sensitivity of paper chromatographic procedures is generally limited by the amount of sample which can be spotted without overloading the paper with plant extractives. This, in turn, is dependent on how well the sample extract has been cleaned up. (As with all chromatographic procedures, there is no substitute for proper cleanup.)

CHLORINATED ORGANIC PESTICIDES
INCLUDING HERBICIDES[3,6,17]

Chromatographic Papers.—Whatman No. 1, 8 × 8 in. sheets. With a hard pencil, rule an origin line 1 in. from the bottom edge and dot with 8 to 10 evenly spaced positions with end dots 1 in. from the sides. Pencil the test number or other identification below each dot. For aqueous systems, wash papers several times with distilled water and dry before use.

Chromogenic Reagent.—Place 1.7 g. silver nitrate in a 200-ml. volumetric flask and add 5 ml. water to dissolve. Add 10 ml. 2-phenoxyethanol, then add Reagent Grade acetone to volume (before making to mark add a drop of 30 percent hydrogen peroxide). Fill into the chromatographic sprayer. (This solution may darken but will remain effective.)

Standard Solutions of Pesticides.—A concentration of 1 mg. per ml. is convenient (1 lambda or 0.001 ml. = 1 μg.). Solvents may be ethyl acetate or hexane.

CHLORINATED INSECTICIDES—DDT, ETC.

Solvent Systems and R_f Values.—Paper chromatography of the chlorinated pesticides involves a two-solvent system. The paper is impregnated with one of the solvents, the immobile solvent, by dipping the paper in an ether solution of the immobile solvent and permitting the ether to evaporate. The second solvent, called the mobile solvent, is used to develop the chromatogram.

Two systems of solvents are generally used, one called the aqueous system, the other nonaqueous. It has been found that for each system there are some pairs of pesticides which have similar R_f values and consequently are not adequately resolved. Use of the other system of solvents usually permits separation of these pesticides.

The order of R_f values is also different for the two systems so that, by using both, the identity of a particular residue can be fixed with greater certainty. Standards should always be run on the same paper as the samples.

Aqueous System. (*1*) *Immobile Solvents.*—Dissolve 25 ml. of mineral oil (USP heavy) in ethyl ether and dilute to 500 ml. Corn, cottonseed, tung, and soya oils may also be used.

(*2*) *Mobile Solvents.*—Dilute 75 ml. of acetone, methylcellosolve, or methanol to 100 ml. with water. Dilute 40 ml. of pyridine to 100 ml. with water.

Nonaqueous System. (*1*) *Immobile Solvents.*—Dilute 175 ml. of N,N-dimethylformamide (DMF) to 500 ml. with ethyl ether. Dimethylcyanamide or 2-phenoxyethanol may. also be used.

(*2*) *Mobile Solvents.*—2,2,4-Trimethylpentane and mixed octanes are used.

Mitchell[18] lists the R_f values in both aqueous and nonaqueous systems for 114 pesticide compounds, including a large number of the chlorinated hydrocarbons.

[18] Mitchell, L. C., J. Assoc. Offic. Agr. Chemists, **41,** 781, 1958.

FOR HERBICIDES—FREE ACIDS AND ESTERS[6]

Solvent Systems and R_f Values.
For Methylated Acids:

Immobile phase	Mobile phase
System (1) 10 percent mineral oil in ether	50 percent acetonitrile in water
System (2) 35 percent dimethylformamide in ether	2,2,4-trimethylpentane

For Esters:

10 percent mineral oil in ether	65 percent acetonitrile in water

System (2) gives good separation of the methylated acids and more compact spots. System (2) also gives a darker background than System (1).

Table 56-7 lists the R_f values for some of the herbicides with these solvent systems.

TABLE 56-7. R_f VALUES FOR HERBICIDES BY PAPER CHROMATOGRAPHY[a]

Compound	System 1	System 2
METHYLATED ACIDS		
2,4-D	0.64	0.39
MCP	0.50	0.58
2,4,5-T	0.48	0.50
2,4-DB	0.34	0.73
2,4,5-TP	0.31	0.82
ESTERS OF 2,4-D		
Iso-octyl		0.32
Isopropyl		0.54
Butoxyethanol		0.53
n-Butyl		0.44
Propylene glycol butyl ether		0.42

[a] Reproduced with permission from Yip, G., J. Assoc. Offic. Agr. Chemists, **47**, 343, 1964.

Some of the esters cannot be resolved by the system listed in Table 56-7. Butoxyethanol ester cannot be separated from isopropyl, nor can butyl from propylene glycol butyl ether. To resolve the first pair, the following system must be used: immobile phase, 10 percent phenoxyethanol in ether; mobile phase, isooctane. Butoxyethanol has an R_f of 0.28; isopropyl, 0.43. To resolve the second pair, the system is: immobile phase, 50 percent DMF in ether; mobile phase, isooctane. Propylene glycol butyl ether has an R_f of 0.76 and n-butyl, 0.60.

Procedure for Chlorinated Pesticides Including Herbicides.[16]—Transfer a suitable aliquot of the purified sample solution to a 15-ml. conical centrifuge tube. (Size of the aliquot may be governed by the tolerance level of the pesticide sought. For most pesticides, the upper limit for good spots is around 10 μg., so if the tolerance for a pesticide is 1 p.p.m., an aliquot representing 5–10 g. of sample may be taken.) Evaporate under a gentle stream of air at room temperature just to dryness (caution). Wash down the sides of the tube with 0.5 ml. ethyl ether, evaporate, and again wash down with 0.1–0.2 ml. ethyl ether. Evaporate and take up the residue (usually invisible) with 0.03–0.04 ml. ethyl ether and transfer to one of the dots on the origin line of the sheet of chromatographic paper, using the 1 lambda pipet repeatedly until the residue is all placed on the one spot. The spot must be allowed to dry after each application to restrict its size. Again wash the tube with 0.03–0.04 ml. ether and transfer to the same spot.

Transfer standard solutions of known pesticides to other spots on the same paper. When the lambda pipet is used for this purpose, one pipetful contains 1 μg. of the compound for a solution containing 1 mg./ml. Varying quantities of a pesticide may be placed on a spot by transferring one or more pipetsful to a single spot. For identification purposes, several compounds may be placed on several spots on the same paper as that containing the unknown. For semiquantitative estimation, varying quantities of a single compound may be chromatographed from adjacent spots.

The choice of pesticides to be used as "tracers" for identification will be governed by the pesticide residues to be expected, as may be indicated by previous knowledge about the sample. If their R_f values allow, several different pesticides may be placed on the same spot. Use 2–5 μg. per spot for identification. For estimations, vary the quantity of the particular standard compound in intervals of 1 or 2 μg. As little as 0.5 μg., or even less of many materials, can be identified; however, it takes about 10 μg. of Perthane to register.

After the samples and knowns are placed on the paper, prepare the chromatography tank. Place 50 ml. of the mobile solvent in the trough; then fill the dipping tank with the desired immobile solvent. Hold the paper by the bottom with a spring clip and immerse it top down into the solution of immobile solvent just to the origin line; then immediately remove it. Hang up the paper to dry for 2 or 3 min., and during this time clip the glass rod which supports the paper in the chromatography tank to the top of the paper (opposite the origin line). Then hang the paper in the chromatography tank so that the bottom (origin end) dips about $\frac{1}{2}$ in. into the trough filled with mobile solvent. Place the glass plate on the tank and seal with masking tape. When the mobile solvent has risen through the paper to within 1 in. of the top (1.5 to 4 hr., depending on the solvent system used), unseal the tank, mark the solvent front, and hang up the paper until it looks dry. When dry, spray the paper uniformly with the chromogenic agent (do not spray so heavily that it will run down the paper). Then dry the paper until most of the solvent is removed, and expose both sides to ultraviolet light (see "Light," page 1493) until the reduced silver spots are developed. The locations, size, and intensity of spots obtained from the unknowns, compared to spots from knowns, serve to identify chlorinated residues and to give an estimate of their quantity. Unknowns and knowns should always be run on the same paper.

ORGANOPHOSPHATES[19]

Paper chromatography of the organophosphates is carried out in a manner similar to that for the chlorinated compounds. However, because of the greater range in polarity of these compounds and their metabolites, a larger number of solvent systems is required to resolve the many combinations of these residues. Two of the most useful solvent systems will be described and the reader is referred to the general literature for additional systems.

The methods of detecting these compounds on the developed chromatograms also

[19] Getz, M. E., J. Assoc. Offic. Agr. Chemists, **45**, 393, 1962.

differ from that used for the chlorinated pesticides. Two useful methods are described.

Solvent Systems. Nonaqueous. (*1*) *Immobile Solvent:* 20 percent dimethylformamide (redistilled at 153°C.) in ethyl ether.

(*2*) *Mobile Solvent:* 2,2,4-trimethylpentane.

Aqueous. (*1*) *Immobile Solvent:* 10 percent Epon 828 resin in acetone (redistilled).

(*2*) *Mobile Solvent:* 40 percent acetonitrile in water.

Chromogenic Reagents.—Two chromogenic reagents which are based on different principles are commonly used.

Chromogenic Reagent for Detecting Thiophosphate Compounds.[4]

(a) 2 Percent silver nitrate in 25 percent water in acetone.

(b) 2 Percent bromcresol green in acetone.

For spraying, mix 95 ml. of (a) with 5 ml. of (b).

Spot paper as described under chlorinated pesticides, using the equivalent of 5 g. of sample. Chromatograph until the solvent front has migrated to within 1 in. from the top of the paper. Remove the paper and dry in an oven at 50°C. for 10 min. Spray the paper with the chromogenic agent. Dry in an oven at 50°C. for 10–15 min.; then immerse the paper for a few minutes in a tray containing 0.02 percent citric acid in distilled water until the spots are discernible. (They are blue spots against a yellow background.) Estimate the amount of residue present by comparing with spots of standard solution chromatographed similarly.

Diazinon may be located and marked just prior to the acid dip. Some of the spots fade rapidly on drying. For record purposes, color photographs may be taken almost immediately after the citric acid dip and while the chromatogram is still moist.

This chromogenic spray reacts only with the sulfur-containing phosphate esters. The intensity of the spot varies with the position of the sulfur in the molecule. The groups exhibit the following degree of intensity: dithio $>$ thiol (bivalent sulfur) $>$ thiono.

Usually 1 μg. of dithio and thiol compounds and 2 μg. of thiono compounds are detectable.

Chromogenic Reagent for Determining Cholinesterase Inhibiting Compounds and Those that Can Be Converted to Inhibitors.[20]—Many organophosphate esters inhibit cholinesterase, whereas the phosphorothioates do not inhibit until oxidized to phosphate by bromine or other agent.

This spot test depends on the ability of the pesticide to inhibit the enzymatic hydrolysis of acetylcholine and to release acetic acid. Areas containing pesticides that inhibit the enzyme activity can be detected by the presence of the basic form of bromthymol blue. In this particular method, bromthymol blue is added to the enzyme solution and sprayed on the paper. This imparts a uniform blue color to the paper. When acetylcholine is sprayed onto the paper, areas with uninhibited enzyme yield acetic acid which changes the indicator to yellow, whereas areas where the enzyme is inhibited remain the original blue.

The size of the spot depends on the activity as well as the quantity of the inhibitory substance present. Therefore, it is possible for 0.01 μg. of one substance to give the same size spot as 1 μg. or more of some other substance. Thus, any quantitative estimation of the amount present requires the use of appropriate standards.

Care must be exercised to be certain no reagents interfere with the enzyme reaction.

METHOD[20]

Materials. Pooled Human Serum.—Any available source (outdated serum from hospitals has been satisfactory). Pool any samples available in order to have more

[20] Getz, M. E., and Friedman, S. J., J. Assoc. Offic. Agr. Chemists, **46,** 707, 1963.

uniform source of enzyme. Distribute pooled serum into a number of small bottles and store frozen until required.

Acetylcholine Bromide.—Reagent Grade (keep refrigerated).

Indicator Solution.—Dissolve 0.15 g. bromthymol blue (Indicator Grade) in 25 ml. 0.1 N sodium hydroxide.

Enzyme-Indicator Solution.—Mix 20 ml. serum, 60 ml. water, 2 ml. 0.1 N sodium hydroxide, and 3.25 ml. indicator solution.

Substrate Solution.—Dissolve 2 g. acetylcholine bromide in 100 ml. water.

Chromatographic Paper.—Thick type, such as Whatman #3MM.

Procedures.—Spot papers, etc., as described under Chlorinated Organic Pesticides, but use the chromatographic systems indicated above for organophosphates. Develop and dry the chromatogram.

Transfer Method.—Spray a sheet of chromatographic paper with enzyme-indicator solution so that paper is moist, but not wet enough to drip. Place in contact with the dried chromatogram, sandwich between stainless-steel plates, and apply moderate pressure. Incubate at room temperature for a definite time (usually 15 min.). Separate the papers and spray the paper containing the enzyme indicator with the substrate solution. After about 10 min. the background begins to change to yellow, and inhibition spots remain blue.

Direct Method.—Spray the dried chromatogram on both sides with the enzyme-indicator solution and place in a tank or cabinet saturated with water vapor. Incubate at room temperature (30 min. is adequate for detecting 1 μg. or less of inhibitors). Remove paper from tank and spray lightly on both sides with substrate solution. In about 10 min. the background starts to turn yellow and the inhibition spots remain bright blue.

Bromination Treatment.—Pipet 0.1 ml. liquid bromine into the bottom of a glass jar or tank and cover to prevent loss of bromine. Let bromine vapors fill the container uniformly. Place the dried chromatogram in the container and let it react for 30 sec. Remove the paper and place in a forced draft cabinet at 50°–60°C. for 15 min., which usually allows all excess bromine to be eliminated. Treat paper by either the direct or transfer method.

The following 12 pesticides produce blue spots without bromination:

Co-Ral (oxygen analog)	Thiol-Systox
DDVP	Thiol-Systox sulfoxide
Dibrom	Thiol-Systox sulfone
Dipterex*a*	TEPP
Phosdrin	Thiol-Imidan
Phosphamidon	Paraoxon

The following 18 pesticides require bromination in order to produce blue spots:

Chlorthion	EPN	Ronnel
Co-Ral	Ethion	Sulfotepp
Delnav	Guthion	Thiono-Systox
Diazinon	Malathion	Thimet
Dimethoate	Methyl parathion	Trithion
Di-Syston	Parathion	Imidan

Many metabolic or alteration products of these compounds produce blue spots without oxidation.

---

a Dipterex inhibits because the basicity of the reagents converts it in part to DDVP.

Solutions of some pesticides used as references may produce inhibition spots other than those expected from the main constituents. This indicates the presence of inhibitory impurities or decomposition products.

The immobile solvents that can be used for the direct chromatographic method must be determined experimentally; some solvents or reagents may be enzyme inhibitors or contain sufficient acid to nullify the test. Some solvents that are suitable for the direct method cannot be used if bromine treatment is required because of formation of bromination products that interfere with the test.

ACKNOWLEDGMENT

The development of this chapter, which presents a relatively uniform system for extraction, cleanup, and determination, by instrumental analysis, for a number of groups of a large number of pesticide chemicals has resulted largely from the research work in Pesticides Branch of Division of Food Chemistry of the Food and Drug Administration.

Much of the work included in this chapter has been taken from publications of members of that Branch. The authors have drawn heavily from the reference publications and are grateful to those authors and the Editors of the *Journal of the Association of Official Agricultural Chemists* for permission to use this material.

Chapter 57

PETROLEUM AND PETROLEUM PRODUCTS

FOREWORD

By J. W. Robinson
Louisiana State University
Baton Rouge, Louisiana

Instrumentation in the field of analytical chemistry is expanding at an unprecedented rate. It is no longer easy or even possible for an "analytical chemist" to move from one area to another and maintain any measure of expertise. For example it is not likely that a man, expert in the field of nuclear magnetic resonance would be much more than a layman in the field of activation analysis.

In general, instruments such as these are in the hands of analytical chemists who are trained and experienced in these fields.

The following sections have been written by a group of chemists, each an expert in his own field. The sections have been written more for the qualified operator than the uninitiated. For this reason less attention has been paid to details of procedures. It was felt that the operator would be cognizant of such details. Rather, the philosophy has been to provide general procedures with (hopefully) enough detail to provide the analyst with a workable procedure.

ATOMIC ABSORPTION SPECTROMETRY

By Richard C. Barras

Atlantic Refining Co.
Philadelphia, Pennsylvania

and

James W. Robinson

Louisiana State University
Baton Rouge, Louisiana

Introduction.—In 1955, A. Walsh proposed that analytical chemists consider the use of atomic absorption spectrometry in the analysis of a variety of materials for trace metal contaminants. He described its potential advantages over optical emission spectrometry and devised suitable equipment that was sufficiently simple, versatile, and inexpensive as to be applicable to the analysis of solutions of a wide variety of elements. The basic advantages of atomic absorption are that it is independent of the excitation potential of the elements present in the sample being analyzed and that it is less subject to interferences than is emission spectrometry. Applications are summarized in Fig. 57-1.

SUMMARY OF PUBLISHED APPLICATIONS OF ATOMIC ABSORPTION SPECTROSCOPY

Element	Sample
Na	Plants, soil extracts, blood sera
K	Soil extracts, blood sera
Cu	Plants, soils, fertilizers, copper alloys, ore concentrates, petroleum, wine
Ag	Lead concentrates
Mg	Plants, soils, blood sera, urine, milks, aluminum, nickel, steel
Ca	Plants, soil extracts, blood sera, urine, saliva
Sr	Plants, soil extracts
Zn	Plants, soils, fertilizers, urine, brasses, wine
Cd	Zirconium, urine
Pb	Urine, copper alloys, steel, wines, petroleum, gasoline, wine
Bi	Urine
Mo	Fertilizers, stainless steel
Mn	Soils, plants
Fe	Plant ash, petroleum, synthetic detergents
Ni	Leaded brass, petroleum, urine
Pt	Reforming catalyst
Hg	Urine
U	U-235/U-238 isotopic ratios
Pt	Commercial samples
Pd	Commercial samples
Rh	Commercial samples
Au	Commercial samples

Fig. 57-1.

The principle of atomic absorption rests on the fact that an atom of an element in the ground state will absorb a photon of incident energy of the proper wavelength. In order to carry out analyses by means of atomic absorption it is necessary to obtain the element of interest in the form of a vapor with most of the atoms in an unexcited state. This sample system must be incorporated within an optical system which permits the irradiating of this volume of vapor with proper electromagnetic radiation, and a means of measuring variations in intensity at pre-selected wavelengths.

The major characteristic that a sample must have in order to be analyzed readily by atomic absorption spectrometry is that it be in a liquid state. Since practically all petroleum oils are in the liquid state at ambient temperatures, it naturally follows that atomic absorption may be applied successfully to the analysis of a wide variety of petroleum fractions separated from crude oil for their trace element content.

APPARATUS

The essential requirements for an atomic absorption spectrometer are as follows:

1. a source of electromagnetic radiation essentially characteristic of the element being determined;

2. a means of vaporizing the sample in order to convert it from its original form to a volume of vapor containing the element being determined in the unexcited state;

3. a means of isolating a pre-selected wavelength;

4. an accurate means of determining variations in intensity of a given wavelength of radiation.

These features are diagramed in Fig. 57-2.

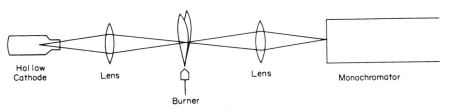

Hollow Cathode   Lens   Burner   Lens   Monochromator

FIG. 57-2.   Diagram of Apparatus.

Source of Radiation.—The most widely used source of radiation is a hollow cathode tube. Hollow cathode tubes consist of an anode and a hollow cathode either composed of, or lined with, the appropriate metal. These are mounted in a sealed glass tube containing one of the rare gases. In operation, bombardment by rare gas ions causes free atoms to be sputtered off the cathode. These are excited by collision with rare gas atoms and emit a strong line spectrum from the confined space inside the cathode where their concentration is relatively high. The filler gas can be either argon or neon. Neon is better if freedom from emission lines in the region of the spectrum where most of the resonance lines exist is desired. However, argon is preferable in most cases because of other desirable features. When a monochromator is used for resonance line isolation, freedom from carrier gas emission is not an essential feature.

Sample Vaporization.—In the most widely used forms of apparatus the solution of the sample being atomized is aspirated by means of a gas mixture under pressure into a flame. A variety of gas mixtures have been found suitable: air-acetylene, air-coal gas, oxy-hydrogen, etc. Upon aspiration into such flames four events occur in rapid succession. First the aspirated aerosol is vaporized with simultaneous vaporization of the solvent leaving the metal in the form of a hydrated particle. Secondly, this residual salt particle is dehydrated. Thirdly, this particle of residue is melted and vaporized. Lastly, the element is transformed to the ground state through dissociation and reduction. The element is now in a form suitable to react with the resonant radiation emitted from the source.

At present, more than thirty-five metals can be determined in solution at the p.p.m. level or lower by atomic absorption spectrometry. While the technique is finding wide acceptance in many applications, there are limitations. At least thirty elements are not susceptible to analysis by present absorption methods because they form refractory oxides or hydroxides in the flame environment. Other elements have their main resonance lines in the vacuum ultraviolet, which is below the region easily accessible to conventional absorption spectrometers. In addition, the sample must be available as a solution. Furthermore, although many of the interferences that plague flame spectrometry and emission spectrometry do not exist in absorption spectrometry, the retention of certain chemical interferences is another problem remaining to be solved. All of these problems stem directly or indirectly from the use of a flame as a sampling device. Much of the present day research is directed toward suitable sampling systems which will eliminate the use of a flame and its associated problems. As yet this research has not led to any other system suitable for routine operation.

Wavelength Isolation.—The use of a line spectrum of the element being determined rather than a continuum as light source makes possible the use of monochromators of low resolving power, or even filters. With the use of a hollow cathode as a light source it is only necessary to isolate the resonance line from the neighboring lines in the source. The resolution required can be lowered even further by the use of a modulated source and an a.c. amplifier tuned to the frequency of modulation. Since, with this system, light from the vaporized sample falling on the detector produces a d.c. signal that is rejected it is only necessary to isolate the resonance line from neighboring lines emitted from the source. The resolution then required depends only on the spectrum emitted from the source. For the transition elements, a resolution of 1 A would be necessary to isolate the strongest resonance lines. With the alkalis and alkaline earths, techniques similar to those used in flame photometry are satisfactory. Since practically all light emitted from a sodium spectral flame is concentrated in the resonance doublet at 5890 and 5896 A, it is possible to determine the presence of sodium without the use of the monochromator or filter if a modulated lamp or a.c. amplifier is used.

Detection and Evaluation.—Photoelectric detectors used in atomic absorption analysis need be no more sensitive than those used in emission analysis because in the former method the concentration of an element is accessed by measuring the reduction in intensity of a resonance line emitted from a source of high intensity. In emission analysis, on the other hand, sensitivity at low concentrations is limited by the detector failing to give adequate signal-to-noise ratio, or failing to measure a spectral line intensity which is small compared to background intensity.

The resonance line of lowest wavelength so far used in atomic absorption analysis is that of zinc at 2138 A. The highest is that of cesium, 8521 A. Between and including these wavelengths RCA 1P22 photomultiplier tubes for the visible and near infrared regions, and the RCA 1P28 for the ultraviolet and visible regions have been used successfully. However, there is no reason why other photomultipliers should not be satisfactory.

The principal factor now limiting the sensitivity of the atomic absorption method is fluctuation of the light source. The conventional method of overcoming such fluctuation is that of double-beam operation. This system is described in Fig. 57-3.

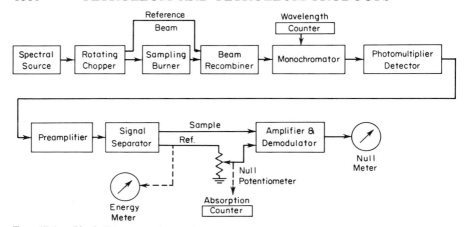

Fɪɢ. 57-3.   Block Diagram of Double-beam Instrument. Emission from the line source is split into sample and reference beams, then is recombined and passed through monochromator. Signal from photodetector is amplified and fed into circuitry which produces a manual electronic null.

QUANTITATIVE ANALYSIS

It is necessary to control a number of variables in order to obtain reproducible quantitative results in atomic absorption. These are:

1. feed rate;
2. solvent;
3. flame position; and
4. burner design.

The effect of these can be traced to their effect on the proficiency of the production of atoms from the solution.

Sample Feed Rate.—Sample feed rate directly affects the number of atoms introduced into the atomizer per unit time. Its effect on atomic absorption is very similar to the effect on flame spectrometry but to a lesser degree. With aqueous solutions when the feed rate is increased, absorption increases up to a maximum. Further increase of feed rate leads to inefficient production of atoms from the residues remaining when each droplet has been evaporated. The effect is not so pronounced with absorption as with emission flame spectrometry, presumably because the extra excitation step of emission methods is unnecessary for absorption. With organic solvents, evaporation is accompanied by combustion and this step is much easier to make than with aqueous solvents. This results in a more efficient production of atoms in the flame.

Solvent.—Generally, organic solvents enhance the degree of absorption by given concentration of metal ions. A possible explanation for this is that the solvent controls the efficiency of the flame in reducing metal atoms from the solution. Also in aspirating burners the viscosity and density of the solvent affect the sample feed rate which is itself a variable.

Flame Position.—When a droplet of solution is introduced into a flame a series of steps takes place. First the droplet must evaporate leaving a residue of solid material including the metal. This residue must than decompose eliminating atoms and finally these atoms may recombine with other constituents in the flame forming such entities as oxides, peroxides, hydroxides, and perhaps even carbon radicals. Since the lifetime of free atoms is usually short under such circumstances, it would be anticipated that the concentration of metal atoms is dependent on flame position. Usually it is comparatively low at the point of introduction at the base of the flame and high in the middle. The signal in the top of the flame depends on the readiness of the metal to form oxides. If oxides do not form, the signal remains high, otherwise it decreases.

Burner Design.—The design of a suitable burner for this work constitutes a considerable challenge to workers in the field of atomic absorption. Under ideal conditions it would be preferable for the solvent to have no effect on the number of atoms produced by the burner and for the feed rate to be independent of the viscosity of samples. These things can come about only when a fixed feed rate is possible. Experimental work has shown that as the concentration of metal increases the noise associated with the signal also increases. Although the mean signal remains stable over a period of time, the observed signal on a continuous basis incorporates a certain amount of signal noise.

ANALYSIS OF LIGHT OILS

Petroleum products boiling under 450°F. can be analyzed by the technique described by Robinson.[1] Samples may be diluted with a suitable solvent such as *n*-heptane or isooctane, if the concentration of the element being sought is too great. It is usually most satisfactory to work in the range of 0 to 20 p.p.m. Beyond this, calibration curves tend to become nonlinear. There will usually be very little viscosity effects to be considered and compensated for when working with light petroleum fractions.

Once the proper dilution of the sample has been determined, solutions of the samples to be analyzed are aspirated in the normal way as described in the manufacturer's instruction manual that accompanies the instrument being used. Suitable standards dissolved in the same solvent should be aspirated along with the samples.

Metallo-organic compounds are the most suitable materials from which to make standards. These are readily available from the National Bureau of Standards, or from the Nuodex Co. Concentrations of desired elements in the samples may be determined from the absorption reading obtained on these standard solutions by plotting absorption *vs.* concentration. This plot is prepared from the readings obtained during the aspiration of the standards.

ANALYSIS OF HEAVY OILS

The analysis of petroleum fractions boiling in excess of 450°F. has been reported by Barras *et al.*[2,3] This method describes a procedure for the determination of copper, iron, and nickel in the gas oil fraction of crude petroleum. It may be adapted to other petroleum fractions by suitable alteration of the solvent dilution step.

Preparation of Standards.—Standard solutions may be prepared by weighing sufficient quantities of National Bureau of Standards or Nuodex concentrates to make 500 p.p.m. in a metal-free gas oil. From this standard solution, a suitable range of calibration standards may be prepared by dilution with metal-free gas oil. Calibration curves should be prepared, covering the range of 0.05 p.p.m. to 20 p.p.m. or any desired portion thereof. As discussed below, the plot is made of delta absorption *vs.* metal concentration. Delta absorption is the difference between the absorption at an absorbing wavelength and absorption at a nonabsorbing wavelength.

Preparation of Sample.—All samples and all calibration standards should be diluted

[1] Robinson, J. W., "Determination of Lead in Gasoline by Atomic Absorption Spectroscopy," Anal. Chim. Acta, **24**, 451, 1961.

[2] Barras, R. C., Boyle, J. F., Smith, H. W., Pittsburgh Conference on Analytical Chemistry, 1963.

[3] Barras, R. C., and Helwig, J. D., 28th Midyear Meeting of the American Petroleum Institute's Division of Refining, Philadelphia, Pa., May 14, 1963.

to an essentially uniform viscosity. This is usually achieved by adding 75 ml. of n-heptane to 25 ml. of each sample and each standard.

Analysis.—Set the necessary parameters on the instrument as indicated in Table 57-1,

TABLE 57-1. INSTRUMENT PARAMETERS

Gas Pressure, p.s.i.:

Air...	16	
Hydrogen.......................................	8	

Tube Current, ma.:

Nickel..	38
Iron...	50
Copper...	30

Detector Voltages:

Nickel..	750
Iron...	810
Copper...	770

Wavelengths, A:	*Absorbing*	*Nonabsorbing*
Nickel.............................	2,320	2319.2
Iron..............................	2,483	2486
Copper............................	3,247	3199.5

aspirate all samples and standards at a single wavelength before setting the monochromator at a new wavelength. Determinations of a single element should be made on all samples and standards before changing to a new hollow-cathode source. Allow suitable warm-up time between elements before proceeding with the analysis. In order to achieve the necessary sensitivity for the analysis of the heavy petroleum fractions for trace element contamination, it has been found necessary to employ a multipass system as diagramed in Fig. 57-4. With this system, the effective path length for absorption of

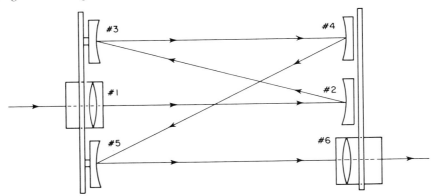

FIG. 57-4. Multiple Pass System.

radiation is increased by passing the source of radiation through the flame five times. Sensitivity further increased by employing three burners instead of one.*

* This equipment is available from Jarrell-Ash Co., Waltham, Mass.

The employment of such a sensitive system emphasizes certain problems inherent in the analysis of heavy petroleum fractions. It has been found that during the aspiration of such samples, some of the irradiating source radiation is scattered by particles of atomic carbon. This will lead to high results unless steps are taken to correct it. Also, certain heavy fractions, particularly those derived from the catalytic cracking of gas oils, may contain a relatively high concentration of polynuclear aromatic hydrocarbons. In the course of combustion of such samples, molecular species are formed which absorb the ultraviolet radiation being used for the analysis. This becomes serious only in the analyses for nickel since short ultraviolet wavelengths are used. These interferences can be adequately corrected by taking absorption readings at the nonabsorbing wavelengths recommended.

Interferences.—One of the major attractions that the atomic absorption technique offers spectrochemical analysis is its relative freedom from interelement interferences. It is not subject to interferences arising from a distribution of atoms over various excited states as is optical emission spectroscopy, nor is it critically dependent on the temperature of the atomic vapor in the flame, as is flame spectrometry. The tendency of an elemental absorption line to undergo self-reversal creates problems in optical emission. In contrast, the phenomenon provides a good indication of sensitivity of the atomic absorption method.

Although this technique is relatively free of interferences, interferences do exist. A brief summary of studies made into chemical interferences in atomic absorption is given below. Further details may be obtained from the literature cited.

Cadmium.[4]—The presence of silicon has been found to affect adversely analysis for cadmium. Sulfuric, hydrochloric, and nitric acids do not interfere.

Calcium.[5]—Aluminum, silicon, and phosphorus interfere but these interferences can be controlled by the addition of about 0.5 percent magnesium and 2 percent sulfuric acid or by the addition of 0.2 percent strontium. Ammonium chloride has been found to afford considerable protection against interferences by silicate but it has little effect on the interferences from phosphorus and aluminum.

The presence of sodium or potassium has been found to enhance the calcium signal by 15 to 30 percent. This can be controlled by the addition of 200 p.p.m. sodium and/or 1500 p.p.m. potassium to both standards and samples.

Magnesium does not interfere with the calcium determination.

The presence of protein interferes in the determination of calcium and must be removed prior to analysis.

Copper.[6]—Sodium and potassium emit a continuum in the region of the best copper lines. Calcium also interferes.

Gold.[7]—Slight interference in the determination of gold arises from the presence of hydrochloric or nitric acids. Sulfuric acid definitely interferes. No interference has been found from ruthenium, rhodium, osmium, or iridium. The presence of relatively massive amounts of palladium and platinum tend to enhance small amounts of gold.

Iron.[4]—No interferences have been reported for the determination of this element.

Lead.[1]—No interferences have been reported for the determination of this element.

Magnesium.[4,8,9]—Sodium, potassium, calcium, titanium, nickel, and phosphorus do not interfere. Aluminum and silicon do interfere. If silicon is present in concentrations less than 0.1 percent and aluminum at less than 0.2 percent, a high concentration of

[4] Atomic Absorption Newsletter No. 5, Perkin-Elmer Corp., Norwalk, Conn.
[5] David, J. D., Analyst, **84**, 536, 1959.
[6] Allan, J. E., Spectrochim. Acta, **17**, 459, 1961.
[7] Strassheim, A., and Wessels, G. J., Applied Spec., **17**, 65, 1963.
[8] Atomic Absorption Newsletter No. 2, Perkin-Elmer Corp., Norwalk, Conn.
[9] Andrews, T. R., and Nickols, P. N. R., Analyst, **87**, 25, 1962.

nickel controls the interference. If silicon is present in excess of 0.1 percent, it must be removed. The interference from aluminum is much less with an air-acetylene flame than with most other flames studied.

Manganese.[4]—Slight interferences have been detected due to the presence of magnesium, calcium, titanium, zirconium, and aluminum in the analysis for manganese. Using an air-acetylene flame, no interference was detected from calcium and magnesium.

Molybdenum.[10]—No interferences have been detected from aluminum, silicon, phosphorus, chlorine, sodium, potassium, nickel, chromium, or zinc. The presence of calcium, strontium, manganese, or iron has been found to interfere, as well as the presence of sulfate. The addition of 1000 p.p.m. of aluminum has been found to completely control these interferences.

Palladium.[7]—No interferences arise from the presence of sodium, ruthenium, rhodium, osmium, iridium, platinum, gold, or ammonium ion. Interferences have been detected from the presence of hydrochloric, nitric, and sulfuric. The problems arising from the presence of HCl or HNO_3 can be eliminated completely by controlling the acidity at 10 to 15 percent.

Platinum.[7]—No interferences arise from the presence of ammonium ion. The presence of hydrochloric acid or gold interferes slightly. Nitric acid interferes but this can be eliminated by controlling the acid concentration. The presence of palladium interferes when its concentration exceeds 125 p.p.m. High concentrations of ruthenium and osmium interfere. Sensitivity is seriously decreased by the presence of sulfuric acid and/or sodium.

Potassium.[8]—No interferences arise from the presence of magnesium, calcium, or phosphorus. Sodium interferes when in high concentrations. Its effect can be overcome by adding similar amounts to standards, or by adding a large amount of sodium to both samples and standards.

Rhodium.[7]—The presence of hydrochloric acid interferes slightly. The interference of nitric acid is significant only with concentrations of rhodium less than 20 p.p.m. No interference arises from the presence of ammonium ion, the presence of which has a buffering action that tends to counteract the interference of sulfuric acid. Low concentrations of sodium enhances the rhodium signal whereas high concentrations reduce sensitivity. At concentrations less than 125 p.p.m. the effect of the presence of palladium and platinum is erratic. At higher concentrations interference is negligible. The presence of gold tends to enhance the signal. Interferences also arise from the presence of ruthenium and osmium.

Sodium.[8]—No interferences arise from the presence of lithium or potassium at 500 to 1 ratios.

Zinc.[4]—Slight interferences arise from the presence of magnesium. The presence of silicon is the only significant interferent found. A large number of other elements have been studied. Their presence has no effect on the determination of zinc.

Detection Limits.—The limit of sensitivity of atomic absorption methods depends on various factors such as the oscillator strength of the line involved, the intensity of the line emitted by the source, and the spectral slit width necessary to isolate the required line. Consequently it is difficult to give any precise figures on sensitivity.

However, the concept of detection limit is more useful for comparing analytical methods because it includes not only the factors that govern analytical sensitivity, but also the factors which control the level of background fluctuation.

For practical purposes, mainly because most authors report so called detection limits as the concentration which will give 1 percent absorption, this concept is used in Fig. 57-5.

[10] Atomic Absorption Newsletter No. 4, Perkin-Elmer Corp., Norwalk, Conn.

IA	IIA												IIIB	IVB	VB	VIB	VIIB	VIIIB
H																		He
Li 0.03	Be 0.02												B 250	C	N	O	F	Ne
Na 0.03	Mg 0.001												Al 10	Si 15	P 100	S	Cl	Ar
K 0.03	Ca 0.08	Sc 5	Ti 12	V 7	Cr 0.05	Mn 0.005	Fe 0.1	Co 0.013	Ni 0.01	Cu 0.003	Zn 0.0003		Ga 1.5	Ge	As 5	Se 5	Br	Kr
Rb 0.1	Sr 0.05	Y 50	Zr	Nb 250	Mo 0.5	Tc	Ru 0.25	Rh 0.1	Pd 0.1	Ag 0.05	Cd 0.0004		In 0.2	Sn 5	Sb 0.1	Te 0.2	I	Xe
Cs 0.15	Ba 5	La	Hf	Ta	W 25	Re 25	Os	Ir 0.2	Pt 0.7	Au 0.2	Hg 0.5		Tl 0.03	Pb 0.02	Bi 0.1	Po	At	Rn
Fr	Ra	Ac																

Ce	Pr	Nd	Pm	Sm	Eu	Gd	Tb	Dy	Ho	Er	Tm	Yb	Lu
Th	Pa	U	Np	Pu	Am	Cm	Bk	Cf	Es	Fm	Md	No	Lw

FIG. 57-5. Detection Limits in Atomic Absorption, p.p.m.

ANALYTICAL NOTES

Calibration Curves.—These should be made from solutions similar to the sample to be analyzed with respect to the solvent and any major components that may be present. Metallo-organic compounds which can be dissolved in organic solvents are generally available through the National Bureau of Standards.[11]

The general procedure is to dissolve a suitable quantity of metallo-organic compound (about 0.1 to 0.2 g.) in xylene (2 ml.) and 2-ethyl-hexanoic acid (5 ml.). This solution is then diluted with pure lube oil to form a stock solution of about 500 p.p.m. of metal. From this, the standard solutions can be made by diluting with a suitable solvent, similar to the samples to be analyzed.

TABLE 57-2.

Element	Sample Type	Absorption Wavelength (A)	Analytical Range (p.p.m.)	Interferences
Ba	Worn lube oils[a,b]	5536	20 to 200	
Ca	Lube oils	4227	0 to 20	Si, Al, PO_4^{3-}, Na, K, Be, Zr, V[e] interferences can be reduced with strontium
Cr	Worn lube oils[a]	3579	2 to 20	
Cu	Worn lube oils[a]	3247	0 to 5	Na, K
	Crude oil[c]	2181	0 to 50	
	Petroleum products[b]	2492	0 to 500	
		2441	0 to 2500	
Fe	Catalysts	2483	0 to 5	
	Feed stocks	3719	0 to 50	
	Worn lube oils[a]	3440	0 to 150	
Pb	Gasoline[d]	2833	0 to 50	
	Lube oils[a,b]	2170	0 to 500	
Mo	Catalysts	3132	0 to 50	Ca, Sr, Mn, Fe
		3209	0 to 500	
		3112		
Ni	Feed stocks[c]	2320	2 to 20	
	Petroleum products[b]	3414	30 to 300	
Pt	Catalysts	2659	0 to 80	
		2175	0 to 150	
K	Lube oils	7665	0 to 5	Na, Li, Cs
		4044	0 to 250	
Na	Worn lube oils	5890	0 to 10	
		3302	0 to 100	
Zn	Worn lube oils	2138	0 to 10	Mg, Si

[a] Analytical Methods for Atomic Absorption, Perkin-Elmer Corp., Norwalk, Conn.
[b] NBS Monograph 54, Oct. 1962.
[c] Barras, R. C., Pittsburgh Conference on Analytical Chemistry, 1963.
[d] Robinson, J. W., Anal. Chim. Acta, **24**, 451, 1961.
[e] Robinson, J. W., unpublished work.

[11] NBS Monograph 54, Oct., 1962.

Barium.—A highly reducing flame is desirable. Lube oils samples can be diluted with n-heptane and the solution analyzed directly.

Calcium.—A rich oxy-acetylene flame is desirable. Lube oil samples may be diluted with n-heptane and the solution analyzed.

Chromium.—A highly reducing flame is desirable. Lube oil samples may be diluted with n-heptane and the solution analyzed.

Copper.—An oxidizing flame is desirable. Liquid samples may be diluted with n-heptane and the solution analyzed.

Iron.—An oxidizing flame is desirable. Liquid samples may be diluted with n-heptane and the solution analyzed.

Lead.—A slightly oxidizing flame is desirable. Gasoline samples may be diluted with n-octane and the solution analyzed. Tetra-ethyl lead should be used in the standards for making up calibration curves. Lube oils may be diluted with n-heptane and the solution analyzed.

Molybdenum.—A highly reducing oxy-acetylene flame is required. The sample is dissolved, and analyzed directly. High concentrations of aluminum or silicon may be troublesome. If necessary they should be removed by hydrofluoric acid treatment, or precipitation.

Platinum.—A reducing flame is desirable. Catalyst samples may be dissolved and analyzed directly. High concentrations of aluminum or silicon should be removed if necessary.

Potassium.—An oxidizing flame is desirable. Liquid samples may be diluted with n-heptane and the solution analyzed.

Sodium.—An oxidizing flame is desirable. Liquid samples may be diluted with n-heptane and the solution analyzed.

Zinc.—An oxidizing flame is desirable. Liquid samples may be diluted with n-heptane and the solution analyzed.

MASS SPECTROMETRY
IN PETROLEUM CHEMISTRY

By D. P. Stevenson and P. A. Wadsworth

Shell Development Co.
Emeryville, California

INTRODUCTION

Mass spectrometry is one of the three tools of the molecular structure chemist that were adapted to the solution of problems in the analytical chemistry of petroleum and its products during the early 1940's. The other two tools are those of infrared and ultra-violet spectrometry. Although these three spectrometries give very different kinds of molecular structure constants to the chemical physicists, their applications in analytical chemistry share many features in common. The most important of the common characteristics the three spectrometries share is that in the present state of molecular structure knowledge one can not describe quantitatively the spectrum of a substance *a priori*. That is, before one can quantitatively identify a substance by means of a spectrum it is necessary to have the corresponding spectrum of an authentic specimen of the substance for comparison. Thus the utility of any one of the three spectrometries in analytical chemistry is largely determined by the size of the available library of spectra of substances of potential interest.

As a result of the cooperation of many laboratories, there have been assembled under the auspices of API Project 44, a large collection of mass spectra of hydrocarbons and those of a considerably lesser number of other substances commonly found in petroleum and petroleum products. Other sources of mass spectra, more or less related to petroleum and petroleum products, are the Manufacturing Chemists Association and the ASTM Plan for the Exchange of Uncertified Spectra. A recent count of the API Project 44 gives the following breakdown with respect to the numbers of substances of various classes for which mass spectra are available.

Substances	*Number of Different Compounds with Mass Spectra*
Aliphatic Hydrocarbons	
Alkanes	165
Cycloalkanes	233
Alkenes (mono and poly)	115
Cycloalkenes (mono and poly)	58
Aromatic Hydrocarbons	
Benzenes	113
Polynuclear	122
Sulfur-containing	161
Oxygen-containing	196
Nitrogen-containing	76

The second characteristic shown by the three spectrometries is that it is possible to develop empirical correlations between the constitution and structure of molecules and the structure of their spectra. Excellent qualitative and frequently semiquantitative predictions of the spectrum that will be associated with a particular constitution and structure can be made by interpolation or extrapolation from the spectra of related substances. In general these correlations of molecular constitution and structure with spectra are much more precise for the intensive aspect of the spectrum than for its extensive aspect.[12,13,14,15]

Mass spectra of substances differ in one important respect from both infrared and ultraviolet absorption spectra. This is in the transferability of measurements of the extensive aspect of the spectrum of a substance from laboratory to laboratory or even instrument to instrument in a single laboratory. The specific intensities associated with the intensive features of the mass spectrum of a substance are much more dependent on the details of construction and operation of the mass spectroscope than is the case in optical spectrometry.[16] The consequence is that while the compilations of mass spectra of substances can be used in qualitative identification of substances and for determining the feasibility of mass spectrometry as a means for the quantitative determination of substances, actual quantitative mass spectrometric analysis requires calibration of the instrument that is to be used with authentic specimens of the substances to be determined.

Although the three spectrometries mentioned above, along with the newer one, proton magnetic resonance spectrometry, are frequently viewed as competitive or alternate methods for the solution of analytical chemical problems, a more accurate view is that these spectrometries are complementary and supplementary to one another. In this complementary set of analytical spectrometries, mass spectrometry plays a unique role. The information derived from either an optical or a magnetic resonance spectrum is in general that of the nature of molecular units, such as the number and kind of bonds

(C—H, C=O, etc.), groups of bonds $\left(\begin{array}{c} C=C-C=C \end{array} , \begin{array}{c} \end{array} , \text{etc.} \right)$, or kinds of

protons (CH_3, CH_2, etc.). From the mass spectrum of a substance, on the other hand, one derives information concerning the whole molecule, that is, more or less unambiguously the molecular formula of the substance. In addition, the mass spectrum of a substance provides some information concerning the gross structural units. Finally, in contrast to the situation that obtains in the case of optical and resonance spectrometries, each substance that can be volatilized has a mass spectrum, whereas many substances and classes of substances do not have experimentally accessible absorption spectra. As a consequence of these unique analytical abilities associated with mass spectrometry, the method has and will probably continue in the future to play a central role in the analysis of petroleum and petroleum products. The authors believe this will continue despite the fact that the method of gas-liquid partition chromatography is now used to handle many of the problems that gave rise to the initial enthusiasm for mass spectrometry.[17]

The single weakness of mass spectrometry, that which keeps it from being an analytical method of complete generality, is the requirement that the material to be analyzed must

[12] McLafferty, F. W., Mass Spectrometry of Organic Ions, Academic Press, New York, 1962.

[13] Benyon, J. H., Mass Spectrometry and Its Application to Organic Chemistry, Elsevier, Amsterdam, 1960.

[14] Bieman, K., Mass Spectrometry, Organic Chemical Application, McGraw-Hill, New York, 1962.

[15] Budzikiewicz, H., Djerassi, C., and Williams, D. H., Interpretation of Mass Spectra of Organic Compounds, Holden-Day Inc., San Francisco, 1964.

[16] Barnard, G. P., Modern Mass Spectrometry, Inst. of Petroleum, London, 1953.

[17] Mass spectrometry has been employed as a rapid and convenient method of identification of the eluate from such a gas-liquid partition chromatographic separation of materials. Dorsey, J. A., Hunt, R. H., O'Neal, M. J., Anal. Chem., 35, 511, 1963.

be capable of complete and quantitative volatilization without decomposition. This fact not only precludes the application of the mass spectrometry analytical method to large numbers of labile substances, but also introduces a serious source of error in quantitative analysis, that of representative sampling. This source of error is greatly exaggerated by the truly micro-chemical character of mass spectrometry.[18]

The normal sample size that is required in analytical mass spectrometry is in the range from 1 to 10 micromoles of which only a few percent actually enter the mass spectroscope proper. For materials that are normally gaseous, or liquid with low vapor pressures at ambient conditions, introducing representative samples of appropriate size presents no serious problem. However, for liquids of high volatility and high melting solids special precautions are clearly necessary to assure that the 1- to 10-micromole sample introduced to the mass spectrometer is truly representative of the material to be analyzed.

Within the limitations imposed by the requirement of finite volatility and a library of reference spectra, mass spectrometry finds application in all the typical analytical problems encountered in analysis of the nonmetallic constituents of petroleum and its products including gases, gasolines, light distillates, heavy distillates, greases, and waxes. These applications include the qualitative identification of constituents of mixtures, the quantitative determination of the individual components of multicomponent mixtures, and the estimation of the relative quantities of types or related groups of substances in very complex mixtures. As indicated above, the strong forte of mass spectroscopic analysis is its ability to distinguish the molecular weight of individual components, and if one were to single out a primary role of mass spectroscopy in the analytical chemistry of petroleum it would be that of determining the distribution of the components of mixtures in molecular weight. The elucidation of the details of molecular structure, or the analyses of mixtures of isomers are generally better done by other methods.

GENERAL PRINCIPLES OF MASS SPECTROMETRIC ANALYSIS

The following brief summary of the principles involved in the use of mass spectroscopes in the analysis of gaseous, liquid, and solid mixtures pertains to the class of spectroscopes that employ electrical detection of the ions of the mass spectra, $i.e.$, mass spectrometers, and those mass spectrometers that employ electron impact ion sources. The mass spectrum of a substance as generated by an electron impact source consists largely (>80 percent) of single charged ions with a small characteristic fraction of doubly charged ions. The mass to charge ratio of the ions (m/q) range down from that characteristic of the molecular formula of the substance, and there are usually found in greater or lesser intensity, ions of m/q corresponding to the formulae of all the fragments into which the original molecule can conceivably dissociate (unimolecularly) by simple bond fission or disproportionation reactions. In general, there are also found ions of m/q corresponding to formulae for fragments that imply molecular rearrangement processes have preceded the fragmentation processes. For example, one may cite the appearance of the ion $m/q = 29$ corresponding to the formula, $C_2H_5^+$, in the mass spectra of isobutylene. In general the most intense ions in the mass spectrum of the hydrocarbons correspond to fragments that may be formed by simple bond fission, as $C_3H_7^+$ ($m/q = 43$) in the mass spectrum of the butanes, or by a simple disproportionation reaction as $C_2H_4^+$ ($m/q = 28$) in the mass spectrum of ethane.

The fraction of the ions in the mass spectrum of a substance that correspond to the molecular formula of the substance, the so-called parent ion, is subject to wide variation.

---

[18] It is to be noted that several workers have suggested that thermally labile substances can be identified by means of the mass spectrum of their thermal decomposition products. Zemany, Anal. Chem., 24, 1709, 1952. Madorsky and coworkers, J. Res. Nat. Bur. Stds., 40, 417, 1948; Ibid., 42, 499, 1949.

Values range from the order of 0.01 percent in the case of neopentane to 98 percent in the case of hydrogen. Ordinarily very low values of this fraction (<1 percent) are found only in the case of alkanes with quaternary carbon atoms. As a general rule, this fraction increases as the formal unsaturation of a hydrocarbon increases, *i.e.*, as z in the formula C_nH_{2n+z} decreases in the series $+2$, 0, -2, etc., and decreases with increasing carbon number in a homologous series, *i.e.*, with n at constant z.

Provided certain simple precautions are observed, the mass spectrum of a mixture of substances is the linear superposition of the mass spectra of the components. That is, the intensity of each ion in the mass spectrum of the mixture is the sum of the intensities of that ion in the mass spectra of the components weighted by the partial pressure of the components. Algebraically, one writes for the intensity of the ion, m/q, in the mass spectrum of a mixture, I_m, the equation

$$I_m = P \sum_{i=1}^{n} X_i I_{mi}^{\circ} \tag{1}$$

where: P = the total pressure of the mixture;
$X_i = P_i/P$ is the mole fraction of the ith component of the mixture of n substances; and
I_{mi}° = the specific intensity of the ion m/q in the mass spectrum of the ith component.

Eq. (1) forms the basis for the use of mass spectrometry in the quantitative component analysis of polycomponent mixtures.

In order that mole fractions, X_i, of an n component mixture shall be determinable from the mass spectrum of the mixture, the necessary and sufficient condition is that there can be found n linearly independent equations of the form of (1), *i.e.*, that there can be found n ions in the mass spectra of the n substances such that

$$|I_{mi}^{\circ}| \neq 0 (m = 1 - n, i = 1 - n) \tag{2}$$

It is of great importance to note that it is not necessary to have either highly reliable mass spectra or even a self-consistent set of mass spectra of a group of n substances in order to determine whether or not mass spectrometric component analysis is feasible and what kind of accuracy may be expected. Quite approximate values of the I_{mi}° in the mass spectra of the substances of interest suffice to determine whether there exist a sufficient number of linearly independent equations of the type of Eq. (1). If a set of linearly independent equations exist, the accuracy with which the various components may be expected to be determinable can be calculated by standard algebraic methods[19] with the assumption that the probable error of determination of the ratio I_m/P characteristic of the mass spectrum of the mixture will be ± 1 percent. If the solutions of the set of Eq. (1), are written in the form

$$X_i = \sum_{m=1}^{n} (I_{mi}^{\circ})^{-1} I_m/P \tag{3}$$

then the probable errors of the X_i, ϵ_i, are given by the equation

$$\epsilon_i = \sqrt{\sum_{m=1}^{n} \{(I_{mi}^{\circ})^{-1}\epsilon_m\}^2} \tag{4}$$

where the ϵ_m are the probable errors of the I_m/P.

[19] Whittaker, E. T., and Robinson, G., Calculus of Observations, Blackie and Sons, London 1929.

In the qualitative identification of substances it has been indicated above that the mass spectroscope is unique in its ability to provide unambiguous information with respect to the molecular formula of a volatilizable substance. In a conventional analytical mass spectrometer with a resolving power in the range 200–500, the molecular weights of the principal isotopic species of a substance are determined to the nearest a.m.u. and the relative concentrations of the principal isotopic species are usually measurable with a probable error of the order of ± 1 percent. The manner in which such data in combination with a knowledge of the natural isotopic abundances of the elements permits the identification of an empirical formula is best described by a simple example. The three substances, tridecane, butyl naphthalene and dibenzothiophene, have as the molecular weight (to the nearest a.m.u.) of their principal isotopic species (^{12}C, H and ^{32}S), $m/q = 184$. Natural carbon and sulfur have isotopes ^{13}C (1.108%) and ^{33}S (0.74%) and ^{34}S (4.19%) respectively, and as a consequence the mass spectra of the three substances will have additional "parent ions" with $m/q = 185, 186,$ and 187. Assuming a random distribution of isotopic atoms in the molecules there can be readily computed by use of the multinomial expansion, the following relative abundances for the respective parent ions in the mass spectra of the three substances.

m/q	$C_{13}H_{28}$	$C_{14}H_{16}$	$C_{12}H_8S$
184	1.	1.	1.
185	0.1456	0.1528	0.1421
186	0.0098	0.0114	0.0534
187	0.0004	0.0005	0.0061

The naphthalene is clearly identifiable in such a group of possibilities from its relatively large intensity at $m/q = 185$, while the dibenzothiophene would be recognized from the relatively large intensity at $m/q = 186$.[20]

When a high resolution mass spectroscope (resolving power ≥ 8000) is available it becomes possible to determine the m/q of the ions in a mass spectrum to within a few parts per million. When such precision of mass determination can be achieved it becomes possible to identify the constitution of an ion from the magnitude of the deviation of the ions m/q from an integer. That is, it becomes possible to make use of the fact that the masses of the atoms are not exactly equal to their mass numbers. In the case of the three substances employed in the example above, the actual masses of the principal isotopic species are $C_{13}H_{28}$ (184.219), $C_{14}H_{16}$ (184.125), and $C_{12}H_8S$ (184.035), differing from one another by the order of 500 p.p.m.

If instead in the above example the paraffin were not tridecane but a $C_{13}H_{28}$ paraffin with quaternary carbon atoms, then little or no parent ion would be observed. In order to establish the molecular weight of this material the rate of effusion of the material through the leak into the mass spectrometer can be measured using one of the ions arising from the fragmentation process. The error in this method of determination of molecular weight can range from 1 to 4 percent.[16]

While the mass spectrum of a particular substance is characteristic of its constitution and structure, it is also true that the kinds of ions (defined by their empirical formulae, C_nH_{2n+z}) that are of greatest intensity in the mass spectrum of a substance are characteristic of the empirical formula of the substance. Thus, it is found that the order of 90 percent of the total intensity of the ions in the mass spectra of the alkanes, C_nH_{2n+2}, and cycloalkanes and alkenes, C_nH_{2n}, is distributed among ions with empirical formulas, C_mH_{2m+1}, C_mH_{2m}, and C_mH_{2m-1} ($m \leq n - 2$), but whereas in the case of alkanes the sums

---

[20] A careful analyst would certainly employ the ultraviolet absorption spectrum of the material to confirm the mass spectrometric identification in a case of this sort.

in the homologous series,

$$\sum_{m=2}^{n-2} I(C_mH_{2m+1}) = \sigma_1, \ \sum_{m=2}^{n-2} I(C_mH_{2m+1}) = \sigma_0 \ \text{and} \ \sum_{m=2}^{n-2} I(C_mH_{2m+1}) = \sigma_{-1} \tag{5}$$

obey the inequality, $\sigma_1 \gg \sigma_1 \sim \sigma_{-1}$, it is found that for the substances with the empirical formulae C_nH_{2n} there obtains $\sigma_1 < \sigma_1 \sim \sigma_{-1}$. While individual substances of particular empirical formula show wide variation in the intensities of the individual ion in any one of the empirical formula series, it is found that the sums, σ_1, σ_0, and σ_{-1} are relatively constant. This invariance of the sums of intensities of characteristic ions in the mass spectra of classes of compounds forms the basis of a modified type of mass spectrometric component analysis. In the place of Eq. (1) that describe the intensities of individual ions in the mass spectrum of a mixture of substances in terms of the concentration of individual substances and their mass spectra, there are written equations describing the sums of intensities of ions in terms of the sums of concentrations of types of substances and the intensity sums characteristic of the types.

If C_z is the concentration of hydrocarbons of empirical formula C_nH_{2n+z} in a mixture, $_z\sigma_i$ the intensity sum characteristic of the hydrocarbon type, and σ_{i0} the intensity sum found for a mixture, the equation that replaces (1) is

$$\sigma_{i0} = \sum_{z=+2}^{z=-10} C_{zz}\sigma_i(i = +2, +1, 0, \cdots, -10) \tag{6}$$

In this equation the $\sigma(\sigma_{i0}$ and $_z\sigma_i)$ are expressed as fractions of the entire mass spectrum and the C_z are in liquid volume fractions. These units are the consequence of the facts that the invariance of the $_z\sigma_i$ appears when these are expressed as fractions of the total ion current in the mass spectrum and that the total intensity in the mass spectra of hydrocarbons is proportional to the volume of liquid hydrocarbon volatilized.[21]

GAS ANALYSIS

The historically first extensive use of mass spectrometry in analytical chemistry was by the oil industry in the analysis of the gaseous streams (i.e., those streams that are overwhelmingly C_4 and lighter) characteristic of modern refineries. These streams include natural gas, waste gas, and gas from thermal and catalytic cracking operations. From its mass spectrum it is in general possible to determine quantitatively with adequate accuracy the individual components of a mixture containing any or all of the following: hydrogen, argon, nitrogen, carbon monoxide, oxygen, hydrogen sulfide, carbon dioxide, carbonyl sulfide, carbon disulfide, methane, acetylene, ethylene, ethane, propylene, propane, butadiene, butenes, and butanes, provided the content of C_5 and higher hydrocarbons does not exceed 1.0 to 2.0 percent m. Water vapor and ammonia usually are undeterminable. The accuracy with which the individual components can be determined varies from component to component and to a greater or lesser extent with the concentration of other components. For those substances whose constitution cause their mass spectra to possess ions of unique mass to charge ratio, m/q, such as, oxygen ($m/q = 32$) hydrogen sulfide ($m/q = 34$), carbon dioxide ($m/q = 22$), carbonyl sulfide ($m/q = 60$) and carbon disulfide ($m/q = 76$), the accuracy of determination of their concentration will be ± 0.01 to ± 0.02 percent m (basis total sample) to $\pm 1 - \pm 2$ percent of the quantity present, whichever is larger. The accuracy of determination of the alkanes, methane, ethane and propane will generally range from ± 0.1 percent (basis sample) to ± 1 percent to ± 2 percent of the actual concentration since these substances have ions in their mass spectra that are relatively absent from the mass spectra of the other possible components.

[21] Otvos, J. W., and Stevenson, D. P., J. Am. Chem. Soc., **78,** 546, 1956; Grable, G. F., and Coggeshall, N. D., Anal. Chem., **30,** 310, 1958.

For a substance for which the ions of its mass spectrum are all coincident with those of another substance, as is the case for sets of isomers, or for alkenes in the presence of alkanes, the accuracy of determination of the substance is strongly dependent on the relative concentrations of the mutually interfering substances. This may be illustrated by a simple example, namely the accuracy of the mass spectrometric determination of the concentrations of normal and isobutane in binary mixture. A suitable pair of ions for such an analysis are those of $m/q = 58$ and 43 equivalent to $C_4H_{10}^+$ and $C_3H_7^+$ respectively. The equations, (1), for the intensities are

$$\frac{I_{58}}{P} = X_n\, 8.24 + X_i\, 2.47$$

$$\frac{I_{43}}{P} = X_n\, 38.3 + X_i\, 43.4$$

(7)

with the solutions

$$X_n = 0.1652\left(\frac{I_{58}}{P}\right) - 0.00940\left(\frac{I_{43}}{P}\right)$$

$$X_i = -0.1456\left(\frac{I_{58}}{P}\right) + 0.0313\left(\frac{I_{43}}{P}\right)$$

(8)

The probable errors in X_n and X_i, the mole fractions of the two butanes are given by the equations

$$\epsilon_n = \sqrt{(0.1652\,\epsilon_{58})^2 + (0.00940\,\epsilon_{43})^2}$$
$$\epsilon_i = \sqrt{(0.1456\,\epsilon_{58})^2 + (0.0313\,\epsilon_{43})^2}$$

(9)

in terms of the probable errors ϵ_{58} and ϵ_{43} of I_{58}/P and I_{43}/P respectively. If we take the probable errors of I_m/P to be ± 1 percent of their value, we find from Eqs. (9) the following probable errors in the determination of the mole fractions of the two butanes:

	ϵ_n	ϵ_i
pure n-butane	± 0.014	± 0.017
pure isobutane	± 0.006	± 0.014

In Table 57-3 there are summarized the analysis of the errors encountered in the analysis of mixtures of C_1–C_4 alkane-alkene mixtures reported by Washburn and co-workers.[22]

Shepard has discussed the accuracy of mass spectrometric analysis of carburated water gas[23] and of natural gas[24] on the basis of the results of the cooperative analysis of standard samples by a large number of laboratories. Starr and Lane[25] have described the results of a very elaborate series of cooperative analyses of mixtures of C_3–C_5 hydrocarbons in which the accuracy of the mass spectrometric analyses was not only evaluated by comparison with the synthetic compositions of the mixtures analyzed, but also with the results of analysis of the mixtures by other standard methods. Special problems associated with the mass spectrometric analysis of liquefied hydrocarbon mixtures of C_3–C_5 alkanes and alkenes have been analyzed and resolved by Dibeler and Mohler.[26]

[22] Washburn, H. W., et al., Ind. Eng. Chem., Anal. Ed., **17**, 74, 1945.
[23] Shepard, M., J. Res. Nat. Bur. Stds., **36**, 313, 1946; **44**, 509, 1950.
[24] Shepard, M., Ibid., **38**, 19, 491, 1947; Anal. Chem., **19**, 635, 1947.
[25] Starr, C. E., and Lane, T., Anal. Chem., **21**, 572, 1949.
[26] Dibeler, V. H., and Mohler, F. L., J. Res. Nat. Bur. Stds., **39**, 149, 1947.

TABLE 57-3.   ERRORS IN MASS SPECTROMETRIC ANALYSIS OF C_1–C_4 HYDROCARBONS

Component	Approximate %m	No. of Analyses	Mean Error %m	90% of Errors Less Than %m
CH_4	15 ⎫			
C_2H_6	20 ⎪			
C_3H_8	20 ⎬	215	0.2	0.4
iso-C_4H_{10}	10 ⎪			
n-C_4H_{10}	8 ⎭			
C_3H_6	10	43	0.2	0.5
1-C_4H_8	5 ⎱	86	0.7	1.4
2-C_4H_8	5 ⎰			
iso-C_4H_8	7	43	0.4	0.7
total C_4H_8	17	43	0.4	0.8

GROUP OR TYPE ANALYSES

In the analysis of gasoline range and higher boiling mixtures from petroleum, the mass spectrometric method is of very limited utility in the determination of individual components. For these very complex mixtures the mass spectrometer has been extensively employed in so-called *type analyses*. That is, the approximate determination of how the components of the mixture are distributed with respect to the z-value of the empirical formulae, C_nH_{2n+z}, and to a greater or lesser extent the distribution in n for particular z-values. It can not be said that these type analyses have a great degree of absolute reliability with respect to their chemical interpretation. Rather their utility is that of providing a semiempirical means of evaluating the mixture with respect to its value as a feed stock for a particular application or for evaluating the effectiveness of a particular chemical or physical process in modifying the mixture. The greater utility of mass spectrometry than of other semiempirical methods for such evaluation, as the N-D-M method of van Ness and Weston[27] or silica gel elution chromatography,[28] lies in the greater number of data available in a mass spectrum as compared to the number of classical physical-chemical measurements that provide independent characterization of a mixture.

With respect to gasoline range hydrocarbons, it is possible to estimate the relative concentration of alkanes, cycloalkanes plus monoalkenes, cycloalkenes plus alkadienes plus acetylenes plus bicycloalkanes, alkyl benzenes, and benzocycloalkanes from the mass spectrum of the gasoline by use of the characteristic sums of ion intensities of these classes of compounds. From the mass spectra of a gasoline before and after chemical treatment to remove the unsaturated hydrocarbons (such as with concentrated sulfuric acid promoted with P_2O_5), the substances of empirical formula C_nH_{2n} can be resolved into cycloalkanes and alkenes, and those of empirical formula C_nH_{2n-2}, into bicycloalkanes and alkadienes plus acetylenes.[29,30,31,32] Because the mass spectra of alkyl benzenes show relatively less variation with isomer structure than is the case for other classes

[27] van Ness, K., and Weston, H. A., Aspects of the Constitution of Mineral Oils, Elsevier, Amsterdam, 1951.
[28] Mair, W. B. J., J. Res. Nat. Bur. Stds., **34**, 435, 1945.
[29] Smit, W. M., Far. Soc. Disc. **7**, 248, 1949.
[30] Brown, R. A., Anal. Chem., **23**, 430, 1951.
[31] Lumpkin, H. E., Thomas, B. W., and Elliott, A., Anal. Chem., **24**, 1389, 1952.
[32] Klaas, P. J., and Sweeney, W. R., Anal. Chem., **34**, 301, 1962.

of hydrocarbon, particularly with respect to the fraction of their mass spectra that the parent ion constitutes, it is also possible in such gasoline type analyses to determine the distribution of alkyl benzenes in carbon number.[33]

The most important use of this kind of gasoline analysis is in connection with catalytic reforming of straight run gasoline to produce highly aromatic motor fuel or aromatic solvents. The determination of the cycloalkane content of the feed naphtha provides a measure of its quality, *i.e.*, the potential aromatic that can be made, while the determination of aromatics and cycloalkanes in the product provides a measure of the effectiveness of the process.

Similar type analyses have been applied to kerosenes and the heavier fractions of petroleum up to and including heavy lubricating oils, *i.e.*, up to hydrocarbons of molecular weight as great as 600.[34] Because there is overlap in the m/q of the characteristic fragment ions of substances of different degree of unsaturation, as for example between alkanes, C_nH_{2n+2}, and alkyl naphthalenes, $C_{n+1}H_{2n-10}$, the application of mass spectrometry to such heavy fractions requires prior separation into types with respect to chemical unsaturation. The usual separation method is that of silica gel elution chromatography[30,33,35] in which fractions consisting of saturated hydrocarbons, monoaromatics,[36] and polyaromatics are prepared and the mass spectra separately examined. The mass spectrometric type analyses of these heavy fractions are more proximate and more empirical than those of gasoline range mixtures. The reason for this is that the mass spectral sums, $_z\sigma_i$, characteristic of the various classes of hydrocarbon must be estimated from a very small number of representatives of a class, or from representative fractions concentrated from petroleum itself.

Two kinds of type analysis of these heavier materials have been described.[34] These are the so-called fragment peak method and the parent peak method. In the fragment peak method there is estimated the distribution of substances in terms of the number of rings per molecule with some breakdown of the polyring molecules into the relative concentrations of condensed ring and noncondensed ring molecules. In this method there are employed only the sums of the intensities of fragment ions believed to be characteristic of the hydrocarbon types. As implied by the name, the parent peak method employs the intensities of ions believed to be due to molecule ions of molecules present in the mixture along with estimated characteristic specific intensities to determine the approximate distribution in both n and z of the hydrocarbons, C_nH_{2n+z}, in the mixture.

LITERATURE OF MASS SPECTROMETRY

There are available two excellent, comprehensive treatises covering all aspects of mass spectrometry including analytical chemical areas. These are those of Ewald and Hintenberg[37] and of McDowell.[38] Two excellent but brief monographs covering the same general ground as the treatises are those of Robertson[39] and Duckworth.[40] Barnard[16] in his volume, Modern Mass Spectrometry, presents an excellent analysis of the problems

[33] Lumpkin, H. E., and Thomas, B. W., Anal. Chem., **23**, 1738, 1951.
[34] O'Neal, M. J., and Wier, T. P., Anal. Chem., **23**, 830, 1951; O'Neal, M. J., Hood, A., Clerc, R. J., Andre, M. L., and Hines, C. K., Proc. 4th World Pet. Congress, Section V/C No. 3.
[35] Fitzgerald, M. E., Cirillo, V. A., and Galbraith, F. J., Anal. Chem., **34**, 2176, 1962.
[36] Stevenson, D. P., and McConnell, H. M., Spectrochim. Acta, **12**, 262, 1958.
[37] Ewald, H., and Hintenberger, H., Methoden und Anwendungen der Massenpektroskopie, Verlag Chemie, G.m.b.H., Weinheim, 1953.
[38] McDowell, C. A., Mass Spectrometry, McGraw-Hill, New York, 1963.
[39] Robertson, A. J. B., Mass Spectrometry, Methuen, New York, 1955.
[40] Duckworth, H. E., Mass Spectroscopy, Cambridge Univ. Press, 1958.

involved in the application of the mass spectrometer to quantitative chemical analyses as well as good descriptions of a well organized mass spectrometry laboratory.

The recent cooperative treatise edited by McLafferty[12] contains authoritative accounts of the chemical processes associated with the origin of mass spectra, and description of the nature of mass spectra of many classes of organic chemicals. Three recent volumes, those of Beynon,[13] Bieman,[14] and Djerassi[15] present exhaustive accounts of the use of mass spectrometry in the determination of the structure of organic chemicals.

As an appendix to the volume, Advances in Mass Spectrometry,[41] the proceedings of a Petroleum Institute sponsored conference on mass spectrometry there is to be found a comprehensive bibliography of the mass spectrometry literature for the period 1938–1957. A similar bibliography covering the period 1958 through 1960 is incorporated as an appendix in Volume 2 of this series, Advances in Mass Spectrometry.[42] Recent reviews of progress in the analytical applications of mass spectrometry are to be found in the Analytical Chemistry review issues.[43,44,45,46,47]

[41] Waldron, J. D., Advances in Mass Spectrometry, Pergamon Press, New York, 1959.
[42] Elliott, R. M., Advances in Mass Spectrometry, Volume 2, Pergamon Press, New York, 1963.
[43] Dibeler, V. H., Anal. Chem., 28, 610, 1956.
[44] Dibeler, V. H., and Reese, R. M., Ibid., 30, 605, 1958.
[45] Dibeler, V. H., and Reese, R. M., Ibid., 32, 211R, 1960.
[46] Reese, R. M., Ibid., 34, 243R, 1962.
[47] Reese, R. M., and Harllee, F. N., Ibid., 36, 278R, 1964.

NUCLEAR ACTIVATION ANALYSIS

By E. L. Steele

General Atomic Division/General Dynamics Corp.
San Diego, California

INTRODUCTION

Nuclear activation analysis is a method of determining elemental composition by means of induced nuclear transitions. The method begins with the bombardment of analytical samples with particles or electromagnetic radiation to create energetically unstable or radioactive nuclei from the stable isotopes. The radiation emitted, as the decaying nuclei return to stable states, is measured as a function of the isotopes present in the original sample. The type and energy of the radiation provides qualitative information about the analytical sample, while the intensity of a characteristic radiation provides a quantitative relationship with the analytical sample.

Analytical applications of induced radioactivity were readily recognized soon after Curie and Joliot described this phenomenon in 1933.[48] Within three years, Hevesy published a paper describing the determination of dysprosium in yttrium using neutrons to induce a transmutation.[49] In 1938, Seaborg determined trace amounts of gallium in iron by bombarding the sample with energetic deuterons.[50] For security reasons, nothing concerning nuclear activation analysis was published during the war years, but the experiences gained during this period were summarized in 1947 by Clark and Overman.[51] By 1952, a substantial number of papers, both theoretical and practical, had appeared in the literature.[51,52,53,54,55] At the present time, the method is widely accepted in research as well as routine analytical applications.

PRINCIPLES OF ACTIVATION ANALYSIS

The basis of the activation analysis method is an induced nuclear transmutation which converts a portion of the stable isotopes of an element into radioactive isotopes. The relationship between this process and elemental analysis is dependent upon the constant isotopic abundance ratios found in nature. The method can be described by the following reaction:

$$X + a \rightarrow Y + b, \text{ that is } X(a, b)Y$$

where: X is the target nucleus;
Y is the product nucleus;
a is the bombarding particle or photon; and
b is the particle or photon emitted in the process of forming Y.

The decay products from Y, as it returns to a configuration that is stable with respect to

[48] Curie, I., and Joliot, F., Compt. Rend., **198**, 254, 1934.
[49] Hevesy, G., and Levi, H., Kgl. Danske Videnskab, Selskab, Math.-fys. Medd., **14**, No. 5, 1936.
[50] Seaborg, G. T., and Livingood, J. J., JACS, **60**, 1784, 1938.
[51] Clark, H. M., and Overman, R. T., USAEC Report No. MDDC-1329, 1947.
[52] Boyd, G. E., Anal. Chem., **21**, 335, 1949.
[53] Gordon, C. L., Anal. Chem., **21**, 96, 1949.
[54] Leddicotte, G. W., and Reynolds, S. A., Nucleonics, **8**, No. 3, 62, 1951.
[55] Sue, P., Bull. Soc. Chim. France, D9, 1951.

radioactive decay, is the usual analytical signal which is measured as a function of the amount of X originally present in the bombarded sample. It is also possible to measure b as a function of the amount of X present in the original sample. However, the experimental difficulties encountered in making analytical radioactivity measurements near nuclear reaction sites limit this latter technique to special applications. In the more conventional case, the samples are exposed to a source of particles or photons with sufficient energy to induce the desired nuclear reactions, then transferred to a suitable place for measurement. For this reason, only those radioactive products with half-lives of one second or longer find extensive analytical applications at the present time.

A variety of nuclear transmutations can be induced in every isotope of each element except protium. This isotope has only one reaction. In practice, however, the method is generally limited to nuclear reactions which involve energy changes of less than 20 million electron-volts (Mev). At energies above this level, both the reaction mechanisms to produce the radionuclides and the resulting decay schemes of these products become increasingly complicated. Within this energy range, nuclear transmutations can be induced in many naturally occurring elements by bombarding the sample with neutrons, protons, deuterons, helions (mass 3 and mass 4), tritons, and photons. The products resulting from the bombardment are a function of the target isotopes, the bombarding particles or photons, and the energies of the bombarding particles or photons. Every nuclear event energetically possible within the perimeter of a given irradiation environment will proceed completely independent of the other nuclei present. Likewise, the sample's induced radioactivity will be a combination of all the radiations emitted by the product radioisotopes.

Two problems arise from this procedure. First, the total amount of radiation emitted from the activated sample may be large as compared to the analytical signal. The task of identifying and measuring the desired activity in a high intensity radiation field is frequently beyond the capabilities of present day electronic analyzer systems. This is a particularly serious problem if a matrix element emits a radiation which is similar to the analytical signal.

Second, it is possible to obtain the same product radioisotope from more than one source. Aluminum-28, for example, is produced in a reactor irradiation by the following reactions:

(1) $_{13}Al^{27} + n(0.025\text{ ev}) \rightarrow {}_{13}Al^{28} + \text{gamma ray}$
(2) $_{15}P^{31} + n(\geq 2\text{ Mev}) \rightarrow {}_{13}Al^{28} + \text{alpha}$
(3) $_{14}Si^{28} + n(\geq 4\text{ Mev}) \rightarrow {}_{13}Al^{28} + \text{proton}$

Other examples, such as phosphorus-32 from sulfur, phosphorus, and chlorine, are quite common. They constitute an appreciable problem for the activation analyst. The general usefulness of activation analysis is seldom limited by a lack of suitable nuclear reactions or sensitivity, but rather by the inability to activate isotopes for examination *selectively*.

The problem of achieving selectivity in the activation analysis method can be approached in four ways. In the *first*, the traditional way, desired radioactive isotopes are chemically separated from the analytical samples after irradiation. This technique has produced good results in many cases where the isotope half-life is sufficiently long. Precision and accuracy fall, however, as the half-life approaches the time required for separation. The method fails in those cases cited above where one isotope is produced via two or more reactions (unless additional measurements are made). The main disadvantages in chemical separations, however, are the appreciable time required per analysis and the need for very experienced analysts.

A *second* procedure commonly used for increased selectivity involves effective utilization of the various half-lives. Since both the buildup and decay of radioactivity are a function of the individual isotope, time can frequently be used to isolate the desired activity. In cases where the isotope in question has a long half-life and the interferences have short half-lives, the analyst simply activates the sample and lets the short-lived material decay before analysis. In the reverse case, the analyst uses a short irradiation time to prevent the long-lived isotope from forming in appreciable quantities, and then counts the sample very soon after the irradiation. It is obvious that either of these techniques has little value when there is no large differential in half-lives.

The *third* approach is to devise detection systems by means of which selectivity may be increased. The best example of this technique is the present-day multichannel pulse-height analyzer. Resolutions of about 50 kev are regularly obtained in gamma-ray spectrometry, and this value will probably continue to improve. There are a variety of other techniques which find special applications, such as (to name a few), the use of coincidence analyzers, Cerenkov detectors, beta spectrometers, scintillators of various sizes, and semiconductor detectors. In general, as the sample under investigation becomes more complex, the effectiveness of all these techniques diminishes. Frequently, their biggest advantage is that they can be used in connection with chemical separations, allowing the analyst to perform only partial separations for complete resolution.

The *fourth* method for increasing selectivity is the technique of specific activations. With this method, the analyst selects an activation procedure which will produce a maximum amount of radioactivity from the element under investigation while minimizing or, in some cases, essentially eliminating matrix interferences. The various types of activation procedures are best described in terms of the bombarding projectile and its energy. For convenience, however, neutron-induced reactions are discussed as either thermal-neutron reactions or fast-neutron reactions.

Thermal-Neutron Activation Analysis.—This is the method most widely employed in activation analysis work. It involves the bombardment of samples with neutrons in thermal equilibrium with their environment. In practice, this is room temperature, thus giving the neutrons an average energy of 0.025 ev. With few exceptions, the only induced reaction possible at this neutron energy is the so-called neutron-gamma (n, γ) or neutron-capture reaction. While the samples are being irradiated, two processes are occurring at the same time. Product nuclei of a given type are constantly being formed, at a rate equal to $Nf\sigma$, where N is the number of target nuclei (of the appropriate type), present in the sample, f is the thermal-neutron flux (in neutrons per square centimeter per second) to which the sample is exposed, and σ is the thermal-neutron capture cross section (capture probability), expressed in units of square centimeters per nucleus.[56] Since these new nuclei are unstable (radioactive), they decay at a rate equal to $N^*\lambda$, where N^* is the number of product nuclei present at any time t, and λ is the radioactive decay constant of the radioactive species. The overall rate of formation of product nuclei is, therefore, the difference in the two rates:

$$\frac{dN^*}{dt} = Nf\sigma - N^*\lambda \tag{1}$$

This is a linear differential equation for which the solution is:

$$N^* = \frac{Nf\sigma}{\lambda} (1 - e^{-\lambda t_i}) \tag{2}$$

Often, it is more convenient to use an activity expression. This is

[56] In tabulations of nuclear reaction cross sections, the σ's are often listed in units of "barns." One barn = 10^{-24} cm^2/nucleus.

$$N^*\lambda = Nf\sigma(1 - e^{-\lambda t_i}) \tag{3}$$

and gives the activity, in disintegrations per second, just at the conclusion of an irradiation of time duration t_i.

In practice, N is a function of the sample weight, percent of the element present, the abundance of the stable isotope in question (amongst the stable isotopes of that element), atomic weight of the element, and Avogadro's number. Hence, Eq. (3) may be also expressed as:

$$A = \frac{(\text{Grams of sample})\left(\dfrac{\% \text{ of El.}}{100}\right)\left(\dfrac{\% \text{ Ab}}{100}\right)(6.02 \times 10^{23})f\sigma(1 - e^{-0.693t_i/T})}{\text{Atomic Wt.}} \tag{4}$$

From Eq. (4), it is obvious that the amount of a given activity produced by the (n, γ) reaction, for a given sample, increases directly with increasing neutron flux, and is a more complex function of the duration of the irradiation. Saturation (steady state) is reached when $t_i \gg T$ (where T is the half-life of the product nuclide). In this case, $(1 - e^{-\lambda t_i})$ approaches unity and A approaches A_{satn}. Similarly, the activity is $\frac{1}{2} A_{\text{satn}}$ at $t_i = T$, $\frac{3}{4} A_{\text{satn}}$ at $t_i = 2T$, $\frac{7}{8} A_{\text{satn}}$ at $t_i = 3T$, and so on.

Fast-Neutron Activation Analysis.—There is no universally accepted definition for activation analysis based upon fast-neutron induced reactions. In general, the term is applied to systems which produce radioactive products by the reaction $X(n, b)Y$, where n is an energetic (fast, high-velocity) neutron, and b is a nuclear particle (not a gamma ray). Thus, such reactions as the (n, p), $(n, 2n)$, (n, α), (n, n'), (n, d), (n, t), and (n, np) are included in the category of fast-neutron reactions. The threshold for these particle-particle reactions, *e.g.*, the energies required to induce the reactions, with few exceptions, are in the 1 Mev and higher region. These reactions are endoergic reactions, since they involve a small mass increase; that is, the mass of the products is slightly higher than the mass of the reactants.

The particular reaction (of several possible ones) that will dominate, under a given set of conditions, is a function of the nucleus involved and the energy of the incoming neutron. It is possible to draw several conclusions from the vast amount of experimental data available in the 1–14 Mev neutron energy region. First, (n, p) reactions generally require less energetic neutrons than $(n, 2n)$ reactions. The probability (cross section) for $(n, 2n)$ reaction is generally zero or very low for neutron energies below about 10 Mev, except for elements of high atomic number. Second, the cross sections for (n, α), (n, d) and (n, t) reactions decrease with increasing atomic number of the product nucleus. Third, the cross section of a particle-particle reaction is usually much larger than the cross section of a neutron capture reaction—with fast neutrons.

A problem involved in calculating sensitivities for fast-neutron induced reactions is the energy dependence of the reaction cross section. As shown in Fig. 57-6, this term varies considerably with neutron energy, and at the present time it is difficult to predict its behavior quantitatively from theory alone. The relationship between σ and E_n is, therefore, usually determined experimentally. In practice, however, this is not a problem, since a standard (reference) sample of the element of interest is activated under the same experimental conditions, thus permitting a concentration calculation by means of a simple ratio comparison method.

Charged-Particle Activation Analysis.—As the name suggests, this is the technique in which the bombarding particle is a small, positively-charged nucleus (*e.g.*, p^+, d^+, t^+, α^{++}). Because of equipment cost and various experimental difficulties, only those reactions induced by protons, deuterons, tritons, helium-3 nuclei, and alpha particles have analytical possibilities at the present time. Indeed, the appreciable Coulomb barrier energies involved in charged-particle induced reactions limit their application in many types of samples.

One very good area of application of charged-particle projectiles is in the study of surface composition. The short range of heavy ionizing particles in solid matter makes them particularly adaptable as tools for the analysis of the composition of surface layers to depths from a few atomic layers to several mils. As is the case with all nuclear reactions, the interaction energies are too large to be influenced significantly by chemical or crystalline binding energies, so that no information is obtained on compounds or

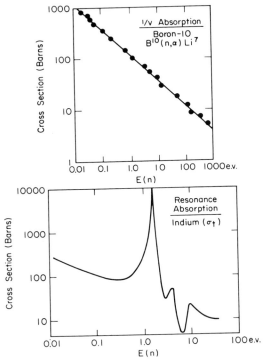

FIG. 57-6.   Cross-section as a Function of Projectile Energy Showing Both 1/V and Resonance Absorption of Thermal Neutrons.

crystal structure by these methods. The large energies do permit individual particles to be detected, and high sensitivities are obtained. Surface concentrations as small as 10^{-8} grams per square centimeter are readily detectable in many cases. Film thickness and continuous variation of concentration with depth can be measured with a resolution of 10^{-2} μ. The best results are achieved with light elements, *e.g.*, below aluminum, but the only barrier to complete analysis is incident particle energy. If nuclear scattering methods are used, rather than nuclear reactions, a source of 2 Mev charged particles is sufficient for the analysis of many heavy elements.

Photon Activation Analysis.—In this technique, samples are irradiated with high-energy *bremsstrahlung* or energetic gamma rays. The most common reactions observed with reasonably priced equipment are the (γ, γ'), (γ, n), and (γ, p). With several important exceptions, isotope formation by the (γ, n) or (γ, p) process requires about 10 Mev, or more, of photon energy.

Prompt-Gamma Ray Activation Analysis.—Prompt-gamma ray activation analysis is not a separate method in the sense of the first four methods listed (thermal-neutron, fast-neutron, charged-particle, photon). Rather, it is a method that differs only in the detection procedure employed—involving the same reactions previously discussed (except the photon-induced reactions). With this method, the prompt gamma radiation emitted is detected and measured, rather than the more conventional subsequent radio-active-decay gamma rays. Prompt-gamma analysis, then, refers to measuring the gamma ray immediately resulting from a nuclear interaction event (such as neutron capture). Prompt radiation usually is emitted within a time period of approximately 10^{-12} to 10^{-14} seconds after the event, so the general techniques of transferring samples to detection systems is not applicable. The sample must be counted *while* it is being irradiated. This technique has considerable potential for continuous analysis.

ACTIVATION ANALYSIS SOURCES

Nuclear Reactors.—Uranium-235 has an exceptionally large fission cross section for thermal neutrons, which accounts for its being the principal nuclear reactor fuel. The moderately high energies associated with neutrons produced in the fission process (mostly in the 1–2 Mev range) also accounts for the extensive use of neutron moderator materials, which is a basic feature of U^{235} reactors. The moderator serves to reduce the energies of fission neutrons to thermal energies, with a minimum of loss by capture or escape mechanisms. As a result, the reactor can be used as a source of neutrons over a considerable range of energies.

The fission spectrum of U^{235} is represented by the equation $N(E) = 1765Ee^{-0.775E}$ The existence of a small but significant number of neutrons with energies as high as 20 Mev is indicated. The flux of fission neutrons is approximately the same as that of thermal neutrons in the region of the core, but they decrease exponentially with distance from the core. The analyst has, then, the choice of in-core, in-pool, thermal-column, or beam-port irradiations. In-pool and in-core irradiations have the advantage of large fluxes, but the neutrons range in energy from thermal energies to 20 Mev. Neutrons with energies below about 0.4 ev can be partially removed by using boron-cadmium shielding. Thermal columns produce nearly pure thermal-neutron fluxes by interposing large amounts of moderator (usually graphite) between the core and the sample position. This additional thermalizing costs the analyst a factor of 1000 or more in neutron flux, but it does reduce the fast-neutron component of the neutron flux experienced by the sample.

Beam-port irradiation techniques are necessary if the analyst wishes to select a variety of neutron energies from the fission spectrum. In these cases, a beam of neutrons is allowed to pass through the reactor shield with a minimum of moderation. Neutron spectrometers are placed in the neutron beam and these devices isolate the desired energies. The analyst uses the isolated narrow energy-range neutron beam as the radiation source. It is obvious that by this procedure the resultant neutron fluxes are many orders of magnitude lower than in-core. This is true whether the analyst uses the crystal or the beam-chopper technique for obtaining a monochromatic source of neutrons. Even in cases where U^{235} is placed in the beam to convert thermal neutrons to fission neutrons, monoenergetic fluxes seldom exceed 10^6 n/cm.²-sec.

One new development in reactor irradiations is the pulsing technique. The reactor pulse or flash is obtained by rapidly ejecting the main control rod from a core which is operating at low power. At this point, the system becomes highly supercritical, and a rapid reactor transient takes place. In the TRIGA Mark 1, for example, the power level rises within a few milliseconds to a peak of about 1000 megawatts, producing a peak total neutron flux of about 3×10^{16} n/cm.^{2}-sec. The effective duration of the pulse is about 15 milliseconds, thus providing an nvt of about 5×10^{14} n/cm.^{2}. The normal steady-state power level of this reactor is 250 kilowatts, which has a corresponding steady total neutron flux of about 10^{13} n/cm.^{2}-sec. With the control rod still ejected, the reactor restores itself to about the normal rated power level of a few hundred kilowatts. The rapid reduction in power is primarily due to the instantaneous heating of the hydrogen in the U-Zr hydride (partially hydrided) fuel to a temperature of 400°–500°C. This reduces the effective U^{235} fission cross section of the moderated neutrons. Within about 5 minutes the fuel elements have cooled sufficiently that the reactor can be reproducibly pulsed again.

Isotopic Neutron Sources.—Certain radioactive isotopes can be used as neutron sources if their decay radiation is energetic enough to induce nuclear reactions in an admixed target element. Alpha emitters and energetic gamma-ray emitters have been used for this purpose. The latter, often called photo-neutron sources, generally have small neutron yields for a given gamma-ray intensity, and must be thoroughly shielded, because of their high gamma-ray intensities. Alpha-neutron sources can be constructed from a variety of materials. As a result of the individual nuclear properties of such materials, a wide range of neutron energies can be obtained in fairly good yields. Neutron energy for a given system is a function of the alpha particle energy and of the nuclear energy levels in the target isotope. Alpha-beryllium sources, for example, produce neutrons in the 2 Mev and 6 Mev region with alpha energies of less than 2 Mev. This is easily explained by the fact that the carbon-12 formed in the reaction can be left in its ground state or in its 4.43 Mev excited state. The neutron spectrum becomes more complicated for energetic alpha-beryllium sources because carbon-12 also has a 7.65 Mev excited state. Multibody breakup processes such as

$$He^4 + Be^9 \rightarrow He^4 + Be^8 + n + 1.66 \text{ Mev}$$
$$\text{and} \quad \rightarrow 3He^4 + n + 1.572 \text{ Mev}$$

also contribute to poor energy resolution.

Characteristic of all isotopic sources is their relatively small neutron yield. Even the best combinations of alpha emitter and target element produce only 500–800 n/10^6 alphas. For radium-beryllium, the neutron yield is approximately 2×10^7 n/sec. per gram of radium. After isolation of the desired neutron energy, usable neutron fluxes of the order of 10^4 n/cm.^{2}-sec. result. The most commonly used isotopic sources are Ra^{226}-Be, Pu^{239}-Be, Po^{210}-Be, and Am^{241}-Be (all α-n sources), and Sb^{124}-Be (a photo-neutron source).

Accelerators.—Any charged particle, accelerated to the proper energy, can provide a suitable source for activation analysis. Positive ions can be used directly, *e.g.*, deuteron irradiations induce (d, n), (d, t), (d, p), (d, γ) and (d, α) reactions. Accelerated protons, tritons, alpha-particles, and He^3 ions induce analogous reactions. Also, the positive ions can be used to generate neutrons, in a suitable target, and the neutrons then used for activation of samples. An example of a suitable reaction of this type is the $Be^9(d, n)B^{10}$ reaction.

There are several reactions which proceed at energies low enough to serve as the basis for relatively inexpensive neutron sources. Commonly referred to as the "D-D" and the "D-T," these reactions of the heavy isotopes of hydrogen produce 2 + Mev and 14 + Mev neutrons, respectively. The reactions are:

$$H^2(D) + H^2(D) \rightarrow He^3 + n^1 + 3.3 \text{ Mev}$$
$$H^2(D) + H^3(T) \rightarrow He^4 + n^1 + 17.6 \text{ Mev}$$

Continuous sources for nearly monoenergetic beams of neutrons, in the energy range of several kev to 20 Mev, are available, using charged-particle reactions where the input energy is kept sufficiently low to avoid excited-state production. In this respect the reactions among the hydrogen isotopes are most useful.

Table 57-4 lists some of the more useful neutron-producing targets, as well as the reactions involved. Neutron yields from these reactions are dependent upon the individual cross sections and the charged-particle energy and beam current. A 3-Mev accelerator with beam currents in the milliampere region will produce neutron fluxes in the 10^8 n/cm.²-sec.–10^{12} n/cm.²-sec. range, depending on the reaction involved.

The energy resolution of the neutron beam is influenced by a number of factors. If the primary beam of charged particles inducing the reaction has a spread in energy, the neutrons produced will likewise share this spread. Input energy spread is a function of the characteristics of the accelerator supplying the particle beam and the degradation of the incident beam in the target. Cockcroft-Walton and Van de Graaff accelerators generally supply a more nearly monoenergetic beam than do cyclotrons. In either case, however, magnetic analysis can sharpen the beams. To minimize beam degradation, thin targets, windowless systems, and temperature control are several mechanisms which have been used successfully. Geometry effects, scattering, and background must be minimized also for good precision.

Accelerated electrons can also induce nuclear reactions, but the reaction cross sections are generally quite small. Often, however, such electrons are instead used to generate *bremsstrahlung* (continuous x-rays) in a high Z target ("converter") such as gold or tungsten. The *bremsstrahlung* can be used directly to induce such nuclear reactions as (γ, γ'), (γ, n), or (γ, p) reactions in samples, or they can be used to generate neutrons, which in turn activate samples. A widely used neutron source of this type is the $Be^9(\gamma, n)Be^8$ reaction.

APPLICATIONS IN THE PETROLEUM INDUSTRY

The petroleum and chemical industry was the first basic industry to include nuclear techniques in their elemental analysis programs. In general, accelerators are used as a source of neutrons for on-site analysis, and reactor installations are utilized for cases where extreme sensitivity is required. Some of the elements determined more or less routinely in the petroleum-petrochemical industry by nuclear activation analysis are oxygen, nitrogen, fluorine, sodium, magnesium, aluminum, silicon, phosphorus, sulfur, chlorine, potassium, calcium, titanium, vanadium, chromium, manganese, iron, cobalt, nickel, copper, zinc, arsenic, selenium, bromine, molybdenum, ruthenium, rhodium, palladium, silver, cadmium, tin, antimony, iodine, barium, tungsten, rhenium, osmium, iridium, platinum, gold, mercury, lead, thorium, and uranium. The materials analyzed vary from crude oil to cracking catalyst, but the organic product has been the principle area of interest. This matrix is particularly convenient for the activation analyst since thermal neutrons do not appreciably activate the elements carbon, hydrogen, nitrogen, or oxygen. Impurities, such as the halogens, arsenic, and most metals, lend themselves to a purely instrumental technique in such a system. Fast neutrons, on the other hand, do produce analytically useful amounts of radioisotopes from oxygen, nitrogen, silicon, and phosphorus.

Thermal Neutron Applications.—Many elements of interest to the petroleum industry have extremely large nuclear cross-sections for the neutron capture reaction. Table 57-5[56a] lists the reactions and sensitivities for these elements using a 250-kw.-TRIGA Mark I reactor. The median limits of detection for the 69 elements listed are approxi-

[56a] Buchanan, J. D., Proc. Intern. Conf. Modern Trends Activation Anal., 72, A & M College, College Station, Texas, December, 1961.

TABLE 57-4. ACCELERATOR TARGETS FOR NEUTRON PRODUCTION

Target	Reaction	E_{Th}(Mev)	E_n Range[a]	Usual Sources and Remarks
H^2	$H^2(d, n)He^3$	<0.1	2.4 Mev–6.2 Mev	D_2O (ice), D_2 (gas), Hydride; monoenergetic
H^3	$H^3(p, n)He^3$	1.02	63.9 kev–2.2 Mev	T_2(gas), Hydride; monoenergetic
H^3	$H^3(d, n)He^4$	<0.1	12.9 Mev–19.6 Mev	T_2(gas), Hydride; monoenergetic
Li^7	$Li^7(p, n)Be^7$	1.88	30 kev–1.3 Mev	LiF, Li metal; monoenergetic
Be^9	$Be^9(d, n)B^{10}$	0.35	0.5 Mev–7 Mev	High yield; polyenergetic
Be^9	$Be^9(\alpha, n)C^{12}$	<0.1	5 Mev–8 Mev	Monoenergetic
Be^9	$Be^9(\gamma, n)Be^8$	1.66	Thermal–8 Mev	Polyenergetic
C^{12}	$C^{12}(d, n)N^{13}$	0.33	3.4 kev–3 Mev	Monoenergetic
C^{13}	$C^{13}(\alpha, n)O^{16}$	<0.1	2 Mev–5 Mev	High yield; monoenergetic
B^{10}	$B^{10}(\alpha, n)N^{13}$		0.1 Mev–3 Mev	Isotopes must be separated for monoenergy
			0.15 Mev–3 Mev	Monoenergetic
Sc^{45}	$Sc^{45}(p, n)Ti^{45}$	2.9	6 kev–500 kev	Monoenergetic
V^{51}	$V^{51}(p, n)Cr^{51}$	1.57	2 kev–1.5 Mev	Stable target; monoenergetic
Cl^{37}	$Cl^{37}(p, n)A^{37}$	1.7	5 kev–1.5 Mev	Monoenergetic
Cu^{65}	$Cu^{65}(p, n)Zn^{65}$	2.2	2 kev–1 Mev	Stable target; monoenergetic

[a] From charged-particle accelerators with a 3 Mev maximum accelerating potential.

TABLE 57-5. ESTIMATED NEUTRON ACTIVATION SENSITIVITIES FOR IRRADIATIONS OF 1 HR. OR LESS IN A THERMAL NEUTRON FLUX OF $(1.8)(10^{12})$ NEUTRONS PER SQ. CM. PER SEC.

Element	Radionuclide Measured[a]	Radiochemical Beta-Ray Sensitivity (Micrograms)	Instrumental Gamma-Ray Sensitivity (Micrograms)
Ag	2.3-m Ag^{108}	0.005	0.005
	24-s Ag^{110}	—	0.0001
Al	2.3-m Al^{28}	0.1	0.01
As	27-h As^{76}	0.001	0.005
Au	2.7-d Au^{198}	0.0005	0.0005
Ba	85-m Ba^{139}	0.05	0.1
Bi	5.0-d Bi^{210}	0.5	—
Br	17.6-m Br^{80}	0.005	0.005
	36-h Br^{82}	0.005	0.01
Ca	8.8-m Ca^{49}	1.0	5
Cd	54-h Cd^{115}	0.05	0.5
Ce	32-d Ce^{141}	1	1
	32-h Ce^{143}	0.1	0.1
Cl	37-m Cl^{38}	0.01	0.1
Co	10.3-m Co^{60m}	0.005	0.1
	5.3-y Co^{60}	0.5	0.5
Cr	27-d Cr^{51}	(No β)	1
Cs	2.2-y Cs^{134}	0.5	0.5
Cu	12.8-h Cu^{64}	0.001	0.001
	5.1-m Cu^{66}	0.01	0.05
Dy	2.3-h Dy^{165}	0.000001	0.000005
Er	9.4-d Er^{169}	0.1	—
	7.5-h Er^{171}	0.001	0.001
Eu	9.3-h Eu^{152m}	0.000005	0.0005
F	11-s F^{20}	—	1
Fe	45-d Fe^{59}	50	200
Ga	14-h Ga^{72}	0.005	0.005
Gd	18-h Gd^{159}	0.01	0.05
Ge	82-m Ge^{75}	0.005	0.05
	11-h Ge^{77}	0.5	—
Hf	19-s Hf^{179m}	—	1
Hg	65-h Hg^{197}	(No β)	0.01
Ho	27-h Ho^{166}	0.0001	0.0001
I	25-m I^{128}	0.005	0.01
In	54-h In^{116m}	0.00005	0.0001
Ir	19-h Ir^{194}	0.0001	0.001
K	12.5-h K^{42}	0.05	0.5
La	40-h La^{140}	0.001	0.005
Lu	3.7-h Lu^{176}	0.00005	0.00005
	6.8-d Lu^{177}	0.0005	0.005
Mg	9.5-m Mg^{27}	0.5	0.5
Mn	2.6-h Mn^{56}	0.00005	0.00005
Mo	15-m Mo^{101}	0.1	5
	67-h Mo^{99}	0.5	0.1
Na	15-h Na^{24}	0.005	0.005
Nb	6.6-m Nb^{24m}	0.005	1
Nd	11.6-d Nd^{147}	0.1	0.1
Ni	2.6-h Ni^{65}	0.05	0.5
Os	31-h Os^{193}	0.05	—
P	14.5-d P^{32}	0.5	—
Pb	3.3-h Pb^{209}	10	—
Pd	4.8-m Pd^{109m}	—	0.05
	13.6-h Pd^{109}	0.0005	5
Pr	19-h Pr^{142}	0.0005	0.05
Pt	31-m Pt^{199}	0.05	0.1
	3.2-d Au^{199}	0.1	0.1
Rb	18.6-d Rb^{86}	0.05	5
Re	91-h Re^{186}	0.001	0.05
	17-h Re^{188}	0.0005	0.001
Rh	4.4-m Rh^{104m}	0.001	0.0005
	4.2-s Rh^{104}	—	0.01
Ru	40-d Ru^{103}	0.5	1
	4.5-h Ru^{105}	0.01	0.05
S	87-d S^{35}	10	—
	5.0-m S^{37}	5	200
Sb	2.8-d Sb^{122}	0.005	0.01
Sc	84-d Sc^{46}	0.01	0.05
Se	120-d Se^{75}	(No β)	5
Si	2.6-h Si^{31}	0.05	500
Sm	47-h Sm^{153}	0.0005	0.005
Sn	9.5-m Sn^{125m}	0.5	0.5
Sr	2.8-h Sr^{87m}	0.005	0.005
	64-d Sr^{85}	50	50
Ta	112-d Ta^{182}	0.05	0.5
Tb	72-d Tb^{160}	0.05	0.1
Te	25-m Te^{131}	0.05	0.05
	8-d I^{131}	5	1
Th	27-d Pa^{233}	0.05	0.05
Ti	5.8-m Ti^{51}	0.5	0.05
Tm	127-d Tm^{170}	0.01	0.1
U	2.3-d Np^{239}	0.005	0.005
V	3.8-m V^{52}	0.005	0.001
W	24-h W^{187}	0.001	0.005
Yb	4.2-d Yb^{175}	0.001	0.01
Zn	14-h Zn^{69m}	0.1	0.1
Zr	17-h Zr^{97}	1	1

[a] s = second; m = minute; h = hour; d = day; y = year.

mately 0.01 μg. Many of the applications, of course, do not require this large neutron flux. Guinn and Wagner[56b] have described a system for 27 common elements using the thermal neutrons produced from a 3-Mev. Van de Graff source. In this case, they used a flux 10,000 times smaller than that obtained from the TRIGA Mark I. Some of the applications they described were polymer analysis for chlorine, organic compounds for bromine, cracking catalyst for aluminum and magnesium, reforming catalyst for aluminum, platinum, and chlorine, hydrodesulfurization catalyst for molybdenum and tungsten, and sulfuric acid for sodium, arsenic, and manganese.

Fast Neutron Applications.—With few exceptions, small positive-ion accelerators employing the D-T reaction are used as a source of 14 Mev. neutrons. Oxygen determi-

[56b] Guinn, V. P., and Wagner, G. D., Anal. Chem., **32**, 317, 1960.

TABLE 57-6. DETECTION LIMITS FOR 43 ELEMENTS VIA ACTIVATION ANALYSIS WITH 14 MEV. NEUTRONS (10^9 N/CM.²-SEC. FLUX, MAX. IRRADIATION TIME OF 5 MIN.)[a]

Element	Nuclear Reaction	Product Half-life	Gamma-ray Energy, Mev.	Irradiation Time, Min.	Counting Time, Min.	Detection Limit, μg.
Aluminum	$Al^{27}(n, p)Mg^{27}$	9.45 min.	0.834	5	10	6
Antimony	$Sb^{121}(n, 2n)Sb^{120}$	16.4 min.	0.51	5	10	7
Arsenic	$As^{75}(n, p)Ge^{75m}$	48 sec.	0.139	1	2	4
Barium	$Ba^{138}(n, 2n)Ba^{137m}$	2.60 min.	0.662	5	10	1
Beryllium	$Be^9(n, \alpha)He^6$	0.82 sec.	(3.2 Mev. β^-)	0.5	0.1	110
Boron	$B^{11}(n, \alpha)Li^8$	0.84 sec.	(13 Mev. β^-)	0.5	0.1	100
Bromine	$Br^{79}(n, n')Br^{79m}$	4.8 sec.	0.20	0.1	0.2	60
Cerium	$Ce^{140}(n, 2n)Ce^{139}$	55 sec.	0.740	1	2	9
Chromium	$Cr^{52}(n, p)V^{52}$	3.74 min.	1.433	5	10	10
Cobalt	$Co^{59}(n, \alpha)Mn^{56}$	2.58 hrs.	0.845	5	10	50
Copper	$Cu^{63}(n, 2n)Cu^{62}$	9.73 min.	0.51	5	10	9
Fluorine	$F^{19}(n, p)O^{19}$	29.4 sec.	0.200	1	2	24
Gallium	$Ga^{69}(n, 2n)Ga^{68}$	1.1 hrs.	1.07	5	10	20
Germanium	$Ge(n, 2n)Ge^{75}$	48 sec.	0.139	1	2	5
Hafnium	$Hf^{180}(n, 2n)Hf^{179}$	19 sec.	0.215	1	2	80
Indium	$In^{113}(n, 2n)In^{112m}$	20.7 min.	0.155	5	10	30
Iron	$Fe^{56}(n, p)Mn^{56}$	2.58 hrs.	0.845	5	10	30
Iodine	$I^{127}(n, 2n)I^{126}$	13.3 days	0.368, 0.650	5	10	80
Lead	$Pb^{208}(n, 2n)Pb^{207}$	0.80 sec.	0.57	0.05	0.1	110
Magnesium	$Mg^{24}(n, p)Na^{24}$	14.97 hrs.	1.368, 2.754	5	10	80
Manganese	$Mn^{55}(n, \alpha)V^{52}$	3.74 min.	1.433	5	10	40
Mercury	$Hg^{200}(n, 2n)Hg^{199m}$	42 min.	0.159	5	10	20
Molybdenum	$Mo^{92}(n, 2n)Mo^{91+91m}$	15.5 min.	0.51 (β^+)	5	10	30
Nickel	$Ni^{60}(n, p)Co^{60m}$	10.47 min.	0.059	5	10	260
Nitrogen	$N^{14}(n, 2n)N^{13}$	10.47 min.	0.51 (β^+)	5	10	90
Oxygen	$O^{16}(n, p)N^{16}$	7.35 sec.	6.1	0.2	0.4	30
Palladium	$Pd^{110}(n, 2n)Pd^{109}$	4.75 min.	0.188	5	10	4
Phosphorus	$P^{31}(n, \alpha)Al^{28}$	2.27 min.	1.78	5	10	8
Platinum	$Pt^{198}(n, 2n)Pt^{197m}$	1.4 hrs.	0.337	5	10	240
Potassium	$K^{39}(n, 2n)K^{38m}$	7.7 min.	0.51 (β^+)	5	10	90
Rubidium	$Rb^{85}(n, 2n)Rb^{84m}$	23 min.	0.239	5	10	1
Scandium	$Sc^{45}(n, 2n)Sc^{44}$	3.92 hrs.	0.51 (β^+)	5	10	20
Selenium	$Se^{78}(n, 2n)Se^{77m}$	17.5 sec.	0.162	1	2	20
Silicon	$Si^{28}(n, p)Al^{28}$	2.3 min.	1.78	5	10	2
Sodium	$Na^{23}(n, p)Ne^{23}$	40.2 sec.	0.439	1	2	20
Strontium	$Sr^{88}(n, 2n)S^{87m}$	2.80 hrs.	0.388	5	10	1
Tantalum	$Ta^{181}(n, 2n)Ta^{180m}$	8.15 hrs.	0.093	5	10	20
Tellurium	$Te^{130}(n, 2n)Te^{129}$	1.2 hrs.	0.475	5	10	60
Tungsten	$W^{186}(n, 2n)W^{185m}$	1.62 min.	0.130, 0.165	5	10	20
Titanium	$Ti^{46}(n, 2n)Ti^{45}$	3.09 hrs.	0.51 (β^+)	5	10	90
Vanadium	$V^{51}(n, p)Ti^{51}$	5.79 min.	0.323	5	10	7
Zinc	$Zn^{64}(n, 2n)Zn^{63}$	38.3 min.	0.51 (β^+)	5	10	30
Zirconium	$Zr^{90}(n, 2n)Zr^{89}$	4.4 min.	0.588	5	10	4

[a] Based on the assumption that the minimum detectable number of photopeak counts is 100.

nations by 14 Mev. neutrons are extremely simple to perform, and sensitivity of 10 μg. is available with moderate equipment. Oxygen determinations, however, are not the only areas of application for these sources. Problems such as barium in lubricating oils and greases, chlorine in polymers, and silicon in feedstock have been handled by fast neutron techniques. Table 57-6 lists the reactions and sensitivities for 43 of the common elements.

X-RAY EMISSION SPECTROMETRY

By S. A. Bartkiewicz

Esso Research Laboratories
Humble Oil & Refining Co.
Baton Rouge, Louisiana

INTRODUCTION

The increasing complexity and diversification of the petroleum industry requires elemental analyses in a wide variety of sample types. In recent years, the rapid development of x-ray emission spectrometry and, to a lesser extent, x-ray absorption has provided many excellent procedures for a large number of these determinations. With the present available equipment one can readily analyze specimens for almost any element of atomic number 11 and greater. More recent developments promise to extend this number down to and including boron. In addition to being nondestructive these methods offer the advantages of speed, accuracy, and sensitivity. With careful use, errors of 0.5 percent or less for element concentrations of 1 percent or higher can be routinely attained. Absolute limits of detection of 100 p.p.m. and lower have been reported in many applications. Samples can be readily handled either as liquids, solids, or powders; in many instances with little or no processing. Since each element has its own unique x-ray spectrum, x-ray emission can be used for qualitative as well as quantitative analysis.

EQUIPMENT

Standard x-ray equipment can be used for emission as well as x-ray absorption analysis. Location of the sample with reference to the x-ray beam and crystal analyzer is the only requirement for either method as shown in Fig. 57-7.

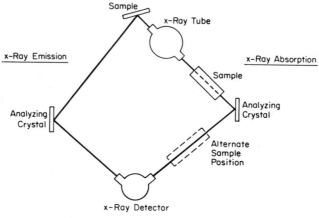

Fig. 57-7.   X-ray Analysis.

1539

QUALITATIVE ANALYSIS

For the qualitative analysis of a sample, a strip chart recording is made over the spectral range of interest. The 2-theta positions of the peak intensities are recorded and identified by reference to published tables.[57,58]

QUANTITATIVE ANALYSIS

SULFUR IN PETROLEUM HYDROCARBONS

Scope.—This is a rapid and accurate method for the direct determination of 0.0005 to 10.0 wt. percent sulfur in petroleum products ranging from gasolines through crude oil. Trace amounts of impurities, less than 1.5 wt. percent, cause negligible interference.[59] Carbon-hydrogen ratio has no significant effect through most of the range. Analysis time is less than 0.1 hour per sample.

Apparatus.—The instrumentation used consisted of an x-ray spectrograph equipped with a flow proportional counter, and a tungsten target x-ray tube. The diffracting crystal was a plane, single crystal of sodium chloride. The optical path was in a helium atmosphere.

Reagents and Materials. **Phenyl Sulfide.**—Highest purity, available from Eastman Kodak Co.

Mineral Oil.—Sulfur free.

Helium.

P-10 Gas.—90% argon—10% methane.

Calibration.—A series of standards containing the following sulfur concentrations is prepared from sulfur free mineral oil and phenyl sulfide:

	% S	Weight % S		% S	
1.	10.00	7.	0.500	13.	0.010
2.	7.50	8.	0.250	14.	0.0075
3.	5.00	9.	0.100	15.	0.0050
4.	2.50	10.	0.075	16.	0.0025
5.	1.00	11.	0.050	17.	0.0010
6.	0.750	12.	0.025	18.	0.0005

Successive standards are prepared by making 10-fold dilutions, with mineral oil, of each preceding group of four standards.

All x-ray measurements on the standards are made relative to a comparison standard of sulfur. A petroleum oil with only its natural sulfur is used for this purpose. Measurements are made as outlined below in "Summary of Routine Procedure." A family of calibration curves is prepared by plotting the counting rate ratio (R) *vs.* sulfur concentration where:

$$R = \frac{I_s}{I_c}$$

I_s = counting rate of sample
I_c = counting rate of comparison standard

[57] Pickett, H. W., X-Ray Wavelengths for Spectrometer, General Electric Co., Milwaukee, 1959.
[58] Powers, M. C., X-Ray Fluorescent Spectrometer Conversion Tables, Philips Electronic Instruments, Mount Vernon, New York, 1960.
[59] Yao, T. C., and Porsche, F. W., Anal. Chem., **31**, 2010, 1959.

For convenience and accuracy in reading the graphs, it is desirable to draw the curves in several concentration ranges, *e.g.*,

0–100 p.p.m.
0–0.1%
0–1%
0–10%

Summary of Routine Procedure.—Set up instrument conditions as follows:

x-ray tube voltage............	50kv.
x-ray tube current............	45 ma.
Analyzing crystal............	NaCl
Goniometer setting..........	144.70 (2θ)
Optical path[60]...............	Helium (gas flow rate 1-CFH)
x-ray detector..............	Flow proportional counter (P-10 gas flow rate, 1-CFH)
Detector voltage............	1600v.
Pulse height analyzer[61]	
Analytical line..............	S Kα = 5.37 A, 2θ = 144.7
Fixed count time............	2 min.

Pour a measured portion of sample into a cell. Place sample cell into x-ray sample chamber and record intensity of unknown. Repeat with comparison standard. Calculate intensity ratio (R) and determine sulfur concentration from plotted analytical curves.[62]

DETERMINATION OF HALOGENS IN PETROLEUM HYDROCARBONS

The procedure for the determination of sulfur in hydrocarbons, described above, can be extended to include chlorine, and with slight modification bromine and iodine. For bromine and iodine, helium would no longer be necessary. It would also be desirable to use a lithium fluoride analyzing crystal in place of sodium chloride and a scintillation detector in place of the flow proportional counter. Interferences for chlorine would be the same as for sulfur while being generally less pronounced for bromine and iodine.

DETERMINATION OF COBALT, ZINC AND IRON IN ORGANIC MATRICES[63]

Scope.—This is a rapid and accurate method for the direct determination of mixtures of cobalt, zinc, and iron in various organic matrices. Copper, as the hydrocarbon soluble octoate or naphthenate, is used as an internal standard to compensate for matrix absorp-

[60] Helium flow through the sample chamber is adjusted to an optimum rate beyond which no further increase in count rate is obtained. In some instruments it may be desirable to have a more rapid rate for a short period immediately after inserting the sample to purge the chamber of air introduced with the sample.

[61] A sufficient number of counts should be taken to satisfy the statistical counting accuracy desired. However, long exposures of the sample to the x-ray beam should be avoided. Prolonged heating of the sample for periods of time greater than 2–3 minutes can result in excessive expansion of the sample, loss of volatile compounds, and the decomposition of some unstable sulfur compounds.

[62] In the low sulfur range (5 to 100 p.p.m.), it becomes necessary to give more consideration to the matrix material of the sample. A major departure in C-H ratio from that of the standards will, in some cases, give a slight change in background which will become significant at these low concentrations. At higher levels the effect becomes negligible and all counts are used including background. Where an excess of interfering materials is present, the effect can be tempered by careful dilution of the sample with sulfur free white oil.

[63] Bartkiewicz, S. A., Hammatt, E. A., Anal. Chem., **36**, 833–836, 1964.

tion effects as well as for instrumental variations. Limit of detection, taken as 3 sigmas above background,[64] is approximately 10 p.p.m. for cobalt, and 5 p.p.m. for zinc and for iron.

Apparatus.—Instrumentation consists of an x-ray spectrometer equipped with a scintillation counter and a tungsten target x-ray tube. The diffracting crystal is a flat, single crystal of lithium fluoride.

Reagents and Materials.—Standard stock solutions of cobalt, zinc, iron, and copper are prepared by dissolving known weights of cobalt (6.0 percent), zinc (8.0 percent), iron (6.0 percent) and copper (6.0 percent) octoates available from the Nuodex Products Co. in Reagent Grade 2-ethyl-1-hexanol. Dilutions are made as required with 2-ethyl-1-hexanol to give the various concentration levels of interest.

Summary of Routine Procedure.—Instrumental conditions are set up as follows:

x-ray tube voltage...........................	45 kv.
x-ray tube current...........................	40 ma.
Analyzing crystal...........................	LiF
x-ray detector.............................	Scintillation
Pulse height analyzer[65]	
Analytical lines.............	Fe Kα = 1.941 A, 2θ = 57.52
	Co Kα = 1.79 A, 2θ = 52.79
	Zn Kα = 1.44 A, 2θ = 41.80
Internal Standard..........	Cu Kα = 1.541 A, 2θ = 45.03
Integration Time...........................	100 sec.

A series of calibration standards is prepared to contain 0–1.00 wt. percent cobalt, zinc, and iron, respectively. The internal standard solution is made to contain 0.200 wt. percent copper. Intensity measurements are made as described below. A family of calibration curves is prepared by plotting the ratio of intensity of metal to intensity of internal standard versus metal concentration. For convenience and accuracy in reading the graphs, it is desirable to draw the curves in several concentration ranges; *e.g.*, 0–100 p.p.m., 0–0.1 wt. percent, and 0–1.0 wt. percent.

Samples are prepared for analysis by pipetting 5 ml. of internal standard into a 10-ml. volumetric flask, diluting to volume with sample and mixing. A portion of the mixture is poured, to mark, into a cell. The cell is inserted into the x-ray spectrometer. The goniometer is set respectively for each element of interest and the intensities in counts per second recorded. The ratios of intensity of unknown metal concentrations to intensity of copper internal standard are calculated and unknown concentration taken from plotted analytical curves.

DETERMINATION OF LEAD IN GASOLINE[66]

The analysis of lead in gasoline is carried out directly on the sample down to a level of less than 1-milliliter of tetraethyl lead per gallon. The instrument is standardized versus an external standard of lead bromide dissolved in a lucite block. A scintillation detector is used in conjunction with a lithium fluoride analyzing crystal and tungsten target x-ray tube. Analytical line is the Lα line of lead appearing at 1.175 A. Calibration standards are prepared from tetraethyl lead and gasoline. Absorption interferences will

[64] Birks, L. S., X-ray Spectrochemical Analysis, Interscience Publishers, Inc., New York, 1959.
[65] Optimum determined for each instrument.
[66] Lamb, F. W., Niebylski, L. M., Kiefer, E. W., Anal. Chem., **27**, 129–132, 1955.

result from variation in sulfur, halogen, and metals concentration[67] as well as from changes in carbon to hydrogen ratio.

DETERMINATION OF TRACE AMOUNTS OF IRON, NICKEL, AND VANADIUM ON CATALYSTS[68]

Scope.—This method is used for the determination of iron, nickel, and vanadium on cracking catalysts or similar type materials. Range of analysis is from less than 0.002 to 1.0 weight percent of each metal, respectively. Expected precision is as follows:

Element	Range, Wt. Percent	Precision, 2σ
Iron	0.1–1.0	3% (relative)
Nickel	0.002–0.10	0.002
Vanadium	0.002–0.10	0.002

Apparatus.—An x-ray spectrograph equipped with a scintillation detector, lithium fluoride analyzing crystal, and tungsten target tube is used.

Calibration.—Standard samples are prepared by impregnating fresh catalyst with iron, nickel, and vanadium from aqueous solutions of nitrates. The excess water is boiled off and the samples ignited in a furnace at 1000°F. Standards are run as described under summary of routine procedure. Calibration curves are prepared by plotting net intensity in counts per second versus concentration of metal.

Summary of Routine Procedure.—Set up instrument conditions as follows:

x-ray tube voltage.............	35 kv.
x-ray tube current............	20 ma.
Goniometer setting:	
Nickel....................	48.50, °2θ
Iron.....................	57.25, °2θ
Background...............	54.00, °2θ
Vanadium................	76.70, °2θ
Background...............	74.00, °2θ
Fixed count	

Standardize instrument for daily operation *vs.* a standard sample.

Grind catalyst samples to less than 200 mesh. Fill sample holder to overflowing and tap gently to pack. Level surface with spatula. Place sample in fluorescence unit and record intensities, subtract background and calculate concentrations from calibration curves.

DETERMINATION OF BARIUM, CALCIUM AND ZINC IN NEW AND USED OILS[69]

Scope.—This method has been developed for the determination of barium, calcium, and zinc in lubricating oils and can be used as well for additives. The oils can be analyzed directly without time-consuming pretreatments. Limits of detection are 1 p.p.m. for barium, calcium, and zinc.

Instrumental Conditions.—Set conditions for barium and zinc as follows:

[67] Yao, T. C., and Porsche, F. W., Anal. Chem., **31,** 2010, 1959.
[68] Dyroff, G. V., and Skiba, P., Anal. Chem., **26,** 1774, 1954.
[69] Davis, E. N., and Van Nordstrand, R. A., Anal. Chem., **26,** 973, 1954.

Excitation: W, 50 Kv., 20 ma.
Crystal: LiF
Detectors: Scintillation
Fixed time: 64 sec.
Ba Lβ line: 2.56 7 A; 2θ, 79.18°
Background: 2θ, 82.00°
Zn Kα: 1.437 A; 2θ, 41.25°

Set conditions for calcium:

Excitation: W, 50 Kv., 20 ma.
Crystal: Pentaerythrite
Beam path: Helium
Detector: Flow proportional
Fixed time: 64 sec.
Ca Kα line: 3.360 A; 2θ, 45.20°
Background: 2θ, 47.00°

Calibration.—Calibration standards are prepared from the metal naphthenates and white oil. Net intensities of metals are plotted as function of concentration. Barium interferes with the determination zinc. Interference is corrected for by preparing calibration curves based on samples containing known concentrations of the interfering element or elements.

Summary of Routine Analysis.—Pour a measured amount of sample into the holder and place in the fluorescence unit. Record line and background intensities. Calculate net intensity and determine metal concentration from prepared analytical curves.

COMBINATION TECHNIQUES AS APPLIED TO COMPLEX HYDROCARBON SYSTEMS

By William L. Senn, Jr.

Esso Research Laboratories
Baton Rouge, Louisiana

and

James W. Robinson

Louisiana State University
Baton Rouge, Louisiana

During recent years great progress has been made in determining the composition of complex hydrocarbon systems. This progress can be primarily attributed to advances made in the fields of gas chromatography, infrared spectrometry, nuclear magnetic resonance, and mass spectrometry. Parallel with these advances in the individual fields, there has been a growing realization of the potential obtainable by combination of these techniques. The purpose of this chapter is to point out how these methods can be most efficiently combined. For specific information on individual techniques the reader is referred to the specialized sections.

The problem normally encountered in organic composition analyses is usually to isolate, identify, and determine a particular component present in a mixture. In the case of complex hydrocarbon mixtures, the possibility of specific compound identification becomes less likely as the number of components in the mixture is increased. Hence, hydrocarbon analyses in the range of C_8 and higher, where the number of isomers generally preclude specific compound identification, require a different means of characterization. One means, which has proven quite useful, is the specification of quantitative amounts of certain atomic groups. The combination of these atomic groupings can be used to describe an "average molecule."

The definition of complex hydrocarbon systems, insofar as this chapter is concerned, is taken to be mixtures of saturates, olefins, and aromatics. If this mixture possesses a rather wide boiling range, it is first fractionated by distillation. Distillation techniques have been reported in detail in many other sources and will not be discussed in this chapter. The distillation cuts are further fractionated by chromatographic means, normally displacement chromatography using silica gel,[70,71] although other techniques are sometimes employed.[72,73,74,75] The results of these consecutive separations are narrow boiling range saturate, olefin and aromatic fractions. At this point the combination of techniques for the analysis of these fractions will be considered.

[70] FIA Method, ASTM Method D1319.
[71] Kearns, G. L., Maranowski, N. C., and Crable, G. F., Anal. Chem., **31**, 1646, 1959.
[72] Snyder, L. R., Anal. Chem., **33**, 1527, 1961.
[73] Snyder, L. R., Anal. Chem., **33**, 1535, 1961.
[74] Snyder, L. R., Anal. Chem., **33**, 1538, 1961.
[75] Snyder, L. R., Anal. Chem., **34**, 771, 1962.

CHARACTERIZATION OF SATURATES

The saturate fraction will contain normal paraffins, isoparaffins, and cycloparaffins. A diagram of techniques used and information obtained is shown in Fig. 57-8. Further fractionation of the saturates is possible through the use of molecular sieves, resulting in normal paraffin and iso- plus cycloparaffin fractions.[76] The normal paraffin fraction may be analyzed by gas chromatography. The iso- plus cycloparaffin fraction may be analyzed by mass spectrometry. This approach yields a breakdown of normal, iso-, cyclo-, and dicycloparaffins. In some cases this approach is not necessary, and the breakdown can be obtained by mass spectrometric examination of the total saturate fraction.

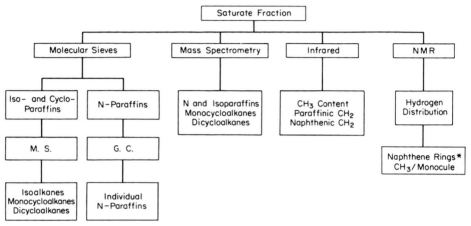

*Requires Knowledge of Total Hydrogen Content and Average Molecular Weight.

FIG. 57-8.

In many cases characterization data may be obtained from infrared (IR) and nuclear magnetic resonance spectrometry (NMR). Infrared examination of hydrocarbon systems is a study of the various types of carbon-hydrogen and carbon-carbon vibration modes. In the case of saturate fractions it is simply a study of methyl and methylene groups and their environment. Infrared analyses have been concerned with determination of methyl, paraffinic methylene, naphthenic methylene contents. One of the most successful approaches has utilized measurements of integrated absorptivities.[77] In this approach the methyl content is determined using the 1380 cm.$^{-1}$ C—H symmetrical bending vibration. The paraffinic methylene content is determined using the 720 cm.$^{-1}$ C—H rocking vibration. Next the entire absorption between approximately 1410 cm.$^{-1}$ and 1510 cm.$^{-1}$ is integrated. The contributions from the asymmetrical methyl C—H bending vibration and the C—H bending vibrations for linear methylene chains are deducted and the naphthenic methylene groups determined by difference.

The NMR characterization of saturates[78,79] requires a knowledge of the total hydrogen

[76] Norris, M. S., and O'Connor, J. G., Anal. Chem., **31,** 275, 1959.

[77] Luther, H., and Oelert, H. H., Z. Anal. Chem., **183,** 161, 1961.

[78] Williams, R. B., ASTM Special Technical Publication No. 224, p. 168, 1958.

[79] Chamberlain, N. F., "Nuclear Magnetic Resonance and Electron Paramagnetic Resonance," in Kolthoff and Elving, Eds., Treatise on Analytical Chemistry, Interscience Publishers, New York, 1964, Part 1, Vol. 4, Chap. 39.

content and an average molecular weight for the fraction. The number of naphthene rings may be calculated from the weight fraction of total hydrogen and the molecular weight. The fraction of hydrogen present in methyl groups may be used to calculate the average number of methyl groups per molecule.

CHARACTERIZATION OF OLEFINIC FRACTIONS

Compound types normally encountered in olefinic fractions are n-monoolefins, iso-monoolefins, cyclomonoolefins, nonconjugated diolefins and conjugated diolefins. A diagram of techniques used and information obtained is shown in Fig. 57-9. Determination

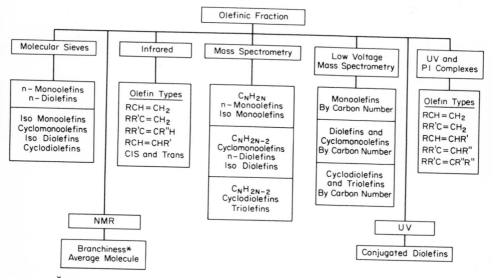

*Requires Knowledge of Total Hydrogen Content, Bromine Number and Molecular Weight.

FIG. 57-9.

of n-monoolefin and n-diolefin content can be accomplished through the use of molecular sieves.[80,81] The molecular sieves are acidic in nature and promote the isomerization of the adsorbed species. Hence the normal monoolefins and diolefins are not recoverable.

Mass spectrometry also yields a compound type analysis. Here the breakdown is made according to the series C_nH_{2n} (monoolefins), C_nH_{2n-2} (cyclomonoolefins and diolefins) and C_nH_{2n-4} (cyclodiolefins and triolefins). The determination of the actual carbon number distribution becomes quite difficult if wide boiling range cuts are used. This is a result of complications caused by fragments of higher molecular weight olefins interfering with lower molecular weight olefins. One means of minimizing this is the use of low voltage mass spectrometry. In this technique the energy of the bombarding electrons is reduced such that the parent mass becomes one of the largest peaks in the spectrum, hence minimizing fragmentation. This, of course, results in much lower total ionization and special techniques are required in its use. Using this approach we can obtain our compound type distribution by carbon number.

[80] O'Connor, J. G., and Norris, M. S., Anal. Chem., **32**, 701, 1960.
[81] Nelson, K. H., Grimes, M. D., and Heinrich, B. J., Anal. Chem., **29**, 1026, 1957.

In many cases an olefin type distribution is desired. The olefin type is designated by the degree of substitution on the double bond. The types and their classification are:

$$R_1\text{—}CH\text{=}CH_2 \qquad \text{Type I}$$
$$R_1\text{—}CH\text{=}CH\text{—}R_2 \qquad \text{Type II-}cis \text{ and -}trans$$
$$R_1R_2C\text{=}CH_2 \qquad \text{Type III}$$
$$R_1R_2C\text{=}CHR_3 \qquad \text{Type IV}$$
$$R_1R_2C\text{=}CR_3R_4 \qquad \text{Type V}$$

The determination of olefin types by infrared spectrometry[82,83] utilizes the characteristic C—H out-of-plane bending mode for those hydrogens substituted on the double bond. As a result Type V olefins are not directly determinable by infrared techniques. The Type I olefins absorb at 990 and 810 cm.[-1], Type II-trans absorption occurs at 980–965 cm.[-1], Type III olefins absorb at 890 cm.[-1], and Types IV and II-cis are more variable absorbing in the range 840–810 and 725–675 cm.[-1] respectively. The analysis is best run by calibrating with standard compounds and establishing a matrix calculation.

Another approach to olefin type analyses is the pi complexation ultraviolet (UV) technique.[84] This approach is based on the fact that the ability of the double bond to donate electrons in the formation of molecular complexes depends upon the degree of substitution. Since the strength of the complexes formed and hence the UV absorption maxima are different, it is possible to set up a UV olefin type procedure. In this case the complexing agent used is iodine. The olefin type and the wavelength of absorption maxima are as follows:

Type	λ max., $m\mu$
$RCH\text{=}CH_2$	275
$R_2C\text{=}CH_2$	290–295
cis $RCH\text{=}CHR$	295–300
trans $RCH\text{=}CHR$	295–300
$R_2C\text{=}CHR$	317
$R_2C\text{=}CR_2$	337

In general the absorptivity increases with increasing substitution on the double bond. This technique is most applicable to Types IV and V olefins. As such it complements the infrared type analysis. Both techniques incorporated into a common calculation matrix have been used for olefin type analyses.

The study of olefinic fractions by NMR yields a measurement of branchiness and the structure of the average molecule.[79] The hydrogen types present that can be distinguished by NMR are: (a) olefinic, (b) methylene and methine alpha to double-bonded carbon, (c) methyl alpha to double-bonded carbon, (d) methyl and methine beta and farther from the double-bonded carbon, and (e) methyl beta and farther from the double-bonded carbon. The quantitative breakdown of these hydrogen types combined with total hydrogen content, bromine number, and molecular weight is used to characterize the olefinic fraction. Terminal and nonterminal olefinic hydrogens are often distinguishable although quantitative analysis is not always possible due to overlap in spin multiplet patterns.

The determination of conjugated diolefins is normally based on UV absorption. In a silica gel separation there is the possibility of aromatics contamination of the diolefin fraction. Simple mononuclear aromatics have little effect on this analysis. Condensed ring systems can cause serious errors in this analysis and precautions for their exclusion

[82] Anderson, J. A., Jr., and Seyfried, W. D., Anal. Chem., **20**, 998, 1948.
[83] Saier, E. L., Pozefsky, A., and Coggeshall, N. D., Anal. Chem., **26**, 1258, 1954.
[84] Long, D. R., and Neuzil, R. W., Anal. Chem., **27**, 1110, 1955.

from higher boiling diolefin cuts must be taken. Nonconjugated diolefins behave as monoolefins and are included in any measurements made specifically for monoolefins.

CHARACTERIZATION OF AROMATIC FRACTIONS

The techniques applied and information obtained are shown diagrammatically in Fig. 57-10. The aromatics fractions are most advantageously studied by mass spectro-

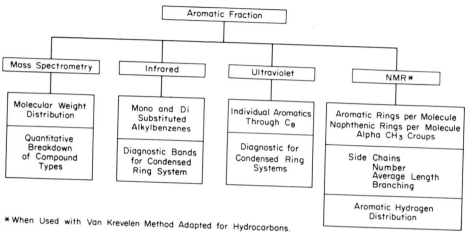

*When Used with Van Krevelen Method Adapted for Hydrocarbons.

FIG. 57-10.

metric techniques. Mass spectrometric analysis yields a molecular weight distribution and a quantitative breakdown of compound types. Normally, aromatic molecules give a parent mass of appreciable intensity. Not only does this aid in analyses but it also decreases interferences.

The infrared study of aromatics fractions[85] utilizes primarily the region of 1000 to 400 cm.$^{-1}$ where absorption due to out-of-plane bending vibrations of aromatic C—H bonds occur. The frequencies of these bonds are characteristic of the number and position of the remaining C—H bonds. Table 57-7 presents a summary.

TABLE 57-7.   CHARACTERISTIC LOW FREQUENCY IR BANDS
OF AROMATIC COMPOUNDS

Structure	Cm.$^{-1}$
1,2-Disubstituted	760–740
1,2,3-Trisubstituted	780–760
1,2,3,4-Tetrasubstituted	810–800
1,2,4,5-Tetrasubstituted	870–855
Pentasubstituted	870

When the fraction is basically condensed ring aromatics it is convenient to develop cor-

[85] Jones, R. Norman, and Sandorfy, Camille, "The Application of Infrared and Raman Spectrometry to the Elucidation of Molecular Structure," in Technique of Organic Chemistry Vol. IX, page 388, A. Weissberger, Ed., Interscience Publishers, New York, 1956.

relations relating to the number of occupied faces rather than carbon atoms.[86] The faces are lettered according to normal nomenclature.[87]

TABLE 57-8. CHARACTERISTIC LOW FREQUENCY IR BANDS
FOR CONDENSED RING AROMATIC COMPOUNDS

Substituted Faces	Cm.$^{-1}$
a	755–720
ab	∼770
ac	815–805
abc	845–830
ad	890–880
abd	∼880

In addition to these classifications, there are some absorption bands between 400 and 500 cm.$^{-1}$ that are characteristic only of linear condensation products such as anthracene, tetracene, pentacene, etc.

Ultraviolet absorption has been applied most productively in the lower molecular weight ranges. When the suitable conditions are present, the individual aromatics through C$_8$ may be analyzed. In the condensed ring classes there are some bands of diagnostic value; however, band overlap from different types precludes their use for quantitative purposes.

Nuclear magnetic resonance hydrogen distribution is used in conjunction with density, elemental analysis, and molecular weight to characterize aromatic fractions. The method developed by Williams and Chamberlain[88] utilizes an adapted Van Krevelen method to determine the number of aromatic rings and the number of naphthene rings per "average molecule." The nuclear magnetic resonance data are then used as a basis for calculating the number of methyl groups on aromatic rings and the number, average length, and amount of branching on the side chains. Under favorable cases the distribution of aromatic ring hydrogens between condensed and noncondensed rings can be determined.

In general a good approach to the analysis of an aromatic fraction is to ascertain the possible aromatics present from mass spectrometry considerations and reduce the possibilities by use of infrared or NMR techniques.

CHROMATOGRAPHIC SEPARATION TECHNIQUES

The analysis of complex mixtures of organic compounds may be resolved by: (a) separation into components by chromatography, and (b) identification of components by other techniques. Two types of mixtures are encountered. First, those whose boiling ranges are low enough that they may be separated by gas chromatography. Using programmed temperature gas chromatography, mixtures which elute below 300°C. can be separated this way. Secondly, higher boiling mixtures may be separated by column chromatography. The molecular types (*e.g.*, acids, paraffins, etc.) of each component are identified by infrared, ultraviolet, nuclear magnetic resonance, or other means. The molecular weight range can be derived from differential thermal analysis. Procedural details are given on p. 1553.

[86] Senn, W. L., Jr., unpublished work.
[87] Patterson, A. M., Capell, L. T., Walker, D. F., The Ring Index, American Chemical Society.
[88] Williams, R. B., and Chamberlain, N. F., Sixth World Petroleum Congress, Section V, Paper 17, 1963.

SEPARATION BY GAS CHROMATOGRAPHY

By far the most elegant technique utilizes a time-of-flight mass spectrograph attached to the exit of a programmed temperature gas chromatograph. The gas chromatograph trace supplies quantitative information and the mass spectrograph is frequently sufficient to provide qualitative data. Failing this combination, trapping procedures must be used.

Equipment. Program Temperature Gas Chromatogram.—A nondestructive detector (*e.g.*, thermal conductivity) column must be used. The exit from the column is fitted with a syringe-needle male joint. It must be heated to about 300°C. to prevent sample drop out. This is achieved by winding with nichrome wire. The current and therefore the temperature is controlled with a rheostat.

Fraction Trap.—Centrifuge tubes (10-ml. capacity) are satisfactory. These are fitted with a rubber cap through which pass two syringe needles. The first dips to the bottom of the solvent, the second is an escape for the scrubbed gas. A convenient quantity (5 ml.) of trapping solvent is put into the tube and glass beads added. These increase contact between the emerging gas fraction and the solvent. The solvent should be chosen so that it is efficient in trapping the G.C. fraction. A high solubility usually insures this. It should also be a suitable solvent for the procedure used in the identification step (*e.g.*, carbon tetrachloride for NMR, etc.). A diagram of the equipment is shown in Fig. 57-11.

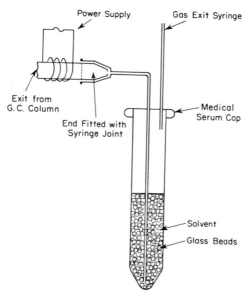

Fig. 57-11. Diagram of Equipment.

Procedure.—A gas chromatogram of the sample is obtained. For many samples the following conditions are satisfactory.

Substrate....................	Silica gel or carbo-wax
Length.....................	12 feet by $\frac{1}{4}$ inch
Carrier gas.................	Helium
Flow rate...................	90 ml./min.

Initial temperature . . . . 80°
Rate of heating . . . . 7.9°C./min.
Cut-off temperature . . . . 300°C.
Block temperature . . . . 350°C.
Sample size . . . . 50 μl.

Based on the results of the chromatogram, adjustments may be made to these conditions for each sample. When satisfactory conditions are decided upon, a final gas chromatogram is taken. The *emergence temperature* rather than the retention time of each pertinent peak should be noted; also the temperature immediately before and after the peak at which nothing is emerging from the column. An example is shown in Fig. 57-12.

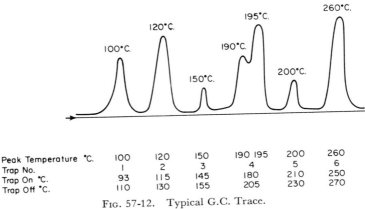

Peak Temperature °C.	100	120	150	190 195	200	260
Trap No.	1	2	3	4	5	6
Trap On °C.	93	115	145	180	210	250
Trap Off °C.	110	130	155	205	230	270

FIG. 57-12. Typical G.C. Trace.

A set of traps is prepared, one for each fraction to be trapped. Each trap (and solvent) is cooled in ice water. For volatile materials, the temperature of the trap may be further reduced by using a dry ice and glycerol bath.

The traps should be carefully numbered and matched to the chromatogram. Further, the temperature at which each trap will be put on and taken off the column exit should also be predetermined from the G.C. traces. Allowance should be made for the difference in time between the detection of the component and its emergence from the G.C. column.

When the equipment is ready, the sample is loaded onto the G.C. column and the components trapped in the corresponding traps. If necessary, higher concentrations of each component may be obtained by repeating the procedure several times, the same trap being used for the same component each time.

After trapping, each component may now be identified by a suitable technique such as infrared, nuclear magnetic resonance, ultraviolet, mass spectrometry, etc. These identifications may be used for subsequent repetitive G.C. analysis of the same sample type.

SEPARATION BY COLUMN CHROMATOGRAPHY

The analysis of residual and other high molecular weight material does not lend itself to gas chromatography. These mixtures are usually too complex for identification of each individual component. However, separation into molecular types can be achieved by column chromatography. An indication of the molecular weight range of each group can then be attained by differential thermal gravimetry.

Equipment. **Chromatographic Column.** *Size.*—24 in. × 1 in. i.d.

Substrate.—Silica gel, Davison grade 923; 200 mesh pretreated at 700°C. for 16 hours.

Column Preparation.—A slurry is made by mixing the silica and heptane. The slurry is poured into a suitable glass tube. Air bubbles are eliminated by vibrating, preferably with a supersonic vibrator. Since the complete treatment may take several days, the glass column should be fitted with a stopcock on the top and the bottom. At all times the silica should be submerged in the solvent.

Procedure.—A weighed sample is mounted on the column. The column is then washed with heptane until no further components of the sample are eluted. The eluate is collected and the heptane evaporated off slowly. The residue is weighed and the percentage calculated.

After washing with heptane, the eluant is changed and a second fraction eluted from the sample. The process is repeated with successive solvents. Suggested solvents and possible eluates are listed below.

Solvent	*Eluate*
Heptane	Paraffins, olefins
Benzene	Esters, aromatics
Ether	Alcohols—esters
Chloroform	Unsaturated ester
Methanol	High molecular weight ester
Formic acid	Acids

DIFFERENTIAL THERMAL ANALYSIS (DTA)

After boiling off the solvent, each fraction is analyzed by DTA up to 600°C. Quantitative interpretation by carbon number is made by: (i) correlating the temperature at which heat was absorbed with the boiling point of the components; and (ii) correlating the amount of heat absorbed with the quantity of material boiling at that temperature. Results based on these assumptions are subject to serious error and allowance should be made. The errors include: (a) recorded temperatures may be inaccurate because DTA is equivalent to a single plate distillation; (b) azeotroping between components would cause serious errors; and (c) the heat absorbed may be due to decomposition, phase changes, or boiling of low molecular weight components. If possible compensation should be made for these sources of error.

GAS CHROMATOGRAPHY

By W. C. Jones, Jr.

Baytown Research and Development Division
Esso Research and Engineering Co.
Baytown, Texas

Analytical laboratories in petroleum refineries and petrochemical plants perhaps have benefited more than any others from gas chromatography. Any mixture that can be vaporized without decomposition can be separated rapidly by gas chromatography into its components or very narrow fractions. The rapid increase in applications of the gas chromatographic technique is borne out by the publication rate. Approximately 10,000 publications on the theory and applications of gas chromatography had accumulated by the end of 1964, and the current rate is about 2000 annually.

Applications of Gas Chromatography in Petroleum Refining.—A petroleum refinery processes by distillation the bulk of its crude oil into gross fractions which might be termed as gases, light naphthas, gasoline base stocks, kerosene and jet fuels, heating oil and diesel fuels, gas oils, lubricating oils or fuel oil, and nondistillable residue or asphalt. In a modern, large refinery some of these materials are further transformed by superfractionation or with catalysts or chemicals, in processes such as catalytic cracking, catalytic hydrogenation, isomerization, alkylation, and polymerization. The more valuable products of these reforming processes include high octane motor fuel, aviation fuel, high quality lubricants, and the vast array of specialties and petrochemicals now on the market.

Gas chromatography may be applied to everything that comes out of petroleum refining except lube oil, asphalts, and high molecular weight polymers. These exceptions are materials which are not distillable at atmospheric pressure. Refinery samples submitted for GC analysis usually fall in the classifications of: gases (C_1–C_4), light naptha (C_5–C_7), gasoline blend stocks (C_5–C_{12}), kerosene or jet fuel (C_{12}–C_{20}), solvents, specialties, and petrochemicals. The actual labels on a sample are more likely to designate the sample as a stream or product from a particular unit, for example, "Pipe Still Side Stream," "Catalytic Cracking Feed," "Finished Alkylate," "Deasphalted Oil," and the like. Since each refinery has its own language for labeling samples it is necessary for the analyst to determine the approximate boiling range of a new sample, the type of compounds, and the customer's requirements before attempting an analysis.

Description of a Gas Chromatograph.—A stream of inert gas passes through one side of a thermal conductivity cell, picks up a vaporized sample, and flows through a tube packed with an inert support, such as firebrick, on which is coated a solvent, usually much higher boiling than the mixture to be separated. In the case of open tube columns the inner walls of the tube serve as a support for the solvent. As the gas mixture flows through the column the various components become separated in the order of their different gas-liquid partition coefficients. The presence of a separated component and the amount are indicated when the gas stream exits through the other side of the thermal conductivity detector. The thermistors or filaments in the two sides of the detector are part of a Wheatstone bridge circuit. The imbalance set up due to differences in thermal conductivity between a component to be measured and the inert carrier gas is registered as a Gaussian type peak by a curve drawing potentiometer recorder. The thermal con-

1554

ductivity detector probably is the most common type. Other types which respond to other properties of the molecules also are quite useful. Figure 57-13 illustrates an example of a gas chromatographic separation of a simple mixture as displayed on the recorder chart.

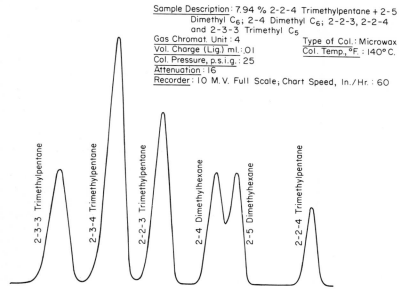

Sample Description: 7.94 % 2-2-4 Trimethylpentane + 2-5 Dimethyl C_6; 2-4 Dimethyl C_6; 2-2-3, 2-2-4 and 2-3-3 Trimethyl C_5

Gas Chromat. Unit : 4

Vol. Charge (Lig.) ml. : .01

Col. Pressure, p.s.i.g. : 25

Attenuation : 16

Recorder : 10 M. V. Full Scale; Chart Speed, In./Hr. : 60

Type of Col.: Microwax

Col. Temp., °F. : 140° C.

FIG. 57-13. Typical Chromatogram of a Hydrocarbon Mixture.

Requirements for a Gas Chromatography Laboratory.—The physical equipment in an analytical gas chromatography laboratory includes the gas chromatograph instrument, installed in a location which preferably is air conditioned, and free from drafts and mechanical vibration. Utilities include a power outlet and various gases depending on the type of instrument. Gases should be pure or filtered. Minimum accessories include a sample charging device and a chromatographic column. For successful operation an analyst unfamiliar with gas chromatography should be trained by an experienced gas chromatographer. An operating manual and wiring diagrams should be available at all times.

Comments on specifications of gas chromatographs are impractical in a summary of this type. There are several dozen well known makes and models on the market. The choice for purchase obviously depends on many factors. The first prerequisite is the processing capability of the instrument for the samples to be analyzed. Most of the inexpensive models, when equipped with a suitable chromatographic column, can furnish useful information on petroleum samples if the sample is quickly vaporized and maintained as a vapor throughout the process. Temperature programming and automatic features add to the cost of the instrument but often are justified based on improvements in accuracy and labor costs. If samples to be analyzed are complex, for example, consisting of wide boiling mixtures of diverse types, a research type instrument is needed. In addition, if a large number of individual components must be measured quantitatively, automatic digitizing equipment may be justified. Some considerations concerning research type equipment are included in the following section.

When the gas chromatography laboratory is ready for samples, the analyst will proceed to obtain the necessary calibrations, which consist of retention times of desired components and their corresponding detector response factors. Explanations of these terms together with data tables for typical columns and separations are included in subsequent sections.

Desirable Features of Capillary Chromatograph and Electronic Integrator.
Capillary Chromatograph with Ionization Detector. *Columns.*—Accommodates capillary columns to at least 500-ft. length. Also accepts $\frac{1}{8}$ in. or $\frac{1}{4}$ in. packed columns at least 10 ft. long.

Temperature Program.—A variety of rates, ranging from about 0.5 to 50°C. per minute, with initial and final holding isothermal options up to 30 minutes. Maximum injection temperature, 500°C. The cooling cycle is rapid and automatic, a change of several hundred degrees Centigrade requires less than 20 minutes. The whole temperature program, once selected and set, is automatic. The heating rate is near linear and highly reproducible.

Electronics.—Signal can be attenuated through a wide range, *e.g.*, 1 to 500,000. Balance control can be set quickly and is stable once adjusted. Noise is in the order of 0.05 mv. or less when using a 5 mv. potentiometer type recorder.

Automatic Digital Chromatograph Readout System.—The automatic integrator system is well designed to accept the output from the ionization chromatograph. The chromatographic peaks are converted to digital recordings of time of occurrence and relative areas. Count rate is at least 10,000 per second full scale, with a linearity of better than 0.1 percent of full scale. Limit of detectability is 15 microvolts per second change in signal, or better. The better instruments incorporate an automatic baseline drift corrector which corrects out any error due to drifting baseline. In order to have a printed record of the digital display on the integrator, most users add a printer unit. Minimum printout speed is about one peak per second for components passing through the chromatograph detector at a high rate.

Qualitative and Quantitative Aspects of Gas Chromatography.—Assuming a sample has been separated in an analytical chromatograph at optimum operating conditions, the analyst will have the resultant chromatogram on a recorder chart for identification. The peaks on the chart represent compounds or groups of unseparated compounds. These peaks are tentatively identified by retention data which the analyst has compiled from his own efforts, using compounds of high purity, or else has adapted from the many literature references which include retention data. For convenience and speed it is suggested that the retention data of interest be entered on a master recorder chart or yard-stick. This consists of a series of marks on a recorder chart, the position of each mark to be at the exact position of elution of the compound whose name is written at the end of the mark. In the absence of retention data because of lack of calibration compounds, such as the higher boiling homologues, fair predictions can be made by extrapolation of data. This is possible because retention position always bears a definite relation to boiling point or carbon number. This is illustrated by the plot in Fig. 57-14. The relation for other types and boiling ranges may be less linear than in this illustration. In such cases the plot should be made on semilog paper with the retention positions plotted off the log axis.

Qualitative problems are the principal limitation of gas chromatography. Positive identifications of unknowns often cannot be made without enlisting the aid of other techniques such as mass spectrometry and infrared spectrometry. This situation may be the exception rather than the rule in many service laboratories which are not scheduled to do detailed composition analyses of complex, wide boiling mixtures or to undertake searches for unknown trace components.

Gas chromatography is an excellent quantitative analytical technique. Precision and accuracy are good over wide concentration ranges. In order to evaluate the recorder chart chromatogram quantitatively, it is necessary first to measure each peak of interest. For fast approximations, concentrations of components can be related to peak height. Correlations with peak areas are recommended for highest accuracy. The peak height method is affected seriously by temperature fluctuations especially if the detector is of the thermal conductivity type.

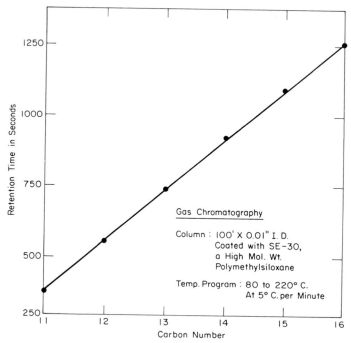

Gas Chromatography

Column : 100' X 0.01" I. D.
Coated with SE-30,
a High Mol. Wt.
Polymethylsiloxane

Temp. Program : 80 to 220° C.
At 5° C. per Minute

FIG. 57-14.   Carbon Number *vs.* Retention Time for n-C$_{11}$ · n-C$_{16}$ Paraffins.

Numerous methods have been suggested for measuring peak areas. Some of these, such as use of a planimeter, counting of squares, or cutting out and weighing of peaks, are quite tedious. Of all the manual methods the most satisfactory is modified triangulation. In this operation, area is simply the product of the peak height and the width measured at a point on the axis which is one-half the peak height. The shape of a peak is the result of many variables, some of which are listed in Table 57-9. There are two principal types of automatic devices for measuring peak area. These are the ball and disc mechanical integrator device and the electronic integrator-digitizer units. The ball and disc devices display the data as a series of hash marks under the peaks on the chromatogram. The number of marks is proportional to the area. Electronic integrators operate directly off the detector signal. They are extremely fast, have a linear response through a wide dynamic range, and display areas numerically. The accuracies obtained with the automatic integrators are not affected by peak shapes.

The measurement of areas of isolated peaks is straightforward. In most chromatograms

TABLE 57-9. FACTORS AFFECTING PEAK SHAPE IN GLC

Sample charging

    Quantity charged
    Time interval for charging
    Flash zone temperature and geometry
    Vaporization properties of sample

Column

    Thermodynamic effects—gas-liquid partition
    Kinetic effects—column efficiency (HETP)
        Dimensions of column
        Description of solvent and support
        Concentration of solvent
        Solute-solvent interaction
        Adsorption effects
        Temperature and back pressure
        Carrier gas and flow rate

Detector

    Type and condition
    Geometry
    Speed of response
    Temperature
    Electric potential
    H_2 and air rates if flame ionization type

Electrometer

    Design and resistances in bridge
    Attenuation

Recorder

    Type and condition
    Attenuation
    Chart speed
    Pen speed

from multicomponent mixtures, however, there are usually some components which are unresolved, *i.e.*, come out in the same peak, and others which are partially resolved. If retention data indicate a peak contains more than one component, the names of all components should be attached to the total equivalent concentration. If there are more than two poorly resolved peaks in a connected series, *i.e.*, there are no saddles between the peaks, there is no satisfactory mathematical or graphical way to resolve the peaks. If only two peaks are poorly resolved, the approximate ratio of their respective areas may be obtained by the following graphical means. Draw tangents to the sides of the combined peak. At the points where the tangents intersect perpendiculars drawn from the retention positions of the pure compounds, draw inside tangents to match. The result should be two overlapping isosceles triangles. The ratio of the areas of these triangles should approximate the ratios of the areas of the poorly resolved peaks. A similar triangulation method can be used for peaks with a saddle between; however, if the saddle is as much as half-way down from the apex of the larger peak, the usual technique is to drop a perpendicular from the bottom of the saddle to the baseline. The peaks on either side of this line are then handled as if they were isolated peaks.

With the aid of automatic integrators the complications of measuring poorly resolved peaks are minimized. Most of these integrators are "triggered" to measure a new area each time the chromatogram goes through zero slope. Poorly resolved peaks may not be detected by the integrator. The user should determine from the manufacturer the exact limitations of the integrator in this connection.

When peak areas or peak heights have been measured, a calibration plot or tabulation of response factors should be available to convert areas or heights into equivalent amounts of compounds. A typical example of such a calibration is shown in Fig. 57-15. Plots of

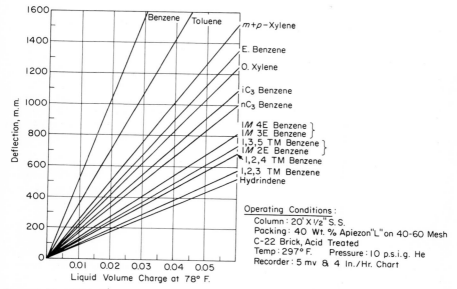

FIG. 57-15. High Temperature Gas-Liquid Partition Chromatography Calibration for Separation of Aromatics.

quantity of a compound as a function of response signal are linear for hydrocarbons as long as the column and detector are not overloaded. Units for concentration and response may be chosen for convenience. The slope of each calibration line should be fixed by at least three points, two which bracket the expected range of concentrations, and one near midrange. After the slope has been established as linear, a tabulation of response factors for the compounds of interest may be used if more convenient than the chart. These factors are expressed as square millimeters per microgram or square millimeters per microliter, and the like.

Care should be exercised in the selection of the laboratory technique used for correlating peak area with concentration. The best practice requires that accurately measured amounts of each calibration standard (compound of certified high purity) be injected into the chromatograph. To save time these can be injected as a synthetic blend simulating the sample to be analyzed. If a blend is used it must be prepared accurately, using an analytical balance. Also, in using a blend, the retention values of the compound should be known in order that response factors which are measured will be assigned to the correct peaks. Quantitative calibration is required in all cases of C_1–C_5 hydrocarbon analysis or if significant quantities (more than 0.1 percent) of a nonhydrocarbon are to be analyzed when using either thermal conductivity or ionization type detectors. For hydrocarbons above C_5 calibrations are recommended if highest accuracy is desired. When analyzing hydrocarbon fractions above C_{10}, or samples covering a wide boiling range, a point is reached when calibration becomes academic. This is true if the chromatogram is a continuum of poorly resolved peaks. Obviously, this condition is influenced by the complexity of the sample, the resolving power of the column and other operating variables.

When a peak area has been converted to quantity of a component a simple computation changes this to percentage basis, for example:

$$\text{Weight percent of component} = \frac{\text{Peak area of component} \times \text{response factor} \times 100}{\text{Weight of sample}}$$

Concentration can be reported in whatever units are desired provided the response factor is in units compatible with the units of peak and sample measurement. Reports from 52 laboratories in a cross-checking program indicated standard deviation of in-lab repeatability to be about 0.37 when analyzing a mixture of hydrocarbons using a packed column and thermal conductivity detector. Precision can be as good as ± 0.2 percent if operating variables are carefully controlled. Precision for trace components (concentrations below 0.1 percent) varies, but ranges between about 10 and 20 percent of the amount present.

Tables of Retention Data for Gas Chromatography.—The examples included in the tables presented here, plus the voluminous literature, will suggest the kinds of columns needed for the specific problems of a particular laboratory. With the exception of a few common nonhydrocarbon gases, this brief compilation is confined to typical applications of GC to the analysis of petroleum hydrocarbon mixtures.

The gas chromatographer has many variables at his command: with this in mind the retention tables are presented in a format which hopefully will be convenient for the analyst. The information includes column dimensions, solvent (except for first example which uses no solvent), description of support, carrier gas and rate, and column temperature. The compounds to be separated and their boiling points are shown opposite columns of retention data. For convenience, the retention values are shown in units of elapsed time, length of recorder chart travel, and on a relative basis. If the chart travel units are used, the analyst must of course use the recorder chart speed specified on the data sheet.

Certain limitations must be observed when using any retention data tables. No two columns are identical. Retention times will be somewhat different for duplicate columns regardless of where prepared. Most of the manufacturers of gas chromatographs offer a selection of ready-made columns for sale and will also make special columns on order. For the analyst who prefers to make his own packed columns, instructions are included in the following section.

Retention tables do not necessarily include all hydrocarbons in the boiling range or carbon number range specified. Compounds of wide interest usually are included but the particular column and operating conditions may be useful for other unlisted isomers.

Although retention times of two compounds may appear to be sufficiently different for separation, good separation is not guaranteed. The variable of concentration has an important effect. A component in high concentration may lead to peak base broadening sufficient to overlap peaks of adjacent components.

A final precaution in use of retention data concerns column temperature. The temperature specified is not necessarily the maximum allowable temperature for the column used. If the temperature is changed, retention times will change; the times will be longer for lower temperatures, shorter for higher temperatures. The analyst may wish to save time, at the expense of resolution, by raising the temperature. Maximum allowable gas chromatography temperatures for solvents are included in Table 57-10.

The various retention data tables are numbered 57-11 to 57-23, inclusive.

TABLE 57-10. MAXIMUM OPERATING TEMPERATURES FOR VARIOUS SOLVENTS
IN PACKED COLUMNS FOR GAS CHROMATOGRAPHY[a]

Paraffins	°C.
Hexadecane	50
2,6,10,15,19,23-Hexamethyltetracosane	140
Hexatriacontane	160
Microcrystalline wax, 195°F. minimum melting point	170

Esters of dibasic acids	
Di(2-ethylhexyl)phthalate	140
Di(2-ethylhexyl)sebacate	140
Di-*n*-Decylphthalate	140
Diethyleneglycol succinate	225

Polymers	
Polyethyleneglycol, avg. M.W. 950–1050	150
Polyethyleneglycol, avg. M.W. 1300–1600	150
Polyethyleneglycol, avg. M.W. 15,000–20,000	200
Polydimethylsiloxane liquid, 100–150 centistokes at 25°C. viscosity	200
Polydimethylsiloxane gum, very viscous rubbery gum	300

Polar solvents	
Dimethylformamide	0
2,4-Dimethylsulfolane	40
Hexamethylphosphoramide	40
β,β'-Oxydipropionitrile	70
2-(Benzyloxy)ethanol	35
Stearonitrile	150

[a] Somewhat lower temperatures may be necessary when using these solvents in open tube columns. Maximum temperature in such a column can be detected as that temperature at which noise from column effluent, and/or temperature drift become excessive. Materials which are solids at room temperature should not be used in open tube columns.

Preparation of Packed Type Gas Chromatographic Columns.—The special materials required are a piece of tubing of material and dimensions recommended in the method, the specified solvent, and the support material. Metal tubing is most commonly used and descriptions such as "$\frac{1}{8}$-inch tubing," "$\frac{1}{4}$-inch tubing," *etc.*, refer to the nominal outside diameter of the tubing. There are now many brands and varieties of support material available. Essentially all of the products offered for use in gas liquid chromatography are some form of diatomaceous earth, usually in the form of crushed and sieved firebrick. The regular, or untreated, variety is pink and granular. Various other forms are offered for sale, and these have been treated with chemicals to reduce adsorption effects. Some common treatments are with acid or flux calcining with alkali. Unless specified otherwise, the regular, pink untreated variety is to be used.

Impregnating Support with Solvent.—Estimate weight of support needed to pack chromatographic column. Include about 20 percent excess to allow for handling losses. Use a balance of 0.1 g. or better sensitivity.

Obtain desired solvent and weigh out an amount equal to 20 percent of the weight of the brick. Do not use a different amount unless the specific gas chromatographic method so directs.

Mix the solvent with anaesthetic ether. The amount of ether required for the packing to fill a 10-foot × ¼-inch column is "1 small can" or ¼ lb. This is a weight ratio of ether to brick of about 3/1 minimum. Ether is generally preferred since it is a good "universal," nonaqueous solvent and can be evaporated out of the solvent rapildy. In special cases where a solvent is not soluble in anaesthetic ether, consult the literature or other information source to determine suitable solvent. All operations with ether must be removed a safe distance from any flame or spark source and, preferably, are conducted under a fume hood.

TABLE 57-11. GAS CHROMATOGRAPHY RETENTION DATA

Application: Gas samples
Column:
  Length: 20 feet
  Diameter: ¼ inch
  Support: 5A molecular sieve, 40–60 mesh
  Mesh: 40–60
  g. Solvent/g. Support: No solvent used
Operating conditions:
  Temp.: 60°C.
  Carrier gas: Helium
  Inlet pressure: 10
  Flow rate, ml./min.: 45
  Chart speed, in./min.: 1

B.P., °C.	Compound	Rel. Retention	Min. Past Air	Mm. Past Air
−252.8	Hydrogen	1.0	0.95	23
−183.0	Oxygen	1.8	1.65	42
−195.8	Nitrogen	2.8	2.56	65
−161.5	Methane	4.7	4.25	108
−190.0	Carbon monoxide	8.6	7.81	198

Pour the ether solution of solvent onto the support with constant stirring. The support may be contained in an evaporating dish or other container of sufficient size. A large culture dish approximately 4¾ inches in diameter × 2½ inches deep has proved to be more convenient.

Place the impregnated support and ether mixture on a steam bath and continue to stir while ether is evaporating. Continue evaporation until support appears dry, but no longer. This is especially important in case of low boiling substrates such as dimethylformamide, acetonylacetone, benzonitrile, triisobutylene, *etc*. Never use a hot plate. If evaporation is at too high a temperature or is prolonged, part or all of low boiling substrates will be lost off of the support. In case ether cannot be used as solvent and some other higher-boiling solvent is substituted, a gentle current of dry nitrogen may be directed onto the surface of the evaporating mixture to speed the evaporation. Do not use air.

Packing Columns with Solvent Impregnated Support.—Secure piece of tubing to be used. This should be the desired length and diameter and reasonably straight. Metal tubing, preferably stainless steel, is recommended. Other corrosion resistant tubing may be substituted. Glass is not recommended because of the extreme care which must be exercised in packing and handling long columns, because it cannot be bent after packing, and because of the difficulties of installing glass columns in most of the laboratory gas chromatographic instruments.

Check tubing for obstructions and make sure both ends are completely open.

Clean out tube with acetone and blow dry.

TABLE 57-12. GAS CHROMATOGRAPHY RETENTION DATA

Application: C_2–C_4 Gas samples
Solvent: Hexadecane
Column:
  Length: 20 feet
  Diameter: $\frac{1}{4}$ inch
  Support: Firebrick
  Mesh: 40–60
  Pretreat: 12 N HNO_3
  g. Solvent/g. Support: 0.4
Operating conditions:
  Temp.: 31°C.
  Carrier gas: Helium
  Inlet pressure: 30
  Flow rate, ml./min.: 60
  Chart speed, in./min.: 1

B.P., °C.	Compound	Rel. Retention	Min. Past Air	Mm. Past Air
−78.5	Carbon dioxide	1.0	0.90	22
−103.9	Ethylene	1.7	1.49	38
−88.6	Ethane	2.7	2.32	59
−47.6	Propylene	8.0	6.96	177
−42.1	Propane	9.3	8.03	204
−34.3	Propadiene	11.5	9.92	252
−11.72	Isobutane	21.2	18.35	466
−6.26 −6.9	1-Butene Isobutylene	26.4	22.81	580
−0.55	n-Butane	32.5	28.10	714
+0.86	trans-2-Butene	35.4	30.60	778
+3.72	cis-2-Butene	39.0	33.71	859

Plug lower end of tube with a small tight ball of Pyrex wool. This is equivalent to about 0.02 g. when using a $\frac{1}{4}$-inch column.

Stand the column up in a vertical position with the lower end resting on a heavy duty vibrator of the hopper type. If the column is longer than about 10 feet it will be desirable to mount the column on a light weight rigid frame first to prevent buckling.

Attach a small funnel to the top of the column with a short piece of Tygon or similar tubing. A thistle tube funnel with all but about 1 inch of the tube cut off is convenient.

Fill the funnel with packing material and keep full or nearly full during remainder of packing operation.

Turn on vibrator. Touch column at several points top to bottom to determine if it is undergoing vigorous and uniform vibration.

NOTE.—To insure reproducibility in case column is to be duplicated or repacked later, the weight of packing material ±1.0 g. required to pack the column should be recorded.

Plug upper end of column with Pyrex wool, as before. If column is not to be put in immediate service see that both ends are also sealed with tape before storing.

When column is put in service for first time a purging period of several hours at room temperature may be required to eliminate residual ether.

TABLE 57-13. GAS CHROMATOGRAPHY RETENTION DATA

Application: C$_4$ Hydrocarbons
Solvent: β,β'-Oxydipropionitrile
Column:
    Length: 50 feet
    Diameter: $\frac{1}{4}$ inch
    Support: Firebrick
    Mesh: 40–60
    Pretreat: 12 N HNO$_3$
    g. Solvent/g. Support: 0.4
Operating conditions:
    Temp.: 34.0°C.
    Carrier gas: Helium
    Inlet pressure: 10
    Flow rate, ml./min.: 22
    Chart speed, in./min.: 1

B.P., °C.	Compound	Rel. Retention	Min. Past Air	Mm. Past Air
−11.7	Isobutane	1.0	3.8	97
−9.55	*n*-Butane	1.4	5.4	138
−6.93	Isobutene	3.0	11.3	287
−6.26	1-Butene	3.3	12.6	319
0.86	*trans*-2-Butene	3.7	14.2	360
3.72	*cis*-2-Butene	4.6	17.6	447
−4.41	1,3-Butadiene	7.6	28.9	735

Capillary Chromatography.—The combination of capillary columns and flame ionization detectors has been used effectively for C$_1$–C$_{40}$ hydrocarbons. The special merit of this instrument design is for wide-boiling samples above C$_6$, any multicomponent narrow fractions, and in applications where sensitivity beyond the range of thermal conductivity detectors is needed for trace analysis. Separations by capillary also are usually faster than by packed column techniques.

Examples of operating conditions for several useful applications of capillary chromatography are shown in Table 57-24. Detailed tabulations of retention times for two general purpose capillary columns are included in Tables 57-22 and 57-23.

A good automatic integrator is a valuable accessory for capillary chromatography. The reasons are obvious when one examines a chart from the type of composition analyses often performed with capillary columns. A typical example is the section from a chart shown in Fig. 57-16. Manual measurement of all the peak areas from such a separation

TABLE 57-14. GAS CHROMATOGRAPHY RETENTION DATA

Application: Analysis of C_4–C_6 Catalytic Cracked Fraction
Solvent: 2-(Benzyloxy)ethanol
Column:
  Length: 20 feet
  Diameter: $\frac{1}{4}$ inch
  Support: Firebrick
  Mesh: 40–60
  Pretreat: 12 N HNO$_3$
  g. Solvent/g. Support: 0.29
Operating conditions:
  Temp.: 35°C.
  Carrier gas: Helium
  Inlet pressure: 8
  Flow rate, ml./min.: 35
  Chart speed, in./min.: 30

B.P., °C.	Compound	Rel. Retention	Min. Past Air	Mm. Past Air
−83.6	Acetylene	1.00	1.69	43.0
−11.72	Isobutane	1.25	2.13	54.0
−0.50	n-Butane	1.91	3.23	82.0
−6.90/−6.26	Isobutene and 1-Butene	2.56	4.33	110.0
−0.88	trans-2-Butene	3.37	5.71	145.0
27.9	Isopentane	3.77	6.38	162.0
3.72	cis-2-Butene	4.05	6.85	174.0
−23.2	Methylacetylene	4.23	7.17	182.0
20.06	3-Methyl-1-butene	4.51	7.64	194.0
−4.41	1,3-Butadiene	4.56	7.72	196.0
36.05	n-Pentane	5.05	8.54	217.0
49.72	2,2-Dimethylbutane	6.28	10.63	270.0
29.97	1-Pentene	6.65	11.26	286.0
31.16	2-Methyl-1-butene	7.47	12.64	321.0
36.35	trans-2-Pentene	8.16	13.82	351.0
36.94	cis-2-Pentene	8.88	15.04	382.0
58.00	2,3-Dimethylbutane	8.98	15.20	386.0
8.07	Ethylacetylene	9.02	15.28	388.0
38.57	2-Methyl-2-butene	9.77	16.54	420.0
63.28	3-Methylpentane	10.74	18.19	462.0
34.06	Isoprene	13.05	22.09	561.0
49.28	Cyclopentane	14.60	24.72	628.0
63.49	1-Hexene	16.74	28.35	720.0
42.03	trans-1,3-Pentadiene	17.19	29.09	739.0
60.73	2-Methyl-1-pentene	17.42	29.49	749.0
67.08	trans-3-Hexene	11.02	30.51	775.0
26.99	Dimethyl acetylene	18.14	30.71	780.0
66.44	cis-3-Hexene	18.44	31.22	793.0
44.24	Cyclopentene	18.53	31.38	797.0
44.86	1,2-Pentadiene	18.65	31.57	802.0
67.89	trans-2-Hexene	18.77	31.77	807.0
44.07	cis-1,3-Pentadiene	19.30	32.67	830.0
67.28	2-Methyl-2-pentene	19.93	33.74	857.0
67.61	trans-3-Methyl-2-pentene	21.17	35.75	908.0
32.5	2-Methyl-1-butene-3-yne	21.77	36.85	936.0
40.3	Propylacetylene	22.21	37.60	955.0
71.84	Methylcyclopentane	23.70	40.12	1019.0
42.5	1,3-Cyclopentadiene	26.51	44.88	1140.0

TABLE 57-15. GAS CHROMATOGRAPHY RETENTION DATA

Application: Paraffins, olefins, cycloparaffins, and cyclo-olefins in C$_5$–C$_7$ fraction
Solvent: 2,4-Dimethylsulfolane
Column:
    Length: 50 feet
    Diameter: $\frac{1}{4}$ inch
    Support: Firebrick
    Mesh: 40–60
    Pretreat: 12 N HNO$_3$
    g. Solvent/g. Support: 0.4
Operating conditions:
    Temp.: 50°C.
    Carrier gas: Helium
    Inlet Pressure: 30
    Flow rate, ml./min.: 40
    Chart speed, in./min.: 2

B.P., °C.	Compound	Rel. Retention	Min. Past Air	Mm. Past Air
49.7	2,2-Dimethylbutane	1.00	8.13	206.5
41.2	3,3-Dimethyl-1-butene	1.18	9.61	244.2
58.0	2,3-Dimethylbutane	1.31	10.68	271.2
60.3	2-Methylpentane	1.34	10.90	277.0
63.2	3-Methylpentane	1.67	13.54	324.0
68.7	n-hexane	1.75	14.24	361.8
54.1	3-Methyl-1-pentene	1.78	14.49	368.0
53.8	4-Methyl-1-pentene	1.83	14.85	377.2
49.3	Cyclopentane	1.93	15.70	398.8
56.3	4-Methyl-cis-2-pentene	1.93	15.70	398.8
58.6	4-Methyl-trans-2-pentene	1.96	15.93	404.5
55.6	2,3-Dimethyl-1-butene	2.13	17.30	439.4
63.5	1-Hexene	2.60	21.11	536.2
67.1	trans-3-Hexene	2.60	21.11	536.2
44.2	Cyclopentene	2.67	21.69	550.8
60.7	2-Methyl-1-pentene	2.67	21.69	550.8
97.6	4,4-Dimethyl-1-pentene	2.77	22.54	572.4
66.4	cis-3-Hexene	2.85	23.15	587.8
67.9	trans-2-Hexene	2.91	23.66	601.0
90.1	2-Methylhexane	2.93	23.79	604.2
75.8	Methylcyclopentene	2.95	23.99	609.4
64.7	2-Ethyl-1-butene	2.99	24.34	618.2
68.8	cis-2-Hexene	3.24	26.32	666.2
67.6	3-Methyl-trans-2-pentene	3.39	27.54	699.5
70.5	3-Methyl-cis-2-pentene	3.60	29.30	744.2
80.4	4,4-Dimethyl-cis-2-pentene	3.65	29.69	754.2
77.9	2,3,3-Trimethyl-1-butene	3.73	30.05	863.5
83.4	2,4-Dimethyl-2-pentene	3.75	30.46	773.6
73.2	2,3-Dimethyl-2-butene	4.34	35.25	895.0
84.2	2,3-Dimethyl-1-pentene	4.34	35.25	895.0
85.3	5-Methyl-1-hexene-1	4.34	35.30	896.7
98.3	2-Heptene, cis and trans	5.79	47.05	1195.0
93.6	1-Heptene	5.82	47.33	1202.2

is tedious and very time consuming. Some considerations for purchase of research chromatographs and integrators are included in "Desirable Features of Capillary Chromatograph and Electronic Integrator" (page 1556).

Trace Analysis.—The gas chromatography laboratory must be able to do trace analysis since, in addition to special plant problems, there are usually specification tests for impurities in trace concentrations. In general, the same gas chromatographic

TABLE 57-16. GAS CHROMATOGRAPHY RETENTION DATA

Application: Octenes
Slovent: Stearonitrile
Column:
Length: 20 feet
Diameter: ¼ inch
Support: Firebrick
Mesh: 42–60
Amount of solvent on support: 16.7% of weight of support
Operating conditions:
Temp.: 100°C.
Carrier gas: Helium
Inlet pressure: 25 p.s.i.g.
Chart speed: 60 ins./hr.

B.P., °C.	Compound	Rel. Retention	Min. Past Air	Mm. Past Air
100.9	2,2-Dimethyl-*trans*-3-hexene	1.00	36.8	933
101.4	2,4,4-Trimethyl-1-pentene	1.20	44.2	1122
104.9	2,4,4-Trimethyl-2-pentene	1.22	45.0	1142
105.4	2,2-Dimethyl-*cis*-3-hexene	1.30	47.8	1212
112	2-Methyl-*trans*-3-heptene	1.47	53.9	1369
112	3,4,4-Trimethyl-*cis*-2-pentene	1.58	58.3	1480
112.2	2,5-Dimethyl-2-hexene	1.62	59.5	1512
121.3	1-Octene	2.22	80.2	2034
121.8	2,3-Dimethyl-2-hexene	2.23	81.8	2075

equipment used for macrotests can be used for trace analysis if it meets certain minimum quality standards. Modern TC detectors are sensitive enough to see a separated peak of a low molecular weight hydrocarbon in a concentration as low as 2 to 5 p.p.m. if a large sample is charged. Lower concentrations require an ionization detector or some means of concentrating the trace component of interest. The minimum detectable limit of concentration of a component can be defined as that amount which gives a signal at least twice the noise. Thus, any measures taken to reduce noise help to lower the minimum detectable limit. When using TC type detectors temperature should vary less than ±0.1°C., and carrier gas flow control should hold the desired rate within ±1 percent. There must be no leaks or obstructions in the gas flow system.

Recorder specifications are rather critical in trace work. Sensitivity of 1 millivolt full scale and 1 second pen speed are desirable. Careful adjustment of the gain is necessary to minimize the dead band. All connections in the calibrated circuit should be soldered, not screw-in or plug-in types. The overall limit of error should not be greater than ±0.3 percent of the range span.

Numerous methods requiring trace analyses may be found in the literature. (See the list of gas chromatography references in the Bibliography.) Examples of recent methods in references available to most petroleum analysts can be found in the ASTM Standards on Petroleum Products. Gas chromatographic methods of interest may be found in the 1963 Manual on Hydrocarbon Analysis, ASTM Special Technical Publication No. 332.

Analysis Requiring Gas Chromatography in Combination with Other Techniques.—The latest advances in gas chromatography instrumentation, while useful for a large number of analytical problems, may require the aid of other techniques, especially for samples boiling above about 300°F. Detailed composition studies of such samples often require systematic planning of an analytical scheme if the maximum information is to

TABLE 57-17. GAS CHROMATOGRAPHY RETENTION DATA

Application: Normal paraffins, C$_6$–C$_{14}$
Solvent: Microcrystalline wax, 195°F. minimum melting point
Column:
  Length: 20 feet
  Diameter: $\frac{1}{4}$ inch
  Support: Firebrick
  Mesh: 40–60
  Pretreat: 12 N HNO$_3$
  g. Solvent/g. Support: 0.22
Operating conditions:
  Temp.: 160°C.
  Carrier gas: Helium
  Inlet pressure: 30
  Flow rate, ml./min.: 97
  Chart speed, in./min.: 0.1

B.P., °C.	Compound	Rel. Retention	Min. Past Air	Mm. Past Air
68.7	n-Hexane	1.0	2.4	6
98.4	n-Heptane	1.8	4.3	11
125.7	n-Octane	3.0	7.1	18
150.8	n-Nonane	5.1	12.2	31
174.1	n-Decane	8.7	20.8	53
195.9	n-Undecane	14.9	35.8	91
216.3	n-Dodecane	25.5	61.4	156
235.5	n-Tridecane	43.7	105.0	267
253.5	n-Tetradecane	74.3	178.0	453

be obtained. For lower boiling samples it is possible to separate essentially all components by re-chromatographing so as to obtain a sufficient volume of unresolved fractions for further analysis. An unknown can often be tentatively identified by its retention time on a gas chromatographic column which separates by boiling point. The tentative identification can be verified if the elution time of the component on several columns of different polarity corresponds to the tentative identification.

As fractions of hydrocarbons increase in carbon number or boiling range the identification of individual compounds becomes less practical. To illustrate, a C$_{10}$ fraction consisting solely of paraffins could contain as many as 75 isomers, not counting stereo-isomers. At C$_{20}$ the theoretical number rises above 350,000. Thus when samples contain fractions boiling above about 345°F., the composition analysis becomes increasingly one of type characterization rather than identification of individual components. In the

TABLE 57-18. GAS CHROMATOGRAPHY RETENTION DATA

Application: Paraffins C_{16}–C_{36}
Solvent: Polydimethylsiloxane gum
Column:
  Length: 5 feet
  Diameter: $\frac{1}{4}$ inch
  Support: Firebrick
  Mesh: 40–60
  Amount of solvent on support: 15% of weight of support
Operating conditions:
  Temp.: 125 to 350°C. at 8°/minute
  Carrier gas: Helium
  Flow rate: 120 ml./min.
  Chart speed: 40 in./hr.

B.P., °C.	Compound	Rel. Retention	Min. Past Air	Mm. Past Air
286.8	*n*-Hexadecane	1.00	5.3	89
329.7	*n*-Nonadecane	1.85	9.8	165
342.7	*n*-Eicosane	2.09	11.0	186
378.3	*n*-Tricosane	2.76	14.5	246
389.2	*n*-Tetracosane	2.98	15.6	265
409.7	*n*-Hexacosane	3.28	17.3	292
428.7	*n*-Octacosane	3.64	19.1	324
463	*n*-Dotriacontane	5.22	22.2	376
493	*n*-Hexatriacontane	5.83	25.4	429

TABLE 57-19. GAS CHROMATOGRAPHY RETENTION DATA

Application: Paraffins, 27.9–150.8°C.; aromatics, 80.1–176.1°C.; naphthenes, 71.8–156.6°C.
Solvent: Microcrystalline wax, 195°F. minimum melting point
Column:
  Length: 30 feet
  Diameter: $\frac{1}{4}$ inch
  Support: Firebrick
  Mesh: 40–60
  Pretreat: 12 N acid
  g. Solvent/g. Support: 0.25
Operating conditions:
  Temp.: 140°C.
  Carrier gas: Helium
  Inlet pressure: 25
  Flow rate, ml./min.: 35
  Chart speed, in./min.: 1

B.P., °C.	Paraffins	Ret. mm.*
36.1	*n*-Pentane	62.0
27.9	2-Methylbutane	54.0
68.7	*n*-Hexane	117.0

* Millimeters of chart travel for a 60 in./hr. chart.

TABLE 57-19 (cont.)

B.P., °C.		Ret. mm.*
	Paraffins (cont.)	
60.3	2-Methylpentane	98.0
63.3	3-Methylpentane	108.0
49.7	2,2-Dimethylbutane	81.0
58.0	2,3-Dimethylbutane	99.0
98.5	*n*-Heptane	221.0
90.1	2-Methylhexane	179.0
91.9	3-Methylhexane	192.0
93.5	3-Ethylpentane	210.0
79.2	2,2-Dimethylpentane	141.0
89.8	2,3-Dimethylpentane	195.0
80.5	2,4-Dimethylpentane	140.0
86.1	3,3-Dimethylpentane	185.0
80.9	2,2,3-Trimethylbutane	164.0
125.7	*n*-Octane	406.0
117.6	2-Methylheptane	327.0
118.9	3-Methylheptane	348.0
117.7	5-Methylheptane	337.0
118.5	3-Ethylhexane	356.0
106.8	2,2-Dimethylhexane	251.0
115.6	2,3-Dimethylhexane	332.0
109.4	2,4-Dimethylhexane	272.0
109.1	2,5-Dimethylhexane	262.0
112.0	3,3-Dimethylhexane	309.0
117.7	3,4-Dimethylhexane	353.0
115.7	2-Methyl-3-ethylpentane	334.0
118.3	3-Methyl-3-ethylpentane	379.0
109.8	2,2,2-Trimethylpentane	292.0
99.2	2,2,4-Trimethylpentane	218.0
114.8	2,3,3-Trimethylpentane	370.0
113.5	2,3,4-Trimethylpentane	324.0
150.8	*n*-Nonane	718.0
	Aromatics	
80.1	Benzene	192
110.6	Toluene	377
136.2	Ethylbenzene	651
138.3	*meta*-Xylene	720
139.1	*para*-Xylene	720
144.4	*ortho*-Xylene	835
152.4	Isopropylbenzene	916
159.2	*n*-Propylbenzene	1111
161.3	1-Methyl-3-ethylbenzene	1187
162.0	1-Methyl-4-ethylbenzene	1216
164.7	1,3,5-Trimethylbenzene	1348
169.4	1,2,4-Trimethylbenzene	1545
176.1	1,2,3-Trimethylbenzene	1844

* Millimeters of chart travel for a 60 in./hr. chart.

TABLE 57-19 (cont.)

B.P., °C.		Ret. mm.*
	Naphthenes	
71.8	Methylcyclopentane	162
91.7	*cis*-1,3-Dimethylcyclopentane	221
87.4–90.7	1,1- and *trans*-1,3-Dimethylcyclopentane	235
91.9	*trans*-1,2-Dimethylcyclopentane	235
80.7	Cyclohexane	217
110.4	*cis-trans-cis*-1,2,3-Trimethylcyclopentane	336
100.9	Methylcyclohexane	316
120.1	*cis*-1,3-Dimethylcyclohexane	450
138.0–139.0	*cis*- and *trans*-1,3,5-Trimethylcyclohexane	635
123.4–119.5	1,1- and *trans*-1,2-Dimethylcyclohexane	470
124.5–124.0	*trans*-1,3- and *cis*-1,4-Dimethylcyclohexane	514
119.3	*trans*-1,4-Dimethylcyclohexane	514
156.6	*n*-Propylcyclohexane	695

* Millimeters of chart travel for a 60 in./hr. chart.

TABLE 57-20. GAS CHROMATOGRAPHY RETENTION DATA

Application: Aromatics
Solvent: Microcrystalline wax, 195°F. minimum melting point
Column:

Length: 20 feet
Diameter: $\frac{1}{4}$ inch
Support: Firebrick
Mesh: 40–60
Pretreat: 12 N HNO$_3$
g. Solvent/g. Support: 0.22

Operating Conditions:

Temp.: 140°C.
Carrier gas: Helium
Inlet pressure: 30
Flow rate, ml./min.: 97
Chart speed, in./min.: 1.0

B.P., °C.	Compound	Rel. Retention	Min. Past Air	Mm. Past Air
80.1	Benzene	1.0	4.8	122
110.6	Toluene	1.9	9.3	236
136.2	Ethylbenzene	3.3	16.0	406
139.1	*meta* ⎫ *para* ⎭ Xylene**	3.7	17.8	452
144.4	Orthoxylene	4.3	20.6	522
152.4	Isopropylbenzene	4.7	22.6	573

** *Meta*- and *para*-xylene isomers cannot be separated on most columns. A solvent which will separate these isomers is 1,8-diaminonaphthalene. A suggested column is 20 feet × $\frac{1}{4}$ inch O.D. with 15 percent of solvent on 40–60 mesh firebrick. Another material which is now widely used for the purpose and which separates most other isomers of a C$_6$–C$_9$ aromatics mixture is a clay known as "Bentone-34." There are several literature references on preparation and use of this material; see Mortimer, J. V., and Gent, P. L., Nature **197**, 789, 1963.

TABLE 57-20 (cont.)

B.P., °C.	Compound	Rel. Retention	Min. Past Air	Mm. Past Air
159.2	n-Propylbenzene	5.7	27.1	690
161.3	1-Methyl-4-ethyl ⎱ benzene 1-Methyl-3-ethyl ⎰	6.2	30.0	762
165.7	1,3,5-Trimethyl ⎱ benzene 1-Methyl-2-ethyl ⎰	7.0	33.4	858
169.4	1,2,4-Trimethylbenzene	8.2	39.5	976
176.1	1,2,3-Trimethylbenzene	9.4	45.3	1155
181.1	1,3-Diethylbenzene	1.0	49.2	125
183.4	1,2-Diethylbenzene ⎱	1.04	52.0	132
183.8	1,4-Diethylbenzene ⎰			
183.7	1,3-Dimethyl-5-ethylbenzene	1.10	54.3	183
186.9	1,4-Dimethyl-2-ethylbenzene	1.20	59.1	150
188.4	1,3-Dimethyl-4-ethylbenzene	1.25	61.8	157
189.8	1,2-Dimethyl-5-ethylbenzene	1.28	63.0	160
196.8	1,2,4,5–Tetramethylbenzene	1.66	81.6	207
198.0	1,2,3,5-Tetramethylbenzene	1.71	84.3	214
205.0	1,2,3,5-Tetramethylbenzene	2.03	99.7	253
217.9	Naphthalene	2.53	125.7	320

TABLE 57-21. GAS CHROMATOGRAPHY RETENTION DATA

Application: Naphthalenes
Solvent: Polyester succinate
Column:
  Length: 12 feet
  Diameter: $\frac{1}{8}$ inch
  Support: Firebrick
  Mesh: 40–60
Operating conditions:
  Temp.: 160°C.
  Carrier gas: Helium
  Inlet pressure: 20 p.s.i.g.
  Chart speed: 15 in./hr.

B.P., °C.	Compound	Rel. Retention	Min. Past Air	Mm. Past Air
218.0	Naphthalene	1.00	12.0	76
241.1	2-Methylnaphthalene	1.38	16.4	105
244.6	1-Methylnaphthalene	1.59	19.2	121
262	2,6-Dimethylnaphthalene	1.95	22.4	148
263	1,6-Dimethylnaphthalene	2.26	27.2	172
268	2,3-Dimethylnaphthalene	2.57	30.8	195
266	1,2-Dimethylnaphthalene	3.06	36.0	232

TABLE 57-22. CAPILLARY RETENTION DATA

Column coating: 400 feet Di(2-ethylhexylphthalate) and 100 feet hexamethyltetracosane
Column size: 400 feet and 100 feet × 0.01 inch
Pressure, lbs.: 30.0
Split gas, ml./min.: 200
Column outlet gas, ml./min.: 0.6
Carrier gas: Argon
Chart speed, in./hr.: 30
Column temp., °C.: 80

Unsaturated Hydrocarbons

B.P., °C.	Formula	Compound	Retention, mm.
20.06	C_5H_{10}	3-Methyl-1-butene	627.4
31.16	C_5H_{10}	2-Methyl-1-butene	655.4
41.25	C_6H_{12}	3,3-Dimethyl-1-butene	662.8
42.03	C_5H_8	1,*trans*-3-Pentadiene	700.8
44.86	C_5H_8	1,2-Pentadiene	701.8
53.87	C_6H_{12}	5-Methyl-1-pentene	703.8
48.27	C_5H_8	2,3-Pentadiene	706.0
54.18	C_6H_{12}	3-Methyl-1-pentene	708.4
56.39	C_6H_{12}	4-Methyl-*cis*-2-pentene	717.0
55.62	C_6H_{12}	2,3-Dimethyl-1-butene	719.3
44.24	C_5H_8	Cyclopentene	724.5
59.46	C_6H_{10}	1,5-Hexadiene	747.8
63.49	C_6H_{12}	1-Hexene	753.2
62.11	C_6H_{12}	2-Methyl-1-pentene	754.2
66.45	C_6H_{12}	*cis*-3-Hexene	766.2
64.79	C_6H_{12}	2-Ethyl-1-butene	769.1
67.31	C_6H_{12}	2-Methyl-2-pentene	777.1
67.88	C_6H_{12}	*trans*-2-Hexene	778.4
72.49	C_7H_{14}	4,4-Dimethyl-1-pentene	781.0
68.89	C_6H_{12}	*cis*-2-Hexene	792.5
77.54	C_7H_{14}	3,3-Dimethyl-1-pentene	828.0
81.00	C_7H_{14}	3,5-Dimethyl-1-pentene	854.6
86.00	C_7H_{14}	2-Methyl-*trans*-3-hexene	866.6
95.35	C_7H_{14}	3-Methyl-*cis*-3-hexene	866.6
86.73	C_7H_{14}	4-Methyl-1-hexene	871.6
85.31	C_7H_{14}	5-Methyl-1-hexene	888.0
84.28	C_7H_{14}	2,3-Dimethyl-1-pentene	893.5
75.80	C_6H_{10}	1-Methylcyclopentene	902.1
86.00	C_7H_{14}	5-Methyl-*trans*-2-hexene	908.0
84.00	C_7H_{14}	3-Methyl-1-hexene	908.7
87.00	C_7H_{14}	3,4-Dimethyl-*trans*-2-pentene	945.5
91.95	C_7H_{14}	2-Methyl-1-hexene	976.4
93.64	C_7H_{14}	1-Heptene	991.3
93.53	C_7H_{14}	3-Methyl-*trans*-3-hexene	995.2
97.95	C_7H_{14}	*trans*-3-heptene	997.2
102	C_8H_{16}	2,5 Dimethyl-*trans*-3-hexene	1000.8
82.98	C_7H_{12}	Cyclohexene	1009.0
86	C_7H_{14}	2-Methyl-*cis*-3-hexene	1014.2
95.44	C_7H_{14}	2-Methyl-2-hexene	1017.3
98.10	C_7H_{12}	3-Ethylcyclopentene	1255.2
116.26	C_8H_{16}	2,3,4-Trimethyl-2-pentene	1404.0
110.00	C_7H_{12}	1-Methylcyclohexene	1475.0
121.28	C_8H_{16}	1-Octene	1527.0
110.50	C_8H_{16}	2,3-Dimethyl-1-hexene	1588.5
97.40	C_7H_{14}	2,3-Dimethyl-2-pentene	1697.0
136.00	C_8H_{14}	1-Ethylcyclohexene	2519.0
137.00	C_8H_{14}	1,2-Dimethylcyclohexene	2612.0
146.87	C_9H_{18}	1-Nonene	2714.6

TABLE 57-23. CAPILLARY RETENTION DATA

Column coating: Polyalkylene glycol derivative, intermediate viscosity grade
Column size: 370 feet × 0.010 inches I.D. (N.S.)
Pressure, lbs.: 30.0
Split gas, ml./min.: 200
Column outlet gas, ml./min.: 1.2
Carrier gas: Argon
Chart speed, in./hr.: 30
Column temp., °C.: 125

Alkyl Benzenes

B.P., °C.	Formula	Compound	Retention, mm.
80.1	C₆H₆	Benzene	223.4
110.6	C₇H₈	Methylbenzene	260.8
136.2	C₈H₁₀	Ethylbenzene	307.0
138.4	C₈H₁₀	1,4-Dimethylbenzene	313.9
139.1	C₈H₁₀	1,3-Dimethylbenzene	317.6
144.4	C₈H₁₀	1,2-Dimethylbenzene	342.4
152.4	C₉H₁₂	Isopropylbenzene	344.6
159.2	C₉H₁₂	n-Propylbenzene	375.5
161.3	C₉H₁₂	1-Methyl-3-ethylbenzene	390.5
162.0	C₉H₁₂	1-Methyl-4-ethylbenzene	391.5
169.1	C₁₀H₁₄	tert-Butylbenzene	407.5
164.7	C₉H₁₂	1,3,5-Trimethylbenzene	412.0
172.8	C₁₀H₁₄	Isobutylbenzene	422.0
165.1	C₉H₁₂	1-Methyl-2-ethylbenzene	425.2
173.3	C₁₀H₁₄	sec-Butylbenzene	427.9
175.1	C₁₀H₁₄	1-Methyl-3-isopropylbenzene	443.8
177.1	C₁₀H₁₄	1-Methyl-4-isopropylbenzene	451.4
169.4	C₉H₁₂	1,2,4-Trimethylbenzene	455.0
178.2	C₁₀H₁₄	1-Methyl-2-isopropylbenzene	486.4
181.1	C₁₀H₁₄	1,3-Diethylbenzene	496.4
181.8	C₁₀H₁₄	1-Methyl-3-propylbenzene	500.6
183.3	C₁₀H₁₄	n-Butylbenzene	506.8
183.3	C₁₀H₁₄	1-Methyl-4-propylbenzene	507.6
183.8	C₁₀H₁₄	1,4-Diethylbenzene	514.0
176.1	C₉H₁₂	1,2,3-Trimethylbenzene	527.8
183.8	C₁₀H₁₄	1,3-Dimethyl-5-ethylbenzene	531.8
183.4	C₁₀H₁₄	1,2-Diethylbenzene	536.8
184.8	C₁₀H₁₄	1-Methyl-2-propylbenzene	547.6
192.8	C₁₁H₁₆	1-Methyl-4-tert-butylbenzene	550.6
192.4	C₁₁H₁₆	2-Phenyl-2-methylbutane	562.0
186.9	C₁₀H₁₄	1-5-Dimethyl-2-ethylbenzene	577.8
188.4	C₁₀H₁₄	1-3-Dimethyl-4-ethylbenzene	590.0
189.8	C₁₀H₁₄	1-2-Dimethyl-4-ethylbenzene	607.0
193.9	C₁₀H₁₄	1-2-Dimethyl-3-ethylbenzene	693.6
196.8	C₁₀H₁₄	1-2-4-5-Tetramethylbenzene	738.6
205.4	C₁₁H₁₆	n-Pentylbenzene	749.0
198.0	C₁₀H₁₄	1,2,3,5-Tetramethylbenzene	767.6
205.0	C₁₀H₁₄	1,2,3,4-Tetramethylbenzene	908.6

TABLE 57-24. CAPILLARY GAS CHROMATOGRAPHY: EXAMPLES OF OPERATING CONDITIONS

	Crude Naphtha 200–350°F.	Aviation Alkylate	Nonaromatic Naphtha C8–C34	Aromatic Naphtha 250–450°F.	Jet Fuel	Narrow Boiling Naphthas		
						350–400°F.	400–500°F.	500–600°F.
Column Dimensions	300 ft. × 0.01 in.	300 ft. × 0.01 in.	100 ft. × 0.01 in.	300 ft. × 0.01 in.	300 ft. × 0.01 in.	100 ft. × 0.01 in.	100 ft. × 0.01 in.	100 ft. × 0.01 in.
	Polydimethylsiloxane			Polyethylene glycol		Polydimethylsiloxane		
Solvent	liquid	liquid	gum		liquid	gum	gum	gum
Program								
Initial °C.	40	35	80	56	70	65	60	60
Final °C.	110	140	220	130	155	165	200	200
Rate, °C./min.	10	4	5	2	2	4	5	5
Holding time, Min.								
Initial	12	18	5	10	10	15	5	5
Final	35	15	30	30	20	20	10	10
Injection temp. °C.	200	190	280	233	180	280	280	280
Gas Pressures, p.s.i.g.								
Hydrogen	15	15	12.5	15	15	15	15	15
Helium	40	40	20	40	40	20	20	20
Air	30	30	30	30	30	30	30	30
Splitter ratio	300/1	300/1	300/1	300/1	300/1	300/1	300/1	300/1
Sample, ml. liquid	0.002	0.002	0.001	0.001	0.001	0.001	0.001	0.001
Chromatograph attenuation	50	100	50	20	20	100	50	20
Recorder, mv.	5	5	5	5	5	5	5	5
Instrument time, total mins.	50	55	40	70	70	25	25	40

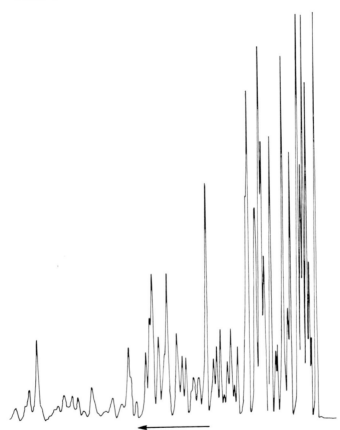

FIG. 57-16.   Capillary Gas Chromatography; Portion of Recorder Chart from Analysis of Fraction of a Cracked Naphtha.

kerosene and gas oil boiling range above about 400°F., the analysis becomes largely one of type analysis by narrow boiling fraction and carbon number.

The foregoing may suggest the logical attack on a wide boiling sample which includes material boiling into the kerosene range or higher. The sample is distilled to obtain narrow boiling fractions. The lower boiling fractions are analyzed directly by gas chromatography with the aid of mass spectrometry to save time. All fractions above 175°F. are then subjected to "FIA type" liquid chromatography (see ASTM D 1319) to separate into aromatics, unsaturates, and paraffins plus naphthenes. Each of the narrow boiling type fractions is then gas chromatographed using a capillary column, the outlet of which is directed to a mass spectrometer. The mass spectrometer is essential for the type characterization part of the analysis, although other refinements, such as the addition of selective dehydrogenation to differentiate between cyclopentanes and cyclohexanes, may aid it.

The elaborate analytical scheme described in the foregoing yields essentially complete hydrocarbon breakdown through 300°F., partial identification to about 400°F., and type analysis from there on. An example of an actual scheme which was used for lower boiling samples, to about 330°F., is shown in Table 57-25. In one noteworthy effort[89]

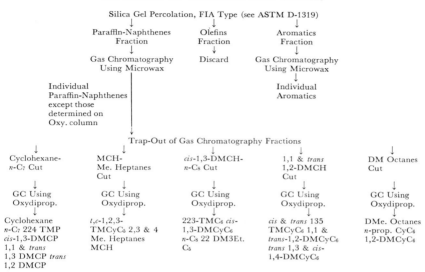

TABLE 57-25. RECOMMENDED CHROMATOGRAPHIC SCHEME FOR ANALYTICAL SEPARATION OF REFORMER FEED SAMPLES

NOTES: Microwax column, 30 feet × ¼ inch at 140°C.
Oxydipropionitrile column, 50 feet × ¼ inch at 71.5°C.

total crudes were analyzed by the combination of distillation, gas chromatography, and mass spectrometry.

SELECTED BIBLIOGRAPHY

The following is a brief compilation of recommended reading and useful references.

Textbooks

Phillips, Courtenay, Gas Chromatography, Academic Press, New York, 1956.
Keulemans, A.I.M., Gas Chromatography, 2nd Ed., Reinhold Publishing Co., New York, 1957.
Pecsok, Robert L., Principles and Practice of Gas Chromatography, John Wiley, New York, 1959.
Bayer, Ernst, Gas Chromatography, Elsevier Publishing Co., Amsterdam, The Netherlands, 1961.
Ambrose, D., and Ambrose, B. A., Gas Chromatography, D. Van Nostrand Co., Princeton, 1962.
Dal Nogare, S., and Juvet, R. S., Gas Chromatography: Theory and Practice, John Wiley, New York, 1962.
Knox, J. H., Gas Chromatography, John Wiley, New York, 1962.
Purnell, Howard, Gas Chromatography, John Wiley, New York, 1962.
Littlewood, A. B., Gas Chromatography: Principles, Techniques and Applications, Academic Press, New York, 1962.

[89] Martin, R. L., Winters, J. C., and Williams, J. A., "Composition of Crude Oils by Gas Chromatography: Geological Significance of Hydrocarbon Distribution," presented at the 6th World Petroleum Congress, Frankfort, Germany, June, 1963.

Kaiser, Rudolf, Gas Phase Chromatography, Butterworth's, London, 1963.
Ettre, L. S., Open Tubular Columns in Gas Chromatography, Plenum Press, New York, 1965.

Symposia

ISA Meetings at Lansing, Michigan:
   1957 meeting, Coates, Noebels, and Fagerson, Academic Press, New York, 1958.
   1959 meeting, Noebels, Wall, and Brenner, Academic Press, New York, 1961.
   1961 meeting, Brenner, Callan, and Weiss, Academic Press, New York, 1962.
   1963 meeting, Lewis Fowler, Academic Press, New York, 1963.
Institute of Petroleum Meetings, Europe and British Isles:
   1956 meeting (London), D. H. Desty, Academic Press, New York, 1957.
   1958 meeting (Amsterdam), D. H. Desty, Academic Press, New York, 1958.
   1960 meeting (Edinburgh), R. P. W. Scott, Butterworth's, London, 1960.
   1962 meeting (Hamburg), M. van Swaay, Butterworth's, London, 1963.

Abstracts (bound volumes)

Knapman, C. E. H., Gas Chromatography Abstracts, Butterworth's, Washington, D. C. Separate volumes for each year; specify year.
Preston, Seaton T., Jr., A Comprehensive Bibliography and Index to the Literature on Gas Chromatography, Preston Technical Abstracts, Co., Evanston, Illinois.
Signeur, Austin V., Guide to Gas Chromatography Literature, Plenum Press, New York.

Journals

Journal of Gas Chromatography, Evanston, Illinois.
Analytical Chemistry, American Chemical Society, Washington, D. C.
Journal of Chromatography, Elsevier Publishing Co., Amsterdam, The Netherlands.

Chapter 58

PLASTICS

By John G. Cobler
The Dow Chemical Co.
Midland, Michigan

A revolution in analytical chemistry is occurring with the introduction of new and improved instrumental methods of analysis. The application of these new instrumental techniques to the study of the composition and structure of plastics provides information which could not have been obtained even a few years ago. In addition, instrumental approaches frequently provide more accurate and/or reproducible data and in a much shorter time than the classical or conventional analytical approach. The fundamental principles of the various instruments have been discussed in the first part of this volume. This chapter will present practical methods for the application ot some of these instruments to the determination of specific plastic components or polymer structural arrangements. Although the methods will be limited in scope to specific applications, the techniques and principles may be applied to the study of plastic materials in general. No attempt has been made to present a schematic system for the complete analysis of individual plastics. Rather, the chapter attempts to show the applicability of instrumental techniques by presenting typical examples utilizing each instrument.

NUCLEAR MAGNETIC RESONANCE SPECTROMETRY

Nuclear magnetic resonance (NMR) spectrometry is being utilized for determining certain physical and chemical structural features, particularly those related to proton or F^{19} resonances.

"Wide-line" (relaxation) spectra obtained with solid polymers provide information concerning the nature and frequency of the motion of polymer molecules as a function of temperature. Crystallinity is observed as a broad band in pure polymers, whereas the amorphous regions are represented by narrow bands. As the temperature rises, motion increases at a faster rate within the amorphous regions than in the crystalline regions, resulting in a narrowing of the lines.[1] Low molecular weight impurities such as water,[2] plasticizers, or solvents[3] may result in a narrowing of lines or the superimposition of a narrow line on the broad line of the solid. Glick, et al.,[4] used wide-line NMR to study irradiated and unirradiated polyethylenes. The first effect of radiation was an increase in segmental mobility due to loss of order in the crystalline regions, as indicated by a change in the second moment derived from line shape vs. temperature. Further irradiation resulted in a loss in mobility as a result of crosslinking.

[1] Collins, R. L., J. Polymer Sci., 27, 67, 1958; Slichter, W. P., and Mandell, E. R., J. Appl. Phys., 29, 1438, 1958; Powles, J. G., and Kail, A. E., J. Polymer Sci., 31, 183, 1958.
[2] Powles, J. G., Polymer, 1, 219, 1960.
[3] Kosfeld, R., and Jenckel, E., Kolloid-Z., 165, 136, 1959; Nolle, A. W., and Billings, J. J., J. Chem. Phys., 30, 84, 1959.
[4] Glick, R. E., Gupta, R. P., Sauer, J. A., and Woodward, A. E., Polymer, 1, 340, 1960.

High resolution spectra, obtainable with moderately dilute polymer solutions, appear to be suitable for determining chemical structure. Naylor and Lasoski[5] found that most of the generalizations previously deduced from small molecules would apply to polymeric materials. Attempts have been made to correlate hyperfine structure with varying degrees of tacticity.

Figure 58-1 shows the spectra for 15 percent solutions of two methyl methacrylate polymers in chloroform.[6] The peak positions are expressed on the "τ-scale," on which the resonance of the methyl group of tetramethylsilane is defined as $+10.000$ p.p.m. The peak at 6.40τ is that of the methoxyl group, whereas the peak at approximately 3τ is that of the chloroform proton. The triplet at 8.78τ, 8.95τ, and 9.09τ is interpreted in terms of isotactic, heterotactic, and syndiotactic sequences, respectively. The spectra show that the n-butyl lithium catalyzed polymer is rich in isotactic sequences, whereas the benzoyl peroxide polymer is rich in syndiotactic sequences.

It appears possible, also, to obtain information concerning the sequences and stereochemical configuration of monomer units in certain copolymer systems.[7] Solutions of 0.10 g. of a styrene-methyl methacrylate copolymer in 0.5 ml. of solvent, containing 2 percent tetramethylsilane as the internal standard, were prepared. The solutions were transferred to Pyrex NMR tubes, which were then evacuated and sealed under 400-mm. nitrogen pressure. Scans were made at 90°C. Carbon tetrachloride and chloroform were both used as solvents. Chloroform is the preferred solvent for obtaining good resolution; however, the chloroform proton resonance obscures the resonance of the phenyl proton of the styrene units. As indicated above, the methoxyl group in the poly(methyl methacrylate) is represented by a single narrow line at 6.40τ. In the styrene-methyl methacrylate copolymers, the resonance of the methoxyl group is influenced by configuration and proximity of styrene units and appears as a multiplicity of peaks in the 6.4τ to 8τ region of the copolymer spectra.

Naylor and Lasoski[8] examined poly(vinylidene) fluoride and ascribed a head-to-head structure on the basis of the assignment of one fluorine resonance. Methods have been developed for determining chain branching in ethylene homopolymers and the copolymer ratio of ethylene-ethyl acrylate and ethylene-vinyl acetate copolymers using a conventional spectrometer probe at 240°C.[9] Chen[10] used NMR to determine the cis-1,4-

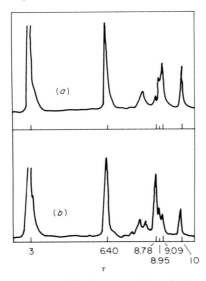

FIG. 58-1. NMR Spectra of Methyl Methacrylate Homopolymers. (a) Polymerization Catalyzed with Benzoyl Peroxide; (b) Polymerization Catalyzed with n-Butyl Lithium. (Courtesy John Wiley and Sons, Inc.)

[5] Naylor, R. E., Jr., and Lasoski, S. W., J. Polymer Sci., 44, 1, 1960.
[6] Bovey, F. A., and Tiers, G. V. D., J. Polymer Sci., 44, 173, 1960.
[7] Bovey, F. A., J. Polymer Sci., 62, 197, 1962. (Courtesy John Wiley and Sons, Inc.)
[8] Naylor, R. E., Jr., and Lasoski, S. W., Jr., J. Polymer Sci., 44, 1, 1960.
[9] Porter, R. S., Nicksic, S. W., and Johnson, J. F., Anal. Chem., 35, 1948, 1963.
[10] Chen, H. Y., Anal. Chem., 34, 1793, 1962.

and *trans*-1,4-contents of polyisoprene with an error of less than 0.5 percent. Johnson and Shoolery[11] determined the total number of hydrogen atoms and the olefin protons in a molecule and used these data to calculate the iodine number and the molecular weight.

DETERMINATION OF THE RATIO OF METHYL METHACRYLATE UNITS TO ETHYL ACRYLATE UNITS IN COPOLYMERS[12]

Scope.—This method is applicable to copolymers containing any ratio of methyl methacrylate to ethyl acrylate units. The method can be extended to other copolymers where a portion of each unit has a resonance not overlapped by that of another unit.

Principle.—The methyl proton resonance of the methoxyl group from −3.3 to −3.7 p.p.m. (Note a) is compared to the methylene proton resonance of the ethoxyl group from −3.7 to −4.5 p.p.m. Since nuclear magnetic resonance peak areas are directly proportional to the number of protons present, the ratio of methyl methacrylate to ethyl acrylate units can be calculated directly from the integral.

Apparatus. Varian A-60 Nuclear Magnetic Resonance Spectrometer and Sample Holder.

Glass Plate for casting the polymer film.

Reagents. Benzene, A.R. grade containing 2 percent tetramethylsilane as the reference standard.

Procedure.—Cast a film of the latex or lacquer on the glass plate. Allow the water, monomers, and other volatiles to evaporate. Dissolve the film in benzene at room temperature by preparing solutions containing from 3 to 7 weight percent polymer and shaking on a mechanical shaker for at least 1 hr. Transfer 1 to 2 ml. of the solution into the NMR sample tube. Adjust the instrument for the best signal-to-noise ratio and resolution. Room temperature scans appear to be the most reliable. Run the spectrum and the integral of the peak areas, using the electronic integrating system incorporated in the instrument (Fig. 58-2).

Calculations (Note b).

$$\text{Mole percent methyl methacrylate} = \frac{\frac{1}{3}Am \times 100}{\frac{1}{2}Ae \times \frac{1}{3}Am}$$

where Am = peak area −3.3 p.p.m. to −3.7 p.p.m. = 3 protons (b) of methyl methacrylate, and

Ae = peak area −3.7 p.p.m. to −4.5 p.p.m. = 2 protons (a) of ethyl acrylate.

Methyl Methacrylate Units	*Ethyl Acrylate Units*
CH₃	—CH₂—CH—
│	│
—CH₂—C—	C=O
│	│
C=O	O
│	│
O	CH₂ (a)
│	│
CH₃ (b)	CH₃

NOTES.—(a) The instrument is adjusted to place the tetramethylsilane peak at the $\delta = 0$ (p.p.m.) position.

$$\delta \text{ (p.p.m.)} = \frac{\Delta \text{ tetramethylsilane} \times 10^6}{\text{oscillator frequency (c/s)}}$$

[11] Johnson, L. F., and Shoolery, J. N., Anal. Chem., **34**, 1136, 1962.
[12] Vander Wal, R. P., The Dow Chemical Company, unpublished manuscript.

Δ is minus where the peaks are downfield and plus where the peaks are upfield. Thus at 10,000 gauss applied field, a δ of -1 p.p.m. implies a line at a field 0.010 gauss lower (downfield) than the reference material. Chemical shifts are sometimes based on the τ-scale where:

$$\tau \text{ (p.p.m.)} = 10 + \frac{\Delta \text{ tetramethylsilane} \times 10^6}{\text{oscillator frequency (c/s)}}$$

Thus a δ of -1 p.p.m. would be equivalent to a τ of 9 p.p.m.
  (b) accuracy is ± 3 percent of the amount present.

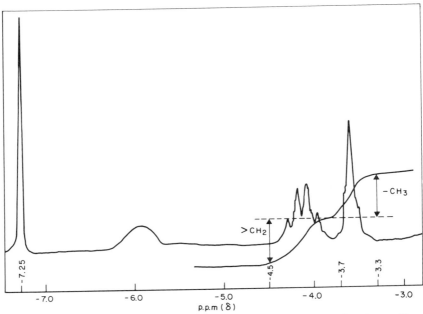

FIG. 58-2.   NMR Spectrum of Methyl Methacrylate–Ethyl Acrylate Copolymer Showing Electronically Determined Integral.

CRYSTALLINITY IN POLYMERS AND X-RAY DIFFRACTION ANALYSIS

It is customary to describe polymers as composites of two highly dispersed solid phases, one of which is amorphous, the other crystalline.[13] A single polymer chain can assume a number of configurations because of freedom of rotation about the bonds connecting the chain atoms. The liquid or amorphous state is characterized by chain units of different molecules arranged in a random array uncoordinated with one another. Under appropriate thermodynamic conditions, polymer chains possessing a sufficient regularity of chain elements undergo a spontaneous ordering of portions of the chain molecules, resulting in a state of three-dimensional configurational order with the freedom of rotation lost.

In the polymer types usually encountered, the crystalline or ordered regions, called

[13] An alternate approach, but one not so amenable to simple calculation, is through the concept of a single "paracrystalline" phase, as discussed by Hosemann, R., and Bagchi, S. N., Direct Analysis of Diffraction by Matter, North-Holland Publishing Co., Amsterdam, 1962.

crystallites, are on the order of 100 A in diameter, and presumably spaced in a matrix of the amorphous phase. A single long-chain polymer molecule, perhaps 5000 A in length, may thus be incorporated into several distinct regions, alternately crystalline and amorphous. Any discussion of polymer crystallinity is somewhat idealized, however. The crystalline state of a polymeric system is highly complex, as evidenced by the polycrystalline character and the fact that the crystallizing entities, repeating chain units, are not isolated structures, but are covalently linked units in molecules comprising many thousands of such units.

In some polymeric substances, such as atactic polystyrene, relatively few crystallites are present. In others, such as linear polyethylene, a relatively large number of crystallites are present and the polymers are highly crystalline. The weight percent of crystallites in a chosen sample is called the degree of crystallinity of that sample. This property depends chiefly on the size and shape of the constituent molecules, on the conditions of polymerization, and on subsequent physical treatment of the resulting polymer. The degree of crystallinity is an extremely important characteristic of a polymer, for it, together with the average molecular weight, largely determines such macroscopic properties as density, melting point, tensile strength, and hardness. The resistance to deformation, or the recovery from it, in fibers and films, is dependent upon the amount of order in an oriented polymer.

Various techniques are available to estimate the degree of crystallinity of polymers; most of these give relative and not absolute values. The practical difficulty is that all of the methods are based on the interpretation of data which are only incidentally related to the degree of crystallinity as defined above. In all of the methods, of course, it is necessary to observe differences in the properties of the two phases present.

One of the simplest of the techniques is based on the determination of density. The density of the ordered crystalline phase of a polymer is greater than that of the disordered amorphous phase, because ordering results in the tighter packing of molecules. If the densities of the crystalline phase and of the amorphous phase of a particular polymer are known, and if one assumes that the degree of crystallinity is a linear function of density, then the determination of crystallinity should be straightforward. Unfortunately, the two "if" clauses represent two weak steps in the argument. For example, the density of amorphous polyethylene at room temperature is not accurately known, and there is evidence that the density of the crystalline phase is not constant, but varies according to physical treatment of the sample. Parameters other than the extent of crystallization affect the apparent density of a polymer sample—inclusions, impurities, surface bubbles, and accidental compressions, to name the more obvious.

Some absorption bands in the infrared spectra of polymers show variations which can be related to changes in crystalline content. The 13.7-μ band of polyethylene and the 10.7-μ band of nylon, for example, are very pronounced in highly crystalline samples of the respective polymers, but are quite unimportant features of the spectra of polymers of low crystallinity. Conversely, some bands are strong in amorphous substances, but decrease in value as crystallinity increases. Observable spectrum differences in various samples of the same polymer type can be seen, but these differences cannot be well related to the degrees of crystallinity established by other methods for the same samples. It is difficult to prepare a polymer sample for infrared analysis without inducing a change either in crystallinity or orientation, which may account for these discrepancies.

A direct method which is sometimes used to estimate crystallinity is that of differential solubility. It is known that the amorphous phase of a polymer usually is more soluble in a selected solvent than is the crystalline phase. This leads to a simple experimental procedure which has been applied to many polymer types. The results are not generally as reproducible as those obtained from other methods.

The heat of fusion of a polymer sample may be used to estimate crystalline content, for the higher the degree of crystallinity, the greater the heat of fusion must be. This also applies to the heat of solution of the polymer. These thermodynamic techniques have been applied principally to polyethylene, as have the other methods already described.

All polymers produce a unique diffraction pattern when a directed beam of mono-chromatic x-radiation strike them. The diffraction pattern shows distinct maxima representative of crystalline and amorphous regions. Techniques based on the analysis of the diffraction pattern are perhaps the most universally used and the most reliable techniques for estimating crystallinity. In fact, it is common to define crystallinity in terms of the orderly lattice array, as determined by x-ray diffraction measurements.

The x-ray crystallinity of polyethylene has been studied by Nichols[14] and by Aggarwal and Tilley.[15] Natta and coworkers[16] and Farrow[17] applied the technique to polypropylene, whereas polyethylene terephthalate was examined by Farrow and Preston.[18]

The following method describes the general x-ray diffraction technique for the estimation of crystallinity employing polyethylene as a specific example.[19]

ESTIMATION OF CRYSTALLINITY IN POLYETHYLENE

Scope.—This procedure is suitable for determining the percent crystallinity in polyethylenes.

Principle.—The x-ray diffraction pattern of the polymer is resolved into the sharp diffraction peaks from the crystalline phase, and the diffuse background from the amorphous phase. The percentage crystallinity is calculated from the integrated intensities (peak areas), assuming equivalence in scattering power of regions of equal mass. Appropriate factors are applied to correct for atomic scattering, absorption, temperature, and diffraction angle.[15]

Apparatus. **Norelco Wide-Range Diffractometer,** Model 4220, or equivalent, with water-cooled diffraction unit and employing, as the monochromatic beam, the characteristic x-radiation of copper filtered through nickel.

Norelco Sample Holder, modified to give a sample area 10 mm. $\times$ 30 mm. in size.

Operating Conditions:

Operating potential	32 kv.
X-ray tube current	20 mA.
Geiger counter	Dead time 280 ms. operated at 100 volts overvoltage
Diffractometer scan	1°(2θ) per minute
Recorder chart	0.5 in. per minute

Procedure.—Although the particle size of the sample has been shown to have a negligible effect on the observed crystallinity, it is preferable to use films or moldings. Powders or pellets are pressed into flat discs at approximately 5000 p.s.i. The discs are trimmed to 10 $\times$ 30 mm. to fit the sample holder.

The diffraction pattern of the sample is recorded on standard chart paper in the range from 10.0° to 30.0° in 2θ (this range is employed for all polymers).

[14] Nichols, J. B., J. Appl. Phys., **25**, 840, 1954.
[15] Aggarwal, S. L., and Tilley, G. P., J. Polymer Sci., **18**, 17, 1955.
[16] Natta, G., Corradini, P., Cesari, M., Atti. accad. Nazl. Lincei Rend., **8**, 11, 1957.
[17] Farrow, G., Polymer (London), **2**, 409, 1961.
[18] Farrow, G., Preston, D., Brit. J. Appl. Phys., **11**, 353, 1960.
[19] Petersen, D. R., The Dow Chemical Company, unpublished manuscript.

Calculation.—The area above the baseline is divided into two parts: a broad diffuse peak representing the diffraction from the amorphous material and several sharp peaks representing diffractions from the crystalline planes.

Draw a baseline tangent to the straight-line portions of the curve at approximately 14.5° and 26.5° (Fig. 58-3a). Draw a line perpendicular from the baseline at 19.5°

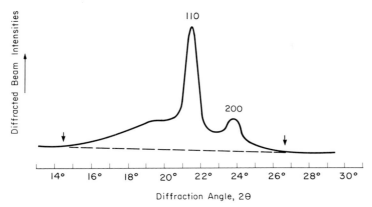

FIG. 58-3a.   X-Ray Diffraction Diagram of Polyethylene Showing Total Intensity Curve.

(center of the amorphous scattering peak) to the maximum of the curve (Fig. 58-3b). The amorphous area is then resolved as a symmetrical curve utilizing the 19.5° peak as the peak height. Drop lines from the maxima of the 110 and 200 peaks to the baseline at 21.5° and 23.8°, respectively. Measure the distance in mm., along these vertical lines,

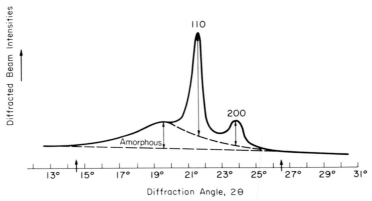

FIG. 58-3b.   Technique for Resolving Total Intensity Curve into Curves for Amorphous and Crystalline Peaks.

from the intersection of the vertical lines and the resolved amorphous curve, to the maxima of the crystalline peaks. These distances represent the calculated peak heights for resolving the 110 and 200 peaks. Resolve the two peaks into symmetrical crystalline

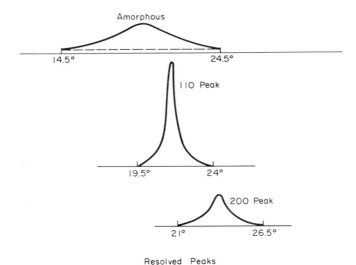

Resolved Peaks

FIG. 58-3c. Total Intensity Curve Resolved into Curves for Diffracted X-Ray Intensities from Amorphous and Crystalline Peaks.

scattering areas (Fig. 58-3c). Measure the area of the two crystalline peaks and of the amorphous peak with a planimeter.

$$\text{Percent of crystallinity} = \frac{A_{110} + 1.43A_{200}}{0.69A_a + A_{110} + 1.43A_{200}} \times 100$$

where A_{110} = area of 110 crystalline peak,
A_{200} = area of 200 crystalline peak, and
A_a = area of amorphous peak.

The numerical value obtained in this way, commonly in the range 65–95 weight percent crystalline, matches reasonably well the value obtained from density measurements.[15]

X-RAY FLUORESCENCE

X-ray fluorescence analysis provides a rapid and nondestructive technique for determining elements with atomic number of 11 (sodium) or higher independent of their chemical bonding. The sample is irradiated with high-intensity x-rays. The resulting energy changes appear as photons with wavelengths characteristic of the atom. These fluorescent x-ray photons characterize the element, and their frequency of occurrence is proportional to the amount of this element present.

The following procedure[20] describes the determination of zinc stearate (as zinc) as a surface additive on plastics employing a single-channel spectrometer. This procedure provides for the separation of the surface additive prior to measurement. Separations or other sample treatment are unnecessary, however, if a total element concentration in a sample is to be determined. Multichannel spectrometers are also available whereby

[20] McLaughlin, E. L., The Dow Chemical Company, unpublished manuscript.

a number of elements may be determined successively in a single run with suitable programming.

DETERMINATION OF ZINC STEARATE AS SURFACE ADDITIVE ON POLYMERS

Scope.—This method provides for the determination of zinc stearate on the surface of polymer granules in the range of 0.05 to 0.1 percent.

Principle.—A weighed portion of the sample is washed with warm dilute nitric acid, after which the supernatant liquor is analyzed for zinc by x-ray fluorescence.

Apparatus. **X-ray Spectrometer** (Philips Electronics X-ray scanning spectrometer or equivalent), single-channel scanning x-ray fluorescence spectrometer having a single LiF crystal, a tungsten target source, a scintillation counter, nickel tube collimation, and helium atmosphere attachment.

Round Stainless-steel Sample Cell in which the area exposed to the x-radiation is 1.5 in. in diameter and 0.25 in. in depth and covered with a Mylar film.

Aluminum Holder for Sample Cell.

Analytical Conditions:

Voltage	50 kv.
Current	20 mA.
Operation	Fixed count
Goniometer	41.74° (may vary slightly)
Scale factors	128 × 8 × 100

Standards.—Dissolve 3.723 g. of zinc nitrate $[Zn(NO_3)_2 \cdot 3H_2O]$ in water and dilute to 100 ml. to obtain a 1 percent zinc solution (1 ml. = 0.01 g. zinc). Prepare dilutions of the 1 percent zinc stock solution as follows: Dilute 10 ml. of the stock solution to 100 ml. to obtain solution A (0.001 mg./ml.).

Dilute 1 ml. of solution A to 100 ml. to obtain a solution 0.005 percent (50 p.p.m.) with respect to zinc (484 p.p.m. with respect to zinc stearate).

Preparation of Calibration Curve.—Transfer portions of the dilute standards to the sample cells and cover with the Mylar film. Care must be taken to see that there are no bubbles under the film.

Scan the samples, recording the time interval for each. Convert the time intervals to counts per second using the formula $102,400/T$, where T equals time in seconds. Prepare an analytical curve by plotting the counts per second *vs.* concentrations of zinc stearate in p.p.m.

Procedure.—Weigh exactly 8.00 g. of the sample into a 50-ml. beaker. Cover the granules with 6–8 ml. of distilled water and 2 ml. of concentrated nitric acid. Heat the mixture on a hot plate for 10–15 min., but do not let the solution come to a vigorous boil. Drain the liquor by decantation into a 150-ml. beaker. Wash the remaining sample at least 3 times with dilute nitric acid, adding each washing to the 150-ml. beaker. Evaporate the wash solution almost to dryness and dilute to exactly 8 ml. with distilled water.

Transfer a portion of the solution to the sample cell and scan as described above, recording the time interval per sample.

Calculations.—Convert the time interval into counts per second using the following formula:

$$\text{Counts per second} = \frac{102,400}{\text{time in seconds}}$$

Read the concentration of zinc stearate in p.p.m. from the analytical curve.

RADIOCHEMICAL ANALYSIS

Polymeric materials are tailored for specific end uses by copolymerizing two or more monomers in definite proportions. Since the exact composition of these polymers frequently differs from the monomer charge, considerable effort has been devoted to the development of methods for their analysis. Infrared spectrometric techniques are rapid and specific; however, it has been shown that the band intensity ratios may vary in going from homopolymer blends to copolymers or terpolymers. Therefore, polymers of known composition are required as standards for calibration. Radiotracer techniques, either alone or combined with standard chemical methods, provide a reliable method for determining the correct composition of polymers. The technique is generally applicable where a component of the polymer can be synthesized from radioactive materials.

Sterling, *et al.*,[21] have reported the standardization of the infrared spectrometric analysis of terpolymer rubbers based on the radioassay of the methylisopropenyl ketone component synthesized from HCHO—C^{14}. Natta, *et al.*,[22] and Lomonte and Tirpak[23] prepared radioactive ethylene-propylene copolymers for standardizing the infrared analysis. Stoffer and Smith[24] described a method for determining the composition of labeled ethylene-propylene copolymer standards involving liquid scintillation counting. The labeled standards were used to develop an infrared method correlating absorbance at 8.7 μ with methyl branching. Drushel and Iddings[25] prepared carbon[14] labeled standards for the examination of ethylene-propylene copolymers by a modification of the Stoffer and Smith technique. Gibson and Heidner[26] applied the radioassay technique to the analysis of acrylonitrile-vinyl acetate copolymers.

A typical application of the radioassay technique is presented below.[27] The method utilizes the radioassay of ethylene-C^{14}-propylene copolymers for standardizing the infrared spectrometric analysis.

THE DETERMINATION OF COMBINED ETHYLENE IN ETHYLENE-PROPYLENE COPOLYMERS

Scope.—This method provides for the infrared spectrometric determination of ethylene in ethylene-propylene copolymers and for the standardization of the technique by radioassay of ethylene-C^{14}-propylene copolymers.

Principle.—Polymer films are scanned from 5 to 16 μ. The intensities of the 7.25-μ band (methyl group) and 6.84-μ band (methylene group) are measured and the ratio obtained. The concentration of ethylene is read from an analytical curve prepared by plotting intensity ratios *vs.* percentage ethylene, as determined by radioassay.

PREPARATION OF RADIOACTIVE ETHYLENE-PROPYLENE COPOLYMERS AND RADIOASSAY

Apparatus. **Mixing Bombs,** 3-liter autoclave bomb.
Gas Chromatograph.

[21] Sterling, G. B., Cobler, J. G., Erley, D. S., Blanchard, F., Anal. Chem., **31**, 1612, 1959.
[22] Natta, G., Mazzanti, G., Valvassori, A., and Pajaro, G., Chim. e ind. (Milan), **39**, 733, 1957.
[23] Lomonte, J. N., and Tirpak, G. A., J. Polymer Sci., Part A, **2**, 705, 1964.
[24] Stoffer, R. L., and Smith, W. E., Anal. Chem., **33**, 1112, 1961; Smith, W. E., Stoffer, R. L., and Hannan, R. B., J. Polymer Sci., **61**, 39, 1962.
[25] Drushel, H. V., and Iddings, F. A., Anal. Chem., **35**, 28, 1963.
[26] Gibson, M. E., Jr., and Heidner, R. H., Anal. Chem., **33**, 1825, 1961.
[27] Burgert, B. E., Blanchard., F. A., Takahashi, I. T., and Johnson, A., The Dow Chemical Company, unpublished manuscript.

Liquid Scintillation Spectrometer, Tri-Carb, Model 314-X. Packard Instrument Company, La Grange, Illinois.

Polymerization Flasks, 1-liter glass flasks.

Reagents. **Ethylene-C^{14},** 50 μC (microcuries), Volk Radio Chemical Company, Chicago, Illinois.

Benzoic-C^{14} Acid, 5000 d.p.m./mg. (disintegrations per minute per milligram), standard source compound. New England Nuclear Corporation, Boston, Massachusetts. Accurately weigh out 500 mg. and dissolve in toluene. Dilute to 50 ml.

Ethylene, polymerization grade.

Propylene, polymerization grade.

Polymerization Catalyst.—Triethyl aluminum: transition-metal or other suitable catalyst system.

Cab-O-Sil®, Ms (99.0 to 97.7 percent SiO$_2$). Cabot Corporation, Boston, Massachusetts.

Scintillator Solution.—Dissolve 4 g. of 2,5-diphenyloxazole (PPO) and 0.1 g. of 1,4-bis-2(5-phenyloxazolyl)benzene (POPOP) in toluene and dilute to 1 liter.

Cab-O-Sil Scintillator Solution.—Add 35 g. of Cab-O-Sil to 1 liter of scintillator solution.

Procedure.—Evacuate the 3-liter autoclave bomb and introduce 50 μC of ethylene-C^{14}. Bring the bomb to atmospheric pressure with the inactive polymerization grade ethylene. The dilution is chosen to give a specific activity which will allow the determination to a 1 percent standard deviation. The specific activity of the diluted ethylene-C^{14} must be accurately determined. In order to do this by liquid scintillation counting techniques, ethylene-C^{14} must be converted into a nonvolatile material which is soluble in the scintillation solution. Ethylene-C^{14} dibromide or toluene-soluble polyethylene-C^{14} are suitable conversion products.[25] The preparation of ethylene-C^{14} dibromide is carried out in a 50-ml. flask equipped with a 28/15 ball joint and sidearm with syringe cap. Pipet 1 ml. liquid bromine into the flask and connect it, through the ball joint, to a microhydrogenator. Wrap the flask with aluminum foil. Evacuate the system with an aspirator. Admit ethylene into the system from a connecting reservoir of the radioactive ethylene. Maintain a slight purge of ethylene on the system. Allow the reaction to proceed until the bromine color just disappears.

Analyze the ethylene dibromide by gas chromatography (or mass spectrometry) and report the concentration of ethylene dibromide in mole percent. Normal concentrations of ethylene dibromide will be 99.8 mole percent or higher.

Transfer aliquots (200–300 mg.) of the ethylene dibromide into 20-ml. counting vials. Cool the vials in a dry-ice bath and pipet 15 ml. of scintillator solution into each vial. Prepare in the same manner background samples containing unlabeled ethylene dibromide. Count the samples in a liquid scintillation spectrometer. The discriminator settings are 10–50 volts and 50–100 volts, with the high voltage adjusted to maximize the counts in the 10–50 volt window. Ten-minute counts on each sample should give more than 10,000 gross counts.

Obtain the counting efficiency by adding aliquots of the standard benzoic acid-C^{14} solution to each sample and recounting the sample. Sufficient internal standard is added to increase the total counts tenfold over the initial sample counts. The counting efficiency of the ethylene dibromide is calculated from the net increase in counts and the known amount of d.p.m. added from the standard.

$$\text{Percent counting efficiency} = \frac{100 \times \text{net increase in counts}}{\text{d.p.m. of standard added}}$$

where d.p.m. is the disintegrations per minute per gram.

The counting efficiency should range from 52 to 58 percent.

Calculate the specific activity of the ethylene-C^{14} dibromide in d.p.m./g. from the activity of the ethylene dibromide after correction for trace impurities.

Specific activity of ethylene-C^{14} (d.p.m./g.)

$$= (K) \left[\frac{\text{EDB gross c.p.m.} - \text{background c.p.m.}}{\text{percent counting efficiency } (0.01)} \right] \frac{1}{\text{g. EDB}} \left[\frac{187.88}{28.05} \right]$$

where K = correction factor derived from the mole percent purity of the ethylene dibromide, the mole percent ethyl bromide, and the other impurities found by the gas chromatographic analysis,

EDB = ethylene dibromide, mol. wt. 187.88, and

c.p.m. = counts per minute.

A typical value (d.p.m./g.) for the ethylene-C^{14} was 7.9×10^4.

Prepare ethylene-propylene copolymers in a reactor equipped with inlets for catalyst, heptane, ethylene, and propylene and with outlets for the purge gas and product withdrawal. The ethylene and propylene are purged through the system to maintain the desired equilibrium monomer concentration in the heptane vehicle. The ethylene content of the feed gas can be varied during the course of the reaction and samples withdrawn periodically to obtain a series of polymers with a range of ethylene content. Precipitate the polymer samples with methanol in a Waring Blendor. Isolate the precipitated polymer and digest with dilute hydrochloric acid in methanol. Wash the precipitate thoroughly and dry in a vacuum oven overnight at 60°C.

Weigh duplicate samples varying from 10 to 100 mg. into the counting vials. Dissolve the polymer in 5 ml. of toluene by heating to 90°C. for 10–200 min. as necessary. Add 15 ml. of Cab-O-Sil scintillator solution directly to the hot solution and then cool to −8°C. and hold for 1 hr. During the cooling, gel formation may occur. The gel is kept in suspension by the Cab-O-Sil in the scintillator solution and has no noticeable effect on the counts.

Count the solutions in the liquid scintillation spectrometer after finding the proper instrument setting to maximize the counts in the 10–50 volt window. Make at least three duplicate 10-min. counts on each sample. Prepare background samples, using nonradioactive polymers, treated in the same manner as the samples. Obtain the counting efficiency using benzoic-C^{14} acid in toluene as the internal standard as described previously.

Calculation.—

Ethylene, weight percent =

$$\frac{(\text{c.p.m., polymer} - \text{c.p.m., background}) \, 100}{(\% \text{ counting efficiency of polymer})(0.01)(\text{g. polymer})(\text{sp. act. ethylene-}C^{14}\text{in d.p.m./g.})}$$

Ethylene, mole percent =

$$\frac{(\text{weight percent ethylene}) \, 100}{(\text{weight percent ethylene}/28.052) + (100\text{-weight percent ethylene}/42.078)}$$

INFRARED SPECTROMETRIC EXAMINATION

Prepare films of the radioactive polymers by pressing under 20,000 p.s.i. pressure or by casting thin films from boiling o-dichlorobenzene solution on rock salt plates. Evaporate the solvent from the films by heating with an infrared lamp under a stream of nitrogen. Control the film thickness to yield an absorbance in the range of 0.6 to 1.0.

Scan the films using a double-beam infrared spectrometer from 5–16 μ. Draw base-lines from the minima at 6.6 μ and 7.1 μ, and from the minima at 7.1 μ and 7.6 μ. Measure the absorbance of the 7.25-μ band (—CH₃) and the 6.84-μ (>CH₂) band and calculate the absorbance ratio 7.25 μ/6.84 μ.

Prepare an analytical curve by plotting the infrared absorbance ratio *vs.* the mole percent ethylene as determined by radioassay (Fig. 58-4).

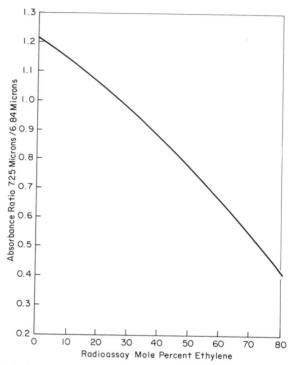

FIG. 58-4.   Analytical Curve for Determining Mole Percent Ethylene in Ethylene-Propylene Copolymers.

APPLICATION OF MICROSCOPY TO THE STUDY OF PLASTICS

Microscopic techniques are finding extensive use in the study of plastics. Some of the more important applications are (a) bright-field microscopy to study occlusions and physical characteristics, (b) oblique reflected light for examining surface characteristics, (c) dark-field techniques for studying occlusions and emulsions, (d) oblique transmitted light for examining inclusions, (e) polarized light for studying crystallinity, and (f) phase-contrast microscopy for studying polyphases and particle size.[28] The general field of high-polymer microscopy (including electron microscopy) has been surveyed by Leigh-Dugmore.[29] Hock and Arbogast[30] determined the melting point of crystalline polymers by noting the disappearance of birefringence. Spherulitic crystallization has

[28] Traylor, P. A., The Dow Chemical Company, personal communication.
[29] Leigh-Dugmore, C. H., Microscopy of Rubber, W. Heffner Sons, Cambridge, 1961.
[30] Hock, C. W., and Arbogast, J. F., Anal. Chem., 33, 462, 1961.

been studied employing the polarizing microscope. Keller[31] presented information on banded spherulites in polyesters, and Hellwege and Hoff[32] studied polyethylene spherulites. A theoretical treatment of the extinction pattern shown by biaxial arrays in spherulites is given by Keith and Padden,[33] and uniaxial arrays are treated by Price.[34] The changes in crystal structure in polypropylene film during oxidative aging at elevated temperatures was discussed by van Schooten.[35]

The advent of reasonably priced electron microscopes has opened a new area (a) for studying the particle size and character of latex (emulsion polymerized) particles, (b) for examining the surface of plastics, (c) for determining the inner structure of multiphase plastics, and (d) for single crystal study.[29] Langton and Stephens[36] discussed in detail the application of optical microscopy and electron microscopy to the examination of high polymers. Bailey[37] correlated spherulitic structure as determined by electron microscopy with physical properties of polyethylene and polypropylene. Combined x-ray and electron microscopy[38] studies were used to demonstrate the form and distribution of radiation-grafted copolymers.

PHASE-CONTRAST MICROSCOPY

The performance of rubber-modified plastics depends, to a large extent, upon the nature and uniformity of the rubber dispersion. Phase-contrast microscopy has found considerable acceptance in the study of the dispersed rubber particles as well as the plastic surface characteristics.[39] The principle of phase-contrast microscopy is based on artificially introducing greater differences in the amplitudes of waves which combine at the eyepoint of the microscope to form images. The effect is that in the image place the relative intensities of background and object structure are modified to enhance contrast. To obtain this effect, the specimen is illuminated by a hollow cone of light from a substage condenser having a special annular stop. As the light moves up from the specimen area, it passes through a special diffraction plate situated at the back focal plane of the objective. Here the light, unaffected by the specimen, is advanced one-quarter wavelength in phase. Due to this advancement, the two wave fronts—the diffracted and undiffracted—interfere at the final image plane to produce an image of increased contrast and detail.

The first consideration in the application of phase-contrast microscopy to the study of rubber-modified plastics is the preparation of suitable specimens.

APPLICATION OF PHASE-CONTRAST MICROSCOPY TO RUBBER-MODIFIED POLYSTYRENES[40]

Scope.—The following method describes the preparation of plastic specimens and their examination by phase-contrast microscopy.

Principle.—A thin plastic specimen is prepared by microtoming and dropping into hot glycerol. On contact with the glycerol, the thin slice flattens out and is immediately

[31] Keller, A., J. Polymer Sci., **39**, 151, 1959.

[32] Hellwege, K. H., and Hoff, G., Kolloid-Z., **170**, 144, 1960.

[33] Keith, H. D., and Padden, F. J., J. Polymer Sci., **39**, 101, 1959.

[34] Price, F. P., J. Polymer Sci., **39**, 139, 1959.

[35] Schooten, J. van, J. Appl. Polymer Sci., **4**, 122, 1960.

[36] Langton, N. H., and Stephens, M., Plastics (London), **23**, 384, 388, 422, 1958; *ibid.*, **25**, 329, 1960.

[37] Bailey, G. W., J. Appl. Phys., **32**, 1635, 1961.

[38] Sella, C., J. Polymer Sci., **48**, 207, 1960.

[39] Keskkula, H., Schmitt, J. A., Cobler, J. G., and Norton, J. W., Jr., Paper Presented at Gordon Research Conference on Elastomers, New London, N. H., August 8, 1958.

[40] Traylor, P. A., Anal. Chem., **33**, 1629, 1961. Copyright 1961 by the American Chemical Society and reprinted with the permission of the copyright owner.

transferred to a microscope slide for microscopic examination. Photomicrographs can be prepared if required.

Apparatus. Microscope.—Bausch and Lomb Model TBR, dark phase-contrast microscope with achromatic optics.

Microtome.—Spencer Model 860 or equivalent.

Photographic Equipment.—Bausch and Lomb H and K type camera.

Glycerol Bath.—Petri dish of glycerol maintained at 100°C.

Reagents. Mounting Liquid.—Dissolve sufficient reagent grade potassium mercuric iodide (K_2HgI_4) in glycerol to raise the refractive index to 1.59 at 25°C. Remove any undissolved solids by filtration or decantation.

Procedure.—Sandwich a piece of the plastic sample between wooden blocks in the object clamp of the microtome. Trim a flat slicing area, with a razor blade, to approximately 1 mm. square. Tilt the microtome knife, which should be very sharp, 30°, and set it at a 45° slicing angle. Lock the automatic feed at 2 μ. Once the knife touches the sample, continue the cut slowly and without hesitation.

Remove the slice from the blade with a soft-bristle brush and transfer it to the hot glycerol bath. The slice should roll out immediately on contact with the hot liquid. If it does not, introduce a new slice. A temperature of 110°C. is suitable for polystyrene plastics. Plastics with higher heat-distortion temperatures may require a higher bath temperature. It should be noted, however, that the use of the heated-bath technique will destroy orientation in the plastic.

Take up the rolled out slice on a microscope slide. Wipe the bottom of the slide with a towel. Blot the glycerol on the top of the slide with filter paper or scrape off with a razor blade. Add a drop of the glycerol–potassium mercuric iodide solution as the mounting medium and cover with a cover glass.

Examine the specimen under the phase-contrast microscope. A photomicrograph may be prepared of representative areas if desired.

Phase-contrast photomicrographs showing the rubber dispersion in a rubber-modified polystyrene and the result of crazing are presented in Fig. 58-5. The rubberized particles appear as white spots or rings on a dark background of polystyrene. In the stressed sample, the cracks appear as white streaks connecting the rubberized particles.

POLARIZING LIGHT MICROSCOPY

A simple method of measuring the crystalline melting point of polymers employs the common "melting-bar"; however, the result obtained by this method is not the crystalline melting point but rather the "fluid" point or the temperature at which the polymer is seen to flow. The use of the polarizing light microscope to determine the crystalline melting point yields relatively accurate results.[41] The microcrystalline structure of most semicrystalline polymers appears, under a polarizing microscope, to consist of spherulites The spherulite is an assembly of crystals radiating from a point in all directions. When a sample of polymer containing spherulites is heated, the spherulites gradually disappear and the crystalline melting point is usually taken as the temperature at which no structure is visible, the entire field of view having become dark.[30]

DETERMINATION OF THE CRYSTALLINE MELTING POINT OF A POLYMER[28]
(First-Order Transition Temperature)

Scope.—This method is believed to be applicable to any thermoplastic polymer with a first-order transition temperature between 100° and 350°C.

[41] Flory, P. J., Principles of Polymer Chemistry, Cornell Univ. Press, 1953; Hill, R., Fibers from Synthetic Polymers, Elsevier Publishing Company, Amsterdam, Holland, 1953.

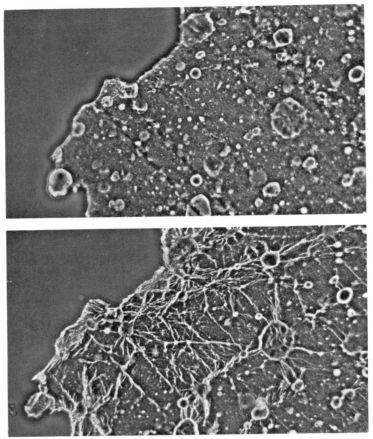

FIG. 58-5. Phase-Contrast Photomicrographs Showing Rubber Dispersion in Rubber-Modified Polystyrene Before (Top) and After (Bottom) Application of Stress.

Principle.—A plastic film with molecular crystallinity, when placed in a special manner between crossed polaroids, serves as a third polaroid to bring about a passage of light to a photocell. This polarizing property is lost when the plastic is heated past its softening or first-order transition temperature. The phenomenon is measured under controlled conditions to obtain a reproducible characterizing temperature.

Apparatus. **Polarizing Light Microscope,** Bausch and Lomb LC Model.

Hot-stage Apparatus, Kofler.

Ortho Illuminator B Lamp, 300-watt, with cooling fan, voltmeter, and variable transformer.

Exposure Meter, Photovolt Model 200M.

Hot Plate, Sunbeam Model 14B.

Microscope Slides.

Procedure.—Molecular crystallinity of the polymer chains is affected by stretching and freezing. The material is first softened on a hot microscope slide and then smeared with a knife blade, or suitable tool, just before the melt hardens. A slide prepared in this manner is placed in the Kofler hot stage between the crossed polaroids of the polarizing light microscope. The specimen is brought into focus and the slide is oriented to place the stretch direction of the plastic at a 45° angle to the vibration planes of the microscope polaroids. The microscope eyepiece is removed and the photocell of the exposure meter is inserted. Light which passes through the specimen is measured on the photocell. The intensity striking the photocell is adjusted to 1.2 ft.-c., or 60 units, on the photovolt exposure meter, and held there until the specimen temperature is no less than 40° below the transition temperature, or 100°C., whichever comes first. From here, no further adjustments are made. The hot-stage transformer is set to give a rise of 3° per minute near the first-order transition temperature.

Simultaneous readings of light transmission and temperature are made as the temperature rises. These are plotted against each other and the curve is extrapolated to zero transmission (Fig. 58-6). This zero transmission point is taken as the first-order transition temperature.

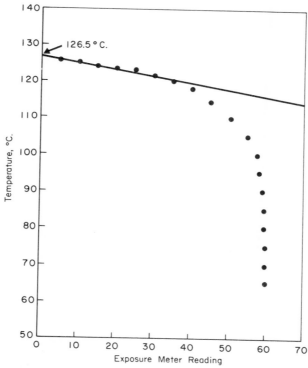

FIG. 58-6.   Crystalline Melting Point of Polyethylene as Measured by Polarizing Light Microscopy.

ULTRAVIOLET SPECTROMETRY

The absorption of radiation in the spectral region from 400 mμ to 200 mμ causes an electronic transition, primarily of the π electrons in conjugated systems, from one energy state to a state of higher energy.[42] Many polymers are therefore essentially transparent (exhibit no distinctive absorption spectra) in this region. For example, poly(methyl methacrylate) containing no conjugated unsaturation is essentially transparent in the ultraviolet region (Fig. 58-7), whereas polystyrene exhibits characteristic absorption bands resulting from the aromatic rings. Although ultraviolet spectrometry will thus have limited application for the identification of plastics, the transparency offers an advantage in that certain structural features, such as end groups incorporated into the polymer chain as a result of the initiation or termination step (catalyst fragments,

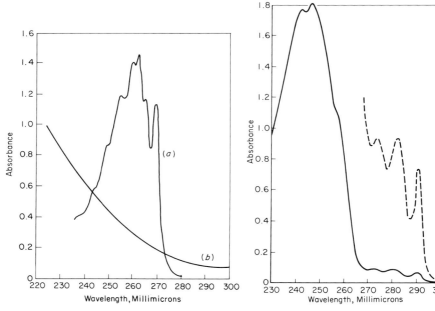

FIG. 58-7. Ultraviolet Spectra of Thin Films of (a) Polystyrene and (b) Poly(Methyl Methacrylate).

FIG. 58-8. Ultraviolet Spectra of Styrene Monomer in Methanol (1 cm. Light Path). 1.26 mg. per 100 ml. (———); 12.63 mg. per 100 ml. (– – –).

chain transfer agents, inhibitors), may be studied. In addition, ultraviolet spectrometry provides an extremely sensitive method for the determination of additives, particularly antioxidants, antiozonants, and light stabilizers.

The electronic group spectra are, however, subject to considerable environmental influence, more so than the infrared band vibrations. In a specific environment, both wavelength and intensity of absorption are important characteristics of a compound. Thus the influence of environment on the absorption spectrum of a compound must be considered when attempting to identify unknown compounds.

Although a large number of solvents are relatively transparent in the ultraviolet region, they are primarily alcohols, aliphatic hydrocarbons, or ethers which are relatively poor solvents for polymers. Films and potassium bromide discs have been

[42] Tyron, M., and Horowitz, E., Anal. Chem. of Polymers, Part II, G. M. Kline, Ed., Interscience Publishers, New York, 1962, p. 269.

employed, although quantitative application of these techniques is limited due to the difficulty in preparing specimens of known size.

A procedure has been described for the determination of combined styrene in styrene-acrylonitrile copolymers by measuring the phenyl ring absorbance at 259 mμ.[43] Combined styrene in styrene-methyl methacrylate copolymers has been determined by measuring the absorbance at 269 mμ.[44] The number of sulfide end groups and the number average molecular weight of poly(methyl methacrylate) was determined by measuring the absorbance at 308 mμ of the complex formed between molecular iodine and the sulfide-sulfur.[45] Hirt, *et al.*,[46] and Shreve and Heether[47] have reported ultraviolet spectrometric methods for studying styrenated alkyd resins. Pepe, Kniel, and Czuha[48] have described a method for determining methylisopropenyl ketone in polymers. Bound styrene in styrene-butadiene copolymers has been determined after conversion to *p*-nitrobenzoic acid.[49] Acrylonitrile-methylvinylpyridine copolymers have been analyzed by determining the pyridine released on acid hydrolysis [50]

Additives are separated from the polymer by extraction or by solution and reprecipitation of the polymer. Phenolic antioxidants may be determined by the direct ultraviolet spectrometric measurement of the extract or, if interferences are present, a differential spectrum may be obtained by scanning an alkaline solution of the phenolic against an identical concentration in neutral or acid solvent.[51] Stafford[52] describes a novel method for determining 2,6-di-*tert.*-butyl-*p*-cresol in the presence of 4,4-thiobis-6-*tert.*-butyl-*p*-cresol by measuring the 365-mμ spectral band produced by oxidizing the former in an alkaline isopropanol solution. The determination of residual styrene monomer in polystyrenes has been described based on measurements at approximately 282 mμ after appropriate treatment (Fig. 58-8).[53]

The determination of tris(nonylated phenyl) phosphite in styrene-butadiene rubber by absorbance measurements before and after treatment with alkali has been described by Nawakowski[54] and Brandt.[55] The procedure has been adapted to the determination of the phosphite in plastics.[56]

DETERMINATION OF TRIS(NONYLATED PHENYL) PHOSPHITE IN PLASTICS

Scope.—This method is suitable for the determination of 0.1 to 1.5 percent tris(nonylated phenyl) phosphite (TNPP) in plastics.

Principle.—The sample is dissolved in chloroform and the polymer precipitated with methanol. After filtration, two aliquots are taken of each filtrate. A pellet of sodium hydroxide is added to one which causes a shift in the absorption peak from 270 mμ to

[43] Welcher, F. J., Ed., Standard Methods of Chemical Analysis, 6th Ed., Vol. II, Part B, D. Van Nostrand Co. Inc., Princeton, N. J., 1963, p. 2062.
[44] Tobolsky, A. V., Eisenberg, A., and O'Driscoll, K. F., Anal. Chem., **31**, 203, 1959.
[45] Rosenthal, I., Frisone, G. J., and Coberg, J. K., Anal. Chem., **32**, 1713, 1960.
[46] Hirt, R. C., Stafford, R. W., King, F. T., and Schmitt, R. G., Anal. Chem., **27**, 226, 1955.
[47] Shreve, O. D., and Heether, M. R., Anal. Chem., **23**, 441, 1951.
[48] Pepe, J. J., Kniel, I., and Czuha, M., Jr., Anal. Chem., **27**, 755, 1955.
[49] Hilton, C. L., Newell, J. E., and Tolsma, J., Anal. Chem., **31**, 915, 1959.
[50] Stafford, C., Jr., and Toren, P. E., Anal. Chem., **31**, 1687, 1959.
[51] Wexler, A. S., Anal. Chem., **35**, 1936, 1963.
[52] Stafford, C., Anal. Chem., **34**, 794, 1962.
[53] Welcher, F. J., Ed., Standard Methods of Chemical Analysis, 6th Ed., Vol. II, Part B, D. Van Nostrand Co. Inc., Princeton, N. J., 1963, p. 2056.
[54] Nawakowski, A. C., Anal. Chem., **30**, 1868, 1958.
[55] Brandt, H. J., Anal. Chem., **33**, 1390, 1961.
[56] Lovestrom, E., and Cobler, J. G., The Dow Chemical Company, unpublished manuscript.

300 mμ (Fig. 58-9). This shift is the basis of calculation of TNPP content of the sample.

Apparatus. **4-Oz. Wide-Mouth Bottles** with foil-lined caps.

Magnetic Stirrer with stirring bar.

Beckman DU Spectrophotometer or equivalent.

1-Cm. Cells, matched.

Reagents. **Chloroform,** reagent grade.

Methanol, reagent grade.

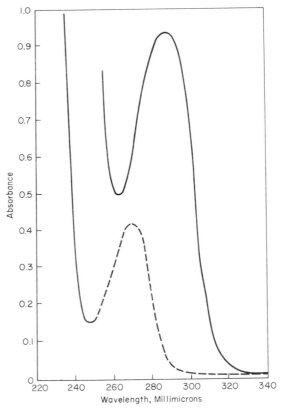

Fɪɢ. 58-9.   Ultraviolet Spectra of 6.0 mg. of Tris(Nonylated Phenyl) Phosphite in 50 ml. of a 1:3 Chloroform-Methanol Solution (1 cm. Light Path); Alkaline Solution (———); Neutral Solution (– – –).

Procedure.—Accurately weigh a 2.000-g. sample of the plastic into a 4-oz. wide-mouth bottle and dissolve in 25 ml. of chloroform added from a pipet or buret. Place a stirring bar in the solution and add 75 ml. of methanol dropwise from a buret while the solution is slowly stirred. The total volume of solvent added must be equal to 100 ml. Mix thoroughly. Filter at least 50 ml. of the solution through No. 42 Whatman paper. If the solution is not clear, filter again to remove turbidity. Pipet a 25-ml. aliquot of the filtered solution into each of two 50-ml. volumetric flasks. Add a pellet of sodium hydroxide to one of the flasks and dilute both solutions to volume with a mixture of 25 parts of chloroform and 75 parts of methanol. Mix thoroughly.

Prepare a standard solution of the phosphite in chloroform. Each ml. is equivalent to 1.0 mg. TNPP. Pipet 5 ml. of the standard solution into each of two 50-ml. volumetric flasks and proceed as directed above.

Read the solutions at 300 mμ in a 1-cm. cell, recording the difference in absorbance between the two aliquots of each sample. The standard solutions are measured in the same manner. Each reading must be taken against a reference cell containing 25 parts chloroform and 75 parts methanol.

Calculations.—Let

$$K = \frac{A}{C}$$

where A = net absorbance of standard, and
C = concentration of standard in grams per 50 ml.

$$\text{TNPP, percent} = \frac{\text{net absorbance of sample} \times 400}{K \times \text{sample weight in g.}}$$

NEAR-INFRARED SPECTROMETRY

Recent advances in instrumentation have expanded spectrometric measurements to the "near" infrared region from 0.6 to 3 μ (600 to 3000 mμ). Equipment for work in the near-infrared region is available as a component (or accessory) of many ultraviolet and visible recording spectrometers and standard or bench-model infrared spectrometers. Absorptions in this region are principally the first and second overtones of the carbon-hydrogen, nitrogen-hydrogen, and oxygen-hydrogen group frequencies found in the 2.5- to 16-μ region. Important bands in the 1.8- to 2.8-μ region are due to binary combinations of hydrogenic stretching modes with hydrogenic deformation or combinations with other vibrations involving the molecule under consideration. Carbon-hydrogen first overtones give a number of bands from 1.6 to 1.8 μ while nitrogen-hydrogen and oxygen-hydrogen first overtones extend to 1.4 μ. Other combination bands which occur from 1.35 to 1.5 μ and the second overtones from 1.0 to 1.2 μ are weak and require very long path lengths. Thus a near-infrared spectrum is less complex than a spectrum in the 2.5- to 16-μ region; however, it also has limited applicability.

Since both quartz and sodium chloride optics are satisfactory as a dispersion medium in the near-infrared region, cells and accessories normally used in ultraviolet or visible spectrometry may be substituted for the sodium chloride cells normally used in infrared spectrometry.

The near-infrared region between 2.7 and 3.0 μ offers a convenient tool for the rapid estimation of phenolic hydroxyl components, particularly of phenolic antioxidants.[57] The hydroxyl number of polyesters and polyethers has been determined by absorption measurements in the 2.0- to 3.2-μ region,[58] whereas the hydroxyl number of alcohols can be measured employing the hydroxyl-stretching overtone band at 1.4 μ.[59] Corish[60] determined the percentage cis-1,4-content of rubber by measuring the CH stretching vibration at 2.46 μ. Goddu[61] calculated the cis-1,4-unsaturation from the absorbance

[57] Goddu, R. F., Anal. Chem., **30**, 2009, 1958.
[58] Hilton, C. L., Anal. Chem., **31**, 1610, 1959.
[59] Crisler, R. O., and Burrill, A. M., Anal. Chem., **31**, 2055, 1959.
[60] Corish, P. J., Rubber Chem. and Tech., **33**, 975, 1960.
[61] Goddu, R. F., Anal. Chem., **29**, 1790, 1957.

at 2.14 μ, while the bands at 1.62 and 2.10 μ were used to determine terminal unsaturation ($>C = CH_2$). Cobler, Miller, and Samsel described the analysis of polyethylene-
polypropylene blends based on the ratio of the $-CH_3$ band at 2.275 μ to the $>CH_2$
band at 2.310 μ.[62] The near-infrared spectra for polypropylene and for linear pol-

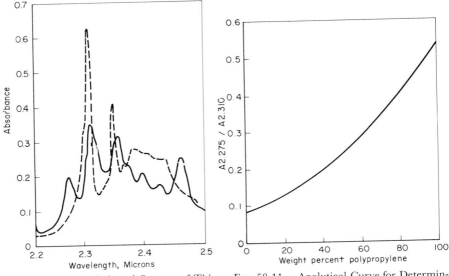

FIG. 58-10.   Near Infrared Spectra of Thin
Films of Polypropylene (——) and Linear
Polyethylene (-----).

FIG. 58-11.   Analytical Curve for Determin-
ining Weight Percent Polypropylene in
Polyethylene-Polypropylene Blends.

yethylene films are shown in Fig. 58-10. A typical calibration curve of absorbance ratio
($A_{2.275}/A_{2.310}$) vs. percentage polypropylene for polypropylene-polyethylene blends is
presented in Fig. 58-11. The near-infrared technique has been adapted by Dannenberg[63]
to study the chemical reaction during the cure of epoxy resins.

DETERMINATION OF α-EPOXIDES IN EPOXY RESINS[63]

Scope.—The following procedure is suitable for the determination of α-epoxides in
liquid or solid epoxy resins.

Principle.—The α-epoxide content of liquid resins is calculated from the measured
absorbance of the 2.205-μ peak after suitable background correction. The α-epoxide
content of solid (or liquid) resins is calculated from the ratio of the variable 2.205-μ
band to a nonvariable absorbance band at 1.668 μ.

The major absorption peak for α-epoxides located at 2.205 μ represents probably
a combination of CH stretching fundamental with the CH_2 deformation fundamental.
The 1.668-μ band probably represents the first overtone of a carbon-hydrogen stretching
mode of aromatic CH groups.

[62] Cobler, J. G., Miller, D. L., Samsel, E. P., Paper presented at ACS Meeting-in-
Miniature, Detroit, Mich., February, 1960.
[63] Dannenberg, H., SPE Transactions, **3**, 78, 1963. (Courtesy SPE Transactions.)

Apparatus. **Cary Model 14 *M* Spectrometer,** or equivalent, with 0.1-cm. sample cell.

Glass Plates with $\frac{1}{16}$-in. Teflon spacer.

Reagents.—Epoxy resins (glycidyl ether of Bisphenol-A) of known epoxy content. Epon 828, Epon 834, and Epon 1001 with epoxy contents, in equivalents/liter, of approximately 6.0, 4.6, and 2.3, respectively, are suitable. The epoxy contents should be determined accurately by chemical means.[64]

Calibration. **A. Liquid Samples (Direct Method).**—Fill a 0.1-cm. cell with the standard liquid resin and record the spectrum from 1.0 to 2.3 μ. Draw a baseline connecting the minima at 2.18 and 2.22 μ. Read the absorbance of the 2.205-μ band measured from the constructed baseline.

Prepare an analytical curve by plotting absorbance values *vs.* epoxy value in equivalents/liter. The correlation between absorbance and epoxy value is also represented by the equation:

$$\text{Epoxy value, equivalents/liter} = \frac{0.881 \times A_{2.205}}{\text{cell length in cm.}} + 0.60$$

The constant 0.60 corrects for the use of a constructed linear background rather than the true, curved background.

B. Solid or Liquid Resins (Relative Method).—The relative method gives the epoxy value relative to the aromatic matter in the specimen independent of thickness and shape of sample. Although the method appears adequate for liquid or low-melting solid resins, the parameters in the calculation will change when the amount of aromatic matter is changed, *e.g.*, by presence of aromatic diluent or curing agent or a different ratio of epichlorohydrin to Bisphenol A in the resin to be analyzed.

Prepare small cast pieces of the standard resins approximately 3 mm. thick by pressing out about 1 ml. of molten resin between glass plates using $\frac{1}{16}$-in. Teflon spacers. After cooling, remove the glass plates and insert the casting into the sample holder of the spectrometer.

Record the spectrum from 1.0 to 2.3 μ. Measure the absorbance of the 2.205 μ peak using the baseline from 1.30 through 1.58 μ, extending it to approximately 1.7 μ. Record the absorbance of the 1.668-μ peak measured from the constructed baseline.

Calculate the absorbance ratio $A_{2.205}/A_{1.668}$. Prepare an analytical curve by plotting the calculated absorbance ratio *vs.* the epoxy value in equivalents per 100 grams. The correlation between the absorbance and the epoxy value is also represented by the following equation:

$$\text{Epoxy value, equivalents/100 g.} = 0.247 \times \frac{A_{2.205}}{A_{1.668}} + 0.022$$

Procedure.—Obtain the spectrum of the sample and measure the absorbance of the appropriate bands as described in A or B above (Fig. 58-12). Calculate the epoxy value in equivalents/liter or equivalents/100 g. from the corresponding equation or read the value from the analytical curve.

The results in equivalents/liter may be converted to equivalents/100 g. by the following equation:

$$\text{Equivalents/100 g.} = \frac{\text{equivalents/liter}}{10 \times \text{sp. gr.}}$$

[64] Dannenberg, H., and Harp, W. R., Anal. Chem., **28,** 86, 1956.

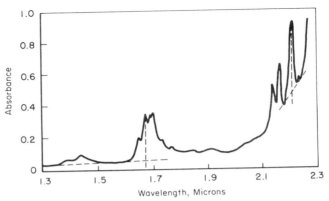

Fig. 58-12.   Near Infrared Spectrum of Liquid Epoxy Resin Showing Method of Evaluating Epoxy Peak at 2.205 μ and Reference Peak at 1.668 μ. (Courtesy SPE Transactions.)

INFRARED SPECTROMETRY

Infrared spectrometry is perhaps the most widely used technique today for the study of polymeric materials. In fact, if the polymer analysis laboratory could afford only one instrument, an infrared spectrometer should be the choice. There are a number of spectrometers available ranging from the relatively low-cost, bench-top models to the high-priced research instruments. The bench-top models, particularly those employing gratings, with the readily available accessories are admirably suited for general plastics analysis work. Instrument quality can be determined by referring to the American Society for Testing Materials publication, "Recommended Practices for Describing and Measuring Performance of Spectrophotometers." [65] The general techniques of infrared spectrometry have been described by Potts.[66]

Identification of most plastics can be made by infrared spectrometry alone at a fraction of the time and cost required for chemical analysis. Copolymer ratios can be calculated from the absorbance of specific functional groups. Infrared spectrometry has also proved suitable for studying oxidation, for monitoring polymerization and the curing of plastics, for characterizing random or block copolymers, for characterizing amorphous and crystalline polymers, and for studying stereoregularity.

A wide variety of sample preparation techniques can be employed: Thin plastic films, solutions, powders mulled in Nujol or perfluorocarbon oil, powders pressed into a disc with potassium bromide, and reflectance measurements from solids.

METHODS OF SAMPLE PREPARATION OF PLASTICS FOR INFRARED SPECTROMETRIC ANALYSIS

Films.—Film thickness in the range of 1 mil (0.025 mm.) is usually satisfactory.

(a) Free Films.—This technique can be applied to samples which have the property of forming self-supporting films and for which a solvent can be readily found. Some of the more useful solvents are methylene dichloride, *o*-dichlorobenzene, benzene, dimethylformamide, ketones, and tetrahydrofuran. In many cases, solution of the

[65] Proceedings, ASTM, Vol. 63, 1963.

[66] Potts, W. J., Jr., Chemical Infrared Spectroscopy, Vol. I, John Wiley and Sons, Inc., New York, 1963.

polymer may be accelerated by gently heating the solvent. The films may be cast directly on glass, tin foil, aluminum foil, or mercury from the polymer solution. Hot solvent film casting on salt plates may require preheating of the plates to avoid fracture. Film thickness can be controlled by using a calibrated drawdown bar or by proper sample dilution. After evaporation of the solvent under an infrared heat lamp, preferably in a nitrogen atmosphere, the film is stripped from the substrate. Immersion of the substrate in warm running water will sometimes facilitate removal of the film. Tin and aluminum foil substrates may be removed by mercury amalgamation and hydrochloric acid etching, respectively.

(b) Mechanical Film Preparation.—Films of suitable thickness may be obtained in some cases by the use of a microtome or by careful shaving with a razor blade.

(c) Cast Films and Liquid Films.—Viscous liquids or semisolids may be spread or flowed over the surface of a rock salt window. A second salt window is then placed on top of the film and the two windows are clamped together to give a film of uniform thickness.

Solid polymers may be dissolved in a suitable solvent and a film then cast directly on a salt window. Films of suitable thickness are obtained by building up several layers of polymer. The films should be freed of most of the solvent at a relatively low temperature to prevent the formation of bubbles in the film. Final drying is then carried out under a nitrogen atmosphere at elevated temperatures, usually with the aid of an infrared heat lamp, or the film may be dried under vacuum. Frequently, the last traces of solvent are difficult to remove from the film. Thus all spectra obtained from films prepared in this manner should be examined carefully for residual solvent bands.

Latexes may be cast on silver chloride or barium fluoride windows which are impervious to water.

Thin polyethylene film is a suitable substrate for casting films from solvents which do not attack it. Polyethylene exhibits only carbon-hydrogen absorption bands which may be cancelled by a compensation technique. Caution should be used in interpreting compensated spectra, since the instrument will be essentially dead in the compensated regions.

(d) Melting.—Some polymers (thermoplastics) may be softened by heat and pressed into a thin film between two rock salt plates.

(e) Compression Molding.—Suitable films may be prepared employing a 10- to 20-ton hydraulic press with heated platens. The films are usually prepared sandwiched between Mylar film.

Method (a) has the disadvantage of sometimes producing interference fringes which are recorded along with the sample spectrum. Lutinski[67] found that interference bands could be eliminated by coating the films with Nujol or perfluorocarbon oil and pressing the coated film against a thick rock salt window. Methods (a), (b), (d), and (e) may cause some difficulties because of possible orientation effects in polymers which exhibit some degree of crystallinity. New bands may appear and frequencies may shift or disappear after thermal treatment.

Mulling.—The sample is finely subdivided by crushing in a mortar (Diamonite), filing, buffing on a coarse abrasive wheel, or grinding in a mill. If the sample is ground, both the sample and mill should be cooled with dry ice or liquid nitrogen prior to grinding. The particle diameters should be reduced to less than 2 μ, particularly for quantitative measurements.

After attrition, the small particles are collected and ground with a mulling agent to form a paste. The paste is collected and sandwiched between two salt windows. A spectrum, entirely free of mulling oil absorptions, is obtained by using a split-mull

[67] Lutinski, C., Anal. Chem., **30**, 2071, 1958.

technique. Perfluorocarbon oil is used for the 2- to 7.5-μ region and Nujol oil for the 7.5- to 16-μ region.

Potassium Bromide Pellet Technique.—A finely divided sample is obtained as described above and ground in a mortar (preferably a motor-driven mortar grinder) with potassium bromide powder. The mixture is placed in a die. Vacuum is applied to the die and it is then pressed under 10 to 20 tons of pressure. A clear disc is thus obtained which can be placed directly in the sample beam.

Solution.—The solution technique is the most suitable for accurate quantitative measurements. Unfortunately, the choice of solvents is small, carbon disulfide and carbon tetrachloride being the most satisfactory. Finely subdivided (less than 2 μ in diameter) particles in stable suspension may also be analyzed satisfactorily.

A 1 to 10 percent solution or suspension of the sample in a suitable solvent is usually satisfactory for scanning in a 0.1-mm. cell.

Variable temperature chambers are available commercially which offer a controlled cell temperature from $-35°$ to $+125°$C. Such a device is particularly useful for polymers which are soluble in solvents only at elevated temperatures.

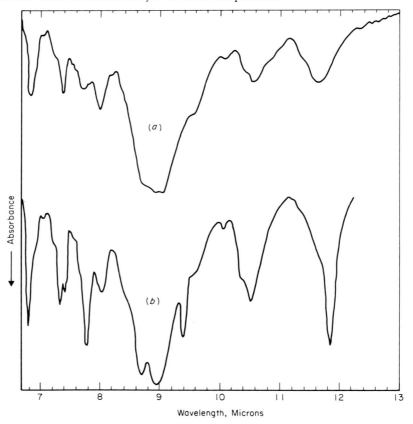

FIG. 58-13. Infrared Spectra of (a) Liquid Poly(Ethylene Glycol) and (b) Solid Poly-(Ethylene Glycol).

QUALITATIVE ANALYSIS

Many functional groups possess a relatively high degree of invariance of both frequency and intensity in different chemical environments and are suitable for both qualitative and quantitative characterization.[68] Nevertheless, there are factors which cause group frequency shifts, thus detracting somewhat from the use of standard frequency tables for absolute characterization. These factors are classified as environmental (change of phase, influence of solvent, and hydrogen bonding) and internal (molecular geometry, masses of substituent groups, mechanical coupling, steric strain, and electrical forces). Thus the most positive method for the identification of polymeric materials is the comparison of the unknown spectrum with standard polymer spectra obtained from samples which have been prepared in exactly the same manner. Although a laboratory engaged in this work will find it advantageous to develop its own library of standard spectra, there are several publications which present a wide variety of polymer spectra suitable for gross identification.[69]

Examples of the difficulty that can be encountered in the interpretation of spectra are shown in Fig. 58-13 and Fig. 58-14. The effect of environment on group frequency and intensity is represented by the spectra for molten and solid poly(ethylene glycol). The amorphous melt spectrum of poly(ethylene glycol) (Fig. 58-13a) is simple when compared to that of the crystalline solid spectrum (Fig. 58-13b). In general, the spectrum of a copolymer is essentially the superposition of the com-

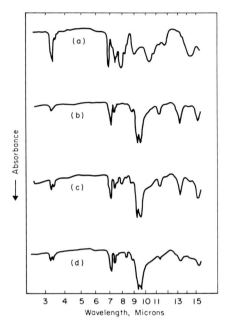

FIG. 58-14. Infrared Spectra of (a) Poly-(Vinyl Chloride); (b) Poly(Vinylidene Chloride); (c) Blend of Poly(Vinyl Chloride) and Poly(Vinylidene Chloride); and (d) Vinylidene Chloride-Vinyl Chloride Copolymer.

ponent homopolymer spectra.[68] However, as mentioned above, the characteristic absorption frequencies of a given functional group may vary, depending on the nature of neighboring groups. Thus a completely random copolymer may not exhibit the same absorption frequencies as a block copolymer or the superimposed spectra of the homopolymers. The vinyl chloride–vinylidene chloride copolymer is a typical example. Figure 58-14a is the spectrum of poly(vinyl chloride), (b) is that of poly-(vinylidene chloride), (c) the spectrum of a mechanical mixture of the two homopolymers, and (d) the random copolymer spectrum. The poly(vinyl chloride) absorption

[68] Potts, W. J., International Symposium on Plastics Testing and Standardization, ASTM, Philadelphia, 1958.

[69] Elliott, A., Advances in Spectroscopy, **1**, 214, 1959; Krimm, S., Fortschr. Hochpolymeren-Forsch, **2**, 51, 1960; Nyquist, R. A., Infrared Spectra of Plastics and Resins, The Dow Chemical Company, Midland, Mich., 1960; U. S. Dept. of Commerce, Office of Technical Services, PB 111438, 1954.

at 8.0 μ, Fig. 58-14a and Fig. 58-14c, has disappeared in the copolymer spectrum, or has been shifted to approximately 8.3 μ.

QUANTITATIVE ANALYSIS

Infrared spectrometry provides the most nearly completely general and reliable technique for the quantitative estimation of (a) copolymer ratios, (b) functional groups, (c) monomer impurities, (d) and additives. The reliability of the technique depends upon the proper selection of the absorption bands. The bands must be characteristic of the component being determined; they should be strong and free of interference. Standarization should be based on samples of known composition, keeping in mind the possible influence of the environmental and internal factors.

Sample Preparation.—The concentration of the sample should be such that in a given cell or film thickness the analytical absorption band will have an absorbance between 0.3 and 0.8. Whenever possible, polymers should be dissolved and measurements made on the solutions. Normally a 1 to 10 percent solution (weight/volume basis) measured in a 0.1-mm. cell is satisfactory. Films may be employed if the polymer is not soluble in suitable solvents. Where it is possible to obtain a fairly uniform film, the thickness may be measured with a micrometer. However, this technique is somewhat less accurate than the solution procedure. Films of unknown or indeterminate thickness are analyzed by the absorbance ratio method. In this, the ratio of one specific component to a second specific component is determined. The percentage of any one component can be determined only if all components have been identified and are included in the calculation. Alternately, a measured amount of a so-called "internal standard" may be added to the sample prior to preparing the film or even prior to making oil mulls or potassium bromide discs. The internal standard may be a dye. The film thickness may then be calculated by absorption measurements in the visible wavelength region. Suitable infrared absorbing materials may also be used. Film thickness may be calculated from the absorbance and concentration of the standard, or the absorbance value may be used to derive the ratio of a film component.

Standardization.—The preparation of suitable standards for quantitative measurement is perhaps the most difficult aspect of quantitative infrared spectrometry. Mechanical blends of homopolymers may be used as standards for many addition copolymers. Elemental or chemical functional group analysis may be employed to establish polymeric materials as standards. Radiotracer methods are finding wide acceptance for standardizing infrared spectrometric techniques. Polymers, synthesized from tagged monomers, are readily analyzed by standard radiotracer techniques. Simple model compounds may be used as standards for functional groups in polymers. This latter method depends on the fact that the absorptivities of functional groups as determined in low molecular weight compounds usually change very little when combined in high molecular weight materials.

INFRARED SPECTROMETRIC ANALYSIS OF POLY(VINYL CHLORIDE)[70]

Scope.—This general method provides for the infrared identification[71] of resins, plasticizers, stabilizers, and fillers in poly(vinyl chloride) (PVC). In many cases, individual components may be measured quantitatively.

Principle.—The sample is solvent extracted to separate the plasticizer from the compound. The resin is dissolved from the remaining compound and the inorganic fillers and stabilizers separated by centrifuging. Organometallic or organic stabilizer, if present,

---

[70] ASTM Standards, D2124-62T, Philadelphia, 1295, 1962. (Courtesy of ASTM.)
[71] ASTM Standards, Part 7, E168-60T, Philadelphia, 1569, 1961.

may partially or wholly separate with either the plasticizer or resin components and should be considered when examining these components. By this technique, the compound is separated into (1) plasticizers, (2) resin, and (3) inorganic stabilizers and fillers. Each may be individually analyzed by infrared techniques to identify and measure the components.

Apparatus. Initial Sample Preparation.—Any of the following apparatus is suitable, depending on shape and size of sample, for reducing solid samples to small particle sizes.

(1) Pencil sharpener or grater and a cold box or container capable of holding at least the temperature of solid carbon dioxide.

(2) Grinding wheel, coarse.

(3) Microtome.

(4) Grinding or cutting mills, commercial, for example, a Wiley Mill (for samples larger than 1 g.).

Soxhlet Extraction Apparatus.—(1) For 0.5- to 1.0-g. samples, an extraction apparatus with a 150-ml. flask and 27 × 100 mm. thimble is suitable.

(2) For 0.2-g. samples, an extraction apparatus with a 30-ml. flask and 10 × 50 mm. thimble is suitable.

Mold and Press for Potassium Bromide Pellets.—A mold assembly capable of pelletizing a ½-in.-diameter pellet under vacuum and a press capable of exerting pressures of at least 20,000 p.s.i. are necessary to press clear suitable potassium bromide pellets.

Infrared Spectrometer.[68]—The spectral region from 2.5 to 15 μ is used. An automatic recording, double-beam infrared spectrometer with sodium chloride prism and an ultimate resolving power in the order of 0.02 μ at 12 μ is satisfactory. Other commercially available infrared spectrophotometers utilizing either double- or single-beam optics may be satisfactory. Their suitability should be proven in the user's laboratory. Demountable cells, 1.0-mm. liquid cells, and potassium bromide pellet holder are accessories used.

Reagents. Purity of Reagents.—Reagent grade chemicals shall be used in all tests. Other grades may be used, provided it is first ascertained that the reagents are of sufficiently high purity to permit their use without lessening the accuracy of the determination.

Alumina, adsorption grade.

Carbon Disulfide (CS₂).

Ether, Anhydrous.

Potassium Bromide (KBr), infrared quality.

Tetrachloroethane, technical.

Tetrahydrofuran, stabilized with 0.1 percent hydroquinone. Pass through an alumina absorption column 6 × 0.5 in. in diameter to remove the hydroquinone prior to use.

Initial Sample Preparation.—PVC samples as received are usually in the form of powders, granules, slabs, or odd-shaped pieces. Powders can be used directly. Granules may be pressed into slabs. Slabs or appropriately shaped pieces may be treated by one of the following techniques:

(1) Buffing on a coarse grinding wheel.

(2) Cooling the sample with solid carbon dioxide and grinding the brittle sample in a clean pencil sharpener or on a grater or clean file.

(3) Shaving thin slices from the sample with a microtome.

Sheets 0.002 to 0.005 cm. thick, molded from individual granules, may also be used for extraction. Any method that will increase the surface area of a sample sufficiently to permit complete plasticizer extraction in a reasonable time is satisfactory.

Plasticizer Extraction.—Weigh approximately 1 g. ± 0.2 mg. of fine particle size PVC sample into a 27 × 100 mm. paper extraction thimble. Place the thimble in a jacketed Soxhlet apparatus fitted with a tared 150-ml. flask, and extract with 120 ml. of ethyl ether for 6 hrs. Remove the tared flask containing the ethyl ether and the extracted plasticizers and heat gently on a steam bath to boil off the ethyl ether. Place the flask in an evacuated desiccator for a minimum of 1 hr. to remove the last traces of ethyl ether. Weigh the flask containing the extracted plasticizers. Calculate the percentage of total plasticizers in the PVC sample as follows:

$$\text{Total plasticizers, percent} = \frac{\text{weight of extracted plasticizers}}{\text{weight of PVC sample}} \times 100$$

Keep the plasticizers for infrared identification or determination.

Separation of Stabilizers and Fillers.—Empty the resin, stabilizers, and fillers remaining in the extraction thimble into a 50-ml. beaker. Add 20 ml. of tetrachloroethane and heat the sample gently until the resin has dissolved. Wash the contents of the beaker quantitatively into a tared 50-ml. centrifuge tube with 20 ml. of tetrahydrofuran, swirl to mix, and centrifuge for 30 min. Decant the solution containing the remaining resin. Repeat the operation. Oven-dry the tared centrifuge tube, containing the stabilizer and filler, at 100°C., for 1 hr., cool, weigh, and calculate the percentage inorganic stabilizer and filler as follows:

$$\text{Inorganic stabilizer and filler, percent} = \frac{\text{weight of stabilizer and filler}}{\text{weight of PVC sample}} \times 100$$

Keep the stabilizer and filler for infrared analysis. Usually, carbon black and color pigments will be included in this portion. Calculate the percentage resin by differences between the initial PVC compound weight and the total of plasticizers, stabilizers, and fillers.

Infrared Analysis of Extracted Plasticizers.—The extracted plasticizers may be run on the infrared spectrometer as liquid films for identification or in carbon disulfide solution for quantitative determinations.

Identification of Plasticizers.—Most plasticizers for PVC are liquid at room temperatures. A few secondary plasticizers may be solid but would be suspended or dissolved in primary plasticizers. A demountable cell with sodium chloride windows and 0.025-mm. spacer usually suffices to give a strong plasticizer spectrum. A capillary film may be satisfactory for the ester plasticizers. Scan the spectrum from 2.5 to 15 μ. By reference to a collection of plasticizer spectra,[72] the plasticizers in the sample may be identified with experience. Rough estimates of concentrations may be made to allow preparation of matching standards for quantitative analysis.

Quantitative Analysis of Plasticizers.—The variety of plasticizers and their possible combinations in PVC compounds is extensive. It is impossible to specify a single procedure that quantitatively determines all plasticizers with equal precision and accuracy. The following procedure is useful for a number of plasticizers and their combinations, particularly if dioctyl phthalate or tricresyl phosphate is the primary plasticizer. The user should decide whether the efficiency, precision, and accuracy of the procedure is satisfactory for a specific combination of plasticizers to be analyzed.

Weigh 60.0 ± 0.2 mg. of extracted plasticizer into a 25-ml. Erlenmeyer flask equipped with a glass stopper; add 20.0 ± 0.2 ml. of carbon disulfide and dissolve the plasticizers. Take care to avoid loss of solvent by keeping the Erlenmeyer flask stoppered when

[72] Kendall, D. N., Hampton, R. R., Hausdorff, H., and Pristera, F., J. Appl. Spectroscopy, **7**, No. 4, 179, 1953; DuVall, R. B., Infrared Spectra of Plasticizers and Other Additives, The Dow Chemical Company, 1962.

possible. Run the resultant 3.0 mg. per ml. plasticizer solution on the infrared spectrometer in a 1.0-mm. liquid cell. Run a compensating 1.0-mm. liquid cell or a varia-
ble-path cell suitably adjusted, filled with carbon disulfide, in the reference beam. After
proper cleaning and drying of the sample cell, an equivalent blank of carbon disulfide
in the sample cell should be run vs. the reference cell. The dioctyl phthalate bands at
5.80 μ, 7.87 μ, and 8.92 μ, and the tricresyl phosphate band at 8.40 μ are satisfactory.
The dioctyl phthalate band chosen will depend in part on secondary plasticizer interferences. Choice of bands for other plasticizers is left to the discretion of the user. At the
analytical band wavelength chosen, measure the absorbances for the sample spectrum
$(A_s + A_b)$ and the blank spectrum (A_b). Net absorbance due to the sample, A_s, is
$(A_s + A_b) - A_b$. If a baseline technique is used for calculating concentrations, the
compensating solvent and blank are unnecessary.

Prepare plasticizer standards in carbon disulfide by dissolving the pure plasticizers of
interest to give a series of standard solutions covering the 3.0 to 0.5 mg. per ml. range
for each plasticizer. These standard plasticizer solutions should be run under identical
conditions to the samples to obtain the net absorbances of the components at a series of
concentrations. Plot Beer's law curves of net absorbance vs. concentration in milligrams
per milliliter for each component.

Use the net absorbance of a specific plasticizer in conjunction with the appropriate
Beer's law curve to determine the concentration in milligrams per milliliter. Calculate
the percentage plasticizer in the PVC as follows:

$$\text{Specific plasticizer, percent} = \frac{AB}{3W} \times 100$$

where A = concentration of plasticizer, in milligrams per milliliter,
  B = total weight of extracted plasticizers, in milligrams, and
  W = weight of PVC sample, in milligrams.

In a two-plasticizer system, one plasticizer may be determined and the other calculated by difference.

Direct Infrared Determination of Plasticizers.—The plasticizers may be determined
directly in a PVC compound using the following sample preparations. The use of this
method usually presupposes that a complete formulation analysis is not required and
that the plasticizers to be determined are known. Weigh approximately 0.25 g. ± 0.2
mg. of fine particle size sample into a 10 × 50 mm. extraction thimble. Place the thimble
in a micro Soxhlet extraction apparatus. Extract for 6 hr. with 20 ml. of carbon disulfide.
Transfer the carbon disulfide containing the extracted plasticizers to a 25-ml. volumetric
flask, dilute to the mark with carbon disulfide, and mix thoroughly. Run this solution
in a 1-mm. cell on the infrared spectrometer.

Calculate the percentage of a specific plasticizer in the PVC compound as follows:

$$\text{Specific plasticizer, percent} = \frac{25A}{W} \times 100$$

where A = concentration of plasticizer, in milligrams per milliliter (from curve), and
  W = weight of PVC sample, in milligrams.

Infrared Analysis of Stabilizers and Fillers.—The stabilizers and fillers, as a dry
powder after separation from the resin, may be identified by running on the infrared
spectrometer as a Nujol mull or potassium bromide pellet. Prepare the Nujol mull by
adding a few milligrams of powder to a drop of Nujol in a small mortar and grind. Run
the resultant mull as a film between two sodium chloride plates held in a demountable

cell mount. Prepare the potassium bromide pellet by adding approximately 1 mg. of powder to 600 mg. of dry potassium bromide powder and mixing for 1 min. in a vibrator mixer. Place the mixture in a mold assembly 0.5 in. in diameter and hold under vacuum for 3 min. Press while still under vacuum for 3 min. at a minimum pressure of 20,000 p.s.i. Higher pressures will produce more stable pellets. Place the resultant pellet in a holder and run on the infrared spectrometer. By comparison with reference spectra, the stabilizer and filler components may be identified in many cases.[73]

Quantitative Analysis of Stabilizers and Fillers.—These components are analyzed by the potassium bromide pellet technique. Weigh approximately 1 ± 0.2 mg. of stabilizer and filler powder and add to approximately 600 ± 0.2 mg. of dry potassium bromide powder, which has also been weighed. Prepare potassium bromide pellets as described in the preceding paragraph. Place in the holder in the sample beam, and run on an infrared spectrometer. Use baseline techniques to determine absorbances of the bands of interest, and plot Beer's law curves of net absorbance *vs.* percentage component in total stabilizers and fillers. The net absorbances are those that would result if the stabilizers and fillers were exactly 1 mg. in 600 mg. of potassium bromide powder. The percentage of component in the PVC sample may be calculated from the weight of stabilizers and fillers in the PVC sample previously determined. Prepare standard samples for preparation of Beer's law curves by mixing the pure compounds of interest in appropriate amounts to give a set of matched standards. The following bands are usable in many cases: Basic lead carbonate, 7.09 μ; calcined clay, 9.30 μ; calcium carbonate, 11.40 μ; antimony oxide, 13.50 μ; basic lead sulfate, 8.85 μ; dibasic lead phthalate, 6.51 μ.

Infrared Analysis of PVC Resin—Identification of Resin.—The resin obtained during component separations is in a tetrachloroethane-tetrahydrofuran solution. Evaporate a few milliliters of the solution, a few drops at a time, on a microscope slide. Gentle heating will accelerate drying. When the resultant film is dry, peel it from the microscope slide. Dry the film in a vacuum desiccator or vacuum oven to reduce solvent spectral interferences. It is advisable to prepare a number of films from each sample in order to obtain one of suitable quality and thickness. Mount the film in the infrared spectrophotometer and record its spectrum from 2.5 to 15 μ.

The PVC may be identified by its overall infrared spectrum. If the resin is a copolymer of vinyl chloride and vinyl acetate, a carbonyl band will be present at 5.74 μ; and if the amount of acetate is greater than approximately 5 percent, a band attributed to the acetate group is present at 9.80 μ. Take care in the interpretation of carbonyl bands in the spectrum of the resin since these may also arise from the following:

(1) Copolymers other than acetate (for example, acrylate).
(2) Incomplete extraction of certain polymeric ester plasticizers.
(3) Oxidation of the resin.
(4) Esterification of the resin by certain compounding ingredients.
(5) Tetrahydrofuran oxidation products.

Usually the carbonyl bands due to residual polymeric plasticizers and to oxidation are at lower frequencies than those due to copolymers or to esterification of the resin.

Precision and Accuracy.—Precisions and accuracies of the order of 1 percent of component values can be achieved for quantitative portions of the method. However, the method is intended as a general procedure to cover a wide range of PVC compounds either qualitatively, semiquantitatively, or quantitatively; and the precision and accuracy will vary according to the specific formulations analyzed.

[73] Hunt, J. M., Wisherd, M. P., and Bonham, L. C., Anal. Chem., **22**, 1478, 1950; Miller, F. A., and Wilkins, C. H., Anal. Chem., **24**, 1253, 1952.

ANALYSIS OF STYRENE-ACRYLONITRILE COPOLYMERS[74]

Scope.—This method is suitable for determining the residual monomer content and the styrene-acrylonitrile ratio of styrene-acrylonitrile copolymers.

Principle.—The residual styrene and acrylonitrile monomers are extracted from the polymer. The extract is scanned and absorbance measurements are made at wavelengths characteristic of each component. The extracted polymer is then dissolved and cast as a film directly on a sodium chloride plate. The film is scanned and absorbance measurements are made at the characteristic wavelengths for acrylonitrile and styrene. The sample absorbances are compared with those obtained from standards of known concentration.

Apparatus. **Infrared Spectrometer,** double beam.
Infrared Cells, 3.0 mm.
Shaker, Burrell Wrist-Action or equivalent.
Reagents. **Carbon Disulfide,** infrared grade.
Methylene Chloride, redistilled.
Styrene-Acrylonitrile Copolymer.
Polystyrene.
Styrene Monomer.
Acrylonitrile Monomer.

Calibration. **Determination of Monomers.**—Prepare individual solutions of styrene monomer and acrylonitrile monomer in carbon disulfide covering the range from 0.1 to 0.5 percent monomer (10 to 50 mg. in 25 ml. carbon disulfide based on a 10-g. sample weight).

Scan the solutions from 2.5 to 16 μ in a 3.0-mm. cell. Draw a baseline from adjacent shoulders of the 10.4-μ (acrylonitrile) and 12.9-μ (styrene) peaks. Measure the absorbance of the peaks and prepare analytical curves by plotting absorbance *vs.* percentage of monomer.

Determination of Copolymer Ratio.—Dissolve the polystyrene and the styrene-acrylonitrile copolymer separately in methylene chloride. Precipitate the polymers by the addition of methanol to produce monomer-free polymer. Recover the purified polymers by filtration and dry at 70°C. *in vacuo.* Calculate the acrylonitrile content of the styrene-acrylonitrile copolymer from the nitrogen content determined by the Kjeldahl procedure.[75] Prepare blends of varying styrene-acrylonitrile content by dissolving known amounts of the polystyrene and the analyzed styrene-acrylonitrile copolymer in methylene chloride.

Cast films from the standard solutions directly on sodium chloride plates and dry under an infrared heat lamp to remove all traces of the solvent. Scan the films from 2.5 to 16 μ. Draw baselines from 4.4 to 4.5 μ and from 6.1 to 6.4 μ and measure the absorbance at 4.45 μ (acrylonitrile) and 6.2 μ (styrene). Calculate the absorbance ratio ($A_{4.45}/A_{6.2}$) and plot an analytical curve of absorbance ratio *vs.* acrylonitrile concentration.

Procedure.—Weigh 10 g. of sample into a 2-oz. narrow-mouth bottle and add 25 ml. of carbon disulfide. Stopper the bottle securely and place on the shaker for 16 hr. Allow the polymer to settle and transfer a portion of the supernatant liquid to the 3.0-mm. cell. Scan from 2.5 to 16 μ. Decant the remaining carbon disulfide from the polymer.

[74] Kiley, L. R., and Scheddel, R. T., The Dow Chemical Company, unpublished manuscript; Scheddel, R. T., Anal. Chem., **30,** 1303, 1958.
[75] Welcher, F. J., ed., Standard Methods of Chemical Analysis, 6th Ed., Vol. II, Part B, D. Van Nostrand Co., Inc., Princeton, N. J., 1963, p. 2063.

Dry the extracted polymer *in vacuo* at 70°C. Weigh 2 g. of the dried polymer into a 2-oz. narrow-mouth bottle and add 50 ml. of methylene chloride. Stopper securely and place the bottle on the shaker until the sample is dissolved. Cast a polymer film approximately 1 mm. thick directly on a sodium chloride plate. Dry the film under an infrared heat lamp and scan from 2.5 to 16 μ.

Calculation.—Measure the absorbances of the characteristic absorption bands as indicated under "Calibration." Read the concentrations of styrene monomer, acrylonitrile monomer, and combined acrylonitrile from the corresponding analytical curves.

DETERMINATION OF METHYL GROUPS IN POLYETHYLENE[76]

Scope.—This method for the estimation of methyl groups is applicable to polyethylene and similar polymers, such as ethylene-propylene copolymers.

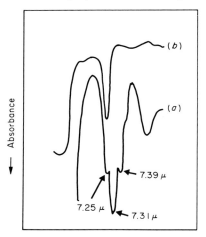

Principle.—The intensity of the 7.25-μ band (symmetrical methyl C—H bending vibration) is independent of crystallinity. The 7.31- and 7.39-μ bands, which interfere with the measurement of the 7.25-μ band, vary with the amorphous content. The interference of those two bands can be eliminated by compensating with a polymethylene wedge (Fig. 58-15). Polymethylene is very similar to polyethylene except that it is void of the methyl side chains which exhibit absorption at 7.25 μ.

Apparatus. **Perkin-Elmer Model 421 Spectrophotometer** or equivalent.

Wabash Hydraulic Press with platens capable of being heated to 170°C., or equivalent.

Smooth-surface Metal Plates.

Brass Shim about 10 mils in thickness with aperature in center about 2 in. × 1 in.

FIG. 58-15. Infrared Spectra of (a) Polyethylene; (b) Polyethylene Compensated with Polymethylene.

Lufkin Micrometer, calibrated in mils, or equivalent.

Polymethylene Wedge.[77]

Reagents. **n-Hexadecane (cetane-$C_{16}H_{34}$),** N.B.S. or equivalent purity.

n-Triacontane ($C_{30}H_{62}$), N.B.S. or equivalent purity.

n-Octapentacontane ($C_{58}H_{118}$), m.p. 97°C.

Calibration.—The calibration is based on the measurement of the 7.25-μ absorption band of model compounds having known concentrations of methyl groups. The Beer-Lambert law is assumed to apply for extrapolation of the calibration curve.

The n-hexadecane is scanned undiluted in a 0.25-mm. cell. The higher melting standards are scanned as 10-mil-thick films.

Place the standard in the sample beam of the spectrometer and scan from 7 to 8 μ.

[76] Melcher, R. G., The Dow Chemical Company, unpublished manuscript. Pertinent References: Bryant, W. M. D., and Voter, R. C., J. Am. Chem. Soc., **75**, 6113, 1953; Jones, R. G., J. Am. Chem. Soc., **69**, 2350, 1947; Willbourn, A. H., J. Polymer Sci., **34**, 569, 1959; Slowinski, E. J., Walter, H., and Miller, R. L., J. Polymer Sci., **19**, 353, 1956.
[77] Harvey, M. C., and Peters, L. L., Anal. Chem., **32**, 1725, 1960.

Place the polymethylene wedge in the reference beam and scan. Adjust the position of the wedge in the reference beam and scan until the 7.31-μ band is completely compensated (absorbance at 7.31 μ equal to absorbance at 7.13 μ). Draw a baseline tangent to the compensated curve from 7.20 to 7.50 μ. Measure the absorbance of the 7.25-μ band. Calculate the specific absorbance (K) using the formula:

$$K_{7.25} = \frac{A_{7.25}}{d \times t}$$

where $A_{7.25}$ = measured absorbance,
d = density in g. per ml., and
t = thickness in cm.

Prepare an analytical curve by plotting the specific absorbance of the known in the 0.25-mm. cell *vs.* the theoretical number of methyl groups per 1000 carbon atoms. Extrapolate the curve to zero concentration.

Procedure.—Mold the polyethylene into film in the following way: Place the brass shim on one of the metal plates. Place sufficient polymer in the aperture of the shim to completely fill it after molding. Place the second metal plate on top of the shim. Place the assembly between the platens of the press which have been preheated to 170°C. Bring the pressure up to 30,000 lb., and hold for 1 min. Release the pressure slowly and, grasping the assembly with pliers, quickly plunge it into cold water. Remove the film and dry it.

Tape the film onto a suitable holder and measure the thickness at several places in the aperture with the micrometer. Record the average thickness.

Measure the density of a clipping from the same film by use of a density gradient tube[78] or other suitable means.

Scan the film from 7 to 8 μ employing the polymethylene wedge for compensation, as described above. Measure the absorbance of the 7.25-μ band and calculate the specific absorbance.

Read the concentration of methyl groups per 1000 carbon atoms from the analytical curve.

DETERMINATION OF CARBONYL GROUPS AND UNSATURATION IN POLYETHYLENE[79]

Scope.—The following procedure is designed for the determination of the number of carbonyl groups, *trans* —CH=CH-unsaturation, and vinyl-1,2-unsaturation per 1000 carbon atoms in polyethylene.

Principle.—The various chemical groupings are determined by comparing the intensity of the characteristic absorption bands to the absorption produced by analogous prototype compounds. This method is completely general for any functional group having a unique infrared absorption.

Apparatus. **Infrared Spectrometer,** double beam.

Hydraulic Press with platens capable of being heated to 170°C.

Brass Shim, 0.4 mm. thick with aperture in center about 2 in. × 1 in.

Reagents. **n-Hexane.**—Phillips Spectro-grade or equivalent.

5-Nonanone (n-Butyl Ketone).

1-Octene.

[78] Welcher, F. J., Standard Methods of Chemical Analysis, 6th Ed., Vol. II, Part B, D. Van Nostrand Co., Inc., Princeton, N. J., 1963, p. 2080.
[79] Potts, W. J., The Dow Chemical Company, unpublished manuscript; Potts, W. J., International Symposium on Plastics Testing and Standardization, ASTM, Philadelphia, 1958.

Trans-4-Octene.

Calibration.—Prepare a solution of 5-nonanone, 1-octene, and *trans*-4-octene in *n*-hexane such that each of the three components is approximately 0.04 molar. The concentration of each component should be known exactly. Transfer a portion of the solution to a 1-mm. cell and scan from 2.5 to 16 μ. Measure the absorbance at the wavelengths indicated in the tabulation below, employing the designated baselines.

Constituent	Wavelength, μ	Baseline, μ
Carbonyl ($>$C$=$O)	5.83	5.6– 6.0
Trans —CH$=$CH—	10.35	10.1–10.8
—CH$=$CH$_2$	11.0	10.8–11.2

Calculate the concentration of the $>$C$=$O, —CH$=$CH—, and —CH$=$CH$_2$ groups in the hexane solution as moles per liter.

Procedure.—Using the technique described in the procedure "Determination of Methyl Groups in Polyethylene," prepare a polyethylene film approximately 0.4 mm. thick, and measure the average thickness and the density of the film.

Scan the film from 2.5 to 16 μ and measure the absorption at 5.83, 10.35, and 11.0 μ by the baseline method.

Calculation.—Calculate the concentration of each chemical group by substituting the corresponding values in the following formula.

$$\text{Group per 1000 carbon atoms} = \frac{A_{\text{poly}}}{A_{\text{prot}}} \times \frac{14 C_{\text{prot}} \times t_{\text{cell}} \times d_{\text{poly}}}{t_{\text{poly}}} \times 1000$$

where A_{poly} = absorbance of band in polymer spectrum,

A_{prot} = analogous absorbance of prototype compound in hexane solution in moles/liter,

C_{prot} = concentration of prototype group in hexane solution in moles/liter,

t_{cell} = cell thickness used in measuring prototype in hexane solution, mm.,

d_{poly} = density of polymer, g./cc., and

t_{poly} = polymer film thickness, mm.

ADDITIVES

Most plastics contain significant amounts of intentional or unintentional additives. Intentional additives are plasticizers, inorganic fillers, antioxidants, mold release agents, light stabilizers, etc., which have been added to the plastic for a specific purpose. Unintentional additives are components, such as residual monomers, solvents, or catalyst residues, which are present as the result of the processing. In most cases, these materials can be removed from the plastic by solvent extraction. In some instances, merely soaking the plastic in a suitable solvent will be satisfactory. Other samples may require prolonged Soxhlet extraction. As a last resort, the plastic may be dissolved. Inorganic additives may then be separated by centrifuging or perhaps by simply filtering. The polymer can then be separated from the soluble additive by precipitation with a nonsolvent. If the additives are present in suffcient concentration and if the polymer is reasonably transparent in the region of the additive absorption bands, polymer films, mulls, or solutions may be scanned directly.

DETERMINATION OF MINERAL OIL IN POLYSTYRENE[80]

Scope.—This method provides for the determination of 0.2 to 8 percent of mineral oil in polystyrenes which contain, in addition to the mineral oil, only styrene-butadiene

[80] Scheddel, R. T., The Dow Chemical Company, unpublished manuscript.

rubber and 2,6-di-*tert*.-butyl-*p*-cresol. It may be used in the presence of other additives if these additives are known and proper corrections applied.

Principle.—The sample is dissolved in carbon disulfide. The polymer and the rubber are separated by precipitation with an equal volume of isopropanol. The carbon disulfide–isopropanol solution, containing the additives, monomer, and some low molecular weight polymer, is filtered and washed with water to remove the isopropanol. The carbon disulfide solution is then scanned and infrared absorption measurements are made at wavelengths characteristic of each component. The sample absorbances are compared with those obtained from pure components. Mineral oil is determined at 3.4 μ after correcting this absorption for interference by the other components.

Apparatus. **Infrared Spectrometer,** sodium chloride optics.
Infrared Cell, 0.9 mm., sodium chloride windows.
Shaker, Burrell Wrist-Action or equivalent.
Separatory Funnel, 500-ml.
Centrifuge.
Reagents. **Isopropanol,** reagent grade.
Carbon Disulfide, infrared grade.
Polystyrene, pure.
Styrene-Butadiene Rubber, GRS-1006 type.
2,6-Di-*tert*.-butyl-*p*-cresol (DBC), pure.
Mineral Oil.

Calibration.—In practice, the only interference encountered on mineral oil will probably be low molecular weight polystyrene, which is soluble in isopropanol. The interferences for DBC, rubber, and isopropanol are included so that it will be possible to determine the mineral oil even though these compounds are present. The method may be extended to include any monomer or additive by calibrating with suitable standards. In this case, solutions and standards should also be scanned in a 3.0-mm. cell to increase the sensitivity.

Weigh into separate 50-ml. volumetric flasks the following amounts of the specified materials. Dilute each flask to volume with carbon disulfide.

Mineral oil: 25, 50, 75, 100, 150, 200 mg.
Polystyrene: 50, 100, 150 mg.
Isopropanol: 50, 100 mg.
DBC: 10, 25 mg.
Styrene-butadiene rubber: 25, 50 mg.

Scan each solution and a carbon disulfide blank from 2 to 16 μ in the 0.9-mm. cell. Measure the absorbances of each solution at the wavelengths indicated in the table, and at 3.4 μ employing the designated baselines.

Constituent	Wavelength, μ	Baseline, μ
Mineral oil	3.4	3.0–4.0
Isopropanol	10.5	10.1–10.6
DBC	8.1	7.9–8.15
Styrene-butadiene rubber	10.4	10.4–10.6
Polystyrene	14.3	13.9–13.6

Subtract the carbon disulfide interference from the 3.4-μ absorbances. Plot analytical and interference curves. Twenty-five mg. of component per 50 ml. of carbon disulfide solution represents 1 percent component in the sample.

Procedure.—Weigh 2.5 g. of sample into a 2-oz. narrow-mouth bottle, and add 50 ml. of carbon disulfide. Place the bottle on the shaker until the sample is dissolved. Any pigment present will not dissolve but will go into suspension and will not interfere with the analysis.

Using a graduate, measure 20 ml. of isopropanol and shake briefly to mix. Centrifuge for 2 min. Filter the carbon disulfide-isopropanol solution into a 500-ml. separatory funnel which has been nearly filled with water. Shake by hand for 1 min. Pour off as much water as possible, retaining the carbon disulfide solution in the funnel. Refill with water and shake again for 1 min. Draw the carbon disulfide solution off the bottom into a 1-oz. bottle. Add salt crystals to take up any water that may have come through. Scan the solution from 2 to 16 μ in a 0.9-mm. cell.

Calculations.—Measure the absorbances, if any, as indicated in the calibration procedure. After applying interference corrections to the 3.4-μ absorbance, read the remaining absorbance, if any, as percent mineral oil from analytical curve.

Accuracy and Sensitivity.—The accuracy is ±0.2 percent and the least amount detectable is 0.2 percent.

DETERMINATION OF 2,6-DI-TERT.-BUTYL-p-CRESOL IN POLYETHYLENE[81]

Scope.—This method is suitable for the determination of 10 to 500 p.p.m. of 2,6-di-*tert.*-butyl-*p*-cresol in polyethylene.

Principle.—The finely ground sample is extracted with carbon disulfide. The carbon disulfide extract is scanned and infrared absorption measurements are made at 8.65 μ.

Apparatus. Infrared Spectrometer with 1.0-cm. cells.

Shaker, Burrell Wrist-Action or equivalent.

Reagents. Carbon Disulfide, infrared grade.

2,6-Di-*tert.*-butyl-*p*-cresol.

Calibration.—Prepare a stock solution by weighing 100 mg. of 2,6-di-*tert.*-butyl-*p*-cresol into a 100-ml. flask. Dissolve the standard in carbon disulfide and dilute to volume with the same solvent.

Transfer, to separate 50-ml. volumetric flasks, 1-, 2.5-,and 5-ml. aliquots of the stock solution and dilute to volume with carbon disulfide. These standards represent 40, 100, and 250 p.p.m. of 2,6-di-*tert.*-butyl-*p*-cresol (DBC) respectively. Scan each solution in a 1-cm. cell from 7.6 to 9 μ. Draw a base line from 8.50 to 8.85 μ and measure the absorbance of the 8.65 μ peak. Prepare an analytical curve by plotting absorbance values versus concentration of DBC.

Procedure.—Weigh 10 g. of finely ground polyethylene into a 2-oz. bottle and add 20-ml. of carbon disulfide. Shake on the mechanical shaker for 2 hrs. Filter the solution into a 1-cm. cell and scan as described above. Measure the absorbance of the 8.65 μ peak. From the analytical curve, read the concentration of DBC in p.p.m. The peak at 8.15 μ may be employed if interference occurs at 8.65 μ.

DETERMINATION OF 9-OCTADECENAMIDE IN POLYETHYLENE[81]

Scope.—This method is suitable for the determination of 100 to 500 p.p.m. of 9-octadecenamide (oleamide) in polyethylene.

Principle.—A film, 5 mil thick, compensated with a film devoid of oleamide in the reference beam is scanned from 5.5 μ to 6.2 μ. Absorption measurements are made at 5.85 μ.

Apparatus. Infrared Spectrometer—double beam.

Hydraulic Press with platens capable of being heated to 300°F.

[81] Spell, H. L., and Eddy, R. D., Anal. Chem., **32,** 1811, 1960. Copyright 1960 by the American Chemical Society and reprinted with the permission of the copyright owner.

Smooth Surface Aluminum or Chrome-Steel Plates.—Brass shim with an aperture in the center at least 2 in. × 1 in. and about 5 mm. thick.

Reagents. **9-Octadecenamide (Oleamide).**

Calibration.—Prepare standard blends of oleamide and polyethylene covering the range from 100 p.p.m. to 500 p.p.m. oleamide. The preferred method of preparation is a Banbury mixing of the polyethylene with the desired amounts of oleamide followed by extrusion of the mix. Prepare a film, 5 mm. thick, of each blend as follows: With the brass shim on one of the smooth plates, place a small amount of polymer in the aperture and cover with the second plate. Place the assembly between the press platens which have been preheated to 300°F. Bring the pressure up to 30,000 lb. and hold for 1 min. Release the pressure and, grasping the assembly with pliers or wearing heavy leather gloves, quickly plunge the assembly into cold water. Remove the film and dry it. Prepare an identical reference film devoid of oleamide for compensation in the reference beam.

Place the reference film in the reference beam. Scan the treated samples from 5.5 μ to 6.2 μ. Draw a baseline from 6.1 μ tangent to the curve at 5.5 μ. Measure the absorbance of the 5.85-μ peak. Prepare an analytical curve by plotting absorbance values *vs.* concentration of oleamide in p.p.m.

Procedure.—Prepare a film 5 mm. thick and scan as described above. Measure the absorbance of the 5.85-μ band and read the concentration of oleamide from the analytical curve.

The lower limit of detection of oleamide by this method is 40 p.p.m. with an accuracy of ±5 p.p.m.

AMORPHOUS, CRYSTALLINE AND STEREOREGULAR POLYMERS[82]

The degree of crystallinity and the stereoregularity of polymers are important factors in determining the physical properties or end-use applications or plastics. Actually, the two terms are interrelated since a crystalline polymer can be obtained only when there is regularity in the succession of configurations of its monomeric units in a long-chain segment, or when enantiomorphous configurations follow each other. Crystallinity and the factors related to its formation influence such polymer characteristics as hardness, melting temperature range, tensile strength, and elasticity.

Asymmetric chain atoms, double bonds, rings of appropriate type, etc., are sites of steric isomerism in a polymer chain and define the type of stereoisomerism as:

(a) Geometrical stereoisomerism which occurs when the same chemical formula may correspond to intrinsically different geometrical configurations (compounds containing double bonds).

(b) Optical stereoisomerism which occurs when a molecule cannot assume, by permissible rotation around a single bond, the enantiomorphous configuration (due to the presence of carbon atoms linked to four different substituents).

Frequently the absorption bands in the infrared spectrum of a polymer differ, depending upon whether the polymer is in the amorphous or crystalline state. Additionally, differences in stereoregularity give rise to variations in frequency or intensity of group absorption bands. Thus it is possible to characterize the microstructure of many polymers by infrared spectrometry. However, it must be recognized that crystallinity measurements by infrared spectrometer techniques are usually less accurate than x-ray diffraction results.

The stereospecific polymerized polybutadienes provide excellent examples of geo-

[82] Pertinent references: Gailey, J. A., Anal. Chem., **33**, 1831, 1961; Huggins, M. L., Natta, G., Desreux, V., and Mark, H., J. Polymer Sci., **56**, 153, 1962; Natta, G., and Corradini, Rubber Chem. and Tech., **33**, 703, 1960.

metrical stereoisomers. The configurations of the geometric isomers are shown in Fig. 58-16.

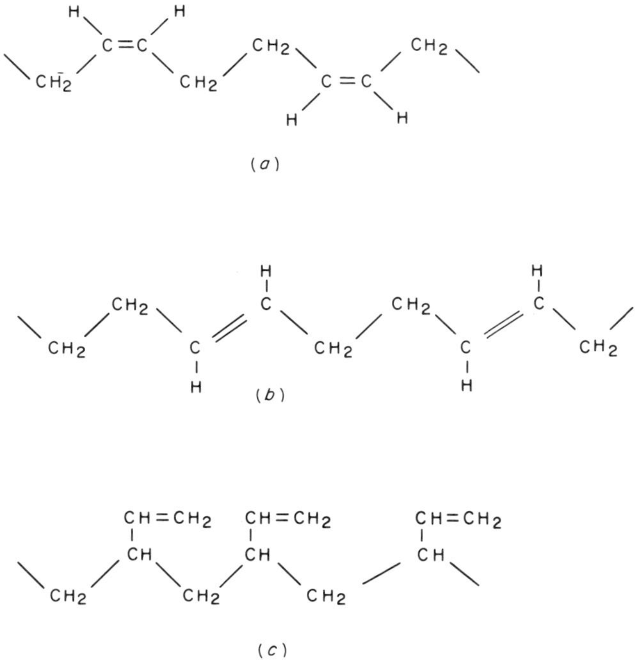

(a)

(b)

(c)

FIG. 58-16.   Structural Formulas for (a) *Cis*-1,4-Polybutadiene; (b) *Trans*-1,4-Polybutadiene; and (c) Vinyl-1,2-Polybutadiene.

A spectral curve for a polybutadiene containing approximately 41 percent *cis*-1,4-, 54 percent *trans*-1,4- and 5 percent vinyl-1,2- configurations is shown in Fig. 58-17. The principal identifying bands occur at 10.34 μ for the *trans*-1,4-configuration, at about 13.5 μ (broad) for the *cis*-1,4-configuration, and at 10.98 μ for the vinyl-1,2-configuration. Infrared spectrometric methods for characterizing polybutadienes have been developed, based on the absorbance of these bands as compared to the absorbance of model low molecular weight olefins, such as *cis*-4-octene, *trans*-4-octene, and 1-octene.[83] When pure standards are not available for calibrating infrared spectrometric analysis, a technique of successive approximation may be employed. This technique has been used by Scheddel[84] to calibrate the procedure for determining the microstructure of polybutadiene.

Optical stereoregular polymers can be classified generally as atactic, isotactic, or syndiotactic. An atactic polymer has complete randomness with regard to the configurations at all the main chain sites of steric isomerism. Many atactic polymers are completely amorphous and cannot be crystallized by any method. Quite possibly, the bulkiness of the side groups (for example, the phenyl group in polystyrene) does not permit

[83] Binder, J. L., and Ransaw, H. C., Anal. Chem., **29,** 503, 1957; Hampton, R. R., Anal. Chem., **21,** 923, 1949.

[84] Scheddel, R. T., The Dow Chemical Company, unpublished manuscript.

the formation of a crystal lattice unless there is an ordered arrangement. An isotactic polymer possesses, as a component of the base unit of the main chain, a carbon atom with two different lateral substituents, both of which are in the steric order along the length of the chain (Fig. 58-18a). A syndiotactic polymer possesses, as a component of

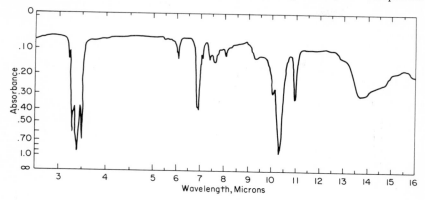

Fig. 58-17. Infrared Spectrum of Polybutadiene.

the base unit of the main chain, a carbon atom with two different lateral substituents. In the progression along the chain, however, the successive units are in opposite steric configuration (Fig. 58-18b).

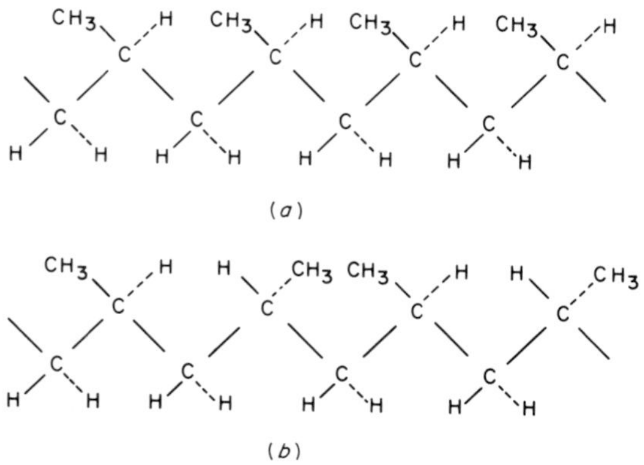

(a)

(b)

Fig. 58-18. Structural Formulas for (a) Isotactic Polypropylene and (b) Syndiotactic Polypropylene.

Isotactic and syndiotactic polymers are characterized by the ability to crystallize under certain conditions. The spectrum of the amorphous form is generally more diffuse than that of the crystalline form; therefore, the study of stereoregularity is generally carried out on solutions, in which the bands due to crystallinity are absent. Spectra of atactic and a primarily isotactic polypropylene are shown in Fig. 58-19. The isotactic polypropylene is characterized by increased intensity of the bands at $10.02\ \mu$ and $11.8\ \mu$

and by the appearance of a relatively strong band at 8.55 μ. Heinen[85] used the absorbance of the 11.8-μ band as a measure of crystallinity, whereas Luongo[86] used the ratio of intensities of the bands at 10.27 and 10.05 μ as a measure of crystallinity.

Although x-ray diffraction analysis is usually a more reliable procedure for measuring crystallinity, the composition of some polymers (such as the chlorine atoms in vinylidene chloride copolymers) interferes with, or distorts, the x-ray diffraction pattern, making

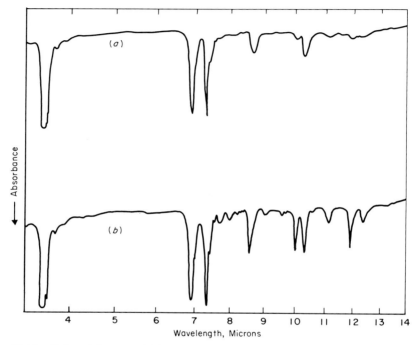

FIG. 58-19. Infrared Spectra of (a) Atactic Polypropylene and (b) Isotactic Polypropylene.

quantitative interpretation difficult. Although absolute crystallinity values for such materials cannot be obtained with any degree of confidence, infrared spectrometry does yield relative information of a quantitative nature. The measurement of crystallinity in vinylidene chloride–acrylonitrile copolymers is a typical example. The infrared spectra of typical amorphous and crystalline polymers are presented in Fig. 58-20a and Fig. 58-20b, respectively. Absorption bands indicative of crystallinity are those at 9.6, 11.3, and 13.35 μ.[87] The 9.35-μ band is primarily indicative of the concentration of the amorphous portion of the polymer, although it is enhanced slightly by crystallization. The relative crystallinity ratio is calculated as the absorbance ratio of 9.6-μ band to the 9.35-μ band measured from a baseline drawn from 8.5 to 12.5 μ. The greater the ratio, the greater is the proportion of crystalline phase to amorphous phase.

[85] Heinen, W., J. Polymer Sci., **38**, 545, 1959.
[86] Luongo, J. P., J. Appl. Polymer Sci., **3**, 302, 1960.
[87] Rector, M. E., The Dow Chemical Company, personal communication; Burton, R. L., Cobbs, W. H., and Haskell, V. C., J. Polymer Sci., **7**, 569, 1951.

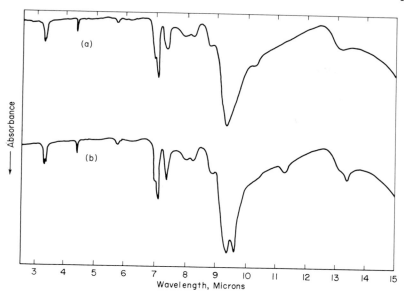

FIG. 58-20. Infrared Spectra of Vinylidene Chloride-Acrylonitrile Copolymer. (a) Amorphous State; (b) Crystalline State.

DETERMINATION OF THE MICROSTRUCTURE OF POLYBUTADIENES[84]

Scope.—The following procedure provides for the determination of *cis*-1,4-, *trans*-1,4-, and vinyl-1,2-unsaturation in polybutadienes.

Principle.—A solution of the polymer is scanned and absorbance measurements are made at wavelengths characteristic of each type of unsaturation. The sample absorbances are compared with absorbances calculated from reference materials by the technique of successive approximation.

Apparatus. **Infrared Spectrometer,** double beam.

Shaker, Burrell Wrist-Action or equivalent.

Reagents. **Carbon Disulfide,** infrared grade.

Reference Polybutadienes.—*Cis*-1,4-polybutadiene (approximately 95 percent *cis*-1,4-unsaturation). *Trans*-1,4-polybutadiene (approximately 98 percent *trans*-1,4-unsaturation. Vinyl-1,2-polybutadiene (approximately 85 percent vinyl-1,2-unsaturation and 15 percent *trans*-1,4-unsaturation).

Calibration.—Weigh 0.5-, 1.0-, and 2.0-g. portions of each reference polybutadiene into separate 2-oz. bottles. Add exactly 50 ml. of carbon disulfide to each bottle and stopper securely. Place on the mechanical shaker until the polybutadiene is completely dissolved. Scan the solutions from 2.5 to 16 μ in a 0.1-mm. cell compensated with pure carbon disulfide in a second 0.1-mm. cell. Measure the absorbances of each solution at the wavelengths given below:

Component	Wavelength, μ	Baseline, μ
Trans-1,4-unsaturation	10.34	9.6–11.6
Vinyl-1,2-unsaturation	10.98	9.6–11.6
Cis-1,4-unsaturation	13.7	12.4–15.4
	3.32	Adjacent shoulders

Calculate corrected absorbances by the technique of successive approximations.

(a) Plot the 10.34-μ absorbances measured on the three solutions of the *trans*-reference polybutadiene *vs.* concentrations assuming 100 percent *trans*-1,4-unsaturation.

(b) Convert the absorbances at 10.34 μ measured on the *cis*-reference solutions to percent *trans*-1,4-unsaturation using the curve plotted in (a).

(c) Calculate the first approximation of *cis*-1,4-unsaturation as 100 minus the percentage of *trans*-1,4-unsaturation from (b).

(d) Use the corrected values for the concentration of *cis*-1,4-unsaturation and prepare a plot of absorbances measured at 3.32 μ and at 13.7 μ on the *cis*-1,4-reference solutions *vs.* percentage *cis*-1,4-unsaturation. The 3.32-μ wavelength for the *cis*-1,4-unsaturation is given as an alternate since, in mixtures, interference is frequently encountered at the 13.7-μ wavelength. However, the 3.32-μ absorbance band should be employed only as a last resort.

(e) Convert the absorbance at 10.34 μ measured on the vinyl reference solution to percentage *trans*-1,4-unsaturation using the curve plotted in (a).

(f) Convert the absorbances at 3.32 μ and at 13.7 μ measured on the vinyl reference polybutadienes to percentage *cis*-1,4-unsaturation using the curve plotted in (d).

(g) Calculate the first approximation of the vinyl-1,2-concentration as 100 minus the sum of the *trans*-1,4-unsaturation and the *cis*-1,4-unsaturation from (e) and (f), respectively.

(h) Use the corrected values for the concentration of vinyl-1,2-unsaturation and prepare a plot of absorbances, measured at 10.98 μ, *vs.* percentage of vinyl-1,2-unsaturation.

(i) Calculate the concentrations of *cis*-1,4-unsaturation and vinyl-1,2-unsaturation in the *trans*-1,4-reference solutions from the curves prepared in (d) and (h).

(j) Calculate the percentage *trans*-1,4-unsaturation in the *trans*-reference solutions as 100 minus the value found in (i).

(k) Prepare a new curve for *trans*-1,4-unsaturation absorbances at 10.34 *vs.* the concentration calculated from (j).

(l) Repeat this re-evaluation of analytical curves using the most recent corrected curves for the three types of unsaturation until no further change occurs in the plotted curves.

Procedure.—Dissolve 2.0 g. of polybutadiene in 50 ml. of carbon disulfide as directed above. Scan the solution from 2.5 to 16 μ using the same cells and instrument conditions as in the calibration. Read the concentrations of *cis*-1,4-, *trans*-1,4-, and vinyl-1,2-unsaturation directly from the corrected analytical curve.

OXIDATION AND POLYMERIZATION STUDIES

The physical properties of many polymers are impaired by thermal oxidation during processing. Knowledge of the molecular changes produced by oxidation is important in devising suitable protective measures. Infrared spectrometry is an excellent means for following molecular changes which occur in thermal treatment.[88]

A typical study shows the changes which occur during the heat treatment of an unstabilized styrene-butadiene rubber. The sample was cast on a glass plate from a latex and allowed to air-dry. After drying, the film was floated from the plate with water and attached to a wire frame suitable for mounting in the spectrometer. The spectrum in Fig. 58-21a represents the characteristic absorption bands of a freshly made polymer film. The spectra in Fig. 58-21b, Fig. 58-21c, and Fig. 58-21d were taken of the same polymer film after 3, 5, and 9 days exposure at 58°C. in the absence of light. Structural changes, as a result of oxidation, are indicated by the appearance of absorption bands

[88] Field, J. E., Woodford, D. E., and Gehman, S. D., Rubber Chem. and Tech., **28**, 770, 1955; Luongo, J. P., J. Polymer Sci., **42**, 139, 1960.

at 2.9 μ (hydroxyl), 5.8 μ (ketonic or aldehydic carbonyl), and at 5.85 μ (acid carbonyl). The intensity of the ketonic carbonyl increases much more rapidly than that for the other groups. Also, as a result of oxidation, there is a general increase in absorption in the 7- to 11-μ range (C—O links) which masks out the normal absorption bands.

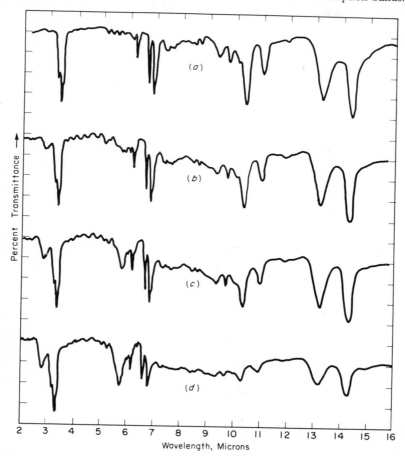

FIG. 58-21. Infrared Spectra of Styrene-Butadiene Rubber Showing Structural Changes as a Result of Thermal Degradation. (a) Initial Film; (b) Three Days Exposure at 58°C.; (c) Five Days Exposure at 58°C.; (d) Nine Days Exposure at 58°C.

Utilizing this technique, it is therefore possible to follow the formation of oxidation products during the heat treatment of many plastics. By the use of prototype compounds, the concentration of the various degradation products can be measured.

Infrared spectrometry provides an excellent technique for following polymerization or curing reactions. An example of the former, the polymerization of diglycidyl ether with Bisphenol A, is shown in Fig. 58-22. Characteristic absorption bands occur at 3.0 μ (phenolic —OH), 2.9 μ (alcoholic —OH), 6.65 μ (phenyl ring vibration) 7.8 μ (C—O—C), 8.23 μ (—OH), and 9.75 μ (C—O—C). As polymerization proceeds, the phenolic —OH band at 3.0 μ decreases and is replaced by the ether absorption bands at 7.8 and 9.75 μ. An alcoholic —OH absorption band appears at 2.9 μ. The phenyl ring absorption at 6.65 μ remains constant throughout the polymerization. Thus, the changes which occur as a result of polymerization may be measured relative to the phenyl ring absorption.

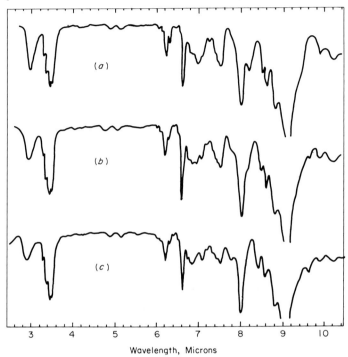

Fig. 58-22.   Infrared Spectra Showing Successive Stages in the Reaction of Bisphenol A with Diglycidyl Ether.

POLARIZED INFRARED RADIATION SPECTROMETRY[89]

When unpolarized radiation is passed through a liquid or an amorphous solid with a purely random spatial arrangement, there is an equal probability of interaction between the radiation and all possible modes of vibration of the molecules. In oriented polymers, however, changes in dipole moments of molecular groups may be restricted to definite directions in relation to the chain axis. Thus, when a beam of plane-polarized radiation is passed through an oriented film, an absorption band will be of maximum intensity if the direction of the dipole moment change accompanying the vibration is parallel to the electric vector of the polarized radiation. If the electric vector of the polarized radiation is perpendicular to the vector of the vibration, the absorption band will be of minimum intensity.

Orientation of the polymer chain can be produced by stretching or by rolling between heated rollers. Uniaxial orientation results from stretching. The long chain crystallo-

[89] Liang, C. Y., Lytton, M. R., and Boone, C. J., J. Polymer Sci., **54**, 523, 1961. (Courtesy John Wiley and Sons, Inc.)

graphic axis becomes aligned parallel to the stretching direction; however, all orientations of the crystallites about this axis will be equally probable. Double orientation is produced by rolling the plastic, whereby the crystallographic axis is aligned with the rolling direction with particular crystallographic planes oriented parallel to the plane of the film.

Two separate infrared spectra of the polymer are obtained by the use of plane-polarized infrared radiation. The sample is rotated 90° between scans, thus giving spectra with the radiation electric vector parallel, then perpendicular, to the direction of orientation. The "dichroic ratio" is calculated as follows:

$$\frac{A\pi}{A\sigma}$$

where $A\pi$ = the absorbance when the electric vector is parallel to orientation, absorption bands of maximum intensity, and

$A\sigma$ = the absorbance when the vector is perpendicular to orientation, absorption bands of minimum intensity.

The dichroic ratio is used to measure the orientation of molecular groups as well as crystalline-amorphous regions, since various configurations and kinds of chain folding produce characteristic ratios.

The polarized infrared radiation spectra of stretched polypropylene provide an excellent example of the application of this technique (Fig. 58-23). Typical parallel

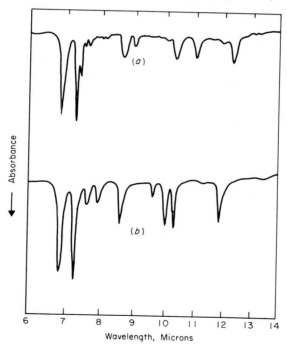

FIG. 58-23. Polarized Infrared Spectra of Polypropylene. (a) Radiation Perpendicular to Direction of Stretch; (b) Radiation Parallel to Direction of Stretch. (Courtesy John Wiley and Sons, Inc.)

polarized modes are those at 7.65 μ (CH bending), 7.96 μ (CH bending), 8.55 μ (CH₃ rocking), 10 μ (skeletal), 10.25 μ (CH₃ rocking), and at 11.92 μ (skeletal).

ATTENUATED TOTAL REFLECTION[90]

From time to time, new techniques are created for analysis by infrared spectroscopy. Potassium bromide pelleting and the use of a variety of transmitting materials are established techniques for the analysis of some of the difficult problems that the spectroscopist would desire to solve. In 1959, J. Fahrenfort[91] introduced the concept of Attenuated Total Reflection whereby an infrared spectrum is obtained by reflectance of light from the surface of a sample instead of by transmission through the sample.

Résumé of the Theory of ATR.—If a beam of radiation is passed into a prism in such a manner that the beam is totally reflected from the back face, a portion of the beam escapes from the face of the prism and then is returned into the prism. Thus, if one assumes that the beam is composed of a series of sine wave motions, part of the beam would escape the totally reflecting face by approximately 1 wavelength and be returned into the prism. The same principle is defined with reflecting crystals shaped in the form of hemicylinders (Fig. 58-24). The flat side or diametrical face is used as the reflecting

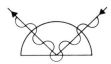

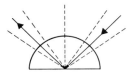

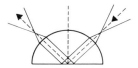

FIG. 58-24. Reflection of Light from Reflecting Crystal Showing the Escape and Return of the Light Beam. (Courtesy Connecticut Instrument Co., now Instrument Division of Barnes Engineering Co.)

FIG. 58-25. Reflection of Light Beam Focused in the Center of a Hemicylinder. (Courtesy Connecticut Instrument Co., now Instrument Division of Barnes Engineering Co.)

FIG. 58-26. Reflection of Light Beam Focused Outside the Surface of a Hemicylinder. (Courtesy Connecticut Instrument Co., now Instrument Division of Barnes Engineering Co.)

interface. The curved surface serves as the entrance and the exit windows for the light beam. If the beam has its focus in the center of the cylinder, it passes the curved surface unrefracted, and thus the angle of incidence may be given any desired value (Fig. 58-25). If, on the other hand, the focus is outside the cylindrical surface of the hemicylinder, a parallel light beam is usually obtained inside the crystal; and the result is a better defined angle of incidence (Fig. 58-26).

Thus, if an absorbing sample is placed in intimate contact with the diametrical face of the hemicylinder, the part of the wave of the beam which escapes the reflecting surface is selectively absorbed by the surface of the sample. In test results, the similarity between the spectrum obtained by transmission becomes apparent. Several unique features of this concept are (1) that spectra can be obtained regardless of sample thickness, (2) that penetration of the beam into the absorbing material is in the order of a wavelength, and (3) that there is ease of sample preparation.

[90] Long, M. W., The Dow Chemical Company, unpublished manuscript. Pertinent references: CIC Newsletter, Connecticut Instrument Co., Wilton, Conn., No. 14, September, 1961; No. 15, January, 1962; No. 16, June, 1962; No. 17, July–August, 1962; No. 18, November, 1962; No. 20, April, 1963; Attenuated Total Reflectance Accessory, Perkin-Elmer Instrument Div., Norwalk, Conn., July, 1963.

[91] Fahrenfort, J., Spectrochimica Acta, **17**, 698, 1961; Fahrenfort, J., and Visser, W. M., *ibid.*, **18**, 1103, 1962.

Many different types of macro and micro attachments with single- and multiple-reflection faces are available. In general, multiple reflection yields a stronger spectrum.

Frequently better spectra may be obtained with instruments equipped with ordinate scale expansion, particularly when using the micro attachment. The micro attachment is more versatile than the macro attachment and is better suited for obtaining ATR spectra on small samples, *i.e.*, chemical impurities, extracts from thin-layer chromatography, fibers, and many other difficult problems. The optical system of the micro ATR (Fig. 58-27) is more complex than the macro system (Fig. 58-28), since the incident beam is consensed at the sampling point by approximately three to one; thus, a

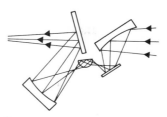

FIG. 58-27. Optical System of a Typical Micro Attenuated Total Reflectance System. (Courtesy Connecticut Instrument Co., now Instrument Division of Barnes Engineering Co.)

sample size of 1 mm. $\times$ 5 mm. or smaller may be analyzed with little energy attenuation. The angle of incidence in both attachments may be varied over a considerable range, usually 30° to 60°, and can be reproduced reasonably well.

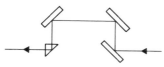

FIG. 58-28. Optical System of a Typical Macro Attenuated Total Reflectance System. (Courtesy Connecticut Instrument Co., now Instrument Division of Barnes Engineering Co.)

Reflective Crystals.—Both single- and multiple-reflection sampling devices may be obtained for the micro ATR attachment in a variety of infrared transmitting crystals. With the proper backing plate for the crystal, solid samples and liquid samples may be adequately analyzed. The selection of the prism or the crystal with the proper index of refraction is important, since the band intensities in an ATR spectrum are a function of the refractive index of both the prism and the sample, *i.e.*, the refractive index of the prism must be higher than the refractive index of the sample to maintain internal reflection. If the refractive index of the sample is greater than the refractive index of the prism, the beam of radiation will transmit through both the prism and the sample, and an adequate spectrum will not be obtained. If, however, the refractive indices of the prism and the sample are nearly equal, the beam of radiation apparently penetrates further into the sample, and a spectrum with more intense bands is obtained.

Selection of Reflective Crystals.—Silver chloride, KRS-5, and germanium perform satisfactorily in-the analyses of the majority of organic liquids and solids. Of these three transmitting media, KRS-5 has the superior qualification of permitting well-defined spectra of nearly all organic materials. KRS-5 is a tough and durable material. Although it is soluble in basic solutions, it may be used in nonoxidizing acid media. KRS-5 IS TOXIC AND SHOULD BE HANDLED WITH THE NECESSARY PRECAUTIONS. Silver chloride is recommended for aqueous sampling, whereas KRS-5 is recommended for solid sampling, since the useful index of refraction of silver chloride overlaps the useful index of refraction of KRS-5. Germanium is recommended for those rare cases with samples of high refractive index. Although silver chloride and KRS-5 are suitable materials for transmitting media, the crystals are subject to physical distortion with usage. Dies are available for the hemicylinders which will reform the distorted crystal into a usable configuration.

Material	Index of Refraction at 5.0 μ	Transmission Range, μ	Comments
Sodium chloride	1.519	1–16	Low index, brittle; for low index organic liquids
Cesium bromide	1.667	1–36	For long-range transmission
Silver chloride	1.997	2–22	For organic liquids and low index solids
KRS-6	2.192	2–20	Intermediate index
Irtran-2	2.245	2–11	Very durable
KRS-5	2.380	2–35	Most useful for organic solids
Germanium	4.017	2.5–15	Highest index

Operation of the ATR Attachment.—Successful operation of the ATR attachment depends upon the intimate contact of the sample with the face of the crystal. For useful spectra, the sample should be at least 10 μ thick. Maximum thickness is controlled only by the physical limitations of the sample mount. Solid samples which have a flat surface or a plastic consistency should be cut to the correct size and shape to fit the sample mount. Identifiable spectra may be obtained of fibrous materials by winding several strands around a piece of cardboard and mounting the sample in the micro ATR attachment. Liquid samples can be analyzed by assembling the liquid sampling plate and gaskets, and introducing the liquid into the area behind the reflective face.

The Correct Angle of Incidence.—If a single unit is to be used in a double-beam instrument, attenuation of the reference beam is necessary to compensate for crystal reflection losses. The angle of incidence determines the apparent depth of beam penetration into the sample. A steep angle produces a deeper penetration than a shallow angle. The optimum angle generally occurs near, but slightly above, the critical angle. For most samples, the optimum angle is between 45° and 50° with a KRS-5 crystal; 50° to 55° with a silver chloride crystal; and 25° to 30° with a germanium crystal. Higher angles may be necessary for certain samples. To determine the approximate critical angle of the crystal-sample combination, the instrument should be set to a nonabsorbing region

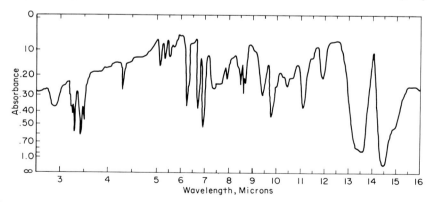

FIG. 58-29.   Attenuated Total Reflectance Spectrum of Polystyrene Obtained with Silver Chloride Prism.

beyond 10 μ. Sufficient reference beam attenuation should be used to place the recording pen near 90 percent transmission with a dial setting of 60°. The dial should be slowly turned toward 25° and the rate of change of transmittance observed. At the critical angle, the transmittance will suddenly decrease rapidly. Near the critical angle the spectrum tends to be "distorted" from the transmission spectrum. The best qualitative results will be obtained 2° to 5° above this angle. Experimentation will determine the angle setting for the most useful results.

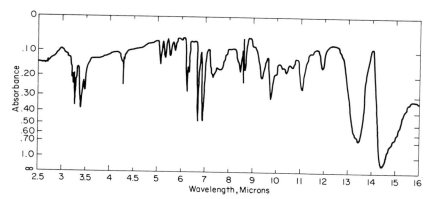

FIG. 58-30. Attenuated Total Reflectance Spectrum of Polystyrene Obtained with KRS-5 Prism.

The dependence of absorption band intensity upon the refractive index of the ATR prism can be illustrated by comparing the ATR spectra of polystyrene in Figs. 58-29, 58-30, and 58-31.

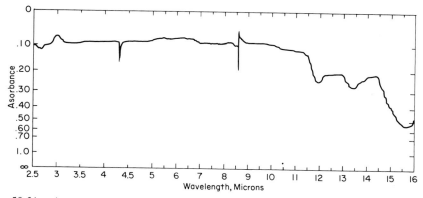

FIG. 58-31. Attenuated Total Reflectance Spectrum of Polystyrene Obtained with Germanium Prism.

Care of Reflective Crystals.—Certain precautions are necessary to ensure a long and useful life of the sampling crystals. It is recommended that a 100 percent transmission line be run for each crystal before it is used for the first analysis. These runs can be saved and used for comparison to determine the condition of the crystal. The sample should be peeled, not scratched, from the surface of the crystal, because the surfaces of most of the crystals are easily marred. Thorough cleaning of the sample units can best be accomplished by disassembly. Generally, if the mounting unit is immersed in an appropriate hydrocarbon solvent and thoroughly flushed and dried, disassembly will be unnecessary. The silver chloride crystals should be removed from contact with the metal of the mount and stored in the absence of light. All crystals should be stored with protection from stress, preferably unmounted. The crystals of germanium should be returned to the instrument company for repolishing. The crystals of silver chloride and KRS-5 will be distorted under pressure, and germanium will fracture under too much pressure from the backing plate; thus precautionary measures should be applied to prevent misuse of the crystals.

THERMOGRAVIMETRIC ANALYSIS

Thermogravimetric analysis is a method of following the weight loss of a sample as a function of temperature. The technique provides a simple and rapid method for assessing the thermal or oxidative stability of plastics and for examining the various reactions occurring during thermal or oxidative degradation. The complete elucidation of degradation mechanisms involves characterization of the reaction products and determination of the molecular weights of the nonvolatile residues in addition to measurement of the weight loss. However, it is possible to estimate the activation energies of the kinetic steps and the order of reaction and to classify the type of degradation reaction, *e.g.*, unzipping or random chain transfer, solely from the weight-loss curves.[92] The technique also has a practical application, since the critical extrusion and molding temperatures of a plastic may be approximated from the thermograms.

Jellinek[93] and Madorsky[94] have described an isothermal technique for evaluating the energy of activation, whereas Freeman and coworkers[95] have developed the nonisothermal technique. Numerous thermal studies, particularly those involving the thermal degradation of poly(methyl methacrylate),[96] poly-α-methylstyrene,[97] polyolefins,[92,93,98] polystyrene,[92,93,95,99] hydrofluoroethylene polymers,[100] and phenolic resins[101] have been reported in recent years. General discussions of pyrolysis and thermogravimetric techniques have been presented by Wall,[102] Garn,[103] Horowitz and Metzger,[104] and Newkirk.[105]

The following methods describe the construction and operation of a simple thermogravimetric balance and the calculation of energies of activation.

[92] Melville, H., Science Progress, **88**, 1950.
[93] Jellinek, H. H. G., J. Polymer Sci., **4**, 13, 1949.
[94] Madorsky, S. L., J. Polymer Sci., **9**, 133, 1952.
[95] Freeman, E. S., and Carroll, B., J. Phys. Chem., **62**, 394, 1958; Anderson, D. A., and Freeman, E. S., J. Polymer Sci., **54**, 253, 1961.
[96] Bywater, S., J. Phys. Chem., **57**, 879, 1953; Grassie, N., and Melville, H. W., Proc. Roy. Soc. (London), **A199**, 1, 1949.
[97] Madorsky, S. L., J. Polymer Sci., **9**, 133, 1952; **11**, 491, 1953.
[98] Wall, L. A., and Straus, S., J. Polymer Sci., **44**, 313, 1960; Straus, S., and Wall, L. A., J. Research Natl. Bur. Standards, **65A**, 221, 1961.
[99] Madorsky, S. L., and Straus, S., J. Research Natl. Bur. Standards, 40, 417, 1948; Grassie, N., and Kerr, W. W., Trans. Faraday Soc., **53**, 234, 1957.
[100] Wall, L. A., and Straus, S., J. Research Natl. Bur. Standards, **65A**, 227, 1961; Madorsky, S. L., and Straus, S., *ibid.*, **64A**, 513, 1960.
[101] Jeffreys, K. D., Brit. Plastics, **36**, 188, 1963.
[102] Wall, L. A., Analytical Chemistry of Polymers, Part II, Interscience Publishers, Inc., New York, **181**, 1962; Wall, L. A., and Florin, R. E., J. Research Natl. Bur. Standards, **60**, 451, 1958.
[103] Garn, P. D., Anal. Chem., **33**, 1247, 1961.
[104] Horowitz, H. H., and Metzger, G., Anal. Chem., **35**, 1464, 1963.
[105] Newkirk, A. E., Anal. Chem., **32**, 1558, 1960.

THE CONSTRUCTION AND OPERATION OF A RECORDING THERMOBALANCE

Scope.—The balance described below is capable of measuring and recording weight changes from 0.5 to 500 mg. The temperature of the furnace can be held constant or can be increased from 25° to 800°C. at a rate which can be varied from 1° to 10° per minute. The unit can be operated under vacuum, at atmospheric pressure, or under an inert atmosphere as desired. The data obtained from the weight-loss curves may be used to calculate the activation energies of the reaction.

Principle of Operation.—A soft iron cylindrical core of a differential transformer is suspended by one end from a quartz spring within a glass housing. The coil of the transformer is slipped around the glass housing and positioned so that the core is in the center of the coil.

The loaded sample boat is suspended from the other end of the core by a quartz rod. As the sample loses or gains weight, the spring contracts or elongates; and the core moves through the coil. This movement of the core causes an induced signal in the secondary winding of the coil proportional in magnitude to the distance the core travels, and thus proportional to the weight change. This signal is amplified and fed to the pen drive of a Brown X–Y recorder.

The sample temperature is measured by a thermocouple positioned just below the sample holder. The thermocouple is connected to the chart drive of the X–Y recorder and hence a plot of weight change *vs.* temperature is obtained.

Apparatus (See Figs. 58-32 and 58-33). **Differential Transformer Coil,** Shaevitz linear variable differential transformer, type 0605-L., serial number 7988, with core.

Quartz Rod, 0.5 mm. in diameter, 290 mm. long.

Platinum Sample Holder, cylindrical, 15 mm. in diameter, 10 mm. deep.

Quartz Spring, so constructed that a 0.5-g. stress will produce a 0.25-in. elongation.

Sample Heating Tube.—The heating element is constructed as follows: Lay a thermocouple (made of 20-gauge glass-fiber coated iron-constantan double thermocouple wire) along the outside wall of a 38-mm. O.D. Vycor tube so that the junction is approximately 3 in. from the lower end of the tube. Wind thirty turns of #23-gauge asbestos coated Nichrome wire tightly around the sample tube and the thermocouple. The windings should extend from the sample-tube outlet to within 1 in. of the lower end of the sample tube. Secure the wire in place by wrapping the tube with three layers of 1-in. asbestos tape. Tie the tape at the top and bottom and finally cover the taped tube with asbestos paper.

Position a stainless-steel sleeve, $4\frac{1}{2}$ in. long, $\frac{7}{8}$ in. inside diameter, 1 in. outside diameter, inside the tube opposite the heating element and equidistant from all points on the inner wall.

Temperature Programmer.

Transducer Amplifier Indicator, Model 300 C with the Type 60 plug-in unit, manufactured by the Datronic Corporation, 2875 Culver Avenue, Dayton 29, Ohio. This instrument is a high-amplification multirange amplifier. By using different amplification range settings, it is possible to obtain full-scale pen deflection from weight-loss changes of 10 to 500 mg.

Recorders, Brown X–Y recorder and strip chart recorder. The strip chart recorder is substituted for the X–Y recorder for constant temperature studies.

Calibration.—Grease all joints lightly with vacuum stopcock grease and assemble the apparatus. Connect two dry-ice traps in series to the sample-tube outlet. Connect the outer trap vent through a manometer and pressure regulator to a suitable vacuum pump. After the system has reached the prescribed pressure, calibrate the balance with zero and 0.500-g. loads. Turn the amplifier phase selector pointer to position A. Set the amplification range pointer at ±0.100. Turn the micrometer adjuster screw (see Fig. 58-32) either up or down until the recorder pen records approximately 100 percent weight loss on the chart paper.

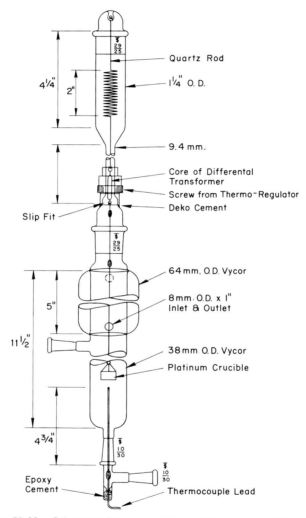

FIG. 58-32.   Schematic Diagram of Thermal Gravimetric Balance.

If it is impossible to raise the transformer coil high enough to bring the pen to the 100 percent weight-loss line by turning the micrometer adjuster screw, the coil can be elevated by placing a shim made from a cross-section of a bored rubber stopper between the coil and the micrometer. After the coil is positioned, it should be possible to move

the recorder pen from the 100 percent to the zero weight-loss line by turning the micrometer screw.

Adjust the recorder pen exactly to the 100 percent weight-loss line by turning the
amplifier zero knob. Place a 0.500-g. weight in the sample holder and adjust the re-

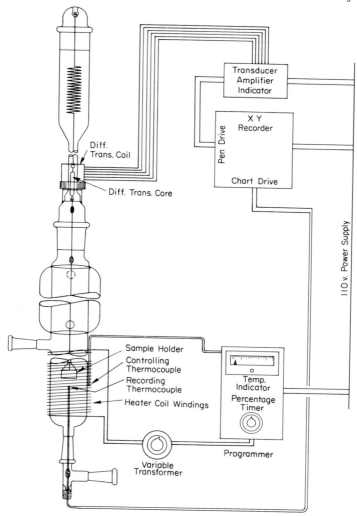

FIG. 58-33.   Wiring Diagram of Thermal Gravimetric Balance.

corder pen exactly to the zero weight-loss line on the chart paper by turning the sensitivity knob on the amplifier.

Procedure for the Study of Weight Loss vs. Time at Constant Temperature.—
Replace the X–Y recorder with a strip chart recorder and connect the recorder output

leads from the amplifier to the terminals on the pen drive. Connect the recording thermo-couple lead wires to the pen drive of a Leeds and Northrup temperature recorder. Set the programmer temperature indicator at the desired temperature. Switch on the temperature recorder. The temperature will increase at the maximum rate until it reaches the indicated temperature which the programmer will maintain over the course of the run.

CALCULATION OF ACTIVATION ENERGY OF THERMAL DEGRADATION OF POLYMERS

The activation energy is the coefficient of the temperature term in the reaction rate-temperature expression. It can be calculated from two isothermal weight-loss *vs.* time curves by substituting the values for the reaction rates, K_1 and K_2, and the inverse temperatures, $1/T_1$ and $1/T_2$ in the following equation:

$$\log \frac{K_2}{K_1} = -\frac{\Delta E}{2.303R}\left(\frac{1}{T_1} - \frac{1}{T_2}\right)$$

where ΔE = the activation energy, and
R = the gas constant (1.99 cal./°C./mole).

It is also possible to calculate ΔE from the nonisothermal weight-loss *vs.* temperature curve by use of the Anderson-Freeman equation:

$$\Delta \log\left(\frac{dw}{dt}\right) = x \, \Delta \log W_r - \left(\frac{\Delta E}{2.303R}\right)\Delta \frac{1}{T}$$

where $(dw)/(dt)$ = the reaction rate in mg. per min.,
x = the order of reaction,
W_r = the amount of material reacting, and
$1/T$ = a constant inverse temperature increment.

Procedure Using Two Isothermal Weight-Loss vs. Temperature Curves.—Obtain a weight-loss *vs.* temperature recording to determine the temperature range over which the polymer undergoes thermal degradation. From the weight-loss *vs.* temperature curve, determine the temperatures at which the cumulative weight loss is 10 and 40 percent.

Record the isothermal time *vs.* weight-loss curve at each of the designated temperatures (Fig. 58-34). From each of these curves, calculate the differential rates (percent weight loss per minute) at 3-min. intervals over the course of the reaction. Plot these rates against the cumulative percentage weight losses at constant Δt to obtain the rate curves. A maximum rate curve is shown in Fig. 58-35. Determine the rates at the maximum of each curve and substitute these rates in the following equation. Alternately, the rates of volatilization may be plotted against percentage of residues for the same time interval. The straight-line portions of these curves are extrapolated to zero conversion:

$$\log \frac{K_2}{K_1} = -\frac{\Delta E}{2.303R}\left(\frac{1}{T_1} - \frac{1}{T_2}\right)$$

where K_1 = rate (percent weight loss per minute) at T_1 (°K),
K_2 = rate (percent weight loss per minute) at T_2 (°K), and
R = gas constant (1.99 cal./°C./mole).

Solve the equation for the activation energy (ΔE). Rate data on polymers which do not exhibit a maximum may be extrapolated to zero conversion to obtain the initial rate.

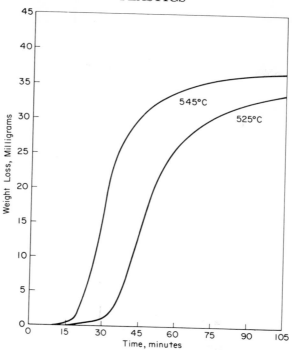

FIG. 58-34. Cumulative Weight Loss Under Isothermal Conditions.

Graphical Procedure Using Two or More Isothermal Curves.—Determine the maximum rate or extrapolated initial rate of each of the above curves and plot the log of the rate against $10^3/[T(°K)]$ as shown in Fig. 58-36. Draw a straight line through the points and calculate the slope. Calculate the activation energy using the following equation:

$$-\Delta E = 2.303R \cdot S$$

where S = slope of line = $x \cdot \Delta \log W_r$ (see following equation),
   ΔE = activation energy, and
   R = gas constant (1.99 cal./°C./mole).

Procedure Using Nonisothermal Temperature vs. Weight-Loss Curve.
A. Calculation in Region Above 10 Percent Weight Loss.—The activation energy can be calculated from a single weight-loss vs. temperature curve by the Anderson-Freeman equation:

$$\Delta \log \frac{dw}{dt} = x \, \Delta \log W_r - \frac{\Delta E}{2.303R} \Delta \left(\frac{1}{T}\right)$$

where $(dw)/(dt)$ = rate of weight loss (mg. wt. loss/minute),
   W_r = (proportional to amount of reactant) = $W_c - \Delta W$,
   W_c = total weight loss,
   ΔW = weight loss at the point $(dw)/(dt)$,
   $\Delta(1/T)$ = constant temperature interval, and
   x = order of reaction.

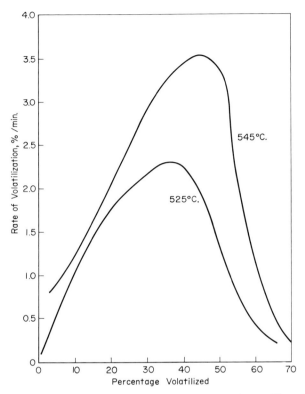

Fɪɢ. 58-35. Volatilization Rate Curve. Percentage Loss per Minute Plotted as a Function of Cumulative Percentage Volatilization.

Record the temperature *vs.* percent weight-loss curve under vacuum (1.0 mm. pressure) at a heating rate of 5°C. per minute. Calculate the differential weight-loss rates (mg. weight loss/°C.) graphically from the above curve at 15°C. temperature intervals and plot against the inverse of the absolute temperatures $(10^3/T)$. Calculate the corresponding W_r values and plot these values against the inverse absolute temperature, $10^3/T$ (Fig. 58-37). Calculate the weight-loss rate and the corresponding W_r values at a constant inverse temperature interval, $\Delta(10^3/T) = 0.025$, over the course of the above curves. Obtain the logarithms of these values and plot the differences of the logarithms of consecutive rates $[\Delta \log (dw)/(dt)]$ against the differences of the logarithms of consecutive W_r values ($\Delta \log W_r$). Draw a straight line through the points and extrapolate to the Y axis. The low temperature points may deviate from the curve (Fig. 58-38). The activation energy (ΔE) is calculated from the Y intercept as follows:

$$Y = -\frac{\Delta E}{2.303R}$$

where $Y = Y$ intercept value and
R = gas constant (1.99 cal./°C./mole).

$$S = x \cdot \Delta \log W_r$$

where S = slope and

x = reaction order.

B. Calculation in Region Below 10 Percent Weight Loss.—The activation energy in the 0 to 10 percent weight-loss region may be calculated from the temperature de-

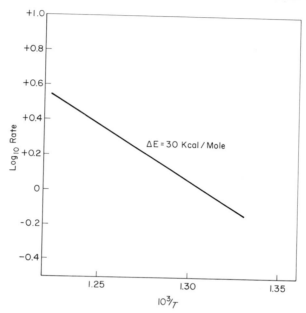

Fig. 58-36.   Logarithms of Maximum Rate Plotted Against the Inverse of the Absolute Temperature. The Slope of the Line Represents the Activation Energy.

pendency plot (Fig. 58-39). Calculate the weight-loss rate (mg./min.) from the original weight-loss *vs.* temperature curve at 10° temperature intervals from 0 to 10 percent weight loss. Plot these rates on semilog paper against the inverse of the temperatures. Calculate the activation energy (ΔE) from the slope of the line:

$$-\Delta E = 2.303 R \cdot S$$

The symbols stand for the same quantities as in the preceding sections.

DIFFERENTIAL THERMAL ANALYSIS

The physical and chemical changes of plastics under the influence of heat are not only directly related to the chemical structure, but are among the most important properties influencing their fabrication and end-uses. Although thermochemical phenomena are usually studied by conventional calorimetry, differential thermal analysis (DTA) provides a rapid and reasonably accurate method for studying physical and chemical transformations which are accompanied by thermal effects. Thus, DTA may be used to study or measure (a) glass-transition temperatures, (b) first-order transition temperatures, heats and entropies of fusion, and degree of crystallinity, (c) characterization of polymers and polymer blends, (d) thermal stability and stabilization, and (e) polymerization and curing reactions.

An idealized thermogram is shown in Fig. 58-40. The physical transformations, such as the melting of crystallites or volatilization, and such chemical reactions as depolym-

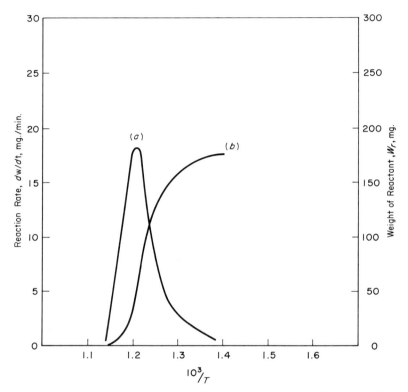

FIG. 58-37.   First Derivative of the Thermal Gravimetric Curve (dw/dt) and the Weight of Reactant (W_r) Plotted as a Function of the Inverse of the Absolute Temperature. (a) First Derivative Plot; (b) Weight Reactant Plot.

erization or thermal decomposition are endothermic in nature, whereas crystallization and the chemical reactions of polymerication, curing, and oxidation are exothermic. There are a number of differential thermal analysis instruments commercially available. Although specific operating details may vary from instrument to instrument (sample size may vary from a few milligrams to several grams, facilities for low-temperature operation and temperature-programmed heating and cooling cycles may vary), the fundamental principles remain essentially the same. A schematic diagram of a simplified DTA apparatus is shown in Fig. 58-41.[106]

[106] Cobler, J. G., and Miller, D. L., Paper presented at 136th Meeting of the Am. Chem. Soc., Atlantic City, September, 1959.

GENERAL PROCEDURE FOR DIFFERENTIAL
THERMAL ANALYSIS

Scope.—This procedure is suitable for detecting and recording physical and chemical transitions of a plastic as a function of the temperature.

Principle.—The polymer is heated at a constant rate in one cell of the sample holder. An inert reference material is heated in a second cell. Any temperature difference occur-

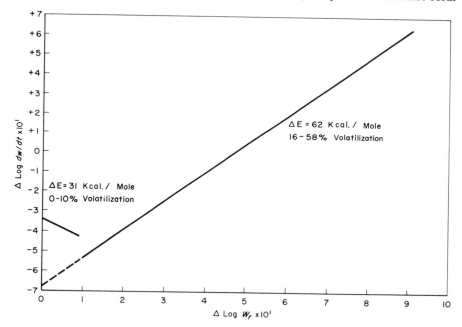

$\Delta E = 62$ Kcal./ Mole
16 – 58% Volatilization

$\Delta E = 31$ Kcal./ Mole
0 – 10% Volatilization

Δ Log $dw/dt \times 10^1$

Δ Log $W_r \times 10^1$

Fig. 58-38.   Kinetic Plot of Thermal Degradation.

ring between the sample and reference material is measured by an opposed or differential thermocouple assembly and recorded on an X–Y recorder as a function of the temperature. Such difference may be caused by physical transitions or chemical reactions.

Apparatus. **Differential Thermal Analysis Instrument.**—DuPont Model 900 B Differential Thermal Analyzer or equivalent.

Calibration.—Weigh exactly 5 mg. of analytical reagent grade benzoic acid and transfer to the sample cell. Warm the cell until the benzoic acid just melts. Insert the sample thermocouple junction and allow the melt to solidify.

Transfer the same weight of inert reference material to the two reference cells. Insert the reference thermocouple junctions into the reference cells. The heat capacity and thermal conductivity of the reference material should be matched as closely as possible with those of the sample. Variations may result in an initial drift in ΔT. The reference material must exhibit no transitions over the temperature range studied.

Place the three cells in the corresponding holes in the heating unit. Set the temperature programmer-controller to give a heating rate of 2°C. per minute. Obtain the thermogram over the temperature range from room temperature to 200°C. in a nitrogen atmosphere.

The melting point of benzoic acid is 122°C. Measure the area of the melting peak with a planimeter. In order to calculate the area, draw a straight-line extension of the

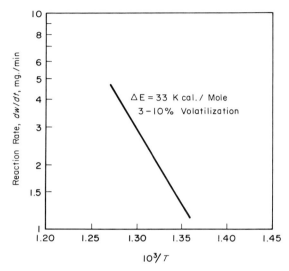

FIG. 58-39. Temperature Dependency Plot of the Low Temperature Stage of Thermal Degradation.

peak to an extrapolated baseline. The thermogram for a melting process (endothermic) should return to an extended baseline of the initial plot. In practice, however, the baseline may vary because of a difference in thermal conductivity of the melt.

The area of the melting endotherm is equivalent to the heat of fusion of the benzoic acid (33.9 cal./g.).

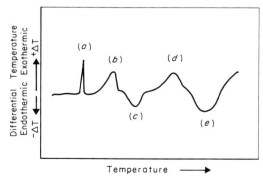

FIG. 58-40. Ideal Differential Thermogram. (a) Polymerization or Curing; (b) Crystallization; (c) Melting; (d) Oxidation; (e) Thermal Decomposition.

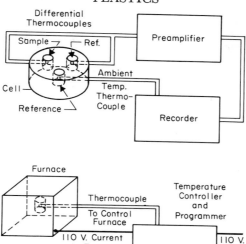

FIG. 58-41.   Schematic Diagram of Differential Thermal Analysis Equipment.

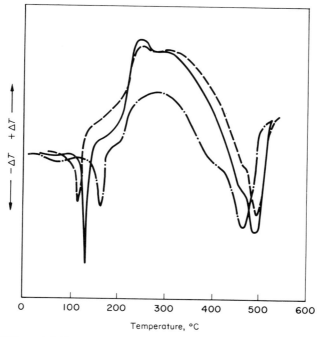

FIG. 58-42.   Differential Thermograms of Branched Polyethylene (– – – – – –); Linear
Polyethylene (————); Polypropylene (——.——.——.).

Sample Preparation.—Several techniques are available for preparing suitable samples. If the results of the study are not dependent on the previous heat history of the sample, the best technique is to melt the sample in the cell and insert the thermocouple junction while the sample is still molten. If melting will change the properties to be measured, the sample may be chilled in liquid nitrogen and ground in a suitable mill. Care must be taken during grinding. If the sample is not kept cold, physical or chemical changes may occur. For quantitative measurement, consistency of sample preparation, sample size, and cell packing is imperative.

Procedure.—Weigh exactly 5 mg. of the prepared sample into a sample cell. Obtain a thermogram as described under "Calibration."

CHARACTERIZATION OF POLYMERS OR POLYMER MIXTURES

Differences in thermal behavior may be employed in the identification of plastics. Anderson and Freeman[107] have classified 33 saturated polyesters by the number of peaks, peak areas, peak temperatures, and inflection points. Various homo- and polyamides have been characterized according to peak shape, position, and area.[108] Homopolyamides were also differentiated from the copolyamides.

DTA can also be used to detect a physical mixture or blend of polymers having sufficiently separated melting points.[109] Each component produces a peak that retains its characteristic shape and area, provided that the mixture does not form a homogenous crystal.

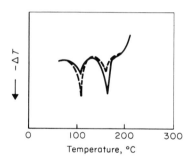

Thermograms for branched and linear polyethylenes and for polypropylene are shown in Fig. 58-42. Endothermic reactions indicative of crystalline melting or first-order transition are observed at 110°C., 135°C., and 165°C., respectively. The thermograms of blends of branched polyethylene and polypropylene are given in Fig. 58-43. The components of the blend can be identified by their characteristic transition peaks. The areas under the peaks are equivalent to the concentrations of the two components.

Thermograms for characterizing the plastics are obtained according to the procedure given in the previous section

Fig. 58-43. Differential Thermograms of Blends of Branched Polyethylene and Polypropylene; 25 Percent Polyethylene and 75 Percent Polypropylene (————); 75 Percent Polyethylene and 25 Percent Polypropylene (– – – –).

with the exception that the heating rate is usually programmed at 10°C. per minute. Studies may be conducted *in vacuo* or in either an inert or a reactive atmosphere. Nitrogen is usually selected as the inert atmosphere and is the preferred atmosphere for studying transition or thermal decomposition reactions, thus avoiding interference from oxidation.

GLASS TRANSITIONS

The glass transition (T_g), or second-order transition, is caused by a relaxation of the chain segments in the amorphous portion of the polymer chain and is not associated

[107] Anderson, D. A., Freeman, E. S., Anal. Chem., **31**, 1697, 1959.
[108] Ke, Bacon, and Sisko, A. W., J. Polymer Sci., **50**, 87, 1961.
[109] Ke, Bacon, J. Polymer Sci., **42**, 15, 1960.

with any latent heat. The relaxation is manifested by a sudden change in specific heat which is proportional to the amount of amorphous material present.

The glass-transition temperature is perhaps the most important characteristic parameter of an amorphous polymer and is an important factor in predicting low-temperature performance. Polymeric materials, and particularly elastomers, stiffen when cooled. Any pronounced stiffening may interfere with low-temperature serviceability; at very low temperatures, plastics will become brittle and may shatter on sudden bending or impact.

The usual methods for determining T_g are those which measure the specific volume $V(t)$ of the polymer as a function of the temperature (dilatometric) or which measure the temperature at which a maximum in change of some mechanical property (stress-strain or mechanical damping) occurs. However, DTA provides a rapid technique for detecting glass-transition temperatures.[108,110] Knox[111] applied DTA to the determination of glass transitions in ethylene-propylene rubbers. The glass transitions in polyethylene-terphthalate were studied by Scott.[112]

Although many plastics exhibit glass transitions near room temperature or above, some transitions occur down to $-100°C.$, or below. Transitions in this latter range are detected after cooling the sample cells and heating block with liquid nitrogen. Prior to cooling the unit, the assembly should be evacuated to remove any moisture. The assembly is then cooled as low as possible by introducing liquid nitrogen. After shutting off the flow of liquid nitrogen, vacuum is applied. Recording of the heating curve is started after sufficient time lapse to allow the assembly to reach an equilibrium temperature.

As shown in Fig. 58-44, the T_g is characterized primarily by a more or less abrupt

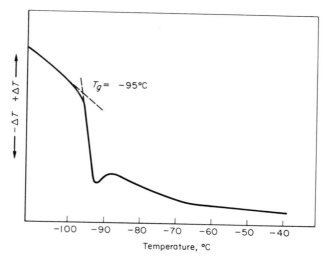

FIG. 58-44.   Low-Temperature Differential Thermogram of Polybutadiene.

baseline shift in the endothermic direction. The T_g is indicated by extrapolating the straight-line portions of the thermogram. Continued warming confers mobility to the

[110] Dannis, M. L., J. Appl. Polymer Sci., **7**, 231, 1963; Strella, S., *ibid.*, **7**, 569, 1963.
[111] Knox, J. R., Abstracts, 140th Meeting ACS, p. 3V, Chicago, September, 1961.
[112] Scott, N. D., Polymer, **1**, 114, 1960.

polymer chains and some of the material may crystallize. The liberated heat thus produces an exothermic break in the thermogram.

HEAT OF FUSION AND DEGREE OF CRYSTALLINITY

Many polymers are partially crystalline, exhibiting geometrically perfect regions or crystallites surrounded by amorphous regions. Transitions in these ordered regions occur when the polymers undergo fusion. DTA is suitable for detecting these first-order transition temperatures and for providing data for calculating the heat of fusion and the degree of crystallinity of polymers.[108,113] Wunderlich and Kashdan[114] found that the degree of crystallinity as determined by DTA agreed with calorimetric data.

The heat of fusion is calculated by comparing the area under the endothermic peak with the area of the peak produced by benzoic acid. The degree of crystallinity is calculated by comparing the area under the peak with the area of the double peak produced by the melting of crystalline dotriacontane. The heat of fusion of a perfect crystalline polyethylene is assumed to be equal to that of the crystalline straight-chain paraffin hydrocarbon.

For convenience in measurement, the same amount of sample and standard are used. All samples are ground and screened through a U. S. standard sieve No. 35. Procedural details must be exactly the same in all runs, including the method of packing the sample in the cell.

Obtain the thermograms of 5-mg. samples in a nitrogen atmosphere and at a programmed heating rate of 10°C. per minute. Measure the peak areas as described previously.

Calculation of Heat of Fusion ($\triangle H$).

$$\Delta H_s \text{ (cal./g.)} = \frac{\Delta H_b \times A_s}{A_b}$$

where ΔH_s = heat of fusion of sample in cal. per g.,
$\quad \Delta H_b$ = heat of fusion of benzoic acid in cal. per g. (33.9),
$\quad A_s$ = area of sample peak in sq. cm., and
$\quad A_b$ = area of benzoic acid peak in sq. cm.

Calculation of Percent Crystallinity.

$$\text{Percent of crystallinity} = \frac{A_s}{A_d} \times 100$$

where A_s = area of sample peak in sq. cm., and
$\quad A_d$ = area of dotriacontane peak in sq. cm.

ANALYSIS OF POLYOLEFIN BLENDS

DTA has also been found useful for characterizing blends of linear and branched polyethylenes,[115] ethylene-propylene rubber,[116] and for investigating comonomer distribution in ethylene-acrylate copolymers.[117]

[113] Vold, M. J., Anal. Chem., **21**, 683, 1949.
[114] Wunderlich, B., and Kashdan, W. H., J. Polymer Sci., **50**, 71, 1961.
[115] Clampitt, B. H., Anal. Chem., **35**, 577, 1963; Stafford, B. B., The Dow Chemical Company, personal communication.
[116] Knox, J. R., Am. Chem. Soc., Div. Polymer Chem. Preprints, **3**, (1), 234, 1962.
[117] Bombaugh, K. J., Cook, C. E., and Clampitt, B. H., Anal. Chem., **35**, 1834, 1963.

CHARACTERIZATION OF POLYETHYLENE BLENDS

Scope.—This procedure is suitable for the characterization of blends of ethylene homopolymers whose crystalline melting points are separated by at least 10°C.

Principle.—Differential thermograms of properly annealed samples are obtained at a linear heating rate of approximately 10°C. per minute. Both the linear and branched polyethylenes produce a peak on the thermogram which is characteristic of the peak of the pure components. The weight concentration of each component is calculated by measuring the peak area of one component and comparing the area, by algebraic proportions, to the peak area of the individual homopolymer.

Standardization.—Prepare standard blends of high and low density (linear and branched polyethylenes) covering the range from 0 to 100 percent high-density polyethylene by preparing approximately 1 percent solutions of suitable polymers in *p*-xylene. Solution is affected by heating the xylene, stabilized with 0.01 percent 2,6-di-*tert.*-butyl-*p*-cresol, to 135°C. Precipitate the dissolved polymer by the addition of methanol while stirring rapidly. Filter and wash the precipitate with additional methanol. Dry the precipitate *in vacuo* at 70°C.

Transfer a suitable amount (weighed accurately) of the dried blend to the sample holder and tamp lightly. Insert the thermocouple junction and place the sample holder in the heating block. Purge the system with nitrogen and increase the temperature to 150°C. at a rate of 20°C. per minute. Check the position of the thermocouple junction to ascertain that it is centered in the sample.

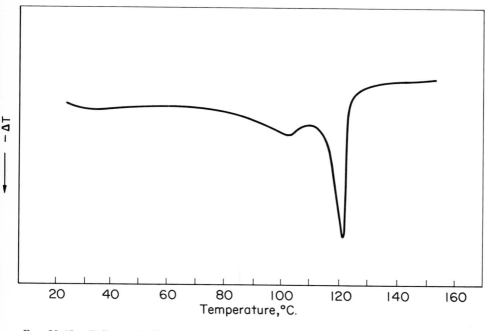

Fig. 58-45.   Differential Thermogram of a Blend of Branched and Linear Polyethylenes Showing Resolved Crystalline Melting Temperatures.

Anneal the sample by programming the cooling from 150° to 25°C. at a rate of 2°C. per minute. (Clampitt[115] advocates annealing at 120°C. for 30 min.) Obtain the heating thermogram at a heating rate of 10°C. per minute. Measure the peak area of the melting endotherm of the high-density (higher melting temperature) polyethylene with a planimeter (Fig. 58-45).

Prepare similar thermograms for all of the prepared blends, employing the same sample weight, and measure the resulting high-density polyethylene endotherms. Prepare a calibration curve by plotting weight percent high-density polyethylene in the blends *vs.* peak areas in square centimeters.

Procedure.—Transfer a portion of the ground sample, weighing exactly the same as the standard blends, to the sample holder. Anneal and obtain the heating thermogram, as described above.

Measure the area of the high-density endotherm and read the concentration of high-density (linear) polyethylene from the standard curve.

STABILITY AND STABILIZATION

Differential thermal analysis is an effective method for showing the oxidative and thermal stability of polymers and the effectiveness of antioxidants for preventing oxidation. The temperature at which oxidation takes place is indicated by an exothermic reaction, whereas depolymerization or thermal decomposition is indicated by a strong

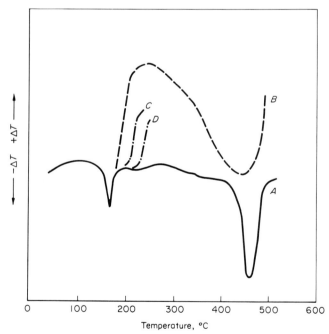

FIG. 58-46. Differential Thermograms of Polypropylene. (A) Unstabilized Polypropylene in Nitrogen Atmosphere;, (B) Unstabilized Polypropylene in Air; (C) and (D) Stabilized Polypropylenes in Air.

endothermic reaction. The measurement of the thermal oxidation was found to be fast and reproducible when using DTA.[118]

Thermograms for polypropylene obtained in air and in a nitrogen atmosphere are shown in Fig. 58-46. The oxidation exotherm observed in the thermogram obtained in air (a) is absent when the air is replaced by nitrogen (b). The effectiveness of anti-oxidants in increasing the oxidation induction period is shown by curves (c) and (d) which represent polypropylenes stabilized by the addition of antioxidants.

CHROMATOGRAPHY

Chromatography is a collective term applied to a number of diverse techniques, each of which utilizes repeated transfer across phase boundaries to affect the separation of components of a mixture. Three chromatographic techniques are finding widespread application for the analysis of plastics: (a) Column chromatography based on the transport of a liquid sample through a column containing, as the stationary phase, a solid adsorbing (or inert) agent, (b) thin-layer chromatography, based on the principles of column chromatography but employing flat surfaces rather than columns, and (c) gas chromatography, based on the transport of a gaseous sample through a column containing a stationary phase which may be either a solid adsorbent or a partitioning liquid supported on an inert solid.

FRACTIONATION OF POLYMERS BY COLUMN CHROMATOGRAPHY

Most polymeric substances are heterogeneous with respect to molecular weight. The separation of a polymer into more nearly homogeneous parts (molecular weight distribution) is important for the elucidation of polymerization mechanisms and for the study of the relationship between molecular weight and the physical and mechanical properties. Fractionation is also important for characterizing polymer blends, copolymers, and block copolymers. Four variations of column chromatography have been employed to fractionate polymers, (a) chromatographic adsorption, (b) column extraction, (c) gradient elution, and (d) gradient elution with superimposed temperature gradient. Schneider[119] discusses some of the factors which control the fractionation of polymers by the elution and thermal gradient techniques.

Polystyrene has been fractionated by adsorption on activated charcoal columns followed by elution with mixtures of tetralin and toluene.[120] Bannister, Phillips, and Williams[121] described a gradient elution modification of the chromatographic adsorption technique for the fractionation of silicon polymers. The polymer was adsorbed onto a column of animal charcoal from a poor solvent (methanol). The development of the zones was commenced with the poor solvent and elution carried on with increasingly more powerful eluting solutions by introducing continuously a good solvent (diethyl ether). A series of fractions was obtained, in which the molecular weight of the polymer in the fractions increased with increasing effluent volume. In general, however, it is wise to avoid adsorption techniques, because frequently it is impossible to elute the higher molecular weight polymer from the adsorbent.

The column extraction technique, pioneered by Desreux[122] and commonly referred

[118] Rudin, A., Schreiber, H. P., and Waldman, M. H., Ind. Eng. Chem., **53**, 137, 1961.
[119] Schneider, N. S., Anal. Chem., **33**, 1829, 1961.
[120] Yeh, Si Jung, and Frisch, H., J. Polymer Sci., **27**, 149, 1958.
[121] Bannister, D. W., Phillips, C. S. G., and Williams, R. J. P., Anal. Chem., **26**, 1451, 1954.
[122] Desreux, V., Rec. Trav. Chim. Pays-Bas, **68**, 789, 1949.

to as the "sand column extraction" technique, has been used extensively for polymer fractionation. An inert supporting material of large surface area is packed in a column and the polymer is deposited on the support from a solvent. Polymer fractions are eluted from the column with a single solvent or a solvent mixture by raising the temperature of the column, or by using progressively richer solvent-nonsolvent mixtures. The technique has been used successfully to study the molecular weight distribution of polyethylenes by Desreux and Spiegels,[123] Francis, Cooke, and Elliott,[124] and Lawrence.[125] Lawrence fractionated high-density polyethylenes at 140°C. employing a solvent-nonsolvent system, composed of tetralin and butyl cellosolve, respectively. Davis and Tobias[126] applied the following procedure to the fractionation of polypropylene.

FRACTIONATION OF POLYPROPYLENE
BY SAND COLUMN EXTRACTION

Scope.—The following procedure is suitable for the fractionation of polypropylene according to molecular weight.

Principle.—The polypropylene is precipitated from solution onto an inert support. Elution from the support is accomplished at an elevated temperature by addition of solvent-nonsolvent mixtures of successively increasing solvent power.

Apparatus. **Vapor-jacketed Extraction Column.**—See Fig. 58-47.

Reagents. **Methanol.**

2-Octanone.

o-**Dichlorobenzene.**

Diethylene Glycol Monomethyl Ether.

Sand.

2,6-Di-*tert*.-butyl-*p*-cresol.

Oxidation Inhibition.—Precautions should be taken to prevent the rapid degradation of polypropylene at elevated temperatures by oxidation. A nitrogen atmosphere must be kept over the polymer solutions at all times. Additionally, the solvent and nonsolvent (*o*-dichlorobenzene and diethylene glycol monomethyl ether, respectively) must contain 0.5 percent 2,6-di-*tert*.-butyl-*p*-cresol as an antioxidant.

Solvent-Nonsolvent Mixtures.—The eluants generally fall within the range of 25 to 58 volume percent of dichlorobenzene for polypropylene. Frequently, however, it is necessary to do a trial extraction to obtain the proper extraction conditions. A trial extraction may be conducted employing 10 eluants containing, respectively, 25, 30, 35, 40, 44, 47, 51, 54, 56, and 58 volume percent *o*-dichlorobenzene.

Procedure.—Fill the extraction column to within 10 cm. of the top with prewashed sand. Add sufficient solvent-nonsolvent mixture (60:40 by volume) to cover the sand completely, but with the level just below the opening of the drain tube of the reservoir. Add 2-octanone (b.p. 170°C.) to the boilers and connect the apparatus as shown in the diagram. Bring the 2-octanone in the boiler of the extraction column to a boil and allow the column to equilibrate at 170°C. Remove the stirrer and open stopcock *A* of the reservoir. Purge the system with nitrogen. After the system is thoroughly purged, close stopcock *A* and reduce the nitrogen flow. Maintain a slight positive nitrogen pressure on the system throughout the determination.

[123] Desreux, V., and Spiegels, M. C., Bull. Soc. Chim. Belg., **59**, 476, 1950.

[124] Francis, P. S., Cooke, R. C., Jr., and Elliott, J. H., J. Polymer Sci., **31**, 453, 1958.

[125] Lawrence, K., Techniques of Polymer Characterization, Ed. P. W. Allen, Academic Press, Inc., New York, 1959, p. 43.

[126] Davis, T. E., and Tobias, R. L., J. Polymer Sci., **50**, 227, 1961. (Courtesy John Wiley and Sons, Inc.)

Introduce 0.5 g. of polypropylene and 38 ml. of *o*-dichlorobenzene to the cold reservoir. Turn the stirrer and boiler on. When the reservoir temperature has reached 170°C. and the polymer is completely dissolved, add 25 ml. of pre-heated nonsolvent slowly. Drain the solvent out of the column and add the polymer solution from the reservoir at such rates that the liquid level remains at the surface of the sand. Rinse the reservoir with 10 ml. of the 60 percent solvent mixture and transfer to the sand.

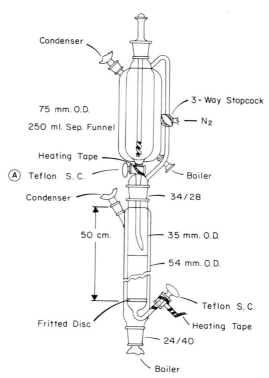

Condenser

75 mm. O.D.

250 ml. Sep. Funnel

Heating Tape

(A) Teflon S. C.

Condenser

50 cm.

Fritted Disc

3 - Way Stopcock

N₂

Boiler

34 / 28

35 mm. O.D.

54 mm. O.D.

Teflon S. C.

Heating Tape

24 / 40

Boiler

FIG. 58-47.   Vapor-jacketed Extraction Column. (Courtesy John Wiley and Sons, Inc.)

Turn the boilers off and allow the column to cool overnight to precipitate the polymer onto the sand. The volumes used were selected so that all except the bottom and top 1 to 2 cm. of sand are coated. A sufficient amount of the 60 percent solvent mixture is added to the top of the sand to ensure that the liquid surface does not drop below the sand surface as the liquid cools.

Rinse the cooled column with nonsolvent and then turn the boilers on. Place 250 ml. of the first eluant mixture in the reservoir and turn the stirrer on. The stirring aids not only in heat transfer, but also in the evolution of dissolved gases from the solvent. Some gas bubbling in the system has no significant effect on the fractionation. However, if channeling of the eluant occurs, the gas pockets can be removed by the application of a slight vacuum to the nitrogen inlet.

Allow the eluants to pass through the column at a rate of about 10 ml. per minute. Only a small amount of polymer is removed by the first and last 50 ml. of eluant. Drain the eluants into a large excess of methanol, which is stirred continuously, to precipitate the polymer.

Recover the precipitated polymer by filtration through a fine porosity-fritted glass filter. Wash the residue with methanol. Dry the polymer in a vacuum open at 110°C. for at least 2 hr.

The gradient elution technique is a modification of the above described column extraction procedure. In this technique, the composition of the eluant is continuously changed by the addition, at a fixed rate, of a good polymer solvent to a known initial volume of a poor polymer solvent. Mixing of the solvents occurs in a chamber, after which the mixture is transferred to the column. Baker and Williams[127] have improved this technique by the addition of a temperature gradient to the column whereby they obtain a multistage extraction-precipitation fractionation. Cooper, Vaughan, Eaves, and Madden[128] applied this principle to the fractionation of 250 mg. of polybutadiene, whereas Pepper and Rutherford[129] devised a preparative column capable of fractionating samples up to 8 g.

Schneider, et al.,[130] proposed the following conditions for the fractionation of "Monodisperse" polystyrene: 0.82-g. sample, 4-cm.-diameter column operating between 10° and 60°C., 1-liter mixing vessel initially filled with 20/80 mixture of ethanol–methyl ethyl ketone fed by a reservoir containing methyl ethyl ketone, and 13-ml. fractions.

Moore[131] and Maley[132] have described a new technique for molecular size fractionations for which the term "gel permeation chromatography" is proposed. Polymers are fractionated on columns packed with beads of permeable styrene-divinylbenzene polymers. The solute molecules are separated by their permeation into the gel which offers different internal volumes to molecules of different sizes. The larger molecules permeate only to a limited extent and thus pass through the column rapidly. The smaller molecules permeate more completely and remain in the column for a longer time. With proper choice of monomer, crosslinker, and diluent system, it should be possible to make gel beads "swellable" in almost any desired solvent system, with any desired permeability, and still retain the strength and rigidity required for high resolution.

THIN-LAYER CHROMATOGRAPHY[133]

Thin-layer chromatography is more commonly useful for the separation of polymer additives than the examination of polymers; however, decomposition products of polymers, residual monomers, and higher oligomers are separable in some systems. Typical applications involve the separation of additives such as light stabilizers, antioxidants, surfactants, plasticizers, brighteners, tints, antistatic agents, surface lubricants, and mold release agents. Commercial polymers contain an increasing variety and number of these additives and separation of three or four components from a concentrate or polymer extract is often necessary prior to identification.

Thin-layer chromatography has nearly all the advantages of conventional liquid-solid adsorption column chromatography and is much faster. It is also more rapid than

[127] Baker, C. A., and Williams, R. J. P., J. Chem. Soc., **1956**, 2352.

[128] Cooper, W., Vaughan, G., Eaves, D. E., and Madden, R. W., J. Polymer Sci., **50**, 159, 1961.

[129] Pepper, D. C., and Rutherford, P. P., J. Appl. Polymer Sci., **2**, 100, 1959.

[130] Schneider, N. S., and Holmes, L. G., J. Polymer Sci., **38**, 552, 1959.

[131] Moore, J. C., J. Polymer Sci., Part A, **2**, 835, 1964.

[132] Maley, L. E., Proc. Natl. Instr. Symp. 9th, Houston, 1963, 131.

[133] Owens, E. G., The Dow Chemical Company, unpublished manuscript. Pertinent References: Peifer, J. J., Mikrochim. Acta, 529, 1962; Mangold, H. K., J. Am. Oil Chemists Soc., **38**, 708, 1961; Barrett, G. C., Nature, **194**, 1171, 1962; Brinkmann Instruments, Inc., Tech. Bull. No. 20, 115 Culter Mill Road, Long Island, New York, 1962.

paper chromatography and has capacity for larger samples. This is convenient especially for qualitative analysis when milligram size samples are needed for identification by infrared spectra. Choice of solvent or solvents is important, but not as critical as in paper chromatography, because the separation process is more dependent on adsorption with less emphasis on liquid-liquid partition. Mild conditions avoid the destructive influence of high temperatures sometimes necessary for distillation or gas chromatography. Volatility is, of course, not required. These are important advantages in this field of application because many of the compounds used as listed above decompose with heat or are not volatile. These practical features often make thin-layer chromatography the first choice technique for isolation of polymer additives.

In common with other chromatographic methods, the separations are not always specific. R_f factors may be the same even for different class compounds, although this is not usually true. In particular, the material which does not migrate and that which moves fast at the solvent front should be examined closely for purity.

Generally, the more polar compounds are most strongly retained. The following series illustrates a gradation from low to high mobility:

Acids, alcohols, amines, ketones, ethers, alkanes

In a parallel way, because they are more strongly adsorbed, the more polar solvents have a stronger eluting action. A series graded from strong to weak eluting power is this:

Water, methanol, methylene chloride, carbon tetrachloride, hexane

The essential features of the technique fall under the classifications:

Preparation of Coated Plates
Activation of the Adsorbent
Application of the Sample
Selection of the Developing Solvent or Mixture
Development
Location of Fractions
Recovery of Fractions

Preparation of Coated Plates.—Silica gel, with calcium sulfate added as a binder, is the most common coating and perhaps the most versatile, judging from its many uses recorded in the literature. Other adsorbents common in column chromatography, such as alumina, cellulose powders, and diatomaceous earth, are also used with added binder. The adsorbent coating is applied from an organic solvent slurry or from a water slurry. The features of each of these are listed below:

Organic Solvent Slurry.—A typical slurry is a mixture of 20–30 percent of silica gel (containing about 10 percent calcium sulfate) in chloroform. Such a system is stable and may be stored for several months. The slurry must be mixed thoroughly just prior to coating, which is usually done by a dip process. After air-drying, the coated plates are steamed. Coatings made in this manner may flake if too thick.

Water Slurry.—A typical water slurry is a mixture of 1 part adsorbent (containing 10–15 percent calcium sulfate) and 2 parts water. Water slurries set up in 10–15 min.; therefore they must be prepared just prior to application to the plates, which is usually done with an applicator of the draw-down bar type. Thicker, more uniform layers, with less tendency to flake, can be prepared from water slurries.

Activation of the Adsorbent.—The adsorbent is activated by heating in an oven, after air-drying, for 30 min. at 110°C., or other times and temperatures as required. Higher temperatures and longer times produce a more retentive adsorbent layer. For separation of hydrophilic mixtures, air-drying without heat may be desirable.

Application of the Sample.—Care should be taken not to overload the plates with sample, because this will result in poor separations. Overloading can sometimes be detected when the developing solvent does not wet the sample spot or takes unusually long to pass the point of application if a series of spots has been applied. Samples may drip in the reverse direction to the solvent advance, due to overloading; or it may be observed that the spot does not dry rapidly after application. It is desirable to dilute samples with a volatile solvent prior to application to help avoid the above behavior. A 5 percent sample solution in a volatile solvent can be applied to the plate with an eye dropper restricted to a capillary opening. After drying, more solution is applied to the same spots. This limits the spots to a small area and results in sharper separations.

Selection of the Developing Solvent or Mixture.—It is usually not necessary to employ complex solvent mixtures for development. Single solvents or binary mixtures are usually satisfactory. It should be emphasized here that these remarks apply to separations that are usually not difficult for thin-layer techniques. This is true when the three or four additives under consideration for separation are from different classes. More elaborate solvent mixtures may be necessary for separation of homologs or isomers, for example. The more volatile solvents allow a faster procedure when the subsequent evaporation step is considered.

It is a convenient practice to make pilot determinations on unknown mixtures using small, coated, microscope slides. The slides are prepared by dipping in an organic solvent slurry containing the adsorbent and binder. The slurry is stable, and the small plates are quickly coated for use as needed from a stock slurry. Several solvents representing a range from polar to nonpolar are investigated simultaneously in 10 to 15 min. using iodine vapor after development to locate the separated components. The most attractive separation condition can then be used on a larger scale perhaps with a thicker layer and larger plates. The larger plates (4 × 8 in.) are prepared from a water slurry using a commercial applicator. Once the essential features of a separation are determined, they can be applied using column techniques if extremely large amounts are needed. For identification purposes, however, enough can be recovered from several of the larger thin layer plates.

Development.—Ascending development is usual. The plates are placed in a beaker with a top, or other airtight enclosure, containing about a centimeter depth of solvent. A small air space around the plate slows down the rate of evaporation of solvent from the surface and is desirable. The use of filter-paper strips to prevent surface evaporation is effective. The paper is placed so that it does not touch the plate and brings more solvent up by a wicking action to help saturate the air space around the plate. It is frequently desirable to repeat separations of closely spaced fractions to obtain high purity.

Location of Fractions.—A nondestructive method of location is desirable. Ultraviolet light may allow location of spots by contrast, even though the spots are not fluorescent. In ordinary light, the spots or bands are sometimes more discernible from the back side of the plate than the front. A common method is exposure to iodine vapor. This is a quick, rather general way to locate most components and is not destructive except for very sensitive compounds and such special classes as organic sulfur compounds. The iodine is absorbed by the fractions staining them brown-yellow to pink in color. This variation is sometimes helpful as a clue to the type of fraction, since it seems to be related to the polar nature of the fraction. Polar compounds are brown-yellow, and nonpolar compounds tend to be pink or violet (compare the color of an aqueous iodine solution to the color of iodine in carbon tetrachloride). The staining is not persistent and disappears in 10 to 15 min. after exposure.

Recovery of Fractions.—Sufficient sample for infrared identification of equally concentrated components can usually be recovered from four or five of the larger plates. The fractions are removed by scraping the adsorbent from the plates. The adsorbed component is dissolved and separated from the insoluble inorganic materials by filtration. Additives are usually present in low concentrations and small extract samples are the rule. If it is suspected that the fractions will be small, it is a good practice to filter the solutions directly into mortars which can be used, after solvent evaporation, to prepare potassium bromide discs or mulls where appropriate. This is convenient because it avoids sample transfer loss and may mean the difference between suitable infrared spectra and insufficient sample from a limited amount of polymer extract. It is often possible to obtain identifiable spectra in this manner from barely visible amounts of fractions. Care should be taken that the eluting solvent is strong enough to desorb the sample. It would not be recommended, for example, that hexane be used to redissolve an acid. Methanol would be better because of its stronger eluting action.

The following specific example illustrates separation of the additives present in a commercial polymer.

Concentration of the Additives in an Extract of the Polymer.—The polymer was precipitated from a methylene chloride solution by the addition of methanol. The insoluble polymer was removed by filtration and the filtrate evaporated to a small volume.

Separation of Components in the Extract.—The components in the residue were separated by thin-layer chromatography on silica gel G with chloroform as the developing solvent. Exposure of the plates to iodine vapor revealed four bands which were scraped off the plates into small aluminum evaporating dishes. Methanol was added to each dish to dissolve the additive. The slurry was filtered to remove the inorganic matter. The methanol was evaporated and it was found that components 1 and 4 were liquids, and 2 and 3 were solids. Examination of the recovered fractions by infrared showed component 1 to be an alkyl phosphite ester; component 2, a long-chain fatty acid; component 3, a substituted benzotriazole; and component 4, a dimer or other low molecular weight oligomer. (Fractions Nos. 1 and 2 were not well resolved under these conditions.)

GAS CHROMATOGRAPHY

Gas chromatographic techniques are finding increasing utility for the identification of polymers, for studying their thermal stability, for elucidation of the mechanisms of thermal degradation, and for determining additives and such other volatile products as residual monomers, solvents, antioxidants, and even plasticizers. In fact, the versatility of the gas chromatograph, especially when combined with other techniques of analysis, has opened up a virtual "Pandora Box" of new approaches to plastics analysis.

The primary criterion for gas chromatographic analysis is that the substances being examined have an appreciable vapor pressure at a temperature below 300° to 350°C. For the examination of polymers per se, the material is pyrolyzed at elevated temperatures and the volatile pyrolysis products subsequently characterized. The separation of components of a mixture is dependent upon the nature of the stationary phase and the length and temperature of the column. The components emerging from the column are recorded, usually as a function of time, by a detector device. Thermal conductivity and hydrogen flame ionization detectors are perhaps the most widely used; however, other devices, such as β-ray ionization, argon detectors, and electron capture (designed primarily for halogenated products), are available. The hydrogen flame detector is considerably more sensitive than the thermal conductivity cell; however, it has the disadvantage of destroying the sample, thereby preventing capture of the emerging components for subsequent identification. This latter step is important in the examination of unknown materials, since the peaks on a gas chromatogram are not characteristic of a functional group or a specific component in the same manner as the peaks in an infrared spectrum. The usual procedure for the characterization of the peaks is to inject known materials under the same conditions as the sample, and then compare retention times for the various peaks. For absolute identification, retention times should be checked on two columns containing different packing materials. An alternate and more reliable procedure is actually to trap the individual products as they emerge from the column as relatively pure materials and characterize them by infrared or mass spectrometry.

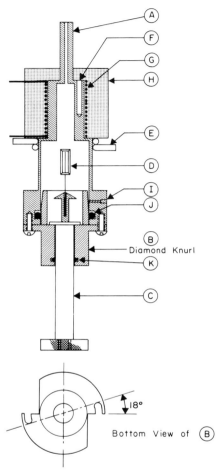

Diamond Knurl

Bottom View of (B)

18°

FIG. 58-48. Polymer Pyrolyzer. (A) ¼-in. O.D. Tube to Take Compression Tube Fittings; (B) Quick Disconnect Sample Loader Sealed with O-Ring; (C) ⅜-in. Polished S.S. Push Rod with Stop and Furnace Seal; (D) Sample Basket; Two Turns -in. Copper Tubing Soldered to Sample Storage Chamber (F) Thermo-couple Well; (G) Double-Layer 26-Gauge Insulated Nichrome Wire; (H) Asbestos Plaster Insulation; (I) Hole for Attaching -in. Carrier Gas Tubing; (J) O-Ring and Static Seal; (K) O-Ring and Dynamic Seal.

IDENTIFICATION OF PLASTICS BY GAS CHROMATOGRAPHY

Pyrolysis of the sample may be carried out by the hot-wire or filament technique, whereby a small particle is laid on a Nichrome or platinum heating spiral or a thin film is deposited on the spiral from a solvent. Alternately, the pyrolysis may be carried out in a furnace or tubular reactor. This latter technique has several advantages over the hot-wire technique: (a) quartz or porcelain boats may be used to hold the sample, thereby avoiding any catalytic effect of metals; (b) thermoset plastics may be studied, since a solution of the polymer is not required; (c) solvent effects are avoided; and (d) the temperature of the reaction zone may be accurately measured. The pyrolysis temperature has been varied from 150° to 950°C.; however, a reactor temperature of 500°C. appears to be satisfactory for most polymers. Although the selection of a column packing is considerably more critical, two of the more useful are 20 percent di-2-ethyl-hexyl sebacate on 20–60 mshe firebrick and 25 percent LAC-2-R-446 (polydiethyleneglycolpentaerythritol adipate) plus 2 percent phosphoric acid on 80–100 mesh Chromosorb W.

A general method for the identification of plastics employing a simple furnace technique was described in an earlier volume.[134] The same equipment was used to study the thermal degradation of various vinyl polymers in the temperature range from 300° to 500°C.[135]

An improved syringe-type pyrolysis unit has been designed (Fig. 58-48) which can be attached directly to the injector system of a gas chromatograph with a Swagelok fitting.[136] The furnace is adjusted to the desired temperature. Five mg. of the sample is weighed into a Coors 00000 porcelain boat, and the boat is placed in the basket of the plunger. After the assembly has been flushed free of air, the sample is pushed into the furnace.

Barrall, Porter, and Johnson[137] analyzed ethylene-vinyl acetate and ethylene-ethyl acrylate copolymers and copolymer blends by pyrolyzing the samples at 350° to 490°C. The pyrolysis products were separated on a Carbowax column (acetic acid) and a propylene carbonate column (ethylene). Acrylate and methacrylate polymers have been studied by a number of investigators.[138] Percival[139] analyzed polyesters by methanolysis of the polymer followed by the gas chromatographic determination of the resulting free glycols and dimethyl esters. The products were chromatographed on 16.7 percent GE Silicone SF96 on Fluoropak 80. The column temperature was programmed from 110° to 180°C. with the injector port and detector cell held at 200°C. Voigt[140] studied the degradation of polyolefins by pyrolyzing 2-mg. samples at 550°C. for 18 seconds. The pyrolysis products were swept into a 6-ft. column (at 75°C.) packed with di-n-decyl phthalate on kieselguhr. The same procedure was also used for the quantitative analysis of ethylene-propylene copolymers.

DETERMINATION OF ADDITIVES

Residual monomer, residual solvents, antioxidants, plasticizers, and other volatile products in plastics may be determined readily by gas chromatography. The plastic may be dissolved in a suitable solvent and an aliquot injected directly. Alternately the additives may be removed by extraction or even liberated from the plastic by mild pyrolysis. Aqueous emulsions or latexes may be dissolved in a solvent such as dimethylformamide prior to injection.

Esposito[141] identified and determined phthalate, phosphate, and sebacate ester plasticizers by the gas chromatographic examination of a polymer extract using a 6-ft. column ($\frac{1}{4}$ in.) packed with 20 percent silicone grease on washed Chromosorb W. The column temperature was programmed from 210° to 290°C. at a rate of 4°C. per minute. The inlet port temperature and the detector cell temperature were 330°C. and 300°C., respectively. Zulaica and Guiochon[142] employed a mild pyrolysis of the sample to liberate the plasticizers directly into the column without prior extraction. The plastic was pyrolyzed at 650°C. for 10 sec. Plasticizers, boiling under 400°C., at atmospheric pressure were eluted from a 6-ft. column packed with 0.5 percent silicone gum SE 30 on 125–160 μ glass beads or from a 10-ft. column packed with 0.5 percent polyneopentyl

[134] Cobler, J. G., in Welcher, F. J., ed., Standard Methods of Chemical Analysis, 6th Ed., Vol. II, Part B, D. Van Nostrand Co., Inc., Princeton, N. J., 1963, p. 2041.
[135] Cobler, J. G., and Samsel, E. P., SPE Transactions, 2, 145, 1962.
[136] Long, M. W., and Hatton, W., The Dow Chemical Company, personal communication.
[137] Barrall, E. M., Porter, R. S., and Johnson, J. F., Anal. Chem., 35, 73, 1963.
[138] Guillet, J. E., Wooten, W. C., and Combs, R. L., J. Appl. Polymer Sci., 3, 61, 1960; Radell, E. A., and Strutz, H. C., Anal. Chem., 31, 1890, 1959; Lehmann, F. A., and Brauer, G. M., Anal. Chem., 33, 673, 1961.
[139] Percival, D. F., Anal. Chem., 35, 236, 1963.
[140] Voigt, J., Kunststoffe, 54, 2, 1964.
[141] Esposito, G. G., Anal. Chem., 35, 1439, 1963.
[142] Zulaica, J., and Guiochon, G., Anal. Chem., 35, 1724, 1963.

glycol adipate on glass beads at 200° to 240°C. Amine antidegradants (such as *N*-phenyl-2-naphthylamine) were determined in rubber extracts employing a 6-ft. column packed with 20 percent Apiezon L on 30–60 mesh Chromosorb W.[143] The column temperature was programmed from 210° to 325°C. The inlet port temperature and the detector cell temperature were held at 340° and 310°C., respectively.

THE DETERMINATION OF HIGH-BOILING ESTERS BY GAS CHROMATOGRAPHY[144]

Scope.—This method is applicable to the determination of dibutyl sebacate, and acetyl tributyl citrate in polymer extracts.

Principle.—The additives are removed from the polymer by extraction with benzene. The additives in the extract are then separated and determined by gas chromatography. Quantitative measurements are made by comparing the peak heights of the sample components to those of a prepared standard.

Apparatus. Gas Chromatograph, Beckman GC-2, or equivalent, equipped with a flame ionization detector, and the sample inlet modified for direct column injection (Fig. 58-49).

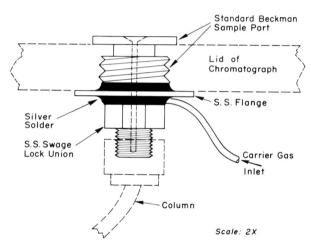

FIG. 58-49.   Modified Sample Port for Direct Column Injection.

Recorder, 0 to 1.05 millivolt.

Column, $\frac{1}{4}$-in. O.D., 0.028-in. wall thickness, stainless-steel tubing, 2 ft. long.

Syringe, Hamilton microliter, No. 701-N, or equivalent.

Reagents. Column Packing.—Five percent by weight LAC-2-R446 and 2 percent by weight phosphoric acid on 80–100 mesh Chromosorb W. The LAC-2-R446 is available from The Cambridge Industries Company, Inc., 101 Potter Street, Cambridge, Massachusetts. The prepared packing is available from Wilkens Instrument and Research, Inc., Walnut Creek, California.

Helium Gas, commercial grade.

Hydrogen Gas, commercial grade.

[143] Wise, R. W., and Sullivan, A. B., Rubber Age, **91**, 773, 1962.
[144] Gill, H. G., and Solomon, R. A., The Dow Chemical Company, unpublished manuscript.

Air, clean and dry.
Dibutyl Sebacate (DBS).
Acetyl Tributyl Citrate.
Benzene, reagent grade.
Chromatographic Conditions.—Carrier gas, helium. Flow rate, 80 ml. per minute as determined by the soap bubble method.

Column temperature, 200°C.
Hydrogen, 20 p.s.i.

Preparation of the Standard.—Prepare a standard using the concentrations of the additives known to be present in the samples. The weights and percentages of the standard components are based on the 10-g. sample to be used in the analysis.

Component	Weight, g.	Percent
Dibutyl sebacate	0.4000	4.00
Acetyl tributyl citrate	0.2250	2.25

Dissolve the standard in 100 ml. of benzene.

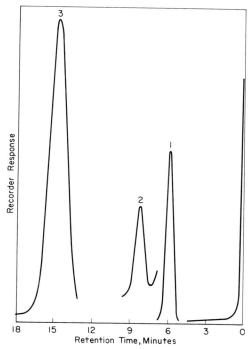

Fig. 58-50. Gas Chromatogram Showing Retention Times for Dibutyl Sebacate (1); Impurity in Dibutyl Sebacate (2); and Acetyl Tributyl Citrate (3).

Calibration.—Using a 5-μl. sample of the standard, obtain a chromatogram of the standard components (Fig. 58-50). The unknown component found in the standard was shown to be present in the dibutyl sebacate standard. Since this value is incorporated in the dibutyl sebacate value, the unknown was not calculated in the samples. Measure the peak height of each component in chart scale divisions.

Procedure.—Take a 10-g. sample of the plastic, weighed to the nearest 0.1 g., and cut into small pieces. Place the sample in a 16-oz. bottle with a foil-lined cap.

Add 100 ml. of benzene and place the sample on the shaker for 1 hr. Inject a 5-μl. sample of the benzene extract into the instrument and record the chromatogram.

Calculation.—Quantitative measurement of the components is made by comparing the peak height of each component of the standard with that of the samples.

$$\text{Percent component} = \frac{\text{peak height (component)} \times \% \text{ standard}}{\text{peak height (standard)}}$$

Reproducibility.—The reproducibility of the procedure is ± 1 chart division. This variation gives an accuracy of 2 percent relative to the amount of the additive present.

DETERMINATION OF RESIDUAL STYRENE MONOMER IN STYRENE POLYMERS

Scope.—This method is suitable for the determination of residual styrene monomer in all types of styrene polymers.

Principle.—The sample is dissolved in methylene chloride. An aliquot of the solution is injected into a gas chromatograph. The amount of styrene monomer present is determined from the area of the resulting peak.

Apparatus. **Gas Chromatograph.**—Beckman GC-2A gas chromatograph with hydrogen flame detector or apparatus of equivalent sensitivity.

Chromatograph Column.—One-quarter inch O.D. stainless-steel tubing (0.028 in. wall thickness), 4 ft. long, packed with 20 percent Carbowax 20 *M*-alkaline on 60/80 mesh firebrick (the packing is a product of Wilkens Instrument and Research, Inc., Walnut Creek, California, Catalog No. 0033).

Recorder. 0–1 millivolt range, chart speed of 30 in. per hour.

Reagents. **Helium Gas.**

Hydrogen Gas.

Compressed Air, purified.

Methylene Chloride, redistilled.

Styrene Monomer, redistilled.

Operating Conditions for the Beckman GC-2A Gas Chromatograph.—The column is operated at a temperature of 100°C. with a helium flow rate of 82 ml. per minute.

The hydrogen burner is operated with 15 p.s.i. of air pressure and 7 p.s.i. of hydrogen pressure.

The attenuation of the hydrogen flame detector is set at 2×10^2.

Standardization.—Prepare a standard solution by weighing accurately 15 to 20 mg. of styrene monomer into a 2-oz. bottle containing 25.0 ml. of methylene chloride. Cap the bottle tightly and shake to thoroughly mix the solution.

By means of a microliter syringe, inject 1 μl. of the standard solution into the gas chromatograph. Measure the area of the styrene monomer peak which emerges after approximately 12 min.

Procedure.—Transfer a 1-g. sample (accurately weighed to the nearest 0.001 g.) to a 2-oz. bottle and add several glass beads. Pipet 20.0 ml. of methylene chloride into the bottle. Cap the bottle tightly and place on a mechanical shaker. Shake until the polymer is completely dissolved. Transfer the solution to a 25-ml. volumetric flask and dilute to volume. If any insoluble residue remains, allow the flask to stand (or centrifuge at a low speed) until a clear supernatant layer appears.

By means of a microliter syringe, inject 3 μl. of the clear supernatant liquid into the gas chromatograph.

Measure the area of the resulting styrene monomer peak. Compare the sample peak area with the area produced by the standard styrene monomer solution.

Calculation.

Percent styrene monomer

$$= \frac{\text{milligrams monomer in standard} \times \text{peak area of sample}}{\text{monomer standard peak area} \times \text{sample weight in gram} \times 30}$$

FRACTION COLLECTION FROM GAS CHROMATOGRAPHY[145]

A variety of techniques and attachments are available for the collection of fractions issuing from the exit port of the gas chromatographic unit. Fundamentally, the gas chromatographic unit has to be equipped with thermal conductivity or other non-destructive detectors, *i.e.*, the fractions cannot be burned for detection purposes. Highly volatile fractions may be transferred directly (by manipulation of valves) into a gas cell located in the sample beam of a high-speed infrared spectrometer,[146] or they may be collected by condensing with liquid nitrogen, adding a suitable solvent, and transferring the diluted sample to a suitable microcell. Less highly volatile samples may be collected by a variety of collector techniques. Such techniques include condensing the fractions directly on micro sodium chloride plates or pressed potassium bromide pellets, condensing on potassium bromide powder, after which the contaminated powder is pressed into a disc, and condensing the fraction in tubes designed to trap a microliter or less of sample. One device for condensing the fraction employs a capillary tube technique,[147] another uses a "V" tube technique.[148] Both devices require that the exit tube be in a horizontal position and preferably heated.

The capillary tube is made according to the diagram (Fig. 58-51). The tube is attached to the exit port in the following manner: A hole is drilled in a Teflon Luerlok male plug, the diameter of which is the external diameter of the exit port. To this Luerlok plug is fitted a 19-gauge syringe needle that has been cut to a length of $1\frac{1}{4}$ in. The capillary tube is inserted into a thimble filled with dry ice which is made by cutting a Soxhlet extraction thimble, 1 in. in diameter, in half, punching holes in the bottom half, and insert-

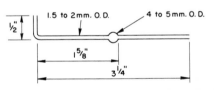

Fig. 58-51. Capillary Tube for Trapping Fractions from Gas Chromatograph.

ing the capillary tube until it emerges from the other side. When the fraction starts to emerge from the exit port, the capillary tube (with the thimble of dry ice) is slipped over the needle attached to the exit port. When the desired fraction has been collected, the capillary tube and the thimble are removed.

The "V" tube is made of 1 mm. capillary tubing (Fig. 58-52) bent at approximately a 90° angle, with a small bubble at the bend This bubble swirls the carrier gas which allows a more efficient fraction collection and facilitates solvent recovery from the trap.

[145] Long, M. W., The Dow Chemical Company, unpublished manuscript.

[146] Brown, R., and Wicks, P. A., Paper presented at the Pittsburgh Conference on Analytical and Applied Spectroscopy, Pittsburgh, 1964; Bartz, A. M., and Ruhl, H. D., *op. cit.*

[147] Moss, R. D., The Dow Chemical Company, personal communication.

[148] Blake, B. H., The Dow Chemical Company, personal communication.

The arms of the trap are made approximately $1\frac{3}{4}$ in. long to enable a microsyringe to be inserted to the bottom of the trap for the removal of the solution.

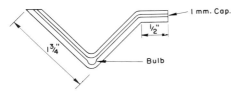

FIG. 58-52. "V" Tube for Trapping Fractions from Gas Chromatograph.

For the attachment of the tube to the chromatograph, a Teflon coupling is made from a piece of rod. The rod is drilled one-half its length to accommodate insertion of the exit port tube. The other end of the rod is drilled one-half its length to allow insertion of the "V" tube. To condense the fractions, a thimble is made by cutting a Soxhlet extraction thimble, 43 ml. in diameter, 2 in. from the bottom and punching holes in the sides of the bottom portion so that the "V" tube may be entirely inserted through the bucket. The bucket is filled with dry ice. When the fraction starts to emerge from the exit port, the "V" tube (with the thimble of dry ice) is inserted into the Teflon coupling. When the desired fraction has been collected, the "V" tube and thimble are removed.

A suitable solvent, carbon disulfide or carbon tetrachloride, is added to the tube (capillary or "V") with a Hamilton microliter syringe. The tube is rocked back and forth to dissolve the sample and the solution withdrawn with the micro syringe. The solution is inserted into any one of a variety of commercially available microcells, the cell sealed, and placed in the sample beam of the spectrometer.

SURVEY OF ADDITIONAL INSTRUMENTAL TECHNIQUES

LIGHT SCATTERING

One of the more useful methods for the measurement of molecular weights above 10,000 is based on the scattering of light from polymer molecules in solution.[149] In fact, the report of the International Union summarizing a study of polystyrenes by viscosity, osmotic pressure, and light-scattering methods concluded that the most consistent results were obtained by the light-scattering technique.[150] The intensity of the light scattered when a beam of monochromatic light passes through a solution of the polymer depends on the polarizability of the polymer molecules compared with that of the solvent, on the size of the molecules, and on their concentration. Thus the technique provides an absolute measurement of molecular weights, since only geometric measurements and fundamental physical constants are required.

Techniques have been described for the study of polystyrene,[151] polyethylene,[152] poly(vinyl alcohol),[153] poly(vinyl acetate),[154] poly(vinyl chloride),[155] and poly(methyl methacrylate).[156] Although the normal molecular weight average obtained by this tech-

[149] Fishman, M. M., Light Scattering by Colloidal Systems, Technical Service Laboratories, River Edge, N. J., 1957; Stacey, K. A., Light Scattering in Physical Chemistry, Academic Press, Inc., New York, 1956; Peaker, F. W., Techniques of Polymer Characterization, Allen, P. W., ed., Academic Press, Inc., New York, 1959, p. 131.

[150] Frank, H. P., and Mark, H., U.P.A.C. Report, J. Polymer Sci., **10**, 129, 1953.

[151] Kunst, E. D., Rec. Trav. Chim. Pays-Bas, **69**, 125, 1950; Zimm, B. H., J. Chem. Phys., **16**, 1099, 1948; Flory, P. J., Fox, T. G., and Bueche, A. M., J. Am. Chem. Soc., **73**, 285, 1951.

[152] Billmeyer, F. W., Jr., J. Am. Chem. Soc., **75**, 6118, 1953; Moore, L. D., J. Polymer Sci., **20**, 137, 1956.

[153] Dieu, H. A., J. Polymer Sci., **12**, 417, 1954.

[154] Bosworth, P., Masson, C. R., Melville, H. W., and Peaker, F. W., J. Polymer Sci., **9**, 565, 1952.

[155] Doty, P., Wagner, H., and Singer, S., J. Phys. Chem., **51**, 32, 1947.

[156] Stockmayer, W. H., and Stanley, H. E., J. Chem. Phys., **18**, 153, 1950.

nique is the weight average ($\overline{M}w$), Benoit[157] showed that, under favorable conditions, both weight average and number average ($\overline{M}n$) molecular weights could be determined.

Data from light-scattering measurements can also give information concerning the molecular size and shape of polymer molecules and the parameters characterizing the interaction between solvent and polymer molecules. Chain branching can be estimated from the angular variation of the scattering, a branched molecule having a more compact structure than a linear molecule with the same degree of polymerization.[158]

ULTRACENTRIFUGE

Ultracentrifugation techniques are perhaps the most intricate of methods for the determination of molecular weights and molecular weight distributions. The general applications of the technique have been discussed by Baldwin and Van Holde[159] and Schachman.[160] The ultracentrifuge consists essentially of a small rotor which is spun at high speed in a vacuum. A small cylindrical cell containing a solution of the polymer is held within the rotor. The progress of sedimentation of the polymer molecules under the influence of the centrifugal field is followed optically by using a beam of light traveling parallel to the axis of rotation and perpendicular to the cell. The refraction of rays passing through different portions of the cell is usually determined by means of schlieren optics[161] or interference optical systems.[162] The molecular weights of the polymer molecules may be determined from the rate of sedimentation or from the ultimate distribution of the polymer molecules within the cell after equilibrium has been attained.

Goldberg[163] discussed the general theory of sedimentation based on thermodynamic considerations. Wales and Van Holde[164] determined the relation between sedimentation constants, concentration, and molecular weights for polystyrene, poly(methyl methacrylate), and polyisobutylene. Newman and Eirich[165] obtained sedimentation data on polystyrene in chloroform, toluene, and methyl ethyl ketone. Additional studies of polystyrene[166] and polyisobutylene[167] have been described. Shashoua and Van Holde[168] employed the ultracentrifuge to characterize graft polymers.

OSMOMETRY

The determination of the number average molecular weight ($\overline{M}n$) of polymers by osmotic pressure measurements has long been a standard but tedious determination. The osmotic pressure may be determined by equilibrium (static elevation) or by dynamic techniques. In the former, the liquid head developed by the influx of solvent into the polymer solution through a semipermeable membrane is measured. The externally applied pressure necessary to counterbalance the osmotic pressure is measured in the dynamic method.

Inexpensive equilibrium osmometers have been described by Wagner and Sands and

[157] Benoit, H., J. Polymer Sci., **11**, 507, 1953.

[158] Thurmond, C. D., and Zimm, B. H., J. Polymer Sci., **8**, 477, 1952; Stockmayer, W. H., and Fixman, M., Ann. N. Y. Acad. Sci., **57**, 334, 1953.

[159] Baldwin, R. L., and Van Holde, K. E., Advances in Polymer Sci., **1**, 451, 1960.

[160] Schachman, H. K., Ultracentrifugation in Biochemistry, Academic Press, Inc., New York, 1959.

[161] Svedberg, T., and Pedersen, K. O., The Ultracentrifuge, Clarendon Press, Oxford, 1940.

[162] Richards, E. G., and Schachman, H. K., J. Phys. Chem., **63**, 1578, 1959.

[163] Goldberg, R. J., J. Phys. Chem., **57**, 194, 1953.

[164] Wales, M., and Van Holde, K. E., J. Polymer Sci., **14**, 81, 1954.

[165] Newman, S., and Eirich, F., J. Colloid. Sci., **5**, 541, 1950.

[166] Gralen, N., and Lagermalm, G., J. Phys. Chem., **56**, 514, 1952.

[167] Mandelkern, L., Williams, L. C., and Weissberg, S. G., J. Phys. Chem., **61**, 271, 1957.

[168] Shashoua, V. E., and Van Holde, K. E., J. Polymer Sci., **28**, 395, 1958.

by Johnson.[169] Block-type osmometers have been developed which permit greater speed in attaining equilibrium, as well as greater precision.[170] Dynamic osmotic pressure techniques have been described[171] in which the rate of permeation is measured as a function of the pressure difference. The rate is extrapolated to zero rate, yielding a calculated pressure equal to the osmotic pressure. A "rate-of-flow" osmometer described by Bruss and Stross,[172] which enables measurements to be made in one day or less, is available commercially.[173] A high-speed negative pressure osmometer has recently been made available.[174] The polymer solution is introduced, displacing the solvent or a previous sample, on the solution side of the membrane. A sensitive optical transducer on the solvent side of the membrane detects the solvent flow toward the membrane. At a signal from the transducer, a servosystem adjusts the pressure to prevent solvent flow through the membrane. This pressure is continuously read directly in centimeters of solvent on the instruments digital readout or via a recorder. Eighteen or twenty osmotic pressure measurements may be made in one day, as opposed to one or less using the equilibrium systems.

MASS SPECTROMETRY

Mass spectrometry offers a valuable technique for characterizing materials having a vapor pressure of at least 1 mm. at 250°C. The molecules in the vapor state are bombarded with electrons causing bond rupture and ionization to occur. The positive ions are accelerated into a magnetic field and travel curved paths, the radii of which are proportional to the square root of the masses. The ions, separated in the magnetic field according to the mass-to-charge ratio, are swept past a collector where the ions are discharged, producing a current proportional to the relative abundance of the ions. These currents are recorded to give the mass spectrum. Simple mixtures may be identified by putting together the fragments, shown in the spectrum, to form molecules. Complex mixtures are usually identified by reference to standard spectra. The general techniques and applications of mass spectrometry have been reviewed by Dibeler and Dunning.[175]

Time-of-flight mass spectrometers based on velocity selection are now available.[176] The main advantage of the time-of-flight spectrometer is the speed with which a spectrum is obtained. Several hundred spectra can, theoretically, be obtained in a second. The instrument has been used to monitor the effluents from gas chromatographs.[177]

Most of the applications of mass spectrometry to plastics have been in the study of the pyrolysis products of plastics, such as polystyrene,[178] polyethylene,[179] and poly(vinyl

[169] Wagner, R. H., Ind. Eng. Chem., Anal. Ed., **16**, 520, 1944; Sands, G. D., and Johnson, B. L., Anal. Chem., **19**, 261, 1947.

[170] Meyer, K. H., Wolff, E., and Boissonnas, C. G., Helv. Chim. Acta, **23**, 430, 1940; Flory, P. J., J. Am. Chem. Soc., **65**, 372, 1943; Krigbaum, W. R., and Flory, P. J., J. Am. Chem. Soc., **75**, 1775, 1953.

[171] Fuoss, R. M., and Mead, D. J., J. Phys. Chem., **47**, 59, 1943; Philipp, H. J., J. Polymer Sci., **6**, 371, 1951.

[172] Bruss, D. B., and Stross, F. H., J. Polymer Sci., **55**, 381, 1961.

[173] J. V. Stabin Company, Brooklyn, N. Y.

[174] Mechrolab Model 501 Membrane Osmometer, Mechrolab Inc., 1062 Linda Vista Ave., Mountain View, Calif.

[175] Dibeler, V. H., Organic Analysis, Vol. 3, Interscience Publishers, Inc., New York, 1956, pp. 387–441; Dunning, W. J., Quart. Rev. (London), **9**, 23, 1955.

[176] Katzenstein, H. S., and Friedland, S. S., Rev. Sci. Instr., **26**, 324, 1955; Wiley, W. C., Science, **124**, 817, 1956.

[177] Gohlke, R. S., Anal. Chem., **31**, 535, 1959.

[178] Bradt, P., Dibeler, V. H., and Mohler, F. L., J. Research Natl. Bur. Standards, **50**, 201, 1953.

[179] Simha, R., and Wall, L. A., J. Polymer Sci., **6**, 39, 1951.

chloride).[180] Bua and Manaresi[181] determined the copolymer ratio of ethylene-propylene copolymers by pyrolysis and analysis of the pyrolysis products by mass spectrometric techniques. Thieme[182] analyzed the gases evolved from plastics, such as polystyrene, poly(methyl methacrylate), and Teflon under vacuum conditions.

SELECTED BIBLIOGRAPHY

Allen, P. W., Ed., Techniques of Polymer Characterization, Academic Press, Inc., New York, 1959.

Kappelmeier, C. P. A., Ed., Chemical Analysis of Resin-Based Coating Materials, Interscience Publishers, Inc., New York, 1959.

Ke, B., Ed., Newer Methods of Polymer Characterization, Polymer Reviews 6, Interscience Publishers, Inc., New York, 1964.

Kline, G. M., Ed., Analytical Chemistry of Polymers, High Polymer Series XII, Interscience Publishers, Inc., New York: Part I—Analysis of Monomers and Polymeric Materials, 1959; Part II—Analysis of Molecular Structure and Chemical Groups, 1962; Part III—Identification Procedures and Chemical Analysis, 1962.

Wake, W. C., The Analysis of Rubber and Rubber-Like Polymers, Maclaren and Sons, Ltd., London, 1958.

The author would like to acknowledge the cooperation of his colleagues in preparing this chapter. He is particularly indebted to Dr. V. A. Stenger for his valuable criticisms of the manuscript.

[180] Bradt, P., and Mohler, F. L., J. Research Natl. Bur. Standards, **55**, 323, 1955.
[181] Bua, E., and Manaresi, P., Anal. Chem., **31**, 2022, 1959.
[182] Thieme, G., Vacuum, **13**, 137, 1963.

Chapter 59

RUBBER AND RUBBER PRODUCTS

By Max Tryon and Emanuel Horowitz

Polymer Characterization Section
National Bureau of Standards
Washington, D. C.

INTRODUCTION

Scope.—The purpose of this chapter is to guide the chemist who is interested in analyzing a rubber or rubber product to a rapid, satisfactory method that is designed to provide information about the polymeric and nonpolymer constituents in the sample.

In contrast to Chapter 43 of Vol. IIB, which dealt with standard procedures accepted by such organizations as the American Society for Testing and Materials, and which was concerned primarily with noninstrumental methods, this chapter stresses instrumental methods not yet accepted as "standard" but of value to the analyst in characterizing the material in question.

Many of these instrumental methods involve, in part at least, standard procedures described in the earlier chapter. The instrumental part of the method serves only as the final measuring act, frequently substituting for one or more tedious or time consuming steps in an existing standard method. On the other hand, there are also methods that are completely independent of any of the accepted standard procedures; these are of value because of the discriminatory power of the technique.

Instrumental methods are defined for the purpose of this chapter as methods using contrived mechanical, electrical, optical, and other means for the measuring or detecting process. For example: titrations using a photoelectric cell, rather than the eye of the operator, to detect the change in an indicator; infrared spectrophotometry; mass spectrometry; nuclear magnetic resonance; conductimetric and amperometric titrations; gas, paper, and liquid chromatography; and others are considered to be properly included in this chapter. In addition, several standard methods not reported in Volume IIB have also been included, as well as some methods judged to merit description.

Conventional "wet" methods not yet accepted as standard procedures will not be included. Only methods that were specifically written as procedures are included. A bibliography of other less specific procedures is included and referenced at the beginning of each section.

Books and review articles of general interest to the rubber analyst include the rather comprehensive book by Frey[1] on methods for the chemical analysis of rubber mixtures; it includes references to both classical and instrumental methods and techniques, the book on the analysis of rubber by Wake,[2] Chapter II in the book on applied science of

---

[1] Frey, H. E., Methoden zur Chemischen Analyse von Gummimischungen, Springer Verlag, Berlin, 1960.

[2] Wake, W. C., The Analysis of Rubber and Rubber-Like Polymers, MacLaren and Sons, Ltd., London, 1958.

rubber, edited by Naunton,[3] the earlier book by Whitby,[4] the review paper by Mitchell and Lord[5] on instrumental methods for polymer analysis, which covers infrared, ultraviolet, nuclear magnetic resonance, and thermal techniques through 1960, and the earlier review paper by Burger,[6] which reviews the literature on rubber analysis up through 1958. The Handbook of Analytical Chemistry[7] has a chapter on rubber analysis which presents a large number of both classical and instrumental methods in abstract or abbreviated form. Standard materials for rubber compounding available from the National Bureau of Standards are described by Roth and Stiehler.[8] These materials include various carbon blacks, synthetic rubbers, and natural rubber as well as sulfur, antioxidants, accelerators, stearic acid, zinc oxide, and magnesia.

Definitions and Nomenclature.—The American Society for Testing and Materials defines rubber as a material that is capable of recovering from large deformations quickly and forcibly.[9] Further, it is capable of being modified to a state in which it can swell but not dissolve in boiling solvents, such as benzene, methyl ethyl ketone, and ethanol-toluene azeotrope.

The definition is quite specific when it states "a rubber in its modified state, free of diluents, retracts within 1 minute to less than 1.5 times its original length after being stretched at room temperature (20° to 27°C.) to twice its length and held for 1 minute before release."

The same standardization organization defines a rubber *product* in somewhat different terms.

"Items of commerce in which the major portion of the filler bearing material is a rubber. Typical examples are rubber bands, rubber balls, rubber tires, etc. The rubber composition in the product as distinct from the fabric or metal to which it may be attached must possess the properties described under the definition of rubber."

In some cases, however, this definition must be modified, as rubbers are used in such ways that the properties described under the definition for rubber are not readily apparent. Examples include flooring and shoe soles where the amount of diluent is very high, in rubber adhesives, in unvulcanized rubber, or where the diluent is a gas as in cellular products. In such cases "the major polymeric constituent must be identified by other means, and if it is identified as one of the well recognized rubbers which without plasticizers or other diluents would pass the prescribed test, the article is a rubber product."

The *rubber polymer nomenclature, family designations* in Vol. IIB, Chapter 43, page 2148 has been extended by ASTM[10] to include polymers containing silicon (the "Si" family) and polymers having a saturated chain of the polymethylene type (the "M" family). These are as follows:

Si—Silicone elastomers having only methyl-containing groups on the polymer chain, such as dimethyl siloxane.

PSi—Silicone elastomers having both methyl- and phenyl-containing groups on the polymer chain.

VSi—Silicone elastomers having both methyl- and vinyl-containing groups on the polymer chain.

[3] Naunton, W. J. S., Ed., The Applied Science of Rubber, Arnold Publishers, London, 1961.
[4] Whitby, G. S., Ed., Synthetic Rubber, John Wiley and Sons, New York, 1954.
[5] Mitchell, J., Jr., and Lord, S. S., Jr., Rubber Chemistry and Technol., **34,** 1553, 1961.
[6] Burger, V. L., Rubber Chemistry and Technol., **32,** 1452, 1959.
[7] Meites, L. B., Ed., Handbook of Analytical Chemistry, McGraw-Hill Book Co., New York, 1963.
[8] Roth, F., and Stiehler, R. D., Rubber Chemistry and Technol., **34,** 788, 1961.
[9] ASTM Standards, 1964, Part 28, D 1566-62T.
[10] ASTM Standards, 1964, Part 28, D 1418-61T.

FSi—Silicone elastomers having both methyl- and fluorine-containing groups on the side chain.

PVSi—Silicone elastomers having methyl-, phenyl-, and vinyl-containing groups on the side chain.

IM—Polyisobutylene.

EPM—Ethylene-propylene copolymer.

CSM—Chloro-sulfonyl-polyethylene.

CFM—Polychloro-trifluoro-ethylene.

FPM—Vinylidine fluoride and hexafluoropropylene copolymer.

ACM—Ethyl or other acrylate and 2-chloroethyl vinyl ether copolymers.

ANM—Ethyl or other acrylate and acrylonitrile copolymers.

Sample Preparation.—The methods of preparation of the sample prior to analysis are varied. The approach is to render the sample tractable to the analytical technique to be employed and/or to reduce the number of possible interfering substances present in the original sample. Elastomers or rubber products usually are a mixture of a wide variety of substances. It is generally wise to extract the sample prior to undertaking any other step in the procedure. The extraction procedures most widely used have been described in Vol. IIB, Chapter 43. For some special analytical problems, variations of these methods have been employed, and these will be described when appropriate or necessary to the procedure.

Often it is necessary to dissolve the sample in a solvent prior to analysis. Solvents for unvulcanized rubbers are available but other restrictions on the solvent may make the solvent choice difficult. Such problems are the spectral transmission of the solvent for use in infrared or ultraviolet analysis or the chemical reactivity of the solvent in colorimetric analysis, etc. Table 59-1 lists a series of solvents used for the dissolution of various rubbers both vulcanized and unvulcanized and their suitability for particular analytical procedures.

TABLE 59-1. SOLVENTS COMMONLY USED FOR THE SOLUTION OF RUBBER

Polymer	Unvulcanized	Vulcanized	Use
All rubber	Ethylene dichloride	o-dichlorobenzene	Film casting or spreading for I.R.[a,b]
Natural rubber, SBR	—	p-cymene + xylene 5:1	Separation of solid filler, from polymer and film casting[c]
Natural rubber, Butyl rubber	Toluene	—	Film casting for I.R.[d]
NBR	Nitropropane	—	Film casting for I.R.[d]
Polybutadiene, SBR	CS₂	—	I.R. solution[e]
SBR	Toluene	—	UV. on solution[f]
SBR	Methylcyclohexane + EtOH	—	UV. on solution[f]
Natural rubber, SBR	—	ASTM Rubber Solvent	Separation of rubber from solid fillers[f]
Polyisoprene	CCl₄	—	I.R. analysis[g]

[a] Dinsmore, H. L., and Smith, D. C., Anal. Chem., **20**, 11, 1948.
[b] Hummel, D., Rubber Chemistry and Technol., **32**, 854, 1959.
[c] Barnes, R. B., Williams, V. Z., Davis, A. R., and Giesecke, P., Ind. Eng. Chem., Anal. Ed., **16**, 9, 1944.
[d] Harms, D. L., Anal. Chem., **25**, 1140, 1953.
[e] Hampton, R. R., Anal. Chem., **21**, 923, 1949.
[f] Volume II, Part B, Chapter 43.
[g] Corish, P. J., Rubber Chemistry and Technol., **33**, 975, 1960.

As might be expected, vulcanized polymers are the most difficult to prepare for investigation. Various methods have been proposed and used successfully for specific applications to vulcanized rubbers. These include: pyrolysis with collection of the products for identification; microtoming for film formation; swollen gel; pressing, either hot or cold; hydrolysis; and mulling.

Ashing may be used as a means for exhaustive removal of polymer and organic filler but obviously this procedure is suitable only for the analysis for certain elements and not specific compounds. The pyrolytic process may also be used as a means for the removal of organic material from fillers, before the collected fractions are subjected to instrumental analysis. Both of these latter processes have been discussed in Vol. IIB, Chapter 43.

POLYMER COMPOSITION

In this section methods are given for both qualitative and quantitative measurements on the materials of interest.

Some of the many methods or approaches to the problems of identification, structural analyses, and composition may also be found in the references in Table 59-2.

TABLE 59-2.

Subject	Method	References[a]
Identification	Infrared with gas chromatography	1, 2, 3, 4, 5, 6, 7, 8, 9, 10, 11, 12, 13, 14
Identification	Gas chromatography	
Identification	Paper chromatography	15
Identification	Pyrolysis	16
Identification	Pyrolysis with infrared	17
Structural composition	Infrared	18, 19, 20, 21, 22, 23, 24, 25, 26, 27, 28, 29, 30, 31
Structural composition	NMR	32, 33, 34
Structural composition	Elution chromatography	35
Quant. copolymer comp.	Ultraviolet	36, 37
Quant. copolymer comp.	Combustion	38
Quant. copolymer comp.	Pyrolysis	39
Quant. copolymer comp.	Gas chromatography	40
Internal structures	DTA	41, 42, 43

[a] Numbers refer to the following works:
1. Barnes, R. B., Gore, R. C., Stafford, R. W., and Williams, V. Z., Anal. Chem., **20**, 402, 1948.
2. Barnes, R. B., Williams, V. Z., Davis, A. R., and Giesecke, P., Ind. Eng. Chem., Anal. Ed., **16**, 9, 1944.
3. Cleverly, B., and Herrmann, R., J. Appl. Chem., **10**, 192, 1960.
4. Davison, W. H. T., Slaney, S., and Wragg, A. L., Chem. and Ind. (London), No. 44, 1356, 1954.
5. Dinsmore, H. L., and Smith, D. C., Anal. Chem., **20**, 11, 1948.
6. Feuerberg, H., Gross, D., and Zimmer, A., Kautschuk u. Gummi, **16**, WT 199, 1963.
7. Fiorenza, A., and Bonomi, G., Rubber Chemistry and Technol., **36**, 1129, 1963; Rassegna Chimica (Rome), **13**, 5, 1961.
8. Jones, C. E. Roland. and Moyles, A. F., Nature, **191**, 663, 1961.
9. Mitzer, B. M., J. Polymer Sci., **21**, 323, 1956; Rubber Chemistry and Technol., **30**, 352, 1957.
10. Sands, J. D., and Turner, G. S., Anal. Chem., **24**, 791, 1952.

TABLE 59-2 (cont.)

11. Feuerberg, H., Kautschuk u. Gummi, **14**, WT 33, 1961.
12. Feuerberg, H., and Weigel, H., Kautschuk u. Gummi, **15**, WT 276, 1962.
13. Voight, J., Kunstoffe, **51**, 18, 1961.
14. *Ibid.*, p. 314.
15. Feuerberg, H., Kretschmer, W., and Weigel, H., Kautschuk u. Gummi, **14**, WT 218, 1961.
16. Straus, S., and Madorsky, S., Rubber Chemistry and Technol., **30**, 93, 1957.
17. McGarvey, J. W., U. S. Department of Commerce, Office of Technical Services, PB Report 138, 408, 1958.
18. Binder, J. L., Rubber Chemistry and Technol., **35**, 57, 1962.
19. Binder, J. L., and Ranshaw, H. C., Anal. Chem., **29**, 503, 1957.
20. Corish, P. J., J. Appl. Polymer. Sci., **4**, 86, 1960.
21. Cunneen, J. I., Higgins, G. M. C., and Watson, W. F., J. Polymer Sci., **40**, 1, 1959.
22. Davison, W. H. T., and Bates, G. R., Rubber Chemistry and Technol., **30**, 771, 1957.
23. Hampton, R. R., Anal. Chem., **21**, 923, 1949.
24. Kimmer, W., and Schmalz, E. O., Rubber Chemistry and Technol., **33**, 639, 1960.
25. Parker, C. A., and Barnes, W. J., Polymer., **2**, 357, 1961.
26. Reding, F. P., and Lovell, C. M., J. Polymer. Sci., **21**, 157, 1956.
27. Richardson, W. S., and Sacher, A. J., J. Polymer. Sci., **10**, 353, 1953.
28. Schooten, J. van, Duck, E. W., and Berkenbosch, R., Polymer., **2**, 357, 1961.
29. Short, J. N., Thornton, V., and Kraus, G., Rubber Chemistry and Technol., **30**, 1118, 1957.
30. Silas, R. S., Yates, J., and Thornton, V., Anal. Chem., **31**, 529, 1959.
31. Wei, P. E., Anal. Chem., **33**, 215, 1961.
32. Chen, H. Y., Anal. Chem., **34**, 1793, 1962.
33. Golub, M. A., Fuqua, S. A., and Bhacca, N. S., Anal. Chem., **29**, 503, 1957; Rubber Chemistry and Technol., **36**, 315, 1963.
34. Slichter, W. P., Rubber Chemistry and Technol., **34**, 1574, 1961.
35. Hulme, J. M., and McLeod, L. A., Rubber Chemistry and Technol., **36**, 502, 1963.
36. Hilton, C. L., Newell, J. E., and Tolsma, J., Anal. Chem., **31**, 915, 1959.
37. Meehan, E. J., J. Polymer Sci., **1**, 175, 1946; Rubber Chemistry and Technol., **19**, 1077, 1946.
38. Wood, L. A., Madorsky, S., and Paulson, R. A., Rubber Chemistry and Technol., **33**, 1132, 1960.
39. Crippen, R. C., and Bonilla, C. F., Anal. Chem., **21**, 927, 1949.
40. Feuerberg, H., Kautschuk u. Gummi, **14**, WT 33, 1961.
41. Ke, B., J. Polymer. Sci., **42**, 15, 1960.
42. Ke, B., J. Polymer. Sci., **61**, 47, 1962.
43. Paciorek, K. L., Lajiness, W. G., and Lenk, C. T., J. Polymer Sci., **60**, 141, 1962.

GENERAL IDENTIFICATION

INFRARED OF LIQUID PYROLYZATES[11]

The method consists of a simple pyrolysis of the sample, collection of the liquid pyrolyzate, and obtaining the infrared absorption spectrum of the liquid product. Such a spectrum is usually specific for the type of rubber in the sample and serves as a qualitative identification when compared to reference spectra of products obtained in the same manner on known rubber samples.

Procedure.—The sample may vary from 2 g. to a few hundred mg., depending upon whether the sample material is estimated to contain a large amount of inert filler or is 100 percent polymer. Small fragments of the material to be tested are placed in a 15- by 120-mm. borosilicate glass test tube. The tube is held nearly horizontal and is heated at its closed end over the inner blue cone of the Bunsen burner flame to 375° to 750°C. The temperature of pyrolysis depends upon the type of sample (Table 59-3). Heat must

[11] Harms, D. L., Anal. Chem., **25**, 1140, 1953.

be applied as rapidly as possible to minimize charring. The vaporous pyrolyzate condenses as a liquid on the cooler portion of the tube and is transferred directly to

TABLE 59-3. TEMPERATURE OF PYROLYSIS FOR VARIOUS POLYMERS

Polymer	Temperature, °C.[a]	Residue
Saran tubing	375–400	Little
Filled rubber except silicone	425–450	Tarry mass
Polythene	440–460	None
Nylon 66 (molded)	450–460	Little
Kel-F	450–500	Little
Silicone rubber	475–500	Fillers, little tar
Formex enamel on copper wire	490–500	Tarry mass
Wood flour phenolic	500–550	Charred mass
Teflon	500–585	Some charring
Asbestos phenolic[b]	600–650	Charred mass
Silicone resin (high methyl)[b]	725–750	Silica, very little charring

[a] Temperatures are measured in pyrolyzing mass with Chromel-Alumel thermocouple and indicate range of a number of readings for each material represented.
[b] Tube walls at sample location were 850–900°C.

Reprinted from Analytical Chemistry, **25**, 1140, 1953. Copyright 1953 by the American Chemical Society and reprinted by permission of the copyright owner.

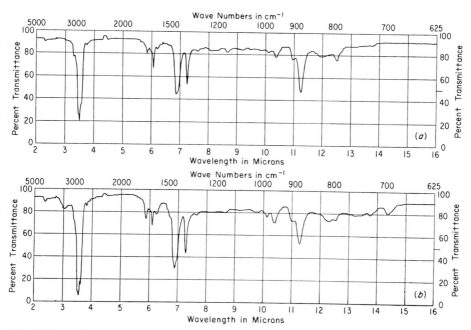

FIG. 59-1. a, Liquid Pyrolyzate of Natural Rubber Gum; b, Liquid Pyrolyzate of Vulcanized, Carbon Black-filled Natural Rubber. (Reprinted from Analytical Chemistry, 25, 1140, 1953. Copyright 1953 by the American Chemical Society and reprinted by permission of the copyright owner.)

sodium chloride window. A "sandwich" is then made by pressing a second sodium chloride window over a few drops of the pyrolyzate on the first window.

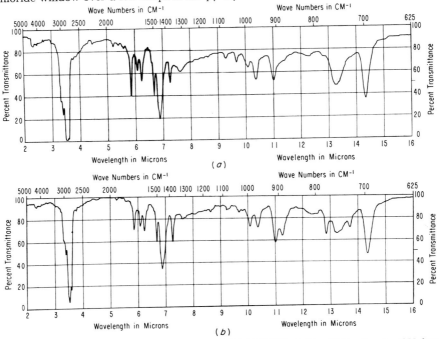

Fig. 59-2.   *a*, Liquid Pyrolyzate of SBR Gum (GR-S 65 SP); *b*, Liquid Pyrolyzate of Vulcanized, Carbon Black-filled SBR-Natural Rubber Mixture. (Reprinted from Analytical Chemistry **25**, 1140, 1953. Copyright 1953 by the American Chemical Society and reprinted by permission of the copyright owner.)

Spectra are obtained in the 2- to 16-μ region using a double-beam recording spectrophotometer.

INFRARED OF GASEOUS PYROLYZATES[12]

The method requires the pyrolysis of the sample in a special apparatus so that gaseous pyrolysis products can be collected directly in a cell suitable for infrared absorption measurements. Such measurements lead to characteristic spectra usually sufficient to identify the rubber.

Procedure.—The apparatus is designed so that gaseous products of pyrolysis as well as liquid or solid products may be collected. The optimum pressure in the gas cell (approximately 50 mm. of mercury for 10-cm. light path) is achieved after pyrolysis by proper manipulation of valves H_1, H_2, and H_3. Infrared spectra are obtained on the liquid phase by pressing a few drops between sodium chloride plates. These spectra in the region 2–16 μ resemble those shown by Harms in the work mentioned previously.[11]

[12] Hummel, D., Rubber Chemistry and Technol., **32**, 854, 1959.

The gas spectra are illustrated in Fig. 59-8, on p. 1674, and in Fig. 59-9, on p. 1676.

INFRARED OF POLYMER FILMS[12]

In this method films are formed from the vulcanized sample by breakdown with *o*-dichlorobenzene and evaporation of the solvent from a coating of the solution on a sodium chloride plate. The resultant film is suitable for measurement by the usual infrared absorption methods.

Procedure.—The vulcanized sample is extracted and dried by an ASTM method (see

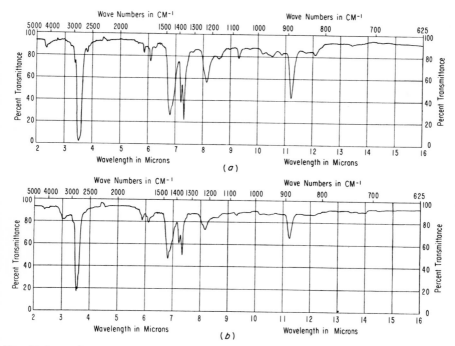

Fig. 59-3. *a*, Liquid Pyrolyzate of IIR Gum (Butyl Rubber); *b*, Liquid Pyrolyzate of Titanium Oxide-Filled, Cured IIR. (Reprinted from Analytical Chemistry **25**, 1140, 1953. Copyright 1953 by the American Chemical Society and reprinted by permission of the copyright owner.)

Chapter 43, Vol. IIB). Then it is milled to breakdown depending on the sample, allowed to swell in *o*-dichlorobenzene at room temperature. The mixture then is heated on a steam bath under nitrogen with stirring. Filter aid is added to the solution, the mixture is heated briefly and centrifuged. The solvent is vacuum distilled from the separated supernatant to leave a syrupy residue. A few drops of this residue are transferred to a sodium chloride disc, and the final solvent is removed in a vacuum oven. The spectrum is obtained on a double-beam infrared spectrometer in the region from 2–16 μ wavelength. Sample spectra are given in Figs. 59-10 and 59-11.

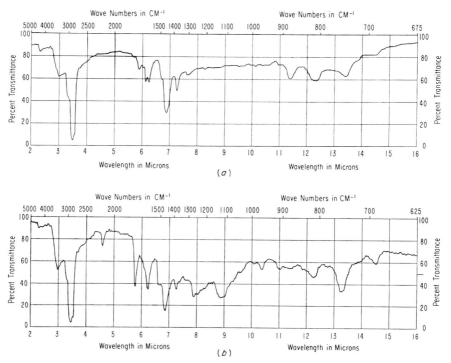

FIG. 59-4. *a*, Liquid Pyrolyzate of Vulcanized CR (Neoprene); *b*, Liquid Pyrolyzate of Vulcanized NBR (Buna N). (Reprinted from Analytical Chemistry, **25**, 1140, 1953. Copyright 1953 by the American Chemical Society and reprinted by permission of the copyright owner.)

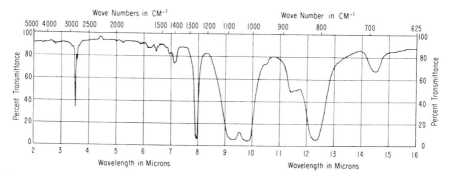

FIG. 59-5. Infrared Spectrum of the Liquid Pyrolyzate of Silica-filled SiR (Silicon Rubber). (Reprinted from Analytical Chemistry **25**, 1140, 1953. Copyright 1953 by the American Chemical Society and reprinted by permission of the copyright owner.)

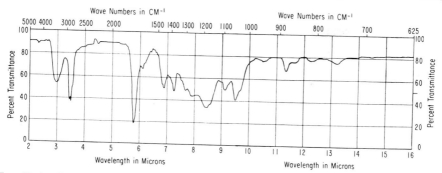

FIG. 59-6. Infrared Spectrum of the Liquid Pyrolyzate of Titanium Oxide-filled, Cured ACM Rubber (Hycar PA.) (Reprinted from Analytical Chemistry, 25, 1140, 1953. Copyright 1953 by the American Chemical Society and reprinted by permission of the copyright owner.)

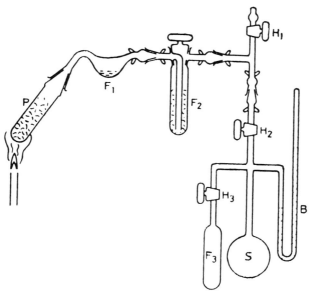

FIG. 59-7. Pyrolysis Apparatus: P, Quartz Tube; F_1, First Trap, Liquid Products; F_2, Aerosol Trap; S, Spectroscopic Gas Cell; F_3, Gas Trap, Cooled With Nitrogen; B, Manometer. (Courtesy Kautschuk und Gummi.)

MASS SPECTROMETRY OF PYROLYSIS PRODUCTS[13]

A special sample holder and adapter is used in this method to allow the volatile pyrolysis products from the sample to be directly introduced into the mass spectrometer inlet system. An empirical method of comparing peak ratios allows the identification of the polymer being investigated.

[13] Phillips, J. K., Appl. Spectroscopy, 17, 9, 1963; Rubber Chemistry, 36, 794, 1963.

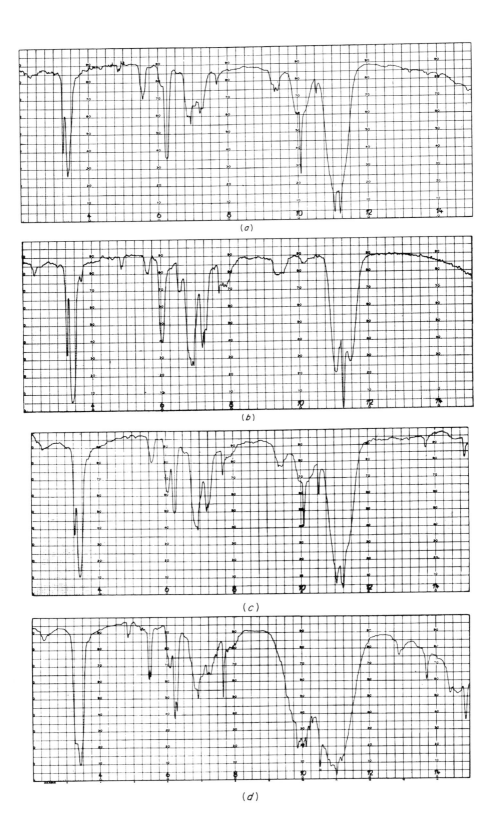

(a)

(b)

(c)

(d)

Procedure.—A small sample of the material to be pyrolyzed (2 to 5 mg.) is inserted into the end of a capillary melting point tube and suspended by means of a metal clip in the center of the outer glass tube, which is then attached to an adapter with stopcock. After evacuating to approximately 10^{-6} mm. mercury on the mass spectrometer inlet system, the sampling tube is precisely mounted in the arc-imaging furnace[14] making sure that the small sample in the capillary tube is centered in the heating area. The carbon arc is then started and allowed to come to equilibrium. The furnace shutter is then opened exposing the sample to the high intensity radiant energy for 2 seconds. A timer is used to turn off the carbon arc automatically after the 2-second exposure period. After the pyrolysis the sampling tube is remounted on the mass spectrometer for analysis of the gaseous pyrolyzates.

The 0.0625-in. o.d. capillary melting point tube is open at both ends to permit free flow of the gaseous pyrolyzates away from the heated zone during the pyrolysis. The tube holder, Fig. 59-12, is a metal clip made from 10-mil stainless steel sheet, bent to fit the inside of the glass tube and also to clamp the melting point tube, holding it in the center of the outer glass tube.

The empirical ratio, R1, used to identify most elastomers is obtained by dividing the sum of the peak heights of mass numbers 53 and 54 by the sum of the peak heights of the mass numbers 68 and 104. This ratio emphasizes the peak heights at the mass number corresponding to the molecular weight of the respective monomers. Butadiene is 54, isoprene 68, and styrene 104. Mass 53 is a high peak in the isoprene pattern resulting from the splitting off of the methyl group from the isoprene molecule.

Empirical ratios, R1, for several common rubber types are shown in Table 59-4.

TABLE 59-4. EMPIRICAL IDENTIFICATION RATIOS
FOR COMMON RUBBER POLYMERS

Rubber type	R1[a]
Natural	1.44
SBR (styrene/butadiene)	20.68
PBD (polybutadiene)	38.61
NBR (acrylonitrile/butadiene)	18.20

[a] R1 = sum of the peak heights of mass numbers 53 and 54 divided by sum of the peak heights of mass numbers 68 and 104.
Table reprinted courtesy of Applied Spectroscopy.

These values were obtained from the gaseous pyrolyzates of compounded and cured rubber samples. Supplemental observations are also made to verify the identifications indicated by the R1 values. Natural rubber, for example, is present if the ratio of mass number 53 to mass number 54 is 1 or greater, and is accompanied by a high peak at mass 68. The presence of SBR (styrene/butadiene rubber) is indicated if there is a peak at mass 104, the molecular weight of styrene monomer.

[14] The arc-imaging furnace used was manufactured by Strong Electric Co., Toledo, Ohio, and designed by Arthur D. Little Co., Cambridge, Mass.

FIG. 59-8. Infrared Spectra of Gaseous Products: *a*, Gas Pyrolyzate (Isoprene), Natural Rubber, Vulcanized; *b*, Gas Pyrolyzate (Isobutylene) IIR (Butyl) Rubber, Vulcanized; *c*, Gas Pyrolyzate 2 Parts Natural and 1 Part IRR, Vulcanized; *d*, Gas Pyrolyzate, SBR (Buna S-3), Vulcanized. (Courtesy Kautschuk und Gummi.)

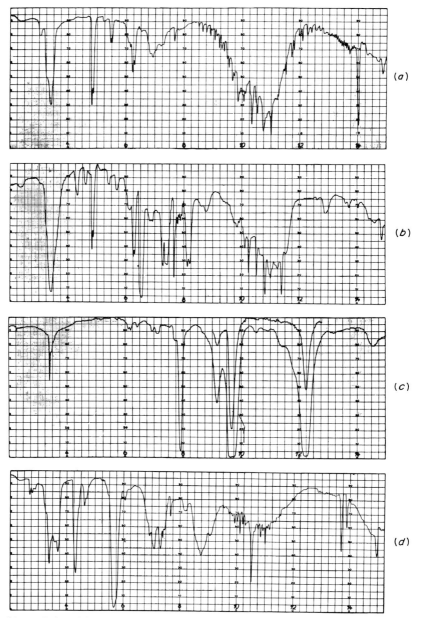

FIG. 59-9.   Infrared Spectra of Gaseous Products: *a*, Gas Pyrolyzate, NBR (Perbunam 2810),
Vulcanized; *b*, Gas Pyrolyzate, CR (Neoprene), Vulcanized; *c*, Gas Pyrolyzate, SiR (Silicon
R-20), Cured; *d*, Gas Pyrolyzate, Urethane Rubber (Vukollen), Cured. (Courtesy Kautschuk
und Gummi.)

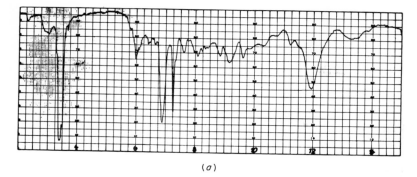

(a)

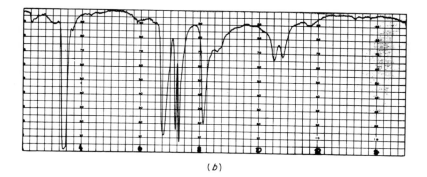

(b)

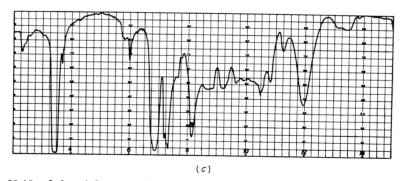

(c)

FIG. 59-10. Infrared Spectra of Partly Degraded Vulcanizates: a, Natural Rubber Vulcanizate Dissolved in o-Dichlorobenzene; b, IIR (Butyl Rubber) Vulcanizate Dissolved in o-Dichlorobenzene, c, Natural Rubber Plus IIR (2:1) Vulcanizate. Residues From Decomposition in o-Dichlorobenzene. (Courtesy Kautschuk und Gummi.)

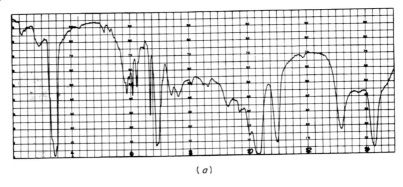

(a)

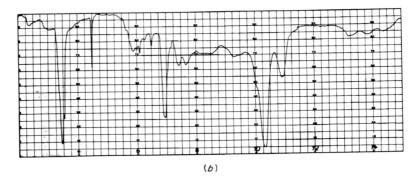

(b)

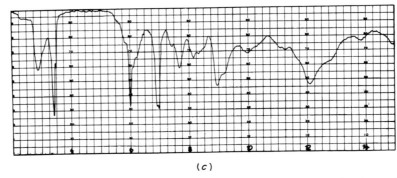

(c)

FIG. 59-11. Infrared Spectra of Partly Degraded Vulcanizates; a, Vulcanizate of SBR (Buna S) Dissolved in o-Dichlorobenzene; b, Vulcanizate of NBR (Perbunam 2810). Residue From Decomposition with o-Dichlorobenzene; c, Vulcanizate of CR (Neoprene) Dissolved in o-Dichlorobenzene. (Courtesy Kautschuk und Gummi.)

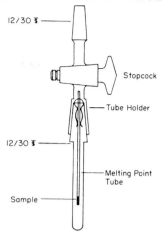

FIG. 59-12. Special Sampling Tube Used for Rubber Pyrolysis. (Courtesy Applied Spectroscopy.)

STRUCTURAL CHARACTERISTICS

POLYURETHANE RUBBERS

INFRARED ON FILMS[15]

This method describes a procedure for forming thin films from polyurethane products by stretching swollen microtomed sections of the sample. Correlations are given for certain structural characteristics with infrared absorption spectra obtained on such films.

Procedure.—Microtome sections, 15×5 mm. in area and 10 to 20 μ thick, from cast or molded samples of polymers. Gum is used to fix the samples to the microtome stage and this is followed by mild freezing. Petroleum ether (or naphtha) may be used as lubricant. The sections are then stretched to three or four times their original length by transparent adhesive tape, fixed to each end. These stretched sections are stuck down on to sample cells and the rest of the cell around the section is masked out with aluminum foil. Typical correlations are given in Table 59-5.

INFRARED OF HYDROLYSIS PRODUCTS[15]

The method gives information as to the compositional structure of polyurethanes by employing hydrolysis, separation of components, and identification of the products by infrared absorption spectroscopy.

Procedure.—One gram of polyurethane is cut in small pieces and loaded into a stainless steel tube. A solution of about 2.5 g. of sodium hydroxide in 15 ml. of water is added and left overnight to swell the sample. The tube is sealed, then heated approximately 24 hours at about 155°C. in an oil bath. The contents are extracted with four 25-ml. portions of ether, which on evaporation gives the diamine, I, derived from the original diisocyanate. The aqueous layer is filtered to remove insoluble disubstituted ureas, II, and the filtrate is distilled to substantial dryness. The distillate is dried in a

[15] Corish, P. J., Anal. Chem., **31**, 1298, 1959.

vacuum desiccator (over phosphorus pentoxide) using water pump vacuum to remove the water from the glycol, III. This procedure must be carefully controlled, because water and glycol codistill; if too high a vacuum or too long a distillation time is used, the glycol may be lost.

NOTE.—The procedure is not suitable for polyurethanes made using hexamethylene diisocyanate. These polymers may be identified by absence of the 1600 cm.$^{-1}$ bond in spectra obtained on microtomed section.

The water-glycol mixture is poured into a Petri dish (large surface area) which is placed beside another Petri dish containing phosphorus pentoxide. Both are placed in a vacuum

TABLE 59-5. INFRARED ABSORPTION BANDS

Structure		Wavelength of Absorption, cm.$^{-1}$
Urethane	*ca.*	3300
		1695
		1540
	ca.	1300
	ca.	1230
Crystallinity bands		700–750
Heat film to 50°C.		bands at 750 and 735 decrease or disappear
Diisocyanates:		
1,5-naphthalene		780–783
p-phenylene		825 doublet
Polyethylene glycol	*ca.*	1120
		945
	ca.	840
Polytetrahydrofuran		1120
		1390
		none at 945 and *ca.* 840
All polyurethanes prepared from polyethers		1230

desiccator and a water pump vacuum applied. The Petri dish is left until only a smear remains at the bottom.

The residue from the previous distillation containing the sodium salts is dissolved in a small amount of water, just acidified with concentrated hydrochloric acid (carbon dioxide evolved) and evaporated to dryness. This gives the dicarboxylic acid, IV, and sodium chloride (which is transparent to infrared).

A modification of the hydrolysis procedure described may be used for further analysis of polyether-urethane polymers.

After hydrolysis for shorter times than needed for polyester-urethane polymers (about 8 hours is sufficient), ether extraction yields the diamine corresponding to the diisocyanate used to form the polymer. On removal of water by distillation, the residue is the polyether: poly(ethylene glycol), poly(propylene glycol), or polytetrahydrofuran.

Method of Separation.—Heat 1 g. of polyurethane with a solution of caustic soda in a sealed tube (stainless steel). Extract with ether.

Ether Layer

Evaporate to dryness

Diamine from diisocyanate, I,
  NH_2—R—NH_2

Residue

N,N'-disubstituted urea, II,
  R'''—NH—CO—NH—R'''

Distillate

Dry over P_2O_5

Glycol from ester wax, III,
  HO—R'—OH

Aqueous Layer

Filter

Filtrate

Distill off aqueous portion

Residue

Dissolve in water, acidify with conc.
  HCl and evaporate to dryness

Residue

Acid from ester wax, IV,
  HOOC—R''—COOH (+ NaCl)

The diamines and dicarboxylic acids are examined spectroscopically as mulls in Nujol or potassium bromide discs. These spectra are compared to reference spectra of known compounds for identification.

SILICONE RUBBERS

INFRARED OF SOLUTIONS[16]

Some polymers are soluble in carbon disulfide and carbon tetrachloride, and solution in these materials is a convenient method for obtaining the spectra for such polymers. However, high viscosity dimethylpolysiloxanes have limited solubility in carbon disulfide, and it may be necessary, if a solution spectrum is desired, to use carbon tetrachloride throughout the entire spectral region or to use some solvent such as 2,2,4-trimethylpentane in the 11- to 16-micron region. Frequently, sufficiently good spectra may be obtained by simply casting a film of the polymer on a polished salt plate from a low-boiling solvent such as chloroform. Hard, brittle materials, such as cured resins, can be run by the mineral oil mull or potassium bromide pressed plate techniques. In cases where a filler or a reinforcing agent is present, the pyrolysis technique of Harms[17] is very useful.

Interpretation of Spectra.—The infrared spectra of silicones are notable for two things: the characteristic vibrations of substituents vary only slightly in wavelength, regardless of the compound in which they are found; and the intensity of the absorption bands lying beyond 7 μ is 5 to 10 times greater than is normal with most organic compounds. These characteristics make silicones relatively easy to identify by their infrared spectra.

Silicone polymers are distinguished by a strong absorption in the 9- to 10-μ region arising from an Si—O stretching vibration in the siloxane backbone of the polymer. Linear and cyclic polymers containing 8 or fewer units can be characterized by the shape and position of the siloxane band.

In commercial polymers the silicon atoms are usually substituted by some combination of methyl, ethyl, phenyl, hydrogen, alkoxy, or hydroxyl groups. Figure 59-13 shows the spectrum of a dimethyl-substituted polysiloxane. This material is occasionally encountered in qualitative organic analysis, when inadvertent extraction of silicone stopcock grease by an organic phase has occurred. The infrared spectrum of a methylsiloxane $(MeHSiO)_x$ polymer is also shown in Fig. 59-13. The strong bands at 4.6 and 11.2 μ indicate the presence of Si—H, and the Si—Me group has a characteristic band

[16] Smith, A. L., and McHard, J. A., Anal. Chem., **31**, 1174, 1959.
[17] Harms, D. L., Anal. Chem., **25**, 1140, 1953.

at 7.95 μ. Figure 59-13 also shows the spectrum of a phenyl methyl-substituted siloxane polymer, and a copolymer of phenyl methyl and dimethyl-substituted polysiloxane.

An all-methyl silicone resin with a high (MeSiO$_{3/2}$) content is shown in Fig. 59-14. The SiO$_{3/2}$ unit can be recognized by a strong band at about 9 μ. Figure 59-14 also shows an ethyl-substituted resin, which is essentially a silsesquioxane. The Et—Si group

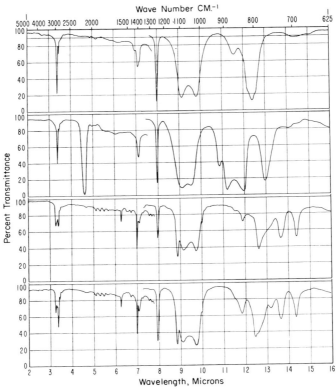

Fig. 59-13.   Spectra of Polysiloxanes. All spectra are measured on solutions of 100 mg. per cc. CCl$_4$ (2–7.5 μ); 20 mg. per cc. CS$_2$ (7.5–16 μ). 1, Poly (dimethylsiloxane), trimethyl end blocked. 2, Poly(methylhydrogen siloxane), trimethyl end blocked. 3, Poly(methyl phenyl siloxane), trimethyl end blocked. 4, Copolymerized methyl phenyl siloxane and dimethyl siloxane, trimethyl end blocked. (Reprinted from Analytical Chemistry, **31**, 1174, 1959. Copyright 1959 by the American Chemical Society and reprinted by permission of the copyright owner.)

is characterized by absorption at 8.0, 9.9, and 10.3 μ. The spectrum of a typical phenyl and methyl-containing silicone resin with mono- and disubstituted silicon and that of a silicone-modified alkyd resin composed of 25 percent silicone, 25 percent fatty acid, and 50 percent glycerol phthalate are also shown in Fig. 59-14. Silicones used to modify organic resins usually contain either the dimethylsiloxane (Me$_2$SiO) group which absorbs at 7.9 and 12.5 μ, or the phenylsilicon group, which shows a needlesharp band at 7.0 μ, or both. A broad absorption in the 9- to 10-μ region indicates the presence of siloxane. Table 59-6 gives a brief compilation of characteristic frequencies of substituted silicones.

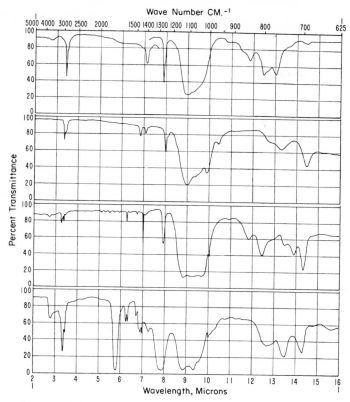

Fig. 59.14. Spectra of Resins. 1, All methyl resin containing $MeSiO_{3/2}$, $MeSiO$, and $MeSiO_{1/2}$, 100 mg. per cc. in CCl_4 (2 to 7.5 μ), 20 mg. per cc. in CS_2 (7.5 to 16 μ). 2, $(EtSiO_{3/2})_x$ type resin, film. 3, Pure silicone resin containing $MeSiO$, $MeSiO_{3/2}$, (phenyl)$_2$ SiO, and phenyl $SiO_{3/2}$, film. 4, Silicone-modified alkyd resin, film. (Reprinted from Analytical Chemistry **31**, 1174, 1959. Copyright 1959 by the American Chemical Society and reprinted by permission of the copyright owner.)

TABLE 59-6.   ABSORPTION DATA*

Group	Absorption, Wavelengths, μ
Si—H	4.4–4.8; 10.5–12.5
Si—CH$_3$	7.8–8.0; 11.6–13.1
Si—CH$_2$CH$_3$	8.0–8.1; 9.8–10.0; 10.3–10.6
Si—C$_6$H$_5$	7.0; 8.9; 13.7; 14.3–14.5
Si—O—CH$_3$	3.5; 8.4
Si—O—CH$_2$—R	8.4–8.9; 9.1–9.3; 10.1–10.6
Si—O—Aryl	10.3–10.9
Si—OH	2.7–3.1; 10.5–12.0
Si—O—Si	8.9–9.9
Si—CH=CH$_2$	6.2–6.3; 9.9–10.0; 10.2–10.6

* Reprinted from Analytical Chemistry, **31**, 1174, 1959. Copyright 1959 by the American Chemical Society and reprinted by permission of the copyright owner.

BUTADIENE-ISOPRENE COPOLYMERS
NUCLEAR MAGNETIC RESONANCE[18]

This method employs nuclear magnetic resonance measurements on solutions of butadiene-styrene copolymers, and permits the calculation of the concentration of various structures in the polymer.

Procedure.—The conditions for measurement are as follows: spectra are obtained at 60 megacycles per second using a Varian V-4302 DP-60 NMR spectrometer equipped with a 12-inch electromagnet and magnetic-flux stabilizer or an equivalent apparatus. The temperature of the probe is held at $25° \pm 1°C$. or better. The polymer solutions are to be made in reagent grade carbon tetrachloride in a 5 percent by weight of sample concentration. Standard 5-mm. tubes are used with tetramethylsilane as the internal standard. Peak shifts are measured using the usual side band technique.

Method for calculating the concentration of the following structures in the copolymer.

$$
\begin{array}{c}
CH_3 \\
| \\
-CH_2-C-CH{=}CH_2 \\
|
\end{array} \qquad (A)
$$

$$
\begin{array}{c}
CH_3 \\
| \\
CH_2{=}C-CH-CH_2- \\
|
\end{array} \qquad (B)
$$

$$
\begin{array}{c}
CH_3 \\
| \\
-CH_2-C{=}CH-CH_2-
\end{array} \qquad (cis \text{ and } trans) \qquad (C)
$$

$$
\begin{array}{c}
| \\
-CH_2-CH-CH{=}CH_2
\end{array} \qquad (D)
$$

$$
-CH_2-CH{=}CH-CH_2- \qquad (cis \text{ and } trans) \qquad (E)
$$

The area under an absorption peak is directly proportional to the concentrations of protons contributing to it, provided $\gamma^2 H_1{}^2 T_1 T_2 \ll 1$, where γ is the gyromagnetic ratio of the proton, H_1 is the rf field strength, and T_1 and T_2 are the spin lattice and spin-spin relaxation constants. Assuming a negligible amount of secondary polymerization through the double bonds in the polymer, the relative concentration of units (A) to (E) can be calculated using the following simultaneous equations. Individual peak areas are expressed as percentages of the total area of all peaks.

$$
\begin{aligned}
3[a] + 2[b] + [c] + 3[d] + 2[e] &= \text{area percent of peaks } 1 + 2 + 3 & (1) \\
[b] + 4[c] + [d] + 4[e] &= \text{area percent of peak } 4 & (2) \\
3[b] + 3[c] &= \text{area percent of peak } 5 & (3) \\
[a] + [d] + 2[e] &= \text{area percent of peak } 1 & (4) \\
2[b] &= \text{area percent of peak } 3 & (5) \\
2[a] &= \text{area percent of peak } 7 & (6)
\end{aligned}
$$

[18] Chen, H. Y., Anal. Chem., **34**, 1134, 1962.

where [a] to [e] are the relative concentrations in mole percent corresponding to the structure forms (A) through (E).

Equations (2) to (6) are used to obtain the concentration of the 5 components ((A) through (E)). These values are substituted in Eq. (1). If the values do not fit, the areas on the right side of Eqs. (2)–(6) are readjusted, keeping the total the same. New values are calculated for [a] to [e] and checked with Eq. (1). Such iteration is continued until the values calculated for [a] to [e] are consistent with all 6 equations.[19] (Table 59-7.)

TABLE 59-7. PEAK ASSIGNMENTS FOR 1 TO 1 BUTADIENE-ISOPRENE COPOLYMER

Peak No.	Measured Peak Shift, p.p.m. from Tetramethylsilane	Type of Proton	Reference Compound	Av. Chem. Shift of Ref. Compound, p.p.m. from Tetramethylsilane
1	5.30	$-CH=CH_2$	1,5-Hexadiene 1-Octene 1-Hexene 1-Pentene	5.56
2	5.03	$-CH=CH-$ $-CH=CH_2$	cis- and trans-polybutadiene 1,5-Hexadiene 1-Octene 1-Hexene 1-Pentene	5.31 4.86
		$-CH=C-$ with CH_3	Natural rubber	5.05
3	4.65	$CH_2=C-$ with CH_3	2-Ethyl-1-butene 2,4,4-Trimethyl-1-pentene	4.63
4	1.98	$CH-C=C$	cis- and trans-polybutadiene	1.98
5	1.58	$CH_3-C=C$	Natural rubber	1.68
6	1.26	$CH-C-C$	. . .	. . .
7	0.92	CH_3-C-C	. . .	. . .

Reprinted from Analytical Chemistry, **34,** 1134, 1962. Copyright 1962 by the American Chemical Society and reprinted by permission of the copyright owner.

[19] The proper operation of the spectrometer for quantitative measurements is discussed in detail in the following references:
Reilly, C. A., Anal. Chem., **32,** 211R, 1960;
Varian Associates, Instrument Div., Instruction Manual, V-3521 NMR Integrator, Publ. 87-100-029;
Varian Associates, NMR and EPR Spectroscopy, Chapter 8, Pergamon Press, New York, 1960;
Williams, R. B., Ann. N. Y., Acad. Sci., **70,** 890, 1958.

QUANTITATIVE COPOLYMER COMPOSITION

ETHYLENE-PROPYLENE COPOLYMERS

INFRARED OF FILMS[20]

This is a quantitative infrared method for determining the propylene content of ethylene-propylene copolymers by measuring the number of methyl branches on the polymer chain.

Procedure.—The sample is dissolved in a hydrocarbon solvent and filtered to remove catalyst. The solvent is removed by evaporation, and the polymer is washed with acetone and vacuum dried at 60°C. for 24 hours. The specimens are prepared by pressing the sample to films 0.25 to 0.30 mm. thick. Spectra are recorded between 7 and 15 μ wavelength on an infrared spectrometer with an ordinate expander. Methyl branching is calculated from the equation:

$$CH_3 \text{ groups/1000 carbons} = 80A/1$$

where: A is the absorbance at 8.7 μ corrected for background by a base line drawn between 8.4 and 9.1 μ; and

1 is the film thickness in mm.

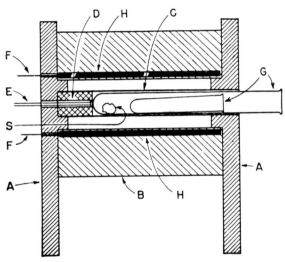

FIG. 59-15. Pyrolysis Furnace. A, Transite sheet. B, Furnace from combustion train. C, Stainless steel tube, thin-wall, approximately 18 mm., i.d. D, Steel plug with hole for thermocouple. E, Thermocouple. F, Heater leads. G, test tubes: large 16 × 150 mm; small, 10 × 75 mm. H, Heater coils. S, Sample. (Reprinted from Analytical Chemistry, **35**, 2172, 1963. Copyright 1963 by the American Chemical Society and reprinted by permission of the copyright owner.)

INFRARED ON LIQUID PYROLYZATES[21]

This is an empirical quantitative infrared method for determining the propylene content of ethylene-propylene copolymers. The method is suitable for vulcanized or

[20] Smith, W. E., Stoffer, R. L., and Hannan, R. B., J. Polymer. Sci., **61**, 39, 1962.
[21] Brown, J. E., Tryon, M., and Mandel, J., Anal. Chem., **35**, 2172, 1963.

unvulcanized polymers since the measurements are made on the liquid pyrolysis products obtained from the sample in a specified manner.

Procedure.—A sample weighing about 0.25 g. is placed in the pyrolysis vessel, as shown in Fig. 59-15. The mouth of a smaller test tube (10 × 75 mm.) is adjusted to within about 5 cm. of the mouth of the larger test tube (16 × 150 mm.) to aid in directing the distillate along the hot wall of the larger tube and thereby assure maximum contact of the initial pyrolyzate with the hot pyrolysis tube. The assembly is placed in the furnace previously heated to about 450°C. The pyrolyzate condensing at the open end of the test tube is allowed to run into a third test tube. When the pyrolysis is complete (about 3 to 5 minutes), a portion of the pyrolyzate is placed between two sodium chloride windows having a 0.025-mm. lead spacer to control cell thickness. The cell is then placed in the infrared beam and scanned through the frequency of 950 cm.$^{-1}$ to 850 cm.$^{-1}$ (10.5 to 11.8 μ wavelength). The instrument controls are set for normal operation with NaCl optics. The absorbances corrected for background are measured. The ratio, R, of the absorbance near 909 cm.$^{-1}$ to that near 889 cm.$^{-1}$ is calculated, *i.e.*, $R = A_{909}$ cm.$^{-1}/A_{889}$ cm.$^{-1}$. Typical calibration curves are shown in Figs. 59-16 and 59-17.

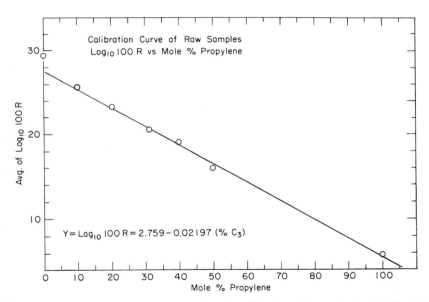

Fig. 59-16. Calibration Curve for Raw Samples. (Reprinted from Analytical Chemistry, **35**, 2172, 1963. Copyright 1963 by the American Chemical Society and reprinted by permission of the copyright owner.)

RADIO-LABELING METHOD[22]

This is a method for determining the ethylene or propylene content of specially prepared ethylene-propylene copolymers. The method uses a radioactively labeled monomer in the polymerization, and describes the important details of the procedure used for determining the content of the labeled monomer in the final copolymer.

Apparatus.—A Model 314 Tricarb liquid-scintillation spectrometer is suitable for all

[22] Stoffer, R. L., and Smith, R. L., Anal. Chem., **33**, 1112, 1961.

counting. Five-dram glass vials are convenient for sample preparation and counting.

Procedure.—A 0.5-g. sample of dried polymer is weighed directly into a 5-dram counting vial. Then 15 ml. of a liquid scintillator, which consists of Research-grade *o*-xylene containing 7.5 g. per liter of Scintillation-grade diphenyloxazole, is added. The vial is heated to between 115° and 125°C. for 15 minutes to dissolve the sample; it is

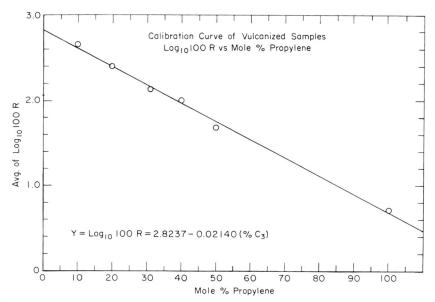

Fig. 59-17. Calibration Curve for Vulcanized Samples. (Reprinted from Analytical Chemistry, **35**, 2172, 1963. Copyright 1963 by the American Chemical Society and reprinted by permission of the copyright owner.)

then cooled to room temperature, capped, wiped clean, shaken well, held at the temperature of the counting chamber for at least 30 minutes, and shaken again just before counting.

The samples are counted with the lower and upper discriminators of the two-channel pulse-height analyzer and the high voltage applied to the multiplier phototubes set to minimize statistical counting errors.

This counting method can also be applied to 0.1-g. polymer samples. In this case, a suspension of polymer in the liquid scintillator is obtained as the counting sample, instead of a gel.

Sample activities are converted into percent labeled monomer by the formula:

$$\% \text{ labeled monomer} = \frac{A \times 100}{CF \times W}$$

where: A is the sample activity in c.p.m.;

CF is a conversion factor (specific activity of labeled monomer in c.p.m. per mg.); and

W is the sample weight in mg.

MASS SPECTROMETRY OF PYROLYZATES[23]

This is an empirical mass spectrometric method for determining the propylene content of ethylene-propylene copolymers. The method is suitable for both vulcanized and unvulcanized materials provided the appropriate calibration is made.

Apparatus.—The pyrolysis is performed in the combustion assembly shown in Fig. 59-18. This assembly consists of a steel block 100 × 100 mm. in diameter, a thermocouple fitted in a central hole, and three holes (depth 60 mm., diameter 12 mm.) for three pyrolysis vessels. The heating block is surrounded by an asbestos-insulated metallic shield. The pyrolysis vessels are borosilicate glass combustion tubes closed at the end by a rubber tubing with a clamp.

Procedure.—A 0.01-g. weighed sample is placed in a pyrolysis vessel, and the vessel is evacuated. Two other vessels are prepared in the same way. The steel block is then heated by a Bunsen burner flame to 530°C. At this temperature the flame is put out, and when the block attains the thermocouple temperature of 520°C., the three pyrolysis tubes are quickly inserted in the holes.

After 5 minutes (the temperature falls to 470°C.) they are removed from the block and are cooled to room temperature. After 30 minutes the volatile products are analyzed by directly connecting the pyrolysis vessels with the sample system of the mass spectrometer. The spectra are obtained on a Consolidated 21 103 B

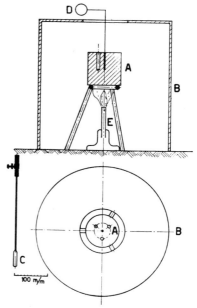

FIG. 59-18. Pyrolysis Apparatus. A, Steel block. B, Asbestos-insulated metallic shield. C, Pyrolysis vessel. D, Thermocouple. E, Bunsen burner. (Reprinted from Analytical Chemistry, **31**, 2022, 1959. Copyright 1959 by the American Chemical Society and reprinted by permission of the copyright owner.)

mass spectrometer or equivalent under the following conditions: an ionizing voltage of 70 volts, an ionizing current of 30 μa., and an ion source temperature of 250°C.

Computation.—Schematic spectra of pyrolyzates from two ethylene-propylene copolymers with different propylene content are shown in Fig. 59-19. The following peak ratio is used for the propylene content computation:

$$R = \frac{A}{B + C - D - E}$$

where: A = peak height at mass 26;
B = peak height at mass 16;
C = peak height at mass 42;
D = peak height at mass 70; and
E = peak height at mass 84.

[23] Bua, E., and Manaresi, P., Anal. Chem., **31**, 2022, 1959.

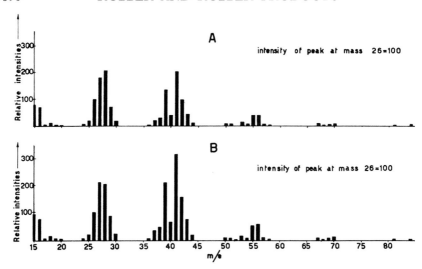

Fig. 59-19.   Schematic Mass Spectra of Pyrolysis Products of Ethylene-Propylene Copolymers. A, Propylene content 32 mole percent. B, Propylene content 68 mole percent. (Reprinted from Analytical Chemistry, **31,** 2022, 1959. Copyright 1959 by the American Chemical
Society and reprinted by permission of the copyright owner.)

Such a ratio was found practically independent of small changes of pyrolysis conditions
and of mass spectrometer peak sensitivities.

INTERNAL STRUCTURES

Cis-1,4 CONTENT OF POLYISOPRENE

NEAR INFRARED ON SOLUTIONS[24]

In this method the near infrared spectral region is employed to measure the absorbance
of the *cis*-1,4-configuration of the isoprene unit in polyisoprene.

An empirical calibration curve relates this measured absorbance with the *cis* content.

Procedure.—A solution of 0.5 g. polymer in carbon tetrachloride is prepared by
allowing the sample to stand overnight in contact with sufficient solvent to cover the
rubber. The sample is shaken in a mechanical shaker until dissolved (about 4 hours).
The solution is made up to 50 ml. with carbon tetrachloride and mixed well. The peak
absorption is measured at 2.46 μ and at 2.315 μ on an infrared
spectrometer, such as a Beckman Model DK-2. Normal settings on this model instrument
are: scanning time of 50; 2 × scale expansion, 0.2 second time constant; sensitivity
100. The ratio of the peak absorbances at the above two wavelengths corrected by typical
base line method are compared to an empirical calibration curve made by similar
measurements on mixtures of natural rubber and gutta percha. This same approach
can be used for films with the proper calibration curve. A typical calibration curve for
solutions is shown in Fig. 59-20.

NOTE.—Benzene interferes and care should be taken to assure its removal from the sample
if this solvent has been used in film formation.

[24] Corish, P. J., Rubber Chemistry and Technol., **33,** 975, 1960.

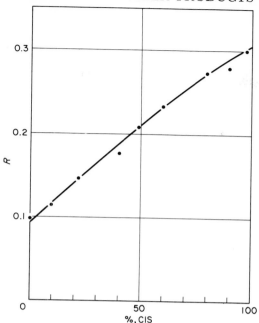

Fig. 59-20. Calibration Curve Obtained on Synthetic Mixtures of Natural Rubber and Gutta Percha. $R = \dfrac{A_{2.46\mu}}{A_{2.315\mu}}$. (Courtesy Spectrochimica Acta.)

QUANTITATIVE COMPOSITION OF POLYMER MIXTURES

TOTAL RUBBER HYDROCARBON

PYROLYSIS METHOD[25]

This is a noninstrumental method for determining the total rubber hydrocarbon in a rubber sample. It is, however, a useful British standard method not covered in Chapter 43 of Volume IIB, and so it is included here. The method is based on a procedure in which the weight loss after controlled pyrolysis of the sample is related to the rubber hydrocarbon content.

Apparatus.—A diagram of the apparatus is shown in Fig. 59-21. It consists of a scavenging train to purify the nitrogen before it passes into the pyrolysis tube, F, in an electric furnace maintained at $550 \pm 25°C$. Drechsel bottles, A and B, contain alkaline pyrogallol and sulphuric acid (sp. gr. 1.84) respectively. Liquid, G, and vapor, H, traps are fitted on the efflux end of the tube. The vapor trap contains xylene.

A glass rod, D, provided with a hook, slides in a T-piece, C, a seal being effected by a rubber sleeve.

Reagents.—All reagents used shall be of analytical reagent quality; demineralized water shall be used whenever water is specified.

Alkaline Pyrogallol.—Dissolve 30 g. of pyrogallol in 100 ml. of 50 percent potassium hydroxide. Prepare fresh for each determination.

[25] British Standard Methods of Testing Vulcanized Rubber, B. S. 903, British Standard Institution, 1960.

Nitrogen.—Oxygen-free.

Sulphuric Acid.—Sp. gr. 1.84.

Xylene.

Procedure.—Weigh accurately a sufficient amount of the sample to contain approximately 0.1 g. of rubber hydrocarbon. Extract the test portion with acetone and with chloroform (see Chapter 43, Vol. IIB). Dry the extracted rubber in an oven at a temperature of 70–100°C. for 1 hour.

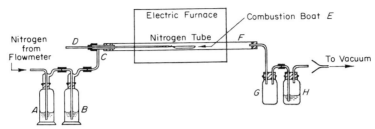

Fig. 59-21. Apparatus for Determination of Total Rubber Hydrocarbon. (Reproduced from B. S. 903 by Permission of British Standards Institution. Copies of the complete standard may be obtained through the American Standards Assn., New York.)

Heat the furnace to a temperature of 550 ± 25°C. Place the test portion into a weighed porcelain or platinum boat, and insert the boat into the entrance of the pyrolysis tube. Insert the hook at the end of the glass rod, *D* (see Fig. 59-21), into the handle of the boat and close the tube with a rubber stopper carrying the T-piece, *C*.

Pass a stream of oxygen-free nitrogen through the apparatus at a rate of 250–300 ml. per minute for 5 minutes before moving the boat slowly into the center of the furnace, taking about 5 minutes for the operation.

Leave the boat in the center part of the furnace for a further 5 minutes, withdraw to the cold portion of the tube and leave for 10 minutes during which time the flow of nitrogen is maintained. Disconnect the gas supply and transfer the boat to a desiccator for further cooling before weighing.

Calculation.—Total apparent hydrocarbon percent $= \dfrac{\text{Loss in weight in g.} \times 100}{\text{Weight of test portion in g.}}$

From the figure so obtained, deduct the rubber-combined sulfur, moisture loss from clay or other fillers, and volatile matter characteristic of the type of any carbon black present.

NATURAL RUBBER-SBR MIXTURE

INFRARED ON LIQUID PYROLYZATES[26]

This is an empirical method using a pyrolysis technique in which measurements of the infrared transmittance of the liquid pyrolyzate obtained from the sample are related to the natural rubber content of a mixture of natural rubber and SBR.

Procedure.—Samples are extracted with acetone by the ASTM method (see Chapter 43, Vol. IIB) and dried in a vacuum oven for 2 hours at 50°C. A 0.5-g. portion is placed in a 16 × 150-mm. test tube and the sample is pyrolyzed in an electric furnace, controlled at 550°C., as shown in Fig. 59-15. The small test tube, *G*, is not used. The

[26] Tryon, M., Horowitz, E., and Mandel, J., J. Research Nat'l Bur. Standards, **55**, 219, 1955.

liquid distillate is collected in a micro test tube. A portion of the distillate is placed between sodium chloride window using a 0.025-mm. lead spacer. The spectrum is obtained between 10 and 12 μ using sodium chloride optics. Peak transmittances are measured at 11.02 and 11.25 μ using baseline correction. The ratio of these corrected peak transmittances is denoted as R. $\left(R = 10\, \dfrac{T\,11.02}{T\,11.25}. \right)$ The percent natural rubber, N, is calculated from the following equation:

$$\log R = 0.730 + 0.00851\,N - .000015\,N^2$$

NBR N-PHENOLIC BLENDS
INFRARED ON LIQUID PYROLYSATES[27]

In this method the ratio of two absorbances obtained on the liquid pyrolyzate is related to the phenolic resin content of an NBR-phenolic mixture, and the absorbance at 4.48 μ wavelength is related to the acrylonitrile content of the NBR.

Apparatus.—The pyrolysis was performed in an especially constructed combustion assembly (Fig. 59-22). It consists of a combustion tube to fit into a Sargent micro-

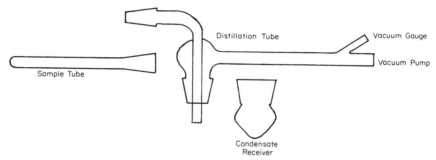

Fig. 59-22. Pyrolysis Apparatus, Unassembled. (Reprinted from Analytical Chemistry, **26**, 1980, 1954. Copyright 1954 by the American Chemical Society and reprinted by permission of the copyright owner.)

combustion furnace, a dry ice trap, and vacuum take-off. The dimensions of the combustion assembly are probably not critical.

Procedure.—A 2-g. sample of rubber is placed in the combustion tube, the pressure is reduced to approximately 2 mm. of mercury, and the sample is pyrolyzed for 15 minutes, during which time the furnace should reach a temperature of 550°C., starting at room temperature. The pyrolysis products which form collect in the dry ice trap and the receiving tube leading to it. The pyrolysis products are washed out of the receiving tube and flask with a 30:70 mixture of acetone and chloroform. All of the washings are combined and the solvent is evaporated under identical conditions for each sample. The resulting tarry pyrolyzate is placed between rock salt plates using a 0.05-mm. spacer, and the infrared spectrum is recorded on an infrared spectrophotometer using a sodium chloride prism in the 2.5 to 5-μ wavelength region. Calibration plots are shown in Figs. 59-23 and 59-24.

[27] Bentley, F. F., and Rappaport, G., Anal. Chem., **26**, 1980, 1954.

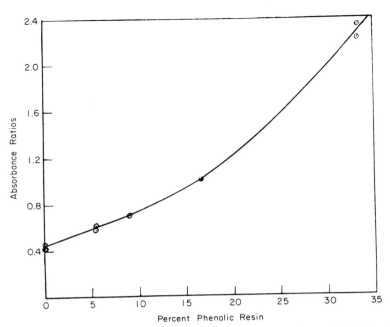

FIG. 59-23. Calibration Curve for NBR Blended with 0 to 33.3% Phenolic Resin. Absorbance ratio $= \dfrac{A_{2.95\mu}}{A_{4.48\mu}}$. (Reprinted from Analytical Chemistry, **26**, 1980, 1954. Copyright 1954 by the American Chemical Society and reprinted by permission of the copyright owner.)

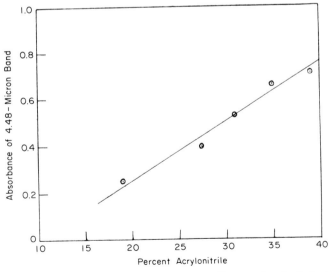

FIG. 59-24. Relation of Absorbance of 4.48-μ Band to Percent Acrylonitrile in NBR. (Reprinted from Analytical Chemistry, **26**, 1980, 1954. Copyright 1954 by the American Chemical Society and reprinted by permission of the copyright owner.)

NONRUBBER CONSTITUENTS

This section deals with methods for materials compounded with rubber to give a finished product. Such materials include both those necessary for the vulcanization process and those added to impart certain properties desirable for ease of manufacture, final properties, or lower cost. The methods given here are specific in nature since the wide range of additives to rubber makes it impossible for a general method to be applicable. The relatively small number of methods available does not truly reflect the importance of this area of rubber analysis, but rather shows the types of additives for which the greatest interest prevails. Undoubtedly many specific methods exist and are in use, but have never been published due to the high degree of specificity and limited application. References not covered by this chapter are given in Table 59-8.

TABLE 59-8.

Subject	Method	References[a]
Identification:		
Accelerators	Chromatography	1, 2, 3, 4, 5
"	Ultraviolet	3, 6, 7
Antioxidants	Chromatography	4, 5, 8
"	Ultraviolet	7, 8, 9
"	Fluorescence	10
Inorganic fillers	Infrared	11, 12
Quantitative analyses:		
Accelerators	Ultraviolet	13
"	Conductometry	14, 15, 16
"	Polarography	17, 18, 19
"	Amperometry	20
"	Argentometric titration	21
"	Chromatography	22
Antioxidants	Ultraviolet	23, 24
"	Chromatography	25, 26
"	Polarography	18, 27
"	Colorimetry	28
"	Potentiometric titration	29
Inorganic fillers	Nephelometry	30
Carbon black	Pyrolysis	31
Sulfur	Photometric titration	32
"	Microcombustion (bomb)	33, 34
"	Combustion (tube)	35
"	Polarography	27, 36
Rubber extender and processing oils	Chromatography	37

[a] Numbers refer to the following works:
1. Bellamy, L. J., Lawrie, J. H., and Press, E. W. S., Rubber Chemistry and Technol., **21**, 195, 734, 1948; Trans. Inst. Rubber Ind., **22**, 308, 1947.
2. Bloomfield, G. F., Rubber Chemistry and Technol., **21**, 735, 1948.
3. Fiorenza, A., Bonomi, G., Piacentini, R., Rubber Chemistry and Technol., **36**, 1119, 1963; Materie Plastiche, 56, January 1963.
4. Parker, C. A., Nature, **170**, 539, 1952.

TABLE 59-8 (cont.)

5. Parker, C. A., and Berriman, J. M., Trans. Inst. Rubber Ind., 28, 279, 1952; Rubber Chemistry and Technol., 26, 449, 1953.
6. Koch, H. P., J. Chem. Soc., 92, 401, 1949.
7. Parker, C. A., J. Royal Inst. Chem., 81, 674, 1957; Rubber Chemistry and Technol., 31, 953, 1958.
8. Hively, R. A., Cole, J. O., Parks, C. R., Field, J. E., and Fink, R., Anal. Chem., 27, 100, 1955.
9. Corish, P. J., J. Appl. Polymer Sci., 7, 727, 1963.
10. Parker, C. A., and Barnes, W. J., Analyst, 82, 606, 1957.
11. Corish, P. J., J. Appl. Polymer Sci., 5, 53, 1961.
12. Miller, F. A., and Wilkins, C. H., Anal. Chem., 24, 1253, 1952.
13. Kress, K. E., Anal. Chem., 23, 313, 1951.
14. Lorenz, O., and Echte, E., Rubber Chemistry and Technol., 30, 1017, 1957; Kautschuk u. Gummi, 9, WT 300, 1956.
15. Scheele, W., and Gensch, C., Kautschuk u. Gummi, 6, WT 147, 1953; Rubber Chemistry and Technol., 29, 1373, 1956.
16. Scheele, W., and Gensch, C., Rubber Chemistry and Technol., 30, 728, 1957.
17. Mocker, F., Kautschuk u. Gummi, 12, WT 368, 1959.
18. Mocker, F., Rubber Chemistry and Technol., 32, 1254, 1959.
19. Mocker, F., and Old, I., Kautschuk u. Gummi, 12, WT 190, 1959.
20. Chatterjee, P. K., Banerjee, D., and Sircar, A. K., Trans. Inst. Rubber Ind., 36, 65 MBT, 1960.
21. Zijp, J. W. H., Rubber Chemistry and Technol., 30, 1175, 1957.
22. Zijp, J. W. H., Rubber Chemistry and Technol., 30, 705, 1957.
23. Banes, F. S., and Eby, L. T., Ind. Eng. Chem., Anal. Ed., 18, 535, 1946.
24. Brandt, H. J., Anal. Chem., 33, 1390, 1961.
25. Zijp, J. W. H., Rubber Chemistry and Technol., 30, 1168, 1957.
26. Zijp, J. W. H., Rubber Chemistry and Technol., 30, 1172, 1957.
27. Poulton, F. C. J., and Tarrant, L., J. Appl. Chem. (London), 1, 29, 1951.
28. Mensik, P., and Broulik, D., Rubber Chemistry and Technol., 29, 647, 1956.
29. Lorenz, O., and Parks, C. R., Rubber Chemistry and Technol., 35, 676, 1962.
30. Frey, H. E., Anal. Chim. Acta, 5, 317, 1951.
31. Glander, F., Rubber Chemistry and Technol., 30, 191, 1951.
32. Walter, R. N., Anal. Chem., 22, 1332, 1950.
33. Mocker, F., Old, I., and Walther, G., Kautschuk u. Gummi, 15, WT 197, 1962.
34. Siegfriedt, R. K., Wiberley, J. S., and Moore, R. W., Anal. Chem., 23, 1008, 1951.
35. Bauminger, B. B., Analyst, 81, 12, 1956.
36. Proske, G., Angew. Chem., A59, 121, 1957.
37. ASTM Standards, 1964, Part 28, D 2007-62 T.

QUALITATIVE METHODS

DETECTION OF DITHIOCARBAMATE ACCELERATORS

LIQUID CHROMATOGRAPHIC METHOD[28]

This method for the detection of dithiocarbamate accelerators combines a silica gel-Celite chromatographic column technique with the formation of the highly colored copper complex of the accelerator to give both selectivity and sensitivity.

Procedure.—Ten g. of the finely divided vulcanized rubber is extracted with acetone for 8 hours in a hot Soxhlet-extraction apparatus. The extract is evaporated under reduced pressure, and the last few cc. of acetone are removed by means of a current of air at room temperature. The residue is finally dried over sulfuric acid. It is then extracted with several portions of warm carbon tetrachloride, the solutions are filtered and made up to 25 cc. Ten cc. of this solution is treated with 1 percent aqueous copper sulfate in 15 percent sodium sulfate solution and extracted with carbon tetrachloride, or, in the

[28] Parker, C. A., and Berriman, J. M., Nature, 170, 539, 1952; Rubber Chemistry and Technol., 27, 1013, 1954.

case of the zinc salts, by shaking a 0.1 percent solution of the dithiocarbamate in carbon tetrachloride with the copper sulfate solution. (Owing to the small solubility of the copper complex of the dimethyl compound in carbon tetrachloride, benzene is used for this compound.) The solution of the copper complex is washed twice with water, dried

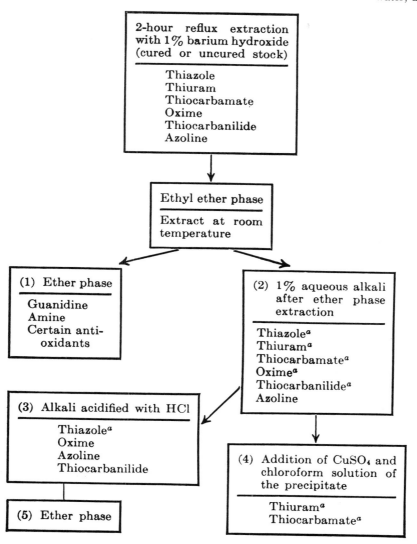

^{a} Major or most reliable test. Other tests are more or less confirmatory and are not always needed for identification.

Fig. 59-25. Outline B: Procedure for Accelerator Identification with Alkali Extract. (Reprinted from Analytical Chemistry, 27, 528, 1955. Copyright 1955 by the American Chemical Society and reprinted by permission of the copyright owner.)

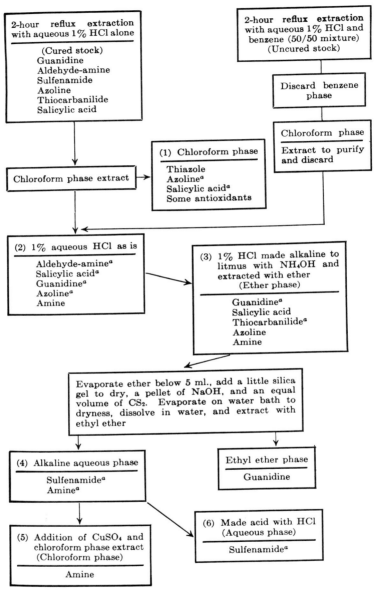

Fig. 59-26.   Outline A: Procedure for Accelerator Identification with Acid Extract. (Reprinted from Analytical Chemistry, **27**, 528, 1955. Copyright 1955 by the American Chemical Society and reprinted by permission of the copyright owner.)

over anhydrous sodium sulfate, and filtered. (This and all other procedures are carried out in subdued light, due to the photosensitivity of copper compounds.)

One cc. of the dried carbon tetrachloride (or benzene) solution is placed on a 1 × 15 cm. column of silica gel-Celite, and developed with 25–50 cc. of 0.25 percent ethyl ether

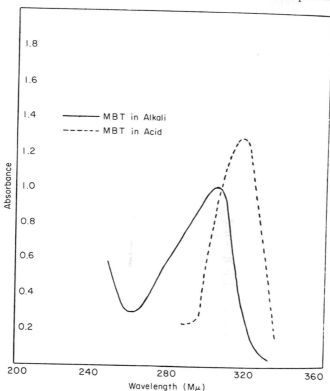

FIG. 59-27. Absorbance Curves for Thiazoles in Aqueous Barium Hydroxide and HCl Solutions. (Reprinted from Analytical Chemistry, **27**, 528, 1955. Copyright 1955 by the American Chemical Society and reprinted by permission of the copyright owner.)

in carbon tetrachloride. The limit of detection is of the order of 0.05 mg. of the copper derivative. This corresponds to 0.01 percent of the accelerators in the original sample when 0.4 g. of rubber is extracted. The bands are identified by parallel tests run with known compounds.

IDENTIFICATION OF ACCELERATORS

ABSORPTIOMETRIC METHOD[29]

This method describes the means for separating accelerators from interfering substances in an extract and gives the characteristics of a number of common accelerators so that they may be readily identified.

[29] Kress, K. E., and Mees, F. G. Stevens, Anal. Chem., **27**, 528, 1955; Rubber Chemistry and Technol. **29**, 319, 1956.

Extraction Procedure. **Alkali.**—The stock to be used for analysis is thoroughly milled and sheeted thinly on a cool mill, and 1 to 2 g. are added to a ground-glass-jointed Erlenmeyer flask. The sample is refluxed in about 50 ml. of 1 percent barium hydroxide, with the flask connected to a condenser fitted with a ground-glass tapered joint. The hot solution, when filtered and cooled, is ready for the spectral analysis indicated in Fig. 59-25.

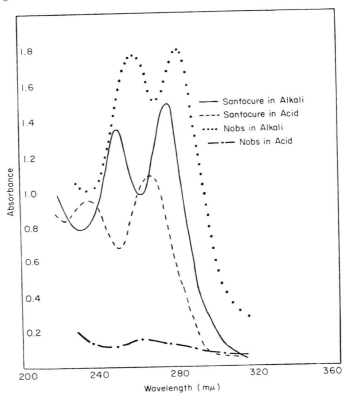

FIG. 59-28. Absorbance Curves for Thiocarbamate Derivatives of Sulfonamides in Aqueous NaOH and HCl. (Reprinted from Analytical Chemistry, **27**, 528, 1955. Copyright 1955 by the American Chemical Society and reprinted by permission of the copyright owner.)

Before a spectral analysis is made, the solution should be liquid-liquid extracted with chloroform or ethyl ether to remove small amounts of dissolved antioxidants and softeners, which are known to be present in the hot alkaline solution, but which are only slightly soluble on cooling. Guanidines may also be present alone or in large quantities.

Acid.—The procedure (Fig. 59-26) is identical to that for the alkali extraction, with the exception of the solvent. Here approximately 50 ml. of 1 percent hydrochloric acid are used if the stock is cured; an additional 50 ml. of benzene are used if an uncured stock is being analyzed. If benzene has been used, the benzene is removed after cooling and the acid solution boiled for a few minutes to remove any traces of benzene. At this stage the acid solution is ready for any special preparation which may be required for the complete analysis.

Thiazoles will be extracted from the aqueous acid by the initial ethyl ether phase extraction, but as they are best determined in the alkaline extract, they may be considered as interfering here.

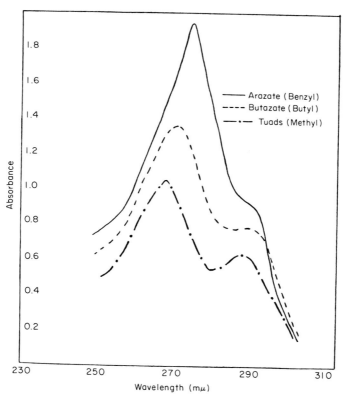

FIG. 59-29.   Absorbance Curves for the Copper Complex of Thiurams and Thiocarbamates in CHCl₃. (Reprinted from Analytical Chemistry, 27, 528, 1955. Copyright 1955 by the American Chemical Society and reprinted by permission of the copyright owner.)

Examples of ultraviolet spectra of some accelerators are given in Figs. 59-27 through 59-31. Spectra are obtained using 1-cm. cells and a Beckman ultraviolet spectrometer or equivalent. The solvent used is taken from Table 59-9.

CHROMATOGRAPHIC SEPARATION AND SPECTRAL ABSORPTION[30]

The method combines liquid elution chromatographic separation of materials in the rubber extract with both ultraviolet and infrared analysis of the separated components in order to identify the compounds of interest.

[30] Fiorenza, A., Bonomi, G., and Piacentini, R., Rubber Chemistry and Technol., **36,** 1119, 1963; Materie Plastiche, 56, January, 1963.

Apparatus.—The column, indicated schematically in Fig. 59-32 consists of:

(a) a 500-ml. receiver that serves as a container for the eluted solvent. It is preceded at the top by a drying tube with stopcock and standard taper joint. At the bottom there is another stopcock for regulating the flow;

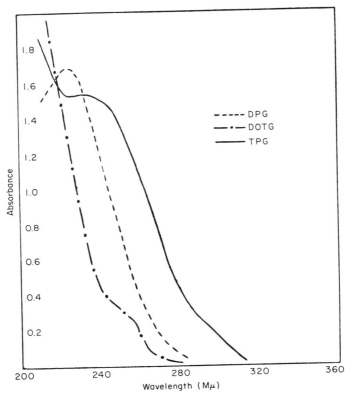

Fig. 59-30. Absorbance Curves for Guanidines in 1 Percent Aqueous HCl. (Reprinted from Analytical Chemistry, **27**, 528, 1955. Copyright 1955 by the American Chemical Society and reprinted by permission of the copyright owner.)

(b) a column which consists of a tube about 23 mm. in diameter and 500 mm. long. It has a tapered portion near the bottom on which rests a small porous sintered glass disc;

(c) a stopcock with double standard taper joints to stop the flow of liquid in case of interruption. This avoids being required to dry the column;

(d) an Auschutz-Thiele collector or similar unit with a 100-ml. reservoir; and

(e) 3 stopcocks for the collection of the fractions.

Spectrometer.—Beckman DK-2 or other suitable spectrometer.

Reagents.—Alumina for chromatographic use, without any particular activation treatment, from B.D.H. (British Drug House). (Selected after trying other types which gave negative results.) The charging of the alumina into the column does not present any particular difficulty. In order to charge the column it is sufficient to keep it vertical and to pour the alumina powder into the column with a funnel. This is done in such a way as to obtain a gradual and continuous filling of the column without vacuum and with successive layers, as far as possible, normal to the axis of the cylinder.

To treat the alumina, the porous glass disc, described previously, is fitted beforehand

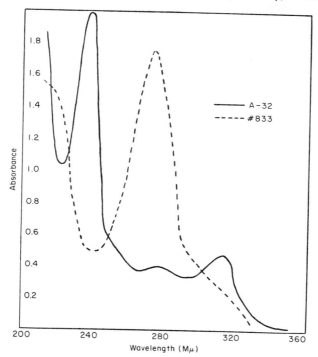

FIG. 59-31. Absorbance Curves for Aldehyde-Amines in Aqueous HCl. (Reprinted from Analytical Chemistry, **27**, 528, 1955. Copyright 1955 by the American Chemical Society and reprinted by permission of the copyright owner.)

with a pad of glass wool. When the charging of the alumina is finished the column is tapped with a rubber hose until it is observed that a further reduction in volume of the alumina does not occur.

When the settling of the alumina is finished, a small layer of glass wool is placed above it; in addition a layer of glass pellets about 1 cm. in diameter is also placed above it; then about 100 ml. of pure benzene are poured on the alumina. The benzene is allowed to flow out until its top level is at the same height as that of the pellets; in this manner the column is made ready for use.

Procedure. **Chromatographic Separation.**—Ten g. of the vulcanizate under examination are extracted in a Soxhlet for 4 hours with a mixture of methyl ethyl ketone and ethyl alcohol in a ratio of 3:1. The extract is dried in a vacuum oven at 50°C. and then taken up in 50 ml. of boiling benzene. After cooling, the solution is poured into the chromatographic column and the liquid is allowed to rise almost to the upper level of the alumina; in this way the so-called "development" of the column is achieved. In

TABLE 59-9. ABSORBANCE CHARACTERISTICS OF ACCELERATOR FRACTIONS

Trade Names	Chemical Names	Index No./Solvent[a]	Wavelength of Maxima, $m\mu$[b]	Absorbance[c] Ratio
Aromatic Thiazoles	2-Mercaptobenzothiazole	A1/C; B5/E	329	$329/274 = 14$
MBT, Captax,			236	$329/236 = 1.8$
Thiotax		B2/B	308	$232/308 = 1.1$
			232	
		B3/A	322	$322/232 = 1.8$
			232	
MBTS, Altax, Thiofide	2,2'-Benzothiazyl disulfide		Identical with MBT	
Santocure	Benzothiazyl-2-monocyclo-		Thiazole portion identical with MBT	
	hexylsulfenamide	A4/B[d]	284, 252	$284/252 = 1.1$
		A6/A	270, 236	$270/236 = 1.1$
Nobs, Amax	N-Oxydiethylene benzothi-	A4/B[d]	286, 262	$286/262 = 1.0$
	azole-2-sulfenamide	A6/A	No maxima	
OXAF, Zenite	Zinc benzothiazyl sulfide		Identical with MBT	
Special				
Aliphatic Thiazoles				
Texas	Mixed ethyl and dimethyl	B5/C	326	$326/276 = 16$
	mercaptothiazoles	B2/B	298	$298/248 = 4.6$
		B3/A	318	$318/266 = 9.5$
Erie	Mixed ethyl and dimethyl	B2/B	294	$294/242 = 3.2$
	thiazyl disulfides	B3/A	314	$314/246 = 3.8$
Guanidines				
DPG	Diphenylguanidine	B1/E	Identical with A3/E	
		A2/A	266	$226/246 = 1.7$
		A3/E	258	$258/278 = 1.6$
DOTG	Di-o-tolylguanidine	B1/E	Identical with A3/E	
		A2/A	254 (shoulder)	$254/274 = 9.3$
		A3/E	254	$254/274 = 1.9$
TPG	Triphenylguanidine	B1/E	Identical with A3/E	
		A2/A	235	$235/226 = 1.02$
		A3/E	263	$263/284 = 1.4$
Permalux	Di-o-tolylguanidine salt of	B2/B	276	$276/250 = 2.8$
	dicatechol borate	A2/A	274	$274/254 = 1.8$
		A3/E	254	$254/274 = 1.9$
Thiocarbamates				
Methyl Zimate,	Zinc dimethyldithio-	B2/B	Identical with methyl Tuads	
Methazate	carbamate	B4/C		
Ethyl Zimate,	Zinc diethyldithio-	B2/B	Identical with ethyl Tuads	
Ethazate	carbamate	B4/C		
Butyl Zimate,	Zinc dibutyldithio-	B2/B	258, 282	$258/282 = 1.0$
Butazate	carbamate	B4/C	274, 290	$274/290 = 1.7$
Arazate	Zinc dibenzyldithio-	B2/B	258, 290	$258/290 = 1.1$
	carbamate	B4/C	276, 294	$276/294 = 2.1$
Selenac	Selenium diethyldithio-	B2/B	Identical with ethyl Tuads	
	carbamate	B4/C		
Pip-Pip	Piperidine pentamethylene-	B2/B	258, 282	$258/282 = 1.3$
	dithiocarbamate			
Thiurams				
TMTD, Methyl	Tetramethylthiuram	B2/B	252, 278	$252/278 = 1.0$
Tuads, Tuex	disulfide	B4/C	268, 290	$268/290 = 1.6$
TETD, Ethyl Tuads	Tetraethylthiuram disulfide	B2/B	258, 282	$258/282 = 1.0$
		B4/C	272, 290	$272/290 = 1.6$
Monex, Thionex	Tetramethylthiuram mono-	B2/B	Identical with methyl Tuads	
	sulfide			
Aldehyde-Amines				
A-32, 808	Butyraldehyde and aniline	B4/C		
	reaction product	A2/A	242, 322, 280	$242/322 = 4.3$
		B2/B	228, 280	$228/280 = 2.2$
Accelerator 833	Butyraldehyde-monobutyl-	A2/A	278	$278/242 = 3.7$
	amine reaction product	B2/B	278	$278/244 = 5.6$
Trimene base	Triethyltrimethylenetri-	A2/A	242, 324	$242/324 = 3.7$
	amine	B2/B	268, 298	$268/298 = 1.3$
A-19	Acetaldehyde-formaldehyde-	A2/A	237, 314	$237/314 = 2.9$
	aniline product			
Azolines				
2-MT	2-Mercaptothiazoline	A2/A	268	$268/230 = 5.0$
		A1/E, A3/E	268, 248	$268/248 = 2.3$

TABLE 59-9 (cont.)

Trade Names	Chemical Names	Index No./Solvent[a]	Wavelength of Maxima, $m\mu$[b]	Absorbance[c] Ratio
		B2/B	246, 264	246/264 = 1.1
NA-22	2-Mercaptoimidazoline	B3/A	268	268/230 = 5.1
		A2/A	268	268/230 = 4.6
		A1/E, A3/E	278, 248	278/248 = 2.2
		B2/B	232	232/252 = 11.3
Special purpose		B3/A	232	232/252 = 6.2
Thiocarbanilide				
		A3/E	240, 288	240/288 = 4.3
		B2/B, B3/A	252	252/272 = 1.4
Aniline		B5/E	280	280/246 = 2.3
		A2/A	240, 280	240/280 = 6.1
Vulcanizing agents				
Dibenzo GMF	p,p'-Dibenzoquinone-dioxime	B2/B	360	360/380 = 3.5
		B3/A	314	314/254 = 2.0
GMF	p-Quinonedioxime	B5/E	313	313/334 = 2.6
		B2/B	317	317/336 = 2.0
		B3/A	316	316/336 = 1.9
Activators		B5/E	314	314/334 = 2.7
Barak	Dibutylammonium oleate	A4/B[d]	258, 282	258/282 = 1.1
		A5/C	274	274/290 = 1.7
DBA	Dibenzylamine	A4/B[d]	258, 284	258/284 = 1.1
		A5/C	276, 294	276/294 = 1.9
Retarders				
Retarder W	Salicylic acid	A2/A	236, 304	236/304 = 2.2
		A1/E	236, 306	236/306 = 1.8
E-S-E-N	Phthalic anhydride	A2/A	230, 280	230/280 = 5.5
		A1/E	224, 276	224/276 = 6.4

Reprinted from Analytical Chemistry, **27**, 528, 1955. Copyright 1955 by the American Chemical Society and reprinted by permission of the copyright owner.

[a] Index No. refers to procedure for accelerator identification—either Outline A (acid) or Outline B (base) with the number representing a given block within each outline. Thus, A3/ indicates acid outline, block 3. For the solvent, the following abbreviations apply: A, aqueous acid; B, aqueous alkali; E, ethyl ether; and C, chloroform. Chloroform and ether may usually be used interchangeably. Where chloroform is used in place of ether, the wave length of the maximum will be shifted about 2 $m\mu$ toward the longer wavelength region.

[b] Primary or most characteristic maximum listed first. In a few cases the secondary maximum is no more than a "shoulder," but it is characteristic.

[c] Ratio of absorbance of strongest and next most intense maximum where two maxima are present. Represents ratio of maximum to adjacent minimum where single maximum is present. If no minimum is present, ratio is that of maximum absorbance to an arbitrarily selected wavelength 20 $m\mu$ toward longer wavelength region. Purpose of ratio is to indicate selectivity or sharpness of maximum, which is important for identification. Ratio given is believed reasonably accurate, but may be expected to vary somewhat depending on purity and amount of interference in extract.

[d] Barium salts are represented in all alkaline solutions except for (A4/B), where absorbance reported is that of sodium salt. Prepared thiocarbamate derivatives of sulfenamides and amine activators are sodium salts.

order to protect it from actinic radiation, which catalyzes many processes of chemical transformation, the column is covered with a suitable protection consisting of a wrapping of aluminum foil.

The column is charged successively in the following manner: 200 ml. of pure benzene, 200 ml. of a mixture of 99.75 percent benzene and 0.25 percent absolute alcohol, 200 ml. of a mixture of 95 percent benzene and 5 percent absolute alcohol, and at the end 1000 ml. of absolute alcohol.

The eluate is collected in fractions of about 50 ml. each, which are progressively numbered; a constant flow rate of about 5 ml. per minute is obtained by means of a light aspiration at the base of the column.

Ultraviolet Spectrophotometric Examination.—From every fraction 1 ml. is withdrawn and evaporated under a vacuum of 20 mm. mercury at 50°C., and then diluted with Spectrograde methyl alcohol in a manner to obtain the concentration most adapted for ultraviolet examination. The degree of the necessary dilution can serve to indicate in which fraction one has the maximum concentration of substances to identify. The spectra obtained are compared with spectra achieved previously, of substances possibly present in the mixture extract.

An example of the results obtained is shown by the spectra in Fig. 59-33; the reference spectra are shown in Fig. 59-34.

Infrared Analysis.—The extraction and chromatographic procedures described above are used to separate the antioxidants from the vulcanizate.

The solvents that are not suitable for infrared examination are distilled from the fractions, and the residue, dried in a vacuum oven at about 50°C., is dissolved in carbon tetrachloride at a concentration more adapted to the execution of the spectrums.

Figure 59-35 illustrates the spectra of the extract itself and of the extract fractions. In Fig. 59-36, the spectra of known materials are shown.

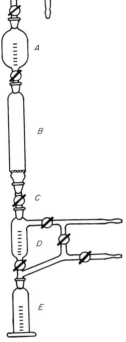

FIG. 59-32. Chromatographic Column. *A*, Receiver. *B*, Column with sintered glass disc at bottom. *C*, Stopcock. *D* and *E*, Collector System. (Courtesy Materie Plastiche ed Elastomeri.)

IDENTIFICATION OF AMINES
X-RAY DIFFRACTION METHOD[31]

This method describes a general procedure for the identification of amines by evaluating the characteristic spacings in the x-ray diffraction pattern of the amine hydrochlorides.

Procedure.—A few drops of the amine or aqueous amine solution is added to a small Petri dish containing 10 ml. of 1 N hydrochloric acid. The resulting solution is stirred and evaporated to dryness in a 110°C. oven. The crystalline product is dissolved in anhydrous ethyl alcohol. The solution is filtered and again evaporated to dryness in a watch glass.

The crystalline hydrochloride is then ground to a fine powder in an agate mortar and packed in a cellulose acetate tube. If only a small amount of derivative is recovered, it may be scraped into a pile on the watch glass and packed into the cellulose acetate tube without grinding.

NOTE.—In some cases, the hydrochlorides are hygroscopic, and in such instances it is necessary to use a few simple precautions in preparing the samples. Satisfactory results are usually obtained by keeping the crystals in a 70°C. oven and removing them intermittently for grinding. After the sample is ground sufficiently, it is quickly packed into a cellulose acetate tube and the open end of the tube is sealed by dipping it into melted paraffin wax. The diffraction diagram should be taken immediately.

Some of the amine hydrochlorides of low molecular weight exist as a melt in the 100°C. oven. In such cases these salts are crystallized in a 70°C. oven.

Tributylamine and triamylamine hydrochlorides are liquids at 70°C. and must be removed from the oven and crystallized, using agitation and cooling with dry ice.

In identifying an unknown amine hydrochloride, the interplanar spacings and relative intensities given in Table 59-10 can be used. However, it is usually more satisfactory to identify the unknown by a direct comparison with a set of standard films or charts. For rapid identification measure the longest spacing, which in many cases is one of the most

---

[31] Brock, M. J., and Hannum, M. J., Anal. Chem., **27**, 1374, 1955.

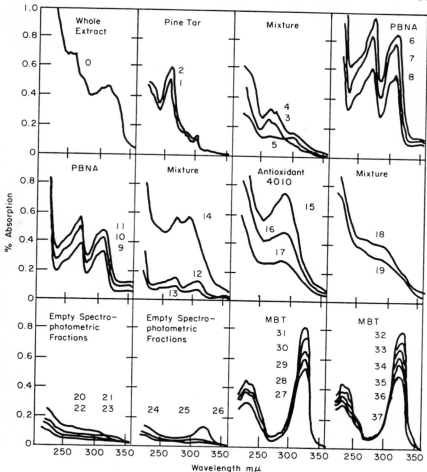

FIG. 59-33. Typical Ultraviolet Absorption Spectra. (Courtesy Materie Plastiche ed Elastomeri.)

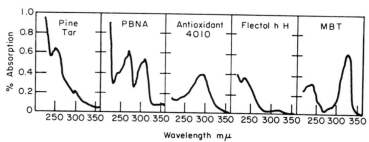

FIG. 59-34. Reference Ultraviolet Absorption Spectra. (Courtesy Materie Plastiche ed Elastomeri.)

intense. The appropriate standards with similar long spacings can then be selected from the file of diagrams of known amine hydrochlorides. Comparison with these standards will give a positive identification.

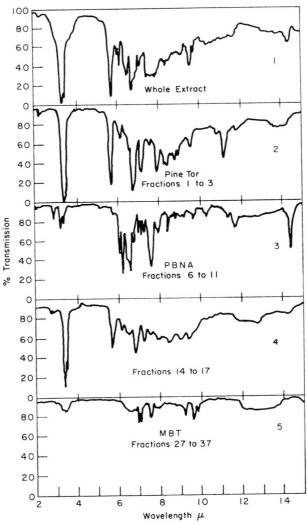

FIG. 59-35. Typical Infrared Transmission Spectra. (Courtesy Materie Plastiche ed Elastomeri.)

Binary mixtures of amines can be readily identified provided the minor component is present in sufficient quantity to give a diffraction pattern. In some cases even ternary mixtures are identifiable.

The diameters of the diffraction maxima were measured with a Philips line-measuring device. Using the 114.59-mm. camera, 2 mm. measured on the film is equivalent to an angle of 1° θ in the Bragg formula, where $\lambda = 2d \sin \theta$. The interplanar spacing values,

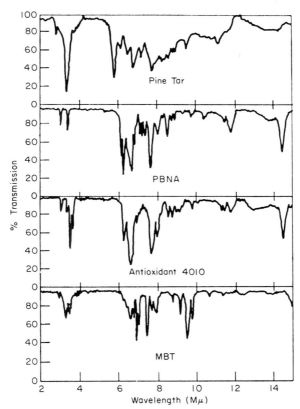

FIG. 59-36.   Reference Infrared Transmission Spectra. (Courtesy Materie Plastiche ed Elastomeri.)

d, were then determined using the charts prepared by Parrish and Irwin[32] for copper Kα radiation ($\lambda = 1.5418$ A).

The interplanar spacings, measured in Angstrom units, for the amine hydrochlorides studied are listed in Table 59-10 together with the visually estimated relative intensities, I/I_1. The relative intensities of the diffraction maxima were determined using photographic standards as recommended by Hanawalt, Rinn, and Frevel.[33]

[32] Parrish, W., and Irwin, B. W., Data for X-ray Analysis, Vol. 1, Philips Technical Library, Irvington-on-Hudson, N. Y., 1953.
[33] Hanawalt, J. D., Rinn, H. W., and Frevel, L. K., Ind. Eng. Chem., Anal. Ed., 10, 457, 1938.

TABLE 59-10. X-RAY DIFFRACTION DATA FOR AMINE HYDROCHLORIDES[a]

Methylamine

d	I/I₁
5.06	0.46
3.89	0.25
3.27	1.00
3.03	0.84
2.83	0.15
2.60	0.25
2.53	0.15
2.40	0.15
2.18	0.25
2.14	0.25
1.98	0.15
1.94	0.15
1.80	0.25
1.63	0.15
1.53	0.15
1.53	0.15

Dimethylamine

d	I/I₁
4.98	0.69
3.64	1.00
3.35	0.04
3.10	0.04
2.94	0.46
2.78	0.29
2.58	0.20
2.29	0.07
2.17	0.07
1.89	0.04

Trimethylamine

d	I/I₁
6.14	0.09
4.61	0.79
3.52	1.00
3.05	0.05
2.91	0.43
2.75	0.09
2.69	0.18
2.49	0.09

Ethylamine

d	I/I₁
8.26	0.35
4.07	0.08
3.88	0.35
3.39	1.00
3.25	0.08
3.14	0.05
3.01	0.65
2.82	0.05
2.74	0.05
2.65	0.15
2.40	0.15
2.37	0.15
2.15	0.05
2.13	0.08
2.03	0.05
1.88	0.05
1.80	0.08
1.69	0.05
1.63	0.05
1.50	0.08

Diethylamine

d	I/I₁
6.54	0.32
4.77	0.19
3.67	1.00
3.38	0.25
3.19	0.25
2.62	0.19
2.44	0.09
2.40	0.06
2.32	0.06
2.26	0.09
2.04	0.09
1.87	0.02
1.83	0.03
1.76	0.03
1.73	0.06
1.65	0.03

Triethylamine

d	I/I₁
7.25	1.00
5.07	0.22
4.18	0.38
3.64	0.22
3.54	1.00
3.22	1.00
2.70	0.22
2.54	0.15
2.41	0.03
2.24	0.03
2.17	0.03
2.09	0.08
1.99	0.05
1.93	0.05
1.79	0.08
1.75	0.03
1.72	0.03
1.63	0.05
1.58	0.03
1.53	0.05
1.44	0.05
1.39	0.02
1.26	0.03

2-Aminoethanol

d	I/I₁
7.08	0.35
3.66	0.24
3.54	0.82
3.44	1.00
3.20	1.00
2.89	0.35
2.74	0.15
2.59	0.49
2.47	0.24
2.32	0.15
2.14	0.04
2.09	0.15
2.02	0.08
1.92	0.08
1.82	0.15
1.59	0.15
1.46	0.08

2,2',2''-Nitrilotriethanol

d	I/I₁
6.08	0.18
4.48	0.58
4.15	0.15
3.83	0.18
3.63	0.03
3.42	1.00
3.04	0.22
2.80	0.46
2.67	0.15
2.45	0.18
2.38	0.02
2.24	0.02
2.18	0.08
2.07	0.15
2.02	0.05
1.93	0.08
1.88	0.11
1.82	0.05
1.75	0.05
1.70	0.03
1.64	0.03
1.50	0.02
1.45	0.03
1.40	0.03
1.34	0.02
1.30	0.02
1.27	0.02
1.21	0.02

Propylamine

d	I/I₁
7.42	0.24
4.78	0.24
4.42	0.15
3.79	1.00
3.12	1.00
2.86	0.35
2.62	0.05
2.38	0.15
2.21	0.24
2.12	0.15
1.91	0.24
1.74	0.07

Dipropylamine

d	I/I₁
9.25	0.46
4.98	0.22
4.61	0.02
3.94	0.27
3.78	0.01
3.64	1.00
3.51	0.01
3.38	0.22
2.86	0.05
2.57	0.11
2.48	0.08
2.35	0.01
2.24	0.02
2.14	0.05
1.95	0.02
1.82	0.02
1.79	0.02
1.62	0.01
1.60	0.01

Tripropylamine

d	I/I₁
8.60	0.31
5.46	0.19
4.97	0.19
4.31	0.19
4.07	0.31
3.66	0.09
3.52	1.00
3.25	0.13
2.95	0.09
2.87	0.13
2.72	0.09
2.39	0.06
2.24	0.03
1.89	0.03
1.76	0.03
1.66	0.03

Isopropylamine

d	I/I₁
9.20	0.29
6.48	0.29
4.85	0.09
4.60	1.00
4.10	0.18
3.87	0.05
3.70	0.79
3.56	0.43
3.41	0.05
3.22	0.05
3.04	0.05
2.89	0.59
2.75	0.05
2.53	0.18
2.33	0.05
2.28	0.29
2.21	0.05
2.15	0.05
2.09	0.18

Diisopropylamine

d	I/I₁
7.05	1.00
5.25	0.41
5.03	0.41
4.18	0.04
4.00	1.00
3.84	0.69
3.68	0.06
3.46	0.84
3.23	0.84
3.01	0.13
2.88	0.20
2.77	0.20
2.72	0.13
2.52	0.13
2.48	0.20
2.37	0.06
2.25	0.06
2.18	0.13
2.11	0.06
2.01	0.06
1.91	0.06
1.84	0.06
1.81	0.04
1.77	0.04
1.75	0.06
1.65	0.04
1.55	0.04
1.34	0.04

Butylamine

d	I/I₁
14.38	0.59
(14.98)	
7.42	0.05
4.77	0.49
4.17	0.49
3.56	1.00
3.46	0.14
2.99	0.05
2.88	0.05
2.58	0.05
2.49	0.14

Dibutylamine

d	I/I₁
11.41	0.79
(11.56)	
5.71	0.02
5.01	0.54
4.27	0.46
3.76	0.02
3.63	1.00
3.46	0.38
3.06	0.06
2.77	0.02
2.62	0.02
2.56	0.09
2.49	0.09
2.34	0.02
2.19	0.03
2.05	0.02
1.80	0.02
1.61	0.02

Tributylamine

d	I/I₁
11.27	1.00
(11.34)	
6.74	0.19
5.71	0.19
4.38	0.31
3.95	0.63
3.69	0.31

Isobutylamine

d	I/I₁
11.75	0.19
(11.91)	
5.95	0.09
5.09	0.09
4.89	0.09
4.08	0.38
3.89	1.00
3.70	0.32
3.25	0.09
2.96	0.19
2.78	0.09
2.68	0.09
2.62	0.09
2.45	0.06
2.37	0.09
2.30	0.09
2.23	0.06
2.12	0.09
1.93	0.03
1.86	0.06
1.70	0.06
1.62	0.03
1.49	0.06

Diisobutylamine

d	I/I₁
10.06	1.00
5.30	0.09
4.98	0.43
4.72	0.43
4.26	0.29
4.07	0.29
3.75	1.00
3.51	0.59
3.37	0.18
3.01	0.29
2.74	0.09
2.65	0.09
2.56	0.18
2.48	0.18
2.41	0.05
2.29	0.09
2.07	0.09
1.86	0.09

sec-Butylamine

d	I/I₁
9.10	0.31
5.17	0.19
4.60	0.19
4.17	0.06
3.74	1.00
3.48	0.31
3.06	0.25
2.90	0.09
2.62	0.06
2.53	0.19
2.37	0.06
2.23	0.03
2.15	0.06
2.10	0.13
1.99	0.03
1.83	0.03
1.76	0.03
1.64	0.03
1.51	0.03
1.40	0.03

Di-sec-Butylamine

d	I/I₁
8.69	1.00
7.82	0.20
6.66	0.20
5.35	0.84
4.24	0.20
4.06	1.00
3.89	0.30
3.81	0.30
3.68	0.20
3.55	0.54
3.43	0.20
3.26	0.30
3.16	0.20
3.06	0.30
2.80	0.06
2.73	0.06
2.68	0.06
2.59	0.12
2.48	0.06
2.37	0.12
2.21	0.06
2.09	0.06

TABLE 59-10 (cont.)

tert-Butylamine

d	I/I₁
9.05	0.21
6.40	0.14
5.94	0.14
5.17	0.60
4.51	1.00
4.37	1.00
4.04	0.29
3.92	0.29
3.67	0.49
3.31	0.14
3.14	0.21
2.99	0.14
2.86	0.39
2.74	0.39
2.51	0.39
2.42	0.29
2.29	0.09
2.18	0.14
2.13	0.04
1.77	0.14

Amylamine

d	I/I₁
15.77	0.84
(16.67)	
4.87	0.70
4.34	0.25
4.13	0.17
3.74	0.17
3.60	1.00
3.52	0.34
3.33	0.05
3.22	0.05
3.03	0.05
2.72	0.15
2.53	0.25
2.44	0.05
2.18	0.05
2.10	0.05

Diamylamine

d	I/I₁
13.05	0.84
(13.38)	
5.07	0.69
4.44	0.54
3.64	1.00
3.51	0.41
3.19	0.13
2.81	0.06
2.58	0.13
2.52	0.13
2.40	0.06
2.23	0.06
2.12	0.04
1.81	0.04

Triamylamine

d	I/I₁
12.58	1.00
(12.85)	
8.50	0.09
7.82	0.09
4.78	1.00
4.32	0.72
3.94	0.15
3.79	0.15
3.64	0.49
3.43	0.31
3.07	0.15
2.83	0.31
2.41	0.09
2.32	0.09

Isoamylamine

d	I/I₁
14.32	1.00
(14.86)	
7.32	0.07
5.37	0.82
5.05	0.15
4.56	0.49
4.18	0.65
3.86	0.82
3.71	0.35
3.56	1.00
3.38	0.82
3.11	0.65
2.87	0.82
2.61	0.15
2.48	0.15
2.32	0.07
2.19	0.07
2.13	0.35
1.87	0.07
1.70	0.15

Diisoamylamine

d	I/I₁
12.42	0.64
(12.63)	
5.22	0.31
4.86	0.31
4.58	0.06
4.40	0.38
4.20	0.06
3.89	0.19
3.62	1.00
3.47	0.06
3.33	0.25
3.16	0.06
2.97	0.09
2.75	0.02
2.66	0.19
2.61	0.09
2.45	0.06
2.24	0.09
2.04	0.06
1.81	0.03
1.67	0.06

Triisoamylamine

d	I/I₁
11.94	1.00
(12.14)	
9.64	0.29
8.00	0.11
7.01	0.09
6.01	0.49
5.53	0.14
4.96	1.00
4.48	0.29
4.35	1.00
3.98	0.29
3.78	0.04
3.66	0.21
3.51	0.49
3.35	0.21
3.19	0.14
3.09	0.49
3.00	0.39
2.91	0.14
2.82	0.09
2.71	0.14
2.62	0.04
2.55	0.21
2.44	0.09
2.32	0.09
2.23	0.09
2.13	0.04
1.75	0.09
1.69	0.09
1.65	0.04
1.42	0.09

sec-Amylamine

d	I/I₁
10.57	0.79
7.55	0.09
5.01	0.18
4.75	0.09
3.76	1.00
3.63	0.38
3.52	0.09
2.95	0.13
2.65	0.13
2.50	0.03
2.32	0.09
2.14	0.13
2.08	0.03
1.99	0.03
1.67	0.03
1.59	0.03

tert-Amylamine

d	I/I₁
13.58	0.04
(13.92)	
11.34	0.09
(11.51)	
9.38	0.29
6.92	0.21
6.39	0.04
5.20	1.00
4.50	0.14
4.17	0.09
3.98	0.09
3.81	0.71
3.62	0.71

tert-Amylamine (Cont.)

d	I/I₁
3.39	0.04
3.23	0.04
3.07	0.04
2.95	0.14
2.88	0.14
2.67	0.21
2.57	0.04
2.47	0.09
2.36	0.04
2.24	0.09
2.13	0.09
1.79	0.09

Hexylamine

d	I/I₁
19.31	1.00
4.86	0.84
4.46	0.13
3.97	0.41
3.52	1.00
3.23	0.04
3.06	0.04
2.86	0.04
2.60	0.06
2.49	0.20
2.40	0.06
2.18	0.04
2.11	0.06

Heptylamine

d	I/I₁
21.80	1.00
7.24	0.02
5.43	0.12
4.96	0.32
4.73	0.24
4.34	0.24
3.89	0.24
3.66	0.02
3.50	1.00
3.37	0.02
3.09	0.04
2.97	0.02
2.71	0.02
2.48	0.17
2.16	0.02
2.09	0.02

Octylamine

d	I/I₁
25.32	1.00
8.50	0.20
6.37	0.13
4.72	0.54
4.48	0.54
4.21	0.84
3.95	0.06
3.49	0.04
3.34	1.00
2.56	0.06
2.35	0.20
1.66	0.06
1.50	0.06

1,1,3,3-Tetramethylbutylamine

d	I/I₁
13.58	0.84
(13.92)	
9.10	0.20
7.89	0.06
6.99	0.06
6.43	0.13
5.88	1.00
4.55	1.00
3.46	0.41
3.21	0.20
3.01	0.20
2.88	0.41
2.81	0.13
2.52	0.20
2.27	0.04
1.80	0.06

Ethylenediamine

d	I/I₁
3.72	0.13
3.48	0.69
3.35	0.54
3.26	0.54
2.99	1.00
2.84	0.04
2.72	0.20
2.63	0.41
2.51	0.06
2.46	0.13
2.41	0.06
2.35	0.20
2.22	0.04
2.15	0.04
2.09	0.20
2.05	0.13
1.88	0.20
1.78	0.20
1.70	0.13
1.64	0.13
1.60	0.29
1.50	0.06

1,3-Propanediamine

d	I/I₁
5.27	0.18
4.72	0.09
4.21	0.79
3.80	0.79
3.62	1.00
3.33	0.43
3.12	0.43
3.02	0.18
2.93	0.29
2.84	0.18
2.62	0.29
2.50	0.18
2.45	0.29
2.37	0.29
2.29	0.09
2.20	0.18
1.96	0.05
1.82	0.09
1.73	0.18

1,3-Butanediamine

d	I/I₁
9.29	0.37
6.85	0.07
5.53	0.12
4.98	0.37
4.54	0.54
3.81	0.54
3.67	0.75
3.51	0.37
3.34	0.23
3.12	1.00
2.99	1.00
2.87	0.23
2.78	0.37
2.55	0.12
2.34	0.23
2.29	0.23
2.24	0.23
2.16	0.23
2.01	0.12
1.85	0.12
1.77	0.12
1.69	0.23
1.62	0.12
1.55	0.07
1.46	0.12
1.43	0.12

1,4-Butanediamine

d	I/I₁
6.61	0.09
4.55	0.09
4.03	0.43
3.89	0.43
3.72	0.59
3.57	0.43
3.29	1.00
3.17	0.59
2.99	0.59
2.69	0.29
2.55	0.18
2.47	0.29
2.38	0.59
2.31	0.18
2.20	0.18
2.15	0.18
2.08	0.09
2.00	0.09
1.93	0.06
1.79	0.18
1.75	0.06
1.70	0.06
1.65	0.06
1.50	0.09
1.41	0.06

1,6-Hexanediamine

d	I/I₁
10.50	0.21
4.62	0.09
4.39	0.04
4.21	0.29
3.97	0.21
3.80	0.14
3.47	1.00

TABLE 59-10 (cont.)

1,6-Hexanediamine (Cont.)

d	I/I₁
3.32	0.09
3.24	0.09
3.12	0.21
3.05	0.14
2.78	0.14
2.63	0.09
2.54	0.09
2.42	0.04
2.29	0.09
2.19	0.09
1.96	0.04
1.92	0.09
1.74	0.04
1.65	0.09

Aniline

d	I/I₁
7.83	0.17
4.45	0.07
4.24	1.00
4.06	0.37
3.90	0.07
3.60	0.17
3.48	0.07
3.35	0.17
3.26	0.17
3.16	0.17
3.02	0.07
2.70	0.07
2.60	0.07
2.53	0.37
2.42	0.07
2.22	0.04
2.14	0.04
2.05	0.07
1.93	0.07
1.87	0.04
1.82	0.07
1.73	0.04
1.66	0.04
1.63	0.07
1.55	0.04

Diphenylamine

d	I/I₁
8.10	0.05
7.31	0.17
6.55	0.17
5.82	0.17
5.47	0.25
5.12	0.17
4.53	0.11
4.12	1.00
3.94	0.84
3.65	0.34
3.49	0.25
3.36	0.11
3.20	0.34
3.05	0.11
2.91	0.17
2.74	0.25
2.60	0.05
2.46	0.05
2.36	0.11
2.28	0.17

Diphenylamine (Cont.)

d	I/I₁
2.19	0.01
2.10	0.05
2.01	0.01
1.93	0.01
1.83	0.05
1.69	0.01

Benzylamine

d	I/I₁
14.14	0.54
(14.75)	
5.68	0.84
5.25	0.29
4.84	0.20
4.30	1.00
4.08	0.29
3.82	0.06
3.54	0.41
3.38	0.41
3.25	0.00
3.15	1.20
2.94	0.54
2.83	0.54
2.62	0.06
2.45	0.13
2.27	0.06
2.08	0.41
1.99	0.06
1.90	0.06
1.77	0.13
1.73	0.13
1.69	0.04
1.47	0.13

Dibenzylamine

d	I/I₁
14.26	0.25
(14.93)	
11.97	0.70
(12.25)	
5.69	0.17
5.18	1.00
4.79	0.03
4.51	1.00
4.28	0.58
4.00	0.70
3.60	0.70
3.51	0.70
3.31	0.70
3.13	0.70
2.94	0.17
2.82	0.17
2.58	0.34
2.46	0.11
2.16	0.03
2.09	0.17
2.00	0.17
1.91	0.03
1.83	0.17

Tribenzylamine

d	I/I₁
7.80	1.00
6.05	0.85
4.79	1.00
4.51	0.49
4.08	0.49
3.89	1.00
3.29	0.85
3.16	0.03
3.03	0.39
2.95	0.29
2.82	0.39
2.61	0.21
2.52	0.21
2.39	0.21
2.27	0.21
2.17	0.14
2.11	0.04
2.02	0.04
1.97	0.29
1.86	0.29
1.80	0.14
1.71	0.04
1.68	0.09
1.65	0.03
1.61	0.03
1.48	0.03
1.41	0.03

Cyclohexylamine

d	I/I₁
11.41	0.13
(11.51)	
7.24	0.09
5.72	0.13
5.22	0.64
4.92	0.19
4.67	0.38
4.32	0.09
4.10	0.64
3.94	0.03
3.78	1.00
3.59	0.09
3.35	0.19
2.97	0.31
2.79	0.25
2.69	0.09
2.58	0.13
2.43	0.03
2.33	0.19
2.22	0.19
2.13	0.03
2.05	0.06
1.92	0.03
1.85	0.06
1.79	0.03
1.75	0.06
1.66	0.03
1.60	0.03
1.49	0.03
1.44	0.03

Dicyclohexylamine

d	I/I₁
10.04	0.54
5.66	0.29
5.37	0.04
4.90	0.54
4.60	0.20
4.42	0.13
3.97	1.00
3.80	0.41
3.65	0.04
3.53	0.06
3.35	0.04
3.18	0.20
2.98	0.20
2.64	0.20
2.57	0.13
2.46	0.04
2.32	0.04
2.23	0.06
1.88	0.04
1.77	0.06

Morpholine

d	I/I₁
5.34	0.15
4.74	1.00
4.20	1.00
3.78	0.82
3.62	0.03
3.45	1.00
3.29	0.24
3.01	0.15
2.83	1.00
2.70	0.24
2.60	0.15
2.46	0.35
2.34	0.24
2.20	0.15
2.14	0.15
2.08	0.03
1.93	0.07
1.88	0.15
1.80	0.15
1.70	0.15
1.67	0.24

Piperazine

d	I/I₁
5.32	1.00
4.62	0.52
3.81	0.79
3.65	0.79
3.42	0.22
3.17	1.00
3.09	0.35
2.97	1.00
2.88	0.22
2.68	0.35
2.58	1.00
2.51	0.22
2.45	0.22
2.32	0.52
2.23	0.11
2.09	0.22
2.02	0.22

Piperazine (Cont.)

d	I/I₁
1.91	0.11
1.78	0.22
1.71	0.11
1.67	0.11
1.62	0.11
1.41	0.11

Piperidine

d	I/I₁
9.91	0.15
4.92	1.00
4.39	0.15
4.08	0.15
3.70	0.84
3.47	0.17
3.30	0.17
3.15	0.15
2.96	0.34
2.86	0.48
2.73	0.17
2.54	0.05
2.46	0.17
2.38	0.05
2.26	0.03
2.20	0.17
2.14	0.03
2.00	0.05
1.86	0.03
1.82	0.03
1.74	0.15
1.71	0.15
1.64	0.15

Pyridine

d	I/I₁
7.70	0.23
5.56	0.12
4.07	0.37
3.83	0.23
3.62	1.00
3.47	0.07
3.11	0.12
2.98	0.12
2.80	0.07
2.56	0.12
2.44	0.07
2.23	0.07

o-Toluidine

d	I/I₁
7.99	0.09
5.87	0.59
5.43	0.18
5.12	0.43
4.45	0.79
3.96	0.05
3.83	1.00
3.61	0.18
3.46	0.79
3.33	1.00
3.13	0.29
2.94	0.18
2.86	0.18
2.72	0.18
2.60	0.18
2.54	0.79

o-Toluidine (Cont.)

d	I/I₁
2.41	0.05
2.30	0.29
2.22	0.09
2.17	0.05
2.10	0.05
1.99	0.05
1.87	0.05
1.86	0.05
1.80	0.05
1.70	0.09
1.67	0.05
1.64	0.09

m-Toluidine

d	I/I₁
12.42	0.58
(12.45)	
6.74	0.46
6.22	0.01
4.93	0.11
4.17	0.17
3.98	0.11
3.79	0.17
3.57	1.00
3.37	0.25
3.30	0.05
2.91	0.25
2.81	0.34
2.69	0.05
2.52	0.11
2.46	0.17
2.24	0.05
2.00	0.11
1.78	0.11

p-Toluidine

d	I/I₁
7.29	0.07
6.40	0.54
5.95	0.07
4.79	0.75
4.53	0.07
4.29	0.75
4.02	1.00
3.86	0.23
3.54	0.37
3.32	0.54
3.12	0.54
2.92	0.23
2.79	0.23
2.73	0.23
2.61	0.23
2.56	0.12
2.47	0.07
2.41	0.07
2.34	0.07
2.27	0.12
2.12	0.07
1.83	0.12

[a] X-ray diffraction diagrams were obtained with a Philips 114.59-mm. powder camera using copper Kα radiation from a Philips x-ray generator operated at 35 kv. and 20 ma. Exposures varied from 1.5 to 2 hours using Kodak No-Screen x-ray film and the recommended developing procedure.

Reprinted from Analytical Chemistry, **27**, 1374, 1955. Copyright 1955 by the American Chemical Society and reprinted by permission of the copyright owner.

IDENTIFICATION OF ANTIOXIDANTS

ULTRAVIOLET ABSORPTION AND X-RAY DIFFRACTION[34]

This method uses the general procedure described above to determine the x-ray diffraction pattern spacings for common amine antioxidants used in rubber. The spacings so determined are characteristic and serve to identify the antioxidant.

Extraction of Antioxidant and Accelerator Fragments from Rubber Products.—
The rubber products are prepared in the usual way by mixing and sheeting out on a rubber mill. Vulcanizates can also be ground in a Wiley mill. Cements are prepared by evaporation to the solids, preferably in a vacuum oven. The solids can then be mixed and sheeted out. Compounded latex and latex products may be prepared in the same way.

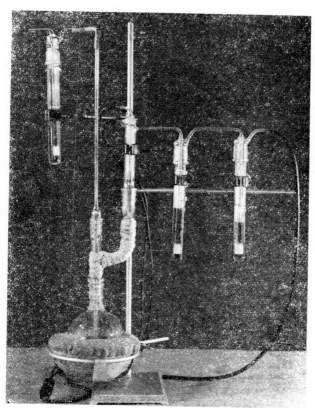

FIG. 59-37.   Apparatus for Extractive Decomposition of Rubber Compounding Materials. (Reprinted from Analytical Chemistry, 27, 1575, 1955. Copyright 1955 by the American Chemical Society and reprinted by permission of the copyright owner.)

Apparatus.—The apparatus used for extracting rubber compounds under reflux is shown in Fig. 59-37. It consists of a 1-liter, single-necked, round-bottomed flask, fitted

[34] Brock, M. J., and Louth, G. D., Anal. Chem., 27, 1575, 1955.

with a Claisen-type adapter which connects it to an air inlet tube, and to a Hopkins-type reflux condenser. The upper end of the air inlet tube is connected to a gas-washing tube containing 0.5 N alcoholic alkali to remove any traces of carbon disulfide and hydrogen sulfide from the incoming air. The lower end of this tube dips below the liquid level in the flask. Connected to the outlet tube of the reflux condenser is another gas-washing tube which contains 50 ml. of 10 percent aqueous copper sulfate to remove any hydrogen sulfide generated during the refluxing period. A third gas-washing tube containing 0.3 N alcoholic sodium hydroxide is used to trap the carbon disulfide that may be liberated from the rubber compound. This tube is connected to a vacuum line.

For distillation of the amines and their absorption in acid, a conventional type of apparatus may be used, such as that illustrated in Fig. 59-38. A modified cylindrical

Fig. 59-38.   Apparatus for Distilling Volatile Amines. (Reprinted from Analytical Chemistry, **27**, 1575, 1955. Copyright 1955 by the American Chemical Society and reprinted by permission of the copyright owner.)

Kjeldahl spray trap is inserted between the distillation flask and the condenser. Modification consists of fusing an insulating jacket around the bulb, to prevent excessive liquid holdup. The receiving adapter has an outlet tip consisting of a small perforated glass bulb.

Procedure.—Place 15 to 20 g. of the prepared rubber product in the 1-liter, single-necked, round-bottomed flask, and add 100 ml. of ethyl alcohol and 100 ml. of 1 N aqueous hydrochloric acid. Connect the flask to the reflux setup, and attach the gas-washing tubes (Fig. 59-37). Apply enough suction to the outlet of the carbon disulfide absorption tube to permit a slow bubbling of air through all the solutions.

Turn on the heating mantle and allow the alcoholic-acid solution to reflux for approxi-

TABLE 59-11. SEPARATION OF NONVOLATILE, NEUTRAL, BASIC, AND ACIDIC MATERIALS

Alkaline Aqueous Solution, Free of Alcohol and Volatile Amine

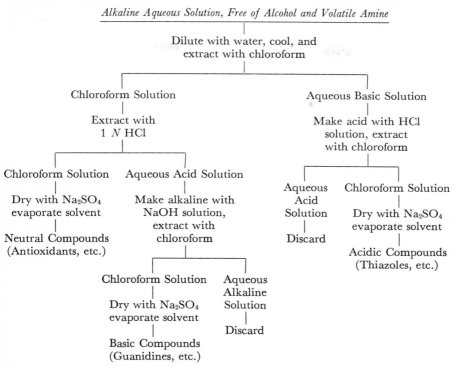

Reprinted from Analytical Chemistry, **27,** 1575, 1955. Copyright 1955 by the American Chemical Society and reprinted by permission of the copyright owner.

TABLE 59-12. ULTRAVIOLET ABSORPTION CHARACTERISTICS OF AMINE ANTIOXIDANTS AND MBT IN ABSOLUTE ETHYL ALCOHOL

	Min., $m\mu$	*Maxima,* $200-250\ m\mu$		*Min.,* $m\mu$	*Maxima,* $250-300\ m\mu$	*Min.,* $m\mu$	*Maxima,* $300-350\ m\mu$
AgeRite Stalite	. . .	208(I)		253	288(II)	. . .	. . . .
BJE	228	208(I)	240(IIIs)[a]	258	. . .	. . .	304(II)
BLE	. . .	208(I)		251	288(II)	. . .	. . . .
Flectol H	225	212(I)	236(II)	285	. . .	. . .	310(IIIs)
Neozone A (PANA)	. . .	217(I)		236	253(II)	288	340(IIIs)
Neozone D (PBNA)	. . .	220(I)		232	272(II)	283	310(III)
Sanoflex AW	. . .	230(I)		. . .	. . .	300	350(IIs)
Sanoflex B	. . .	. . .		. . .	256(I)	278	310(II)
Sanoflex BX	. . .	208(I)		219	256(II)	278	310(III)
Stabilite	218	212(I)	250(II)	272	294(IIIs)	. . .	. . . .
Thermoflex	234	208(I)	245(IIIs)	253	288(II)	. . .	. . . .
Thermoflex A	. . .	220(I)		232	272(III)	282	300–310(II)
MBT	234	230(II)	238(III)	. . .	. . .	272	325(I)

For each antioxidant, maxima are designated I, II, and III in descending order of intensity. [a]s denotes slight maximum.

Reprinted from Analytical Chemistry, **27,** 1575, 1955. Copyright 1955 by The American Chemical Society and reprinted by permission of the copyright owner.

mately 2 hours. After the heat is turned off, allow air to bubble through the solutions for about 5 minutes. Disconnect the apparatus and filter the alcoholic-acid solution into a 500-ml. single-necked, round-bottomed flask. Wash the rubber residue with 100 ml. of water and add the washings to the main solution.

Distillation, Recovery, and Identification of Amine.—Make the cooled alcoholic acid solution alkaline with approximately 25 percent aqueous sodium hydroxide solution, connect the flask to the distillation apparatus, turn on the heating mantle, and distill the amine into 35 ml. of 0.5 N aqueous hydrochloric acid. Continue until most of the alcohol has been distilled from the mixture. The appearance of foam in the boil-

TABLE 59-13.   X-RAY DIFFRACTION DATA OF GUANIDINES

Diphenylguanidine (DPG)		Triphenylguanidine (TPG)		Di-o-tolylguanidine (DOTG)	
d^a	$I/I_1{}^b$	d	I/I_1	d	I/I_1
10.36	0.82	9.15	1.00	10.33	0.46
6.96	0.07	8.24	0.38	6.79	0.25
6.43	0.12	7.05	0.06	6.18	1.00
6.07	0.07	6.50	0.03	5.22	0.25
5.06	0.17	5.37	0.46	4.63	1.00
4.68	1.00	5.00	0.03	4.04	0.46
4.51	0.24	4.72	0.25	3.88	0.17
4.19	0.32	4.52	0.31	3.76	0.46
3.95	0.24	4.34	0.46	3.37	0.05
3.80	0.17	4.07	0.38	3.18	0.11
3.63	0.40	3.79	0.19	3.03	0.05
3.49	0.24	3.56	0.38	2.50	0.05
3.26	0.04	3.42	0.03	2.43	0.05
3.09	0.07	3.08	0.25	2.09	0.03
2.99	0.07	2.70	0.19		
2.91	0.04				
2.64	0.02				
2.54	0.04				
2.44	0.02				
2.41	0.02				
2.31	0.04				
2.21	0.04				
2.14	0.04				
2.01	0.02				
1.93	0.02				
1.86	0.04				
1.69	0.04				

[a] d = interplanar spacing in Angstrom units calculated from Bragg's law where:

$$d = \frac{\lambda}{2 \sin \theta}.$$

λ is wave length of characteristic CuKα radiation, and θ is one half the angle of diffraction.
[b] I/I_1 = relative intensity.

Reprinted from Analytical Chemistry, **27**, 1575, 1955. Copyright 1955 by the American Chemical Society and reprinted by permission of the copyright owner.

ing, alkaline solution indicates that the bulk of the alcohol has been distilled. Concentrate the distillate by boiling, and finally evaporate to dryness in a 100°C. oven. Boil the dried residue gently with 2 or 3 ml. of chloroform and filter to separate the more soluble amine hydrochloride from the sodium and ammonium chlorides. Evaporate the chloroform at 70°C. and identify the dried amine hydrochloride by the x-ray diffraction method of Brock and Hannum described previously.

COLORIMETRIC METHOD[35]

In this method the antioxidant in an extract from the sample is coupled with the diazonium salt of p-nitroaniline to give compounds with characteristic absorption spectra in the visible region. Comparison with spectra of known compounds serves as a means for identification.

Apparatus.—Use a Beckman Model DK-2 recording spectrophotometer or similar instrument with a temperature-regulated cell holder. The instrument settings for the Beckman Model DK-2 are as follows: scanning time, 10; scale expanded, IX; time constant, 0.1; sensitivity, 50. The multiplier phototube is used in the IX position. At this sensitivity, the nominal slit widths are 0.048 mm. at 700 mμ, 0.022 mm. at 650 mμ, 0.013 mm. at 450 mμ, and 0.019 at 400 mμ. Quartz cells having a light path of 1.000 $\pm$ 0.005 cm. are used.

Reagents. **Ethyl Alcohol,** 95 percent.

Sodium Hydroxide Pellets.—Reagent grade, 4 N; 160 g. of sodium hydroxide per liter of distilled water.

*p***-Nitroaniline.**—Melting point 146° to 147°C.

Sodium Nitrite.—Reagent grade.

Coupling Agent.—Dissolve 2.800 g. (0.0203 mole) of p-nitroaniline in 32 ml. of hot concentrated hydrochloric acid and dilute with water to 250 ml. After cooling to room temperature adjust the volume of the liquid to exactly 250 ml. Prepare a second solution containing 1.44 g. (0.0209 mole) of sodium nitrite in exactly 250 ml. of distilled water. Both of the above solutions are reputed to be stable indefinitely.

Twenty-five milliliters of each of these solutions are pipetted into separate 100-ml. beakers and are chilled in ice to below 10°C. The contents are mixed by combining the solutions and pouring them back and forth from one beaker to the other. Pure nitrogen is bubbled through the mixture as it is allowed to warm to room temperature. Finally, 10 mg. of urea (or 1 ml. of 0.1 g. per 10 ml. of solution) are added to destroy any excess nitrous acid. The reagent becomes cloudy after an hour or so but is suitable for use for several hours. Fresh reagent should be made every day.

Procedure.—The sample to be analyzed must be very thinly sheeted (or powdered by passing through a Wiley mill). A 2.000 $\pm$ 0.020-g. sample is accurately weighed and wrapped with extraction cloth which has been previously extracted to remove sizing, etc. The wrapped sample is placed in an Underwriter's extraction cup and extracted for 16 hours with 95 percent ethanol or methanol. The alcohol extract is transferred to a 100-ml. volumetric flask, cooled to room temperature, and brought to the mark with the extraction solvent. A 10-ml. aliquot is transferred to a 100-ml. volumetric flask. Two milliliters of coupling reagent are added. The solution is thoroughly mixed and 3 ml. of 4 N sodium hydroxide solution are added. The solution is then brought to the mark with 95 percent ethanol or methanol. (The sample weight, the size of the aliquot, or both may be adjusted to give a more satisfactory color. However, the total volume at the time of adding the coupling solution must be 10 ml.)

The absorption spectrum from 700 to 400 mμ is determined. The color formation is

[35] Hilton, C. L., Anal. Chem., **32**, 383, 1960.

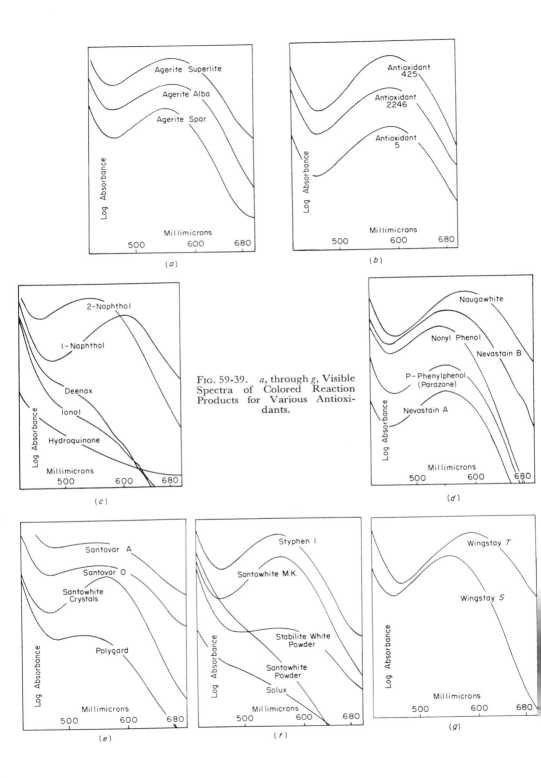

FIG. 59-39. *a*, through *g*, Visible Spectra of Colored Reaction Products for Various Antioxidants.

complete by the time the solution is brought to the mark. The color is stable for at least 2 hours. Ethyl alcohol is used in the reference cell unless the alcohol extract is strongly colored. In this case, the reference solvent is taken to be a 10-ml. aliquot of the ethyl alcohol extract diluted to 100-ml. with ethyl alcohol. The absorbance readings are plotted on Keuffel and Esser semilogarithmic graph paper No. 358-63, 2 cycles × 10½ inches. The resulting spectrum is compared with Fig. 59-39, a through g for identification of the antioxidant.

IDENTIFICATION OF INORGANIC FILLERS
INFRARED METHOD[36]

A procedure is given for the preparation of suitably fine powders from inorganic fillers used in rubber so that infrared absorption spectra may be obtained directly. Such spectra often are sufficient for identification of the filler material when compared to spectra obtained in a similar way on known compounds.

Procedure.—The absorption spectra are obtained from powders having particle diameters smaller than 5 μ in all cases except for those minerals which are difficult to disperse by sedimentation. About 0.2 g. of powder smaller than 5 μ is sufficient for analysis. This can be obtained by grinding about 5 g. of the sample to a fineness that will pass a 150-mesh screen. This powder is added to 250 ml. of distilled water with a small amount of a dispersing agent. For carbonates, silicates, and inorganic chemicals, the dispersing agent is 5 drops of sodium metasilicate. The mixture is violently agitated in a Waring Blendor for about 10 minutes. The suspension which forms is poured from the blender into a 250-ml. graduated cylinder and allowed to stand 2 hours. At the end of this time the upper 5 inches of the suspension will contain particles less than 5 μ in diameter. The upper 5 inches (12.5 cm.) of suspension are drawn off and centrifuged to separate the sediment from the solution of the dispersing agent. The sediment is then dried in an oven at 105° to 110°C. for 24 hours, and placed in a desiccator prior to use. The oven-dried sample is crushed in a small mortar to separate particles which have adhered together, and some of the powder is placed on a standard sodium chloride window. A few drops of isopropyl alcohol are added to form a paste. The paste is smoothed out on the window with a microscope slide whose edges have been beveled and polished to prevent scratching. When the slide is removed, the alcohol evaporates, leaving a thin film of sample on the window.

The window with the powder film on it is inserted in the sample beam and a blank sodium chloride window is placed in the reference beam. Typical spectra are shown in Fig. 59-40. Miller and Wilkins[37] have also reported infrared spectra for inorganic compounds, some of which may be used as reference standards for comparative purposes. More recent techniques involve the preparation of specimens in the form of KBr pellets as described in the section on infrared spectrophotometry in footnote 7 and in Chapter 37 of Volume II, Part B of this work.

IDENTIFICATION OF MAGNESIUM CARBONATE AND MAGNESIUM OXIDE
X-RAY DIFFRACTION METHOD[38]

The method uses special cellulose acetate tubes as sample holders in an x-ray diffraction apparatus, and gives the important factors in obtaining diffraction patterns adequate for identification of inorganic fillers isolated from rubber compounds.

[36] Hunt, J. M., Wisherd, M. P., and Bonham, L. C., Anal. Chem., **22**, 1478, 1950.
[37] Miller, F. A., and Wilkins, C. H., Anal. Chem., **24**, 1253, 1952.
[38] Endter, F., Rubber Chemistry and Technol., **30**, 180, 1957.

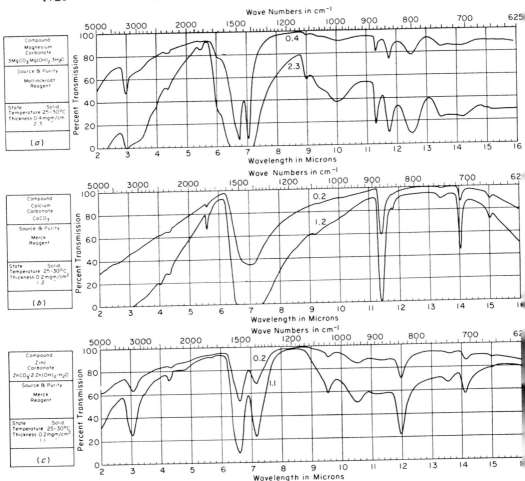

Fig. 59-40.   Infrared Spectra of Powder Films. *A*, Magnesium carbonate. *B*, Calcium Carbonate. *C*, Zinc Carbonate. (Reprinted from Analytical Chemistry, **22**, 1478, 1950. Copyright 1950 by the American Chemical Society and reprinted by permission of the copyright owner.)

Procedure.—For taking x-ray photographs, rod-shaped specimens 0.4–0.5 mm. in diameter and 15 mm. long are used. For testing the vulcanizate itself, a small amount, usually 3–4 mm.^{3}, is finely divided. Filler mixtures isolated are pulverized in an agate mortar and, if necessary, are brushed through a fine screen.

The finely divided or powdered samples are compressed into cellulose acetate capillary tubes. These capillaries can be easily made by following the directions of Fricke, Lohrmann, and Schröder.[39] A warning should be advanced against the use of commerical

[39] Fricke, R. von, Lohrmann, O., and Schröder, W., Z. Elektrochem., **47**, 374, 1941.

medullary tubes of special glass or quartz for they give a central ring in the same position on the x-ray diagram as some of the amorphous substances used for vulcanizates.

In general, the resolving power of a Debye-Scherrer camera with 57.5-mm. diameter is sufficient for taking x-ray diagrams of fillers. Larger camera radii mean considerably longer times of exposure.

Most substances give clear diagrams with nickel-filtered copper Kα-radiation. In the presence of relatively high proportions of amorphous substances, which cause a general blackening of the background of the diagram, an aluminum foil 0.1 mm. thick placed on the film gives better results. Vulcanizates containing large amounts of iron oxide can be more expediently taken with cobalt or molybdenum radiation. When copper radiation is used, a tube voltage of about 40 kv. and an emission current of 20 ma. are sufficient.

Determination of a Combination of Fillers from X-ray Photographs of a Vulcanizate and a Pyrolysis Residue.—As is evident from a comparison of the photograph in Fig. 59-41 of a vulcanizate (B), with standard photographs of magnesium

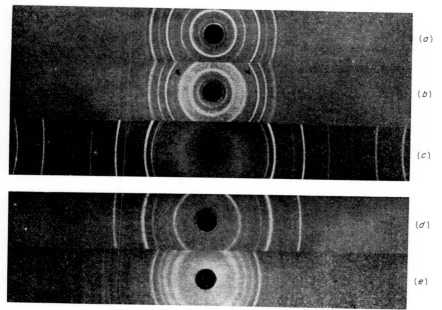

FIG. 59-41. X-ray Diffraction Patterns. *A*, Standard pattern of magnesium carbonate. *B*, Pattern obtained on vulcanizate. *C*, Standard pattern of magnesium oxide. *D*, Pattern obtained on syrolysis residue. *E*, Standard pattern of diatomaceous earth. (Courtesy Kautschuk und Gummi.)

carbonate (*A*), and of magnesium oxide (*C*), the majority of the lines of the analytical diagram pertain to these two compounds. At the point marked x on the standard photograph there is, however, a line of strong texture. This indicates the presence of another component. The diagram (*D*) of the vulcanizate pyrolyzed in vacuum shows that all magnesium carbonate has been converted into magnesium oxide. According to the extent that the several lines in the middle of the diagram disappear as a result of decomposition of the magnesium oxide, the line texture becomes clearer. A comparison with standard photographs shows that the innermost five lines of the diagram of the pyrolysis residue are characteristic of diatomaceous earth (E).

If the pyrolysis residue is calcined, the magnesium oxide diagram becomes very much sharper, while at the same time new lines which appear show that certain of the components in the filler mixture have reacted with one another during calcination.

QUANTITATIVE METHODS

DETERMINATION OF SULFUR

PEROXIDE BOMB FUSION METHOD[40]

This method is a modification of the usual peroxide bomb fusion procedure for sulfur in organic compounds. As it is considered an important method for sulfur in rubber it has been included.

Procedure.—The rubber sample must be finely divided; this is accomplished by rasping, buffing, cutting, or milling. For the 22-ml. ignition type of bomb the following procedure shall be used.

Accurately weigh a sample containing not more than 0.20 g. rubber hydrocarbon, mix thoroughly with 0.50 g. of potassium perchlorate accelerator, 0.50 g. powdered sucrose and 11 g. of sodium peroxide in the fusion cup. Add 4 g. of sodium peroxide as an unmixed layer on top of the thoroughly mixed, leveled surface of the charge, and ignite in accordance with the operating instructions given for the bomb.

When the 22-ml. electric ignition type of bomb is used, follow the above procedure except that 15 g. of sodium peroxide are thoroughly mixed with the charge and the 4-g. layer of peroxide is omitted. In this case the charge is ignited in accordance with the instructions given for electric ignition.

After ignition, cool and open the bomb, wash the head with hot distilled water, and collect the washings in a 600-ml. beaker. Transfer the fusion cup to the beaker containing about 75 ml. of warm distilled water and dissolve the melt. Then remove the cup with tongs, washing the cup with about 25 ml. of hot distilled water.

Neutralize the solution with concentrated hydrochloric acid and add 0.5 ml. of excess acid. After neutralizing with ammonia or ammonium carbonate, add 15 g. more of ammonium carbonate and boil the solution for 30 minutes. Filter any precipitate and wash with a dilute sodium carbonate solution. Add concentrated hydrochloric acid until the filtrate is acid and drive off the carbon dioxide by boiling. If ferric chloride is present, precipitate the iron with ammonia and filter the precipitate. Add 5 ml. of concentrated hydrochloric acid to the filtrate, dilute to 400 ml., heat to boiling, and slowly add 20 ml. of 10 percent barium chloride while stirring the solution slowly. Place the covered beaker on the steam bath overnight, filter, ignite, weigh, and calculate the sulfur content.

$$\text{Sulfur, } \% = \frac{\text{wt. BaSO}_4 \times 13.734}{\text{wt. sample}}$$

ABSORPTIMETRIC METHOD[41]

The method employs the absorption of lead chloride at 270 mμ wavelength as an indirect measure of sulfur in a sample. The sample is oxidized in a solution containing lead nitrate, nitric acid, bromine, and perchloric acid to convert the sulfur to sulfate ion. The precipitated lead sulfate is separated and purified, converted to soluble lead

[40] Manual No. 121, Parr Instruments Co., Moline, Illinois.
[41] Kress, K. E., Anal. Chem., **27**, 1618, 1955.

chloride, and the lead is estimated by ultraviolet absorption measurement. The sulfur content is calculated from this absorbance value.

Apparatus. Sample Test Tubes.—Such as 15 × 100 mm. lipless culture tubes, of 12- to 15-ml. volume.

Capillary-tipped Pipet.—Connected to a water pump vacuum source.

Standard High Speed Semimicrocentrifuge.—Capable of holding sample tubes.

Finger Stall.—Pure gum rubber, or a finger from a rubber glove, extracted with a solution of 5 percent hydrochloric acid in acetone.

Beckman DU Quartz Ultraviolet Spectrophotometer.—With ultraviolet accessories, or a similar instrument.

Roller-Smith Microbalance.—Torsion type, of 25-mg. capacity with V-shaped pan, or similar balance weighing to 0.01 mg.

Reagents. Concentrated Nitric Acid-Bromine.—Add Reagent Grade bromine to concentrated Reagent Grade nitric acid, in an all-glass dropper bottle with clean rubber or Tygon bulb. Have a layer of excess bromine on the bottom at all times.

Perchloric Acid.—70 to 72 percent Reagent Grade used as received.

Acetone, Reagent Grade.—This must be redistilled if a brown residue is present after evaporation of the acetone following the precipitation and washing step.

Hydrochloric Acid, 50 percent by volume.—Mix equal volumes of concentrated hydrochloric acid (35 to 38 percent Reagent, sp. gr. 1.1778 to 1.1923 range) and distilled water, using the same volumetric flask to measure the acid and water.

Lead Nitrate, 10 percent.—Dissolve 10.0 g. of lead nitrate in water and dilute to 100 ml.

Calibration.—The average specific absorbance or K value of lead at 270 mμ is 54.0. The exact figure should be determined for each instrument for greatest accuracy.

Prepare a stock solution containing 1000 p.p.m. of lead by dissolving 0.160 g. of Reagent Grade lead nitrate in distilled water in a 100-ml. volumetric flask and diluting to volume. Pipet 10.0 ml. into a second 100-ml. volumetric flask and dilute to volume for a 100 p.p.m. lead standard. Deliver different volumes between 0.5 and 8.0 ml. of the 100 p.p.m. standard into a clean glass Erlenmeyer flask. Add enough distilled water to make exactly 10.0-ml. total volume of lead solution. Pipet 10.0 ml. of concentrated hydrochloric acid reagent into the flask. Shake well and measure absorbance of the 50 percent hydrochloric acid solution at 270 mμ in 1.00-cm. quartz sample cells. Calculate K_{Pb} as follows:

$$K_{Pb} = \frac{A_{270m\mu}}{bc}$$

where: A is instrument absorbance at 270 mμ;

> b is internal cell thickness, and is neglected as long as it is 1.00 ± 0.005 cm.;
>
> c is concentration of lead in g. per liter at the dilution for which absorbance is measured; *e.g.*, 100 p.p.m. × 4 ml./20 ml. = 20 p.p.m. or 0.020 g. per liter.

The K value to be used is the average of the data over the range of linear instrument absorbance (usually considered 0.1 to 1.8).

Procedure.—Weigh 1 to 3 mg. of well milled representative sample. Sheet as thin as possible and weigh to 0.01 mg. on a suitable microbalance. Transfer the sample directly into the labeled sample tube, add 0.25 ml. of 10 percent lead nitrate solution, then add about 1 ml. of prepared concentrated nitric acid-bromine reagent and 3 drops (1 ml.)

of 70 percent perchloric acid reagent. *While oxidation procedures using perchloric acid must always be handled with caution, this method is reported to be safe.*

After the oxidation reaction is completed, cool the tubes to room temperature and rapidly pour 10 ml. of acetone into the reaction tube. Cover the tube mouth and shake gently to mix the acid and the acetone.

Immerse the sample tubes in a water bath at 50°C. for 15 minutes, then centrifuge for 1–2 minutes. Carefully withdraw all but 0.5 ml. of the liquid layer. Wash the precipitated lead sulfate twice with 10 ml. of acetone, centrifuge and remove washings. Add 2 drops of distilled water, evaporate to complete dryness, and cool. The residue should be white but if brown coloration is present, heat the residue at 550°C. for about 15 minutes until residue is white. When tube is cool, add 10.0 ml. of 50 percent hydrochloric acid. Using rubber finger stall as stopper, shake tube until all the lead sulfate is dissolved. Centrifuge down any acid-insoluble matter.

Record absorbance at 270 mμ using a 50 percent hydrochloric acid blank. If absorbance is above 1.80, dilute with 50 percent hydrochloric acid.

Calculate the percent sulfur in the sample as follows with a spectrophotometer cell thickness of 1.00 cm. A reagent blank normally amounts to about 0.010 absorbance or less, which is about 0.01 to 0.02 percent sulfur. Therefore, the analyst may neglect the reagent blank, except for the most exacting work.

$$\% \text{ sulfur} = \frac{A \times \dfrac{S(32.07)}{\text{Pb}(207.2)} \times 100}{K_{\text{Pb}} \times c(\text{mg./ml.})} = \frac{A_{270\ m\mu} \times 0.155 \times 100}{54.0 \times (\text{wt. mg./10 ml. acid})}$$

For 10.0 ml. of acid, this reduces to

$$\% \text{ sulfur} = \frac{(2.87)A_{270\ m\mu}}{\text{mg. of sample}}$$

If 1 to 1 volume dilution is necessary (20-ml. volume), the factor is doubled and is 5.74.

COMBUSTION METHOD[42]

This is a British Standards Institution method using a special combustion train and collection traps to convert the sulfur in the rubber sample to sulfuric acid and a titration procedure for final measurement of sulfur. A special titration procedure is given for samples containing acrylonitrile.

This semimicromethod occupies a total time of about 1 hour. The result will include all sulfur present. Alternative finishes are given for samples containing acrylonitrile type polymers and chlorine compounds.

Reagents.—All reagents used shall be of recognized analytical reagent quality, and demineralized water shall be used wherever water is specified.

Calcium Chloride.—Anhydrous, approximately 14–22 mesh.

Catalyst.—Heat some vanadium pentoxide in a shallow dish at 140–160°C. for 16 hours, and cool in a desiccator. Weigh 0.8 g. of the dry vanadium pentoxide and 0.2 g. of zinc oxide for each determination.

Hydrogen Peroxide Solution.—3 g. of H_2O_2 in 100 ml. water.

Indicator Solution.—0.125 g. of methyl red and 0.083 g. methylene blue in 100 ml. ethanol.

Magnesium Perchlorate (Anhydrone), 14–22 mesh.

Supply of Oxygen.

Soda Asbestos.—14–22 mesh, preferably self-indicating type.

[42] British Standard Methods of Testing Vulcanized Rubber, B. S. 903, Parts B6-B10, 1958.

Sodium Hydroxide.—0.02 N solution.

Additional reagents for samples containing chlorine compounds and acrylonitrile type polymers.

Ammonium Chloride.

Ammonia Solution, sp. gr. 0.880.

Barium Chloride, 0.01 M solution.

Congo Red Test Paper.

Disodium Dihydrogen Ethylenediaminetetraacetate (EDTA), 0.01 M solution.

Eriochrome Black T or Solochrome Black WDFA Indicator.—Dissolve by warming 0.5 g. of Eriochrome Black T or Solochrome Black WDFA in 100 ml. of ethanol, and add 4.5 g. of hydroxylamine hydrochloride. Allow to stand overnight and centrifuge or filter. This indicator solution should not be kept for more than 1 month.

Hydrochloric Acid, dilute.—Dilute 1 volume of concentrated acid (sp. gr. 1.18) with 3 volumes of water.

Zinc Disodium Ethylenediaminetetraacetate.—Dissolve by warming 5.0 g. disodium dihydrogen ethylenediaminetetraacetate dihydrate in 100 ml. of water. Add 1.5 g. of zinc oxide to the hot solution, stir, and heat to boiling to dissolve as much as possible of the zinc oxide. Cool to room temperature and filter the excess of zinc oxide. Evaporate the solution to dryness on a water bath with occasional stirring.

Apparatus.—The assembly of the apparatus is shown in Fig. 59-42.

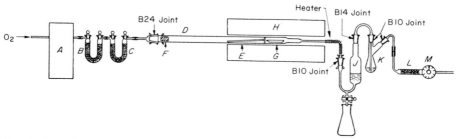

FIG. 59-42. Apparatus for the Determination of Total Sulfur by the Combustion Method. *A,* Flowmeter. *B* and *C,* Purifying train. *D,* Silica combustion tube. *E,* Silica rod with handle and button. *F,* Magnetic block. *G,* Combustion boat. *H,* Combustion furnace. *J,* Primary absorbing vessel. *K,* Secondary absorbing vessel. *L,* Calcium chloride tube. *M,* Needle valve. (Reproduced from B. S. 903 by permission of British Standards Institution. Copies of the complete standard may be obtained through the American Standards Assn., Inc., New York.)

Flow Meter.—To indicate 50–60 ml. per minute.

Purifying Train.

Silica Combustion Tube.—Equipped with heater for bent end. Total horizontal length 650–670 mm.

Silica Rod.—Equipped with handle and button. Diameter of rod 7–8 mm. Diameter of button 12–13 mm. Overall length 125 mm.

Magnetic Stainless Steel Cylinder Block.—Diameter 13–14 mm. Length 10–11 mm.

Combustion Boat (Transparent Silica) with Handle.—Outside measurements; overall length 53–55 mm., width 11–13 mm., depth 7–9 mm.

Combustion Furnace (Electric).—Equipped with temperature indicator and controller. Length about 320 mm.

Primary Absorbing Vessel.—See Fig. 59–43.

Secondary Absorbing Vessel.
Calcium Chloride Tube.
Needle Valve.
Magnet.—Capable of moving magnetic cylinder block, *F*, from outside silica combustion tube.

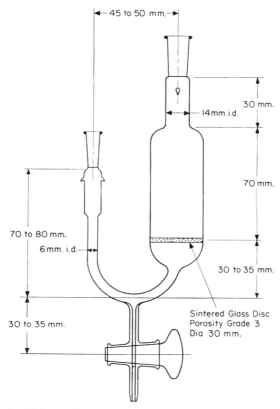

Fig. 59-43.   Detail of Primary Absorbing Vessel, *J*. (Reproduced from B. S. 903 by permission of British Standards Institution. Copies of the complete standard may be obtained through the American Standards Assn., Inc., New York.)

Description of Apparatus.—The combustion tube, *D*, consists of a satin or transparent silica tube 16 mm. i.d., fused at one end to a transparent silica tube which narrows to 7-mm. i.d. The other end is fused to a B24 cone provided with hooks. The overall measurement across the B24 cone and hooks must not exceed 30 mm. The length of the wide tube is 480 mm.; the narrower tube is horizontal for 170–190 mm. and then bends downwards at a right angle and continues for a further 77 mm., including a B10 cone with hooks in the same plane as the bend: the cone is greased with sulfur-free, high-temperature-resisting silicone grease.

To prevent condensation of vapor in the bent end of the combustion tube and in the neighboring ground glass joint, the bent portion is electrically heated to a temperature to 400–500°C. which is controlled by suitable means.

The B24 cone is fitted with a socket provided with hooks, and this is connected by rubber tubing to U-tube, C, of the purifying train.

An asbestos screen is fixed at the exit end of the combustion tube so that radiated heat from the furnace does not affect the solution in the absorbing vessels.

The absorption train consists of two vessels. The primary vessel, J, is the shape of a U-tube, and is joined to the combustion tube by a B10 socket which is 70–80 mm. (measured vertically) from the bottom of the U-tube. The internal diameter of this limb is 6 mm. and the stopcock is 30–35 mm. from the bottom of the tube. A sintered glass disc (porosity 3), 30-mm. diameter, is sealed in the other limb at the lower end of the expanded portion, which is 70 mm. long and 30 mm. in diameter. This limb then narrows to a 14-mm. diameter for 30 mm. and terminates in a B14 socket.

The secondary vessel, K, consists of a 20- or 25-ml. pear-shaped flask with B10 sockets at the neck and side arm. The side arm is fitted with a B10 cone and delivery tube, which is connected via a calcium chloride tube, L, to a needle valve, M, and suction line. The two absorbing vessels are connected to each other by an inverted U-tube, 7-mm. i.d., with a B14 cone at one end and a B10 cone and delivery tube at the other. The delivery tube ends not more than 1 mm. from the bottom of the secondary vessel. All ground-glass joints of the absorption train are secured by springs and no grease is used.

The purifying train consists of two U-tubes, B and C. B contains magnesium perchlorate, and is connected to the exit of the calibrated flow meter, A. The second U-tube contains soda asbestos.

Procedure.—Heat the combustion furnace to 1000 ± 20°C., and the bent end of the combustion tube to 400–500°C.

Place a layer of catalyst (about 0.3 g.) in the ignited combustion boat. Weigh accurately about 50 mg. (10 mg. in the case of ebonite or thioplasts) of the sample, and distribute the test portion in the prepared boat. Cover with the remainder of the catalyst.

Connect the absorbing vessels to the combustion tube, remove the inverted U-tube and from a graduated pipet add 15 ml. of hydrogen peroxide solution to the primary absorbing vessel via the B14 socket and 5 ml. to the secondary absorbing vessel. Replace the inverted U-tube and connect the side arm of the secondary absorbing vessel via the calcium chloride tube to the needle valve attached to the suction line.

Connect the oxygen to the flow meter and purifying train, and adjust the supply of oxygen so that the rate of flow is 50 ml. per minute. To ensure a steady stream of oxygen a pressure of not less than 25 lb./sq. in. should be shown on the pressure gauge of the cylinder. Disconnect the oxygen from the flow meter without changing the setting of the oxygen regulator.

Insert the boat in the mouth of the combustion tube followed by the silica rod and steel cylinder. Close the combustion tube with the B24 socket and connect to the purifying train and flow meter. Adjust the suction to draw purified air through the combustion tube and absorbing vessels at a rate of 60 ml. per minute as indicated by the flow meter. Connect the oxygen to the flow meter so that the previously adjusted oxygen is drawn through the combustion tube and absorption train.

By means of the magnet (steel cylinder and silica rod), slide the boat to a position 1 cm. from the furnace and leave it for 2 minutes. In order to maintain a steady combustion rate, propel the boat slowly forward (about 0.5 cm. per minute) to the hottest zone of the furnace. (If the advance of the boat into the hot zone is too rapid, excessive fluctuations of the flow meter level will be noted.) Withdraw the steel cylinder to the mouth of the tube as soon as the boat reaches the hottest zone of the furnace. When destruction of the organic material is complete, as indicated by stability of the flow meter, continue the combustion for a further 30 minutes to ensure decomposition of alkaline earth sulfates.

Switch off the current to the bent end heater, disconnect the oxygen from the flow meter, and cool the hot B10 joint of the primary absorbing vessel to room temperature, *e.g.*, with a jet of compressed air. Then disconnect the suction from the side arm of the secondary absorbing vessel and remove the silica rod and boat.[43]

Connect hand bellows to the side arm and gently blow the liquid from the secondary absorbing vessel into the primary absorbing vessel and round the lower U-tube until it is just below the B10 joint. Carefully open the stopcock, allow the liquid to run slowly into a flask, and continue blowing until all the solution is transferred. For samples containing no chlorine compounds or acrylonitrile-type polymers, collect the solution in a 100-ml. conical flask. For samples containing these compounds, collect the solution in a 50-ml. volumetric flask.

Add about 8 ml. of water through the side arm of the secondary absorbing vessel and with the hand bellows transfer the liquid to the primary vessel, wash the U-tube just above the B10 joint, and collect the washings in the flask. Disconnect the apparatus at the B14 joint and rinse down the side of the wide limb of the U-tube with 10 ml. of water. Replace the B14 joint and force the liquid into the U-tube and thence through the stop cock into the flask. Repeat the washing with a further 10 ml. of water, and then titrate according to the appropriate finish.

Make a blank determination on the reagents by carrying out the complete procedure using the appropriate titrimetric finish and calculate the sulfur content from the corrected titration figure.

Titrimetric Finish for Samples Containing No Acrylonitrile Type Polymers or Chlorine Compounds.—Add to the liquid in the 100-ml. conical flask 2 drops of methyl red–methylene blue indicator solution, and titrate using 0.02 N sodium hydroxide from a 10-ml. microburet.

Titrimetric Finish for Samples Containing Acrylonitrile Type Polymers and Chlorine Compounds.—Make up the liquid in the 50-ml. volumetric flask to the mark with water and proceed as follows.

(*a*) *For samples containing acrylonitrile type polymers.*—Pipet 20 ml. of the solution into a 100-ml. conical flask, add a small piece of Congo red indicator paper, and neutralize with 0.02 N sodium hydroxide. Add 5 drops of dilute hydrochloric acid, heat to boiling, add by pipet 5 ml. of 0.01 M barium chloride, and boil for 1 minute. Cool the solution to 15 $\pm$ 2°C., and add 0.1 g. ammonium chloride, 0.02 g. of zinc EDTA complex, 5 ml. of ammonia solution, and 5 drops of Eriochrome Black T or Solochrome Black WDFA. Titrate to the first pseudo end point with 0.01 M EDTA, add a further 5 ml. of ammonia solution, and titrate to the blue end point (Y ml.).

Carry out a blank titration using the same quantities of reagents as above (X ml.).

(*b*) *For samples containing chlorine compounds with or without acrylonitrile type polymers.*—Proceed exactly as described under (*a*) with the following addition.

Pipet a further 20 ml. into a 100-ml. conical flask, add 5 drops of dilute hydrochloric acid, and boil for 1 minute. Cool the solution to 15 $\pm$ 2°C., add 0.1 g. of ammonium chloride, 5 ml. of ammonia solution, and 5 drops of Eriochrome Black T or Solochrome Black WDFA indicator. Titrate as described in (*a*) with 0.01 M EDTA (Z ml.).

---

[43] In order to clean the boat for further determinations, it is advisable to withdraw it while the contents are still molten, and quickly pour the molten mass into a beaker containing silica, applying heat to the boat if necessary. Suspend the cool boat in warm concentrated hydrochloric acid, then remove all traces of acid by washing with water, and ignite.

Calculation of Results.—Samples containing no acrylonitrile type polymers or chlorine compounds:

$$\text{Total sulfur} = \frac{V \times 0.032}{W} \text{ percent}$$

where: V = corrected volume of 0.02 N sodium hydroxide, in milliliters; and
W = weight of sample, in grams.

Samples containing acrylonitrile type polymers:

$$\text{Total sulfur} = \frac{0.08(X - Y)}{W} \text{ percent}$$

where W = weight of sample, in grams.

Samples containing chlorine compounds with or without acrylonitrile type polymers:

$$\text{Total sulfur} = \frac{0.08(X + Z - Y)}{W} \text{ percent}$$

where W = weight of sample, in grams.

FREE SULFUR IN ACCELERATORS: BY POLAROGRAPHIC METHOD[44]

This polarographic method uses liquid elution chromatography to separate free sulfur from accelerators and determines the eluted free sulfur by polarographic analysis of a pyridine solution of the sulfur.

Apparatus. Chromatographic Tube.—Regular length, similar to size II, Cat. No. J-1664, Scientific Glass Apparatus Co., Bloomfield, N. J.

Polarograph.—Either manual or recording, with dropping mercury electrode and saturated calomel reference electrode. Sensitivity ranges of approximately 5 and 20 microamperes full scale deflection are required. The damping is set at the galvanometer equivalent. Drop time is 6 seconds.

Thermostat.—To maintain the polarographic cell at 25 $\pm$ 1°C.

Bottle, Gas Washing.—Tall form with fritted cylinder, 125-ml. capacity, similar to Cat. No. 31770, Corning Glass Works, Corning, N. Y.

Reagents. Sulfur.—Purify by recrystallizing from benzene.

Buffer Solution.—0.175 M acetic acid and 0.175 M sodium acetate. Dissolve 10.5 g. of acetic acid and 14.4 g. of anhydrous sodium acetate in a liter of water. Filter the solution.

Alumina, Activated.—Chromatographic powdered catalyst grade, similar to AL-0109P (90 percent Al_2O_3), Harshaw Chemical Co., Cleveland, Ohio. Put 1800 g. of alumina and 2250 ml. of ethyl acetate in a covered container and let stand for 48 hours. Filter on a Buchner funnel, wash with $4\frac{1}{2}$ liters of water and $4\frac{1}{2}$ liters of methanol, and dry to a free-flowing powder by drawing air through it. Place the alumina in a furnace at 360°C. for 5 hours. Transfer it to a bottle and put the bottle on a roller for several hours. Ignite a 2-g. sample at 900°C. for 2 hours and calculate the loss in weight as water. Add sufficient water to make the water content 10.0 $\pm$ 0.5 percent, and put the alumina on a roller overnight. Redetermine the water.

Pyridine.—Redistill, collecting the middle 80 percent.

Nitrogen.—Lamp Grade, similar to that furnished by General Electric Co.

[44] Hively, R. A., and Wadelin, C. W., Rubber Chemistry and Technol., **32**, 123, 1959.

Benzene.
Methanol.
Calibration.—Weigh accurately about 100 mg. of sulfur, dissolve it in pyridine in a 100-ml. volumetric flask, and dilute to the mark. Using aliquots of this solution, prepare solutions A and B, containing 0.100 and 0.600 mg. of sulfur/ml. of pyridine, respectively.

Transfer 0, 1.0, 3.0, 6.0, and 10.0 ml. of solution A to 50-ml. beakers, add enough pyridine to make a total of 10.0 ml., and add, with a pipet, 20.0 ml. of methanol and 10.0 ml. of buffer solution. Mix well, rinse the polarographic cell, and fill it. Degas the solution for 15 min. with Lamp Grade nitrogen which has been presaturated by passing it through a gas washing bottle containing 1 part pyridine, 2 parts methanol, and 1 part water by volume.

Measure the average galvanometer deflection at −0.75 volts *vs.* the saturated calomel electrode using a galvanometer sensitivity of 5 microamperes full scale, temperature 25 ± 1°C., and drop time of 3 to 6 seconds.

In a similar manner, transfer 0, 1.0, 2.0, 4.0, and 6.0-ml. portions of solution B to beakers, treat as above, and measure the average galvanometer deflections using a sensitivity of 20 microamperes full scale.

Subtract the average galvanometer deflection for 0 mg. of sulfur (residual current) from each of the other average galvanometer deflections measured at the same sensitivity, and plot a graph of (average galvanometer deflection-residual current) *vs.* mg. of sulfur for each series.

Procedure.—Weigh accurately about 100 mg. of accelerator. Dissolve it in 5 ml. of benzene, warming if necessary. Pour the solution onto a column of alumina, 10 cm. in height, 19 mm. in diameter. Rinse the sample container with 5 ml. of benzene and pour it onto the column when the level of the sample solution reaches the top of the alumina. Repeat the rinsing once more. When the level of the second portion of rinse solution reaches the top of the alumina, add about 25 ml. of benzene. Collect the first 15 ml. of eluate. A little pressure on top of the column or vacuum on the receiver may be used to speed the elution, but the flow rate should not exceed 3 ml./min.

Evaporate the eluted solution at a temperature just below the boiling point. Remove the beaker from the heat just before it reaches dryness and complete the evaporation to dryness at room temperature.

Dissolve the sulfur residue in 10.0 ml. of pyridine measured with a pipet, warming slightly to insure complete dissolution. Add methanol and buffer solution, degas, and measure as in the calibration procedure. If less than 1 mg. of sulfur is expected, measure at 5 microamperes full scale deflection. If from 1 to 3.6 mg. are expected, measure at 20 microamperes full scale.

At least once each day run a blank determination. Subtract the residual current from the sample reading and refer the corrected average galvanometer deflection to the calibration plot to find the amount of sulfur present.

DETERMINATION OF SOLUBILITY, DIFFUSIVITY, AND BLOOMING OF SULFUR IN RUBBER: TRACER METHOD[45]

The method of Auerbach and Gehman uses the radioactive sulfur-35 isotope to measure the solubility of sulfur in opaque rubber samples by comparing the equilibrium counting rate with a calibration curve of counts for samples containing known amounts of radioactive sulfur. Diffusivity of sulfur in rubber is determined by suitable application of these procedures. The blooming of sulfur in rubber specimens is also evaluated by this method.

[45] Auerbach, I., and Gehman, S. D., Anal. Chem., **26**, 685, 1954.

CARBON BLACK IN MASTERBATCHES

PYROLYSIS METHOD[46]

This method determines the carbon black in unvulcanized masterbatches by the pyrolysis of rubber at 550°C., under reduced pressure in a stream of helium gas.

The volatile products are removed as they are formed, and the carbon black is determined by weighing the residue after pyrolysis and correcting for the ash content.

Apparatus. **Drying Oven.**

Porcelain Crucibles.—No. 00000, tared.

Weighing Bottles.—Tared.

Combustion Boat.—The boat may be prepared of stainless steel to hold about 12 crucibles, depending on the length of the furnace. A rod should be attached to one end of the boat to permit removing it.

Combustion Tube.—Vycor 30 in. by 1 in. in diameter.

Rack.—To hold combustion tube when out of furnace.

Combustion Furnace.—The furnace should open by lifting up the top half so that the combustion tube may be inserted or removed, without interrupting the gas train.

Reduced Pressure Device.—For producing a pressure of either 4–5 mm. or 40–45 mm. in the combustion tube when the other end of the tube is attached to a good mechanical vacuum pump.

The device shown in Fig. 59-44, as an example, is designed so that the restriction of the flow when the stopcock is closed results in a reduction in pressure of 10:1 as compared

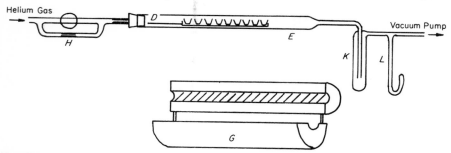

FIG. 59-44. Pyrolysis Apparatus for Determination of Carbon Black. *D*, Combustion boat. *E*, Combustion tube. *G*, Combustion furnace. *H*, Pressure-controlling device. *K*, Dry ice trap. *L*, Manometer.

to the pressure with the stopcock open. The actual pressure achieved is selected by proper balance of the gas inlet pressure and the limits of the mechanical vacuum pump used.

Vacuum Pump.

Two-stage Reducing Valve.—For helium tank.

Dry Ice Trap.—To prevent pyrolysis products from getting into manometer and vacuum pump.

Manometer.—To measure pressure in the combustion tube just before vacuum pump.

Tank of Helium Gas.

Preparation of Sample.—Blend 200 g. of dried sample by passing it 5 times between the rolls of a laboratory mill. Maintain the roll temperature at 50 ± 5°C. and a distance

[46] Linnig, F. J., and Cohen, R. I., unpublished work.

between the rolls of 0.020 ± 0.005 in. After blending, sheet the sample from the mill in such a manner as to obtain a thickness of less than 0.030 in. Dry approximately 2 g. of the blended, sheeted material in the oven at 105°C. for 1 hr. Keep the dried sheet in a desiccator until the samples are weighed. Accurately weigh three 0.2- to 0.5-g. samples from the sheet of material being tested into the previously weighed porcelain crucibles. If the most precise values are desired, test at the same time three samples from a similarly prepared sheet of standard SBR black determinate. Due to the hygroscopic nature of the samples, and, particularly, to the rapid pick-up of atmospheric moisture after pyrolysis, weigh the crucible and contents in previously weighed weighing bottles.

Place the crucibles in the combustion boat in an order random with respect to the order of weighing. Insert the combustion boat into the combustion tube placed in the rack and flow helium through the combustion tube (with the pump on) at a pressure of about 40–45 mm. Sweep the tube for about 30 minutes in this manner, then reduce the gas flow so that the pressure in the combustion tube is reduced to 4–5 mm., and place the combustion tube in the combustion furnace maintained at 550 ± 25°C. The vacuum pump is kept running during the entire process. Distill off the rubber hydrocarbon and allow the combustion tube to remain in the furnace at 550 ± 25°C. for 20 minutes, continuing to pass helium through the tube at a pressure of 4–5 mm. At the end of this period remove the combustion tube from the furnace to the rack. Allow it to cool, meanwhile continuing the flow of helium through it at 4–5 mm. pressure. When the tube has cooled to about 125°C., turn off the pump, shut off the gas flow, and remove the sample boat from the combustion tube. Place the crucibles in the previously weighed weighing bottles, and put these in a desiccator until they have cooled to room temperature. Weigh the weighing bottles containing the crucibles in an order random with respect to the position of the crucibles in the boat. After weighing place the crucibles and contents in a muffle furnace maintained at 550 ± 25°C. and burn off the carbon. After the carbon has been completely removed, take the crucibles from the furnace, place in the weighed weighing bottles, and allow them to cool in a desiccator. Weigh the weighing bottles containing the crucibles. Calculate the percentage of ash, A, in the sample

$$A = \frac{(F - E)}{D - E} \times 100$$

where: F = weight of the crucible plus the ash after ignition of the carbon black;
E = weight of crucible; and
D = weight of the original dry sample plus the crucible.

Calculate the carbon black contents of each of the samples of the material tested on a dry ash-free basis as follows:

$$c = \frac{100(Q - F)}{(D - E)(1 - 0.01\,A)}$$

where: Q = weight of the crucible plus the carbon black residue after the distillation of hydrocarbon. F, D, E, and A are defined as above.

Calculate in a similar manner the carbon black contents of each of the samples of the standard SBR carbon black determinate C' on a dry, ash-free basis.

Calculate the corrected percent of carbon black in the material tested as follows.

$$\text{Carbon black, percent} = C + B - C'$$

where: C = average of the three values for percent carbon black in the material
tested;

B = percentage of carbon black assigned as the standard value for the
determinate sample; and

C' = average of the three values for percent carbon black in the determinate sample.

If a determinate sample is not used, rough values are obtained which may be inaccurate by as much as several percent, depending on the SBR-black combination tested. For more accurate values, a determinate sample should be used prepared from the same SBR-black combination as that present in the material tested.

DETERMINATION OF PHENOLIC ANTIOXIDANTS
COLORIMETRIC METHOD[35]

This method uses the absorbance of the colored product formed in the reaction of the diazonium salt of p-nitroaniline and the antioxidant as a measure of the amount of phenolic antioxidant present.

Procedure.—The procedure described for colorimetric identification (under the section on phenolic antioxidants) is followed, and the percent antioxidant is calculated as follows.

As the absorptivity of an antioxidant will vary from batch to batch, it is essential that a new absorptivity be calculated each time a different batch of antioxidant is used. Absorptivity equals A/bc where A is the absorbance of the solution, b is the optical path in centimeters, and c is the concentration in grams per liter. Pertinent information about the antioxidants is given in Table 59-14. (The absorbance at 700 mμ is subtracted from that at the maximum to eliminate some of the error in the case of turbid solutions.)

The equations for the quantitative determination of the antioxidants are developed by calculating the absorptivity of the solution, multiplying by 100, and dividing by the absorptivity of the antioxidant. If a 1.000-cm. cell is used and a 10-ml. aliquot is taken from 100 ml. of extract, the absorptivity can be calculated as follows:

$$a = \frac{A_{\mathrm{maximum}} - A_{700}}{(1.000) \text{ sample weight in grams}}$$

The sample weight in grams is substituted for the concentration in grams per liter because the original extract is in 100 ml. and a 10-ml. aliquot is diluted to 100 ml. Thus, the concentration in grams per liter is equal to the sample weight.

ULTRAVIOLET ABSORPTION METHOD[47]

The change in the absorbance of phenolic antioxidants as a function of pH is used to measure quantitatively the antioxidant content in a rubber sample.

Apparatus.—Absorbance measurements are made with a Cary Model 11 spectrophotometer, a Beckman Model DU spectrophotometer, or another suitable spectrophotometer.

Measurements are made in matched pairs of 1-cm. quartz cells, using solvent blanks in the reference cell. Absorption intensities are plotted in terms of absorptivity, a, liter gram^{-1} centimeter^{-1}.

[47] Wadelin, C. W., Anal. Chem., **28**, 1530, 1956.

TABLE 59-14. COMPOSITION AND ABSORPTIVITY DATA FOR PHENOLIC ANTIOXIDANTS

Antioxidant	Composition	Absorptivity, a	Wavelength Max., mμ
AgeRite Alba[a]	Hydroquinone monobenzyl ether	31.48	565
AgeRite Spar[a]	Styrenated phenol	44.06	548
AgeRite Superlite[a]	A polyalkyl polyphenol	23.40	560
Antioxidant 5[a]	Not disclosed	18.81	585
Antioxidant 425[a]	2,2'-Methylenebis(6-tert-butyl-4-methylphenol)	22.30	585
Antioxidant 2246[a]	2,2'-Methylenebis(6-tert-butyl-4-methylphenol)	20.60	578
Deenax[a]	2,6-Di-tert-butyl-p-cresol	Does not couple	
Ionol[a]	2,6-Di-tert-p-cresol	Does not couple	
1-Naphthol	1-Naphthol	120.2	598
2-Naphthol	2-Naphthol	115.1	540
Naugawhite[a]	Alkylated phenol	8.20	580
Nevastain A[a]	Not disclosed	12.44	550
Nevastain B[a]	Not disclosed	6.62	550
Nonyl phenol	Nonyl phenol	36.25	538
p-Phenyl phenol	p-Phenyl phenol	80.80	548
Polygard[a]	Tris(nonylated phenyl) phosphite	Must be hydrolyzed before it will couple	
Santovar A[a]	2,5-Di-tert-amylhydroquinone	Color too weak	
Santovar O[a]	2,5-Di-tert-butylhydroquinone	Color too weak	
Santowhite Crystals[a]	4,4'-Thiobis(6-tert-butyl-2-methylphenol)	78.84	565
Santowhite MK[a]	Reaction product of 6-tert-butyl-m-cresol and SCl$_2$	66.94	560
Santowhite Powder[a]	4,4'-Butylidene-bis(3-methyl-6-tert-butylphenol)	Color too weak	
Solux[a]	N-p-Hydroxyphenylmorpholine	Color too weak	
Stabilite White powder[a]	Not disclosed	Color too weak	
Styphen I[a]	Styrenated phenol	22.61	558
Wingstay S[a]	Styrenated phenol	50.82	545
Wingstay T[a]	A hindered phenol	10.27	590

[a] Trademark.

Reprinted from Analytical Chemistry, **32,** 383, 1960. Copyright 1960 by the American Chemical Society and reprinted by permission of the copyright owner.

Reagents.—A 1 M solution of potassium hydroxide is prepared by grinding 22.4 g. of the reagent with 50-ml. portions of absolute ethyl alcohol until it dissolves and then diluting to 400 ml. with absolute ethyl alcohol. The solution is allowed to stand overnight for potassium carbonate to settle. When the solution begins to turn yellow, it is discarded. The solution should be between 0.9 and 1.1 M.

Commerical grade antioxidants are used without purification.

Procedure.—Sheet the sample to a thickness of 0.020 inch and cut into strips 1 × 5 cm. Weigh a 6-g. sample and add it to 100 ml. of absolute ethyl alcohol, one strip at a time to prevent sticking together. Reflux for 60 minutes, pour off the solvent, add 100 ml. of fresh absolute ethyl alcohol, and reflux 60 minutes more. Pour this off and rinse the sample with three 10-ml. portions of absolute ethyl alcohol. Combine all extracts and washings in a 250-ml. volumetric flask. Cool to room temperature and dilute to the mark with absolute ethyl alcohol.

Transfer 5-ml. aliquots of the extract to two 50-ml. volumetric flasks. Add 5 ml. of 1 M alcoholic potassium hydroxide to one of the flasks. Dilute both solutions to the mark with absolute alcohol. Prepare a blank solution by diluting 5 ml. of the 1 M alcoholic potassium hydroxide to 50 ml. with absolute alcohol.

Measure the absorbances of the extract solutions at 301 mμ in 1-cm. cells, using absolute ethyl alcohol in the reference cell for the neutral solution and the alcoholic potassium hydroxide blank solution in the reference cell for the basic solution.

For calibration prepare a solution of 0.300 g. of Wingstay S per liter of absolute ethyl alcohol, preferably from the same lot of Wingstay S as that used in the samples. Transfer 5-ml. aliquots of this solution to two 50-ml. volumetric flasks. Treat and measure in the same manner as with the sample extracts.

From the measurements on the standards:

$$\alpha = \frac{A_{base} - A_{neutral}}{c \times b}$$

From the measurements of the sample:

$$\% \text{ Wingstay S} = \frac{A_{base} - A_{neutral} \times V \times E \times 0.1}{S \times \alpha \times D \times b}$$

where:

α = absorptivity, liter gram^{-1} centimeter $^{-1}$;
A_{base} = absorbance in basic solution;
$A_{neutral}$ = absorbance in neutral solution;
c = concentration in grams/liter;
b = cell length, centimeters;
S = sample weight in grams;
V = volume of combined extracts, milliliters;
D = volume of aliquot, milliliters; and
E = volume of which aliquot is diluted.

DETERMINATION OF AMINE ANTIOXIDANTS

COLORIMETRIC METHOD[48]

The absorbance of the colored products formed in the reaction of the diazonium salt of p-nitroaniline and the antioxidant is used to determine the antioxidant content of the sample.

Apparatus.—The absorption measurements may be made on a Cary Model II or similar spectrophotometer using quartz cells having a light path of 1.000 cm.

Reagents.—Methanol (99.85 percent).

Hydrochloric Acid.—Analyzed Reagent Grade, sp. gr. 1.188 (37.2 percent hydrochloric acid by weight).

p-Nitroaniline, m.p. 146° to 147°C.

Sodium Nitrite.—Analyzed Reagent Grade. See "Identification of Antioxidants, Colorimetric Method, Reagents."

Methanol-hydrochloric Acid Solvent.—Three volumes of methanol are placed in a glass-stoppered bottle and 1 volume of concentrated hydrochloric acid is added gradually with gentle mixing. The mixture is allowed to come to room temperature before carrying out the analyses.

[48] Hilton, C. L., Rubber Chemistry and Technol., **32**, 844, 1959.

Procedure.—The sample to be analyzed must be very thinly sheeted (or powdered by passing through a Wiley mill). Weigh a 1.0000 ± .0005 g. sample. Wrap with extraction cloth which has been previously extracted to remove sizing, etc. Place wrapped sample in an Underwriter's extraction cup and extract for 16 hours with 95 percent ethanol or methanol. Transfer the alcohol extract to a 100-ml. volumetric flask. Cool to room temperature and bring to the mark with the extraction solvent. Transfer a 10-ml. aliquot to a 100-ml. volumetric flask. Add 15 ml. of methanol-hydrochloric acid solution and 1 ml. of coupling agent. Place in the dark for 1½ hours and then bring to the mark with methanol-hydrochloric acid. Determine the absorption spectrum from 700 mμ to 350 mμ.

Plot the absorbance readings on Keuffel and Esser semilogarithmic graph paper 359-H-71, 3 cycles × 10 to the inch. Compare the resulting spectrum with Fig. 59-45, *a* through *i* for identification of the antioxidant. Calculate amount of antioxidant present using constant given in Table 59-15.

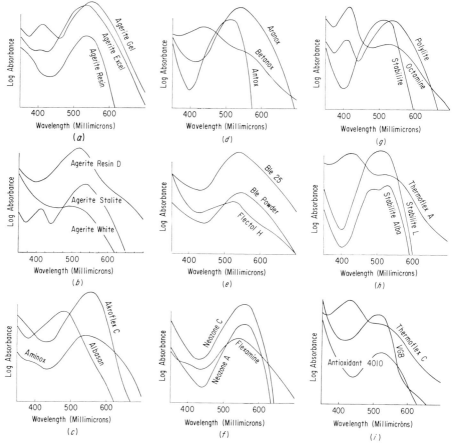

Fig. 59-45. Spectra of Colored Reaction Products of Various Antioxidants. (Courtesy Rubber Age.)

TABLE 59-15. EQUATIONS FOR ANTIOXIDANTS WHICH CAN BE DETERMINED
BY THE REGULAR PROCEDURE

Antioxidant	Equation % antioxidant =	Antioxidant	Equation % antioxidant =
Agerite Excel	$1.30\ A_{534}$	Flectol H	$3.02\ A_{525}$
Agerite Gel	$1.76\ A_{535}$	Flexamine	$1.61\ A_{540}$
Agerite Resin	$1.13\ A_{534}$	Neozone A	$0.443\ A_{557}$
Agerite Resin D	$3.10\ A_{522}$	Neozone C	$0.606\ A_{557}$
Agerite Stalite	$1.37\ A_{537}$	Octamine	$3.79\ A_{419}$
Akroflex C	$0.778\ A_{555}$	Polylite	$2.07\ A_{537}$
Albasan	$3.99\ A_{495}$	Stabilite	$1.40\ A_{522}$
Aminox	$1.18\ A_{547}$	Stabilite ALBA	$0.668\ A_{522}$
Antox	$1.49\ A_{512}$	Stabilite L	$0.573\ A_{515}$
Aranox	$0.902\ A_{540}$	Thermoflex A	$2.98\ A_{425}$
Betanox[a]	$3.13\ A_{438}$	Thermoflex C	$2.87\ A_{425}$
BLE-25	$0.720\ A_{538}$	VGB	$2.62\ A_{515}$
BLE Powder	$1.43\ A_{538}$		

[a] Coupled color insoluble in methanol-hydrochloric acid. Equation is for sample coupled in methanol-hydrochloric acid and diluted with glacial acetic acid.
Reproduced courtesy of Rubber Age.

NOTE.—If a red color is formed immediately upon coupling, and the color then fades to an amber or brown, it is likely that one of the antioxidants containing phenyl-2-naphthylamine (PBNA) is present. In this case an alternate procedure must be used.

Alternate Procedure for PBNA.—Extract as indicated in the regular procedure. Take a 10-ml. aliquot from the 100-ml. volumetric flask. Bring almost to the mark with methanol-hydrochloric acid mixture and add 1 ml. of coupling agent. Bring exactly to the mark, mix, and immediately determine the absorbance. The absorbance will rise to a maximum in 2 to 5 minutes after coupling. Use this maximum absorbance in calculating the amount of antioxidant present (Table 59-16).

TABLE 59-16. EQUATIONS FOR ANTIOXIDANTS CONTAINING PBNA
REQUIRING ALTERNATE PROCEDURE

Antioxidant	Equation % antioxidant =	Antioxidant	Equation % antioxidant =
Agerite HIPAR	$1.67\ A_{534}$	Neozone D	$1.25\ A_{534}$
Agerite HP	$2.47\ A_{534}$	PBNA	$1.25\ A_{534}$
Agerite Powder	$1.25\ A_{534}$	Thermoflex A	$2.49\ A_{534}$
Akroflex CD	$1.92\ A_{534}$	Thermoflex C	$2.12\ A_{534}$

Reproduced courtesy of Rubber Age.

Calculation.

$$\text{Let } W = AC \tag{7}$$

where: W = weight of antioxidant in grams;
   A = absorbance at the wavelength concerned; and
   C = concentration in grams of antioxidant per 100 ml. required for absorbance of 1.000.

Then

$$\% \text{ Antioxidant} = \frac{100 \ (AC)}{0.1 \ (\text{sample weight})} \tag{8}$$

The factor 0.1 is used because of a 10-ml., aliquot which is taken from a 100-ml. sample. If a 1.00-g. sample is always taken, then

$$\% \text{ Antioxidant} = 1000 \ (AC) \tag{9}$$

NOTE.—The antioxidants for which the method has been found to be unsatisfactory are Agerite White, Antioxidant 4010, BXA, Eastozone 32, JZF (DPPD), OZO 88, Santoflex AW, Santoflex BX, Santoflex DD, Santoflex 35, Santoflex 75, Tenamine 2, Tenamine 30, Tonox, Tonox D, U.O.P. 88 and U.O.P. 288.

GAS CHROMATOGRAPHIC METHOD[49]

A gas chromatographic method for a series of antioxidants is given in which an internal standard allows the calculation of characteristic retention times, relative retention times, and response factors. The method uses both isothermal and programmed temperature procedures.

Apparatus.—Dual-column, high-temperature gas chromatograph described by Wise and Sullivan, or other suitable gas chromatographic equipment.

TABLE 59-17. GAS CHROMATOGRAPHIC CALIBRATION DATA
OF SOME AMINE ANTIOXIDANTS

Antioxidant Chemical Name	Symbol	Internal Standard	Column temp., °C.	Retention time (min.) Antioxidant	Retention time (min.) Internal std.	Relative retention time[a]	Response[b]
1,2-Dihydro-2,2,4-trimethyl-6-ethoxyquinoline	DTEQ	DPA[e]	220	9.22	7.37	1.25	0.82
N,N'-Dimethyl-N,N'-di-(1-methyl-propyl)-p-phenylenediamine	DMD[MP]PD	DPA	220	13.97	6.70	2.08	0.86
N-Isopropyl-N'-phenyl-p-phenylenediamine	IPPD	PBNA	290	4.33	7.27	0.60	1.04
Di-(1-methylpropyl)-p-phenylenediamine	D[MP]PD	DPA	220	9.67	6.70	1.44	0.93
N,N'-Di-3-(5-methylheptyl)-p-phenylenediamine	D[MH]PD	IPPD	290	6.20	4.33	1.43	0.86
N-Phenyl-2-naphthylamine	PBNA	IPPD	290	7.27	4.33	1.68	0.96
N-N'-Di-2-octyl-p-phenylenediamine	DOPD	CPPD	300	8.17	12.60	0.65	0.98
N-Cyclohexyl-N'-phenyl-p-phenylenediamine	CPPD	DOPD	300	12.60	8.17	1.54	1.02
N,N'-Diphenyl-p-phenylenediamine	DPPD	DCPD[d]	310	11.38	8.12	1.40	0.99

a $\dfrac{\text{Retention Time, Antioxidant}}{\text{Retention Time, Internal Std.}}$

b $\dfrac{\text{Area Antioxidant per gram}}{\text{Area Internal Std. per gram}}$

e Diphenylamine

d N,N'-Dicyclohexyl-p-phenylenediamine

Operating Conditions: 2-meter column of 20% Apiezon L on 30–60 mesh Chromosorb W, 150 ml./min. of (helium) detector at 310°C., injector at 340°C.

Reproduced courtesy Rubber Chemistry and Technology.

Calibration.—The calibration data needed for quantitative analysis are obtained by determining the relative response of a series of purified antioxidants, with respect to an appropriate internal standard. Approximately 0.5 g. of the purified antioxidant is ac-

[49] Wise, R. W., and Sullivan, A. B., Rubber Chemistry and Technol., **35**, 684, 1962.

curately weighed and then dissolved in 10 ml. of the appropriate internal standard solution. The internal standard and chromatographic conditions used for each anti-oxidant are given in Table 59.17. Apprxomately 20 μl. of the calibration solution are chromatographed under these conditions. The response of the antioxidant with respect to the internal standard is calculated from the area of their respective peaks.

$$\text{Response} = \frac{\text{area of antioxidant peak/gram}}{\text{area of internal standard peak/gram}}$$

Reagents.—The antioxidants listed in the table are prepared by purifying commercial materials. The compounds which are liquids at room temperature are purified by fractional distillation at reduced pressure. The solid compounds are twice recrystallized from *n*-heptane under a nitrogen atmosphere.

An internal standard solution is prepared by diluting 5.0 g. of internal standard to 100 ml. with Reagent Grade benzene. The internal standard used for the analysis of each antioxidant is given in Table 59-17.

Procedure.—The rubber sample is first cut into small sections approximately $\frac{1}{16}$ inch square. A 15- to 25-g. sample of rubber is then accurately weighed into a Soxhlet ex-traction thimble. The sample is extracted for 16 hours in a Soxhlet extraction apparatus with approximately 100 ml. of boiling acetone. A 10-ml. aliquot of the appropriate internal standard solution containing 0.5 g. of internal standard is added to the acetone extract. The resulting solution is evaporated at 50°C. under reduced pressure to a total volume of approximately 10 ml. A 20 μl. portion of this solution is chromatographed on 2-meter Apiezon L column using a helium flow rate of 150 ml./min. The column temperature selected for the analysis of the particular antioxidants is given in Table 59-17.

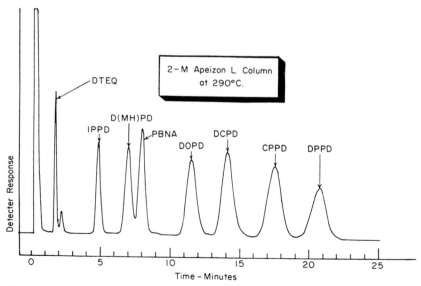

Fig. 59-46. Isothermal Gas Chromatogram of a Mixture of Amine Antioxidants. (Courtesy Rubber Chemistry and Technology.)

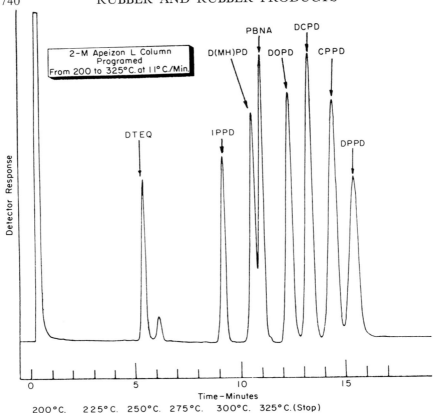

Fig. 59-47.   Programmed Temperature Gas Chromatogram of a Mixture of Amine Anti-oxidants. (Courtesy Rubber Chemistry and Technology.)

Calculation.—The antioxidant content is calculated as follows:

$$\% \text{ Antioxidant} = \frac{\text{area of antioxidant peak} \times 100 \times \text{weight of internal standard}}{\text{area of internal standard peak} \times \text{response} \times \text{sample weight}}$$

Chromatograms.—Chromatograms for a synthetic sample of a mixture of wide-boiling-range antioxidants under isothermal and program temperature conditions are shown in Figs. 59-46 and 59-47, respectively. Figure 59-48 gives the chromatogram for DPPD extracted from vulcanized rubber. The chemical name and abbreviation for each antioxidant is given in Table 59-17.

DETERMINATION OF ACCELERATORS

ULTRAVIOLET ABSORPTION METHOD[50]

In this method the ultraviolet absorbance of the reaction product of the volatile accelerator fragments of dithiocarbamate accelerators and dimethylamine is used to calculate the accelerator content of the sample.

[50] Hilton, C. L., and Newell, J. E., Rubber Age (New York) **83**, 981, 1958.

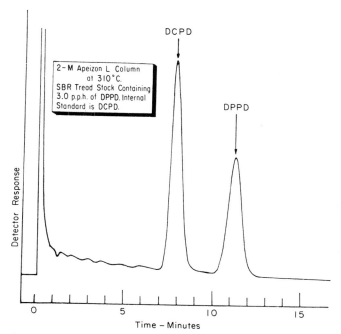

2-M Apeizon L Column
at 310°C.
SBR Tread Stock Containing
3.0 p.p.h. of DPPD. Internal
Standard is DCPD.

FIG. 59-48. Isothermal Chromatogram of an Extract from Vulcanized Rubber Containing *N*,*N'*-diphenyl-*p*-phenylenediamine (DPPD). (Courtesy Rubber Chemistry and Technology.)

Apparatus. Beckman Model DU Ultraviolet Spectrophotometer.—Or an equivalent spectrophotometer.

Quartz transmission cells.—Having 1-cm. light path.

Procedure.—An accurately weighed sample of exactly 0.5000 g. of thinly sheeted stock or cured foam rubber is placed in a 500-ml., three-necked, round-bottomed flask. For thinly sheeted stocks, it is advisable to shake overnight. For foam stocks, it is only necessary to tear the stock into pieces approximately $\frac{1}{8}$-inch in diameter. The analysis can then be run immediately. A few boiling chips, 400 ml. of 95 percent ethanol, and 1 ml. of concentrated (85 percent) phosphoric acid are added. Distillation at the rate of 3 to 4 ml. per minute is carried out using a Glas-Col heating mantle.

The receiver is a 250-ml. volumetric flask containing 5 ml. of a 5 percent dimethylamine solution (aqueous) and 15 ml. of 95 percent ethanol. An adapter which extends to the bottom of the volumetric flask should be used. The receiving flask should be placed in such a position that it can be lowered as the distillation proceeds. In this way, the adapter can be kept slightly below the level of the distillate at all times.

When the distillate has reached a total volume of 250 ml., the contents are mixed thoroughly and the absorbance of the distillate at 287 mμ, using 95 percent ethanol in the blank cell, is measured. The percent dithiocarbamate accelerator is calculated from Eqs. 10 through 14.

The residue is then neutralized with 100 ml. of a 0.1 N sodium hydroxide solution. A solution of 0.100 g. of sodium hydrogen sulfite in 100 ml. of water and 50 ml. of 95 percent ethanol are added and the distillation is repeated. The percent thiuram sulfide accelerator is determined using the absorbance at 285 mμ. The equations for this determination are (15), (16), and (17).

Calculations.—The percent accelerator is given by:

$$\% \text{ accelerator} = \frac{100 \, AC}{\text{Weight of sample in grams}}$$

where: A is the absorbance at the point of maximum absorption; and
C is the concentration in grams of accelerator per 250 ml. of distillate required to give a value of 1.000 for A.

If the sample weight is always taken as exactly 0.5000 g., the equations for the accelerators are as follows:

% Methazate (zinc dimethyldithiocarbamate) = 0.55 (Absorbance at 287 mμ)   (10)
% Ethazate (zinc diethyldithiocarbamate)   = 0.65 (Absorbance at 287 mμ)   (11)
% Butazate (zinc dibutyldithiocarbamate)   = 0.85 (Absorbance at 287 mμ)   (12)
% Arazate (zinc dibenzyldithiocarbamate)   = 1.10 (Absorbance at 287 mμ)   (13)
% Pipazate (zinc N-pentamethylene dithio-
    carbamate)   = 0.69 (Absorbance at 287 mμ)   (14)
% Tuex (Tetramethyl thiuram disulfide)   = 0.438 (Absorbance at 285 mμ)   (15)
% Ethyl Tuex (Tetraethyl thiuram disulfide) = 0.586 (Absorbance at 285 mμ)   (16)
% Monex (Tetramethyl thiuram sulfide)   = 0.750 (Absorbance at 285 mμ)   (17)

NOTE.—The values for C and, thus, the final equations, should be determined for each instrument to be used. The values listed were obtained with a Beckman Model DU spectrophotometer using 1.000-cm. quartz cells. The slit widths were 0.875 mm. at 287 mμ for Eqs. (10) through (14) and 0.905 mm. at 285 mμ for Eqs. (15) through (17). Usual corrections should be made for variations in cell transmission characteristics.

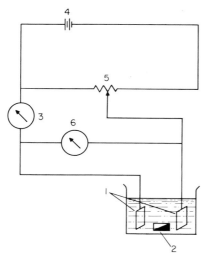

FIG. 59-49. Apparatus for Titration. 1, Two silver plate electrodes (area approximately 25 mm.²). 2, Magnetic stirrer. 3, Mirror galvanometer with a sensitivity of 2×10^{-8} A/mm., a light source, and a scale. 4, Battery. 5, Rheostat, 2000 ohm. 6, Voltmeter. (Courtesy Soviet Rubber Technology, Maclaren & Sons, Ltd.)

DETERMINATION OF MERCAPTOBENZOTHIAZOLE

AMPEROMETRIC METHOD[51]

The method employs an amperometric titration procedure to back titrate the excess silver after treating the extract from a rubber sample with a standard solution of silver nitrate. The amount of MBT present in the sample is calculated by determining the amount of silver that has reacted with the MBT.

Procedure.—Two g. of finely cut uncured rubber mix or vulcanizate in a filter paper thimble are extracted with 40 ml. of alcohol for 2 hours in a Soxhlet microextractor. The extract is transferred to a measuring flask and alcohol is added to bring the volume to 50 ml. Ten ml. of the solution are withdrawn into a flask for electrolysis (see Fig. 59-49) and 40 ml. of alcohol and 2 ml. of 0.01 M silver

[51] Gordon, B. E., Melamed, E. A., and Belova, N. A., Sov. Rubber Technol., **21**, 46, 1962; Kauchuk i Rezina, **21**, 46, 1962.

nitrate solution are added. The magnetic stirrer is then switched on, and a constant voltage of 0.1 volt is applied to the silver electrodes, which are then immersed in the solution. The initial reading of the mirror galvanometer is noted and the titration is conducted with a 0.01 M solution of sodium chloride, the latter being added in amounts of 0.1 ml., noting the readings of the galvanometer; the minimum reading corresponds to the end point (see Fig. 59-50).

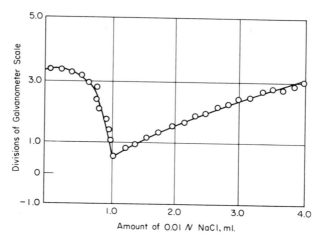

FIG. 59-50.   Example of Back Titration of an Excess of Silver with 0.01 N NaCl Solution (1 ml. of 0.01 M MBT Solution, 4 ml. of 0.005 AgNO$_3$ Solution, Made up to 50 ml. with alcohol). (Courtesy Soviet Rubber Technology, Maclaren & Sons, Ltd.)

Calculation.

$$x\% = \frac{M(a - b)xv_1 \times 100}{100 \times 1000 \times v_2H} = \frac{0.167(2 - b)5}{H}$$

where: M is the molecular weight of MBT;
H is the weight of the specimen, g.;
a is the number of ml. of 0.01 M AgNO$_3$ solution;
b is the number of ml. of 0.01 M NaCl solution used in titration;
v_1 is the volume of the extract; and
v_2 is the volume of the extract taken for titration.

DETERMINATION OF TETRAMETHYL THIURAM DISULFIDE

ABSORPTIMETRIC METHOD[52]

The absorbance of the reaction product between TMTD and Copper(I) N,N-diethyldithiocarbamate is used to determine the amount of TMTD present.

Apparatus.—**Beckman spectrophotometer**—Model B or equivalent.
Transmission Cells. – Glass, 1-cm.
Solvent and Reagent. Chloroform.—Reagent Grade.
Copper (I) N, N-diethyldithiocarbamate.

Procedure.—A sample containing 0.1–0.3 mg. of TMTD is weighed in and diluted with chloroform to 50 ml. About 3 ml. of this solution is required for the zero-adjusting

[52] Akerstrom, S., and Bjorn Lindahl, P. E., Rubber Chemistry and Technol. **36**, 305, 1963.

of the spectrophotometer. To the rest of the solution 1–10 mg. of copper(I) N,N-diethyl-dithiocarbamate is added and shaken well for 10 seconds. The absorbance of the solution is measured at 433 mμ.

$$\% \text{ TMTD} = (s \times 100)/W$$

where: s = mg. of TMTD per 50 ml. of solution read from an absorbance
calibration curve; and
W = amount of sample in mg.

DETERMINATION OF ZINC OXIDE
ABSORPTIMETRIC METHOD[53]

The absorbance of zinc diethyldithiocarbamate is used as a measure of the zinc oxide present in a rubber compound. A procedure for converting the zinc oxide to the above derivative and for eliminating interferences is given.

Apparatus. Cylinders.—25 and 50 ml., graduated to 1 ml., with close fitting, ground-glass stoppers.

Borosilicate Glass Beakers.—5 ml.

Stirring Rod.—Equipped with short platinum wire bent at an angle at the end.

Section of 2- to 4-cm. Diameter Glass Tubing.—Tubing should be restricted at one end to serve as an adsorption column for ether purification.

Spectrophotometer.—Beckman Model DU or similar spectrophotometer with conventional ultraviolet accessories, including 1.000 ± 0.005-cm. quartz cells. Also, a Beckman Model B or similar spectrophotometer with 1.00-cm. Corex cells.

Reagents. Chromatographic Grade Adsorption Alumina.—80- to 200-mesh.

Anhydrous Ethyl Ether.—ACS Reagent Grade, purified further by filtering through a short column of alumina (about a 4-cm. depth in a column 4 cm. in diameter) to remove iron. This purification step also removes peroxides.

Hydrochloric Acid, 10 percent by volume.—Dilute 10 ml. of 37 percent acid to 100 ml. with distilled water.

Sodium Carbonate, approximately 10 percent.—Dissolve 10 g. of Reagent Grade anhydrous sodium carbonate in distilled water, dilute to 100 ml., and purify (see below) for absorptimetric analysis.

Sodium Diethyl Dithiocarbamate, approximately 1 percent.—Dissolve 1.0 g. of Reagent Grade material in distilled water and dilute to 100 ml. Purify with ether as described below. Store in an actinic brown bottle. This is referred to hereafter as 1 percent carbamate reagent or indicator.

Ammonium Hydroxide, 10 percent by Volume.—Dilute 10 ml. of the concentrated reagent to 100 ml. with distilled water.

Ammonium Hydroxide, Concentrated.—Purify as described below.

Gum Arabic, about 5 percent.—Make a paste with distilled water and 5 g. of Reagent Grade gum arabic; then dilute to 100 ml. There should be no detectable increase in yellow coloration or turbidity when an aliquot of the filtered solution is tested by adding a few drops of 1 percent carbamate reagent. Never heat this reagent.

Standard Zinc Solution, 500 p.p.m.—Weigh 0.1000 g. of zinc metal, and place in a 200-ml. volumetric flask. Add 2 ml. of concentrated hydrochloric acid and allow to stand until all the zinc is in solution, warming if necessary. Dilute to the mark with distilled water.

All aqueous alkaline reagents for the absorptiometric method must be purified before use. Add about 2 drops of 1 percent carbamate reagent per 100 ml. of reagent to be

[53] Kress, K. E., Anal. Chem., **30**, 432, 1958.

purified, then extract with purified ethyl ether to remove any trace metal impurities (such as copper in ammonia), which form a carbamate complex. Extract three or more times until the ether is colorless; discard the ether each time. The sodium carbonate may be warmed to drive off the ether, but do not warm the ammonium hydroxide. These purified reagents are usable for 1 month or more.

Calibration.—Determine the absorptivity, *a*, of the zinc diethyldithiocarbamate solution in ether at each wavelength where data are to be recorded. A fixed slit width may be assigned, but as the absorbance maximum (262 mμ) is relatively broad, the slit width is not normally critical.

Dilute the standard zinc solution 1:10 and use different volumes to establish the calibration curve. Calibrations have given absorptivity values of 550, 282, and 85 to 262, 280, and 295 mμ, respectively.

Procedure.—Weigh 2 to 4 mg. of a well-milled, homogeneous sample to the nearest 0.01 mg. if absorbance is to be measured at 262 mμ. If absorbance is measured at 280 mμ, use a 5- to 10-mg. sample. Place in a 5-ml. borosilicate glass beaker and ash at 550°C. for 30 minutes or until completely ashed. Alternatively, drive off volatile matter at 550°C. for 5 to 10 minutes and complete ashing in a muffle at 800° to 1000°C. by placing the beaker inside the door just long enough to burn off the carbon black (1 to 2 minutes).

NOTE.—A combination of wet and dry ashing ensures total recovery of zinc from neoprene rubber products which may contain zinc chloride. The sample is first taken to dryness on a hot plate with a few drops of concentrated sulfuric acid, then ashed in the 550°C. muffle as usual.

Remove from the muffle carefully to avoid loss of ash, and allow to cool somewhat. While still warm to the touch, add about 1 ml. of 10 percent hydrochloric acid from a dropping pipet to wash down the side of the beaker. If necessary, break up any caked residue with the stirring rod tipped with platinum wire and stir the sample a little. Add 2 to 4 ml. of distilled water, using a small jet from a wash bottle to aid mixing the sample, then pour the solution into a clean, glass-stoppered, 50-ml. graduated cylinder. Wash the beaker twice with 1 to 2 ml. of water and add to the cylinder. Keep the total volume below 8 ml.

Add litmus paper and then 10 percent ammonium hydroxide, drop by drop, while shaking vigorously, until the aqueous solution is just alkaline. Then carefully add 1 drop more. Add 0.5 ± 0.1 ml. of sodium carbonate reagent. Mix, then add 0.05 ml. of carbamate reagent. Dilute carefully to 10.0 ml. with distilled water, then dilute to the 50.0-ml. mark with purified ethyl ether. Stopper the cylinder and shake vigorously for about 30 seconds.

Clean the 1.00-cm. quartz cells with ether and check for transparency correction if necessary. (Disregard the transparency correction if the absorbance with ether alone is ±0.005 or less.) Place purified ether in the first cell as an instrument blank. Decant the separated ether layer of the reagent blank and the sample solution into the remaining cells. Take readings at the 262-mμ absorbance maximum of zinc diethyldithiocarbamate in ether. If the absorbance is over 1.8, repeat the measurement at 280 or 295 mμ to provide three levels of sensitivity for the determination. This eliminates the need for dilution or concentration of the zinc solution.

If the ether solution is colored or if lead is present, add 10 ml. of purified concentrated ammonium hydroxide directly to the sample in the 50-ml. graduate. Stopper and mix vigorously to re-extract the zinc into the 50 percent aqueous ammonium hydroxide layer. Again measure the absorbance of the ether layer at the same wavelength as used for the initial measurements, use this reading as the blank absorbance. The loss in absorbance is that due to zinc, while residual absorbance is due to interfering elements.

NOTE.—There should be no visible trace of yellow coloration in the ether solution when observed through its 12-cm. depth against a white background. Avoid mistaking the reflected color of precipitated ferric hydroxide as coloration in the ether layer. When the ether layer is uncolored, any interference from iron, copper, cobalt, nickel, or bismuth may then be considered negligible, particularly if the absorbance of the zinc complex itself at 262 mμ is relatively strong (above 0.5).

Calculation.

$$\% \text{ ZnO} = \frac{(A_s - A_b) \times 1.245 \times 100}{a_{Zn} \times c} \tag{1}$$

where: A_s is absorbance measured at a given wavelength;

A_b is absorbance of the blank at the same wavelength; and

a_{Zn} is absorptivity at the same wavelength as determined with Reagent Grade zinc metal, with concentration (c) in mg. per ml. or g. per liter $(a_{Zn} = A/c)$.

Cell thickness is a constant and need not be included in the calculation.

Blank.—Always run a reagent blank. It should be measured against ether as the instrument blank rather than used to zero the spectrophotometer. This ensures that the reagent blank is low enough to provide satisfactory accuracy. A blank above 0.050 at 280 mμ indicates that some reagent needs further purification. A blank absorbance as high as 0.10 may be tolerated if the sample absorbance is relatively high, preferably more more than 10 times that of the blank. Any dilution of the sample (ether extract) requires a comparable dilution of the blank.

Certain samples, notably the high silicate samples, may need to be wet ashed. The use of perchloric acid for wet ashing in rubber chemistry is restricted in routine analysis because of the potential explosive hazard when used on a macroscale. These hazards are increased by the introduction of synthetic rubbers, such as Butyl and Vistanex polymers, which are harder to oxidize than natural rubber. Oxidation of samples of Butyl rubber of about 100 mg. with either concentrated or fuming nitric acid mixed with a few drops of perchloric acid has resulted in explosive oxidation.

The sensitivity of the absorptiometric procedure makes it possible to work in a micro-sample range, where perchloric acid oxidation is reported to be safe.

Digest a 5- to 15-mg. sample in a borosilicate glass test tube (16 × 100 mm.) with about 0.5 ml. of fuming nitric acid and 5 drops of 70 percent perchloric acid. After complete oxidation add 1 ml. of water and 2 drops of purified saturated ammonium chloride solution, then transfer to a 50-ml. graduate with water. Neutralize the sample to litmus with sodium carbonate (no ammonia) and proceed with the absorptiometric method.

DETERMINATION OF ZINC

POLAROGRAPHIC METHOD[54]

This method describes the steps and conditions for preparing an ashed rubber sample for the polarographic analysis of the zinc content.

Procedure.—Weigh a sample of the compounded rubber into a porcelain crucible and heat carefully to remove all organic matter. Add 0.5 ml. of concentrated hydro-chloric acid to the ash, heat just to dryness, moisten with dilute acetic acid (equal volumes glacial acid and water), and dilute with a few ml. of warm water. Boil the solu-tion with 2 ml. of 5 percent aqueous potassium iodide solution until the brown color of

[54] Poulton, F. C. J., and Tarrant, L., Trans. Inst. Rubber Ind., 25, 328, 1950; Rubber Chemistry and Technol., 23, 975, 1950.

any liberated iodine is discharged, cool and transfer to a 50-ml. standard volumetric flask containing 10 ml. of the following base solution:

Potassium thiocyanate	24 g.	
Ammonium acetate	76 g.	made up to 1 liter
Methyl red sodium salt (0.02 percent solution)	25 ml.	with water
Gelatin (1 percent aqueous solution)	20 ml.	

Adjust the pH of the solution to a value of 4–5 by adding acetic acid until the methyl red is just red and dilute to volume with water. The solution is then ready for polarographing. After the removal of dissolved oxygen by bubbling pure nitrogen through the cell for 5 minutes, polarograph the solution over the voltage range −0.5 to −1.2 volt. Standard calibration curves are prepared by treating zinc oxide of analytical quality similarly. Oxygen-free nitrogen is obtained by following the procedure of Meites and Meites.[55]

X-RAY DIFFRACTION METHOD[56]

In this method no special sample preparation is necessary except for cutting the sample to fit the standard sample holder of the x-ray diffraction apparatus.[57]

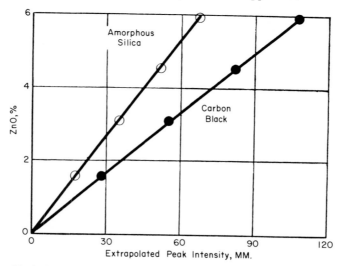

FIG. 59-51.   Variation of Peak Intensity with Zinc Oxide Concentration in Vulcanizates with Different Types of Fillers. (Courtesy Journal of Applied Polymer Science.)

Procedure.—The cured sample measuring about $1\frac{3}{8} \times 1\frac{1}{2}$ inch is placed on top of a standard x-ray sample holder made from aluminum and then inserted in the goniometer for scanning. A Norelco Geiger counter diffractometer employing CuKα radiation may be used in the determinations. The operating conditions are: 35 kv., 15 ma.

[55] Meites, L., and Meites, T., Anal. Chem., **20**, 984, 1948.
[56] Laning, S. H., Wagner, M. P., and Sellers, J. W., J. Appl. Polymer Sci., **2**, 225, 1959; Rubber Chemistry and Technol., **33**, 890, 1960.
[57] The method was developed for samples containing natural rubber amorphous silica or HAF black, zinc oxide, curatives (sulfur, MBTS, DOTG, TEA, and PBNA), and stearic acid.

on a copper target tube, a nickel filter to remove CuKβ radiation, a 1° divergent slit, 0.006-inch receiving slit, 1° scatter slit, and the usual Soller slits to collimate the beam. The sample is scanned at the rate of $\frac{1}{2}$° per minute from an angle of 37° to 35° 2θ, with a scale factor of 32 and a time constant of 2 seconds. The variation in x-ray intensity may be recorded on a strip chart. Two determinations are made on each side of the sample. From the diffraction pattern, the intensity of the zinc oxide peak above background, at an angle of 36.2° 2θ is measured for each determination. The average of the four measurements is then plotted against the corresponding time of cure. Smooth curves are drawn through each series of points and extrapolated to zero cure time. The values of the peak intensity at zero cure time, obtained by extrapolation, then corresponds to the initial zinc oxide concentration. Calibration curves are obtained by plotting this extrapolated peak intensity against the initial percentage of zinc oxide (Fig. 59-51).

NOTE.   Though the peak intensity-cure time curves are nonlinear, smooth curves through the experimentally determined points permit extrapolation with an estimated relative error of less than ±5 percent. This error will vary depending on the slope of the curve at zero time of cure. This, in turn, is dependent on the rate of disappearance of the zinc oxide.

DETERMINATION OF LEAD

ABSORPTIMETRIC METHOD[58]

The absorbance of lead ion in hydrochloric acid solution is used to determine the amount of lead in a rubber sample or in zinc oxide.

Apparatus. **Spectrophotometer.**—Beckman Model DU or similar spectrophotometer with 1.00-cm. quartz cells.

Borosilicate Glass Beakers.—5 ml., for dry ashing or test tubes, 16 × 100 mm., for wet ashing.

Glass-stoppered Graduated Cylinder, 10 ml.

Reagents. **Hydrochloric Acid,** 50 percent by volume.—Make an exact 1:1 dilution of Reagent Grade concentrated hydrochloric acid (37 percent).

Instrument Calibration. —Refer to the calibration procedure outlined in the section "Determination of Sulfur, Absorptimetric Method" (page 1723).

Procedure. **1. For Lead.**—Homogenize the sample in a rubber mill, then weigh a 1- to 10-mg. sample, or more if less than 1 percent lead is expected. Ash in a 5-ml. beaker at 550°C. for about 10 minutes, then in the front of a high-temperature muffle (900°C.) for 1 or 2 minutes until ashing is complete.

Cool the beaker, then dissolve the ash in about 2 ml. of 50 percent hydrochloric acid, stirring with a glass rod if necessary. Transfer to a 10-ml. glass-stoppered cylinder using 50 percent acid wash. Dilute to volume with 50 percent acid and mix well.

Measure the absorbance at 250, 270, and 289 mμ, using a blank of 50 percent acid. If absorbance is above 1.8, dilute with 50 percent acid as needed. Include all dilutions in calculating sample concentration, c.

Substitute appropriate absorbance values in the following equation to determine lead content of the sample.

$$\Delta A_{270}^s = (A_{270} - A_{289}) - \frac{(A_{250} - A_{289})}{2} \tag{18}$$

$$\% \text{ lead} = \frac{\Delta A_{270}^s \times 100}{\Delta a_{270}^{Pb} \times c(\text{mg./ml.})} \tag{19}$$

2. Lead in Zinc Oxide.—The sample size of zinc oxide is determined by the normal lead content as follows.

[58] Kress, K. E., Anal. Chem., **29,** 803, 1957.

Normal Lead Sulfate Content, %	Approximate Sample Weight, g. (g.ZnO/10 ml.)
Below 0.004	1 to 2
0.03	0.4
0.1	0.1
1	0.01

The weights given are close to the maximum allowable in 10 ml. of 50 percent acid without further dilution.

Weigh an appropriate amount of the zinc oxide and transfer to the 10-ml. cylinder. Add just enough concentrated hydrochloric acid to dissolve the sample with vigorous shaking. Add the last of the acid drop by drop.

Dilute to 5.0 ml. with distilled water, then to 10.0 ml. with concentrated hydrochloric acid. Mix well and measure the absorbance at 250, 270, and 289 mμ. Thereafter, follow the procedure for determination of lead in rubber products. The results are usually multiplied by 1.46 to convert to lead sulfate.

ORGANIC ACID IN SBR

PHOTOMETRIC TITRATION METHOD[59]

The solution of the unvulcanized SBR sample is treated with a complexing agent to prevent the reaction of aluminum in alum-coagulated SBR during the titration procedure. The indicator chosen has two color changes allowing a measure of both mineral acid and organic acid in the sample.

Apparatus.—Fisher Electrophotometer or equivalent, equipped with a number 525-B(green) filter.

Reagents. Toluene, C.P.

8-Hydroxyquinoline.

Ethanol, 95 percent.

Meta-cresol Purple Indicator Solution.—A 0.3 percent solution in 95 percent ethanol, neutralizing each 0.1 g. of indicator with 2.62 ml. of 0.1 N sodium hydroxide.

Tank N$_2$ Gas.

0.1 N Sodium Hydroxide.—Dissolve 5.2 ml. of 50 percent aqueous sodium hydroxide in absolute ethanol.

0.05 N Alcoholic Hydrochloric Acid.—Use concentrated hydrochloric acid and absolute ethanol.

Procedure.—Take approximately 2 g. of the thinly-sheeted alum-coagulated SBR and cut it into strips or small pieces to facilitate solution. Weigh the specimen. Place a single sheet of 9-cm. filter paper, perforated with small holes, on the bottom of a 400-ml. rubber extraction flask containing 125 ml. of toluene.

Add the weighed specimen piece by piece to the rubber extraction flask, being certain that the pieces remain on top of the filter paper, thus preventing the rubber from sticking and burning on the bottom of the flask during heating. Dissolve the sample by refluxing in a rubber extraction apparatus. Swirl the flask if necessary to prevent the rubber from sticking to the glass.

When the sample has completely dissolved, transfer the solution to a 250-ml. beaker. Add 15 ml. of toluene to the extraction flask and reflux it for 3 to 5 minutes with frequent swirling of the flask. Pour the rinsing into the beaker. Rinse the extraction flask with 2

[59] Linnig, F. J., Rubber Age (New York), **90**, 440, 1961.

additional 15-ml. portions of toluene, refluxing if necessary to remove any rubber adhering to the flask.

NOTE.—Bubbles which persistently adhere to the surface of the glass after removal from the
hot plate indicate the presence of undissolved rubber.

Reflux and treat 125 ml. of solvent in the same manner as the rubber solution to serve
as a blank. Solvents should be selected so that the mineral acid blank is no more than a
few hundredths of a milliliter.

Add 2 ml. of a toluene solution of 8-hydroxyquinoline containing 0.125 g. per ml.
Cover the beaker and heat at the boiling temperature for 1½ hours, being careful to keep

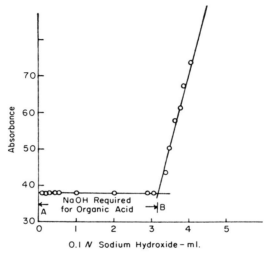

FIG. 59-52. Typical Titration Curve for SBR Solution Containing No Mineral Acid.
(Courtesy Rubber Age.)

the rubber from sticking to the bottom of the beaker by frequent stirring. Cool the
solution to room temperature. Slowly add 30 ml. of 95 percent ethanol while stirring the
solution. (*Caution:* Do not boil the solution following the addition of ethanol.) Add 7
drops of meta-cresol purple indicator solution.

Set the beaker in the photometer so that it is directly in the path of the light. Fit the
photometer with a special lid which has two openings: one to permit the addition of the
sodium hydroxide by means of a buret; the other to permit the entrance of a glass tube
(0.5 cm. inside diameter) through which a stream of inert gas is passed into the solution
to expel carbon dioxide and to mix the solution during the titration. In placing the holes,
be certain that the gas lead-in tube does not fall in the path of the light.

Regulate the flow of gas by maintaining a pressure of 7–11 cm. of water. Using a
green filter with a maximum transmittance at 525 mμ, regulate the initial null to give
the lowest possible reading on the scale representing absorbance. Titrate the solution
with 0.1 N sodium hydroxide, using a 5-ml. buret graduated to 0.01 ml. divisions.

Make the titration in increments of 0.02 ml. until no further drop in absorbance is
detected, if it occurs at all, then continue the titration in 1-ml. increments until only a
few tenths of a milliliter remain to be titrated before the end point. If no initial drop in
absorbance occurs for the first 0.3 ml., continue the titration in 1-ml. increments as just

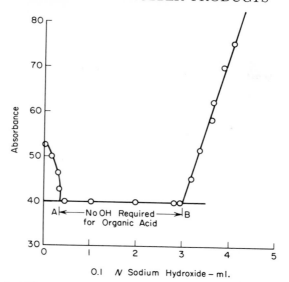

FIG. 59-53. Typical Titration Curve for SBR Solution Containing Mineral Acid. (Courtesy Rubber Age.)

described. In either case complete the titration in increments of 0.1 ml., taking about 6 points after the absorbance begins to show a steady rise.

Add 30 ml. of 95 percent ethanol and 7 drops of the indicator to the blank and, using 0.01-ml. increments, titrate the blank with 0.05 N alcoholic hydrochloric acid (prepared from concentrated hydrochloric acid and absolute ethanol) until the period of marked increase in absorbance is past.

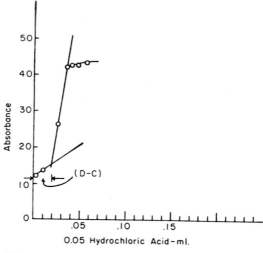

FIG. 59-54. Typical Titration Blank Used as a Check on the Quality of the Solvent. (Courtesy Rubber Age.)

Plot changes in absorbance against the corresponding number of milliliters of sodium hydroxide used (Fig. 59-52). If an initial drop in absorbance takes place within the first few tenths of a milliliter, a change of the color of the indicator from pink to yellow has occurred and indicates the presence of mineral acid.

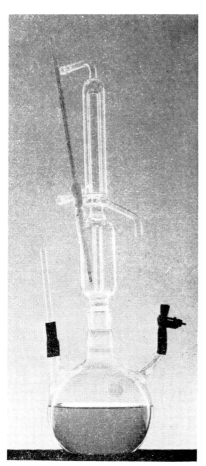

In these cases make a separate plot of this portion of the curve on an increased scale to determine this end point. Draw straight or curved lines through the points preceding and following this discontinuity. Extrapolate these lines to the point of intersection A shown in Fig. 59-53. The difference B–A shown in these figures represents the number of milliliters of reagent consumed by the organic acid.

To determine the solvent blank as a check on the quality of the solvent, plot the changes in optical density against the corresponding number of milliliters of hydrochloric acid required for the blank titration. Using the extrapolation procedure just described, the blank is represented by the difference (D–C) in Fig. 59-54. It is not necessary to titrate a blank for the change from yellow to purple.

Calculations.

$$\text{Organic acid, percent} = \frac{(M_B \times N_B)K}{W}$$

where: W = weight of the original dry sample;

M_B = milliliters of standard sodium hydroxide solution used to titrate the organic acid [(B–A) in Figs. 59-54 and 59-55];

N_B = normality of the sodium hydroxide solution; and

K = 28.4 when the organic acid is determined as stearic acid, and

= 34.6 when the organic acid is determined as rosin acid.

FIG. 59-55. Distilling Apparatus. (Reprinted from Analytical Chemistry, **29**, 140, 1957. Copyright 1957 by the American Chemical Society and reprinted by permission of the copyright owner.)

DETERMINATION OF FLUORINE

MICROBOMB METHOD[60]

In this method sodium fusion in a microbomb is used followed by steam distillation to prepare the sample for photometric titration of the fluorine in the sample.

[60] Ma, T. S., and Gwirtsman, J., Anal. Chem., **29**, 140, 1957.

Apparatus. **Parr Microbomb.**—2.5-ml. capacity, Series 2300, No. A1MB, from Parr Instrument Co., Moline, Ill. Copper gaskets are cut from a sheet of copper 0.5 mm. thick.

Distilling Apparatus.—This apparatus is adapted from the regular steam-dillation apparatus of Mavrodineanu and Gwirtsman[61] for fluorine determination. A complete single unit is shown in Fig. 59-55. The lower section is the steam generator made from a 1-liter, flat-bottomed borosilicate glass flask. It is provided with a safety tube and a side arm which serves as the outlet and is closed by a screw clamp. The upper section comprises the distilling flask and condenser, shown in detail in Fig. 59-56. As indicated by the arrows, steam, S, travels along the ground-glass joint, J_1, passes through two concentric tubes, IT_1 and ET_1, and reaches the distilling flask, D, through the two openings. The vapors enter the condenser, C, which consists of three concentric tubes: In IT_2 and ET_2 the vapors are condensed, and the cooling water circulates in ET_3. The ground-glass joint, J_2, serves as the opening for the introduction of the sodium fluoride solution as well as the seat of a thermometer (150°C.) during distillation with the mercury bulb immersed in the liquid, L.

As the steam distillation from a perchloric acid solution requires a temperature of 135°C., an additional heating system is provided by the electric heating jacket, H. This is made from nickel wire, W (resistance, 2.120 ohms per foot), 600 cm. long. The actual length of the resistance spiral is 420 cm., the rest being used for terminals (3 × 30 cm. bent and twisted at each end). A glass cylinder, 48 mm. in diameter, is covered with aluminum foil on which a sheet of asbestos is affixed. The Nichrome spiral is then wound on the cylinder and covered with a layer of Insulate cement (Fisher Scientific Co., No. 4-760), asbestos, and an external layer of cement. After drying at 105°C. for 48 hours, the jacket is taken off the cylinder and placed on ring, R. The assembled apparatus is placed on a 500 watt electric hot plate, and the heating jacket is connected to a Powerstat (Type 116, 0-135 volts, 7.5 amperes).

pH Meter.—Beckman Model G.

Microburet.—5-ml. capacity, graduated in 0.01 ml.

Equipment for Photoelectric Titration.—Photoelectric filter photometer. (A commercial model is available from Marley Products Co., New Hyde Park, N. Y.)

Reagents. **Fluorine-free Water.**—Obtained by passing distilled water through an ion exchange-type deionizing column.

Sodium Metal.—Reagent Grade, stored under kerosene.

Perchloric Acid.—70 to 72 percent.

Silver Perchlorate.—25 percent aqueous solution.

Hydrochloric Acid and Sodium Hydroxide Solutions.—Approximately 1 N, 0.1 N, and 0.01 N, for pH adjustment.

Sodium Alizarinsulfonate.—0.01 percent, for back titration or direct titration in the range up to 100 μg. of fluorine, 0.035 percent for direct titration up to 1000 μg. of fluorine.

Standard Thorium Nitrate Solution.—0.1 N for photoelectric titration. Dissolve 13.805 g. of thorium nitrate tetrahydrate in water and dilute to 1 liter. From this prepare 0.01 N and 0.001 N solutions.

Sodium Fluoride Stock Solution.—This should contain 1 mg. of fluorine per ml. Dissolve 2.210 g. of C.P. sodium fluoride (dried over phosphorus pentoxide for 48 hours) in water and dilute to 1 liter. From this prepare solutions containing 100 and 10 μg. of fluorine per ml. Check the thorium nitrate and sodium fluoride solutions against each other (by steam distillation of the fluoride from perchloric acid and titration with the thorium nitrate).

[61] Mavrodineanu, R., Gwirtsman, J., Contrib. Boyce Thompson Inst., **17**, 489, 1954.

Note.—Store the reagents, especially the sodium fluoride solutions, in polyethylene containers, if possible.

Procedure. Sodium Fusion.—A 1- to 5-mg. sample (containing 0.1 to 0.5 mg. of fluorine) is accurately weighed out and transferred to the thoroughly cleaned Parr microbomb. Solids are weighed by means of a charging tube. Viscous liquids are weighed in microglass cups made by sealing one end of a 4-mm. glass tubing. Volatile liquids are weighed in capillaries described by Steyermark[62] with slight modifications to fit the dimensions of the microbomb. The capillary should have a bore of about 2 mm. and a length of 15 mm., with a tip of the same length and 1-mm. bore. The capillary is first weighed empty, the sample is introduced by means of a syringe or a micropipet drawn to a fine tip, and then the capillary is sealed before the final weighing. The tip of the capillary is broken off with an ampoule cutter and both the tip and the capillary are placed in the microbomb. The sealed capillary may be chilled in dry ice until ready for analysis.

A piece of sodium is wiped and sliced, and a portion of about 30 to 50 mg. is introduced into the microbomb, which is closed tightly, the copper gasket providing a resistant seal. The microbomb is ignited over a Bunsen burner for 5 to 10 minutes. Upon cooling, the microbomb is opened and the underside of the lid is washed with fluorine-free distilled water into a 100-ml. beaker. A trace of unreacted sodium in the microbomb is destroyed by carefully adding 1 or 2 drops of water or alcohol. More water is then introduced to dissolve the fusion product and the solution is transferred into the 100-ml. beaker. Any adhering material is removed by means of a glass rod, and the microbomb is washed thoroughly with a jet of water.

Steam Distillation from Perchloric Acid.—The contents of the 100-ml. beaker are transferred quantitatively into the distilling apparatus through a funnel with ground joint fitted to opening J_2 (Fig. 59-56). The beaker is then rinsed with 20 ml. of 70 to 72 percent perchloric acid, which is also transferred to the still. One milliliter of silver perchlorate solution and 8 to 10 glass beads are then added, the thermometer is inserted, and the distillation is ready to start. The hot plate switch is turned to the position "high" and the Powerstat dial is set at 80 (to deliver 2.8 amperes at approximately 80 volts). The opening of the outlet tube of the steam generator is so regulated by the screw clamp that a pressure corresponding to 20 to 30 mm. of water column in the safety tube is maintained inside the flask. When the temperature of the sample solution (Fig. 59-56, L) reaches 130°C., the screw clamp is closed and the steam distillation starts. At this moment the dial of the Powerstat is set at 45 (to deliver 1.5 amperes at approximately 45 volts), and the distilling temperature is maintained at 135° ± 2°C. during the entire operation. In about 45 minutes 250 ml. of distillate will have been collected in the glass cell. In order to stop the steam distillation, the Powerstat is turned off, and when a drop in temperature is noticeable, the outlet tube of the steam generator is opened and the hot plate is switched off.

The distilling apparatus is cleaned by connecting the base of the distilling flask, D, to a water aspirator through a glass tube with ground joint to fit J_1. At the same time, the outlet tube of the condenser is fitted with rubber tubing dipping into fluorine-free water. The washing liquid is thus sucked through the entire apparatus.

Determination of Fluoride.—The distillate, or a suitable aliquot thereof, is made up to 250 ml. in the glass cell of the filter photometer and is adjusted to pH 3.0 ± 0.05; 2.0 ml. of sodium alizarinsulfonate indicator are added. A blank cell is prepared containing 250 ml. of fluorine-free distilled water of the same pH and same amount of indicator. The two cells are placed in the filter photometer. After the light source and the

[62] Steyermark, A., Quantitative Organic Microanalysis, Blakiston, Philadelphia, 1951, p. 33.

magnetic stirrer have been turned on, the optical system is balanced by means of the iris diaphragms (spot of galvanometer at 0). Standard thorium nitrate solution is now added from a microburet to the sample cell through an opening on the top of the enclosure. So long as the titrant reacts with the fluoride ions, no change is detected by the

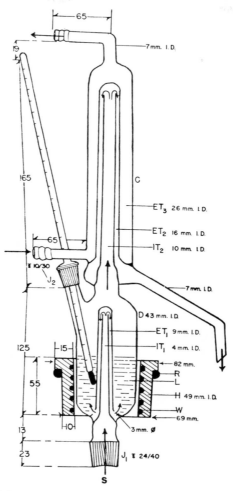

Fig. 59-56. Detail of Upper Section of Distilling Apparatus. (Reprinted from Analytical Chemistry, **29**, 140, 1957. Copyright 1957 by the American Chemical Society and reprinted by permission of the copyright owner.)

galvanometer. As soon as an excess of thorium nitrate is present, the pink lake which is formed changes the light transmittance of the system and causes the galvanometer to deflect. A deflection of 25 divisions is arbitrarily chosen for measurements. A blank representing the volume of thorium nitrate required to produce this deflection by a fluorine-free solution is also determined. A calibration curve is prepared relating the volumes of standard thorium nitrate solution in milliliters and the quantities of fluorine in micrograms. This curve is linear up to 300 μg. of fluorine. The concentration of fluorine in an unknown sample is obtained from the volume of thorium nitrate used (after subtracting the blank) and the calibration curve, frequently checked by means of the standard sodium fluoride solutions.

MISCELLANEOUS ANALYSES

The methods included in this section are all either related to rubber analysis or are complementary to those already covered in this series of methods. It is difficult to decide the limitations to be imposed on the choice of methods related to rubber analysis because of the large variety of materials that have been, can be, and are included in rubber compounds. The advent of synthetic elastomers of structures and compositions extremely different from natural rubber also extends the range of additives as well as the needs for special types of analytical methods. The few methods given here were chosen to indicate some of the variety of measurements important to such analyses.

TABLE 59-18.

Subject	Method	References[a]
Latex	Light scattering	1, 2, 3, 4, 5
Latex	Electron microscopy	6
Dispersion of fillers	Electron microscopy	1, 7
Carbon black	Electron microscopy	8, 9
	pH by glass electrode	10
Rubber	Microscopy	11
Specific gravity of rubber chemicals	Pycnometer	12

[a] Numbers refer to the following reference works:
1. Ladd, W. A., and Ladd, M. W., Rubber Chemistry and Technol., **34,** 697, 1961.
2. Maron, S. H., and Elder, M. E., J. Colloid Sci., **18,** 107, 1963.
3. Maron, S. H., and Elder, M. E., J. Colloid Sci., **18,** 199, 1963.
4. Maron, S. H., Pierce, P. E., and Elder, M. E., J. Colloid Sci., **18,** 391, 1963.
5. Maron, S. H., Pierce, P. E., and Ulevitch, I. N., J. Colloid Sci., **18,** 470, 1963.
6. Rupar, W., and Mitchell, J. M., Rubber Chemistry and Technol., **35,** 1028, 1962.
7. Suito, E., Arakawa, M., Hasegawa, H., and Furusawa, Y., J. Soc. Rubber Ind. (Japan), **28,** 1, 1955; Rubber Chemistry and Technol., **29,** 1003, 1956.
8. Endter, F., Kautschuk u. Gummi, **3,** WT 273, 1950.
9. Prestridge, E. B., J. Appl. Polymer Sci., **7,** 27, 1963.
10. ASTM Standards, 1964, Part 28, D1512-60.
11. Leigh-Dugmore, C. H., Microscopy in Rubber, The Institution of the Rubber Industry, London, England, 1961.
12. ASTM Standards, 1964, Part 28, D 1817-61T.

TOTAL SOAP IN LATEX

CONDUCTANCE METHOD[63]

This method involves a conductance back titration of a latex solution in a mixture of water and isopropanol after addition of a known amount of standard hydrochloric acid solution.

Procedure.—Weigh to the nearest milligram a 10-g. sample of latex and transfer the asmple quantitatively to a 600-ml. beaker. Add the following reagents to the latex,

[63] Federal Standard No. 90, Rubber, Synthetic: Specification Limits, Sampling and Testing, April 12, 1956, General Services Administration, Washington, D. C.

continually stirring the latex during the addition, and being sure to add the reagents in the order given in order to avoid coagulation.

(1) 200 ml. of carbon dioxide-free distilled water.

(2) 200 ml. of isopropanol (99 percent minimum purity).

Introduce into the latex solution a pair of platinized platinum electrodes, protected by a perforated glass shield, and connect them to a suitable conductivity bridge (for example Leeds and Northrup Portable Conductivity Bridge No. 4866). Stir the latex solution continuously with an automatic stirrer during the determination.

Add to the solution 25 ml. of 0.1 N standard hydrochloric acid solution. Determine the conductance of the solution. From a buret, add 1.0 ml. of 0.1 N standard sodium hydroxide solution. Determine the conductance of the solution. Continue the titration by adding successive 1.0-ml.

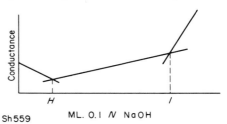

FIG. 59-57. Typical Conductance Titration Curve for Soap in Latex. (Courtesy General Services Administration.)

increments of standard 0.1 N sodium hydroxide solution, determining the conductance after the addition of each increment, until four or five conductance values have been obtained beyond a sharp increase in conductance (point I in Fig. 59-57).

Plot conductance as ordinate against milliliters of standard 0.1 N sodium hydroxide solution as abscissa. Draw three straight lines through the plotted points as indicated in Fig. 59-59.

Calculation.

$$\text{Total soap, percent} = \frac{(I - H) \times J \times K}{L}$$

$(I - H)$ = the milliliters of standard sodium hydroxide solution equivalent to soap;

J = the normality of the standard sodium hydroxide solution

K = the soap equivalent weight factor; 35.5 for GR-S-2003 latex and GR-S-2004 latex; and

L = the weight of the latex sample.

DISPERSION OF FILLERS

LIGHT MICROSCOPY METHOD[64]

This method describes a procedure for sample preparation and a means for quantitatively assessing filler dispersion in rubber by means of a light microscopic examination.

Procedure.—Cut sections of rubber with a sledge microtome while they are frozen, using the technique of Tidmus and Parkinson.[65]

The only change in the original method of sectioning is to substitute glass for steel knives.[66] Rhomboid-shaped pieces are cut from quarter-inch or 0.375-inch plate glass and the acute-angled edges of about 45° are used for cutting. The only way that has been found practicable for removing sections from the knife edge and mounting them for examination involves flooding them with naphtha. This causes swelling and increases the area of a vulcanized rubber about twice. Vulcanized rubber sections swell uniformly,

[64] Leigh-Dugmore, C. H., Rubber Chemistry and Technol. **29**, 1303, 1956.

[65] Tidmus. J. S., and Parkinson, D., Trans. Inst. Rubber Ind., **13**, 52, 1937.

[66] Latta and Hartman, Proc. Soc. Expt. Bio. Med., **74**, 436, 1950.

unvulcanized ones do not. If the piece of vulcanized rubber which is to be sectioned is measured beforehand (say with the vernier attachment on the microscope stage) and the mounted section is measured again afterwards the amount of swelling can be recorded as the areal swelling factor, s, which is the ratio of these two areas.

Assessment of Dispersion.—The sections are examined in a light microscope with a micrometer ruled in squares in the eyepiece, using transmitted light and a total magnification about 70 to $100\times$. The area of agglomerates in the field of view is measured in units of one square of the micrometer by counting the number of squares covered by agglomerates which are each larger than half a square. If the section thickness is small compared with the smallest agglomerates counted, the total area, U, of agglomerates in the field can be taken as proportional to the total volume, V, of agglomerates in the field. So, if the unswollen thickness was t,

$$V = Ut$$

If L percent by volume of the whole unswollen stock is carbon black, a is the unswollen area and t is the thickness, the total volume of black in the field viewed is

$$\frac{Lat}{100}$$

and the proportion of this in the form of agglomerates which have been counted is

$$R = \frac{U}{La} \times 10^4 \text{ percent}$$

If the micrometer has 10^4 squares, and the field they cover had area a unswollen,

$$sa = 10^4$$

where s is the areal swelling factor, and

$$R = \frac{U_s}{L} \text{ percent}$$

The percentage of the total black content which has been dispersed as agglomerates smaller than those counted is then the dispersion coefficient,

$$D = 100 - R \text{ percent}$$

$$= 100 - \frac{U_s}{L} \text{ percent}$$

Because an areal measurement, U, is used to provide a volume assessment, D, of the dispersion, the smallest agglomerates counted should be larger than the section thickness.

GENERAL TECHNIQUES OF LIGHT MICROSCOPY, MICRORADIOGRAPHY, AND ELECTRON MICROSCOPY FOR RUBBER ANALYSIS[67]

This method contains a description of a procedure for microtoming thin sections from rubber samples, and discusses the areas of usefulness of light microscopy, microradiography, and electron microscopy when applied to fillers in rubber.

Procedure. Microtoming Techniques.—Completely immerse the specimens in liq-

---

[67] Hess, W. M., Rubber Chemistry and Technol., **35**, 228, 1962.

uid nitrogen for a set amount of time, making it possible to duplicate freezing conditions quite closely from one operation to another.

Two different types of microtome may be employed for frozen section work. These are the Leitz Sledge Microtome (E. Leitz, Inc., N. Y., N. Y.) and the Porter-Blum Rotary Microtome (Ivan Sorvall, Inc., Norwalk, Conn.). The latter instrument is used exclusively for preparing electron microscope specimens, while the former is used for all of the light microscope and x-ray work as well as some electron microscope studies.

In order to maintain the frozen state of the specimen while it is being sectioned, a simple but very effective specimen mount is employed. For the Leitz microtome, this consists of a cylinder of brass which is threaded into a rectangular block of Teflon. The rubber specimen to be microtomed is first embedded in a slightly thickened water soluble mucilage on the top surface of the brass. This surface is deeply scored to provide a firm mount. After immersion in liquid nitrogen the brass quickly assumes a low temperature and will keep the rubber and supporting glue frozen for several minutes. The Teflon insulation permits a very slow temperature rise.

For most rubber samples a 1-minute freezing time is sufficient. This will keep the specimen frozen for about 3-8 minutes and allows ample time for alignment and paring down. For a given set of operating conditions, the optimum time for sectioning can be readily determined.

Thin sectioning for light or electron microscopy may be accomplished most efficiently with a glass knife. However, the relatively large, thick sections that are employed for x-ray studies can be more easily cut with a steel knife.

Specimens of the order of 2-μ thick are necessary for good light transmission of rubber compounds that are highly loaded with carbon black. At this thickness the sections curl badly and stick to the knife edge. In order to uncurl them and subsequently to brush them out flat they must be swelled in a suitable solvent such as naphtha or xylene. The knife should be continually lubricated during the sectioning operation.

Specimens in the thickness range of 10–40 μ are suitable for examination by microradiography. These can be readily handled without swelling. A steel knife lubricated with water or alcohol reduces the tendency toward curling, and the sections can simply be picked up with tweezers.

The Leitz Sledge Microtome is also capable of cutting frozen sections of rubber thin enough for the electron microscope. This can be done by setting the mechanical specimen advance at "0" and relying on thermal expansion to raise the specimen. Sections in the thickness range of 1000–500 A can then be cut quite easily. As for the light microscope, these specimens must also be uncurled in a solvent. However, in this instance they are mounted on standard 200 mesh EM specimen grids containing thin supporting substrates.

To eliminate the necessity of uncurling specimens for the electron microscope, the sections are cut on a Porter-Blum Rotary Microtome. The freezing mount is essentially the same as the one used for the Leitz instrument. It is cylindrical in shape and partially capped with Teflon to provide more complete insulation of the brass core. The frozen state of the specimen can thus be maintained for a longer period of time.

As the sections are cut they are floated directly onto a water surface where they are subsequently picked up on 200 mesh specimen grids. No swelling or brushing is necessary.

This set-up is capable of producing sections of SBR, IIR, and NR in the thickness range of 500 A. Polymers such as polybutadiene and silicone rubber are usually given a more vigorous freezing action. By means of a container that plugs into the top of the holder, liquid nitrogen can be kept in thermal contact with the rubber as it is sectioned. The specimen can then be kept frozen longer at a higher hardness level.

Light Microscopy.—This technique is particularly suitable for resolving undispersed agglomerates of carbon black; it has been applied extensively to the analysis of tread stocks. (Poor black dispersion has consistently been associated with a significant loss of wear.)

Figure 59-58 is a light photomicrograph of poor black dispersions in butyl and silicone rubber, and serves to illustrate the present technique.

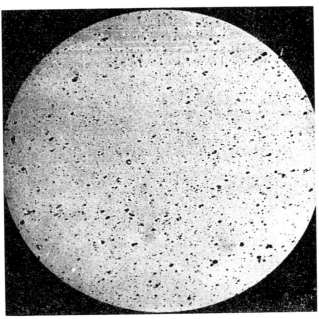

FIG. 59-58. Light Micrograph of Carbon Black in IIR (Butyl Rubber), Poor Dispersion. Loading: 50 PHR. (Courtesy Rubber World.)

Microradiography.—These analyses are carried out on a Phillips Contact Microradiography Unit,[68] which is capable of producing extremely soft x-rays in the 1–5 kv. range (6 to 8-A wavelength). The rubber specimens are mounted directly onto the emulsion of the fine grain recording film. A typical exposure for a 20-μ thick sample is 4 minutes at 3.5 kv. To increase contrast the wavelength of the x-ray beam is increased, and thinner specimens are used. At 1.5 kv., exposures on 10-μ thick sections run about 25 minutes, and the specimen chamber must be put under vacuum to prevent air absorption of the x-rays.

Since contact microradiograms are the actual size of the specimen, they must subsequently be enlarged optically. This is best done under a light microscope where the negatives can be either directly examined or rephotographed and printed at higher magnification.

Figure 59-59 shows a light micrograph of an SBR white sidewall compound containing 50 percent by weight of an 80:20 blend of zinc and titanium oxides. Section thickness was 10 μ. Figure 59-60 shows a negative microradiogram of the identical area. Regions

[68] Phillips Electronics, Mount Vernon, N. Y.

of high x-ray absorption appear white. The obvious improvement in resolution over the light microscope method is quite apparent. The outlines of the pigment agglomerations are much more clearly defined by microradiography. In a carbon-loaded stock, agglomerates similar to these are even more difficult to resolve by light microscopy.

Electron Microscopy.—The use of the electron microscope as a tool for dispersion

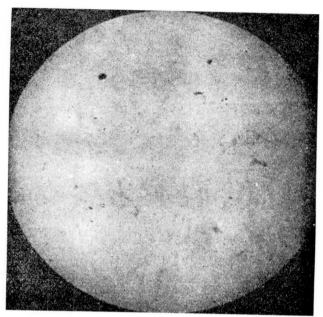

Fig. 59-59. Light Micrograph of White Sidewall Compound (50 by Weight of 80:20 Blend of ZnO and TiO$_2$). (Courtesy Rubber World.)

analysis is somewhat restricted, due to the small size of the specimen that can be examined. It is used as shown in Fig. 59-61 to resolve the size and shape of the ultimate pigment particles, and it is also employed to compare dispersion quality when other methods have failed to show differences.

Silicone rubber and polybutadiene, both with very low glass transition temperatures, have been the most difficult polymers to section thin enough for electron microscopy. Nevertheless, with care, they can be microtomed to a thickness of 1000–500 A with reasonable consistency. Sections of IIR, SBR, and NR can be cut quite routinely.

DETERMINATION OF ISOCYANATE GROUP IN BONDING AGENTS

POTENTIOMETRIC METHOD[69]

In this method the isocyanate content present in the bonding agent is determined by back titrating an added excess of diisobutylamine with a standard solution of hydrochloric acid, using a glass electrode indicator for the end point.

[69] Williamson, A. G., Analyst, **77**, 372, 1952.

Procedure.—Dissolve sufficient concentrated hydrochloric acid, sp. gr. 1.18, to make a normal solution in a medium consisting of monochlorobenzene (30 volumes) and methanol (100 volumes), and standardize this solution by direct two-phase colorimetric titration with aqueous standard alkali solution, using methyl orange as indicator.

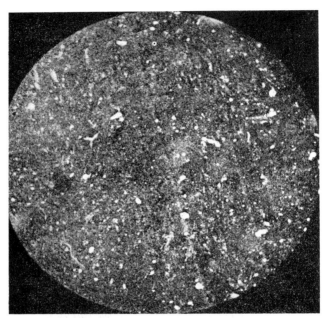

Fig. 59-60.   Negative Microradiogram of the SBR Compound in Fig. 59-59. (Courtesy Rubber World.)

Take a 1.5 to 2 *N* solution of diisobutylamine in monochlorobenzene, and transfer exactly 10 ml. to a small flask. Add sufficient monochlorobenzene to bring the final volume of inert solution to about 20 ml. and weigh, *e.g.*, from a Lunge-Ray pipet, sufficient isocyanate solution to react with 5 to 7 ml. of the diisobutylamine solution. Agitate the flask gently, then cork it and set it aside for about 10 minutes to complete the reaction. Pour the contents of the flask into a titration beaker provided with an automatic stirrer, wash the flask with a known quantity of distilled methanol, equivalent to 100 volumes for 30 volumes of inert solvent present in the reaction flask, and add the washings to the beaker. Add 13 volumes of water, slowly, with stirring.

Insert the glass electrode and one arm of an agar bridge connected to a calomel electrode in the solution. Couple the cell so formed into the measuring circuit. With continuous stirring, titrate the excess of diisobutylamine with a standard normal solution of hydrochloric acid made up from concentrated aqueous acid and a medium containing 30 volumes of monochlorobenzene to 100 volumes of methanol. In the region of the equivalence point, take readings after the addition of each drop of titrant and plot the cell potential against the amount, in milliliters, of titrant added. The equivalance point

FIG. 59-61. Electron Micrograph of the SBR Compound in Fig. 59-59. One-half inch equals one micron. (Courtesy Rubber World.)

is accurately found from the resulting curve. Carry out a blank determination, omitting the isocyanate.

NOTE.—In some isocyanate samples, carbamyl chlorides formed as intermediates in the isocyanate preparation may be found as impurities. These interfere as they do in other methods based on the reaction of the isocyanate with an amine. The true isocyanate content of such a mixture can be found by combining the results of potentiometric titration with those of gravimetric determination as given by Stagg.[70]

[70] Stagg, H. L., Analyst, **7**, 557, 1946.

Chapter **60**

SEMICONDUCTORS

By Philip F. Kane

Central Research Laboratories
Texas Instruments Inc.
Dallas, Texas

INTRODUCTION[1]

The analytical chemistry of semiconductor materials differs from the analysis of other materials in that probably in no other area does so little mean so much. The proper functioning of a solid state electronic device is implicitly dependent upon having a very precisely controlled level of just the right kind of impurities in the material from which the device is made. Just a few parts per million of the wrong impurity in, for instance, either silicon or germanium can bring the value of these materials down from several hundred to a few dollars per pound.

CONDUCTION IN SEMICONDUCTORS

To appreciate the effect of trace impurities in semiconductor materials, some considerations of the mechanisms of conduction in such materials is essential. For the sake of brevity, some of the concepts in the following discussion have been simplified but the description of the phenomenon in its most elementary form should be helpful to the uninitiated.

Figure 60-1 is a two-dimensional representation of the silicon crystal lattice; germanium and most other semiconductors have similar structures. An excited electron in a perfect crystal is acted upon solely by the lattice forces and, subject to these forces, can wander through the interstices of the crystal lattice. Such an electron is called a conduction electron, as contrasted to valence electrons whose movements are restricted to orbital paths about given lattice sites. If a valence electron is excited to the conduction state, it wanders away and a one-electron bond is left behind. This one-electron bond is referred to as a hole. Such a hole can migrate by a valence electron jumping from an adjacent bond to the one-electron bond, thus filling one hole but creating a second. The process can continue randomly, propagating itself, and in effect the hole wanders through the lattice like a conduction electron. At any one temperature, the electrons and holes are in equilibrium.

If an electric field is applied to the lattice, as in Fig. 60-2, the electrons will tend to move toward the positive pole; it follows that holes must move against the electron flow to the negative pole. This type of electronic conduction, in which the current is carried by electrons or holes formed by thermal excitation of electrons derived from the basic lattice material, is termed intrinsic conduction. It is an inherent property of the material and does not lend itself to control.

[1] Reprinted in part from a paper by T. S. Burkhalter, Analytical Chemistry, **33**, 21A, 1961. Copyright 1961 by the American Chemical Society and reprinted by permission of the copyright owner.

1764

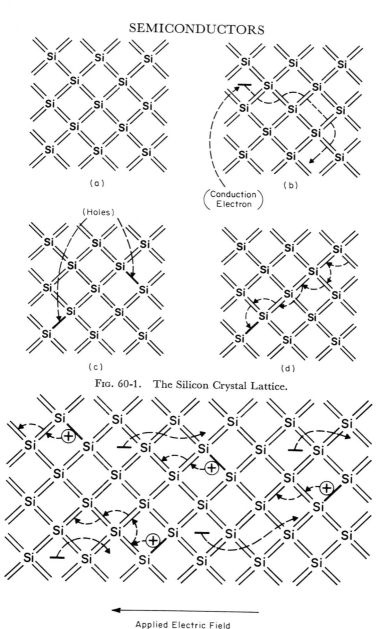

(a)

(b)

$\left(\begin{array}{c}\text{Conduction} \\ \text{Electron}\end{array}\right)$

(Holes)

(c)

(d)

FIG. 60-1. The Silicon Crystal Lattice.

Applied Electric Field

FIG. 60-2. The Effect of an Electric Field on the Silicon Lattice.

A second and controllable source of electrons or holes is provided by the substitution at lattice sites of atoms with one valence electron more or less than the four valence electrons normally associated with the silicon or germanium atom. An arsenic atom, for instance, at a site in a germanium crystal, readily donates its fifth electron to the conduction band and is thus called a donor. An indium atom with its three electrons readily accepts an electron from an adjacent bond pair creating a hole and is thus called an acceptor. Collectively such atoms are called dopants and the electrons and holes thus formed can migrate in an electric field in just the same way as in intrinsic conduction. This type of conduction, where the electrons or holes are derived from other than the basic lattice material, is termed extrinsic conduction.

CONTROLLED ADDITION OF DOPANTS

It is the presence of these mobile electrons or holes in a solid lattice that gives the semiconductor materials their unique properties. Control of the numbers of these electrons and holes, or carriers, makes possible the operations of such devices as transistors. Since the intrinsic conduction is of thermal origin, it follows that the required control must be achieved through adjustment of the extrinsic conduction, that is, by addition of dopants to the material. However, the content of dopants must be very carefully controlled and the presence of too many, or of other foreign atoms, either substitutionally or interstitially, can drastically degrade the material to the point where it is useless for the production of semiconductor devices.

The required number of dopant atoms, and also the number of other atoms which can be tolerated, varies widely with the particular device to be made but, as a general rule of thumb, a desirable level is about 10^{16} dopant atoms per cubic centimeter (cc.) of base material and as few other impurity atoms as possible. A common practice for preparing semiconductor materials is to obtain the base material in the purest possible form and then to add dopant to give the required number of carriers. This raises the question of how pure is pure and introduces the analytical chemist to a new and exciting field of endeavor. If the total impurities can be reduced to about 10^{14} atoms per cubic centimeter, then the level is about 100 times lower than the dopant concentration and will usually be considered adequate. This description of impurity levels in terms of atoms per cubic centimeter is not generally familiar to the analyst who usually talks in terms of parts per million or parts per billion. A typical conversion, that of 10^{14} atoms per cubic centimeter of boron in silicon, is as follows:

$$\text{Parts per billion} = \text{atoms per cc.} \times \frac{M \times 10^9}{A \times d}$$

where M = atomic weight of impurity,
   A = Avogadro's number, and
   d = density of bulk material.

For boron in silicon, $M = 10.8$,
           $d = 2.4$, and
           $A = 6 \times 10^{23}$

i.e., boron content $= 10^{14} \times \dfrac{10.8 \times 10^9}{6 \times 10^{23} \times 2.4} = 0.75$ p.p.b.

Thus, the required purity of silicon, 10^{14} atoms per cubic centimeter, is equivalent to 0.75 p.p.b., a level which, without question, calls for the most sophisticated approach to trace analysis.

CARRIER CONCENTRATIONS BY ELECTRICAL MEASUREMENTS

An approximation of the number of carriers can be arrived at by purely physical means. The conductivity, σ, is given by

$$\sigma = e.n.\mu_e + e.p.\mu_p \tag{1}$$

where e = charge on the electron,
   n = number of electrons per cubic centimeter,
   μ_e = drift mobility of electrons,
   p = number of holes per cubic centimeter, and
   μ_p = drift mobility of holes.

The drift mobility is the velocity attained in a unit electric field. In the extrinsic case, either n or p is always greatly in excess and Eq. (1) simplifies to

$$\sigma = e.n.\mu_e \tag{2}$$

or

$$\sigma = e.p.\mu_p \tag{3}$$

depending on whether the electrons are the majority carriers, an n-type material, or the holes are the majority carriers, a p-type material.

Another important electrical parameter is the Hall coefficient. This can be shown to be:

$$R_H = \frac{\pm\mu_H}{c.\sigma} \tag{4}$$

where μ_H = Hall mobility, and
   c = velocity of light.
μ_H should approximate to the drift mobility, so that combining Eqs. (2) and (4)

$$R_H = \frac{1}{n.e.c.} \tag{5}$$

which defines the Hall coefficient in terms of the number of carriers and is thus an indication of the number of dopant atoms. The conductivity can be used in conjunction with this to give an estimate of the mobility which in turn gives an insight into and some estimate of the other impurities present. The foregoing is greatly simplified but further consideration would be beyond the scope of this chapter. For a more complete treatment of this, and of other properties of these materials, reference should be made to Hannay's work.[2]

The determinations of conductivity and Hall coefficient are standard procedures in any semiconductor materials laboratory, and will be described here only very briefly. Figure 60-3 shows the so-called two-point probe method for measuring conductivity. The method consists of passing a known current in the longitudinal direction through a rectangular bar of known dimensions and, by means of probes separated by a fixed distance, measuring the potential drop along the length of the bar

$$\sigma = \frac{\Delta s.I}{\Delta V.w.t.} \tag{6}$$

where the quantities are as shown in the figure. The same apparatus can be used to obtain the Hall coefficient. If a d.c. current is passed through a rectangular bar in the X direction concurrent with the imposition of a magnetic field in the Y direction, a potential difference known as the Hall voltage results in the Z direction. It is this Hall voltage which is actually measured and the Hall coefficient is calculated from

$$R_H = \frac{V_H t.10^8}{I.H} \tag{7}$$

[2] Hannay, N. B., Semiconductors, Reinhold, New York, 1959.

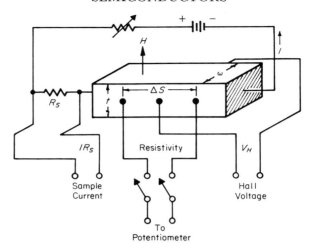

F<small>IG</small>. 60-3.   Apparatus for Determining Resistivity and Hall Coefficient.

where V_H = Hall voltage,
       t = thickness of the bar, and
       H = magnetic field.

IDENTIFICATION OF IMPURITIES

The physical parameters are extremely useful in assessing the quality of a semi-conductor material, and will usually be the criteria for acceptance or rejection. However, like most measurements of physical properties, they do not give any indication of the identity of the impurities which may be present nor, in most cases, of the dopant present. In seeking any particular element, absorptiometric or, sometimes, fluorimetric methods are often considered first since, as Feigl said, they can be made "specific, selective and sensitive"; in fact, a considerable volume of literature exists on the analysis of semiconductors for a very wide selection of elements. A review of some of the more important has been made by Parker and Rees.[3]

These methods, however, suffer from one major drawback, that is, that the reagents which are normally available are more impure than the materials being examined. For example, potassium pyrosulfate, commonly used for fusing refractory materials, has a maximum allowable concentration of 20 p.p.m. iron according to the American Chemical Society specifications for analytical grade material; semiconductor materials must contain over 1000 times less than this. It is usually possible to reduce the level for any one element to an acceptably low blank, but the methods employed are often tedious and involved. Moreover, the very specificity of the absorptiometric methods implies a multiplicity of determinations, each with its specially purified set of reagents. Consequently, despite the effort that has gone into these methods, they are, with a few exceptions, seldom used in practice.

The problem of the blank is usually met by the adoption of physical methods in which the reagents can be reduced to a minimum. In semiconductor analysis, perhaps the most widely used has been emission spectrography, although in more recent years it has been displaced to some extent by solids mass spectrography. Both methods have

[3] Parker, C. A., and Rees, W. T., Trace Analysis of Semiconductor Materials, J. Paul Cali, Ed., Macmillan, New York, 1964.

the advantages of high sensitivity and broad coverage which are essential to any assessment of a semiconductor material, with the mass spectrograph having better coverage and, in general, higher sensitivity. The greatest sensitivity can be achieved by activation analysis but it is more tedious, less widely applicable and, of course, requires access to a neutron source. These techniques, together with some others that have specialized application, will be dealt with in succeeding sections.

Semiconductors include a large number of materials, but in practice only a handful have commercial significance. Almost all solid state electronic devices are made of either germanium or silicon together with a small but significant group composed of combinations of elements from group IIIA with those from group VA of the periodic table. Of these III–V compounds, gallium arsenide, indium arsenide, and indium antimonide are probably the most important. Other semiconductors have been used, boron and silicon carbide, for example, but they have little commercial application. There are a number of photosensitive devices prepared from combinations of elements from group IIB with those from group VIA, in particular cadmium sulfide and cadmium selenide, but these are not in the same high state of purity. The impurity levels are generally in the parts per million range and conventional emission spectrography can be used in their analysis. The following methods have been restricted, therefore, to germanium, silicon, and the III–V compounds, including the constituent elements.

WORKING WITH SEMICONDUCTORS

The analyst starting out on the analysis of ultrapure materials such as semiconductors will usually find it necessary to refine his laboratory techniques. He must constantly bear in mind at every step of the analysis that the impurity he is seeking is in the nanogram range. He must cultivate habits that will guard against adventitious contamination on a vanishingly small scale.

Ideally, the working area should be free of dust, but a normally air-conditioned laboratory is acceptable with certain precautions. Bench tops must be kept scrupulously clean. Reagent racks above the working surface should be avoided. Covers should be kept on all material in beakers and other unprotected containers. Fume hoods are a frequent source of contamination due to corrosion products falling from the upper surfaces; hoods with make-up air are particularly prone to this since there is a draft blowing down toward the working area. In laboratories which are not air-conditioned, these problems become even more acute and in this case a glove-box may be the only solution.

Equally as important as a scrupulously clean working area is meticulous care of the analyst's working tools. Contamination of or by glassware is a common source of error and all such apparatus must be handled and stored accordingly. Soft glass is readily attacked by many reagents and should never be used. Hard glass is usually satisfactory but must be leached with aqua regia and rinsed thoroughly before use. Teflon is suitable for hydrofluoric acid solutions, and either Teflon or polyethylene can be used for longer term storage. Very dilute solutions, such as standards, may tend to deplete by adsorption on the walls of the container and must, therefore, be freshly prepared. Conversely, containers that have been used for stronger solutions may desorb ions into weaker ones; very dilute solutions are best prepared in new, freshly leached containers.

Reagents are a constant problem. The most important is, of course, the water, and a very high purity, deionized water is essential. A resistivity of 14 MΩ-cm. is a good criterion although dissolved carbon dioxide is not important. Care should be taken to see that it is free from particulate matter. Other reagents should be the purest available. Some manufacturers[4] are supplying purer reagents especially for use in this industry; these are referred to in the following methods as semiconductor grade. However, even these are not always sufficiently pure and where large volumes are required, for example,

[4] Included are Allied Chemical, J. T. Baker, and Mallinkrodt.

of hydrofluoric acid for treating silicon, it may be necessary to redistil or otherwise purify them.

In time initially pure reagents may become heavily contaminated because of storage in unsuitable containers or careless handling. The reagents specified in these methods will give acceptable results; however, they are often specified as the best available and if anything better can be obtained it should generally be employed. Unlike most methods, the materials used as calibration standards need not be so rigidly controlled since they finish up at such a low dilution that even 1 percent impurity can be neglected. However, cross-contamination must be avoided. In pipetting a series of standards, the most dilute should be taken first, working up the series to the more concentrated.

In every case, it can be assumed that the samples received by the analyst have contaminated surfaces, and every procedure will include a preliminary etch to remove this surface. All subsequent operations must include precautions to avoid recontaminating the sample; the use of plastic-tipped tweezers to transfer solid material is essential.

Only a punctilious attention to the finer points of good laboratory practice will allow meaningful results to be obtained.

EMISSION SPECTROGRAPHY

Emission spectrography is usually considered first when a sensitive method with broad coverage is required; for the usual concept of pure materials this is an excellent choice. However, for semiconductors, a sensitivity of about 1 p.p.b. is required and this is two to three orders of magnitude lower than the conventional spectrographic methods. The extension of this technique has followed two lines; either a preliminary concentration is used followed by application of existing methods, or the technique itself has been refined to improve sensitivity.

A number of applications of the concentration approach have been made. Several Russian workers[5,6,7,8,9,10,11,12] have determined impurities in silicon by volatilizing the matrix as silicon tetrafluoride; Keck et al.[13] and Borovskii et al.[14] concentrated the impurities by vacuum distillation. Morrison and Rupp[15] determined boron in silicon by using an electrolytic preconcentration. Several workers[16,17,18] separated germanium

[5] Peizulaev, Sh. I., Karabash, A. G., Krauz, L. S., Kostareva, F. A., Smirnova-Averina, N. I., Babina, F. L., Kondrat'eva, L. I., Voronova, E. F., and Meshkova, V. M., Zavod. Lab., **24**, 723–731, 1958.

[6] Zil'bershtein, Kh. I., Kaliteevskii, N. I., Razumovskii, A. N., and Fedorov, Yu. F., Zavod. Lab., **28**, 43–45, 1962.

[7] Vasilevskaya, L. S., Kondrashina, A. I., and Shifrina, G. G., Zavod. Lab., **28**, 674–676, 1962.

[8] Morachevskii, Yu. V., Zil'bershtein, Kh. I., Piryutko, M. M., and Nikitina, O. N., Zhur. Anal. Khim., **17**, 614–620, 1962.

[9] Morachevskii, Yu. V., Zil'bershtein, Kh. I., Piryutko, M. M., and Nikitina, O. N., Vestn. Leningr. Univ., Ser. Fiz. i Khim., 140–145, 1962.

[10] Rudnevskii, N. K., Sokolova, L. N., and Tsvetkov, S. G., Trudy Khim. i Khim. Tekhnol. (Gor'kii), 341–345, 1962.

[11] Semov, M. P., Zavod. Lab., **29**, 1450–1451, 1963.

[12] Lifshits, E. V., Erko, V. F., Bugaiova, N. I., and Mosova, L. M., Ukr. Fiz. Zhur., **6**, 846–850, 1961.

[13] Keck, P. H., MacDonald, A. L., and Mellichamp, J. W., Anal. Chem., **28**, 995–996, 1956.

[14] Borovskii, I. M., Shteinberg, A. N., and Bugulova, V. V., Trudy Inst. Metallurgii, Akad. Nauk S.S.S.R., 283–288, 1958.

[15] Morrison, G. H., and Rupp, R. L., Anal. Chem., **29**, 892–895, 1957.

[16] Karabash, A. G., Peizulaev, Sh. I., Morozova, G. G., and Smirenkina, I. I., Trudy Komiss. Anal. Khim., Akad. Nauk S.S.S.R., **12**, 25–35, 1960.

[17] Vasilevskaya, L. S., Notkina, M. A., Sadof'eva, S. A., and Kondrashina, A. I., Zavod. Lab., **28**, 678–680, 1962.

[18] Dvorak, J., and Dobremyslova, I., Chem. Prumysl, **13**, 136–138, 1963.

by volatilizing as the chloride, and Veleker[19] extracted arsenic and bismuth from germanium by solvent extraction of the diethyldithiocarbamates.

Removal of the matrix by solvent extraction has been described by Owens for the analysis of gallium,[20] and Caldararu for indium.[21] Solvent extraction was also used for the separation of gallium in gallium arsenide by Oldfield and Mack,[22] who removed the arsenic by volatilizing the chloride, and by Kataev and Otmakhova,[23] who separated arsenic on an ion-exchange column. Neeb[24] concentrated zinc from gallium or indium by distillation. Mack[25] determined impurities in arsenic by evaporating the chloride.

All these methods suffer from the criticism leveled at the colorimetric methods, namely that the reagents employed may be impure. Moreover, the handling required may lead to further adventitious contamination. But probably the most serious objection is that the broad coverage required is not there. In separating the major elements one may also separate some of the trace elements and, consequently, only a limited number of elements may be sought. The final analysis leaves a considerable area of uncertainty.

The alternative approach is to apply the technique to the sample with the minimum of pretreatment. Conventional total burn techniques have been used for silicon carbide[26,27,28,29] and for silicon,[30,31,32] but in general these do not have the necessary sensitivity. Morrison et al.[33,34] applied a "selective" volatilization technique to the analysis of silicon carbide, and this same principle was used by Jones et al.[35] in the analysis of gallium arsenide. Briefly, the technique splits the burn into a number of successive exposures; this has the effect of substantially reducing the background while not significantly lowering the signal from most of the elements. Figure 60-4 shows the intensity of radiation as a function of time for three impurity lines and the background from a sample of gallium arsenide. It is apparent that, if a first and last cut is made of the total burn, then a better "signal-to-noise" ratio can be obtained. This is the basis of the methods described below for general application.

The method used for III-V compounds has been found very useful: sensitivities as low as 1 p.p.b. can be obtained for copper and magnesium; and most of the other elements of interest are detectable between 0.01 and 1 p.p.m. The method can be refined further for the volatile elements mercury, phosphorus, tellurium, and zinc by the addition of a boiler cap[36] to the electrode to enhance the separation. A separate procedure for the alkali metals is described since this utilizes a different region of the spectrum.

[19] Veleker, T. J., Anal. Chem., **34**, 87–89, 1962.
[20] Owens, E. B., Appl. Spectroscopy, **13**, 105–108, 1959.
[21] Caldararu, H., Rev. Chim., Bucharest, **14**, 39–41, 1963.
[22] Oldfield, J. H., and Mack, D. L., Analyst, **87**, 778–785, 1962.
[23] Kataev, G. A., and Otmakhova, Z. I., Zhur. Anal. Khim., **18**, 339–341, 1963.
[24] Neeb, K. H., Z. anal. Chem., **194**, 255–264, 1963.
[25] Mack, D. L., Analyst, **88**, 481–482, 1963.
[26] Hegemann, F., Giesen, K., and Von Sybel, C., Ber. dtsch. Keram. Ges., **32**, 329–333, 1955.
[27] Rost, F., Mikrochim. Acta, 343–352, 1956.
[28] Hegemann, F., Giesen, K., and Von Sybel, C., Ber. dtsch. Keram. Ges., **33**, 387–390, 1956.
[29] Ehrlich, G., Gerbatsch, R., and Freitag, G., Chem. Anal., Warsaw, **7**, 435–443, 1962.
[30] Shvangiradze, R. R., and Mozgovaya, T. A., Zhur. Anal. Khim., **12**, 708–713, 1957.
[31] Vecsernyes, L., Magyar Kem. Foly., **66**, 513–516, 1960.
[32] Vecsernyes, L., Z. anal. Chem., **182**, 429–435, 1961.
[33] Rupp, R. L., and Morrison, G. H., U. S. Government Report AFCRL-62-130, 1960.
[34] Morrison, G. H., Rupp, R. L., and Klecak, G. L., Anal. Chem., **32**, 933–935, 1960.
[35] Jones, C. E., Andrychuk, D., and Massengale, J. F., Pittsburgh Conf. on Anal. Chem. and Appl. Spec., 1961.
[36] This is a well established procedure. See, for example, C. E. Harvey, Spectrochemical Procedures, A.R.L., Glendale, California, 1950.

The elements of groups III and V, with the exception of arsenic, can be analyzed by the same procedures. Arsenic is too volatile to allow a split-burn technique to be applied.

The emission spectrographic method is considerably less valuable for silicon and germanium. Since a higher temperature is required to volatilize them into the arc, a smaller cup electrode must be used. This reduces the sample volume, and the weight is lowered still more by the lower density of these materials. Moreover, the oxides formed in air

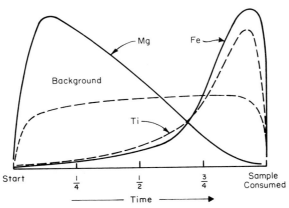

FIG. 60-4.   Emission as a Function of Time During a Spectrographic Burn. (Reprinted from Analytical Chemistry, **33**, 21A, 1961. Copyright 1961 by the American Chemical Society and reprinted by permission of the copyright owner.)

give a band structure which obscures the lines; it is desirable to arc in an inert atmosphere. This inert atmosphere, however, tends to repress the volatilization of the sample and to give rise to excessively long exposures. The method described is a compromise and has value in examining material which may be suspected of being heavily contaminated. In general, the levels of sensitivity are 10 to 20 times higher than for the III-V materials.

SPECTROGRAPHIC ANALYSIS OF III-V COMPOUNDS AND ELEMENTS[37]

SAMPLE PREPARATION

For Gallium Arsenide, Indium Antimonide, Indium Arsenide, Antimony, and Indium.—Samples will usually be received as ingots. The material may or may not be single crystal, but in any case one cannot assume it to be homogeneous; a sampling problem will always exist. Slight variation in trace element distribution can be expected along the length of the ingot and in cross-section. A center section can usually be regarded as representative, but for highest accuracy several sections should be sampled.

Using a diamond saw, cut a section 0.75 mm. (0.030 in.) thick, perpendicular to the length of the ingot. Remove the mounting wax by boiling the sample in methanol, semiconductor grade. Transfer it, using Teflon-coated tweezers, to a polypropylene spoon (see Fig. 60-5) and immerse in boiling aqua regia (3:1 hydrochloric acid:nitric acid, both semiconductor grade) for 1 minute. Rinse twice in hot, deionized water (1

[37] In collaboration with J. F. Massengale.

minute) followed by boiling methanol, semiconductor grade (1 minute). Tip from spoon to bibulous paper, and allow it to dry in the air (as free of dust as possible). When it is dry, transfer it, using tweezers, to fresh bibulous paper and cover with a second sheet. Transfer the sample, still between the sheets, to a clean agate or tungsten carbide mortar and break by tapping the covered slice with the pestle. Reduce to fragments less than 2 mm. on a side. Roll the fragments between the sheets to mix.

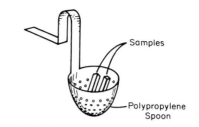

FIG. 60-5. Polypropylene Spoon for Sample Transfer.

For Gallium.—Gallium melts at 29.8°C. (85.6°F.); consequently, it is usually packed and shipped in polyethylene bottles.

Liquefy the sample by immersing the bottle in warm, deionized water. Transfer it to the electrode as a liquid, using a clean polyethylene or glass dropper.

ELECTRODES

Lower.—$\frac{1}{4}$ in. undercut cup electrode, N.C. 4018, Ultracarbon 1989.

Upper.—$\frac{3}{16}$ in. shaped counter electrode, N.C. 3951, Ultracarbon 105U.

Preburn the electrodes, with the lower as the anode, at 20 amps. d.c. for 10 seconds using a 3-mm. gap. Transfer to a covered electrode stand.

SPLIT-BURN TECHNIQUE

STANDARDS

Silicon-Boron Solution. Standard 1A.—1 mg. per ml. Weigh exactly 1.012 g. of sodium metasilicate, reagent grade, and 0.822 g. of sodium tetraborate, ACS reagent grade, into a 100-ml. volumetric flask. Add deionized water, shake to dissolve, and dilute to volume.

Standard 1B.—10 μg. per ml. Pipet 1 ml. of standard 1A into a 100-ml. volumetric flask and dilute to volume with deionized water. Mix. This dilution must be made on the day of use.

Working Standards.—Into a series of 100-ml. volumetric flasks, pipet 1, 4, 10 and 40 ml. of standard 1B. Dilute to volume with deionized water and mix.

Nitrate Solution. Standard 2A.—1 mg. per ml. Weigh out 0.100 g. of the following metals, all reagent grade: bismuth, cadmium, copper, lead, magnesium, nickel, and silver. Transfer to a 100-ml. beaker. Add 10 ml. of concentrated nitric acid, semiconductor grade, and heat for 1 hour. Cool and add 50 ml. of deionized water.[38] Transfer to a 100-ml. volumetric flask, dilute to volume with deionized water, and mix.

Standard 2B.—Prepare standard 2B and working standards as described for series 1.

Chloride Solution. Standard 3A.—1 mg. per ml. Weigh out 0.100 g. of the following metals, all reagent grade: aluminum, beryllium, chromium, cobalt, iron, manganese, tin, and titanium. Transfer to a 100-ml. beaker. Add 10 ml. of concentrated hydrochloric acid, semiconductor grade, and heat to dissolve. Cool. Transfer to a 100-ml. volumetric flask, dilute to volume with deionized water, and mix.

Standard 3B.—Prepare standard 3B and working standards as described for series 1.

Gold Solution. Standard 4A.—1 mg. Au per ml. Weigh 0.100 g. of pure gold wire

---

[38] All the metals will dissolve in concentrated nitric acid; the lead salt, however, will re-precipitate as a white powder in this acid. On the addition of water, it will redissolve.

into a beaker. Add 10 ml. of aqua regia (1 part nitric acid, semiconductor grade, with 3 parts hydrochloric acid, semiconductor grade) and allow to dissolve. Transfer to a 100-ml. volumetric flask, dilute to volume with deionized water, and mix.

Standard 4B.—Prepare standard 4B and working standards as described for series 1.

Preparation of Calibration Standards.[39]—Wetproof the preburned lower electrodes by filling the cup with a dilution of Duco cement (cellulose cement), 1 part cement with 20 parts ethyl acetate, ACS reagent. Allow to dry.

To a series of 10 wet-proofed electrodes, add 25- and 50-μl. aliquots of standard 1B and its working standards, as shown in the following table.

Electrode No.	1	2	3	4	5	6	7	8	9	10
Working Standard, 1%, μl.	25	50								
Working Standard, 4%, μl.			25	50						
Working Standard, 10%, μl.					25	50				
Working Standard, 40%, μl.							25	50		
Standard 1B, μl.									25	50
Wt. of each element, ng.	2.5	5	10	20	25	50	100	200	250	500

Dry under an infrared heat lamp. Repeat using series 2, 3, and 4. The result is a series of electrodes containing the weights of each element shown in the table. To each of these electrodes and a blank electrode, add a weighed amount (175 to 225 mg.) of the intended matrix,[40] prepared as described for the sample.

Sample Loading.—Weigh accurately between 175 and 225 mg. of sample, prepared as given above, into a preburned lower electrode.

Procedure.—Adjust the spectrograph to record in the range 2400 to 3600 A. Adjust the slit width so that the background of the final spectrum is at least 20 percent transmission in the short wavelength end; a neutral filter in the external optics or adjustment of the grating mask may be necessary to achieve this. Use a convenient slit length and corresponding plate rack (2-mm. length and 2.5-mm. rack is suggested).

Check the spectrograph alignment.

Mount a loaded electrode in the lower electrode holder and a counter electrode in the upper. Connect a source of d.c. to the electrodes, making the lower (sample) electrode the anode. Adjust the analytical gap to 3 mm.

Load the camera with Eastman Kodak 103-0 plate or film.

Open the shutter and strike the arc, adjusting the current to 18 amps. At the same time start a timer. Maintain the analytical gap at 3 mm.

After 40 seconds, rack the plate to the next position, maintaining the burn. Continue until the bead of metal is about 1 mm. in diameter. Rack the plate again.

Continue the burn until the sample is completely consumed (usually 20–30 seconds). Switch off d.c. supply. Close shutter. Rack the plate for the next sample (or standard).

Plate Development.—Develop in Kodak D-19 for 3 minutes at 70°F. Stop, fix, wash, and dry.

Densitometry.—For each sample (or standard), there will be three exposures.

For the first exposure, measure the densities of the following lines and their adjacent backgrounds.

[39] Because of the wide coverage, no single internal standard was felt suitable, and an absolute method was adopted.

[40] The standard matrix presents a problem since it should be the purest specimen available. However, in setting up, this may well be the sample itself. In this case, the analysis can be made by using the sample here and determining the impurities as given in the section on calibration curves.

Al	3092.7 (for Ga and GaAs 3082.2)
Be	3130.4
Bi	3067.7
B	2497.7 (not applicable to Ga and GaAs)
Cd	3466.2
Pb	2833.1
Mg	2853.1
Si	2516.1

Using the plate calibration for the particular emulsion batch, transform density to intensity. Subtract the background intensity from the line intensity and record the corrected line intensity.

Examine the second exposure. If any of the above lines are present, measure and obtain corrected line intensity as above. Add these two corrected intensities to obtain the total corrected line intensity.

For the last exposure, measure the densities of the following lines and their adjacent backgrounds.

Cr	3021.6
Co	3453.5
Cu	3247.5
Au	2676.0
Fe	3020.6
Mn	2605.7
Ni	3002.5
Ag	3280.7
Sn	2840.0
Ti	3234.5

Obtain the corrected line intensities as before.

Re-examine the second exposure. If any of these lines are present, measure and add to obtain the total corrected line intensities as before.

Calibration Curves.—For each element listed above, and for each particular matrix, construct a graph of intensity against concentration, expressed as nanograms per gram and calculated on the weight of matrix added to each individual electrode. Draw the best straight line through these points.

If the curve passes through the origin, the matrix was free from the element being considered. Replot the curve as intensity against weight, in nanograms.

If the curve does not pass through the origin, extrapolate to cut the abscissa. The intercept on the abscissa is the concentration, in nanograms per gram, of the element in the matrix. Calculate, in nanograms, the weight of the standard element present in each of the matrix additions, and add to the standard amount to obtain corrected element addition. Replot the curve as intensity against weight, in nanograms.

Sample Calculation.—Using the appropriate calibration curve, determine the weight in nanograms corresponding to the total corrected line intensity. Divide by the sample weight in grams to obtain the concentration in nanograms per gram (p.p.b.).

ALKALI METALS

STANDARDS

Alkali Metal Solution. Standard 5A.—1 mg. per ml. Weigh into a clean 100-ml. volumetric flask the following amounts of salts: calcium carbonate, ACS Reagent, 250 mg.; lithium carbonate, Reagent, 532 mg.; potassium chloride, ACS reagent, 191 mg.;

rubidium chloride, purified, 141 mg.; and sodium chloride, ACS Reagent, 254 mg. Add 10 ml. of concentrated hydrochloric acid, semiconductor grade, and 10 ml. of deionized water. Shake to dissolve. Dilute to volume with deionized water. Mix.

Standard 5B.—Prepare standard 5B and working standards as described in series 1.

Preparation of Calibration Standards.—To a series of 10 preburned electrodes, add 25- and 50-μl. aliquots of the working standards and of standard 5B, one aliquot to each, starting with the lowest strength as described for the split-burn technique. Dry under an infrared heat lamp. The result is a series of electrodes containing the following weights of each element.

Electrode No.	1	2	3	4	5	6	7	8	9	10
Wt. of each element, μg.	0.025	0.050	0.100	0.200	0.250	0.500	1.00	2.00	2.50	5.00

To each of these electrodes and a blank electrode, add a weighed amount (175 to 225 mg.) of the intended matrix, prepared as given under sample preparation.

Sample Loading.—Weigh accurately between 175 and 225 mg. of sample, prepared as given above, into a preburned lower electrode.

Procedure.—Set the spectrograph to record in the range 4000–8000 A. (On some instruments, this will require two exposures; obviously the whole procedure must then be duplicated.) Adjust the slit width so that the background of the final spectrum shows at least 20 percent transmission at the long wavelength end; a neutral filter in the external optics or adjustment of the grating mask may be necessary to achieve this. Use a convenient slit length and corresponding plate rack (2-mm. length and 2.5-mm. rack is suggested).

Check the spectrograph alignment.

Mount a loaded electrode in the lower electrode holder and a counter-electrode in the upper. Connect a source of d.c. to the electrodes, making the lower (sample) electrode the anode. Adjust the analytical gap to 3 mm. Load the camera with Eastman Kodak 1 N plate or film.

Open the shutter. Strike the arc, adjusting the current to 18 amps.; at the same time start a timer. Maintain the analytical gap at 3 mm.

After 20 seconds close the shutter. Switch off d.c. supply. Rack plate for next sample (or standard).

Plate Development.—Develop in Kodak D-19 for 3 minutes at 70°F. Stop, fix, wash, and dry.

Densitometry.—Measure the densities of the following lines and their adjacent backgrounds.

Ca	4226.7
Li	6707.8
K	7699.0
Rb	7800.2
Na	5895.9

Using the plate calibration for the particular emulsion batch, transform density to intensity. Subtract the background intensity from the line intensity and record the corrected line intensity.

Calibration Curves.—Construct as described for the split-burn technique but express concentration as micrograms per gram.

Sample Calculation.—Using the appropriate calibration curve, determine the weight in micrograms corresponding to the corrected line intensity. Divide by the sample weight in grams to obtain the concentration in micrograms per gram (p.p.m.).

BOILER CAP

STANDARDS

Volatile Element Solution. **Standard 6A.**—1 mg. per ml. Weigh into a clean 100-ml. volumetric flask the following amounts of salts: mercuric chloride, $HgCl_2$, ACS Reagent, 135 mg.; sodium phosphate, dibasic, crystal, $Na_2HPO_4 \cdot 7H_2O$, ACS Reagent, 866 mg.; tellurium dioxide, TeO_2, purified, 125 mg.; and zinc sulfate, crystal, $ZnSO_4 \cdot 7H_2O$, ACS Reagent, 441 mg.

Add 10 ml. of concentrated hydrochloric acid, semiconductor grade, and 10 ml. of deionized water. Shake to dissolve. Dilute to volume with deionized water. Mix.

Standard 6B.—Prepare Standard 6B and working standards as described for series 1.

Preparation of Calibration Standards.—To a series of 10 preburned electrodes, add 25- and 50-μl. aliquots of the working standards and of standard 6B, one aliquot to each, starting with the lowest strength as described for the split-burn technique. Dry under an infrared heat lamp. The result is a series of electrodes containing the following weights of each element.

Electrode No.	1	2	3	4	5	6	7	8	9	10
Wt. of each element, μg.	0.025	0.050	0.100	0.200	0.250	0.500	1.00	2.00	2.50	5.00

To each of these electrodes and a blank electrode, add a weighed amount (175 to 225 mg.) of the intended matrix, prepared as given under sample preparation.

Close each electrode with a boiler cap, NC L3915 or Ultracarbon 300.

Sample Loading.—Weigh accurately between 175 and 225 mg. of sample, prepared as given above, into a preburned lower electrode. Close the electrode with a boiler cap, NC L3915 or Ultracarbon 300.

Procedure.—Adjust the spectrograph to record in the range 2400 to 3500 A. Adjust the slit width so that the background of the final spectrum shows at least 20 percent transmission at the short wavelength end; a neutral filter in the external optics or adjustment of the grating mask may be necessary to achieve this. Use a convenient slit length and corresponding plate rack (2-mm. length and 2.5-mm. rack is suggested).

Check the spectrograph alignment.

Mount a loaded, capped electrode in the lower electrode holder and a counter electrode in the upper. Connect a source of d.c. to the electrodes, making the lower (sample) electrode the anode. Adjust the analytical gap to 3 mm.

Load the camera with Eastman Kodak 103-0 plate or film.

Open the shutter. Strike the arc, adjusting the current to 18 amps.; at the same time, start a timer. Maintain the analytical gap at 3 mm.

After 30 seconds, close the shutter. Switch off d.c. supply. Rack plate for next sample (or standard).

Plate Development.—Develop in Kodak D-19 for 3 minutes at 70°F. Stop, fix, wash, and dry.

Densitometry.—Measure the densities of the following lines and their adjacent backgrounds.

Hg	2536.5
P	2535.7
Te	2385.8
Zn	3302.6

Using the plate calibration for the particular emulsion batch, transform density to intensity. Subtract the background intensity from the line intensity, and record the corrected line intensity.

Calibration Curves.—Construct as described for the split-burn method but express concentration as micrograms per gram.

Sample Calculation.—Using the appropriate calibration curve, determine the weight in micrograms corresponding to the corrected line intensity. Divide by the sample weight in grams to obtain the concentration in micrograms per gram (p.p.m.).

SPECTROGRAPHIC ANALYSIS OF ARSENIC[37]

SAMPLE PREPARATION

Reagents. Bromine-methanol Etch.—10 percent bromine, ACS reagent, in methanol, semiconductor grade.

Methanol.—Semiconductor grade.

Procedure.—This material is usually received broken into randomly sized fragments. Place sample between sheets of bibulous paper and transfer to an agate or tungsten carbide mortar. Break by tapping with the pestle to fragments less than 2 mm. on a side. Roll the fragments between the sheets to mix and transfer from the paper to a clean beaker. Add sufficient bromine-methanol etch to cover the sample and etch for 3 minutes at room temperature. Decant off and rinse the sample three times with methanol.

ELECTRODES

Lower.—$\frac{1}{4}$ in. undercut cup electrode, N.C. 4012 or Ultracarbon 1988.

Upper.—$\frac{3}{16}$ in. shaped counter electrode, N.C. 3951 or Ultracarbon 105U.

Preburn the electrodes, with the lower as the anode, at 20 amps. d.c. for 10 seconds using a 3-mm. gap. Transfer to a covered electrode stand.

STANDARDS

Silicon-Boron Solution.—Series 1 prepared as given for the IIIV compounds.

Nitrate Solution.—Series 2 prepared as given for the III-V compounds.

Chloride Solution.—Series 3 prepared as given for the III-V compounds.

Gold Solution.—Series 4 prepared as given for the III-V compounds.

Volatile Element Solution.—Series 6 prepared as given for the III-V compounds.

Preparation of Calibration Standards.—Wetproof the preburned lower electrodes by filling the cup with a dilution of Duco cement (cellulose cement), 1 part cement with 20 parts ethyl acetate, ACS reagent. Allow to dry.

To a series of 10 wet-proofed electrodes, add 25- and 50-μl. aliquots of standard 1B and its working standards, one aliquot to each, starting with the lowest strength as described for the split-burn technique. Repeat using series 2, 3, 4, and 6. The result is a series of electrodes containing the following weights of elements.

Electrode No.	1	2	3	4	5	6	7	8	9	10
Wt. of each element, excluding Hg, P, Te, Zn, ng.	2.5	5	10	20	25	50	100	200	250	500
Hg, P, Te, Zn, μg.	0.025	0.050	0.100	0.200	0.250	0.500	1.00	2.00	2.50	5.00

To each of these electrodes and a blank electrode, add a weighed amount of arsenic, 175 to 225 mg., prepared as given under sample preparation.

Sample Loading.—Weigh accurately between 175 and 225 mg. of sample, prepared as given above, into a preburned lower electrode.

Procedure.—Adjust the spectrograph to record in the range 2400 to 3600 A. Adjust the slit width so that the background of the final spectrum has at least 20 percent transmission at the short wavelength end; a neutral filter in the external optics or adjustment of the grating mask may be necessary to achieve this. Use a convenient slit length and corresponding plate rack (2-mm. length and 2.5-mm. rack is suggested).

Check the spectrograph alignment.

Mount a loaded electrode in the lower electrode holder and a counter electrode in the upper. Connect a source of d.c. to the electrodes, making the lower (sample) electrode the anode. Adjust the analytical gap to 2 mm.

Load the camera with Eastman Kodak 103-0 plate or film.

Open the shutter. Strike the arc, adjusting the current to 10 amps. Burn to completion (about 20 seconds).

Close shutter. Switch off d.c. supply. Rack plate for next sample (or standard).

Plate Development.—Develop in Kodak D-19 for 3 minutes at 70°F. Stop, fix, wash, and dry.

Densitometry.—Measure the densities of the following lines and their adjacent backgrounds.

Al	3092.7 A
Be	3130.4
Bi	3067.7
B	2497.7
Cd	3466.2
Cr	3021.6
Co	3453.5
Cu	3247.5
Au	2676.0
Fe	3020.6
Pb	2833.1
Mg	2795.5
Mn	2605.7
Hg	2536.5
Ni	3002.5
P	2535.7
Si	2516.1
Ag	3280.7

Te	2385.8
Sn	2840.0
Ti	3234.5
Zn	3302.6

Using the plate calibration for the particular emulsion batch, transform density to intensity. Subtract the background intensity from the line intensity and record the corrected line intensity.

Calibration Curves.—Construct as described for the split-burn method for III-V compounds, but note that the additions of mercury, phosphorus, tellurium, and zinc are in micrograms.

Sample Calculation.—Using the appropriate calibration curve, determine the weight in nanograms corresponding to the corrected line intensity. Divide by the sample weight in grams to obtain the concentration in nanograms per gram (p.p.b.).

SPECTROGRAPHIC ANALYSIS OF SILICON AND GERMANIUM[37]

SAMPLE PREPARATION

Reagents. **Planar Etch.**—15:5:2 nitric acid:acetic acid:hydrofluoric acid, all semiconductor grade.

Methanol.—Semiconductor grade.

Water.—Deionized.

Procedure.—Samples will usually be received as ingots, and should be treated as described for the III-V compounds with the exception that the above planar etch at room temperature should be substituted for the boiling aqua regia; the etch time remains 1 minute.

ELECTRODES

Lower.—$\frac{3}{16}$ in. undercut cup electrode N.C. 4206, Ultracarbon 105S.

Upper.—$\frac{3}{16}$ in. shaped counter electrode, N.C. 3951, Ultracarbon 105U.

Preburn the electrodes with the lower as anode at 20 amps. d.c. for 10 seconds using a 3-mm. gap. Transfer to a covered electrode stand.

STANDARDS

Silicon Boron Solution.—Series 1 prepared as given for the III-V compounds.

Nitrate Solution.—Series 2 prepared as given for the III-V compounds.

Chloride Solution.—Series 3 prepared as given for the III-V compounds.

Gold Solution.—Series 4 prepared as given for the III-V compounds.

Aqua Regia Solution. **Standard 7A.**—1 mg. per ml. Weigh out 0.100 g. of the following metals, all reagent grade: antimony, arsenic, germanium, and indium, and 0.134 g. of gallium oxide, Ga_2O_3, spectrographic grade. Add 10 ml. of aqua regia (1 part nitric acid, semiconductor grade, with 3 parts hydrochloric acid, semiconductor grade) and allow to dissolve. Transfer to a 100-ml. volumetric flask, dilute to volume with deionized water, and mix.

Standard 7B.—Prepare standard 7B and working standards as described for series 1 under "III-V compounds."

Volatile Element Solution.—Series 6 prepared as given for the III-V compounds.

Preparation of Calibration Standards.—Wetproof the preburned lower electrodes by filling the cup with a dilution of Duco cement (cellulose cement), 1 part cement with 20 parts ethyl acetate, ACS reagent. Allow to dry.

To a series of 10 wet-proofed electrodes, add 25- and 50-μl. aliquots of standard 1B and its working standards, one aliquot to each, starting with the lowest strength as described for the split-burn technique. Dry under an infrared lamp. Repeat using series 2, 3, 4, 6, and 7. The result is a series of electrodes containing the following weights of each element.

Electrode No.	1	2	3	4	5	6	7	8	9	10
Wt. of each element, excluding Hg, P, Te, Zn, ng.	2.5	5	10	20	25	50	100	200	250	500
Hg, P, Te, Zn, μg.	0.025	0.050	0.100	0.200	0.250	0.500	1.00	2.00	2.50	5.00

To each of these electrodes and a blank electrode, add a weighed amount of the intended matrix, 17.5 to 22.5 mg. of silicon or 35 to 45 mg. of germanium, prepared as described for the sample.

Sample Loading.—Weigh accurately between 17.5 and 22.5 mg. of silicon or 35 to 45 mg. of germanium, prepared as given above, into a preburned lower electrode.

Procedure.—Adjust the spectrograph to record in the range 2400 to 3600 A. Adjust the slit width so that the background of the final spectrum has at least 20 percent transmission at the short wavelength end; a neutral filter in the external optics or adjustment of the grating mask may be necessary to achieve this. Use a convenient slit length and corresponding plate rack. (2-mm. length and 2.5-mm. rack is suggested.)

Check the spectrograph alignment.

Fit the excitation stand with an enclosed Stallwood jet[41] or similar chamber able to switch readily from an inert atmosphere to air. Mount a loaded electrode in the lower electrode holder and cover with the quartz dome. Pass argon into the chamber at 5 cu. ft. per hr. Mount a counter electrode in the upper electrode holder, and adjust the analytical gap to 3 mm. Allow argon to flush the chamber for 5 minutes. Connect a source of d.c. to the electrodes making the lower (sample) electrode the anode.

Load the camera with Eastman Kodak SA-1 plate or film.

Open the shutter and strike the arc, adjusting the current to 15 amps. At the same time start a timer. Maintain the analytical gap at 3 mm.

After 60 seconds close the shutter, switch off d.c. supply, stop the argon flow, and remove the quartz dome.

Adjust the analytical gap to 3 mm.; rack the plate to the next position and open the shutter. Strike the arc, at the same time starting the timer. After 30 seconds, rack the plate to the next position, maintaining the burn. Continue to burn until the sample is consumed (10–30 seconds).

Switch off d.c. supply and close shutter.

Plate Development.—Develop in Kodak D-19 for 3 minutes at 70°F. Stop, fix, wash, and dry.

Densitometry.—For each sample (or standard), there will be three exposures.

For the first exposure, measure the densities of the following lines and their adjacent backgrounds.

[41] Spex Industries, Inc. accessory No. 9025 is suitable.

Sb	2528.5
As	2780.2
Be	3130.4
Bi	3067.7
Cd	3466.2
Pb	2833.1
Mg	2852.1
Hg	2536.5
P	2535.7
Si	2528.5 (in Ge only)
Te	2385.8
Zn	3345.0

Using the plate calibration for the particular emulsion batch, convert the density values to relative intensities. Subtract the background intensity from the line intensity and record the corrected line intensity.

Examine the second exposure. If any of the above lines are present, measure and obtain corrected line intensity as above. Add these two corrected intensities to obtain the total corrected line intensity.

For the last exposure, measure the densities of the following lines and their adjacent backgrounds.

Al	3092.7
B	2497.7
Co	3453.5
Cu	3247.5
Cr	3021.6
Ga	2943.6
Ge	3039.1 (in Si only)
Au	2676.0
In	3256.1
Fe	3020.6
Mn	2576.1
Ni	3002.5
Ag	3280.7
Sn	2840.0

Obtain the corrected line intensities as before.

Re-examine the second exposure. If any of these lines are present, measure and add to obtain the corrected line intensities as before. In a few cases, these lines will also appear in the first exposure when a further correction must be made; this is particularly true of boron, germanium (in silicon), and silver.

Calibration Curves.—Construct as described for the split-burn method for III-V compounds, but note that the additions of mercury, phosphorus, tellurium, and zinc are in micrograms.

Sample Calculation.—Using the appropriate calibration curve, determine the weight in nanograms corresponding to the total corrected line intensity. Divide by the sample weight in milligrams to obtain the concentration in micrograms per gram (p.p.m.).

MASS SPECTROMETRY

As can be seen from the previous section, emission spectrography is a very valuable means of assessing the quality of a semiconductor material. However, it is limited because the sensitivity for some elements is poor and, for still others, no suitable analysis lines exist. This latter case includes many electrically important impurities such as sulfur and the halogens. Recently, this technique has been complemented by a more sensitive method which does not suffer from these limitations, namely mass spectrometric analysis.

Honig[42] and Hannay and Ahearn[43] were probably among the first to apply mass spectrometry to the analysis of semiconductors. Honig vaporized germanium into the electron source of a 180° spectrometer and determined impurities in the 10 p.p.m. atomic range. However, Hannay and Ahearn applied the vacuum spark source in a double-focusing instrument and pioneered what is now the generally accepted technique. This instrument was subsequently made available commercially by Associated Electrical Industries Limited (A.E.I.) as their Type MS7 instrument, and by Consolidated Electro-dynamics Corporation (C.E.C.) as their Model 21-110.

Since the introduction of commercial instruments, considerable work has been carried out on semiconductor materials. Descriptions of the techniques used have been given by Craig and his coworkers,[44,45,46] Ahearn,[47,48] Duke,[49] Willardson,[50] and Honig.[51] The methods given in the following sections are largely based on those devised for the A.E.I. MS7 by Craig and his colleagues, but can readily be adapted to the C.E.C. Model 21-110. The method is basically the same for all solid samples with minor variations in the source parameters to keep the temperature below the volatilization point. In the case of gallium, a cold finger modification due to Wolstenholme[52] is used to maintain the sample as a solid.

In the field of mass spectrometry, it is conventional to refer to concentrations in p.p.m atomic. This is related to p.p.m. by weight as follows:

$$\text{p.p.m. by weight} = \text{p.p.m. atomic} \times \frac{M_i}{M_b}$$

where M_i = atomic weight of impurity, and

M_b = atomic (or equivalent) weight of bulk material.

Referring back to the earlier example of boron in silicon, if the concentration were 0.002 p.p.m. atomic, then

$$\text{p.p.m. by weight} = 0.002 \times \frac{10.8}{28}$$

$$= 0.00075 \text{ p.p.m.}$$
$$= 0.75 \text{ p.p.b.}$$

[42] Honig, R. E., Anal. Chem., **25**, 1530–1535, 1953.

[43] Hannay, N. B., and Ahearn, A. J., Anal. Chem., **26**, 1056–1058, 1954.

[44] Craig, R. D., Errock, G. A., and Waldron, J. D., in Advances in Mass Spectrometry, J. D. Waldron, Ed., Pergamon Press, London, 1959.

[45] Brown, R., Craig, R. D., James, J. A., and Wilson, C. M., in Ultrapurification of Semiconductor Materials, M. S. Brooks and J. K. Kennedy, Eds., Macmillan, New York, 1962.

[46] Brown, R., Craig, R. D., and Elliott, R. M., in Advances in Mass Spectrometry, Vol. 2, R. M. Elliott, Ed., Pergamon Press, Oxford, 1963.

[47] Ahearn, A. J., in Proceedings of the 10th Colloquium Spectroscopicum Internationale, E. R. Lippincott and M. Margoshes, Eds., Spartan Books, Washington, 1963.

[48] Ahearn, A. J., 11th Annual Conference on Mass Spectrometry and Allied Topics, ASTM Committee E-14, San Francisco, 1963.

[49] Duke, J. F., in Ultrapurification of Semiconductor Materials, M. S. Brooks and J. K. Kennnedy, Eds., Macmillan, New York, 1962.

[50] Willardson, R. K., in Ultrapurification of Semiconductor Materials, M. S. Brooks and J. K. Kennedy, Eds., Macmillan, New York, 1962.

[51] Honig, R. E., in Trace Analysis of Semiconductor Materials, J. P. Cali, Ed., Pergamon Press, Oxford, 1964.

[52] Wolstenholme, W. A., Appl. Spectroscopy, **17**, 51, 1963.

By simple substitution,

$$\text{atoms per cc.} = \text{p.p.b. atomic} \times \frac{A \times d}{M_b \times 10^9}$$

where A = Avogadro's number, and
d = density of bulk material.

Again, for the case of 2 p.p.b. atomic boron in silicon,

$$\text{atoms per cc.} = 2 \times \frac{6 \times 10^{23} \times 2.4}{28 \times 10^9}$$

$$= 10^{14}$$

MASS SPECTROMETRIC ANALYSIS[53]

Sample Preparation.—Samples will normally be received as ingots. These may not be homogeneous and for best results should be sampled at a number of points.

Using a diamond saw, cut a slice of material 1 mm. (0.040 in.) thick from the center of the bar. This may be regarded as typical of the bulk of the ingot, but, if possible, additional slices should be taken near the ends.

Through a diameter of the slice, make a cut through the material. Make additional parallel cuts 1 mm. (0.040 in.) apart sufficient to provide at least two bars not less than 2 cm. long. Trim to this length.

Note that the ingot may not be homogeneous in cross-section as well; if this is significant, cut the end which is to go in the holder with a diagonal cut.

Clean the wax from the bars with a suitable solvent.

Etch the bars as follows:

Silicon and Germanium.—Prepare a mixture of 10 parts by volume of nitric acid, semiconductor grade, and 1 part by volume hydrofluoric acid, semiconductor grade, in a 50-ml. PTFE (Teflon) beaker. Place the bars in a polypropylene spoon (Fig. 60-5) and immerse in the etch for about 1 minute. Remove. Rinse twice in fresh portions of hot, deionized water. Allow to dry in air and transfer directly to the holders, using Teflon tipped tweezers.

Gallium Arsenide, Indium Antimonide, Indium Arsenide, Indium.—Prepare a mixture of 3 parts by volume hydrochloric acid, semiconductor grade, and 1 part nitric acid, semiconductor grade, in a 50-ml. Pyrex beaker. Bring to incipient boiling. Place the bars in a polypropylene spoon and immerse spoon in the etch for about 30 seconds. Remove. Rinse twice in fresh portions of hot, deionized water. Allow to dry in air and transfer directly to the holders, using Teflon tipped tweezers.

Procedure.—Switch on rotary pumps, diffusion pumps, and gauge supplies. Close valves to auxiliary pump and open all other valves to the main vacuum system. Continue pumping until a pressure of 10^{-6} torr is reached on analyzer and source gauges. Fill liquid nitrogen traps. Continue pumping to less than 10^{-7} torr on both gauges. If this is not achieved, blow out traps and bake out system. Refill traps and pump. Repeat until the required vacuum is achieved.

Switch on amplifiers and magnet power supply; these must run for at least 24 hours before an analysis. Adjust magnet current for mass range required.

Close necessary valves to isolate plate magazine. Release vacuum on magazine. Load with Ilford Q2 or Kodak SWR plates. Seal magazine and open to auxiliary rotary pump.

[53] In collaboration with A. M. Bryant.

When thermocouple gauge indicates 0.1 mm., close to auxiliary pump and open to main vacuum system; do not connect to analyzer. Allow to equilibrate for 12 hours.

The machine is now in the standby condition (A).

Isolate source from main vacuum system and analyzer and vent. Remove face-plate, shutter, and electrode shield.

Insert one pair of sample bars in the electrode holders with the diagonal cuts (if any) in the holders. Using the inspection lamp, adjust one electrode so that the tip is aligned with the ion gun slits (Fig. 60-6). Adjust the other electrode so that it overlaps the first

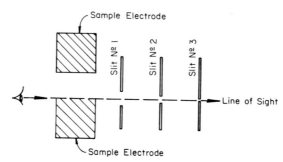

FIG. 60-6.   Ion Gun Slit Alignment.

by 1.5 mm. but is about 0.1 mm. above it. Slide the spark shield and shutter into place. Check the sample assembly to ensure there will be no electrical shorts. Replace the face-plate.

Connect source to auxiliary rotary pump. Pump down to 0.1 mm. on thermocouple gauge. Close to auxiliary pump and open to main vacuum system and analyzer. Pump down the source to 10^{-7} torr.

Align desired plate in magazine, ready for transfer. Set the plate rack in the analyzer to the center position. Open sliding valve to analyzer. Transfer plate through valve to rack; withdraw ramrod and close sliding valve. Rack plate to blank position.

Switch on the 20-kv. supply to the accelerating plate and the power to the r.f. supply; the time delay in this high voltage power supply will take about 3 minutes to operate.

Initially, set the spark voltage to 30 percent (about 30 kv.), the pulse repetition rate to 10 c.p.s., the pulse length to 25 μsec. and the timer to infinity. Switch on the spark; if it fails to strike, adjust the electrode gap until it does. Switch on the beam. Adjust the electrode gap and pulse repetition rate so that the integrator travels full scale in not less than 3 seconds with the range switches on this and the monitor at unity. Switch off beam; switch off spark.

Rack plate to position No. 1. Switch on spark; the spark should strike. Using the auxiliary beam switch, maintain for a time such that the integrator registers 10^{-13} coulombs (10 percent of the integrator when the range switch for this and the monitor are at 1). Switch off spark.

Repeat this exposure procedure for the following integrated charges: 0.0003, 0.001, 0.003, 0.01, 0.03, 0.1, 0.3, 1, 3, 10, 30, 100, 300, 1000 nanocoulombs (nC). To maintain a reasonable exposure time, it will be necessary to increase the pulse repetition rate with increasing charge. If for an exposure, the integrator takes more than 2 minutes for full scale deflection, increase the pulse repetition rate to the next setting on the *next* exposure. If the sample glows red, the maximum rate has been reached; immediately return the setting to the next lowest.

Switch off the 20-kv. supply to the accelerating plate and the power to the r.f. supply.

Set the plate rack in the center position. Open sliding valve to the analyzer. Push ramrod forward and engage cassette; withdraw plate to magazine, close sliding valve.

The machine is again in the standby condition.

For similar samples, the procedure from point (A) can be repeated, merely substituting the new sample electrodes for the old. If the memory effect is important, it may be necessary to clean the tantalum shields in hydrofluoric acid.

When all the plates in the magazine have been exposed, isolate from main vacuum system and vent.

Plate Development. Ilford Q2.—Develop in ID-19 for 2.5 minutes at 70°F. Rinse. Fix in acid fix (Ansco) for 1.5 minutes at 70°F. Wash for 3 minutes in 70°F. water. Allow to dry.

Kodak SWR.—Develop in 50 percent ID-19 (equal parts with water) for 2.5 minutes at 70°F. Rinse. Fix in acid fix (Ansco) for 1.5 minutes at 70°F. Wash for 3 minutes in 70°F. water. Allow to dry.

Plate Interpretation.—Using the known isotopic masses for the matrix element(s), construct a scale of mass to charge ratios (m/e). The presence of multiply-charged ions and polyatomic ions will give further reference points across the spectrum.

Visual Estimation.—Select a line due to a minor isotope of the major (or one of the major) elements. Note the exposure at which this line is just detectable; check the next shortest exposure to verify that it has disappeared. Let this "just detectable" exposure be E_s.

If the standard line does not disappear, and assuming this is the least abundant isotope, a comparison method may be used. Select any nearby line that does disappear before the shortest exposure. Determine at which exposure (E_y) the line is equal in density to the standard line in the shortest exposure (0.0001 nC.). Determine at which exposure this line becomes "just detectable" (E_z). Then

$$E_s = \frac{E_y}{E_z} \times 0.0001 \text{ nC.}$$

The plate sensitivity, S_p, is defined as the actual concentration of any isotope in p.p.m. atomic that is "just detectable" at the longest exposure and is calculated from the expression

$$S_p = \frac{E_s}{E_{max}} \times \frac{X}{100} \times \frac{I_s}{100} \times 10^6$$

where E_{max} = longest exposure on plate (1000 nC. if full series is run),
X = atomic percent concentration of internal standard element (100 percent for elemental semiconductors, 50 percent for compound), and
I_s = isotopic abundance of chosen isotope.

For compound semiconductors, selective volatilization may reduce the accuracy of the plate sensitivity. For the best results, a separate calibration run should be made for each batch of plates using an element such as tin.

Starting at the high mass end, attempt to identify every line. Many lines will remain unidentified since these will be due to charge exchange processes and hydrocarbons from the pump oil. Positive identification of an element must depend on: (a) identification of lines of at least two isotopes of the element in the correct relative intensity ratio; and (b) identification of lines due to multiply-charged ions at $\frac{1}{2}$ or $\frac{1}{3}$ of the mass of the major isotope.

In the case of elements which have only one isotope, *e.g.*, arsenic, manganese, aluminum, and bismuth, condition (b) should include identification of lines due to multiply-charged ions at both $\frac{1}{2}$ and $\frac{1}{3}$ of the mass. For some cases, it may be necessary to make additional exposures at a lower magnet current in order to resolve lines to satisfy condition (a). This is particularly true for silicon as an impurity.

Having identified the impurities present, determine their concentrations. For each impurity, identify the line for the singly-charged ion of the most abundant isotope. Determine the exposure at which this becomes "just detectable" (E_i). Then,

$$\text{concentration of impurity in p.p.m. atomic} = S_p \times \frac{E_{\max}}{E_i} \times \frac{100}{I_i}$$

where I_i = isotopic abundance of impurity isotope.

In many cases, this particular line will suffer interference, in which case select a singly-charged ion for a less abundant isotope. If this is not possible, a doubly-charged ion may be selected and the correction factor of 4 applied to the result. (This value of 4 is the approximate ratio of singly- to doubly-charged ions.)

Photometric Determination.—Calibrate each batch of plates by running one series of exposures using a standard of suitable isotope concentration; tin is recommended for this purpose since it has a number of isotopes of different abundances so that suitable density may be chosen. An alloy containing about 0.02 percent tin is suitable; NBS iron, No. 461, containing 0.022 percent tin is available in $\frac{7}{32}$ in. rod which may be cut into quadrants, and degreased in alcohol to give suitable electrodes.

Obtain a series of exposures for this material by the method given above. In this case, a maximum exposure of 1 nC. should be sufficient.

Mark in the mass scale as described in the previous section. Measure the transmission of the lines due to each tin isotope on each exposure. Select the isotope whose transmission is most evenly spread over the exposure series. Using semilog graph paper, construct a curve of transmission against logarithm of exposure (Fig. 60-7). This is the calibration curve applicable to this particular batch of plates.

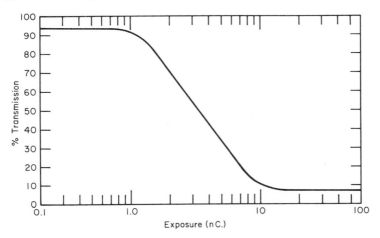

FIG. 60-7. Typical Plate Calibration Curve.

From the sample exposures, select that in which the impurity line is closest to 50 percent transmission; let this be E_i nC. Measure the transmission of this line; using the calibration curve for this batch of plates, find the exposure E_s, corresponding to this transmission. Then

$$\text{concentration, p.p.m. atomic} = \frac{E_i}{E_s} \times \frac{I_s}{I_i} \times n \times 10^4$$

where I_s = isotopic abundance of tin isotope selected,
$\quad I_i$ = isotopic abundance of impurity isotope selected, and
$\quad n$ = concentration of the tin in the standard as atomic percentage.

$$= \frac{a \times 55.85}{118.7} \% \text{ atomic for the NBS Standard 461}$$

where a = concentration of tin as weight percentage.

Note that although this method is more accurate, it is less sensitive than the visual method since "just detectable" lines are not usable. Only the straight-line portion of the calibration curve is applicable.

MASS SPECTROMETRIC ANALYSIS OF GALLIUM

Sample Preparation.—This material melts at 29.8°C. (85.6°F.); consequently, it is usually packed and shipped in polyethylene bottles.

Liquefy the sample by immersing bottle in warm deionized water. Transfer enough gallium to a clean, dry, 50-ml. beaker to form a layer 1 mm. thick. Dip the beaker into

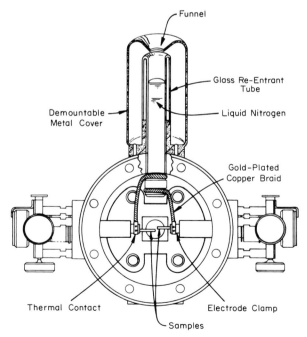

FIG. 60-8. Cold Finder Attachment for the Analysis of Gallium. (Reprinted with permission from Applied Spectroscopy, **17**, 51, 1963.)

liquid nitrogen to freeze the sample. Invert the beaker over a clean dry filter paper; the disc of gallium will easily separate. Using a jeweler's saw, cut two bars 1 mm. wide and 2 cm. long. Care must be taken to avoid melting the gallium by warmth from the hand; if the sample temperature begins to rise, cool by immersing in liquid nitrogen. Into a 250-ml. beaker, pour about 10 ml. of concentrated hydrochloric acid, semiconductor grade. Place a thermometer in the acid; the temperature must be less than 25°C. Etch the bars in this acid for 5 minutes. Rinse twice in cold (less than 25°C.) deionized water. Allow to dry in air and transfer directly to the holders using Teflon tipped tweezers.

Apparatus.—Replace the shutter mechanism, mounted to the top of the source, with a cold finger (see Fig. 60-8). This finger is obtainable from A.E.I. It consists of a glass tube, closed at its lower end, and carrying two copper leads which clamp to the holders to disperse heat. The tube is surrounded by a jacket and mounted on a metal flange. The jacket exhausts into the source to form a vacuum insulator.

Method.—After inserting the sample bars, reduce the source pressure to 10^{-6} torr. Fill the tube with liquid nitrogen and allow to cool for 10 minutes.

Proceed with the method as given above. Maintain the liquid nitrogen level throughout the analysis.

ACTIVATION ANALYSIS[54]

Undoubtedly the most sensitive method for trace analysis is the technique of activation analysis, usually neutron activation analysis. This has been quite extensively applied to semiconductors, and a number of reviews of the subject are available. The most up-to-date, and certainly the most pertinent, is by Cali.[55] Generally, the method involves activation in a high flux (at least 10^{12} neutrons per cm.² per sec.) followed by chemical separation of the particular element being determined. The final determination is made by counting the induced activity from the radiochemically pure element.

The activation of the trace impurity is accomplished by bombarding the sample either with fast or thermal neutrons, or high energy particles such as protons, tritons, or doubly-ionized helium nuclei. The ultimate sensitivity of the method is, of course, dependent upon the amount of radioactivity induced in the impurity under analysis. The amount of activity is given by the following equation

$$N_{d.p.s.} = \varphi \sigma N (1 - e^{-\lambda t})$$

where $N_{d.p.s.}$ = induced activity (decompositions per second),
   φ = flux (neutrons per second per cm.²),
   σ = cross section (barns),
   N = number of atoms of target nuclide,
   λ = decay constant = 0.693/half life, and
   t = time of irradiation.

Since σ, N and λ are properties of the material, the sensitivity of the method is dependent on the flux and the time of irradiation.

The cost of accelerators required for high energy particle activation is too high for any laboratory to justify solely on the basis of activation analysis. The commercially available fast neutron generators have too low a flux ($10^8 - 10^9$ n./sec./cm.²) for impurity analysis at the level found in semiconductors. The capture cross-sections for fast neutron reactions are generally lower than thermal neutron cross-sections, which again restricts the sensitivity of fast neutron activation analyses. There are some cases

---

[54] In collaboration with G. B. Larrabee.
[55] Cali, J. P., in Trace Analysis of Semiconductor Materials, Pergamon Press, Oxford, 1964.

($O^{16}(n, p)N^{16}$) where fast neutron activation is useful, but in general its use in trace analysis is very restricted.

The availability of high thermal neutron fluxes in nuclear reactors makes this method of activation analysis by far the most useful. However, most companies interested in utilizing thermal neutron activation will not have a reactor, and this is undoubtedly the most serious drawback of the method. Moreover, the samples after irradiation are sufficiently high in activity to require a license (A.E.C. or equivalent) for their handling. As a consequence, most laboratories not already actively engaged in handling isotopes will prefer to avoid the legal complications involved by using an alternative technique. If the high sensitivity is a must, then the activation analysis services offered by General Atomics, Union Carbide, or Harwell may offer the best solution.

If a license is held, then samples irradiated at, for example, Oak Ridge, Harwell, or Chalk River may be separated and measured. However, this method is by no means of universal application; many elements of interest, e.g., boron, have no active isotopes or the isotopes are so short-lived that they have decayed before the sample returns from the reactor. Moreover, although chemical interferences are avoided by this method, another type of interference is encountered in that transmutations are possible. For example, phosphorus in silicon is determined by an n, γ reaction as P^{32}; however, silicon almost always contains some chlorine which can be converted by the fast neutrons present in the reactor flux to P^{32} by an n, α reaction.

It is apparent that this technique is severely limited in its application. Nevertheless, when it is applicable, its extreme sensitivity can give very valuable information, unobtainable by any other means.

Smales and Pate[56] determined arsenic in germanium, and Szekely[57] determined copper in the same matrix, both at the p.p.b. level. Morrison and Cosgrove[58] extended the method to a few other trace elements, but at the p.p.m. level. Yakovlev et al.[59] mentioned the determination of several elements in germanium using gamma-ray spectroscopy, but gave no details, and, with Gottfried,[60] described a method for copper in germanium using a chemical separation. Leliaert[61] determined phosphorus and arsenic in germanium, and the latter determination was also carried out by Jaskolska and Wodkiewicz.[62] Rytchkov and Glukhareva[63] have outlined a method for gold, copper, antimony, zinc, indium, gallium, and manganese in germanium using a multichannel analyzer, but again no details were given.

Silicon was analyzed for several impurities by Morrison and Cosgrove[64] using γ-ray spectroscopy, and Kant et al.[65] determined twelve impurities using a radiochemical separation. James and Richards[66] determined arsenic by separating with a carrier and counting; they later reported[67] that they had determined twelve elements by radiochemical separation. Other early work was carried out by Smales et al.[68] and by

[56] Smales, A. A., and Pate, B. D., Anal. Chem., 24, 717–721, 1952.
[57] Szekely, G., Anal. Chem., 26, 1500–1502, 1954.
[58] Morrison, G. H., and Cosgrove, J. F., Anal. Chem., 28, 320–323, 1956.
[59] Yakovlev, Y. V., Kulak, A. I., Ryakukhin, V. A., and Rytchkov, R. S., Proc. 2nd U. N. Intern. Conf. oi. Peaceful Uses of Atomic Energy, Paper P/2023, U. N., Geneva, 1958.
[60] Gottfried, J., and Yakovlev, Y. V., Chem. Prumysl, 9, 179–182, 1959.
[61] Leliaert, G., Pure and Appl. Chem., 1, 121–126, 1960.
[62] Jaskolska, H., and Wodkiewicz, L., Chem. Anal., Warsaw, 6, 161–165, 1961.
[63] Rytchkov, R. S., and Glukhareva, N. A., Zavod. Lab., 27, 1246–1250, 1961.
[64] Morrison, G. H., and Cosgrove, J. F., Anal. Chem., 27, 810–813, 1955.
[65] Kant, A., Cali, J. P., and Thompson, H. D., Anal. Chem., 28, 1867–1871, 1956.
[66] James, J. A., and Richards, D. H., Nature, 175, 769–770, 1955.
[67] James, J. A., and Richards, D. H., J. Electronics and Control, 3, 500–506, 1957.
[68] Smales, A. A., Mapper, D., Wood, A. J., and Salmon, L., AERE Report C/R2254, 1957.

Yakovlev et al.[59] A detailed separation scheme was devised by Thompson et al.[69] Since then, considerable work has been carried out in Japan[70,71,72,73] and Russia.[63,74,75,76,77]

The work on III–V compounds is much less extensive due to the high level of activity induced in the matrix. Rytchkov and Glukhareva[63] determined sulfur, selenium, and tellurium in gallium arsenide, and Green et al.[78] determined silicon, zinc, and magnesium by applying a technique of short irradiation and rapid separation. Oxygen was determined in gallium arsenide by Bailey and Ross[79] using an $O^{16}(T, n)F^{18}$ reaction; the tritons were generated in a neutron flux by surrounding the sample with lithium to give a $Li^6(n, T)He^4$ reaction.

Hoste and Van den Berghe[80] determined about 40 p.p.m. indium in gallium by activating with a radium-beryllium source and extracting the indium as the bromide with diethyl ether. Lerch and Kreienbuhl[81] determined calcium in gallium by precipitation as the hydroxide, and zinc by an isotope dilution method. Kulak[82] described a radio-chemical separation for copper, arsenic, tellurium, nickel, and cobalt in antimony, and Rakovskii et al.,[83] determined phosphorus, chromium, manganese, copper, zinc, gallium, and arsenic in zone-refined antimony.

All the above irradiations were carried out using thermal neutrons. Gill[84] used 20 MeV. protons to determine boron in silicon by the $B^{11}(p, n)C^{11}$ reaction, and Breger et al.[85] used high-energy (24 MeV.) gamma-radiation to determine oxygen by the $O^{16}(\gamma, n)O^{15}$ reaction.

The simplest method of activation analysis consists of irradiating the sample, allowing the matrix activity to decay, and then identifying and determining the impurities by gamma-ray spectroscopy. Such a method could be applied to, say, 0.1 p.p.m. of indium or gallium in silicon but such levels can be dealt with more readily by other techniques. For very low level determinations, less than 1 p.p.b., the matrix activity remains too high for too long and a chemical separation is necessary.

The most comprehensive procedure for silicon is due to Thompson, et al.[69] The silicon is removed as the fluoride and the residue is submitted to a scheme for separating 23 elements. This separation is based on classical analytical separations and will not be detailed here. Usually, only some of these elements will be required and the analyst

[69] Thompson, B. A., Strause, B. M., and Leboeuf, M. B., Anal. Chem., 30, 1023–1027, 1958.

[70] Nakai, T., Yajima, S., Fujii, I., and Okada, M., Japan Analyst, 8, 367–372, 1959.

[71] Nozaki, T., Baba, H., and Araki, H., Bull. Chem. Soc. Japan, 33, 320–322, 1960.

[72] Nozaki, T., Kawashima, T., Baba, H., and Araki, H., Bull. Chem. Soc. Japan, 33, 1428–1430, 1960.

[73] Chiba, M., Trans. Nat. Inst. Met., Japan, 4, 143–150, 1962.

[74] Erokhina, K. I., Lemberg, I. K., Makasheva, I. E., Maslov, I. A., and Obukhov, A. P., Zavod. Lab., 26, 821–827, 1960

[75] Kalinin, A. I., Kuznetsov, R. A., and Moiseev, V. V., Radiokhimiya, 4, 575–581, 1962.

[76] Lobanov, E. M., Zvyagin, V. I., and Zverev, B. P., Dokl. Akad. Nauk UzSSR, 13–16, 1962.

[77] Lobanov, E. M., Zvyagin, V. I., Kist, A. A., Zverev, B. P., Suiridova, A. I., and Moskovtseva, G. A., Zhur. Anal. Khim., 18, 1349–1355, 1963.

[78] Green, D. E., Helsop, J. A. B., and Whitley, J. E., Analyst, 88, 522–528, 1963.

[79] Bailey, R. F., and Ross, D. A., Anal. Chem., 35, 791–794, 1963.

[80] Hoste, J., and Van den Berghe, H., Mikrochim. Acta, 797–803, 1956.

[81] Lerch, P., and Kreienbuhl, L., Chimia, 15, 519–522, 1961.

[82] Kulak, A. I., Zhur. Anal. Khim., 12, 727–730, 1957.

[83] Rakovskii, E. E., Smakhtin, L. A., and Yakovlev, Y. V., Zavod. Lab., 26, 1199–1200, 1960.

[84] Gill, R. A., AERE Report C/R 2758, 1958.

[85] Breger, A. K., Ormont, B. F., Viting, B. I., Grizhko, V. M., Kozlov, V. A., Kutseva, V. S., Chapyzhnikov, B. A., and Chepel, L. V., Trudy Komiss. Anal. Khim., Akad. Nauk SSSR, 10, 137–141, 1960.

will adapt the procedure accordingly. This method, in common with all radiochemical methods, has the advantage that adventitious contamination is not a problem and normal analytical reagents can be used in the separations. It differs from the usual analytical separation only in that carriers are added to avoid loss of the active material and that the final determination is based on the specific activity of the final precipitate instead of the weight.

The method of Kant et al.[65] is similar but describes a somewhat shorter procedure for 12 elements in silicon; this group includes several of the more important impurities.

For germanium, there is no detailed separation scheme published. Most of those referred to above were either used at higher levels of impurity, or the details of the separations were not given. Probably the most useful is the method of Smales and Pate.[56] The germanium is distilled as the chloride. The arsenic is subsequently distilled as the bromide and counted. The method of Thompson et al.[69] could probably be applied to the distillation residue for more extensive analyses.

Due to the high activities induced in the matrices, no procedures can be recommended for the analysis of III–V compounds.

THE ACTIVATION ANALYSIS OF SILICON[86]

INTRODUCTION

The published methods, while comprehensive, include many elements which are either rarely met in semiconductor material or are electrically insignificant. A shorter procedure, covering eight of the most important trace elements, has been devised by Heinen and Larrabee[87] at Texas Instruments. This scheme is based on the necessity of separating the short-lived isotopes first. With practice, the complete analysis can be finished within two working days.

The outline of the separation is shown in Fig. 60-9. Since the exact flux at a point in any reactor is unknown, a series of monitors is carried through simultaneously and provides counting standards.

Reagents. **Acetic acid, glacial, ACS.**
Hydrochloric acid, concentrated, ACS.
Hydrofluoric acid, 48 percent, ACS.
Nitric acid, concentrated, ACS.
Sulfuric acid, concentrated, ACS.
Ammonium hydroxide, concentrated, ACS.
Acetone, 99 percent, ACS.
Ammonium chloride, ACS.
Ethyl ether, anhydrous, ACS.
Hydrogen sulfide, 99.9 percent pure.
Potassium nitrite, crystal.
Aerosol OT, 1 percent.—Dilute 10 ml. of Aerosol OT, 10 percent, to 100 ml. with deionized water.

Ammonium hydroxide, 4 M.—Dilute 135 ml. of concentrated ammonium hydroxide to 500 ml. with deionized water.

Chromous chloride, 1 M.—Place about 200 g. of zinc, 20-mesh granular, ACS reagent, into a 250-ml. beaker, cover with 1 M hydrochloric acid and stir for 1 minute. Add 50 ml. of saturated mercuric chloride solution (prepared from ACS reagent powder) and stir for 3 minutes. Decant the liquid and wash the amalgam three times with

---

[86] In collaboration with K. G. Heinen.
[87] Heinen, K. G., and Larrabee, G. B., unpublished procedure.

deionized water. Fill a Jones reductor (ASTM type) with 0.01 M hydrochloric acid and transfer the amalgam to the column.

Prepare 1 M chromic chloride by dissolving 266 g. of chromic chloride crystals, $CrCl_3 \cdot 6H_2O$, ACS reagent, in 1 liter of 0.5 M hydrochloric acid.

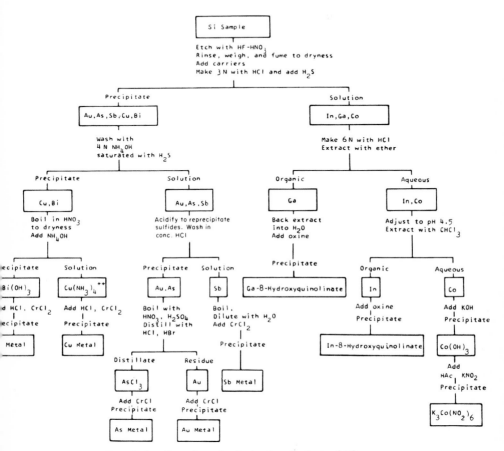

FIG. 60-9. Procedure for Activation Analysis of Silicon.

Immediately before use, lower the level in the column to just above the amalgam and add 1 M chromic chloride. Allow liquid to pass through the column until the effluent is blue.

After use, wash the column with 0.01 M hydrochloric acid and store under this acid.

Hydrochloric acid, 0.3 M wash solution.—Dilute 12.5 ml. of concentrated hydrochloric acid to 500 ml. with deionized water.

Hydrobromic acid, 3:2.—Dilute 300 ml. of fuming hydrobromic acid, ACS reagent, to 500 ml. with deionized water.

8-Hydroxyquinoline, 50 g. per liter.—Dissolve 5 g. of 8-hydroxyquinoline, ACS reagent, in 100 ml. of 2 M acetic acid.

8-Hydroxyquinoline, 0.02 M.—Dissolve 1.45 g. of 8-hydroxyquinoline, ACS reagent, in 500 ml. of chloroform, ACS reagent.

Potassium hydroxide, 6 M.—Dissolve 335 g. of potassium hydroxide pellets, ACS reagent, in 1 liter of deionized water. Store in a polyethylene bottle.

Potassium permanganate, 10 percent.—Dissolve 10 g. of potassium permanganate crystals, ACS reagent, in 100 ml. of deionized water.

Sodium acetate, 6 M.—Dissolve 410 g. of sodium acetate crystals, ACS reagent, in 500 ml. of deionized water.

Carrier solutions, 10 mg. metal per ml. nominal.—Weigh accurately about 1 g. of each of the following metals, all reagent grade; antimony, arsenic, bismuth, copper, cobalt, gallium, gold, and indium. Place each in a 100-ml. volumetric flask and dissolve in 5 to 30 ml. of aqua regia (1:3 nitric acid:hydrochloric acid). Dilute to volume with deionized water. Record the actual strength of each solution in milligrams per milliliter.

Carrier solutions, 10 μg. per ml. nominal.—Pipet 100 μl. of each of the 10 mg. per ml. carrier solutions into a series of 100-ml. flasks, and dilute to volume with deionized water.

Recording Data.—Use the table shown in Fig. 60-10 to record data as the analysis proceeds.

Irradiation.—Weigh 1–10 g. of sample and wrap in aluminum foil.

Into a series of ultrapure quartz[88] ampoules of 5-mm. internal diameter, introduce about 1 mg., accurately weighed on a microbalance, of each of the following materials, all of 99.999 percent purity;[89] antimony, arsenic, bismuth, cobalt, copper, gallium oxide,[90] gold, and indium. Record the weights in column A.[91] Seal the ampoules.

Forward the samples and monitors to a reactor for irradiation. The total integrated neutron dose must be at least 1.5×10^{16} neutrons. If the flux is known, the irradiation time can be calculated from the formula given in the introduction. For example, if the flux is 2×10^{12} n. per sec. per cm.[2] then the time will be 2.5 hours; at a flux of 2×10^{11} n. per sec. per cm.[2] the time must be increased to 24 hours.

Sample Reduction.—1. Etch the irradiated sample in a mixture of equal parts of concentrated nitric and hydrofluoric acids in a platinum dish for 5 to 20 seconds.

2. Remove, using platinum tipped tongs, and rinse in deionized water. Rinse in acetone and air dry. Weigh. Record the weight in column a.

3. Transfer the sample to a clean platinum dish containing 1 ml. of the carrier solutions, 10 μg. per ml.

4. Carefully add a mixture of equal parts of concentrated nitric and hydrofluoric acids until the sample has dissolved. Cover with a Teflon watch glass. When the vigorous reaction has subsided, place the dish on a warm hot plate and evaporate almost to dryness.

5. Add 15 ml. of concentrated hydrofluoric acid and evaporate almost to dryness. Repeat twice more.

6. Add 1 ml. of each of the carrier solutions, 10 mg. per ml. nominal. Record the actual weights added in column b. Transfer the solution to a 40-ml. centrifuge tube; let this be tube A. Add 2 ml. of concentrated hydrochloric acid to the platinum dish and heat briefly. Transfer this wash solution to tube A. Wash the dish again with 6 ml. of deionized water, and add this to tube A.

7. Add 1 g. of ammonium chloride and 10 percent potassium permanganate

[88] Type 204 tubing from General Electric is satisfactory.
[89] Suitable metals are available from Leytess Metal and Chemical Corp., 500 Fifth Avenue, New York 36, New York, and from Koch Light Laboratories Ltd., Colnbrook, Bucks, England.
[90] Gallium metal is not allowed in any reactor.
[91] For gallium, multiply the weight of oxide by 0.744 to correct to metal.

	a	b	c	d	e	f	g	h	j	k	ℓ	m	n	p
	Sample wt., g.	Carrier Added, mg.	Wt. of ppt., mg.	Gravimetric Factor	Elemental Yield, $c \times d$ mg.	Fractional Yield, e/b	Count Corrected for Background c.p.m.	Yield Corrected Count, g/f	Time of Count, Date and Hour	Time Difference J-j Hours	Half Life Hours	Decay Factor, $e^{-0.693k/\ell}$	Time Corrected Count, h/m	Conc. $n \times L \times 10^6 / a$ µg. per g.
Gallium				0.14							14.1			
Antimony				1.0							67.2			
Arsenic				1.0							26.5			
Gold				1.0							64.8			
Copper				1.0							12.9			
Bismuth				1.0							120			
Indium				0.21							1200			
Cobalt				0.13							46,200			

	A	B	C	D	E	F	G	H	J	K	L
	Wt. of Monitor, mg.	Aliquot Taken, µℓ.	Carrier Added, mg.	Wt. of ppt., mg.	Elemental Yield, $D \times d$, mg.	Fractional Yield, E/C	Count Corrected for Background Count, c.p.m.	Yield Corrected Count, G/F	Time of Count, Date and Hour	Wt. of Monitor Used, g. $A \times B/10^7$	Standard Factor, K/H
Gallium*											
Antimony											
Arsenic											
Gold											
Copper											
Bismuth											
Indium											
Cobalt											

* For gallium, A = wt. of $Ga_2O_3 \times 0.744$

FIG. 60-10. Chart for Recording Data During Analysis.

dropwise until the solution retains a strawlike color. Saturate with hydrogen sulfide for 5 minutes. Place in a hot water bath and continue to saturate with hydrogen sulfide for an additional 2 minutes. Add 3 drops of 1 percent Aerosol OT and centrifuge for 10 minutes.

8. Transfer the supernatant liquid to a 125-ml. separatory funnel and reserve for Step 13.

9. Wash the precipitate with 5 ml. of 0.3 M hydrochloric acid for 3 minutes in a water bath. Centrifuge and add the liquid to the separatory funnel. Repeat twice more.

10. To the precipitate, add 5 ml. of 4 M ammonium hydroxide and saturate with hydrogen sulfide while heating in a water bath for 3 minutes.[92] Centrifuge and transfer the yellow solution to a second centrifuge tube B.

11. Repeat Step 10 twice more, adding the liquid to tube B. Reserve this solution for Step 17.

12. Add 5 ml. of concentrated nitric acid to the black precipitate of bismuth and copper sulfides in tube A and heat almost to dryness.[93] Reserve for Step 26.

Gallium Precipitation.[94]—13. Add 25 ml. of concentrated hydrochloric acid to the separatory funnel. Extract 3 times with 15-ml. portions of ethyl ether. Transfer the ether extract containing the gallium to a clean 60-ml. separatory funnel. Transfer the aqueous portion to a 100-ml. beaker. Cover the beaker and reserve for Step 41.

14. Re-extract the ether portion using three 10-ml. portions of deionized water. Transfer the water extract to centrifuge tube C, and heat to drive off all traces of ether.

15. Adjust the temperature of the solution to 60°C. Add 1.5 ml. of 8-hydroxyquinoline solution, 50 g. per liter. Add 6 M sodium acetate dropwise until a permanent yellow precipitate has formed. Add 5 drops in excess.[95]

16. Within 5 minutes of the final addition, proceed as described in Steps 52 thru 58.

Antimony Precipitation.—17. Acidify the solution in tube B with hydrochloric acid and bubble with hydrogen sulfide for 2 minutes to reprecipitate the sulfides. Centrifuge and discard the supernatant liquid.

18. Wash the precipitate with 0.3 M hydrochloric acid saturated with hydrogen sulfide, and discard the supernatant liquid. Repeat twice more.

19. Add 5 ml. of concentrated hydrochloric acid to the precipitate and heat for 3 minutes in a hot water bath. Centrifuge and transfer the solution to centrifuge tube D.

20. Repeat Step 19 twice more using 2 ml. of concentrated hydrochloric acid and adding the liquid to tube D.

21. Add 3 ml. of concentrated nitric acid to the insoluble residue in tube B and evaporate almost to dryness. Repeat with 3 ml. more concentrated nitric acid. Reserve for Step 32.

22. Dilute the solution in tube D to 30 ml. Reprecipitate antimony trisulfide by saturating with hydrogen sulfide for 3 minutes. Add 3 drops of 1 percent Aerosol OT and centrifuge for 5 minutes. Discard the liquid.

23. Wash the precipitate twice with hot water and discard the wash solutions.

24. Add 3 ml. of concentrated hydrochloric acid to the precipitate. Heat to dissolve the precipitate and to expel the hydrogen sulfide. Dilute to 15 ml. with deionized water.

---

[92] Should the solution contain a reddish-orange suspension, increase the alkalinity very slightly using a few drops of ammonium hydroxide. Do not prepare a solution of ammonium hydroxide saturated with hydrogen sulfide in advance, since polysulfides which are formed on standing will dissolve the copper sulfide. Greater alkalinity will also partially dissolve the copper sulfide.

[93] This can best be done by standing the tube in an empty beaker on the hot plate.

[94] This should be carried out in parallel with Steps 9 to 12.

[95] If too great an excess of sodium acetate is added, the precipitate may contain recrystallized 8-hydroxyquinoline.

Heat the solution to near boiling, and add 20 ml. of freshly prepared chromous chloride from the Jones reductor. Heat to near boiling for 20 minutes.

25. Proceed as described in Steps 52 thru 58.

Copper and Bismuth Precipitations.—26. To tube A, which has evaporated to dryness, add 7 ml. of concentrated ammonium hydroxide. Centrifuge for 10 minutes and transfer the blue solution of copper ammine complex to centrifuge tube E.

27. Wash the precipitate twice with 3-ml. portions of concentrated ammonium hydroxide and centrifuge each time for 5 minutes. Add the wash solutions to tube E.

28. Acidify the copper solution in tube E with concentrated hydrochloric acid and add one drop in excess. Heat to near boiling and add 20 ml. of freshly prepared chromous chloride from the Jones reductor. Heat to near boiling for 20 minutes.

29. Proceed as described in Steps 52 thru 58.

30. Dissolve the bismuth hydroxide precipitate in tube A by adding 3 ml. of concentrated hydrochloric acid. Dilute to 10 ml. with deionized water and heat almost to boiling. Add 20 ml. of freshly prepared chromous chloride from the Jones reductor.

31. Proceed as described in Steps 52 thru 58.

Arsenic and Gold Precipitations.—32. To tube B, which has evaporated almost to dryness, add 7 ml. of concentrated sulfuric acid and heat to fumes. Cool.

33. Set up a distillation apparatus as shown in Fig. 60-11.

34. Transfer the solution from tube B to the flask through the funnel. Wash tube B with 40 ml. of concentrated hydrochloric acid and add this through the funnel. Add 25 ml. of 3:2 hydrobromic acid through the funnel. Close the stopcock and pass nitrogen through the apparatus.

35. Cool the receiver in ice. Add deionized water sufficient to cover the frit. Heat the distillation flask and distil until 30 ml. has collected in the receiver.

36. Add an additional 25 ml. of concentrated hydrochloric acid and 25 ml. of 3:2 hydrobromic acid rapidly through the funnel. Continue distilling until 30 ml. more of distillate has collected.

37. Transfer the distillate to a 250-ml. Erlenmeyer flask. Heat to near boiling. Add 20 ml. of freshly prepared chromous chloride from the Jones reductor. Heat for 10 minutes. Add an additional 15 ml. of chromous chloride.

38. Proceed as described in Steps 52 thru 58.

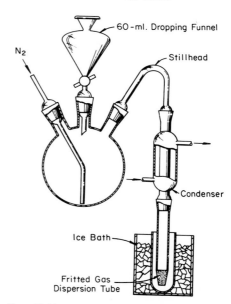

Fig. 60-11.   Arsenic Distillation Apparatus.

39. Transfer the residue in the distillation flask to a beaker and heat to near boiling. Add 20 ml. of chromous chloride from the Jones reductor and heat to near boiling for 20 minutes.

40. Proceed as described in Steps 52 thru 58.

Indium and Cobalt Precipitations.—41. Heat the solution in the beaker from Step 13 to remove *all* traces of ether. Cool to room temperature and adjust the pH to 4.0 to 5.0 with concentrated ammonium hydroxide using a pH meter.

42. Prepare 250 ml. of dilute hydrochloric acid of pH 4.5 with the aid of a pH meter, and equilibrate 200 ml. of 0.02 M chloroformate solution of 8-hydroxyquinoline with 100 ml. of this acid.

43. Transfer the solution from the beaker to a 60-ml. separatory funnel and extract three times with 15-ml. portions of the 8-hydroxyquinoline solution. Reserve the aqueous phase for the cobalt analysis in Step 47.

44. Transfer the organic phase to a clean separatory funnel and back extract using seven 5-ml. portions of 0.1 M hydrochloric acid. Collect the aqueous phase in a 100-ml. beaker and heat to remove *all* traces of chloroform.

45. Add 1 ml. of 8-hydroxyquinoline solution 50 g. per liter, and add 6 M sodium acetate dropwise until a permanent precipitate forms. Add 1 ml. in excess.

46. Within 5 minutes, proceed as described in Steps 52 thru 58.

47. Evaporate the solution containing the cobalt (from Step 43) to approximately 20 ml. Add 6 M potassium hydroxide dropwise until the solution is basic and the pink cobalt hydroxide has precipitated. Heat the mixture in a water bath for 5 minutes.

48. Centrifuge and discard the supernatant liquid. Wash the precipitate with 5 ml. of deionized water containing 2–3 drops of 6 M potassium hydroxide solution. Centrifuge and discard the wash solution.

49. Dissolve the precipitate in 5 ml. of concentrated acetic acid. Add 5 ml. of deionized water.

50. Add 8 ml. of 4 M acetic acid saturated with potassium nitrite. Heat in a water bath at 60°C. for 10 minutes. Chill in an ice bath.

51. Proceed as described in Steps 52 thru 58.

Treatment of Precipitates.—52. Filter the precipitate onto weighed 2.5-cm. Whatman No. 542 filter paper, backed with a Millipore support pad, using a glass funnel fitted with a coarse grade fritted support.

53. Wash the precipitate three times with hot water. Wash all precipitates except gallium and indium with acetone. Since the 8-hydroxyquinolates are soluble in organic solvents, wash the gallium and indium with water only.

54. Dry the precipitate for 10 minutes in a 110°C. oven. Increase the drying time for gallium and indium to 1 hour.

55. Cool the precipitate to room temperature and weigh on a microbalance. Record the weight of the precipitate minus that of the paper in column c (for the sample) or in column C (for the monitors).

56. Mount the paper on a ring-and-clip holder (Fig. 60-12). Cover the precipitate with a thin sheet of Mylar before the clip is snapped into place.

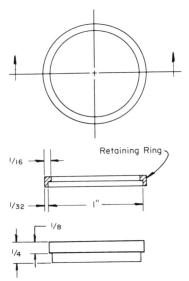

Fig. 60-12.   Ring-and-Clip Sample Holder.

57. Count the precipitates to a minimum accumulated count of 1000 using a gas flow proportional detector with a 100 microgram per cm.^{2} window. Record the counts per minute minus the background counts per minute in column g (for the

sample) or column G (for the monitors), and record the time, *i.e.*, date and time of day, in column j or column J, respectively.

58. Confirm the radiochemical purity by: determining the γ-ray spectrum and checking that the major peaks are at the correct energy;[96] or determining a decay curve by plotting the β count over at least five half lives.[97] Plot with logarithm of count as ordinate and time as abscissa. Purity is indicated by a straight line.[98] Identification of the isotope is made by determining the slope and calculating the half-life, $t_{1/2}$[99,100]

$$t_{1/2} = -\frac{0.300}{\text{slope}}$$

providing logarithms to base 10 are used; $t_{1/2}$ will be in the units of the graph.

Preparation of Standards.—1. During the dissolution of the silicon sample, open the quartz ampoules and transfer the irradiated monitors to a series of 10-ml. volumetric flasks.

2. Add to each 2–4 ml. of aqua regia (1:3 nitric acid:hydrochloric acid) and dissolve. Dilute to volume with water.

3. Add a suitable aliquot of each dilution,[101] to 1 ml. of the appropriate carrier solution in a series of 50-ml. beakers or, for bismuth and cobalt, 40-ml. centrifuge tubes. Record the volume of the aliquot in column B.

Gallium Standard.—4. To the beaker containing the gallium solution, add concentrated ammonium hydroxide dropwise until alkaline to litmus. Just acidify to litmus with 2 N acetic acid.

5. Place the tube in a 60°C. water bath. Add 1.5 ml. of 8-hydroxyquinoline, 50 g. per liter. Add 6 M sodium acetate dropwise until a permanent yellow precipitate forms, and add 5 drops in excess.

6. Proceed within 5 minutes as described in Steps 52 thru 58.[102]

Gold, Arsenic, and Antimony Standards.—7. To the beaker containing the metal solution, add 5 ml. of concentrated hydrochloric acid and dilute to 15 ml. with deionized water.

8. Add 20 ml. of freshly prepared chromous chloride solution from the Jones reductor. Heat to near boiling for 15 minutes.

9. Proceed as described in Steps 52 thru 58.

Copper Standard.—10. To the beaker containing the copper solution, add concentrated ammonium hydroxide dropwise. A deep blue color indicates it to be basic.

11. Add concentrated hydrochloric acid dropwise until neutral to litmus and then one drop in excess. Heat to near boiling and add 20 ml. of freshly prepared chromous chloride solution from the Jones reductor.

12. Proceed as described in Steps 52 thru 58.

---

[96] This cannot be used for bismuth since Bi^{210m} is a pure β emitter; the alternative method must be used.

[97] This cannot be used for cobalt and indium; Co^{60} has a 5.27-year half-life, and In^{114M} a 50-day half-life.

[98] Antimony gives a curve which tails off; Sb^{122} is the major isotope and dominates early, but Sb^{124} becomes more important with time.

[99] Antimony and gold cannot be distinguished by this method. Sb^{122} has a half-life of 67.2 hours and Au^{198} 64.8 hours.

[100] This calculation for $t_{1/2}$ is derived from the equation for radioactive decay, $N = N_0 e^{-\lambda t}$ where λ, the decay constant, $= \dfrac{0.693}{t_{1/2}}$.

[101] The most suitable count rate is 20,000 counts per minute. A preliminary measurement will indicate an aliquot corresponding to this.

[102] Step 58 is recommended as a check against contamination.

Bismuth Standard.—13. To the tube containing the bismuth solution, add concentrated ammonium hydroxide until the white bismuth hydroxide is completely precipitated. Centrifuge for 5 minutes and discard the supernatant liquid.

14. Add 3 ml. of concentrated hydrochloric acid to the precipitate and warm to dissolve. Dilute to 10 ml. with deionized water and heat to near boiling.

15. Add 20 ml. of freshly prepared chromous chloride solution from the Jones reductor. Heat in a water bath for 10 minutes.

16. Proceed as described in Steps 52 thru 58.

Indium Standard.—17. To the beaker containing the indium solution, add 4 M ammonium hydroxide to pH 4.0 to 5.0, using a pH meter.

18. Prepare 250 ml. of dilute hydrochloric acid to pH 4.5 with the aid of a pH meter. Equilibrate 200 ml. of 0.02 M chloroformate solution of 8-hydroxyquinoline with 100 ml. of the pH 4.5 acid.

19. Extract the indium solution with three 15-ml. portions of 8-hydroxyquinoline solution in a separatory funnel. Collect the chloroform phase in a second separatory funnel and reject the aqueous phase.

20. Extract the indium from the chloroform phase using seven 5-ml. portions of 0.1 M hydrochloric acid. Collect the aqueous phase in an Erlenmeyer flask and heat to remove all traces of chloroform.

21. Add 1 ml. of 8-hydroxyquinoline, 50 g. per liter. Add 6 M sodium acetate dropwise until a permanent precipitate forms, and add 1 ml. in excess.

22. Proceed within 5 minutes as described in Steps 52 thru 58.

Cobalt Standard.—23. To the tube containing the cobalt solution, add 6 M potassium hydroxide until alkaline. Heat the mixture. Centrifuge and discard the supernatant liquid.

24. Wash the pink precipitate with 5 ml. of deionized water containing 2–3 drops of 6 M potassium hydroxide. Centrifuge and discard the supernatant liquid.

25. Dissolve the precipitate in 10 ml. of 3 M acetic acid. Add 8 ml. of 6 M acetic acid saturated with potassium nitrite. Heat for 10 minutes in a water bath at 60°C. Chill in an ice bath.

26. Proceed as described in Steps 52 thru 58.

Calculation.—This is included in the table. Results are as p.p.m. (μg. per g.).

POLAROGRAPHY

INTRODUCTION

Conventional polarographic methods have been little applied to the analysis of semiconductors since they lack the necessary sensitivity. The only application to silicon is by Ardelt et al.,[103] who determined copper and iron by both conventional and oscillographic polarography in technical silicon carbide. Pohl[104] described a method for the determination of copper and cadmium in gold by removing the major element by isopropyl ether extraction and subsequently determining the impurities polarographically; he claimed this to be also applicable to indium, gallium, antimony, and arsenic, among other elements. In another publication, Pohl and Bonsels[105] described the method for indium in more detail, extending it to the determination of zinc, bismuth, and lead as well as copper and cadmium. Sensitivities down to 10 p.p.b. were claimed. Rozanova and Kamaev[106] separated copper and iron from arsenic in an acid solution

103 Ardelt, H. W., Opel, P. H., and Kiessling, H., Z. Chem., **3**, 70–72, 1963.
104 Pohl, F. A., J. Polarographic Soc., **1**, 8–10, 1958.
105 Pohl, F. A., and Bonsels, W., Z. anal. Chem., **161**, 108–114, 1958.
106 Rozanova, L. N., and Kamaev, G. A., Zhur. Prikl. Khim., **32**, 2574–2575, 1959.

by ion exchange; the adsorbed impurities were subsequently eluted and determined polarographically. Towndrow et al.[107] determined zinc in semiconductor grade indium by separating on a cellulose column and subsequently polarographing; about 10 p.p.m. is the indicated sensitivity. Kopanica and Pribil[108] complexed indium with 1,2-diamino-cyclohexane-NNN'N'-tetraacetic acid and were able to determine cadmium polarographically. Sinyakova et al.[109] described an involved chemical separation, involving coprecipitation and organic extraction, of indium from gallium prior to its polarographic determination; a sensitivity of 10 p.p.b. was claimed. Sulcek et al.[110] separated tin from antimony on a silica gel column and were able to determine 5 p.p.m. polarographing the eluate. Conradi and Kopanica[111] used a combination of solvent extraction and complexation to determine copper, lead, cadmium, bismuth, thallium, and iron in indium; the sensitivity with a polarographic finish was about 10 p.p.m. but could, it was claimed, be increased by using microtechniques.

These conventional polarographic procedures require chemical concentration steps prior to determination, all of which are sources of contamination. Increased sensitivity is claimed for oscillographic polarography and this was applied to some of those above[103,109] but to little advantage. Pohl and Bonsels[112] adapted their extraction procedure to the determination of a number of impurities in silicon, using a Southern Instruments cathode-ray polarograph; their sensitivity limits were about 1 p.p.m. Gokhstein et al.[113] determined copper, lead, zinc, nickel, iron, and silver in germanium by distilling off as the chloride and polarographing the residue using an oscillographic instrument. They were able to detect as little as 10 p.p.b. for most impurities.

Some of the above methods have been detailed by Parker and Rees,[114] but in general they suffer from the same drawbacks as the colorimetric methods. They are inherently not sensitive enough and a concentration step is necessary prior to measurement. This leads to the problem of purifying numerous reagents.

More sensitive techniques have been applied. Shirai[115] applied alternating current polarography to the determination of lead, cadmium, and zinc in indium. Jennings[116] determined copper and lead in indium arsenide and bismuth, copper, indium, and cadmium in gallium arsenide,[117] using a square wave polarograph. Sensitivities of about 0.1 p.p.m. were achieved for some of these impurities. The same level of sensitivity was achieved by Kaplan et al.[118] for the determination of copper in indium using the same technique. However, the instrumentation is complex and expensive.

Recently, a few applications of stripping polarography have appeared. This technique has been reviewed by Kemula and Kublik.[119] Briefly, the base electrolyte containing the impurity is electrolyzed using a stationary mercury electrode as the cathode. When

[107] Towndrow, E. G., Hutchinson, R., and Webb, H. W., Analyst, **85**, 769–770, 1960.

[108] Kopanica, M., and Pribil, R., Coll. Czech. Chem. Commun., **26**, 398–402, 1961.

[109] Sinyakova, S. I., Rudnev, N. A., Shen, Yu-Ch'ih, and Dzhumaev, R., Zhur. Anal. Khim., **16**, 32–35, 1961.

[110] Sulcek, Z., Dolezal, J., Michal, J., and Sychra, V., Talanta, **10**, 3–11, 1963.

[111] Conradi, G., and Kopanica, M., Chemist-Analyst, **53**, 4–6, 1964.

[112] Pohl, F. A., and Bonsels, W., Mikrochim. Acta, 641–649, 1960.

[113] Gokhstein, Ya. P., Volynets, M. P., and Yukhtanova, V. D., Trudy Komiss, Anal. Khim., Akad. Nauk SSSR, **12**, 5–24, 1960.

[114] Parker, C. A., and Rees, W. T., in Trace Analysis of Semiconductor Materials, J. P. Cali, Ed., Pergamon Press, Oxford, 1964.

[115] Shirai, H., Japan Analyst, **9**, 206–209, 1960.

[116] Jennings, V. J., Analyst, **85**, 62–68, 1960.

[117] Jennings, V. J., Analyst, **87**, 548–557, 1962.

[118] Kaplan, B. Ya., Sorokovskaya, I. A., and Smirnova, G. A., Zavod. Lab., **28**, 1188–1191, 1962.

[119] Kemula, W., and Kublik, Z., in Advances in Analytical Chemistry and Instrumentation, Vol. 2, C. N. Reilley, Ed., Interscience, New York, 1963.

a suitable amount of impurity is amalgamated, the potential is reversed and scanned rapidly; an anodic wave is obtained. Provasnik and Mojzis[120] used a sessile drop electrode to determine lead in gallium down to 0.3 p.p.m. and in arsenic and antimony down to 0.6 p.p.m. Kataev and Zakharova[121] used a hanging drop electrode to analyze arsenic for lead down to 0.2 p.p.m. and copper to 0.08 p.p.m. Sinyakova *et al.*[122] adapted the isopropyl ether extraction method to a hanging drop electrode and determined copper, lead, cadmium, and zinc in indium; the sensitivity claimed was 10 p.p.b.

This method is attractive in that the concentration step takes place in the base electrolyte and in the same vessel as the final measurement. Moreover, there is no lower limit, at least theoretically, to the detection, since a large sample can be concentrated into a very small drop. In practice, the lower limit is set by the reagent impurities but these can be significantly fewer than in a chemical concentration. Conventional polarographs can be used with minor modifications and the electrodes are simple to prepare. Any normal polarographic method can be readily adapted to this technique. It is limited to those metals which form amalgams with mercury, but this includes many of the common impurities.

HMDE POLAROGRAPHIC ANALYSIS OF SEMICONDUCTORS[123]

Apparatus.—The essential feature of a polarograph suitable for stripping analysis is a fast sweep. Such an instrument is available from Sargent, their Model FS. However, their Model XV is readily adapted by substituting three motors: the synchronous sweep motor, converting the sweep time from 10 minutes to 1 minute; the chart speed motor, increasing the speed from 1 in. per minute to 10 in. per minute; and the pen drive motor, increasing the response from 10 seconds to 1 second full scale.

Any other conventional polarograph that can be converted to this specification would be suitable.

The hanging mercury drop electrode (HMDE) cell is shown in Fig. 60-13.[124] The HMDE itself is constructed from a piece of 26 gauge (0.404 mm.) platinum wire mounted in 6-mm. glass tubing. The wire is sealed, cut off, and the end is polished flat. It is then etched back to a depth of 0.5 to 1 mm. by boiling in aqua regia (1:3 nitric acid:hydrochloric acid, both semiconductor grade). The platinum must be mercury plated before use as described below.

The rest of the cell consists of a conventional dropping mercury electrode (DME) to measure out the mercury, a small cup to catch the mercury and transfer it to the HMDE, a saturated calomel electrode (SCE), and a gas dispersion tube. The cell is supported on a magnetic stirrer and thermostatted at 25°C.

Plating the HMDE.—Prepare a solution of 20 g. mercuric oxide, ACS reagent, in 100 ml. of 1 M perchloric acid (9 ml. of 70 percent perchloric acid, ACS reagent, diluted to 100 ml. with deionized water). Transfer to an electrolysis cell with a mercury pool. Allow to stand until reaction has subsided (several hours); the solution now contains mercurous perchlorate. Suspend the HMDE in the solution, fill the tube with mercury to act as a contact and connect to the negative terminal of a 1.5-volt battery. Make the mercury pool the anode, and plate until gassing ceases and well-formed drops of mercury are seen falling from the HDME.

Store in deionized water when not in use.

[120] Provasnik, J., and Mojzis, J., Chem. Listy, **55**, 1299–1303, 1961.
[121] Kataev, G. A., and Zakharova, E. A., Zavod. Lab., **29**, 524–526, 1963.
[122] Sinyakova, S. I., Dudareva, A. G., Markova, I. V., and Talalaeva, I. N., Zhur. Anal. Khim., **18**, 377–384, 1963.
[123] In collaboration with K. R. Burson.
[124] Available from E. H. Sargent and Co., Cat. No. S-29314.

Reagents. **Hydrochloric Acid, Concentrated.**—Semiconductor grade acid, redistilled once in a hard glass still.

Hydrofluoric Acid, Concentrated.—Semiconductor grade acid, redistilled once in a Teflon still.

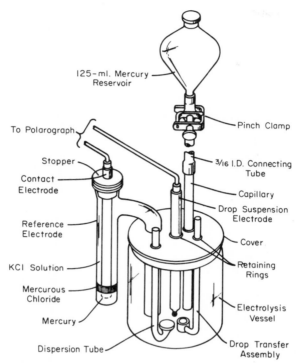

125-ml. Mercury Reservoir

Pinch Clamp

To Polarograph

3/16 I.D. Connecting Tube

Stopper

Contact Electrode

Capillary

Drop Suspension Electrode

Reference Electrode

Cover

KCl Solution

Retaining Rings

Mercurous Chloride

Mercury

Electrolysis Vessel

Dispersion Tube

Drop Transfer Assembly

Fig. 60-13. The Hanging Mercury Drop Electrode. (Courtesy E. H. Sargent and Co.)

Nitric Acid, Concentrated.—Semiconductor grade acid, redistilled once in a hard glass still.

Sulfuric Acid, Concentrated.—Semiconductor grade.

Perchloric Acid, 70 percent.—ACS reagent.

Isopropyl Ether.—Reagent grade.

Hydrobromic Acid, 1:1.—Dilute fuming hydrobromic acid, ACS reagent, with an equal volume of deionized water.

Hydrochloric Acid, 1:1.—Dilute concentrated hydrochloric acid, redistilled semiconductor grade, with an equal volume of deionized water.

Hydrochloric Acid, 1 *M*.—Dilute 100 ml. of concentrated hydrochloric acid, redistilled semiconductor grade, to 1 liter with deionized water.

Nitric Acid, 1:1.—Dilute concentrated nitric acid, redistilled semiconductor grade, with an equal volume of deionized water.

Nitric Acid, 1 *M*.—Dilute 65 ml. of concentrated nitric acid, redistilled semiconductor grade, to 1 liter with deionized water.

Ammonium Hydroxide, 6 *M*.—Place 500 ml. of concentrated ammonium hydroxide, semiconductor grade, in the lower half of a large desiccator. Place a 1-liter beaker containing 400 ml. of deionized water on the divider shelf. Close the desiccator and allow to equilibrate overnight.

Sodium Hydroxide, 1 M.—Dissolve 42 g. of sodium hydroxide, semiconductor grade, in deionized water, and dilute to 1 liter.

Phosphoric Acid, 0.1 M.—Pour 7 ml. of phosphoric acid, H_3PO_4, ACS reagent, into 1 liter of deionized water, stirring thoroughly. Prepare a cation exchange column by slurrying sufficient Dowex 50W-X4 (100–200 mesh) in deionized water to form a column 7 in. long and $\frac{3}{4}$ in. in diameter. Wash with deionized water. Pass the 0.1 M acid through this column and collect.

Standard Metal Solutions. Bismuth, 0.1 μg. per ml.—Weigh accurately about 0.1 g. of bismuth metal, granular, into a 100-ml. beaker; let this weight be Wg. Add 10 ml. of 1:1 nitric acid and heat to dissolve. Transfer to a 1-liter volumetric flask and dilute to volume with 1 M nitric acid. This stock solution contains approximately 100 μg. of Bi per ml.

On the day of use, dilute 1 ml. of the stock solution to 1 liter with deionized water to give the working standard.

Bismuth content, F, $= W$ μg. per ml.

Cadmium, 0.1 μg. per ml.—Dissolve exactly 0.163 g. of cadmium chloride, anhydrous, ACS reagent, previously dried at 150°C. for 3 hours, in deionized water and dilute to 1 liter with deionized water. This stock solution contains 100 μg. of Cd per ml.

On the day of use, dilute 1 ml. of the stock solution to 1 liter with deionized water to give the working standard.

Cadmium content, F, $= 0.100$ μg. per ml.

Copper, 0.1 μg. per ml.—Weigh accurately about 0.1 g. of copper shot, ACS reagent, into a 100-ml. beaker; let this weight be Wg. Add 10 ml. of 1:1 nitric acid and heat to dissolve. Transfer to a 1-liter volumetric flask and dilute to volume with deionized water. This stock solution contains approximately 100 μg. of Cu per ml.

On the day of use, dilute 1 ml. of the stock solution to 1 liter with deionized water to give the working standard.

Copper content, F, $= W$ μg. per ml.

Indium. 0.1 μg. per ml.—Weigh out accurately about 0.1 g. of indium metal, reagent grade, and proceed as for bismuth.

Lead, 0.1 μg. per ml.—Weigh out accurately about 0.1 g. of lead, granular, reagent grade, and proceed as for copper.

Thallium, 0.1 μg. per ml.—Dissolve exactly 0.130 g. of thallium nitrate, $TlNO_3$, purified, previously dried at 110°C. for 3 hours, in deionized water and dilute to 1 liter with deionized water. This stock solution contains 100 μg. Tl per ml.

On the day of use, dilute 1 ml. of the stock solution to 1 liter with deionized water to give the working standard.

Thallium content, F, $= 0.100$ μg. per ml.

Tin, 0.1 μg. per ml.—Weigh accurately about 0.1 g. of tin metal, powder, reagent grade, into a 100-ml. beaker; let this weight be Wg. Add 10 ml. of concentrated hydrochloric acid, redistilled semiconductor grade, and heat to dissolve. Transfer to a 100-ml. volumetric flask and dilute to volume with 1:1 hydrochloric acid. This stock solution contains approximately 1 mg. of Sn. per ml., and is stable for 2 weeks only.

On the day of use, dilute 10 ml. of the stock solution to 1 liter with 1 M hydrochloric acid. This intermediate solution contains approximately 10 μg. of Sn per ml.

Dilute 10 ml. of the intermediate solution to 1 liter with 1 M hydrochloric acid to give the working solution.

Tin content, F, $= W$ μg. per ml.

Zinc, 0.1 μg. per ml.—Weigh out accurately about 0.1 g. of zinc metal, granular, ACS reagent, and proceed as for copper.

Procedure. (a) For Silicon.—Prepare the sample as described under "Emission Spectrography," page 1780. Weigh accurately about 5 g. into a Teflon beaker; let this be Wg. Add 20 ml. of 1:1 nitric acid. Cover the beaker, and heat, adding 45 ml. of concentrated hydrofluoric acid, redistilled semiconductor grade, dropwise to avoid too vigorous a reaction. Remove the beaker cover and heat to dryness. Dissolve the residue in 100 ml. of 6 M ammonium hydroxide and transfer to the polarographic cell.

Deaerate the solution for 20 minutes with oxygen-free nitrogen or helium. Hang a mercury drop on the platinum wire. This is measured by collecting two or three drops from the DME in the cup; a standard number must be used for each series of determinations.[125] Plate from solution at -1.5 volts for 30 minutes, stirring at a constant and reproducible speed.[126]

Set the current at maximum sensitivity and scan from -1.5 to -0.1 volts at a rate of 0.033 volts/sec.

Examine the polarogram for peaks as follows:[127]

Zinc	-1.04 volts
Indium	-0.84
Cadmium	-0.80
Tin	-0.76
	-0.61
Lead	-0.55
Copper	-0.45
	-0.22
Thallium	-0.37
Bismuth	-0.24

If any are present, remove the drop from the platinum wire with the cup, add 1 ml. ($\equiv$ 0.1 μg.) of the appropriate standard(s) and repeat the electrolysis and scan.

Let the peak height be A mm. for the sample and B mm. for the sample and standard combined.

Carry a reagent blank through the method.[128] Let the peak height for the appropriate impurity be C mm.

Then

$$\text{impurity content} = \frac{1000\,(A - C)\,F}{W\,(B - A)} \text{ ng. per g. (p.p.b.)}$$

where F = strength of standard solution in μg. per ml.

(b) For Germanium.—Prepare the sample as described under "Emission Spectrography," page 1780. Weigh accurately about 5 g. into a Teflon beaker; let this weight be Wg. Add 3 ml. of concentrated sulfuric acid, semiconductor grade, and 10 ml. of concentrated hydrofluoric acid, redistilled semiconductor grade. Heat to incipient boiling and add concentrated nitric acid, redistilled semiconductor grade, dropwise

[125] The drop size will affect the peak height, and each HMDE must contain the same number of drops from the DME.
[126] The rate of stirring will affect the amount of metal plated from solution. The sample, standard, and blank runs must be carried out using the same stirring speed.
[127] Mutual interference is possible but in practice only exceptional material will contain significant amounts of any one.
[128] It is essential that the reagent blanks in these methods be identical. Where the instruction reads "add a few drops," these drops must be counted and the same number added to the reagent blank which is being carried through simultaneously.

until solution is complete. Take to fumes. Add 10 ml. of concentrated hydrochloric acid, redistilled semiconductor grade, and again take to fumes. Cool and add 100 ml. of 6 M ammonium hydroxide. Dissolve any residue and transfer to the polarographic cell.

Polarograph and determine impurity contents as described above for silicon.

(c) For Gallium Arsenide.—Prepare the sample as described under "Emission Spectrography," page 1772. Weigh accurately about 5 g. into a Teflon beaker; let this weight be Wg. Add 20 ml. of 1:1 nitric acid and 2 ml. of concentrated hydrochloric acid, redistilled semiconductor grade, and evaporate to dryness. Proceed by either (i) or (ii).

(i) *Impurities other than Zinc.*—Add 100 ml. of 6 M ammonium hydroxide to dissolve the residue and transfer to the polarographic cell.

Deaerate the solution for 20 minutes with oxygen-free nitrogen or helium. Prepare a HMDE and electrolyze for 30 minutes at −1.0 volt. Scan from −1.0 to −0.1 volt at a rate of 0.033 volts/sec.

(ii) *Zinc Determination.*—Add 100 ml. of 1 M sodium hydroxide to dissolve, and transfer to the polarographic cell.

Deaerate the solution for 20 minutes with oxygen-free nitrogen or helium. Prepare a HMDE and electrolyze for 30 minutes at −1.5 volt. Scan from −1.5 to −0.1 volt at a rate of 0.033 volts/sec.

In either case, add the appropriate standard(s) and repeat. Carry a reagent blank through the procedure. Calculate the impurity concentrations as given above for silicon.

(d) For Indium Arsenide, Indium Antimonide, and Indium.—Prepare the sample as described under "Emission Spectrography," page 1772. Weigh accurately about 5 g. into a Teflon beaker; let this weight be Wg. Add 20 ml. of 1:1 nitric acid and 2 ml. of concentrated hydrochloric acid, redistilled semiconductor grade. Proceed by either (i) or (ii).

(i) *General Method.*—Evaporate to dryness. Treat the residue three times with 2-ml. aliquots of 1:1 hydrobromic acid, evaporating to dryness each time. Add 2 ml. of 1:1 hydrobromic acid to dissolve the residue and transfer to a 50-ml. separating funnel. Repeat this twice more with additional 2-ml. portions of hydrobromic acid to effect a quantitative transfer. Add 15 ml. of isopropyl ether, shake for 5 minutes, allow to separate, and reject the ether layer. Repeat four times with 15-ml. portions of isopropyl ether. Transfer the aqueous layer to a beaker and evaporate to small volume. Add a few drops of 70 percent perchloric acid and evaporate to dryness. If the residue is not white, add a few drops more perchloric acid and again evaporate to dryness. Add 2–3 drops sulfuric acid and evaporate to fumes. Dissolve the residue in 100 ml. of 6 M ammonium hydroxide.

Polarograph and determine impurity contents as described above for silicon.

(ii) *Short Method for Copper, Lead, Bismuth, and Tin.*—Bring to incipient boiling until the sample is dissolved. Evaporate to dryness and dissolve the residue in 100 ml. of 0.1 M phosphoric acid. Transfer to the polarographic cell.

Deaerate the solution for 20 minutes with oxygen-free nitrogen or helium. Prepare a HMDE and electrolyze at −0.49 volt for 30 minutes. Scan from −0.49 to +0.5 volts at a rate of 0.033 volts/sec.

Examine the polarogram for peaks as follows:

Tin	−0.38 volts
Lead	−0.33
Bismuth	+0.05
Copper	+0.08

If any are present, renew the HMDE, add 1 ml. of the appropriate standard(s) and repeat the electrolysis and scan.

Carry a reagent blank through the method.

Calculate the impurity content(s) as described for silicon.

VACUUM FUSION ANALYSIS

Introduction.—Guldner[129] in Volume II of this work, has given detailed descriptions of the techniques of vacuum fusion and inert gas fusion. Generally, the latter is less sensitive than vacuum fusion and will not be applied to semiconductors. Even vacuum fusion is somewhat insensitive, being limited to a few p.p.m. for hydrogen, oxygen, and nitrogen. It has some value, however, in examining suspect samples and is, therefore, described here. For most single crystal material, these gases will be present below the detection limit.

Gases in silicon were determined by Beach and Guldner[130] using an iron bath, and a similar technique was used by Donovan *et al.*[131] for the determination of oxygen in silicon. Turovtseva *et al.*[132,133] used a platinum bath for gases in silicon; the same bath was used by a UKAEA group[134] for gases in silicon carbide. Beach and Guldner[130] also determined gases in germanium using a dry bath. Wilson *et al.*[135] employed a copper bath for gallium arsenide and indium antimonide and a dry bath for gallium metal. Vasileva *et al.*[136] also used a dry bath for the determination of oxygen and hydrogen in gallium and indium metals.

The methods given below for silicon and germanium have been well used, at least for oxygen, and are given in detail in the references quoted above. Information on the III–V compounds, on the other hand, is scanty. The references quoted do not contain details of the methods and there is some doubt about the recovery of oxygen from the possibly volatile oxides. Consequently, methods for these materials are not included.

ANALYSIS OF SILICON[137]

Procedure.—Break the sample into chunks of approximately 0.5 g. each. Choose a piece of a shape such that it will pass through the graphite funnel (Guldner's Fig. 36-24 in Vol. II). Etch in 1:1 nitric acid–hydrofluoric acid mixture (semiconductor grade) for 10 seconds at room temperature. Rinse in deionized water followed by methanol, semiconductor grade. Blow dry with air. Store in desiccator till used.

Weigh the sample; let this weight be Wg.

Cut $\frac{1}{4}$-in. diameter, vacuum-melted steel rod into $\frac{3}{8}$-in. lengths, and degrease with trichloroethylene, semiconductor grade. Weigh approximately 10 g. for each two silicon

[129] Guldner, W. G., in Standard Methods of Chemical Analysis, 6th Ed., Vol. II, Part B, F. J. Welcher, Ed., D. Van Nostrand Co., Princeton, N. J., 1963, pp. 1563–1615.

[130] Beach, A. L., and Guldner, W. G., in "Symposium on Determination of Gases in Metals," ASTM Special Technical Publication No. 222, 15–24, American Society for Testing and Materials, Philadelphia, 1958.

[131] Donovan, P. D., Evans, J. L., and Bush, G. M., Analyst, **88**, 771–781, 1963.

[132] Turovtseva, Z. M., Litvinova, N. F., Vasileva, N. M., and Semenyuk, K. G., Trudy Komiss. Anal. Khim., Akad. Nauk SSSR, **10**, 109–116, 1960.

[133] Turovtseva, Z. M., and Kunin, L. L., Analysis of Gases in Metals, English Trans., Consultants Bureau, New York, 1959.

[134] United Kingdom Atomic Energy Authority Report PG381(s), 1962.

[135] Wilson, C. M., Hazelby, D., Aspinal, M. L., and James, J. A., CVD Research Report RP4/3, Report No. G1374, Associated Electrical Industries (Rugby) Ltd., 1962.

[136] Vasileva, V. M., Litvinova, N. F., and Turovtseva, Z. M., Zhur. Anal. Khim., **18**, 250–254, 1963.

[137] In collaboration with H. J. Belknap.

samples. Place in the loading arm, followed by two silicon samples. Repeat this sequence, if necessary. Insert magnetic pusher and seal.

Load a new, dry crucible into the furnace, seal the equipment, and pump down as described in Vol. II, page 1585.

The intermittent bath technique is used (Vol. II, page 1592). Outgas the crucible at 2200°C. for 2 hours. Reduce the temperature to 1700°C. and collect gas for 10 minutes. Determine gas content; this is the crucible blank and should be less than 5 cc. mm. (or less than 10^{-6} torr if an ion gauge is available). If higher, outgas further at 2200°C. Transfer iron to crucible and melt. Outgas for 30 minutes (the pressure at this time should be 10^{-6} torr or less). Collect gas for 10 minutes and analyze; this is the bath blank and should be less than 5 cc. mm. total.

Introduce the first sample and collect gas for 10 minutes. Analyze and deduct appropriate blank.

Introduce second sample and analyze.

Introduce second iron bath and determine new bath blank after outgassing. Two more samples may be determined in this bath, after which a new crucible must be used.

$$\text{Oxygen} = \frac{Q \times 0.8605}{W} \, \mu g. \text{ per g. (p.p.m.)}$$

where Q = volume of CO in cc. mm.

Usually, oxygen is the only gas that need be considered. If hydrogen or nitrogen is required, calculate as given in Vol. II, page 1589.

ANALYSIS OF GERMANIUM[137]

Procedure.—Break the sample into chunks of 1–2 grams each. Choose several pieces of such shape that they will pass through the graphite funnel (Vol. II, Fig. 36-24). Etch in CD etch (3.5 parts nitric acid, 1.8 parts acetic acid, 1 part hydrofluoric acid, all semiconductor grade) for 30 seconds, rinse with deionized water, followed by methanol, semiconductor grade, and blow dry with air.

Weigh each piece and choose several that will total 5–6 grams. Let the weight be Wg. Weigh other aggregate samples in the same manner.

Place the samples in the sample loading arm. (Up to six samples can be conveniently loaded and analyzed.) Insert magnetic pusher and seal.

Load a new, dry crucible into the furnace, seal the equipment, and pump down as described in Vol. II, page 1585.

Outgas the crucible at 2200°C. for 2 hours or until the furnace pressure is 10^{-6} torr or less at the operating temperature of 1550°C. Determine the furnace blank at 1550°C. by collecting gas for 10 minutes. Analyze the gas by the procedure in Vol. II, page 1586. This is the blank to be subtracted from the sample.

Introduce the first sample and collect gas for 10 minutes. Analyze as before and deduct blank from sample. Analyze the other samples in the same manner.

$$\text{Oxygen} = \frac{Q \times 0.8605}{W} \, \mu g. \text{ per g. (p.p.m.)}$$

where Q = volume of CO in cc. mm.

Usually, oxygen is the only gas that need be considered. If hydrogen or nitrogen is required, calculate as given in Vol. II, page 1589.

INFRARED SPECTROMETRY

In the introduction to this chapter, intrinsic conduction was attributed to thermal excitation of valence electrons to a state in which they could wander through the lattice, leaving behind holes which could similarly move against the flow of electrons. If the crystal could be reduced to absolute zero temperature, then these electrons would all return to the valence band and a perfect insulator would result. An infrared spectrum of this crystal would then be as shown in Fig. 60-14.

An absorption edge would appear at a wavelength corresponding to the thermal energy required to raise the electrons from the valence band to the conduction band.

Apart from some minor lattice vibrational modes, this would be the only absorption in a perfect crystal of silicon

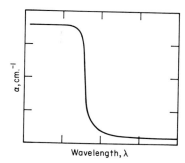

Fig. 60-14.   Infrared Absorption Spectrum of Perfect Crystal at Absolute Zero.

or germanium; in the III–V compounds the lattice vibrational modes are more important and are termed reststrahlen bands. These modes appear at longer wavelengths (20 μ or more). The absorption edges at room temperature are, for silicon, 1.1 μ, for germanium, 1.8 μ, and for gallium arsenide, 0.9 μ. They go to shorter wavelengths with reduced temperatures.

In practice, no crystal can be perfect, and, due to either physical defects or to substitutional impurities in the lattice, extrinsic conduction is always exhibited. The electrons giving rise to this form of conduction do not originate in the valence band but in some other energy level. A donor, or n-type dopant, originates at a level much closer to the conduction band and consequently requires much less energy to raise it to that level. An acceptor, or p-type dopant, originates at a level close to the valence band; electrons are readily raised from the valence band to that level leaving the valence band positively charged, i.e., with "holes." In either case the energy required is much less than that required to transfer electrons right across the energy gap, and the absorption peaks for these impurities are at a longer wavelength.

Theoretically, it should be possible to determine the dopants by infrared absorption. In fact, the above description is a simplification of a very complex and difficult field which has been the object of considerable investigation. A detailed description is given in books by Hannay,[2] Moss,[138] and Hilsum and Rose-Innes.[139] The various possible interactions between the energy levels make identification of the dopants difficult and a quantitative determination almost impossible. However, a number of impurity levels have been assigned, at least in silicon and germanium, and are given in the literature.[2,138]

Since the activation energy of these levels is small compared with that for the intrinsic electrons, it is necessary to obtain these spectra at liquid nitrogen (or in some cases liquid helium) temperature and to avoid spurious emission monochromatic light must be used in the incident beam. So far, no analytical application of these levels has been published but they are inherently highly sensitive. They might have specialized applications in confirming the presence of specific impurities.

[138] Moss, T. S., Optical Properties of Semiconductors, Butterworths, London, 1959.

[139] Hilsum, C., and Rose-Innes, A. C., Semiconducting III–V Compounds, Pergamon Press, Oxford, 1961.

The case of oxygen in single-crystal silicon is significantly different. This is an interstitial impurity and as such does not take part in the electronic transitions described above. It forms a chemical bond with silicon to form SiO which gives rise to an absorption peak at 9 μ. This has been used by Kaiser et al.[140,141] to determine the oxygen concentration over the range 1 to 20 p.p.m. They used vacuum fusion analysis to calibrate and this method would usually be employed. However, for some applications, it would be more convenient to use infrared absorption since this method is nondestructive. It is sufficiently accurate for most purposes to use Kaiser's absorption coefficient, and this is incorporated in the method given below. It is applicable only to high resistivity material (to eliminate free charge carrier absorption, a high background due to excessive extrinsic carriers), and there is a correction required due to interfering lattice vibrations. Since the oxygen content is high compared with other impurities, the measurements may be made with polychromatic incident light at room temperature.

A similar method has been applied by Kaiser and Thurmond[142] to the determination of oxygen in germanium. In this case the GeO vibration is at 11.7 μ. They calibrated their method up to about 3 p.p.m. by vacuum fusion.

In both cases, the results are for dissolved oxygen. At higher levels, above 2×10^{18} atoms per cc.[141,142] (22 p.p.m. for silicon or 10 p.p.m. for germanium), the dioxide begins to precipitate and results will no longer correlate with vacuum fusion.

DETERMINATION OF OXYGEN IN SINGLE CRYSTAL SILICON[143,144]

Sample Preparation.—Samples will usually be received as ingots. Slight variations in oxygen distribution can be expected along the length of the ingot, but a center section can usually be regarded as representative. For the highest accuracy, several sections should be analyzed.

Using a diamond saw, cut a section 5 mm. thick perpendicular to the length of the ingot. The section should be about 1 in. in diameter. Remove mounting wax by boiling in methanol. Optically polish both sides.

Method.—Using a micrometer, measure the thickness of the slice at its center, taking care not to damage the surfaces. Let this be κ cm. Measure the transmission at room temperature at a wavelength of 9.0 μ. Let this be $T\%$.

Calculation.[145]

[140] Kaiser, W., Keck, P. H., and Lange, C. F., Phys. Rev., **101**, 1264, 1956.
[141] Kaiser, W., and Keck, P. H., J. Appl. Phys., **28**, 882, 1957.
[142] Kaiser, W., and Thurmond, C. D., J. Appl. Phys., **32**, 115–118, 1961.
[143] In collaboration with C. E. Jones.
[144] Applicable only to material having a resistivity higher than 10 ohm-cm.
[145] The transmittance, t, can be shown to be

$$t = \frac{I}{I_0} = \frac{(1 - R)^2 e^{-\alpha\kappa}}{1 - R^2 e^{-2\alpha\kappa}} \tag{1}$$

where α = absorption coefficient, cm.$^{-1}$,
κ = thickness, cm., and
R = reflectivity

$$R = \frac{(n - 1)^2 + K^2}{(n + 1)^2 + K^2} \tag{2}$$

where n = refractive index, and
K = extinction coefficient

$$K = \frac{\alpha}{4\pi\bar{v}} \tag{3}$$

where $\bar{v}$ = wave number, cm.$^{-1}$.

DETERMINATION OF OXYGEN IN SINGLE CRYSTAL GERMANIUM[143,146]

Sample Preparation.—As for silicon.

Method.—Using a micrometer, measure the thickness of the slice at its center, taking care not to damage the surfaces. Let this be κ cm.

Measure the transmission at room temperature at a wavelength of 11.7 μ. Let this be $T\%$.

Calculation.[145]

$$\text{Concentration, p.p.m.} = 0.25 \left(\frac{2.3(2.00 - \log_{10} T) - 0.90}{\kappa} - 0.1 \right)$$

$$\text{Oxygen content, p.p.m.} = 3.2 \left(\frac{2.3(2.00 - \log_{10} T) - 0.71}{\kappa} - 0.8 \right)$$

For any particular material at a given wavelength,

$$R = \text{constant}$$
$$= 0.299 \text{ for silicon,}$$
$$= 0.360 \text{ for germanium.}$$

In these two cases,

$$e^{2\alpha x} \gg R^2$$

so that the expression reduces to

$$t = (1 - R)^2 e^{-\alpha\kappa} \tag{4}$$

Kaiser's calibration for silicon[141] can be expressed as

$$\text{concentration, p.p.m.} = 3.2 \, (\alpha - 0.8) \tag{5}$$

and for germanium[142] as

$$\text{concentration, p.p.m.} = 0.25 \, (\alpha - 0.1). \tag{6}$$

Combining Eq. (4) with Eqs. (5) or (6) leads to the formulas given in the methods.

[146] Applicable only to material having a resistivity higher than 1 ohm-cm.

Chapter 61

SOAPS AND SYNTHETIC DETERGENTS

By E. W. Blank and R. M. Kelley

Colgate-Palmolive Research Center
Piscataway, New Jersey

The essential similarities and distinctions between soaps and detergents have been discussed previously by R. C. Stillman in Chapter 45 of Volume II of this work. In brief, soap is the product formed by saponification or neutralization of fats, oils, waxes, rosins, or their acids with organic or inorganic bases. A synthetic detergent is the result of chemical synthesis, and comprises an organic composition other than soap. The term synthetic detergent is frequently contracted to syndet or surfactant. Further information on the chemistry of soaps and synthetic detergents is available in a number of published sources.[1,2]

SCOPE

Many excellent schemes of analysis are available for the systematic or complete analysis of soaps and detergents by the classical, or so-called wet methods of analytical chemistry. It is only lately that instrumental methods of analysis have been developed and applied to the analysis of these materials. At the present time it is not possible to perform a complete analysis of a soap or detergent by the use of instruments, but instrumentation complements and significantly increases the scope of analysis. Furthermore, instruments have extended the analytical potential, and many determinations that were formerly extremely difficult to accomplish are now readily performed.

A concise tabular scheme of analysis for soaps and detergents can be found in the Handbook of Analytical Chemistry, edited by L. Meites.[3] A review of the information available in this book will assist the analyst, particularly if not versed in the field, in obtaining a broad view of the potential application of instrumentation to the determinations required for a complete analysis of soaps and detergents.

SAMPLING

The successful accomplishment of a satisfactory analysis begins with proper sampling. Acceptable sampling methods conform generally to the procedures of the American

[1] Schwartz, A. M., and Perry, J. W., Surface Active Agents: Their Chemistry and Technology, Vol. 1, Interscience Publishers, New York, 1949; Schwartz, A. M., Perry, J. W., and Berch, J., Surface Active Agents and Detergents, Vol. 2, Interscience Publishers, New York, 1958.

[2] Martin, G., The Modern Soap and Detergent Industry, 3rd Ed., revised by E. I., Cooke, 2 Vols., The Technical Press, London, 1950–51. The massive opus of Lewkowitsch, J., Chemical Technology and Analysis of Oils, Fats and Waxes, 6th Ed., G. H. Warburton, Ed., 3 Vols., Macmillan and Co., Ltd., London, 1921–23, although out of date is still valuable.

[3] Handbook of Analytical Chemistry, L. Meites, Ed., McGraw-Hill Book Co., New York, 1963, Section 13-257.

Society for Testing and Materials. For more complete details reference should be made to ASTM Methods D 460-60 and D 1570-60T. These methods of sampling have been summarized by R. C. Stillman in Volume II, Chapter 45 of this work, and need not be repeated here.

As has been indicated in the literature,[4] the sampling of cake soaps or combination bars (soap + syndet formulations) requires special precautions as follows:

Grind the bars in a food chopper or dice in $\frac{1}{4}$-in. cubes by hand. If a large number of bars is to be sampled it is permissible to take a full corner quarter of each bar for grinding. The ground sample should consist of at least 3 lb. Mix all ground samples thoroughly and as rapidly as possible on a dry, nonabsorbent, impervious surface with a metal or porcelain spatula. The familiar operation of quartering is then performed to reduce the size of the sample to approximately 2 lb. Store the sample in a clean, dry, glass-stoppered container.

It is extremely difficult to sample dry mixed formulations consisting of variously sized particles. Such samples should be quartered to a suitable size and the entire quarter weighed and dissolved in a suitable volume of water. Aliquots of this solution containing an appropriate sample weight should be transferred to a beaker and dried to constant weight in an oven or on the steam bath. The entire weight of the sample in the beaker should then be taken for a particular analysis. Mixtures of this type can sometimes be rendered homogeneous by transferring approximately 50 g. or more of the well mixed sample to a plastic bag and pulverizing in the sealed bag with a rolling pin. This technique eliminates errors resulting from loss of moisture.

Slurry samples (alkyl benzene sulfonates prior to spraying) should be received as soon as possible from the crutcher and stored in tightly closed containers in an oven maintained at 40–50°C. until start of the analytical work. Slurry samples received warm and stored as described can be readily mixed in the original container with a spatula to yield a representative sample.

Slurry samples that have been allowed to cool with resulting separation and crystallization should be heated, in the tightly closed original container, to 40–50°C. in an oven or on the steam bath. The entire contents of the sample bottle are then thoroughly mixed by mechanical means (Waring Blendor or Effenbach Homo-Mixer). Avoid unnecessary or excessive transfer of the sample. Stirring and sampling must be accomplished in as short a period of time as possible to avoid moisture loss.

SEPARATIONS

The characterization of a soap or synthetic detergent occurring singly is not difficult but the current formulation of commercial products is becoming increasingly complex and most samples encountered by the analyst represent mixtures.

To achieve a satisfactory analysis of commercial products it is necessary to perform preliminary separations. An extensive knowledge of separations comes only from experience, but the following brief summary will serve to orient the analyst attempting work in this field for the first time. A wealth of information is available[5,6] and should be consulted for the successful analysis of complex mixtures.

High molecular weight alkyl aryl sulfonates (alkyl chain lengths of 4 carbon atoms or more) can be separated from short chain sulfonates, such as toluene sulfonate, by

[4] Gildenberg, L., and Blank, E. W., "Error in the Sampling of Soap and Detergent Bars for Moisture Determination," J. Am. Oil Chem. Soc., **35**, 102, 1958.

[5] Blank, E. W., and Kelley, R. M., "The Analytical Separation of Surface Active Agents," J. Am. Oil Chem. Soc., **41**, 137, 1964.

[6] Rosen, M. J., and Goldsmith, H. A., Systematic Analysis of Surface-Active Agents, Interscience Publishers, New York, 1960.

extraction from an acidified aqueous solution with ethyl ether. The alkyl benzene sulfonate content of the ether layer may be determined by ultraviolet spectrophotometry, and the same technique can be applied to the determination of toluene sulfonate remaining in the extracted water after removal of the residual ethyl ether.

Mixtures of alkyl benzene sulfonate and fatty alcohol sulfate can be separated by dissolving the sample in hot alcohol, removing insoluble salts by filtration, evaporating the alcoholic filtrate to dryness and hydrolyzing the fatty alcohol sulfate by refluxing with 25 percent hydrochloric acid. Allow the refluxed mixture to cool, neutralize with sodium hydroxide and extract the desulfated fatty alcohol with n-pentane. The fatty alcohol may be characterized by infrared or vapor phase chromatography. The extracted solution contains the alkyl benzene sulfonate which can be determined by ultraviolet spectrophotometry.

Nonionics of the alkyl phenoxy polyoxyethylene ethanol type can be determined by ultraviolet absorption in the presence of alkyl benzene sulfonate. The absorbance of the nonionic or mixture of nonionics should be determined at 283 and 300 mμ. The absorbance of the alkyl benzene sulfonate alone (sample without the addition of the nonionic) should also be determined at 283 and 300 mμ. Calculate the ratio of the absorbances and multiply the background reading at 300 mμ of the nonionic and alkyl benzene sulfonate mixture by the ratio to eliminate interference due to alkyl benzene sulfonate at the wavelength of 283 mμ. This procedure may also be applied to admixtures of nonionics and fatty alcohol sulfates.

Mixtures of alkyl benzene sulfonate and nonionics can also be separated by ion exchange. To accomplish such a separation, pass an aqueous alcohol solution of the mixture through a column packed in series with anionic and cationic exchange resins. The nonionic elutes can be recovered by evaporation of the eluted solution. The sulfonate retained by the resin can be recovered by eluting with a 2 percent sodium hydroxide solution in 1:1 isopropanol and water. The nonionic and alkyl benzene sulfonate can be characterized by applicable instrumental techniques.

The ion exchange technique can also be applied to mixtures of sulfates, sulfonates, and alkanolamides. The latter will elute. If other nonionics are present they will also elute with the alkanolamide, but frequently they can be identified by infrared or ultraviolet absorption.

The general methods of separation described in the preceding paragraphs should be kept in mind when dealing with samples of complex formulation. In many instances their application will permit a subsequent analysis by slight modification of the instrumental techniques described in the remainder of this chapter. The characterization of pure compounds by instrumentation is relatively easy and straightforward; the principal difficulty invariably lies in isolation of the compound from a mixture in a sufficiently pure state to eliminate false conclusions arising from the presence of interferences.

NOTE.—Persistent emulsions are frequently encountered in the analysis of soaps and syndets. Solutions can sometimes be defoamed by the addition of 1 or 2 drops of Dow Corning Antifoam A, octyl alcohol or ethyl alcohol. Of course no antifoaming agent can be used that will interfere in subsequent steps of the analysis. Emulsions also are frequently broken by the addition of small amounts (10–20 mg.) of sodium chloride or sodium sulfate.

Ultrasonic vibration is probably the simplest way to disrupt emulsions. A Norda SonBlaster, obtainable from Dyna Sonics, 200 Michael Drive, Syossett, Long Island, New York has been found serviceable in this operation. Set the vessel (extraction cylinder or separatory funnel) containing the emulsion in the stainless steel chamber for fifteen to twenty minutes.

PURITY OF REAGENTS

Reagent grade chemicals shall be used in all tests. All reagents shall conform to the specifications of the Committee on Analytical Reagents of the American Chemical

Society[7] unless otherwise indicated. If such specifications are not available, other grades may be utilized, provided one ascertains previously that the reagent is of sufficient purity to permit its use without decreasing the accuracy of the determination.

Unless otherwise indicated, references to water shall be understood to mean reagent water conforming to the Specifications for Reagent Water (ASTM Designation D 1193).[8]

Where special reagents or Optical Grade reagents are required, this requirement will be indicated in the method of determination.

Ethyl alcohol (95 percent) conforming to either Formula No. 3A or No. 30 of the U. S. Bureau of Internal Revenue is acceptable for use unless specifically indicated otherwise.

VISIBLE SPECTROMETRY

DETERMINATION OF SODIUM CARBOXYMETHYLCELLULOSE IN SYNDETS

Scope.—This method is applicable to the determination of carboxymethylcellulose (NaCMC) in commercial syndet formulations.

Principle.—The method is colorimetric, based upon the cleavage of CMC with concentrated acid to produce glycolic acid and, subsequently, formaldehyde. The latter is condensed with 2,7-dihydroxynaphthalene to form a red-colored complex. The absorbance of the red-colored complex is related to the amount of NaCMC present in the sample by reference to a standard curve prepared using an authentic sample of NaCMC.[9]

Apparatus.—Any suitable spectrometer capable of reading absorbance or percent transmission at a wavelength of 537 mμ.

Reagents. **2,7-Dihydroxynaphthalene Solution.**—The solution is prepared by dissolving 0.050 g. of 2,7-dihydroxynaphthalene in 500 ml. of sulfuric acid. Allow to stand until the yellow color disappears. Store in the dark.

Standard Glycolic Acid Solution (0.01 percent).—Dry the glycolic acid in a vacuum desiccator overnight at room temperature. Accurately weigh 0.0250 g., transfer to a 250-ml. volumetric flask, dilute to the mark with water, and mix well.

Preparation of Calibration Curve.—Using a semimicroburet, accurately measure 1.0, 0.8, 0.6, 0.4, and 0.2 ml. of standard glycolic acid solution into separate 50-ml. volumetric flasks. Accurately pipet 25 ml. of 2,7-dihydroxynaphthalene solution into each flask. Suspend the flasks in a boiling water bath for 20 minutes. Cool the flasks and cautiously add ice-chilled water slowly to each flask while swirling. Add the water in small increments keeping the solution chilled. Finally dilute to the mark with water and mix well. Using 1-cm. cells, measure the absorbance of each solution *vs.* a blank at 540 and 700 mμ. Using rectilinear graph paper, plot corrected absorbance (A_{570}–A_{700}) as the ordinate and the corresponding milligrams of glycolic acid as the abscissa. Draw the best possible straight line through the points with the intercept at the origin.

Procedure.—Accurately weigh a representative sample containing 5 to 10 mg. of NaCMC into a 250-ml. Erlenmeyer flask. Add 50 ml. of concentrated hydrochloric acid, place on a hot plate in a hood, and boil gently for 1 hour. Transfer the solution

---

[7] Reagent Chemicals, American Chemical Society Specifications, American Chemical Society, Washington, 1960. For suggestions on the testing of reagents not listed by the ACS, refer to Reagent Chemicals and Standards, 4th Ed., by Joseph Rosin, D. Van Nostrand Co., Princeton, N. J., 1961, and the United States Pharmacopeia, 17th Revision, Washington, 1965.

[8] Book of ASTM Standards, Part 10, 1958, p. 1132.

[9] Eyler, R. W., and Hall, R. T., "Determination of Carboxymethyl-cellulose in Paper," Paper Trade Journal, **125**, 59, 1947.

to a 50-ml. volumetric flask, cool, and dilute to volume with water. Mix well. Filter the solution and pipet 2 ml. of the clear filtrate into a 50-ml. volumetric flask. Slowly pipet in 25 ml. of 2,7-dihydroxynaphthalene solution and suspend the flask in a boiling water bath for 90 minutes. Prepare a blank in a 50-ml. volumetric flask containing 25 ml. of 2,7-dihydroxynaphthalene, and heat for the same length of time. Cool the flasks and carefully and slowly add ice-chilled water and finally dilute to volume (see preparation of calibration graph). Using 1-cm. cells, measure the absorbance of the sample solution *vs.* that of the blank at 537 and 700 mμ.

Using the corrected absorbance (A_{537}–A_{700}) refer to the calibration graph to obtain the milligrams of glycolic acid. Calculate as follows:

$$\frac{\text{milligrams of glycolic acid (from graph)} \times 25 \times 100}{\text{weight of sample in grams} \times 1000} = \text{percent glycolic acid in product}$$

The percent glycolic acid in the NaCMC should be applied to the grade of NaCMC used in the product. Accurately weigh 5–30 mg. of NaCMC and transfer to a 250-ml. Erlenmeyer flask. Add 50 ml. of concentrated hydrochloric acid, and proceed as described for analysis of the product. Calculate the percent glycolic acid in the NaCMC as shown above.

Calculate the NaCMC in the sample as follows:

$$\frac{\text{percent glycolic acid in product}}{\text{percent glycolic acid in CMC}} = \text{percent sodium carboxymethylcellulose}$$

DETERMINATION OF COPPER IN SOAP

Scope.—This method is applicable to the determination of trace levels of copper in soap and soap products.

Principle.—After removal of the soap fatty acids by an initial extraction from acid solution, the copper is complexed with sodium diethyldithiocarbamate at a controlled pH. The colored complex is extracted with a solvent and the absorbance is read by a suitable spectrometer. The copper content is calculated by reference to a standard calibration graph.[10]

Apparatus.—Any suitable spectrometer capable of reading absorbance at a wavelength of 440 mμ and equipped with 1-cm. cells.

Reagents. Electrolytic Copper.—ACS grade.

Nitric Acid (1:1).

Citric Acid Solution (30 percent).—Dissolve 30 g. of citric acid in 80 ml. of water, and dilute to 100 ml.

Hydrochloric Acid.—Concentrated, Reagent Grade (redistilled).

Ammonium Hydroxide.—Concentrated, Reagent Grade (redistilled).

Ethyl Alcohol (3:1).—Mix 750 ml. of Reagent ethyl alcohol with 250 ml. of distilled water.

Carbon Tetrachloride.—Reagent Grade.

Sodium Diethyldithiocarbamate Reagent, 0.2 percent (Aq.).—Dissolve 1 g. of the reagent in 500 ml. of distilled water. Extract the solution once with 200 ml. of carbon tetrachloride and discard the solvent. Prepare the solution fresh weekly and store in a refrigerator.

Phenol Red Indicator Solution.—Dissolve 0.1 g. of the indicator in a mixture of 20 ml. of ethyl alcohol and 80 ml. of water.

---

[10] Official and Tentative Methods of the American Oil Chemists' Society, AOCS Official Method Da 31–58, American Oil Chemists' Society, Chicago, 1963.

Standard Copper Solution (1 ml. = 8 μg. of copper).—Weigh 0.2 g. ($\pm$0.0001 g.) of clean electrolytic copper into a 50-ml. beaker. Add 10 ml. of 1:1 nitric acid and cover the beaker with a watch glass. After reaction has ceased, add approximately 20 ml. of water, and transfer to a 500-ml. volumetric flask. Dilute to volume with water at room temperature and mix well. Pipet 10 ml. of this stock solution into a 500-ml. volumetric flask, and again dilute to volume with water at room temperature. This solution constitutes the working standard.

Procedure.—Weigh 2.00 ($\pm$0.002 g.) of sample and transfer to a 100-ml. beaker. Add 40 ml. of ethyl alcohol solution (3:1) and 1 ml. of concentrated hydrochloric acid. Heat to dissolve the sample. Transfer to a 125-ml. separatory funnel, and wash out the beaker with a small volume of ethyl alcohol solution. Cool and add 25 ml. of carbon tetrachloride and 2 ml. of 30 percent citric acid solution. Shake the contents of the separatory funnel for 30 seconds. Discard the lower solvent layer, repeat the extraction once more with carbon tetrachloride, and again discard the extract. Add 2 drops of phenol red indicator solution and concentrated ammonium hydroxide dropwise until the solution just turns red. Add 5 ml. of sodium diethyldithiocarbamate reagent. Shake the mixture with 3 ml. of carbon tetrachloride for at least 30 seconds. Let the solvent settle and filter the carbon tetrachloride layer through a cotton plug inserted in the stem of a small funnel collecting the filtrate in a 10-ml. volumetric flask. Extract the solution in the separatory funnel twice more with 3-ml. portions of carbon tetrachloride, again collecting the filtered extracts in the volumetric flask. Wash the cotton plug with a small volume of solvent, collecting the washings in the volumetric flask. Dilute to volume with carbon tetrachloride and mix well. The solution should be clear. If not clear, filter through a plug of cotton taking precautions to prevent evaporation. Transfer a portion of the solution to a 1-cm. cell, cover, and read the absorbance at 440 mμ with a suitable spectrometer using carbon tetrachloride as a blank. Prepare a blank following all steps of the procedure but omitting the sample.

Calculation.

$$\frac{\text{micrograms of copper (sample)} - \text{micrograms of copper (blank)}}{\text{weight of sample}} = \text{copper in p.p.m.}$$

The micrograms of copper are obtained by reference to the standard curve.

Preparation of the Standard Curve.—Place 50 ml. of ethyl alcohol solution (3:1) into each of four 125-ml. separatory funnels and add to each funnel, respectively, 1.00, 3.00, 6.00, and 10.00 ml. of standard copper solution. Measure these volumes using a 10-ml. buret. Add 2 ml. of 30 percent citric acid solution to each funnel, and extract the contents of each with two 25-ml. portions of carbon tetrachloride. Discard the extracts. Add 2 drops of phenol red indicator solution and add concentrated ammonium hydroxide dropwise until the solution just turns red. Add 2 ml. of sodium diethyldithiocarbamate reagent and proceed with the solvent extraction of each solution as previously described under procedure. Read the absorbance of each solvent solution at 440 mμ, using a 1-cm. cell, against carbon tetrachloride, on a suitable spectrometer. Calculate the corrected absorbance for each solution by subtracting the blank reading from the sample readings. Plot the corrected absorbance of each solution as the ordinate, and the corresponding micrograms of copper as the abscissa using linear graph paper. The points should fall on a straight line passing through the origin.

DETERMINATION OF IRON IN SYNDETS

Scope.—This method is applicable to the determination of trace levels of iron in surfactants and commercial syndet formulations.

Principle.—After destruction of the organic matter by ashing, the sample is dissolved in acid and the solution is buffered at pH 5. The solution is reacted with bathophenanthroline (4,7-diphenyl-1,10-phenanthroline), the resulting color complex is extracted with chloroform, and the absorbance is read at 533 mμ. Reference to a previously prepared calibration graph permits the calculation of iron level.[11,12,13]

Reagents. **Bathophenanthroline Reagent (0.001 M).**—Dissolve 0.0332 g. in Reagent alcohol and dilute to 100 ml.

Hydroxylamine Hydrochloride Solution, 20 percent, Aq.

Perchloric Acid, 70–72 percent.

Sodium Acetate Solution, 10 percent, Aq.

Chloroform, Reagent Grade.

Perchloric Acid Solution, 10 percent, Aq.

Standard Iron Solution, 1 ml. = 10 μg. of Iron.—Dissolve 0.1000 g. of pure iron wire in concentrated hydrochloric acid and dilute to 1 liter with water. Pipet a 10-ml. aliquot into a 100-ml. volumetric flask, dilute to volume with water at room temperature, and mix well.

Procedure.—Accurately weigh the sample into a clean platinum dish. The sample size should be chosen so as to yield final absorbance readings on scale:

Iron Expected, p.p.m.	Grams of Sample
5–15	1
2–5	2
less than 2	10

Evaporate to dryness, if necessary, and ash the residue using a Bunsen burner. Add 20 ml. of 1:1 hydrochloric acid and evaporate the solution to a volume of approximately 5 ml. Transfer the solution with about 25 ml. of water to a 150-ml. beaker. Add 2.5 ml. of 70–72 percent perchloric acid, 5 ml. of hydroxylamine hydrochloride solution, 10 ml. of bathophenanthroline reagent, and 5 ml. of sodium acetate solution. Adjust the pH to 5.0 with concentrated ammonium hydroxide. Remove the electrodes while rinsing with small volumes of Reagent alcohol and water, and permit the solution to stand 20 minutes. Transfer the solution to a 125-ml. separatory funnel. Add 3 ml. of chloroform to the beaker and transfer to the separatory funnel. Shake for 30 seconds. Permit the chloroform to settle and draw it off through a small funnel containing a plug of glass wool, collecting the solvent in a 10-ml. volumetric flask. Repeat the extraction with an additional 3 ml. of chloroform, collecting the solvent in the volumetric flask. Dilute to volume with reagent alcohol, washing the glass wool plug thoroughly. Prepare a blank following the procedure but omitting the sample. Measure the absorbance of the sample *vs.* the blank at 533 mμ, using a suitable spectrometer and 1-cm. cells.

Calculations.

$$\frac{\text{micrograms of iron (from curve)}}{\text{weight of sample}} = \text{p.p.m. iron}$$

Preparation of Standard Curve.—Using a 5-ml. buret, measure 0.25, 0.50, 1.00,

[11] Case, F. H., "Substituted 1, 10-Phenanthrolines: V. Phenyl Derivatives," J. Org. Chem., **16**, 1541, 1951.

[12] Smith, G. F., McCurdy, W. H., Jr., and Diehl, H., "The Colorimetric Determination of Iron in Raw and Treated Municipal Water Supplies using 4,7-Diphenyl-1,10-phenanthroline," Analyst, **77**, 418, 1952.

[13] Cluley, H. J., and Newman, E. J., "The Determination of Small Amounts of Iron," Analyst, **88**, 3, 1963.

1.25, and 1.50 ml. of standard iron solution into separate 100-ml. beakers. Add 25 ml. of water and 2.5 ml. of 70–72 percent perchloric acid to each beaker. Add 5 ml. of hydroxylamine hydrochloride solution, 10 ml. of bathophenanthroline reagent, and 5 ml. of sodium acetate to each beaker. Adjust the pH of each solution to 5.0 with concentrated ammonium hydroxide, using a pH meter. Remove electrodes and rinse with small volumes of Reagent alcohol and water. Permit the solution to stand 20 minutes. Transfer the solutions to separate 125-ml. separatory funnels and follow the procedure as described for sample analysis. Prepare a calibration graph by plotting micrograms of iron as the abscissa and absorbance as the ordinate. The points should fall on a straight line which passes through the origin.

DETERMINATION OF LOW LEVEL SURFACTANTS[14]

Scope.—This method is applicable to the determination of low level (p.p.m.) concentrations of anionic surfactants, and is used mainly for studies of biodegradability of surfactants in water and various synthetic media.

Principle.—The method is based upon the formation of a chloroform-soluble blue complex from the reaction of aqueous solutions of methylene blue and anionic detergents. The intensity of the color, which is proportional to concentration, is measured spectrometrically at a wavelength of 652 mμ.

Apparatus. **Separatory Funnels, 500-ml.**

Volumetric Flasks, 100-ml.

Spectrometer.—Equipped with 1-cm. cells, capable of being used at 652 mμ.

Reagents. **Phenolphthalein Indicator Solution.**—Dissolve 5 g. of phenolphthalein in 500 ml. of water. Make faintly pink by adding 0.02 N sodium hydroxide dropwise.

Sodium Hydroxide, 1 N.

Sulfuric Acid, 1 N.

Chloroform, C.P.

Methylene Blue Reagent.—Dissolve 0.100 g. of methylene blue (Eastman No. P573) in 100 ml. of water. Transfer 30 ml. of this solution to a 1000-ml. volumetric flask. Add 500 ml. of water, 6.8 ml. of concentrated sulfuric acid, and 50 g. of sodium dihydrogen phosphate, monohydrate ($NaH_2PO_4 \cdot H_2O$). Shake to dissolve and dilute to volume.

Wash Solution.—Add 6.8 ml. of concentrated sulfuric acid to 500 ml. of water in a 1000-ml. volumetric flask. Add 50 g. of $NaH_2PO_4 \cdot H_2O$ and shake to dissolve. Dilute to volume.

Preparation of Calibration Graph.—Using a sample of the surfactant under test, weigh a sample of sufficient size to yield 1.000 g. of active ingredient. Transfer to a 1000-ml. volumetric flask, shake to dissolve, dilute to volume with water, and mix well. Addition of a few drops of 95 percent ethanol will help break foam during final adjustment to volume. Pipet 10 ml. of this solution into a clean 1000-ml. volumetric flask, dilute to volume with water, and mix well. Add to separate 500-ml. separatory funnels 1.00-, 3.00-, 5.00-, 7.00-, 9.00-, 11.00-, 15.00-, 20.00-, and 25.00-ml. volumes of the dilute surfactant solution measured from a buret. Dilute each sample to 100 ml. with water. Make slightly alkaline to phenolphthalein with 1 N sodium hydroxide. Then just acidify with 1 N sulfuric acid. Add 10 ml. of chloroform and 25 ml. of methylene blue reagent to each funnel. Rock the samples to mix the phases and allow the chloroform to settle. Excessive shaking may result in emulsions. Draw off each chloroform layer into separate 500-ml. separatory funnels. Repeat the extraction 3 times using 10 ml. of

[14] Standard Methods for the Examination of Water and Wastewater, prepared and published jointly by the American Public Health Association, the American Water Works Association, and the Water Pollution Control Federation, 11th Ed., 1960, p. 246.

chloroform for each extraction. The color of the aqueous methylene blue phase should remain blue after the final extraction. To each combined extraction add 50 ml. of wash solution and shake for 30 seconds. Allow to settle and draw off the chloroform layer through a funnel containing glass wool, collecting the filtrate in 100-ml. volumetric flasks. Extract the wash solution twice more with 10 ml. of chloroform for each extraction, collecting the chloroform in the volumetric flasks. Rinse the funnel with chloroform, dilute the combined filtrates to volume with chloroform, and mix well. Using a suitable spectrometer, measure the absorbance of the solution, using 1-cm. cells at 652 mμ *vs.* a blank of chloroform. Using rectilinear graph paper, plot the absorbance as the ordinate and the equivalent milligrams of surfactant as the abscissa. Draw a straight line through the points with the intercept passing through zero.

Sample Analysis.—Pipet an aliquot of the surfactant solution under test of a size sufficient to yield an amount of surfactant covered by the calibration graph. Best results are obtained by adjusting the sample size to yield absorbance readings in the middle range of the graph. If the aliquot taken is less than 100 ml., dilute to 100 ml. with water. If the aliquot taken is over 100 ml., proceed with the analysis. Make the solution alkaline to phenolphthalein with 1 *N* sodium hydroxide, then just acidity with 1 *N* sulfuric acid. Proceed from this point on as described in directions given under preparation of calibration graph. Refer to the calibration graph to convert the observed absorbance reading to equivalent milligrams of surfactant and calculate the level as follows:

$$\frac{\text{milligrams of surfactant (from curve)} \times 1000}{\text{volume of sample taken}} = \text{p.p.m. of surfactant}$$

Note.—It is very important that all glassware used in this test be thoroughly cleaned and rinsed before use to prevent contamination.

BIODEGRADABILITY OF ANIONIC DETERGENTS

RIVER DIE-AWAY PROCEDURE

This technique is one of several approaches for measuring the rate of degradation of anionic detergents. Use of this method with the proper controls will yield information of the approximate rate of decay of surface active agents.

Apparatus. **Mason jars.**—2-quart capacity, with screw caps.
Pipets.—1-, 5-, 10-, 20-, 50- and 100-ml. capacities.
pH Meter.
Magnetic Stirrer plus Stirring Bars.

Reagents. **River Water.**—This must be picked up in sufficient quantity and used within two days. The river should be chosen at a site where excessive tidal and abnormal industrial contamination are at a minimum. Upon receipt in the laboratory, the total amount of water should be combined in a large container, mixed well, and permitted to settle overnight. The clear upper layer is siphoned off for usage. This water should have a sufficient bacterial level for degradation to proceed at a reasonable rate. This can be determined by running control samples of detergents of known degradation rate during the test. The chloride level of the water should be no greater than 0.5 percent chloride and the pH should be between 6.5 and 8.0. The detergent level should be less than 1 p.p.m.

Procedure.—Prepare a 1000-p.p.m. solution (active ingredient basis) of the detergents under test, and prepare also control solutions of the same strength. These solutions should be freshly prepared. Measure 990 ml. of clear river water into each of several Mason jars allowing one jar for each detergent under test and one jar for a blank. Pipet 10 ml. of each detergent solution into its respective jar. The solutions so prepared will have a level of 10 p.p.m. active ingredient present. Add a magnetic stirring bar and stir vigorously for 1 minute to aerate the sample. With the stirrer on, withdraw a sufficient quantity of each solution for analysis, remove stirring bar, place screw cap in place, and permit the solution to stand undisturbed for the next sampling. Sampling in the manner described is continued at 3-day intervals (or as desired), the sampling always being performed after stirring for 1 minute and while stirring.

The analysis on each sample and blank is performed by the methylene blue colorimetric method described under determination of low level surfactants.

Calculations.—Correct each run for blank.

$$\frac{Pz - Px}{Pz} \, 100 = \% \text{ degraded in } X \text{ days}$$

where Pz = p.p.m. active ingredient − zero day, and
Px = p.p.m. active ingredient − X day.

ULTRAVIOLET SPECTROMETRY

DETERMINATION OF SODIUM ALKYL BENZENE SULFONATE[15,16]

Apparatus. **Beckman DU Quartz Spectrometer or Equivalent Instrument.**

Absorption Cells, Quartz.—These should be matched pairs of optical path length 1.000 ± 0.005 cm. The cells in a pair, when filled with distilled water, should match within 1 percent transmittance at 224 and 270 mμ. Otherwise, calibrate the cells and use the correction factor for each cell.

Before each series of analyses, fill the quartz cells with distilled water and determine that the cells match within 1 percent transmittance. This practice is necessary to check cleanliness of the cells. Clean cells, if necessary, with dichromate cleaning solution, until the desired transmittance is restored.

All glassware used in the determination must be rinsed with distilled water before use.

Procedure.—In the case of powders (commercial synthetic detergents and built detergent formulations) accurately weigh to the nearest 0.1 mg. a representative sample containing 0.30 to 0.45 g. of active ingredient. As a general rule in determining sample size, most commercial syndets contain 25 to 40 percent of active ingredient. Dissolve the sample in water and dilute to 500 ml. with water at room temperature in a 500-ml. volumetric flask. Mix thoroughly by inverting the flask several times. The sample must be completely dissolved if satisfactory results are to be obtained. In the case of samples difficult to dissolve, transfer the weighed sample to the volumetric flask and dilute to about 400 ml. with water. Carefully insert a plastic-covered stirring magnet, and agitate vigorously on a magnetic stirrer for 15 to 20 minutes. Retrieve the stirring bar and bring the solution to volume with water at room temperature.

In the case of slurry samples, accurately weigh (to the nearest 1 mg.) a sample containing 6 to 9 g. of active ingredient. Add 50 ml. of alcohol and mix to disperse the sample. Ethyl alcohol (95 percent) conforming to either Formula No. 3A or No. 30 of the U. S. Bureau of Internal Revenue may be used. Add water to dissolve the sample and finally dilute the solution to 1000 ml. with water at room temperature, employing a 1-liter volumetric flask. Pipet a 50-ml. aliquot into a 500-ml. volumetric flask, dilute to volume with water at room temperature, and mix thoroughly.

[15] ASTM Standards on Soaps and Other Detergents, prepared by ASTM Committee D-12, 9th Ed., American Society for Testing and Materials, Philadelphia, 1960, p. 144.
[16] Official and Tentative Methods of the American Oil Chemists' Society, AOCS Tentative Method Dd 3-60, American Oil Chemists' Society, Chicago, 1963.

Pipet a 5-ml. aliquot of the diluted sample solution into a 250-ml. volumetric flask and dilute to volume with water at room temperature. Thoroughly mix the solution by inverting the flask several times.

Using 1-cm. cells, measure the absorbance of the solution at 224 (maximum absorbance) and 270 mμ (background absorbance), employing a cell filled with distilled water as a blank. The observed absorbance readings should fall between 0.2 and 0.9. If the readings fall outside this range, take a different sample weight or vary the aliquot volume.

Calculations.—The sodium alkyl benzene sulfonate content of the sample is calculated by use of the following expression:

$$\frac{(A_{224} - A_{270}) \times 25 \times 100}{W \times a} = \% \text{ sodium alkyl benzene sulfonate}$$

where: A = observed absorbance at 224 and 270 mμ,
W = grams of sample taken for analysis (powder samples) or grams of sample represented by the aliquot used (slurry samples), and
a = absorptivity value for the particular sodium alkyl benzene sulfonate being determined.

The calculation as given above is applicable to the described dilution and aliquoting scheme. For general use (change in weight of sample or volume of aliquot) the calculation may be modified as follows:

$$\frac{A_{224} - A_{270}}{c \times b} \times \frac{100}{a} = \% \text{ sodium alkyl benzene sulfonate}$$

where: A = observed absorbance,
b = cell length in centimeters,
c = concentration of final dilution in grams per 1000 ml., and
a = absorptivity value.

Determination of Absorptivity, a.—The absorptivity value, a, should be determined for each particular sulfonate being analyzed.

On a separate sample of the powder or slurry under analysis, perform the following determinations, as described in Volume 2, Part B, Chapter 45 of this work:

> Moisture by the oven method, p. 2280, or by distillation, p. 2281;
> Alcohol Insoluble, p. 2280;
> Chlorides, p. 2303;
> Unsulfonated Material (neutral oil), p. 2295.

From the results obtained in the above determinations, the percentage of sodium alkyl benzene sulfonate (organic alcohol soluble) may be calculated as follows:

$$100 - (M + A + B + C) = \% \text{ sodium alkyl benzene sulfonate}$$

where: M = percent of alcohol insoluble matter,
A = percent of moisture,
B = percent of sodium chloride, and
C = percent of unsulfonated material.

The absorptivity value, $a = \dfrac{A_{224} - A_{270}}{Sbc} \times 100$

where: A = observed absorbance,
   S = percent of organic alcohol soluble (sodium alkyl benzene sulfonate)
      (average of three determinations),
   b = cell length in centimeters, and
   c = concentration of final dilution in grams per 1000 ml.

Typical values for absorptivity, a, are given below, but each analyst should establish the absorptivity for the particular sodium alkyl benzene sulfonate under examination.

Material	Average Mol. Wt.	Absorptivity, a
Sodium dodecylbenzene sulfonate (sodium alkyl benzene sulfonate)	352	22
Sodium tridecyl benzene sulfonate	360	21.5
Sodium pentadecyl benzene sulfonate	380	20.4

For large numbers of samples, the rapidity of replicate analyses may be considerably increased by use of a flow cell.[17]

NOTE.—The described method is not applicable in the presence of organic additives such as amides. If the latter are present they should be removed by ion exchange. Optical dyes do not interfere. Short chain sulfonates, such as toluene sulfonate, will interfere and must be removed as described under the determination of toluene sulfonate.

DETERMINATION OF SODIUM TOLUENE SULFONATE

This method is applicable to the determination of sodium toluene sulfonate in slurries and in finished products formulated with alkyl benzene sulfonates, fatty alcohol sulfates, and ethanolamide additives. Formulations which contain compounds that exhibit ultraviolet absorbance and are not removed in the extraction step cannot be analyzed by this procedure.

The procedure is based on the ultraviolet absorptivity of sodium toluene sulfonate. Higher molecular weight alkyl benzene sulfonates (alkyl chain length of 4 carbons or more), when present, are removed from an acidified aqueous solution of the sample by extraction with ethyl ether. The separation is based on the fact that relatively short chain sulfonic acids, such as obtained from sodium toluene sulfonate, upon acidification are considerably more soluble in aqueous acid medium than are their long chain, high molecular weight homologs (*e.g.*, dodecyl benzene sulfonic acids) which are more soluble in ethyl ether.[18] The total sodium toluene sulfonate in the aqueous acid layer is determined by ultraviolet spectrometry.

Apparatus.—The same apparatus and calibrated cells utilized for the determination of sodium alkyl benzene sulfonate are employed in this method.

Procedure.—In the case of commercial synthetic detergents (powders) accurately weigh (to the nearest 0.1 mg.) a representative sample containing 0.025 to 0.075 g. of sodium toluene sulfonate, and transfer to a 500-ml. extraction cylinder. Add 250 ml. of water and shake the contents of the cylinder to dissolve the sample.

In the case of slurry samples accurately weigh (to the nearest milligram) a representative sample containing 0.250 to 0.750 g. of sodium toluene sulfonate. Dissolve the sample in approximately 800 ml. of water and dilute to 1 liter with water at room

[17] Kelley, R. M., Blank, E. W., Thompson, W. E., and Fine, R., "The Determination of Alkyl Aryl Sulfonates by Ultraviolet Absorption," ASTM Bulletin, April, 1959, p. 70.
[18] House, R., and Darragh, J. L., "Analysis of Synthetic Anionic Detergent Compositions," Anal. Chem., **26**, 1492, 1954.

temperature, employing a 1-liter volumetric flask. Mix well. Pipet a 100-ml. aliquot of the solution into a 500-ml. extraction cylinder, and add 150 ml. of water.

In either case, add 50 ml. of 1:1 hydrochloric acid to the solution in the extraction cylinder. Swirl to mix and cool the contents of the cylinder to 20°C. or less. Add 100 ml. of ethyl ether, stopper the cylinder, and shake, first by inverting the cylinder several times, followed by shaking vertically. During the shaking operation it is important to release the pressure at frequent intervals as a matter of safety. Remove the stopper and wash it and the internal walls of the cylinder with a small volume of ethyl ether. Allow the cylinder and contents to stand quietly until the layers separate cleanly.

Siphon off the upper ethyl ether layer into a 500-ml. Erlenmeyer flask. Extreme care should be taken not to siphon off any of the lower water layer with the ether extract. The end of the siphon tube should be near the upper surface of the ethyl ether layer at the start of the siphoning operation and away from the cylinder wall. During the siphoning the tube is pushed down gradually, as far as possible without contamination, to within $\frac{1}{8}$ to $\frac{1}{4}$ inches of the interface separating the ethyl ether and water layers. If the operation of siphoning off the ether extract is carefully performed, no water will be siphoned off with the ether layer.

Repeat the extraction two more times using 100 ml. of ethyl ether each time.

Quantitatively transfer the extracted water layer remaining in the extraction cylinder to a 600-ml. beaker with the aid of a small volume of water. Remove the residual ethyl ether by placing the beaker on a steam bath and evaporating using a stream of clean, dry air and occasional stirring. When no odor of ethyl ether is detectable, remove the beaker and contents from the steam bath and cool to room temperature.

Quantitatively transfer the aqueous solution to a 500-ml. volumetric flask, dilute to volume with water at room temperature and mix thoroughly. Pipet a 10-ml. aliquot of the latter solution into a 100-ml. volumetric flask and dilute to volume with water at room temperature. Mix thoroughly.

Using 1-cm. cells measure the absorbance of the solution at 220 and 240 mμ employing a cell filled with distilled water as a blank.

Calculation.—The sodium toluene sulfonate content of the sample is calculated as follows:

$$\frac{(A_{220} - A_{240}) \times 500}{\text{wt. of sample in aliquot (slurry) or wt. of sample (powder)} \times a}$$

$$= \% \text{ low molecular weight sulfonates calculated as sodium toluene sulfonate}$$

where: A = observed absorbance at 220 and 240 mμ,
    500 = dilution factor for aliquoting scheme specified, and
    a = absorptivity for sodium toluene sulfonate at the specified analytical wavelengths. The absorptivity is defined as the absorbance, A, divided by the product of the concentration, in grams of solute per 1 liter of solution, c, and the cell path length, in cm., b. That is, $a = A/bc$.

The calculation given above is based upon the diluting and aliquoting scheme described in the procedure. The calculation may be adapted to any other dilution as follows:

$$\frac{(A_{220} - A_{240}) \times 100}{c \times a}$$

$$= \% \text{ low molecular weight sulfonates calculated as sodium toluene sulfonate}$$

where c = concentration of final dilution in grams per liter.

The approximate value of the absorptivity, a, for sodium toluene sulfonate is 54.5, but each analyst should establish the absorptivity for the particular sodium toluene sulfonate under examination.

DETERMINATION OF SODIUM XYLENE SULFONATE

Scope.—This method is applicable to commercial light duty liquid detergent products for the determination of sodium xylene sulfonate in the presence of sulfated alkylphenoxypoly (ethyleneoxy) ethanols (anionic), alkylphenoxypoly (ethyleneoxy) ethanols (nonionic), and alkyl benzene sulfonate. Other nonextractable ultraviolet absorbing materials will interfere.

Apparatus.—The same apparatus and calibrated cells utilized for the determination of sodium alkyl benzene sulfonate are employed in this method.

Procedure.—Accurately weigh approximately 5 g. of sample (to the nearest 0.1 mg.) into a 150-ml. flat bottom flask. Add 10 ml. of 1:1 hydrochloric acid and several glass beads, and boil the contents of the flask under a reflux condenser for 1 hour.

Allow the solution to cool, add 50 ml. of water, and swirl until complete solution is attained. Quantitatively transfer the solution to a 250-ml. extraction cylinder using a small volume of water to complete the transfer. Add 25 ml. of 1:1 hydrochloric acid and sufficient water to result in a total volume of 150 ml.

Add 75 ml. of ethyl ether to the contents of the extraction cylinder. Shake the cylinder, first by inverting the cylinder several times, then by shaking up and down vertically. During the shaking operation it is important to release the pressure at frequent intervals as a safety precaution. Continue to shake the cylinder vigorously for 1 minute. Remove the stopper and wash it and the internal wall of the cylinder with a small volume of ethyl ether. Allow the contents of the cylinder to stand until the emulsion breaks and both layers are perfectly clear.

Siphon the ethyl ether layer into a 250-ml. Erlenmeyer flask. Care should be taken not to siphon off any of the bottom water layer with the ether extract. The end of the siphon tube should be near the top of the ethyl ether layer at the start of the siphoning operation and away from the cylinder wall. During the siphoning operation, the tube is pushed down gradually as far as possible without contamination to within $\frac{1}{8}$ to $\frac{1}{4}$ inch of the boundary between the ether and water layers. If the operation of siphoning off the ether extract is carefully carried out, no water will be siphoned off with the ether layer. Continue with four more ethyl ether extractions. If desired, the ethyl ether extracts may be collected, evaporated to dryness, and the residue analyzed for the alkyl benzene sulfonate content as described previously.

Quantitatively transfer the lower aqueous acid layer to a 500-ml. volumetric flask using water to complete the transfer. Place the flask in a water bath maintained at 70° to 80°C., or on the steam bath, and gently agitate to remove the residual ethyl ether. Cool the flask and contents to room temperature.

Add 250 ml. of ethyl alcohol and dilute to volume with water at room temperature. Mix thoroughly. Ethyl alcohol (95 percent) conforming to either Formula No. 3A or No. 30 of the U. S. Bureau of Internal Revenue may be used.

Using 1-cm. cells measure the absorbance of the solution at 275 and 300 mμ, using a cell filled with 1:1 ethyl alcohol-water as the blank. A blue sensitive phototube must be employed.

Calculation.—The sodium xylene sulfonate content of the sample is calculated as follows:

$$\frac{(A_{275} - A_{300}) \times 50}{\text{weight of sample} \times a} = \% \text{ sodium xylene sulfonate}$$

where: A = observed absorbance at 275 and 300 mμ,

  50 = dilution factor for aliquoting scheme specified, and

  a = absorptivity for sodium xylene sulfonate at the specified analytical wavelengths. The absorptivity is defined as the absorbance, A, divided by the product of the concentration, in grams of solute per 1 liter of solution, c, and the cell path length, in cm., b. That is, $a = A/bc$.

Each analyst should establish the absorptivity for the particular sodium xylene sulfonate under examination. If a quantity of the original sodium xylene sulfonate employed in formulation of the product is available, no particular difficulty will be encountered in establishing the value of the absorptivity, a.

If the sodium xylene sulfonate has already been incorporated in a product, a portion of the product should be dried in an oven, the alcohol insoluble material removed as described under the determination of alkyl benzene sulfonate, the alcohol soluble material recovered from the alcoholic filtrate by evaporation, and finally dried at 135°C. for 1 hour. This residue can be employed to determine an apparent absorptivity of the product under examination, but since the recovered alcohol soluble material also contains other alcohol soluble compounds, the absorptivity is specific for the particular product only and is valid only for use in replicate analyses of the same product for which the apparent absorptivity was determined.

DETERMINATION OF GERMICIDES IN SOAPS AND DETERGENTS

DETERMINATION OF 2,2-METHYLENE BIS(3,4,6-TRICHLOROPHENOL)

Procedure.—Transfer a weighed (to the nearest 0.1 mg.), finely divided sample containing approximately 9 to 11 mg. of the compound sought, to a 100-ml. beaker. The weight of sample to take for analysis can be estimated from the following table:

2,2-Methylene Bis-(3,4,6-trichlorophenol) Content	Sample Size in Grams
0.25%	4.0 ± 0.3
0.50	2.0 ± 0.1
0.75	1.33 ± 0.1
1.00	1.0 ± 0.1

Add 50 ml. of ethyl alcohol to the sample in the beaker and heat, no longer than necessary, on the steam bath until the sample is in solution.[19] At this point ignore any turbidity due to titanium dioxide present in the sample. Transfer the solution to a 100-ml. volumetric flask, cool to room temperature, and dilute to volume with ethyl alcohol at room temperature. Mix thoroughly. If turbidity persists, filter the solution through a dry No. 3 Whatman filter paper, collecting at least 80 ml. of the filtrate.

Pipet a 10-ml. aliquot of the filtrate into each of two 50-ml. volumetric flasks. Pipet 2 ml. of concentrated ammonium hydroxide into one of the flasks and 10 ml. of glacial acetic acid into the other. Dilute to volume with ethyl alcohol at room temperature and mix thoroughly.

Using 1-cm. cells and the blue sensitive phototube, measure the absorbance of the

[19] Jungermann, E., and Beck, E. C., in "Determination of Germicide Mixtures in Soaps and Detergents," J. Am. Oil Chem. Soc., **38**, 513, 1961, recommend the use of dimethylformamide as a solvent in place of ethyl alcohol. The dimethylformamide is evaporated to dryness to recover the germicide, which is then taken up in both acidic and basic ethyl alcohol. The ultraviolet spectra obtained under these conditions are typical of the various germicides and are used both to identify them and to estimate their concentration.

basic solution at a wavelength of 314 mμ with a Beckman DU spectrophotometer. Use a 1-cm. cell filled with the acidic solution as the blank.

The 2,2-methylene bis(3,4,6-trichlorophenol) content of the sample is calculated as follows:

$$\frac{A_{314} \times 50}{\text{wt. sample} \times a} = \% \text{ 2,2-methylene bis(3,4,6-trichlorophenol)}$$

where: A = observed absorbance at a wavelength of 314 mμ,
50 = dilution factor for aliquoting scheme specified, and
a = differential absorptivity value for 2,2-methylene bis(3,4,6-trichlorophenol) at the specified analytical wavelength. The absorptivity is defined as the absorbance, A, divided by the product of the concentration, in grams of solute per 1 liter of solution, c, and the cell path length, in cm., b. That is, $a = A/bc$.

The analyst should determine the value of the absorptivity, a, on a pure sample of 2,2-methylene bis(3,4,6-trichlorophenol) or the material utilized in formulating the product. The value, a, is approximately 15.4.

The procedure described above is of general applicability to soap and detergent products. Slight modification of the method is necessary in some cases as noted in the following determinations.

DETERMINATION OF 3,5,3',4'-TETRACHLOROSALICYLANILIDE

Procedure.—Follow the procedure given for 2,2-methylene bis(3,4,6-trichlorophenol) and finally pipet a 25-ml. aliquot of the filtered solution into each of two 50-ml. volumetric flasks.

Pipet 2 ml. of concentrated ammonium hydroxide into one of the flasks and 2 ml. of glacial acetic acid into the other. Dilute to volume with ethyl alcohol at room temperature and mix well. Using 1-cm. cells and the blue sensitive phototube in the Beckman spectrophotometer, measure the absorbance of the basic solution at a wavelength of 364 mμ. Use a 1-cm. cell filled with acidic solution as the blank. Establish the absorptivity value on a pure sample of 3,5,3',4'-tetrachlorosalicylanilide or the material used in formulation of the product.

DETERMINATION OF 3,4,4'-TRICHLOROCARBANILIDE

Procedure.—Accurately weigh an amount of sample that contains 4 to 5 mg. of 3,4,4'-trichlorocarbanilide, and transfer to a 250-ml. volumetric flask. Dissolve in alcohol and bring to volume with ethyl alcohol at room temperature. Filter and pipet a 10-ml. aliquot of the clear filtrate into a 100-ml. volumetric flask, dilute to volume with ethyl alcohol at room temperature and mix well.

Using 1-cm. cells and the blue sensitive phototube in the Beckman DU spectrophotometer, measure the absorbance at wavelengths of 265 and 300 mμ. Use a 1-cm. cell filled with ethyl alcohol as the blank.

The 3,4,4'-trichlorocarbanilide content of the sample is calculated as follows:

$$\frac{(A_{265} - A_{300}) \times 250}{\text{wt. sample} \times a} = \% \text{ 3,4,4'-trichlorocarbanilide}$$

where: A = observed absorbance at wavelengths 265 and 300 mμ,
250 = dilution factor for aliquoting scheme specified, and
a = absorptivity value for 3,4,4'-trichlorocarbanilide.

DETERMINATION OF 2,2′-THIOBIS(4,6-DICHLOROPHENOL)

Procedure.—Accurately weigh an amount of sample that contains about 15 mg. of 2,2′-thiobis(4,6-dichlorophenol), and transfer to a 250-ml. beaker. Add 50 ml. of ethyl alcohol and heat to complete solution (disregard any turbidity). Cool and transfer the solution to a 100-ml. volumetric flask, using ethyl alcohol to complete the transfer. Bring to volume with ethyl alcohol at room temperature. Filter the solution, if necessary, and pipet a 10-ml. aliquot of the clear filtrate into each of two 50-ml. volumetric flasks.

Pipet 2 ml. of concentrated ammonium hydroxide into one of the flasks and 2 ml. of glacial acetic acid into the other. Dilute the contents of each flask to volume with ethyl alcohol at room temperature and mix well.

Using a 1-cm. cell and the blue sensitive phototube in the Beckman DU spectrophotometer, measure the absorbance at 334 mμ. Use a 1-cm. cell filled with the acidic solution as a blank.

The 2,2′-thiobis(4,6-dichlorophenol) content of the sample is calculated as follows:

$$\frac{A_{334} \times 500}{\text{wt. sample} \times a} = \%\ 2,2'\text{-thiobis(4,6-dichlorophenol)}$$

where: A = observed absorbance at a wavelength of 334 mμ,
      500 = dilution factor for aliquoting scheme described, and
      a = absorptivity value for 2,2′-thiobis(4,6-dichlorophenol).

The value of a should be determined on a pure sample of 2,2′-thiobis(4,6-dichlorophenol) or on a sample of the material used in the formulation.

DETERMINATION OF 2,2′-THIOBIS(4,4′-CHLOROPHENOL)

Procedure.—The preceding method for the determination of 2,2′-thiobis(4,6-dichlorophenol) can be used to determine 2,2′-thiobis(4,4′-chlorophenol) by reading the absorbance at 324 mμ and establishing the absorptivity, a, for this particular compound.

DETERMINATION OF NONIONICS
(ALKYL PHENOXYPOLYOXYETHYLENE ETHANOL TYPE) IN THE PRESENCE OF ALKYL BENZENE SULFONATE

Scope.—This method is applicable to commercial, low foaming detergent formulations for the determination of nonionics of the alkyl phenoxypolyoxyethylene ethanol type in admixture with alkyl benzene sulfonates. The ultraviolet absorptivity of the nonionic is utilized to determine the amount present. A factor must be established to correct for ultraviolet absorption resulting from the presence of alkyl benzene sulfonate.

Apparatus.—The same apparatus and calibrated cells utilized for the determination of sodium alkyl benzene sulfonate are employed in this method.

Procedure.—Accurately weigh (to the nearest 0.1 mg.) a representative sample containing 47 to 53 mg. of the nonionic, and transfer to a 250-ml. beaker. The weight of sample to take for analysis can be calculated as follows:

$$\frac{0.050 \times 100}{\text{percent nonionic anticipated}} = \text{grams sample weight required}$$

Add 150 ml. of ethyl alcohol to the weighed sample and heat the contents of the beaker to boiling on a steam bath to dissolve the alcohol soluble organic matter.

Quantitatively transfer the contents of the beaker to a 250-ml. volumetric flask with the aid of hot ethyl alcohol. Cool the volumetric flask and contents to room temperature and dilute to volume with ethyl alcohol. Mix thoroughly. Allow the flask and contents to stand for several minutes to permit the insoluble, inorganic salts to settle.

Filter approximately 100 to 150 ml. of the supernatant alcoholic solution through a filter paper (rapid filtering speed) into a flask and stopper to prevent evaporation of the alcohol. The filtrate should be clear. Do not wash the filter paper or in any way alter the concentration of the filtrate.

Using 1-cm. quartz cells and a Beckman DU spectrophotometer, measure the absorbance of the filtrate at 283 and 300 mμ. Use a 1-cm. cell filled with ethyl alcohol as a blank.

Calculation.—The nonionic (alkyl phenoxy polyoxyethylene ethanol type) content of the sample is calculated as follows:

$$\frac{[(A_{283}) - (F)(A_{300})] \times 25}{\text{wt. of sample} \times a} = \% \text{ nonionic (alkyl phenoxy polyoxyethylene ethanol type)}$$

where: A = observed absorbance at wavelengths of 283 and 300 mμ,
$\quad\quad\quad F$ = factor to correct for the ultraviolet absorption of alkyl benzene sulfonate at 283 mμ,
$\quad\quad\quad 25$ = dilution factor for aliquoting scheme specified, and
$\quad\quad\quad a$ = absorptivity for the nonionic (or mixture) at the specified analytical wavelengths.

The absorptivity value must be determined for each nonionic or mixture of nonionics (of the alkyl phenoxy polyoxyethylene ethanol type) employed in the formulation of the product.

For the determination of nonionic content of detergent formulations containing alkyl benzene sulfonate, a correction must be made for the absorbance contributed by alkyl benzene sulfonate to the absorbance of the nonionic at 283 mμ. The error produced by alkyl benzene sulfonate is eliminated by obtaining a spectrum of the detergent formulation containing all of its normal components with the exception of the nonionic or mixture of nonionics. The absorbance of the detergent formulation that does not contain the nonionic or mixture of nonionics is read at 283 and 300 mμ and the correction factor, F, is calculated as the ratio of the respective absorbances:

$$F = \frac{A_{283}}{A_{300}}$$

INFRARED SPECTROMETRY

IDENTIFICATION OF SURFACE ACTIVE AGENTS

GENERAL INFRARED ABSORPTION METHOD FOR THE IDENTIFICATION OF SURFACTANTS

This method is widely applicable to all classes of surfactants. Individual surfactants may be examined directly if no inorganic salts or water are present. Usually sodium sulfate and water are present and must be removed. In order to identify successfully the surface active agents present in commercial detergent products, which usually contain phosphates, carbonates, sulfates, etc., it is first necessary to remove the inorganic salts. The usual method of elimination involves their removal as alcohol insoluble material.

Procedure.—Transfer about 10 g. of the sample to a 250-ml. beaker and add approximately 100 ml. of ethyl alcohol. Heat the contents of the beaker to boiling on a hot plate and break up any lumps of sample by crushing with a stirring rod flattened on one end. Filter while hot through a fine porosity filter paper and evaporate the filtrate to dryness on the steam bath. Significant amounts of sodium chloride are dissolved by ethyl alcohol and will be admixed with the alcohol soluble organic material if present in the original sample. This does not interfere in the subsequent examination of the sample by infrared. However, traces of sodium carbonate, sodium bicarbonate, or sodium tetraborate contaminate the filtrate when appreciable amounts are present in the original sample. If contamination with any, or all of these compounds is suspected, dissolve the organic alcohol soluble in a small volume of a mixture of 1:1 ethyl ether and acetone, filter, and evaporate the solvent mixture on the steam bath to recover the soluble organic material.[20]

If soap is present in the original product, in addition to a surfactant, the former can be removed by dissolving the sample in hot water, adding sufficient 10 percent sulfuric acid to precipitate the fatty acids (acid to methyl orange indicator), extracting the latter with ethyl ether, and evaporating the aqueous extracted solution to dryness to recover the surfactant. The latter will also contain the inorganic salts originally present in the product and must be subjected to the ethyl alcohol insoluble separation described above.

To examine the sample by infrared absorption, it is necessary to prepare the sample either as a mineral oil mull or to incorporate it in a pressed potassium bromide pellet.

In the first method, proceed to form the mull by adding 2 to 3 drops of mineral oil (U.S.P.) to a small quantity of the sample (free of inorganic salts) contained in a polished surface agate or glass mortar, and grinding for 5 to 10 minutes. Grinding should be continued until the sample is completely dispersed in the oil and the mixture becomes a slurry of uniform consistency. Place a portion of the sample between sodium chloride plates and record the spectra over the range of 2 to 15 μ following the manufacturer's instructions for operation of the instrument in use.

If the sample is a dry powder that can be ground in a mortar without becoming tacky, add approximately 1 part of the sample to 19 parts of dry, powdered, 325-mesh, potassium bromide (Infrared Quality) and grind in a mortar to a fine powder. By means of a press, form a pellet at room temperature, under vacuum, employing a pressure of 10 to 30 tons per square inch. Mount the pellet in the infrared spectrometer and record the spectra between the limits of 2 and 15 μ.

The surfactant (or mixture of surfactants) is identified by comparison with reference spectra of known surfactants prepared in the same manner as the unknown samples. Comparison of two spectra is most readily accomplished by superimposing one chart on the other and viewing them on an opaque glass plate electrically illuminated from below.

NOTE.—The above described procedure is satisfactory only in an elementary sense. The subject is complex, and additional information should be sought.[21,22]

Extensive collections of infrared data are obtainable from the National Research Council Committee on Infrared Spectra, National Bureau of Standards, Washington 25, D. C., American Society for Testing and Materials, 1916 Race Street, Philadelphia 3,

[20] Ross, L. U., and Blank, E. W., "Error in the Determination of Active Ingredient in Detergent Products," J. Am. Oil Chem. Soc., **34**, 70, 1957.

[21] Rao, C. N. R., Chemical Applications of Infrared Spectroscopy, Academic Press, New York, 1963.

[22] Nakanishi, K., Infrared Absorption Spectroscopy, Holden-Day, Inc., San Francisco, 1962. This volume constitutes a practical approach to the subject of infrared spectroscopy. The detailed tables of characteristic frequencies will be found useful and unusually complete. A chart indicating the location of characteristic frequencies of functional groups is included in Chapter 1.

Pennsylvania, and, more importantly from a detergent viewpoint, S. P. Sadler and Son, Inc., 2100 Arch Street, Philadelphia 3, Pennsylvania. Section C of the Sadler file comprises surface active agents. Up to and including the year 1963, Section C contained 1700 spectra.

The enormous variety of commercial detergents currently available and in use by industry is shown in McCutcheon's Detergents and Emulsifiers, revised annually. It is published by John W. McCutcheon, Inc., 236 Mt. Kemble Avenue, Morristown, N. J.

IDENTIFICATION OF SULFATES AND SULFONATES BY INFRARED ABSORPTION OF BARIUM SALTS

This method is applicable only to anionic sulfates and sulfonates. Commercial products should be purified by extraction with ethyl alcohol to remove inorganic salts as described in the preceding general method.

Procedure.—Dissolve 0.2 to 0.4 g. of the alcohol soluble organic material (sulfate or sulfonate) in approximately 150 ml. of water heated to about 50°C. Add with stirring, 25 ml. of a 10 percent aqueous solution of barium chloride, dihydrate. Allow the solution to stand on the steam bath until the precipitate settles and the supernatant liquid is clear.

Collect the precipitated barium salt on a filter paper and wash thoroughly with water. Allow to dry and then slurry the precipitate with 100 ml. of n-pentane, again collect the precipitate on a filter paper, air dry, and finally complete the drying at 80°C. for 1 hour.[23]

Mix 10 mg. of the barium salt with 1.2 g. of 325-mesh potassium bromide (Infrared Quality) in a glass mortar, together with a sufficient volume of chloroform to insure intimate mixing. Evaporate the chloroform by means of a stream of clean, dry air and preserve the resulting, fine, dry powder for infrared examination.

A pelleting die with vacuum attachment is used to prepare a potassium bromide pellet as described under the general method. Mount the pellet in the infrared spectrometer and record the spectra between 2 and 15 mμ.

The data contained in the following summary of absorption peaks exhibited by barium salts of sulfates and sulfonates, while necessarily incomplete, should prove useful in the identification of the more common anionic sulfates and sulfonates.

FATTY ACID ETHANOLAMIDES—DETERMINATION OF ESTER

Scope.—This method is applicable to the determination of ester in ethanolamide fatty acid derivatives such as lauric diethanolamide.

Apparatus. **Automatic Recording Infrared Spectrometer.**—This should have sealed liquid absorption cells. Cell spacing should be 0.1 mm. with calcium fluoride windows.

Hypodermic Syringe, 1-ml. Capacity.

Reagents. **Lauric Diethanolamide.**—Ester free.

Lauric Diethanolamide Monolaurate.—Methyl palmitate may be used as a substitute ester standard if the pure monolaurate ester is not available.

Chloroform, Reagent Grade.

Sodium Sulfate, Anhydrous.

Adjustment of Spectrometer.—Using the manufacturer's instruction manual as a guide, adjust the spectrometer as follows:

Close both shutters on the source housing and adjust the balance on the amplifier until no drift exists. Set the slit program control at 960. With the reference shutter open, close

[23] Jenkins, J. W., and Kellenbach, K. O., "Identification of Anionic Surface Active Agents by Infrared Absorption of the Barium Salts," Anal. Chem., **31,** 1056, 1959.

INFRARED ABSORPTION DATA; IDENTIFICATION OF ACTIVE INGREDIENT TYPE
BY EXAMINATION OF BARIUM SALTS

			Absorptions, μ			
Barium Salt of Compound	Car- bonyl	CH₃	Sulfates, Sulfonates, C—O Ester Stretching	C—O Hydroxyl Stretching	Peaks Charac- teristic for Compound	Phenyl Ring Substitution
Alkyl Sulfates						
Barium Dodecane-1-Sulfate	—	7.30	7.86, 8.06, 8.21 max., 8.38	—	9.30–12.15	—
Tetradecane-1-Sulfate	—	7.30	7.85, 8.08, 8.21 max., 8.38	—	9.28–12.15	—
Hexadecane-1-Sulfate	—		7.84, 8.08, 8.20 max., 8.38	—	9.30–12.15	—
Tridecane-2-Sulfate	—	7.24	7.72, 7.95, 8.10, 8.38 max., 8.59	—	9.32–10.53	—
Alkyl and Alkyl Aryl Sulfonates						
Barium Dodecane-1-Sulfonate	—	—	8.25, 8.68 max.	—	9.44, 9.60, 12.60	—
Barium *p*-Phenyldodecane Sulfonate	—	—	8.30, 8.52 max., 8.80	—	9.49–9.84	11.88, 12.27 (para)
Ester Sulfates						
Barium Salt Monoglyceride Sulfate from Coconut Fatty Acid	5.81ᵃ	—	7.57, 8.10 max., 8.40	8.90 Second	9.32–12.38	—
Derived from Hydrogenated Coconut Fatty Acid	5.80ᵃ	—	7.55, 8.10 max., 8.35	8.88 Second	9.28–12.35	—
Ester Sulfonate						
Barium Salt Monoglyceride Sulfonate Derived from Coconut Fatty Acid	5.76ᵃ	—	8.00, 8.28, 8.50–8.60 max.	9.02 Second	9.58–13.16	—
Amide and Sulfonate						
Barium Salt N-Methyl-N-Acyl Taurine Sulfonate Derived from Coconut Fatty Acidᶜ	6.11ᵇ	7.28	7.90, 8.05, 8.40 max., 8.58	—	9.40–13.10	—

ᵃ Ester.
ᵇ Disubstituted amide.
ᶜ Igepon TC.

the sample shutter slowly and adjust the instrument to read zero transmittance. Open the sample shutter and balance the instrument to read 100 percent transmittance.

Determination of Ester.—Accurately weigh 0.900 to 1.100 g. of sample into a clean, dry 10-ml. volumetric flask. Do not heat or melt the sample. Add 5 ml. of chloroform and swirl to dissolve the sample. Dilute to volume with chloroform and mix well. If the sample is turbid due to the presence of an impurity such as soap, filter the solution after dilution to volume. If the solution is turbid due to moisture, add several milligrams of anhydrous sodium sulfate after diluting to volume. Filter before proceeding. Using a hypodermic syringe, inject a sufficient volume of the chloroform solution to fill a clean, dry absorption cell. Place the cell in the sample beam of the spectrophotometer and record the spectrum from 5.0 to 6.5 μ. Measure the absorbance at the maximum peak (5.74 μ) using the base line method. Calculate the ester factor for the sample.

$$\frac{\text{absorbance at } 5.74\ \mu}{\text{cell thickness (mm.)} \times \text{weight of sample} \times 10} = F = \text{ester factor}$$

Determine the percent ester by reference to a calibration graph prepared as follows:

Accurately weigh the following proportions of lauric diethanolamide and lauric diethanolamide monolaurate into separate 10-ml. volumetric flasks. Methyl palmitate may be substituted for the monolaurate ester.

Flask No.	Grams Amide	Grams Ester
1	1.000	0.000
2	0.980	0.020
3	0.950	0.050
4	0.900	0.100

Add 5 ml. of chloroform to each flask and swirl to dissolve. Dilute to volume and mix well. The prepared standards represent 0.0, 2.0, 5.0, and 10.0 percent ester. Using a hypodermic syringe, inject a sufficient volume of each standard into separate, clean, dry absorption cells. Place the cells in the spectrophotometer sample beam and record the spectrum from 5.5 to 6.5 μ. The scanning speed should be set at 1 μ per 1.75 minutes. Measure the absorbance for each standard at the peak maximum (5.74 μ) using the base line method. Calculate the ester factor for each standard as follows:

$$\frac{\text{absorbance at } 5.74\ \mu}{\text{cell thickness (mm.)} \times \text{weight of sample} \times 10} = F = \text{ester factor}$$

To convert the ester factor for methyl palmitate to the ester factor for monolaurate, multiply by 0.518.

Using rectilinear graph paper, plot the ester factor, F, as the ordinate and the corresponding percent ester as the abscissa. Draw the best possible straight line through the plotted points. Any point not falling on the line should be checked. The line should intercept the origin at zero.

DETERMINATION OF ALKYL BENZENE SULFONATES IN SEWAGE AND ESTIMATION OF BRANCHING

An important quality of modern surfactants is the extent to which the surfactant will degrade biologically in waste water treatment. Branched chain alkyl aryl sulfonates are far more resistant to biodegradation than are sulfonates from alkanes possessing a straight (linear) chain structure. The term linear alkylate sulfonate (LAS) has been adopted by industry to identify new straight chain paraffin-derived alkyl benzene sulfonates which are currently under commercial development and which will ultimately (1966) replace the branched chain alkyl benzene sulfonates now incorporated in practically all domestic detergent products.

ISOLATION OF ALKYL BENZENE SULFONATE FROM SEWAGE

The following procedure describes the isolation of alkyl benzene sulfonate from sewage[24] and the subsequent examination by infrared to determine the relative amounts of branched and linear chain isomers.[25,26]

Principle.—The sample is mixed with Celite and filtered. The filter cake is then washed with hot ethyl alcohol to remove adsorbed alkyl benzene sulfonate. The combined filtrate and alcohol washes are reduced to a volume of approximately 300 ml. by

[24] Foote, J. K., "Determination of Alkyl Benzene Sulfonates in Sewage," Journal Water Pollution Control Federation, 33, No. 1, 85, 1961.

[25] Frazee, C. D., and Crisler, R. O., "Infrared Determination of Alkyl Branching in Detergent ABS," J. Am. Oil Chem. Soc., 41, 334, 1964.

[26] Ogden, C. P., Webster, H. L., and Halliday, J., "Determination of Biologically Soft and Hard Alkylbenzene Sulphonates in Detergents and Sewage," Analyst, 86, 22, 1961.

distillation. The concentrated sample is acidified with hydrochloric acid, hydrolyzed under reflux, and the alkyl benzene sulfonate is extracted with ethyl ether. The ethyl ether is evaporated and the extract is dissolved in a mixture of water, hydrochloric acid, and ethyl alcohol. This solution is then extracted with petroleum ether, the extracted solution is evaporated, and the residue is converted to the 1-methylheptylamine salt which in turn is converted to the octylamine salt for infrared examination.

NOTE.—In the present state of knowledge, it has not been determined whether the 1-methylheptylamine salt must be prepared as an intermediate step in the isolation or whether the octylamine salt can be prepared directly.

Procedure.—Pour the sewage sample through a 20-mesh screen to remove any gross solids that may be present. Estimate the alkyl benzene sulfonate content by the methylene blue colorimetric procedure described under the determination of low level surfactants.

The value obtained for alkyl benzene sulfonate content will be an approximation sufficiently accurate to permit calculation of the correct sample size to take for analysis.

A volume of the sewage containing from 5 to 15 mg. of alkyl benzene sulfonate should be taken for analysis. Add 2 g. of Celite No. 545 for each 500 ml. of sample taken for analysis and filter through a Whatman No. 2 filter paper employing a Büchner funnel and vacuum.

Slurry the Celite cake and filter paper in a 250-ml. beaker with 100 ml. of hot 70 percent ethyl alcohol, and filter through a paper in a glass funnel. Wash the filter cake with approximately 50 ml. of hot 70 percent ethyl alcohol. Combine the original alcohol filtrate and washes, and reduce the volume to approximately 300 ml. by distillation through a 6-in. Vigreux column. If the solution foams excessively, add 1 or 2 ml. of concentrated hydrochloric acid.

Allow the solution in the distilling flask to cool slightly and replace the Vigreux column with a reflux condenser. Add 75 ml. of concentrated hydrochloric acid and reflux the mixture for 1 hour.

Cool and transfer the refluxed solution to a 1-liter separatory funnel, rinsing the flask three times with 20-ml. volumes of 3 N hydrochloric acid. Wash the flask once with 200 ml. of ethyl ether. Save the latter for the first extraction described in the next step of the procedure.

Extract the solution in the separatory funnel with two 200-ml. volumes of ethyl ether. Combine the ethyl ether extracts and evaporate to approximately 100 ml. in a 250-ml. beaker. Transfer the ethyl ether solution to a 250-ml. separatory funnel and wash twice with 50-ml. volumes of 3·N hydrochloric acid. Transfer the acid layers to a 250-ml. separatory funnel and wash with 100 ml. of ethyl ether. Combine the latter ethyl ether wash with the previous ethyl ether washes and evaporate to dryness in a 250-ml. beaker.

Dissolve the dry residue in 25 ml. of ethyl alcohol, warming if necessary, and transfer the solution to a 250-ml. separatory funnel. Rinse the beaker with 25 ml. of 6 N hydrochloric acid, followed by two rinses of 10 ml. of washing solution consisting of a 1:1 by volume mixture of ethyl alcohol and 6 N hydrochloric acid. Complete the washing with 50 ml. of petroleum ether. Retain and use the petroleum ether wash for the first extraction described in the next step of the procedure.

Combine the original residue solution and rinses and extract twice with 50-ml. volumes of petroleum ether. Evaporate the combined petroleum ether extracts to a volume of approximately 50 ml. and transfer to a small separatory funnel, completing the transfer with small volumes of petroleum ether. Wash the petroleum ether three times with 25-ml. portions of a 1:1 by volume mixture of ethyl alcohol and 6 N hydrochloric acid.

Combine all of the 1:1 ethyl alcohol and 6 N hydrochloric acid fractions in a 250-ml.

beaker, and evaporate to dryness on the steam bath employing a stream of clean, dry air to facilitate the evaporation.

Dissolve the residue in 20 ml. of 0.025 N sodium hydroxide solution. Transfer the solution quantitatively to a 250-ml. separatory funnel employing a minimum volume of the sodium hydroxide solution to complete the transfer. Neutralize to a pH of 6 to 7 by the addition of 0.5 N sulfuric acid. Add 50 ml. of buffer solution (previously prepared by dissolving 6.8 g. of potassium dihydrogen phosphate (KH_2PO_4) in 1 liter of water and adjusting to a pH of 6.8 to 6.9 by the dropwise addition of 25 percent sodium hydroxide solution). Add 2 drops of 1-methylheptylamine. Mix thoroughly.

Add 75 ml. of chloroform containing three drops of 1-methylheptylamine to the contents of the separatory funnel and shake the mixture for 3 minutes. Draw off and save the chloroform extract. A small layer of insoluble froth usually collects at the interface of the two layers. The latter should be left with the water layer.

Add an additional 75 ml. of chloroform containing 3 drops of 1-methylheptylamine and shake the contents of the funnel. Draw off the chloroform layer and wash twice more, once with 50 ml. of chloroform containing 1 drop of 1-methylheptylamine and finally with 50 ml. of chloroform alone.

Combine the chloroform extracts and evaporate to dryness in a small, 20-ml. beaker on the steam bath. Heat for an additional 15 minutes to expel excess amine. Transfer the residue quantitatively with 10 ml. or less of carbon tetrachloride to a 20-ml. beaker and evaporate to dryness. Transfer to a 2-ml. volumetric flask with carbon tetrachloride and dilute to volume. Run an infrared spectrum from 9.0 to 10.5 μ using double beam operation and 0.5-mm. matched cells. The spectrometer must be adjusted to give maximum absorbance at the 9.9 μ peak. From the peak height calculate the amount of alkyl benzene sulfonate present by reference to a standard curve.

The standard curve is prepared by dissolving 2.0 g. of an alkyl benzene sulfonate of known active ingredient content and structure in 100 ml. of 3 N hydrochloric acid. Extract three times with 100-ml. portions of ethyl ether and evaporate the combined extracts to dryness. Redissolve the residue in ethyl ether and neutralize with an excess of 1-methylheptylamine. Evaporate to dryness and heat in a vacuum oven for 18 hours at 50°C. and 10 mm. pressure. Dissolve the complex in carbon tetrachloride and dilute to 25 ml. in a volumetric flask. Pipet a 50-lambda aliquot, add 2 drops of 20 percent sodium hydroxide and evaporate to dryness. Determine the percent alkyl benzene sulfonate present by following the methylene blue method previously described under the determination of low level surfactants. Prepare a series of carbon tetrachloride solutions of the salt containing 0, 2.5, 5, 7.5, 10, 12.5 and 15.0 mg. per ml. Scan each solution in the infrared from 9.0 to 10.5 μ following the directions previously described. Plot two calibration curves of adsorption *vs.* alkyl benzene sulfonate concentration (as sodium salt), one for the 9.6-μ peak and one for the 9.9-μ peak. The base line should be the one running from the high shoulder of the 9.6 μ peak and the low shoulder of the 9.9-μ peak.

Evaporate a small volume of the solution (from the 2-ml. volumetric flask) on a salt flat and scan by infrared from 2 to 15 μ to prove identity of the sample.

Evaporate a 200-lambda aliquot of the solution to dryness in a small beaker, add 1 drop of 20 percent sodium hydroxide and 5 to 10 ml. of water, mix, and again evaporate to dryness. Dissolve the residue in water, transfer the solution to a 100-ml. volumetric flask, and bring to volume with water. A 5-ml. aliquot of this solution can be used to determine the alkyl benzene sulfonate by the methylene blue procedure described under the determination of low level surfactants. Multiply the milligrams of alkyl benzene sulfonate found in the 5-ml. aliquot by 200 to obtain the total milligrams of alkyl benzene sulfonate in the sample. The remaining volume of carbon tetrachloride solution may be used in the determination of the extent of branching according to the procedure immediately following.[25]

DETERMINATION OF EXTENT OF BRANCHING

Reagents. Basic Solution.—Prepare by transferring 15 g. of sodium chloride, 40 ml. of ethyl alcohol, 25 ml. of 0.5 N sodium hydroxide solution, and 3 ml. of 0.1 percent chlorophenol red indicator solution to a 500-ml. volumetric flask. Bring to volume with water and mix thoroughly.

Phosphate Buffer, pH 6.8.—Prepare by dissolving 6.8 g. of potassium dihydrogen phosphate (KH_2PO_4) in 1 liter of water and adjusting the solution to a pH of 6.8 to 6.9 by the addition of 25 percent sodium hydroxide solution. The 25 percent sodium hydroxide solution must be added dropwise.

Procedure.—Transfer the carbon tetrachloride solution of the methylheptylamine-alkyl benzene sulfonate residue to a 50-ml. extraction cylinder and remove the carbon tetrachloride by evaporating with a stream of nitrogen. Add 20 ml. of the basic solution to the residue in the cylinder and shake the contents to insure complete solution. Extract the solution with a 25-ml. volume of petroleum ether. Shake vigorously during the extraction and remove the petroleum ether layer by means of a glass siphon. The extraction and removal of the petroleum ether layer must be repeated twice more. The petroleum ether extracts may be discarded.

Neutralize the aqueous layer to the chlorophenol red end point by the addition of 0.5 N hydrochloric acid. Add 10 ml. of the phosphate buffer solution and 2 drops of n-octylamine. Mix the contents of the cylinder thoroughly. Extract three times with 20-ml. volumes of petroleum ether containing 1 drop of n-octylamine. Siphon the petroleum ether extracts into a 100-ml. beaker and evaporate them on a steam bath until complete dryness has been attained. During evaporation one must utilize a stream of nitrogen to protect the residue.

Dissolve the residue in the required volume of carbon tetrachloride to yield a 2 percent solution on the sodium alkyl benzene sulfonate basis. The volume of carbon tetrachloride required can be calculated from the amount of alkyl benzene sulfonate found in the 200-lambda aliquot analyzed by methylene blue as described in a previous step of this procedure. A correction must be applied for the 200-lambda aliquot withdrawn for analysis in calculating the weight of alkyl benzene sulfonate to arrive at a 2 percent solution.

Scan the 2 percent solution of alkyl benzene sulfonate in carbon tetrachloride over the spectral range of 6.895 to 7.42 μ employing a 1-mm. cell for the purpose. A carbon tetrachloride blank should be used together with a fivefold expansion of the wavelength scale. Measure the absorbance of the analytical peaks which appear at 70.9 μ and 7.315 μ.

Subtract the background absorbance and determine the absorbance ratio of the peaks. Read the relative amounts of straight and branched chain isomers from a calibration curve, which will be prepared from samples of linear and branched alkyl benzene sulfonates, as described in the following paragraph.

The calibration curve is prepared from known samples of linear and branched alkyl benzene sulfonates. The sulfonates are converted to their n-octylamine salts and a series of mixtures ranging from 5 to 95 percent of each standard is dissolved in carbon tetrachloride at a 2 percent concentration. The standards are then scanned in the same manner as described for the sample, and a calibration graph is drawn plotting the absorbance ratio (7.315-μ and 7.09-μ peaks) against the concentration ratio of the respective standards mixture.

EMISSION FLAME PHOTOMETRY

DETERMINATION OF SODIUM AND POTASSIUM IN SOAPS AND SYNDETS

Scope.—This method is applicable to the determination of sodium and potassium either singly or in combination in soaps and syndets.

Principle.—After excitation of the elements in a flame, the intensities of the resulting flame spectra are measured spectrophotometrically at designated wavelengths. Because of the complexity and variations of instrument adjustments required in this technique, it is recommended that the instrument supplier's manual be consulted.[27]

Apparatus.—Beckman Model DU spectrometer with flame attachment or equivalent instrument. Platinum crucibles.

Reagents. Potassium Chloride, Reagent Grade.
Sodium Chloride, Reagent Grade.
Oxygen, Extra Dry Grade.
Acetylene, Purified Grade.

Preparation of Standard Curves.—Several calibration graphs covering wide ranges of concentrations of each element may need to be prepared. Because of the wide ranges in levels of potassium and sodium encountered in various products, it is usually necessary to determine the number of curves needed experimentally.

Stock solutions of potassium chloride and sodium chloride are prepared separately in distilled water. These solutions should possess sufficient strength to permit dilution of aliquots to 100 ml., the diluted solutions yielding instrumental readings over the calibration range desired.

Following the manufacturer's instructions, set the instrument for optimum operation. This includes the adjustment of sensitivity and slit and photomultiplier settings. Set the wavelength at the proper setting, 766 mμ for potassium and 589 mμ for sodium. Introduce a small amount of distilled water into the flame to assure thorough cleanout of lines. Set the percent transmission to 100 percent, and introduce the most concentrated solution in the range desired into the instrument. Use the slit to make the final adjustment to 100 percent transmission. Remove the standard from the instrument and introduce a small volume of distilled water into the flame. Remove the water and introduce the second strongest concentration of standard in the set into the instrument. Repeat the water purge and follow the cycle through the series of standards, finishing with the solution of lowest concentration. The instrument must be checked periodically for stable operation following the manufacturer's instructions. Record the percent transmission for each standard introduced.

The observed transmission readings are plotted against concentration of either sodium or potassium. In actual practice it is well to check standards when analyzing samples to compensate for fluctuations in flame characteristics and instrument drift. This is best done by running standard concentrations falling on either side of sample reading. For optimum operation an oxygen pressure of 13 lbs. and an acetylene pressure of 3 lbs. is recommended.

Procedure.—Depending upon the concentration expected, accurately weigh 0.5 to 1.0 g. of sample into a clean platinum dish. Dry liquid samples in an oven or under an infrared lamp. Ash the dry sample at a low temperature, dissolve in water, and dilute

[27] Beck, E. C., Wilson, K. J., Jungermann, E. C., "The Determination of Sodium, Potassium and Magnesium in Surfactants by Flame Photometry," J. Am. Oil Chem. Soc., **40**, 515, 1963.

to a volume of 100 ml. with water. For samples high in potassium or sodium, appropriate higher dilutions may be made. Introduce a portion of the well-mixed solution into the flame, and, following the directions previously given under preparation of standard curves, measure the percent transmission. Obtain the concentration of either potassium or sodium by reference to the standard curve, or calculate the levels present in the sample by running standards that yield instrumental readings on either side of the sample reading. Each time a sample or standard solution is fed into the flame it should be followed by a distilled water feed (30 seconds in burner) to permit removal of any salts deposited in the burner tube or near the burner nozzle.

X-RAY DIFFRACTION

IDENTIFICATION OF WATER INSOLUBLE MATERIALS IN SOAP AND SYNDET PRODUCTS

Scope.—This method is applicable to the identification of water insoluble materials in commercial soap and syndet formulations including cleansers.

Principle.—The water insoluble material is isolated and dried. X-ray diffraction patterns are obtained by the powder diffraction method. Comparison of the line spacings obtained with spacings of known compounds permits the identification of the insoluble fraction.

Apparatus. **Norelco X-ray Power Supply and X-ray Tube.**—This should have a copper target (Phillips Electronic Instruments, Mount Vernon, N. Y.). An equivalent type of instrumentation may be used.

Powder Cameras.—Recommended size 114.59 mm. diameter. The 57.3 mm. camera may also be used.

X-ray Film.—$1\frac{3}{8}$-inch width. Kodak No Screen Medical x-ray Type.

Film Developer.—Kodak x-ray Type.

Film Fixer.—Kodak x-ray Type.

Procedure.—Isolate the water insoluble fraction of the sample and dry in an oven at 105°C. In a mortar and pestle grind the material fine enough to pass through a 200-mesh sieve. Prepare a small diameter (0.7 mm. or less), thin-walled melting point tube and fill it with the finely powdered sample, tapping the tube to effect filling. Following the manufacturer's instructions, align the camera for optimum operation. Place the tube in the chuck at the center of the powder camera, fixing it in place with wax or modeling clay. Orient the sample tube so it rotates axially without wobbling. Follow the manufacturer's instructions for sample alignment. Load the camera with film (darkroom) punching out holes in the film so that the collimator and beam trap can be inserted. Insert the collimator and beam trap and place the cover on the camera. Place the camera on the x-ray unit and expose for the optimum time required for good exposure (1–3 hours). This exposure time can vary, and trial may be necessary to determine the best exposure time. Remove the film from the camera in the darkroom. Develop, fix, an wash the film, and place it in rack for drying.

Measurements and Calculations.—Any film, after exposure and processing will shrink to a degree. It is possible to correct for this shrinkage in the following manner. The film is laid flat on the film measuring device and a zero degree (0°) reference point in the forward reflection region is established by bisecting the distance between the corresponding diffraction line on each side of the beam receiving tube hole in the film. To determine the 180° reference point, the same procedure is followed for the back reflection region, without changing the position of the film. Bisect the distance between the corresponding diffraction line on each side of the beam collimating tube hole in the film. The distance between the 0° reference point and the 180° reference point should be 180 mm. If it does not measure 180 mm., the correction factor will be the ratio of 180 mm. to the actual measurement. For example, if the film length is found to be 176 mm. then all the measured distances must be multiplied by 180/176 to obtain the corrected value. The distance of the various diffraction lines from the zero reference point is determined by reading from the scale, and the correction factor is then applied. Divide the value so obtained by 2. This value yields the Bragg angle in degrees since 2 mm. equals 1° Bragg on the 114.59-mm. camera. If a 57.3 mm. camera is employed, the corrected value is not divided by 2 since 1 mm. on the film equals 1° Bragg for this camera. Calculate 2 sin θ (Bragg angle) and then d from the following formula:

$$d = \frac{\lambda}{2 \sin \theta}$$

where: λ = wavelength of characteristic radiation in Angstroms,
     $2 \sin \theta$ is as calculated, and
 d = interplaner spacing in Angstroms.

Estimate the relative intensity values of the lines designating 100 as the strongest line.

By reference to the numerical (Hanawalt) index of the powder diffraction card index file,[28] locate the proper Hanawalt group for the strongest line of the given pattern. Read down the second column to find the closest match to the second strongest line of the given pattern. Compare the three strongest lines and relative intensities of the entry with the given pattern. Refer to the indicated data card for complete data. Comparison of the data obtained on the sample with the card reference data will permit identification of the insoluble fraction.

TURBIDIMETRY

CLOUD POINT OF DETERGENTS

Scope.—This method is applicable to the determination of cloud point of nonionic surfactants and liquid detergent compositions.

Principle.—The cloud point is the temperature at which material begins to crystallize from solution thereby causing cloudiness.

PART I—NONIONICS

Apparatus.—Centigrade thermometer of suitable range—to 0.1°C.

Procedure.—Prepare a 1 percent solution of the nonionic in distilled water using a suitable beaker. Heat the solution slowly until a cloud appears, while stirring with a thermometer. Remove from the heat and, while stirring, allow the solution to cool. Record the cloud point as the temperature at which the solution clears.

PART II—LIQUID DETERGENTS

Apparatus.—Suitable cooling bath capable of reaching temperatures of 5 to 10°C. below the expected cloud point. This bath may consist of ice, water, salt, calcium chloride, acetone, alcohol, or Dry Ice® mixed in proportions suitable for the desired temperature.

Procedure.—Pour the sample into a 6-inch test tube, insert a thermometer, and place the tube in the appropriate cooling bath. Stir the sample carefully taking precautions to

[28] Index (Inorganic) to the Powder Diffraction File, ASTM Special Technical Publication 48-M2, American Society for Testing and Materials, Philadelphia, Pennsylvania, 1963.

prevent incroporation of air. At 10° above the cloud point, stir at a uniform rate. As temperature of the sample drops, remove the test tube from the bath at 2° intervals and examine for cloud. Report the temperature at which the first cloud appears as the cloud point.

POTENTIOMETRIC TITRATIONS

DETERMINATION OF THE COMPOSITION OF UPPER LAYER RESULTING FROM THE SULFONATION OF ALKYLATE

During the sulfonation of alkylate an upper layer is obtained which contains both alkyl benzene sulfonate and free sulfuric acid. A potentiometric titration is applicable to the determination of the respective amounts of alkyl benzene sulfonic acid and free sulfuric acid.

Apparatus. **A pH Meter.**—Equipped with glass and calomel pH electrodes, suitable for potentiometric titration.

Continuous Stirrer, Nonmagnetic.

Reagents. **Morpholine Solution.**—The titrant is an 0.5 N solution of morpholine in acetonitrile prepared by dissolving 43.5 ml. of C.P. morpholine in one liter of acetonitrile. Standardize the morpholine solution as follows:

From a buret, accurately measure 40 ± 0.05 ml. of 0.5 N sulfuric acid into a 250-ml. beaker. Place the beaker on a titration stand and insert a continuous stirrer (nonmagnetic). Insert glass and calomel pH electrodes and titrate the standardized sulfuric acid with the morpholine solution to a pH of 5.4.

Calculate the normality of the morpholine solution as follows:

$$\frac{\text{normality of sulfuric acid} \times \text{ml. sulfuric acid}}{\text{ml. morpholine}} = \frac{\text{normality of morpholine}}{\text{in acetonitrile solution}}$$

Ethylene Glycol-Isopropyl Alcohol Mixture.—Mix equal volumes of ethylene glycol and isopropyl alcohol.

Procedure.—Accurately weigh 1.9 to 2.1 g. of sample (weighed to the nearest 0.1 mg.) into a 400-ml. beaker. Add 150 ml. of 1:1 ethylene glycol-isopropyl alcohol mixture. Insert the pH electrodes and a continuous stirrer (nonmagnetic) into the solution. Titrate the solution with 0.5 N morpholine in acetonitrile to the first equivalence point (pH of approximately 1.5). This point should be determined by plotting the milliliters of 0.5 N morpholine added against the apparent pH. In the vicinity of the end point, add the morpholine solution in 0.1-ml. increments, taking care that the pH and milliliters added are accurately recorded after each addition of titrant. Continue the titration in this fashion until it is certain that the potentiometric break (equivalence point) has been passed. This first point of inflection in the curve is equivalent to all the sulfonic acid plus one-half of the sulfuric acid present in the sample.

Using the titration data, plot the ratios of the change (Δ pH) of electrode potential, for the addition of a definite small volume (0.1 ml.) of titrant, to the volume, ΔV, that is, Δ pH/ΔV (ml.), against the total volume of titrant added. This step is necessary in order to determine the potentiometric end point with precision. Provided ΔV is not large, Δ pH/ΔV is a close approximation to the slope of the titration curve and exhibits a maximum value at the end point.

Continue the titration to the second equivalence point (pH of approximately 5.7) and determine the second potentiometric end point in the same manner as previously described. The second equivalence point is equal to the sulfonic acid plus all of the sulfuric acid present. The difference between the two equivalence points is equivalent to one-half of the sulfuric acid present in the sample.

Calculation.

$$\frac{(\text{ml. morpholine, 2nd end point} - \text{ml. morpholine, 1st end point}) \times N \times 9.8}{\text{weight of sample}} = \% \text{ sulfuric acid}$$

$$\frac{2(\text{ml. morpholine, 1st end point}) - (\text{ml. morpholine, 2nd end point}) \times N \times 0.1 \times \text{mol. wt. of sulfonic acid}}{\text{weight of sample}}$$
$$= \% \text{ sulfonic acid}$$

The molecular weight of dodecylbenzene sulfonic acid = 326.
The molecular weight of pentadecylbenzene sulfonic acid = 368.

DETERMINATION OF WATER AT HIGH LEVELS BY KARL FISCHER TITRATION

In this method the water is titrated with a relatively high water equivalent variation of the Karl Fischer reagent, employing an electrometric "dead stop" apparatus to detect the titration end point. At the end point the unreacted iodine in the Karl Fischer reagent exerts a depolarizing effect upon the electrodes of the titrimeter resulting in a sudden surge of current indicative of the titration end point. Samples containing as high as 40 percent of water can be successfully titrated.

Apparatus.—A commercial type "dead stop" end point titrimeter equipped with a titrating vessel which can be sealed against adsorption of atmospheric moisture is required. An automatic buret, of amber colored glass, should also be available.

Reagents. **Karl Fischer Reagent, Single Solution.**—This reagent is prepared with ethylene glycol monomethyl ether[29] instead of the usual methanol specified in the original Karl Fischer reagent.[30] The reagent may be prepared as follows:

In a well ventilated hood add 300 ml. of anhydrous pyridine to a dry 2-liter round bottom flask. Place the flask in a Dry Ice®-alcohol bath and slowly add to the flask, in small increments, 133.5 ml. of liquid sulfur dioxide. During the addition of the sulfur dioxide, mix the solution with the aid of a magnetic stirrer to minimize spattering. Close the flask with a stopper equipped with a drying tube containing Drierite between additions of the sulfur dioxide. Add an additional 500 ml. of anhydrous pyridine with constant stirring.

Add 250 g. of iodine, C.P., resublimed, in small amounts at a time, and finally add 175 ml. of anhydrous ethylene glycol monomethyl ether. The latter solvent is obtainable from the Union Carbide Corp. under their trade mark "Methyl Cellosolve." Continue to stir the solution for 5 minutes. If after this period of time the iodine has not completely dissolved, remove the flask from the cooling bath and continue to stir until the iodine is completely dissolved. Close the flask with the stopper containing the drying tube filled with Drierite and allow the reagent to stand in the dark for at least 24 hours before use. This reagent will possess a water equivalent of 9 to 10 mg. per ml.

Methyl Alcohol, Anhydrous.—The acceptable water tolerance should not exceed 0.1 percent weight. A blank should be run on each batch of alcohol.

Procedure.—Assemble the titration apparatus and add 75 to 100 ml. of anhydrous methanol to the titration vessel. Immediately seal the vessel to prevent adsorption of atmospheric moisture by the anhydrous alcohol. Other than for the required additions of alcohol, water, and sample, the titration vessel must be kept tightly covered throughout the determination.

[29] Peters, E. D., and Jungnickel, J. L., "Improvements in Karl Fischer Method for Determination of Water," Anal. Chem., **27**, 450, 1955.

[30] Fischer, K., "A New Method for the Analytical Determination of the Water Content of Liquids and Solids," Angew. Chem., **48**, 394, 1935.

Adjust the magnetic stirrer to a moderately slow speed to minimize vortexing and splashing of the alcohol, and titrate the contents of the vessel with Karl Fischer reagent added at a fairly rapid rate. Avoid any readjustment of the stirring speed throughout the balance of the procedure.

Approach of the end point is evidenced by small oscillations of the needle of the microampere scale. At this point, add the Karl Fischer reagent slowly in a dropwise manner. At the end point, the microampere scale needle will be deflected suddenly to a steady high value and will remain constant for at least 30 seconds. Do not over-titrate. Record the microampere reading as the end point reading for subsequent titrations of the water equivalent and sample.

After the titration, immediately refill the buret. Refilling of the buret at this point precludes the formation of a sticky film and poor drainage of the reagent in subsequent titrations.

Accurately weigh a Hill weighing bottle, containing approximately 15 ml. of water, to the nearest 0.1 mg. Rapidly transfer 350 to 450 mg. of water from the weighing bottle to the titration vessel. Run in the prescribed weight of water in one volume rather than dropwise, to prevent loss by evaporation. In order to eliminate errors resulting from loss by evaporation, do not allow the gound glass surfaces of the weighing bottle to become wet.

Titrate the standard water solution in the same manner as described for the titration of the anhydrous methanol. The end point is indicated by a sudden deflection of the microampere scale needle to the same steady high value obtained in the titration of the methanol.

Record the milliliters of Karl Fischer reagent required for titration of the standard water solution. Refill the buret.

Immediately add an amount of the sample containing 350 to 450 mg. of water from a Hill weighing bottle. The weight of sample to take for analysis can be approximated as follows:

$$\frac{0.400 \times 100}{\text{percent water expected}} = \text{sample required in grams}$$

Add the sample in one volume rather than dropwise. Titrate with Karl Fischer reagent as previously described.

Calculation.

$$\frac{\text{grams H}_2\text{O taken for standardization}}{\text{milliliters of Karl Fischer reagent}} = \text{grams of water equivalent to 1 ml. of Karl Fischer reagent}$$

$$\frac{(\text{milliliters of Karl Fischer reagent required for sample}) \times (\text{grams of water equivalent to 1 ml. of Karl Fischer reagent})}{\text{weight of sample}}$$
$$\times 100 = \% \text{ water in sample}$$

NOTES.—Several samples may be run in succession provided the titration vessel is sufficiently large. When necessary, the spent solution is siphoned off with the aid of a suction flask and vacuum line. For each titration, sufficient excess methanol must be present to assure a stoichiometric reaction. The amount of methanol (75–100 ml.) specified in the above procedure is sufficient to run 3 or 4 samples. Fresh, anhydrous methanol must be added each time the spent contents of the vessel are siphoned off.

To improve the precision of the determination and to minimize drifting of the microampere scale needle, it is recommended to add the sample from the weighing bottle and complete the titration before reweighing to determine the exact weight of sample taken for analysis.

For maximum precision the Karl Fischer reagent should be standardized in duplicate before each set of samples (up to 6 replicates) is run. The mean deviation of the standardization should be no greater than 2×10^{-5} g. of water per milliliter of Karl Fischer reagent.

DETERMINATION OF SOAP IN COMMERCIAL PRODUCTS CONTAINING SYNTHETIC DETERGENTS

Scope.—This method is applicable to commercial detergent products containing soap in admixture with synthetic surface active agents and inorganic fillers such as carbonates, phosphates, etc. The soap in the sample is titrated with standard acid in a 1:1 ethylene glycol-isopropyl alcohol mixture.[31]

Preparation of 0.1 N Hydrochloric Acid in Ethylene Glycol-Isopropyl Alcohol.—Transfer 9.6 ml. of concentrated hydrochloric acid (sp. gr. 1.18) to a 1000-ml. volumetric flask. Dilute to volume with ethylene glycol-isopropyl alcohol mixture prepared by mixing equal volumes of C.P. ethylene glycol and 98 percent isopropyl alcohol. Mix thoroughly. In using this solution, dispense from an automatic buret protected from the atmosphere by means of a drying tube containing Drierite (anhydrous calcium sulfate). For use in very accurate work the coefficient of expansion of this solution has been experimentally determined to be 0.00075 ml. per °C. between 20 and 30°C.

NOTE.—This reagent is subject to deterioration upon standing and, therefore, limited quantities should be prepared at one time. The reagent should be standardized at least once a week, as follows.

The reagent is standardized against tris(hydroxy methyl)-aminomethane ($C_4H_{11}NO_3$), Fisher certified reagent, obtainable from the Fisher Scientific Co., New York 14, N. Y. under their registered trade name, Tham. Before use, grind to break up any lumps, dry at 100–105°C. for one hour and then regrind. Tham has a tendency to form hard lumps upon drying. Do not dry the Tham for more than 1 hour.

Accurately weigh 0.50 to 0.55 g. (to the nearest 0.1 mg.) of dried primary standard Tham and transfer to a 250-ml. beaker. Add 100 ml. of 1:1 ethylene glycol-isopropyl alcohol mixture. Stir to dissolve.

Titrate the solution with the 0.1 N hydrochloric acid in ethylene glycol-isopropyl alcohol mixture to a pH of 2.7 using a pH meter and an air stirrer.

$$\frac{\text{weight of Tham}}{\text{milliliters of HCl} \times 0.12114} = \frac{\text{normality of hydrochloric acid in ethylene}}{\text{glycol-isopropyl alcohol mixture.}}$$

NOTE.—The pH meter should be standardized before use, using pH 4.0 and 7.0 buffers. A magnetic stirrer cannot be used in this determination due to electrical interference with the pH meter.

Determination.—Accurately weigh 1 to 4 g. (to the nearest 0.1 mg.) of sample, the actual weight to be taken depending upon the anticipated soap content, into a 250-ml. beaker. Add approximately 100 ml. of ethyl alcohol, and heat the contents of the beaker to boiling. Filter the hot alcoholic solution through a fluted No. 41 Whatman filter of suitable diameter, and collect the filtrate in a 400-ml. beaker. Thoroughly wash the residue on the paper (inorganic constituents) with several washes of hot ethyl alcohol.

Cool the filtrate to room temperature and insert the blade of an air stirrer. Insert pH electrodes and slowly titrate the solution to a pH of 5.4 with the 0.1 N hydrochloric acid in ethylene glycol-isopropyl alcohol mixture.

$$\frac{\text{milliliters of HCl} \times N \times 0.303 \times 100}{\text{weight of sample}} = \% \text{ anhydrous sodium soap}$$

[31] Palit, S. R., "A Direct Volumetric Method for the Analysis of Soap," Oil and Soap, **23**, 58, 1946.

NOTES.—The factor 0.303 is based on fatty acids possessing an average acid value of 20.0 percent potassium hydroxide. If fatty acids having a different acid value are present in the product the factor can be calculated as follows.

$$\frac{56.1 \times 100}{\text{acid value as } \% \text{ KOH}} = \text{mean molecular weight of fatty acids}$$

mean molecular weight of fatty acids $+ 22 =$ mean molecular weight of sodium soap

$$\frac{\text{mean molecular of sodium soap}}{1000} = \text{factor (milliequivalent).}$$

MASS SPECTROMETRY

EXAMINATION OF DETERGENT ALKYLATES BY MASS SPECTROMETRY

Mass spectrometry is a highly specialized branch of analytical chemistry. A large number of commercial mass spectrometers is available on the market, and it is assumed that the individual is familiar with the working of the instrument available to him. The mass spectrometer is extensively used in the examination of petroleum and petroleum by-products, and is of value to the detergent industry as a means of examining alkylates before sulfonation.

The determination of the individual mass spectra of an alkylate is a routine proposition and more properly belongs to the field of petroleum research.[32,33] In view of the current widespread shift of emphasis from branched to linear chain alkylates as the starting material for the production of detergents, the following discussion of the mass spectra obtained from a typical branched and linear alkylate may be of interest.

TABLE 61-1. COMPARISON OF THE MASSES AND PEAK HEIGHTS OF LINEAR AND BRANCHED CHAIN ALKYLATES

m/e	Linear Alkylate	Branched Alkylate
91	100.—	38.35
92	9.62	3.23
103	3.70	3.90
104	8.95	3.08
105	70.75	47.07
106	8.92	6.35
117	7.04	5.18
118	2.49	9.82
119	14.53	100.—
120	2.02	11.31
133	8.06	12.40
134	1.15	1.65
,,	,,	,,
,,	,,	,,
,,	,,	,,

[32] Brown, R. A., Skahan, D. J., Cirillo, V. A., and Melpolder, F. W., "High Mass Spectrometry: Propylene Polymer, Alkylated Benzene, and Wax Analysis," Anal. Chem., 31, 1531, 1959.
[33] Boyer, E. W., Hamming, M. C., and Ford, H. T., "Rearrangement Technique for Analysis of Alkylbenzenes by Mass Spectrometry," Anal. Chem., 35, 1168, 1963.

DIFFERENTIATION OF BRANCHED CHAIN AND LINEAR ALKYLATES

In Table 61-1, the first column lists the masses at which peaks occur in the mass spectra. The second and third columns record the peak heights obtained in the examination of a typical linear alkylate and branched chain alkylate, respectively. The spectra were obtained employing a 70-volt ionizing voltage and 10-microampere ionizing current.

In the most general case, linear and branched chain alkylates can be differentiated by comparison of their respective fragmentation at m/e 91 and m/e 119. In the case of a linear alkylate the peak height at m/e 91 will be very large in relation to the peak height at m/e 119. Conversely, if the m/e 119 peak is greater than the m/e 91 peak the alkylate chain is considered branched.

Notes.—(a) The limited volatility of alkyl aryl sulfonates precludes their direct examination by mass spectrometry. This is true, also, for vapor phase chromatography which is of general application in this work.[34] Sulfonates can, however, be reduced to the original alkylate by desulfonation with phosphoric acid.[35,36]

(b) A correlation of mass spectra with performance properties of detergents has been demonstrated[37,38] for the straight-chain alkylbenzenes.

ABSORPTION CHROMATOGRAPHY

DETERMINATION OF NONIONICS IN SYNDETS

Scope.—This method is applicable to the determination of total nonionic surfactants in commercial syndets. Other nonionic material, such as fatty alcohols and free oil, will interfere.

Principle.—The sample is extracted with alcohol to obtain the active ingredients. An aliquot of the alcoholic solution is treated with a monobed ion exchange resin which removes ionic materials. The solution after filtration is evaporated to yield the nonionic fraction.[39,40]

Apparatus.—Magnetic stirrer with Teflon coated stirring bar.

Reagents. **Reagent Alcohol.**—U. S. Formula 3A or equivalent.

Amberlite MB-1 Monobed Ion Exchange Resin, Analytical Grade.—Prior to use wash the resin several times with Reagent alcohol.

Procedure.—Weigh a sample of sufficient size to yield approximately 0.5 g. of nonionic material, and transfer to a 100-ml. beaker. Add 50 ml. of hot Reagent alcohol and

[34] Carnes, W. J., "Composition of Straight Chain Alkylbenzenes by Gas Chromatography," Anal. Chem., **36**, 1197, 1964.

[35] Knight, J. D., and House, R., "Analysis of Surfactant Mixtures, I.," J. Am. Oil Chem. Soc., **36**, 195, 1959.

[36] Setzkorn, E. A., and Carel, A. B., "The Analysis of Alkyl Aryl Sulfonates by Micro Desulfonation and Gas Chromatography," J. Am. Oil Chem. Soc., **40**, 57, 1963.

[37] Rubinfeld, J., Emery, E. M., Cross III, H. D., Straight-Chain Alkylbenzenes: Structure and Performance Property Relations, paper presented at American Oil Chemists' Society Meeting, New Orleans, April, 1964.

[38] Rubinfeld, J., Emery, E. M., Cross III, H. D., Straight-Chain Alkylbenzenes: Structure and Performance Property Relations, II. Pure Isomer Correlations, paper presented at the 148th National Meeting of the American Chemical Society, August, 1964.

[39] Rosen, M. J., "Separation of Non-ionic Surface Active Agents from Mixtures with Anionics by Batch Ion-exchange," Anal. Chem., **29**, 1675, 1957.

[40] Rosen, M. J., "Analysis of Mixtures of Ionic and Nonionic Surface-Active Agents; Separation and Recovery of Components by Batch Ion Exchange," J. Am. Oil Chem. Soc., **38**, 218, 1961.

boil on a steam bath for approximately 5 minutes. Allow the insoluble matter to settle, and filter the supernatant liquid through a fast filter paper collecting the filtrate in a 100-ml. volumetric flask. Repeat the extraction of the insolubles three times with 15-ml. portions of hot, Reagent alcohol. Cool the solution and dilute to volume with Reagent alcohol. Pipet a 25-ml. aliquot into a 150-ml. beaker. Add 25 ml. of Reagent alcohol and 30 g. of MBl monobed resin. Add a Teflon coated stirring bar and stir on a magnetic stirrer for 20 minutes. Filter the mixture through a rapid filter paper collecting the filtrate in a tared flask. Wash the resin well with 3 separate portions of Reagent alcohol, and filter. Evaporate the combined filtrates to dryness on a steam bath. Dry the residue to constant weight at 105°C.

Calculation.

$$\frac{\text{weight of residue} \times 4 \times 100}{\text{weight of sample}} = \% \text{ total nonionic matter}$$

DETERMINATION OF AMIDE CONTENT OF FATTY ACID ETHANOLAMIDES

Scope.—This method is applicable to the assay of commercial high active fatty alkanolamides.

Principle.—The sample in alcoholic solution is treated with a monobed ion exchange resin which retains ionic impurities. Filtration and evaporation of the filtrate yields the nonionic fraction (ester plus amide). A separate determination of ester allows the calculation of amide content by difference.

Apparatus.—Magnetic Stirrer with Teflon coated stirring bars.

Reagents. **Reagent Alcohol.**—U. S. Formula 3A or equivalent.

Amberlite MB-1 Monobed Ion Exchange Resin, Analytical Grade.—Prior to use wash the resin several times with reagent alcohol.

Procedure.—Accurately weigh 1 g. of sample and transfer to a 250-ml. beaker. Add 100 ml. of Reagent alcohol and warm to dissolve. Add 15 g. of MB-1 Monobed ion-exchange resin, insert a Teflon coated magnet bar and stir on a magnetic stirrer for 15 minutes. Filter the mixture through a fast filter paper collecting the filtrate in a tared 250-ml. beaker. Wash the resin well with 25-ml. portions of Reagent alcohol. Evaporate the combined alcoholic extracts to dryness on a steam bath, and dry the residue to constant weight for 10-minute periods at 105°C. Calculate the total nonionic as follows:

$$\frac{\text{weight of dried residue}}{\text{weight of sample}} \times 100 = \text{total nonionic matter}$$

The amide content is calculated as follows:

$$(\% \text{ total nonionic matter}) - (\% \text{ ester}) = \% \text{ amide}$$

PENTA-SODIUM TRIPOLYPHOSPHATE (TRIPHOSPHATE)— DETERMINATION OF PURITY OF RAW MATERIAL AND DETERMINATION OF AMOUNT IN COMMERCIAL DETERGENT PRODUCTS BY DIRECT FLOW ION EXCHANGE

Scope.—Method 1 describes a relatively rapid control procedure in which the tripolyphosphate and higher phosphates are obtained by difference. Method 2 describes a more specific procedure in which the tripolyphosphate content is determined by direct elution.[41]

[41] ASTM Tentative Method D 501-59T, ASTM Standards on Soaps and Other Detergents, prepared by ASTM Committee D-12, 9th Ed., p. 107, American Society for Testing and

Principle.—Both methods are based on: the exchange, with the help of an ion exchange column, of all exchangeable ions of the same charge for other ions of the same charge; and the internal separation, based on differences in exchange potentials, in an adsorption column, of the phosphate ions upon eluting with a common ion electrolyte.

$$2R—Cl \quad + HPO_4^= \qquad \rightarrow R_2 - HPO_4 + 2Cl^-$$
Anion Resin
Column   orthophosphate

$$2R—Cl \quad + H_2P_2O_7^= \qquad \rightarrow R_2 - H_2P_2O_7 + 2Cl^-$$
pyrophosphate

$$2R—Cl \quad + H_3P_3O_{10}^= \qquad \rightarrow R_2 - H_3P_3O_{10} + 2Cl^-$$
tripolyphosphate

R represents the nonexchangeable insoluble polymeric portion of the resin.

The sample is dissolved and an aliquot of the solution is transferred to an anion exchange column. The column is eluted with potassium chloride solution, and the phosphate content of each eluted fraction is determined. The separation point for ortho-, pyro-, and tripolyphosphate and the number of fractions to collect are dependent upon the elution rate and the respective phosphate recoveries per fraction determined from a standard curve.

In Method 1 the orthophosphates and pyrophosphates are determined directly from the phosphate content of the eluted sample, and the percentage of tripolyphosphate plus higher phosphates is calculated by substracting the total ortho- and pyrophosphate content as percent P_2O_5 from the total percent of P_2O_5.

Method 2 is similar to Method 1 except that the tripolyphosphate is obtained directly by further elution of the sample. Any remaining P_2O_5, not resulting from ortho-, pyro-, and tripolyphosphate, is attributed to small amounts of trimeta-, tetrameta- or tetraphosphate and Graham's salt.

Apparatus.—Refer to Fig. 61-1 for the arrangement of the assembled apparatus.

Reservoir Bottles.—Four are needed, as follows: capacity 4 liters; narrow mouth; equipped with a tight fitting rubber stopper through which passes a glass tube vent for pressure regulation and a glass siphon tube with stopcock (both tubes should extend to the bottom of the reservoir).

Capillary Manifold.—Thick-walled capillary tubing equipped with 4 stopcocks, securely mounted under the reservoir platform.

Chromatographic Glass Tube.—The tube should be fitted with a fritted glass disc of coarse porosity, overall length 30 cm., tube length above the fritted disc 23.5 cm., internal diameter 2.5 cm. Attach a glass stopcock with buret tip by means of a short piece of rubber tubing to the lower outlet end of the tube. Equip the tube with a tight fitting rubber stopper through which passes a glass tube vent assembly and an inlet delivery tube provided with a stopcock. Both tubes should extend about 1 cm. below the rubber stopper.

Perforated Polyethylene Disc.—The disc should have 2-cm. diameter, 1-mm. thickness, and 3 equidistant holes about 6 mm. in diameter. This disc is placed on the surface of the resin bed in the column.

Materials, Philadelphia, 1960, describes a reverse-flow ion exchange method for the quantitative separation and measurement of various phosphates. In the latter method, the eluant enters the bottom of the column and the eluted phosphates are recovered from the top of the column. The direct flow elution is considerably quicker and has given excellent results in commerical practice. For these reasons the direct flow elution procedure has been selected by the authors for descriptive treatment.

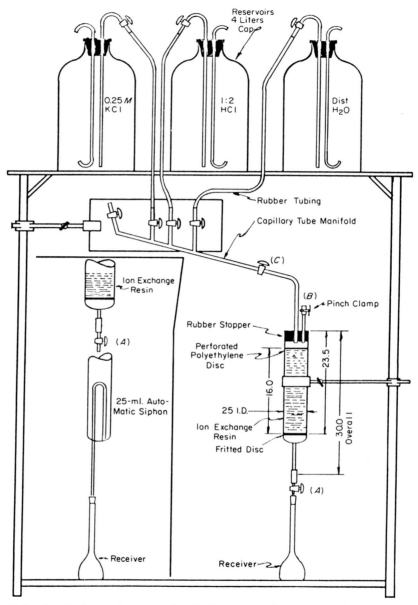

Fig. 61-1. Ion Exchange Apparatus for the Separation of Phosphates. (All dimensions in centimeters.)

in 25 ml. of concentrated hydrochloric acid. Store in a glass-stoppered brown bottle and prepare fresh at least every month.

Reducing Solution.—Dilute 0.5 ml. of stannous chloride stock solution to 100 ml. with 1:35 sulfuric acid-water solution. Prepare this solution fresh daily.

Phosphate Reference Solution.—Dissolve about 0.4 g. of potassium dihydrogen phosphate (KH_2PO_4), 0.7 g. of sodium pyrophosphate ($Na_4P_2O_7\cdot10H_2O$), 0.5 g. of triphosphate ($Na_5P_3O_{10}\cdot6H_2O$), and 0.35 g. of trimetaphosphate ($NaPO_3)_3$ in 250 ml. of water.

Isobutyl Alcohol-Benzene Mixture.—Mix equal volumes of Reagent grade isobutyl alcohol and benzene.

Sulfuric Acid, Alcoholic.—Mix 20 ml. of concentrated sulfuric acid with 980 ml. of Reagent Grade Methyl alcohol.

Acid Solvent.—Mix 735 ml. of isopropyl alcohol with a solution of 50 g. of trichloroacetic acid in 265 ml. of water. Add 2.5 ml. of concentrated ammonium hydroxide.

Chromatographic Spray.—Mix 5 ml. of perchloric acid (60–72 percent), 1 ml. of concentrated hydrochloric acid, and 1 g. of ammonium molybdate $(NH_4)_6Mo_7O_{24}\cdot4H_2O$ and dilute to 100 ml. with water.

Preparation of Chromatographic Paper.—Using a pencil, mark the sheet as follows: place the sheet on a flat surface and draw a horizontal line 1 inch from the bottom and parallel with the 9-inch side. Draw two vertical lines, each 4 inches from the side (separated by 1 inch) and parallel with the 6-inch side. Mark two reference spots one-half inch in from each edge of the paper, and located on the initial horizontal line. Place 8 marks on each side of the horizontal line, separated from each other by $\frac{5}{16}$ inch and located 1 inch in from the reference spots. A total of 16 such spots will be available on one sheet of paper. The 1-inch section in the center is a blank area, and paper marked in the way described allows for two analyses to be conducted on one sheet of paper, the left side for one sample and the right side for a second. Fold the paper into a cylinder by clipping together the centers of the 6-inch edges with 1-inch pieces of platinum wire in such a way that the edges do not touch.

Procedure for One Directional Analysis.—Dissolve a representative sample of the material in water and dilute to 1000 ml. For commercial triphosphate, take 6.0 ± 0.1 g. of sample. A correspondingly larger weight of sample must be taken for samples containing lower levels of triphosphate in the formulation. Using a micropipet, deliver equal amounts (sufficient for optimum separation) to each mark on the paper. In the same way deliver an equal amount of reference solution to the reference mark. Allow the spots to dry. Under very humid conditions dry the paper in a desiccator. Expose the sheet to the vapors of acid solvent in a battery jar for 40 minutes, avoiding contact of the sheet with the liquid. Place 150 ml. of acid solvent in a 1-gallon cylindrical jar. Transfer the sheet, without delay, to the jar with the starting line down. Avoid splashing. Cover the jar and allow the solvent to ascend 5 inches from the bottom of the paper. This requires from 1 to 2.5 hours. Remove the paper sheet from the jar by deforming at the top into a cone. Remove the excess solvent by gently touching the bottom of the paper to an absorbent paper towel. Leave the sheet stand on a paper towel for 10 minutes. Dry 10 minutes in a 50°C. oven. Remove the platinum wire and bend the sheet flat. Evenly apply a fine mist of chromatographic spray solution over the entire sheet using a spray bottle. Avoid the formation of droplets on the paper. Dry the paper at 50°C. for 10 minutes and irradiate under the ultraviolet lamp. The bands of the phosphate species should appear as blue zones. In very dry atmospheres, it may be necessary to spray the sheet again in order for the zones to be visible. In very moist atmospheres, a blue background may obscure the zones. This background may be removed by exposing the sheet to ammonia vapor.

Using the reference zones as a guide, mark the zones corresponding to the various phosphate species with a pencil. This is done horizontally across the sheet so as to include all of the various fractions obtained from each initial application. The reference chromatograph is discarded. Cut the various bands and a corresponding strip of blank paper. The paper areas must match within one-fourth square inch as the quantity of paper taken affects the subsequent colorimetric results. The cuts between the pyrophosphate and triphosphate bands should be taken so as to include as much as possible of the space between the bands in the triphosphate cut. The cuts between the triphosphate and high molecular weight bands should be made just below the trimetaphosphate level as indicated in the reference chromatogram. For samples containing only small amounts of orthophosphate and high molecular weight phosphates, time can be saved by cutting out only the pyrophosphate and triphosphate fractions.

Insert each strip into a 25-ml. volumetric flask, cutting into small pieces for handling. Add 1 ml. of 8 N ammonium hydroxide and about 7 ml. of water to each flask. Swirl and allow to stand for 5 to 10 minutes then add 3 ml. of 8 N sulfuric acid to each flask. Place the flasks in a boiling water bath and allow to stand for 20 minutes. Remove the flasks and allow to cool to room temperature. Add exactly 10 ml. of benzene-butyl alcohol mixture to each flask followed by 2 ml. of ammonium molybdate solution. Dilute to volume with water and shake vigorously for at least 20 seconds. Allow to stand, withdraw exactly 5 ml. of the supernatant liquid from each flask, and transfer to separate 25-ml. volumetric flasks. Dilute contents of each flask with about 10 ml. of alcoholic sulfuric acid. Swirl and add 1 ml. of reducing solution. Mix well and dilute to volume with alcoholic sulfuric acid. Mix and after 10 minutes read the absorbance of each solution at 650 mμ against a blank solution prepared using the blank paper area cut.

Calculations.

$$\frac{Ax}{At} \times 100 = Px$$

where: Ax = absorbance of fraction,
   At = total absorbance of all fractions, and
   Px = percentage P_2O_5 of total P_2O_5 for any given fraction.

The triphosphate fraction will include the trimetaphosphate fraction in this scheme of analysis. Separation of these two entities will require additional work employing two-directional paper chromatography.

$$\left[\left(\frac{Px}{100} \right) (Pt) \right] \times Ps = Zi$$

where: Px = as determined above,
   Ps = factor for converting P_2O_5 to the phosphate entity desired,
   Pt = total P_2O_5 of sample in percent as determined by any standard method, and
   Zi = percent of desired phosphate entity in sample.

Ps values for the various phosphates are given below:

Phosphate Entity	Ps
$Na_5P_3O_{10}$	1.7277
$Na_4P_2O_7$	1.8734
Na_3PO_4	2.3100
$(NaPO_3)_3$	1.4368
High Molecular Weight Phosphates	1.4368

Corrections for Calculations.—When operating at excessively high temperatures for extended runs, apply hydrolysis corrections for temperatures above 20°C. during this scheme of analysis as follows.

Correction for Triphosphate.—Add to the percentage of triphosphate and subtract from the percentage of pyrophosphate the correction calculated as follows.

$$F \times t \times \text{percentage of triphosphate in sample}$$

where: F = 0.002 for 22°C., 0.003 for 25°C., and 0.007 for 30°C., and

t = time the solvent was allowed to ascend in this scheme of analysis.

GAS CHROMATOGRAPHY

DETERMINATION OF FATTY ACIDS

This method is applicable to animal and vegetable fatty acids containing from 8 to 20 carbon atoms. Saturated and unsaturated fatty acids are determined separately. Epoxy, oxidized, and polymerized fatty acids will interfere in the determination. The method is essentially that described in the Official and Tentative Methods of the American Oil Chemists' Society.[44] The fatty acids may be commercial products, or they may result from the hydrolysis of soaps, detergents, and other organic compounds (builders) commonly used in the formulation of commercial detergent products. The fatty acids are converted into methyl esters and the latter are separated and determined by gas chromatography.

Preparation of Methyl Esters.—Boron trifluoride reagent is required in the preparation of the methyl esters. Handling boron trifluoride gas is hazardous; it is recommended that the reagent be purchased as a solution of boron trifluoride in methanol (125 g. boron trifluoride per liter of anhydrous methanol). It is obtainable from Eastman Organic Chemicals.

Place 100 to 150 mg. of fatty acids in a small, round-bottom flask equipped with a standard taper glass joint and vertical condenser. If the fatty acids solidify, warm the flask slightly to melt the acids. Immediately add 1 ml. of methanol to maintain the fatty acids in the liquid state. Nitrogen gas should be passed into the flask during this operation.

Add 3 ml. of boron trifluoride reagent to the contents of the flask and heat the flask on a steam bath in a hood. Boil the mixture under reflux for 3 to 4 minutes, agitating the mixture constantly throughout the operation. Cool the flask and contents, wash down the inside wall of the condenser with several milliliters of petroleum ether, and transfer the mixture to a 125-ml. separatory funnel, using 30 ml. of petroleum ether and 20 ml. of water to complete the transfer. Thoroughly mix by shaking the stoppered funnel, and allow to stand until the layers separate cleanly. Withdraw and discard the aqueous layer.

Wash the petroleum ether layer twice with separate 25-ml. volumes of water. After withdrawal of the second water wash, dry the inside of the stem of the funnel with absorbent cotton. Place a layer of anhydrous sodium sulfate in a No. 4 Whatman paper fitted in a short stem funnel. Filter the ether solution through the sodium sulfate, catching the dried petroleum ether solution in a small beaker. Remove most of the petroleum ether by evaporation on the steam bath while passing a stream of nitrogen into the beaker. To prevent the evaporation of volatile, short chain fatty acids, evaporate to a minimum volume of 1 ml. Quickly transfer the methyl esters to a screw cap vial or other

---

[44] Official and Tentative Methods of the American Oil Chemists' Society, AOCS Tentative Method Ce 1-62, American Oil Chemists' Society, Chicago, 1963.

suitable container and subject the esters to chromatographic analysis within a short period of time. If this is not possible, refrigerate the esters for longer periods of storage under an atmosphere of nitrogen gas.[45]

Alternative Preparation of Methyl Esters.—Transfer about 1 g. of the fatty acids to a 250-ml. round-bottom flask equipped with a glass joint and reflux condenser. Add 150 ml. of anhydrous methyl alcohol containing 0.1 ml. of concentrated sulfuric acid. Add several boiling chips to the contents of the flask and actively reflux for a period of 3 hours. Cool and transfer the solution to a 1-liter separatory funnel. Extract the esters with 200 ml. of petroleum ether. Discard the lower layer and wash the petroleum ether layer three times using 200 ml. of water for each wash. Dry the petroleum ether extract by adding anhydrous sodium sulfate, filter the solution through paper and evaporate the petroleum ether on the steam bath. Observe the handling and storage precautions detailed for the esterification with boron trifluoride.[46]

Gas Chromatographic Unit.—The gas chromatograph should possess the following characteristics:

(a) Temperature of the sample inlet port should exceed the column temperature by approximately 50°C.

(b) The column should be 4 to 10 feet long, with a $\frac{1}{4}$-inch outside diameter, and may be made of glass, stainless steel, aluminum, or copper. It should be packed with 20 percent polyester (polydiethylene glycol succinate is satisfactory) on 60- to 80-mesh, acid washed Chromosorb P or W. The column should be operated at a constant temperature between 190° and 210°C.

(c) The instrument should be equipped with a thermal conductivity detector maintained at the column temperature or at a temperature not more than 25°C. above that of the column.

(d) The recorder should have a 0 to 1 millivolt range and a 1 second full scale deflection with a chart speed of $\frac{1}{2}$ to 1 inch per minute. An attenuation switch is required to alter the recorder range.

Determination of Fatty Acid Composition.[47]—Flow helium gas through the apparatus and adjust the operating conditions. Record a base line to check the stability of the unit. A new column must be preconditioned by maintaining it at 5° to 10°C. above the operating temperature under a constant flow of helium for a period of 24 hours.

The proper gas flow is such that the C_{18} and shorter chain methyl esters will elute within 30 minutes. This must be determined for each instrument and column. The inlet gas pressure should not exceed 40 p.s.i. The gas flow should be maintained constant throughout the duration of an analysis to insure linearity of signal response.

Measure an ester sample of 0.5 to 4 μl. in a hypodermic syringe of 0.01-ml. capacity. Clean the needle tip by wiping, pierce the septum of the sample inlet port, quickly discharge the sample from the syringe, and immediately withdraw the needle. Note on the recorder chart the small peak caused by air which marks the sample introduction reference point. This will be followed immediately by the petroleum ether solvent peak. The sample size must be such that the major peak is not attenuated more than 5 times, preferably less.

[45] Metcalfe, L. D., and Schmitz, A. A., "The Rapid Preparation of Fatty Acid Esters for Gas Chromatographic Analysis," Anal. Chem., **33**, 363, 1961.

[46] Mehlenbacher, The Analysis of Fats and Oils, The Garrard Press, Champaign, Ill., 1960, p. 574.

[47] Herb, S. F., Magidman, P., and Riemenschneider, R. W., "Analysis of Fats and Oils by Gas-Liquid Chromatography and by Ultraviolet Spectrophotometry," J. Am. Oil Chem. Soc., **37**, 127, 1960.

Observe the recorder pen throughout the run, and if automatic attenuation is not provided, change the attenuation, as necessary, to keep the peaks on the chart paper. Note the attenuation on the chart at the point that changes are made. After all the peaks have been traced and the pen has returned to the base line, remove the chart from the recorder.

Calculation.—Determine the area of each methyl ester peak appearing on the chart compensating for attenuation. If the recorder is equipped with an integrator, follow the manufacturer's instructions for its operation. Otherwise, determine the peak area by multiplying the height by half the base (peak height times $\frac{1}{2}$ the width at $\frac{1}{2}$ the height) using calipers. Summate the areas of all the peaks, and calculate the percentage of each as area percent. These percentages are not equivalent to either weight percent or mole percent, and may be in error to a variable extent. For all ordinary work, however, they may be regarded as the percentage of each component present.

Calibration factors can be determined to correct for the nonlinearity of the instrument response and for molecular weight differences by analyzing mixtures of known composition similar to that of the sample itself. The area of each peak as obtained above can then be corrected for instrumental variation by dividing the area by the relative response values obtained from the known mixture. Summating and calculating the corrected area as percent fatty acid will yield results closely approximating true weight percent from which mole percent can be calculated.

Peak Identification.—Peaks are identified by their position (under constant gas flow) on the chart relative to the air or petroleum ether peak. The esters appear in order of increasing number of carbon atoms and of increasing unsaturation for the same number of carbon atoms, *e.g.*, the C_{18} esters appear in this order: stearate; oleate; linoleate; and linolenate. The C_{20} saturated (arachidic) ester usually appears after $C_{18:3}$ (linolenic) ester, but may be reversed in some cases. Identities are established by analyzing mixtures of known composition.

Checking Instrument and Column Performance.—Analyze a known sample containing approximately equal weights of oleate and stearate esters, adjusting the sample size so that the resulting peaks are 25 to 50 percent of the chart width. Calculate the peak resolution as follows:

$$\frac{2X}{S + O} = \text{peak resolution}$$

where: X = distance between the peak maxima for stearate and oleate esters,
$\quad\quad S$ = the base width of the stearate peak, and
$\quad\quad O$ = the base width of the oleate peak.

If the peak resolution is equal to or greater than 1.0, the column and instrument are operating satisfactorily. Columns age under use and exhibit a gradual loss in peak resolution. When the peak resolution decreases to 1.0, a new column should be installed in the instrument.

Rosin fatty acids will interfere in this procedure as they do not completely elute from the column. As a general rule, rosin acids will be found only in the fatty acids isolated from soap. Chemical procedures are available for the determination of rosin acids in fatty acids,[48] in soap and soap products,[49] and in soap containing synthetic detergents.[50]

[48] Official and Tentative Methods of the American Oil Chemists' Society, AOCS Official Method L 14a-58, American Oil Chemists' Society, Chicago, 1963.

[49] Official and Tentative Methods of the American Oil Chemists' Society, AOCS Official Method Da 12-48, American Oil Chemists' Society, Chicago, 1963.

[50] Official and Tentative Methods of the American Oil Chemists' Society, AOCS Official Method Db 11-48, American Oil Chemists' Society, Chicago, 1963.

If it is desired to determine rosin acids (or other nonesterifiable materials) by gas chromatography, it is necessary to take an accurately weighed sample of about 0.34 g. of the acids for esterification with the boron trifluoride reagent. Add to the sample about 0.05 g. (accurately weighed) of margaric acid or pentadecylic acid to serve as an internal standard, and esterify the mixture with 3 ml. of boron trifluoride reagent as already described. Follow the usual procedure for chromatographing the methyl esters.

Calculate the percent of each fatty acid (omitting the margaric or pentadecylic acid) as follows:

$$\frac{Cau}{Cam} \times \frac{Wm}{Wu} \times 100 = \% \text{ fatty acid}$$

where: Cau = corrected area for the unknown fatty acid methyl ester,
Cam = corrected area for the margaric methyl ester,
Wm = weight of margaric acid, and
Wu = weight of unknown fatty acids before addition of margaric acid.

Add the percentages obtained from the above calculation to determine the total eluted fatty acids. The content of noneluted material is obtained by subtracting the total percentage of eluted fatty acid methyl esters from 100 percent.

DETERMINATION OF ETHYL ALCOHOL IN LIQUID DETERGENTS

Scope.—This method is applicable to the determination of ethyl alcohol in liquid detergents.

Principle.—The alcohol is determined by measuring the ratio of peak heights of an internal standard, acetone, and ethyl alcohol. Reference to a curve prepared from known mixtures of alcohol and acetone permits a calculation of alcohol content.[51]

Apparatus. Gas Chromatograph.—Aerograph A-90-C (Wilkens Instrument and Research, Inc., Walnut Creek, Calif.) equipped with a 0–1 millivolt recorder and a $\frac{1}{4}$-inch stainless steel column, 6 feet long, packed with 25 percent Carbowax 20M on acid washed Chromosorb W. Any gas chromatographic instrument of a similar type may be used.

Hypodermic Syringe, 0.01-ml. Capacity.

Vials.—Approximately 7-ml. capacity with tight seal caps or ground glass stoppers.

Reagents. Acetone, Reagent Grade.

Ethyl Alcohol, Reagent Grade, Absolute.

Preparation of Standard Curve.—Equilibrate the gas chromatograph with the column temperature at 100°C., the helium flow rate at 60 cc. per minute and the attenuator set at 8. For instruments containing injector and detector controls, maintain the injector temperature between 265 and 275°C. and the detector controls between 240 and 250°C. Accurately weigh the required amounts of ethyl alcohol and acetone (as shown below) into 7-ml. vials. Take precautions to prevent losses by evaporation during weighing and subsequent handling of standards. Use of septum closed vials is advisable.

| | Standard Mixture | | | |
	1	*2*	*3*	*4*
Weight of ethyl alcohol (grams)	0.200	0.350	0.500	0.650
Weight of acetone (grams)	0.500	0.500	0.500	0.500

[51] Bouthilet, R. J., Caputi, A., Jr., and Ueda, M., "Analysis of Ethanol in Wine by Gas-Liquid Partition Chromatography," J. Assn. Off. Agr. Chemists, **44**, 410, 1961.

Add 1.5 to 2.0 ml. of water to each mixture, stopper, and mix well. Using a 0.01-ml. syringe inject 0.0005 ml. of Standard Mixture 1 into the instrument. Three recorder peaks should be obtained, the acetone appearing first, alcohol second, and water last. The amount injected should be sufficient to develop peak heights of between 60 and 150 mm. It is not necessary to measure an exact volume since the ratio of peak heights is used in subsequent calculations. When the pen has returned to the base line, inject Standard Mixture 2 and record the chromatogram. Repeat for Standard Mixtures 3 and 4. Measure the heights of the alcohol and acetone peaks for each standard mixture. Calculate peak height ratios by dividing the height of the acetone peak for each mixture. Calculate the corresponding weight ratios of the mixtures. Prepare a calibration graph using weight ratios as the abscissa and peak heights as the ordinate.

Sample Analysis.—Accurately weigh the required amount of sample into a 7-ml. vial, and stopper immediately. Add water, if necessary.

Percent expected Ethyl Alcohol Content	Weight of Sample (grams)
0–15	3.000
greater than 15	1.000

Water is added to dissolve any precipitate that may form upon the addition of acetone and to reduce the viscosity of the sample for easier handling in the syringe. Up to 2 ml. of water may be employed for this purpose. Accurately weigh a sufficient amount of acetone into the vial so that an approximate 1:1 weight ratio of alcohol-acetone exists. Stopper and mix well. Using a 0.01-ml. syringe, inject 0.0005 ml. of sample into the instrument. The volume of sample injected should be such that peak heights between 60 and 150 mm. are obtained. Measure the peak heights of the alcohol and acetone and calculate the alcohol-acetone peak height ratio. Determine the weight ratio by reference to the calibration graph.

Calculation.

$$\frac{(\text{weight ratio}) \times (\text{weight of acetone}) \times (100)}{\text{weight of sample}} = \% \text{ ethyl alcohol}$$

MISCELLANEOUS

DETERMINATION OF THE COLOR OF DETERGENT SLURRIES

This method of color determination is applicable to detergent slurries and to powders comprised of alkyl benzene sulfonate, alcohol sulfates, monoglyceride sulfates, or mixtures of these materials and to nonionic polyethylene oxide type materials.

A 5 percent solution (active ingredient or solids basis) is prepared in a solvent mixture and the color read utilizing a Klett-Summerson Colorimeter and a No. 42 blue filter.

Preparation of Sample.—Slurry samples should be received from the source without delay and stored in an oven maintained at 40 to 50°C., in tightly closed containers, until ready for analysis. Samples received warm and stored as above can be readily mixed in the original container with a spatula to yield a representative sample. Slurries that have been allowed to cool and are crystallized should be treated as described in the section on sampling. Powders, chips, and sprayed materials present no special problem beyond representative sampling.

Color on Active Ingredient Content Basis.—Determine the active ingredient content of the sample by ultraviolet absorption. Weigh an amount of sample equivalent to 5.0 g. of active ingredient into a 150-ml. beaker.

$$\frac{5.0 \times 100}{\% \text{ active ingredient}} = \text{sample weight}$$

Color on Solids Basis.   Determine the solids content of the sample by distillation as described in Standard Methods of Chemical Analysis, Vol. 2, Part B, page 2281.

Weigh an amount of sample equivalent to 5.0 g. of solids into a 150-ml. beaker.

$$\frac{5.0 \times 100}{\% \text{ solids}} = \text{sample weight}$$

Initial Treatment of Slurries.—If the sample is a slurry, add 5 ml. of ethylene glycol monobutyl ether (sold by Union Carbide Corp. under the proprietary name of Butyl Cellosolve) to the sample in the beaker, and mix thoroughly while heating to a temperature not exceeding 50°C. Stir thoroughly until all solid particles are completely dispersed or dissolved. The appearance of two layers at this point is normal.

NOTE.—Samples of alcohol sulfates and monoglyceride sulfates require the addition of 10 ml. of ethylene glycol monobutyl ether.

Nonionics of the polyethylene oxide type require special treatment. In the case of the latter mix 5.0 g. of the sample with 12.5 ml. of ethylene glycol monobutyl ether in a 100-ml. volumetric flask. Dilute to volume with a 2:1 water-acetone solution (weight basis) and mix thoroughly. Proceed as directed for the measurement of color using a 12.5 percent ethylene glycol monobutyl ether-87.5 percent water-acetone (2:1) solution as a blank.

Initial Treatment of Solids.—If the sample is a powder, add 10 to 20 ml. of water and prepare a slurry by mixing thoroughly while heating to a temperature not exceeding 50°C. Add 5 ml. of ethylene glycol monobutyl ether and mix as described for slurry samples.

Determination of Color.—Add 50 ml. of water to the mixture in the beaker (either slurry or powder sample prepared as described) and stir thoroughly while warming slightly (30 to 40°C.) until the solution clears and becomes transparent. In the case of detergents that contain alkyl benzene sulfonate, add 5 to 10 ml. of acetone and mix thoroughly. An additional 10 to 15 ml. of water may be necessary in some cases to yield a transparent solution.

Quantitatively transfer the clear solution to a 100-ml. volumetric flask and dilute to volume with water at room temperature. Mix well. Transfer 70 to 80 ml. of the solution to a 100-ml. centrifuge tube and centrifuge for 15 to 20 minutes.

Transfer a sufficient volume of the supernatant solution to a 40 × 20 mm. Klett cell. Using the 40-mm. cell light path, a No. 42 blue filter, and a 5 percent aqueous ethylene glycol monobutyl ether solution as a blank, read the Klett number directly from the Klett-Summerson colorimeter.

NOTE.—In some cases a 5 percent solution is impractical as a result of limited solubility of the sample. In such cases a 2.5 percent solution may be prepared and the color reading multiplied by a factor of 2.

If the solution is permitted to stand for any length of time, turbidity may result. Slight warming (30 to 40°C.) will restore clarity. It is recommended that the determination of color be made without interruption.

Use the No. 42 blue filter and a 10 percent aqueous solution of ethylene glycol monobutyl ether as a blank when determining the color of alcohol sulfates and monoglyceride sulfates.

Klett-Summerson colorimeters are available from the Klett Manufacturing Co., New York, N. Y.

AUTOMATIC ANALYSIS TRAINS
AUTOMATED DETERMINATION OF TOTAL PHOSPHORUS IN SYNDETS

Scope.—This method is applicable to the determination of total phosphates present in soaps and detergents.

Principle.—A solution of the sample is subjected to an acid hydrolysis which converts the various phosphate species to the ortho-form. The orthophosphate is reacted with ammonium molybdate and hydrazine sulfate to form the molybdenum blue complex. The intensity of color developed measures the amount of phosphate in the sample. This automated procedure relies on the use of the Autoanalyzer, a registered trade name for the instrument manufactured by Technicon Controls, Inc., Chauncey, N. Y. This device permits the rapid automatic analysis of replicate samples with a great saving of

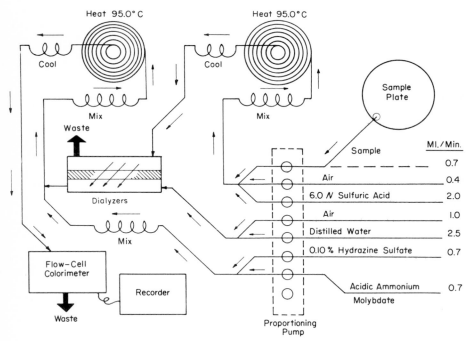

FIG. 61-2.   Autoanalyzer Flow Diagram for the Determination of Total Phosphorus in Syndets.

time. The instrument is equipped to perform the entire analysis including hydrolysis, reagent addition, color development, and read-out.[52]

[52] Lundgren, D. L., "Phosphate Analysis with the Technicon Autoanalyzer," Anal. Chem., **32,** 824, 1960.

Apparatus. **Autoanalyzer Unit.**—The apparatus for this analysis requires the use of the following modules: sampler, pump, heating baths (2), dialyzer, colorimeter (with 6-mm. tubular flow cell), and recorder. Accessory tubing, mixing coils, and recorder paper calibrated in absorbance units are also needed.

Assembling Units.—The modules are assembled in the following order: sampler, pump, heating bath for hydrolysis, dialyzer, heating bath for color development, colorimeter, and recorder. Figure 61-2 shows a schematic drawing of the recommended tubing and coil system. The designated rates of flow are controlled by the tubing diameter, the various sizes being color coded for identification. For further details on assembly and check-out refer to the manufacturer's manual.

Sample Analysis.—Depending on the total P_2O_5 level in the sample, accurately weigh between 0.2 to 0.5 g. of sample and dissolve in water. Dilute to 500 ml. in a volumetric flask. Mix well and fill sample cups with the solution. It is recommended that, initially, a minimum of two cups be used for each sample, the final results being averaged. Insert the cups in the sample holder placing a cup of distilled water between each sample. Make certain that the heating baths are up to temperature (95°C.) and start the flow, passing water through first. The subsequent analyses follow automatically.

Standard solutions of phosphate containing 100, 150, 200, and 300 p.p.m. (or any other range desired) are prepared from pure potassium dihydrogen phosphate (KH_2PO_4). These are passed through the instrument as described. Plot the average absorbance of each standard *vs.* the concentration of P_2O_5.

From the peak height (absorbance) of the unknown, calculate the equivalent P_2O_5 content using the prepared calibration curve.

Chapter 62

SOILS

By Edward J. Rubins
Professor of Agronomy
University of Connecticut
Storrs, Connecticut

LIGHT ABSORPTION SPECTROMETRY

Photometric methods are used routinely in soil analysis for the determination of several elements. Detailed procedures for the application of some of these to soils have been given previously.[1] It is assumed that the reader is familiar with the routine operations of the technique. Therefore, such details as the preparation of stock and working standards, the construction of calibration curves, and the calculation of results have been omitted from the procedures that follow. Reagent blanks should be carried with each set of determinations. The methods given are for quantitative procedures. Semiquantitative colorimetric spot plate or "quick-test" methods are not included.[2]

ALUMINUM

ALUMINON METHOD

The usual method for the determination of small quantities of aluminum in soil extracts has been the aluminon (aurintricarboxylic acid) method. Serious interference is encountered from several ions occurring in soil digests and extracts. Prevention of interference has been accomplished in various ways.[3] The following procedure is adapted to the determination of aluminum isolated from soil digests by hydroxide separation[4] or by ion-exchange separation.[5]

Reagent Solutions. **Acetate Buffer.**—Dilute 60 ml. of glacial acetic acid to 900 ml. with water. Add 100 ml. of 10 percent sodium hydroxide. Adjust the pH to 4.2.

Aluminon.—Dissolve 0.200 g. of aluminon (aurintricarboxylic acid) in 100 ml. of the acetate buffer solution. Dilute with water to 500 ml.

Procedure.—Place an aliquot of test solution containing up to 50 μg. of aluminum in a 50-ml. volumetric flask. The aliquot should contain sufficient hydrochloric acid to bring the pH to 3.7–4.0 after addition of the acetate buffer and aluminon solutions. Heat on the steam bath for 30 min. Cool and dilute to a 25-ml. volume. Add 10 ml. of acetate buffer and exactly 10.0 ml. of aluminon solution. Make to volume with water, mix, and determine transmittancy at 520 mμ.

[1] Welcher, F. J., Ed., Standard Methods of Chemical Analysis, 6th Ed., D. Van Nostrand Co., Inc., Princeton, N. J., Vol. II, Part B, pp. 2310–2337.

[2] See Lunt, *et al.*, Conn. Agr. Exp. Sta. Bull., 541, 1958, for details of tests and bibliography.

[3] See Yuan and Fiskell, J. Agr. Food Chem., 7, 115–117, 1959; and Hsu, Soil Sci., **96**, 230–238, 1963.

[4] Jackson, M. L., Soil Chemical Analysis, Prentice-Hall, Inc., Englewood Cliffs, N. J., 1958, pp. 297–300.

[5] Page and Bingham, Soil Sci. Soc. Am. Proc., **26**, 351–355, 1962.

AMMONIA

Ammonia is sometimes determined by direct nesslerization of soil extracts. It is usually preferable to treat the extract with alkali, distill, and nesslerize an aliquot of the distillate.[6]

BORON

CURCUMIN METHOD

Procedures for the determination of total boron and available boron in soils with quinalizarin have been given previously.[7] A simplified method using curcumin has been applied to boron determinations in soils.[8] It offers several advantages over the quinalizarin procedure, including the fact that color development and measurement do not take place in concentrated sulfuric acid. The precautions and procedures for obtaining the test solutions are the same as those given for the quinalizarin method, except that 0.10 N hydrochloric acid is used in place of 0.36 N sulfuric acid in preparing test solutions for color development.

Reagent Solution. **Curcumin-Oxalic Acid.**—Dissolve 0.04 g. of finely ground curcumin and 5 g. of oxalic acid in 100 ml. of 95 percent ethyl alcohol. Store in a refrigerator. Prepare a fresh supply weekly.

Procedure.—Transfer a 1-ml. aliquot of test solution containing up to 2.0 μg. of boron in 0.10 N hydrochloric acid to a 250-ml. beaker of boron-free glass. Add 4 ml. of curcumin-oxalic acid solution and rotate the beaker to mix thoroughly. Evaporate to dryness at 55°C. $\pm$ 3°C. and continue to bake at this temperature for at least 15 min. When cool, take up the residue in 25 ml. of 95 percent ethyl alcohol. Filter into a comparison tube through Whatman No. 2 or similar paper. Read transmittancy at 540 mμ.

COPPER, ZINC, AND COBALT

Several methods of sample preparation, digestion or extraction, and photometric estimation have been reported. These biologically important metallic elements occur in soils in trace amounts. The analyst must keep in mind the possibility of contamination from equipment, glassware, and reagents at every step. Each laboratory tends to develop with experience its own ritual for the cleansing of glassware and the purification of reagents. The redistillation of water, hydrochloric acid, nitric acid, and ammonia from all-Pyrex stills, while usually called for, may not always be necessary. The source of contamination and the measures needed for its elimination will vary from laboratory to laboratory. The following alternatives are offered for consideration: The use of Vycor in place of Pyrex ware for wet digestions; the use of deionized water in place of redistilled water; the storage of water and reagent solutions in polyethylene bottles; and the use of separatory funnels equipped with Teflon valves.

PREPARATION OF TEST SOLUTION

Sieving.—Pass a well-mixed air-dried sample through a 2-mm. iron sieve or a screen mesh of Nylon or similar material. For total analysis, reduce the sample to 5–10 g. by quartering and grind in an agate mortar until the entire subsample passes a 100-mesh sieve of Nylon or similar nonmetallic material.

[6] Welcher, F. J., Ed., Standard Methods of Chemical Analysis, 6th Ed., D. Van Nostrand Co., Inc., Princeton, N. J., Vol. II, Part B, 1963, pp. 2316–2317 and 2327–2328.
[7] *Ibid.*, pp. 2323–2324 and 2336.
[8] Dible, *et al.*, Anal. Chem., **26**, 418–421, 1954.

***Decomposition with Hydrofluoric Acid for Total Analysis.*[9]**—Place 0.1 to 0.3 g. of 100-mesh soil in a platinum crucible. Ignite in a muffle furnace at 400°–500°C. to destroy organic matter. Cool, add a few ml. of water, 0.5–1.0 ml. of 70 percent perchloric acid, and 3 ml. of hydrofluoric acid. Evaporate to dryness on the sand bath at 180°C. Repeat the addition and evaporation of water and acid until virtually all the silica has disappeared. Then add 1 ml. of perchloric acid and evaporate. Add 2 ml. of redistilled (constant boiling) hydrochloric acid and a few ml. of water to the residue and heat to boiling. Transfer the solution or a suitable aliquot to a separatory funnel for separation and determination of copper, zinc, or cobalt.

Digestion with Perchloric Acid.—Digestions of 100-mesh soil have been carried out with perchloric acid or perchloric-sulfuric acid mixtures in micro-Kjeldahl flasks, digestion tubes, or conical flasks. The question has been raised concerning the quantity of trace metal ion retained by the silica residue in this process. Complete recovery has been claimed when digestions were carried out with 60 percent perchloric acid in 100-ml. wide-mouth conical flasks equipped with special reflux cover glasses.[10] Boiling for 1 hr. followed by evaporation almost to dryness was found to dehydrate silica without its retention of copper, zinc, cobalt, or lead. The residue was then taken up in hydrochloric acid, heated under reflux conditions for 20 to 30 min., and a suitable aliquot of the solution taken for analysis.

Other Extraction Procedures.—Many extractants have been used in attempts to measure that portion of the total soil content of copper or zinc that is available for use by living organisms.[11] Soil that has passed a 2-mm. or 1-mm. mesh sieve is used in place of 100-mesh soil.

DETERMINATION OF COPPER—
DIBENZYLDITHIOCARBAMATE (ARAZATE) METHOD

Copper in soil digests or extracts has been separated in citrate buffer and determined as the dithizonate. But it is preferable to destroy the dithizonate by digestion with nitric and perchloric acids, take the residue up in dilute hydrochloric acid, adjust the pH to 8.5 with ammonia, and determine copper as the diethyldithiocarbamate.[12] Other procedures call for the direct determination of copper as carbamate without first forming the dithizonate.[13] A still simpler technique is to determine copper as the dibenzyldithiocarbamate (arazate).[14] The colored complex forms in acid solutions so that it is not necessary to neutralize soil digests or extracts made up in strong mineral acid. Metallic ions ordinarily present in soils do not interfere.

Reagent Solution. Zinc Dibenzyldithiocarbamate.—Dissolve 0.25 g. of zinc dibenzyldithiocarbamate (arazate) in 500 ml. of Reagent Grade or redistilled carbon tetrachloride.

Procedure.—Transfer to a separatory funnel an aliquot of acid test solution (below pH 2) containing up to 20 μg. of copper. Add 5 ml. of zinc dibenzyldithiocarbamate solution and shake for 30 sec. After the phases have separated, pass the organic layer through Pyrex filtering fiber into a 10-ml. volumetric flask. Repeat the extraction and separation with another 5-ml. portion of solution, make to volume, and measure the transmittancy at 440 mμ.

[9] Adapted from Hanna, in Bear, F., Ed., Chemistry of the Soil, 2nd Ed., 1964, Reinhold Publishing Corp., New York, 1964, pp. 485–489.
[10] Holmes, Soil Sci., **59**, 77–84, 1945.
[11] Jackson, M. L., Soil Chemical Analysis, Prentice-Hall, Inc., Englewood Cliffs, N. J., 1958, pp. 400–402, 406–408.
[12] Holmes, Soil Sci., **59**, 77–84, 1945.
[13] Bear, F., Chemistry of the Soil, 2nd Ed., 1964, 486–487; and Jackson, M. L., Soil Chemical Analysis, Prentice-Hall, Inc., Englewood Cliffs, N. J., 1958, pp. 396–398.
[14] Hagstrom and Rubins, Bull. 360, Storrs Agr. Exp. Sta., 1961.

DETERMINATION OF ZINC AND COBALT[15]

Several modifications of the dithizone method have been used. Ammonium citrate is added to prevent interference by aluminum and iron. Copper may be removed and determined as the dithizonate prior to extraction of zinc dithizonate at pH 8.3. If not removed, carbamate or thiosulfate has been added to prevent interference by copper and other metals with the zinc separation. Dithizone is used to isolate cobalt from soil digests prior to determination with o-nitrosocresol.

IRON

ORTHOPHENANTHROLINE METHOD

Several reagents have been employed for the photometric determination of small quantities of iron in soil extracts. The orthophenanthroline method is convenient and is free from interference by ions occurring in soil extracts.

Reagent Solutions. Hydroxylamine Hydrochloride.—Dissolve 10 g. of hydroxylamine hydrochloride in 100 ml. of water. Store in the refrigerator.

Orthophenanthroline.—Heat 400 ml. of water to boiling. Add 1 g. of orthophenanthroline and stir until dissolved. Cool, replace any water lost by evaporation by diluting to 400 ml., and store in the refrigerator.

Procedure.—Transfer an aliquot of the test solution (adjusted to pH 2 to 4) to a 50-ml. volumetric flask. Add 1 ml. of hydroxylamine hydrochloride solution and 4 ml. of orthophenanthroline solution. Make to volume, mix, and measure transmittancy at 515 mμ.

OTHER METHODS

Two other reagents have found special application in analysis of soils. Tiron (disodium 1,2-dihydroxybenzene-3,5-disulfonate) has been used to determine both iron and titanium in the same aliquot of test solution.[16] Bathophenanthroline has been used to determine total ferrous iron. The solubility of the colored ferrous bathophenanthroline complex in nitrobenzene or isoamyl alcohol permits the concentration and determination of very small quantities.[17]

MAGNESIUM

Magnesium in soil extracts has been determined indirectly by precipitation as magnesium ammonium phosphate in calcium-free solution followed by analysis for phosphorus by the molybdenum blue method.[18] It has also been determined as the colored compound formed with 8-hydroxyquinoline.[19] Many procedures have been based on the absorption of titan yellow or thiazol yellow on magnesium hydroxide. Several elements ordinarily present in soil extracts interfere. Some procedures call for the prior removal of these by precipitation with various reagents, whereas others require the addition to standards and unknowns of compensating solutions containing the

[15] Soil Sci., **59**, 77–84, 1945; Jackson, M. L., Soil Chemical Analysis, Prentice-Hall, Inc., Englewood Cliffs, N. J., 1958, pp. 402–405; and Bear, F., Chemistry of the Soil, 2nd Ed., 1964, Reinhold Publishing Corp., New York, 1964, pp. 484–490.
[16] Jackson, M. L., Soil Chemical Analysis, Prentice-Hall, Inc., Englewood Cliffs, N. J., 1958, pp. 291–293.
[17] Walker and Sherman, Soil Sci., **93**, 325–328, 1962.
[18] Reitemeier, Ind. Eng. Chem., Anal. Ed., **15**, 393–402, 1943.
[19] Jackson, M. L., Soil Chemical Analysis, Prentice-Hall, Inc., Englewood Cliffs, N. J., 1958, pp. 100–102.

interfering ions.[20] The need for the development of a reliable and simple photometric method for the determination of magnesium in soils and soil extracts has been lessened recently by improvements in flame spectrometry and the introduction of atomic absorption methods.[21]

MANGANESE

PERIODATE METHOD

Manganese in various soil extracts is determined by periodate oxidation in phosphoric acid solution. The test solution should be free of reducing substances (organic matter, halides, ammonium) and, preferably, of sulfate as well. The following convenient final preparative treatment has been suggested:[22] Evaporate the test solution to dryness in a 150-ml. beaker. Digest with nitric acid and hydrogen peroxide, and, finally, evaporate once more to dryness.

Procedure.—Add 10 ml. of 85 percent orthophosphoric acid to the residue in the 150-ml. beaker and heat on the steam bath. Then add 50 ml. of water and 0.2 g. of potassium metaperiodate or sodium paraperiodate. Digest on the steam bath for 40 min., adding a little more periodate toward the end of the digestion period. Cool and make to volume with dilute phosphoric acid solution. (Prepare by boiling a mixture of 100 ml. of 85 percent phosphoric acid, 1000 ml. of water, and 1 g. of periodate). Read the transmittancy at 540 mμ.

MOLYBDENUM

Molybdenum has been determined by the thiocyanate method[23] and by the dithiol method.[24] For total analysis the soil is decomposed by sodium carbonate fusion. Extraction of molybdenum from the fusion products has been carried out with water (alkaline slurry method)[25] or with hydrochloric acid.

PREPARATION OF TEST SOLUTION

Sodium Carbonate Fusion for Total Analysis.—Mix 2.00 g. of 100-mesh soil with 4.0 g. of sodium carbonate in a platinum crucible. Ignite in the open over a Meker-type burner for 30 min., gradually increasing the flame from low to high heat during the first 10 min. Cool the melt and detach the fusion cake into a 250-ml. beaker. Wash the crucible with small portions of water and combine the washings (30 to 40 ml.) with the fusion cake in the beaker. Add 20 ml. of concentrated hydrochloric acid, cover, and digest on the steam bath for at least 2 hr. Fusion in the muffle furnace or the addition of hydrochloric acid to the fusion cake in the crucible may remove sufficient platinum to interfere with subsequent photometric determination by the dithiol method.

Evaporate the solution nearly to dryness on the steam bath, stirring frequently as dryness is approached. Terminate the evaporation when the nearly dry residue no

[20] Peech and English, Soil Sci., **57**, 167–195, 1944; Drosdoff and Nearpass, Anal. Chem., **20**, 673–674, 1948; Mikkelson, *et al.*, Soil Sci., **66**, 385–392, 1948; and Toth, *et al.*, Soil Sci., **66**, 459–466, 1948.

[21] See pp. 1874–1876.

[22] Jackson, M. L., Soil Chemical Analysis, Prentice-Hall, Inc., Englewood Cliffs, N. J., 1958, pp. 104–105.

[23] Purvis and Peterson, Soil Sci., **81**, 223–228, 1956; Johnson and Arkley, Anal. Chem., **26**, 572–573, 1954.

[24] Clark and Axley, Anal. Chem., **27**, 2000–2003, 1955; Bingley, J. Agr. Food Chem., **7**, 269–270, 1959.

[25] Jackson, M. L., Soil Chemical Analysis, Prentice-Hall, Inc., Englewood Cliffs, N. J., 1958, pp. 411–413.

longer adheres to the tip of the stirring rod. The odor of hydrochloric acid should still be perceptible from the residue in the beaker. Add 5 ml. concentrated hydrochloric acid and 25 ml. water to the cooled residue, stir and heat on the steam bath for 15 min. Filter into a 100-ml. volumetric flask. Wash with small portions of hot 0.25 N hydrochloric acid and finally with water. For colorimetric determination by dithiol, the entire solution should contain approximately 6 ml. of concentrated hydrochloric acid.

Soil Extracts.[26]—Molybdenum has been determined in various soil extracts in attempts to measure the portion available to plants. Such extracts should be treated to remove organic matter and made up in hydrochloric acid. The presence of 2 to 10 mg. of iron is necessary for complete color development with both the thiocyanate and the dithiol methods. The addition of iron as a solution of ferric chloride should be made to soil extracts prior to color development. Iron should not be added to the test solution from sodium carbonate fusion for total molybdenum determination.

THIOCYANATE METHOD

Reagent Solutions. **Stannous Chloride.**—Dissolve 20 g. stannous chloride in 20 ml. concentrated hydrochloric acid by warming almost to boiling. Add 100 ml. distilled water. Prepare fresh daily.

Ammonium Thiocyanate.—Dissolve 10 g. of ammonium thiocyanate in water and dilute to 100 ml.

Sodium Nitrate.—Dissolve 42.5 g. of sodium nitrate in water and dilute to 100 ml.

Extraction Mixture.—Mix Reagent Grade or redistilled carbon tetrachloride with an equal volume of Reagent Grade or redistilled isoamyl alcohol.

Procedure.—Transfer the entire test solution from the sodium carbonate fusion to a separatory funnel. Add sufficient extraction mixture to saturate the aqueous phase. Shake thoroughly, allow the phases to separate, and discard the excess organic layer. Add 1 ml. sodium nitrate solution, 5 ml. ammonium thiocyanate solution, and 5 ml. stannous chloride solution, shaking thoroughly after each addition. Add a measured volume of extraction mixture (usually 5.00 to 10.00 ml., depending upon molybdenum concentration) and shake for 2 min. Allow the phases to separate. Pass the organic layer through Pyrex filtering fiber into absorption tubes or cells and measure transmittancy at 470 mμ.

DITHIOL METHOD

Reagent Solutions. **Potassium Iodide.**—Dissolve 10 g. of potassium iodide in 20 ml. of water. Prepare fresh solution daily.

Sodium Thiosulfate.—Dissolve 10 g. of sodium thiosulfate ($Na_2S_2O_3 \cdot 5H_2O$) in water and dilute to 100 ml. Store in a refrigerator.

Tartaric Acid.—Dissolve 50 g. of tartaric acid in water and dilute to 100 ml.

Extraction Mixture.—Mix one volume of Reagent Grade or redistilled benzene with 4 volumes of Reagent Grade or redistilled chloroform.

Dithiol.—Warm a 1-g. vial of dithiol (4-methyl-1,2-dimercaptobenzene) to 38°C. Dissolve in 500 ml. of 1 percent sodium hydroxide solution also warmed to 38°C. Add thioglycolic acid slowly until a faint turbidity persists. Transfer to glass-stoppered reagent bottles and store in a refrigerator. Reagent stored under refrigeration in unopened, completely filled bottles will keep for 4 weeks or longer.

Procedure.—Transfer an aliquot of test solution from sodium carbonate fusion containing approximately 1.5 ml. of concentrated hydrochloric acid to a separatory funnel. Add 10 ml. of concentrated hydrochloric acid and 1 ml. of freshly prepared

[26] See Jackson, M. L., Soil Chemical Analysis, Prentice-Hall, Inc., Englewood Cliffs, N. J., 1958, p. 414; and Soil Sci., **81**, 223–238, 1956.

potassium iodide solution. Mix by swirling and allow to stand 10 min. Add sodium thiosulfate solution dropwise until the color of free iodine is just discharged. Add 1 ml. of tartaric acid solution and mix thoroughly. Add 2 ml. of dithiol solution, shake 30 sec., and let stand 10 min. Add 5.00 ml. of extraction mixture, shake 30 sec., and allow the phases to separate. Draw off the organic layer through Pyrex filtering fiber into an absorption tube or cell and measure transmittancy at 680 mμ.

NITRATE

Nitrate may be determined by extracting the soil with dilute copper sulfate solution followed by color development with phenol-2,4-disulfonic acid as previously described.[27] Extraction has also been made with water or with water in the presence of calcium oxide, followed by treatment of the extracts with activated charcoal or with hydrogen peroxide to destroy organic matter. Chlorides interfere in the determination if present in the soil in excess of 10 p.p.m. The interference is removed by addition of silver sulfate to the copper sulfate extracting solution.[28]

PHOSPHORUS

A number of methods for the determination of phosphorus in soils and in soil extracts have been based upon the molybdophosphoric blue color and upon the vanadomolybdo-phosphoric yellow color. The choice of method has depended upon the sensitivity required and the interferences encountered.

MOLYBDOPHOSPHORIC BLUE METHOD

Details of several molybdophosphoric blue methods for soils and soil extracts have been given.[29] In one of these, molybdenum metal serves as the reducing agent and is incorporated in the molybdate reagent. The method is moderately sensitive with a working range of 0.1 to 2 p.p.m. phosphorus in the final solution. Provision is made for the elimination of interference from silicon, pentavalent arsenic, and ferric iron. In contrast to other molybdophosphoric blue methods, the color is stable but pretreatment and color development are relatively lengthy. Development of the molybdophosphoric color with stannous chloride as reducing agent is more rapid, but the color is not stable and photometric readings must be made within prescribed time limits. The greater sensitivity (working range 0.02–1 p.p.m. phosphorus) of this modification is often required for soil extracts.

VANADOMOLYBDOPHOSPHORIC YELLOW METHOD

Vanadomolybdophosphoric yellow methods are convenient to carry out and are relatively free of ion interferences. The color is stable and develops rapidly. Unfortunately, relatively low sensitivity (working range 1–20 p.p.m. phosphorus) limits its use in soils work. Jackson has given two adaptations, one originally applied to analysis of steel, and the other to phosphate rock.[30]

Reagent Solutions. Ammonium Metavanadate.—Dissolve 2.35 g. of ammonium metavanadate in 500 ml. of hot water. Add 10 ml. of concentrated nitric acid. Dilute the solution to 1 liter when cool.

[27] Welcher, F. J., Ed., Standard Methods of Chemical Analysis, 6th Ed., D. Van Nostrand Co., Inc., Princeton, N. J., Vol. II, Part B, 1963, pp. 2317–2318.
[28] Jackson, M. L., Soil Chemical Analysis, Prentice-Hall, Inc., Englewood Cliffs, N. J., 1958, pp. 198–199; Soil Sci., **59**, 47–52, 1945.
[29] Welcher, F. J., Ed., Standard Methods of Chemical Analysis, 6th Ed., D. Van Nostrand Co., Inc., Princeton, N. J., Vol. II, Part B, 1963, pp. 2322–2323, 2334–2336.
[30] Jackson, M. L., Soil Chemical Analysis, Prentice-Hall, Inc., Englewood Cliffs, N. J., 1958, pp. 151–154.

Ammonium Molybdate.—Dissolve 100 g. of ammonium molybdate in 500 ml. of warm water (50°C.) containing 10 ml. of concentrated ammonium hydroxide. Filter and dilute to 1 liter. Store in the dark.

Procedure.—An aliquot of test solution containing up to 400 μg. of phosphorus is placed in a 50-ml. volumetric flask. Add sufficient 1:1 nitric acid to bring the acidity to approximately 0.75 M when diluted to 50 ml. Dilute with water to 35–40 ml. Add 2.5 ml. ammonium metavanadate solution and mix by swirling. Add 2.5 ml. ammonium molybdate solution. Dilute to the mark, mix, and determine transmittancy at 420 mμ.

TITANIUM

Titanium in soils is usually determined with peroxide following sodium carbonate fusion.[31]

EMISSION SPECTROMETRY

Emission spectrometry by the arc technique has been applied to the total analysis of soils and to the analysis of soil extracts. The spark method has had more limited use. Flame emission methods are discussed elsewhere.[32]

The greatest usefulness of arc spectrometry is realized when simultaneous determination of several elements is required, particularly of those that occur in the soil in trace amounts. The determination of a single trace element or of those occurring in larger quantities is usually carried out more conveniently by other techniques. Mitchell has summarized the scope and limitations of emission spectrometry in soil analysis.[33] The complex nature of the soil and its variable composition present the analyst with problems not encountered with many other materials.

The direct current arc has been used for total analysis in surveys of the trace element status of soils. Some of these elements are important in plant and animal nutrition and, since they may vary greatly in content from soil to soil, rapid semiquantitative determinations may furnish clues toward the solution of nutritional problems caused by the presence of an element in toxic or deficient amounts.

With soil extracts it is usually necessary to employ chemical separation before attempting spectrographic analysis for trace elements. Various extractants have been used in attempts to measure the availability to the biosphere of soil constituents. For a given element, the "available" fraction thus extracted may represent only a small portion of the total quantity in the soil. For trace constituents, a considerable concentration factor is needed for satisfactory spectrographic work. Spectrographic instrumentation and its application to soil analysis has been presented in considerable detail.[34]

In this, as in all work with trace constituents, care must be taken to reduce the hazard of contamination. Sources of contamination from equipment, laboratory fixtures, or reagents may vary from laboratory to laboratory and from time to time. Continued careful evaluation of each step in the sampling and analytical process is required. Suggested procedures to be used in the laboratory for the purification of reagents and the care of equipment have been detailed.[35] Recommendations include the use of silica-

---

[31] Welcher, F. J., Ed., Standard Methods of Chemical Analysis, 6th Ed., D. Van Nostrand Co., Inc., Princeton, N. J., Vol. II, Part B, 1963, p. 2263.
[32] See p. 1874.
[33] Soil Sci., **83**, 1–13, 1957.
[34] Jackson, M. L., ed., Soil Chemical Analysis, Prentice-Hall, Inc., Englewood Cliffs, N. J., 1958, pp. 452–485; Soil Sci., **83**, 1–83, 1957.
[35] Mitchell, Commonwealth Bur. Soil Sci., Tech. Commun., **44**, 1948.

lined muffle furnaces for ignition and the coating with plastic paint of metallic surfaces in the laboratory. There is a hazard of mutual contamination of plant and soil samples. It is suggested that the latter be taken with an iron auger, kept in nonmetallic containers, dried on clean sheets of paper lining nonmetallic or aluminum trays, and passed through sieves made of aluminum.

TOTAL ANALYSIS FOR TRACE CONSTITUENTS

RAPID SEMIQUANTITATIVE ESTIMATION[36]

Procedure.—Pass the soil sample through a 2-mm. aluminum sieve. Quarter the sample to give a 20-g. aliquot. Grind in a mechanical agate mortar for 30 to 60 min. to about 100-mesh size. Ignite at 450°C. in a silica-lined muffle furnace to destroy organic matter. Place directly in the crater of a carbon electrode and excite in the direct current cathode arc.

SODIUM NITRATE BUFFER METHOD[37]

Procedure.—Place 2.0 g. of 100-mesh, oven-dry soil in a platinum crucible. Add 1 ml. sulfuric acid, 3 ml. nitric acid, and 2 ml. of perchloric acid. Heat on the sand bath, adding further portions of nitric acid when white fumes are evolved. Continue to heat until all organic matter is destroyed and all the nitric and perchloric acid has been volatilized. Dilute the remaining sulfuric acid with a little water, add 2 ml. of hydrofluoric acid, and heat on the sand bath to volatilize the silica. Repeat the hydrofluoric acid treatment until all the silica has been removed, adding a little sulfuric acid if necessary to avoid taking the residue to complete dryness.

Transfer the contents of the platinum crucible to a volumetric flask and make to volume. Aluminum, calcium copper, iron, magnesium, potassium, strontium, and titanium are determined suitable aliquots of this solution, using molybdenum as internal standard. The aliquot is evaporated to a small volume in a beaker. Sodium nitrate, nitric acid, and molybdate are added, and the mixture is made to an exact final volume so chosen that each ml. contains 0.20 g. sodium nitrate, 0.05 ml. nitric acid, and 0.20 mg. molybdenum. Determine with the alternating current arc.

Al_2O_3—Fe_2O_3—GRAPHITE MATRIX METHOD

Procedure.—To determine bismuth, cadmium, cobalt, chromium, gallium, lead, molybdenum, nickel, tin, vanadium, and zinc, a suitable aliquot is taken of the solution prepared by hydrofluoric acid treatment as described under "Sodium Nitrate Buffer Method," above. The elements are concentrated and determined as described under "Analysis of Soil Extracts."

ANALYSIS OF SOIL EXTRACTS

Some soil extractants lend themselves to subsequent spectroscopic examination more readily than others. Ammonium acetate or acetic acid solutions are convenient. Their organic content can be removed readily, following evaporation. Extracting solutions that contain metallic cations, such as sodium acetate or barium acetate, should be avoided, as should those that may require extensive treatment to remove organic matter, such as citric acid or ammonium oxalate. Unfortunately, an extractant that is suitable from a spectrographic point of view may not provide the desired information regarding the biological availability of the element.

[36] *Ibid.*

[37] Bear, F., Chemistry of the Soil, Reinhold Publishing Corp., New York, 1964, pp. 492–493.

CHEMICAL CONCENTRATION AND DETERMINATION[38]

Reagent Solutions. Ammonium Acetate.—Prepare a 2 M solution.

Acetic Acid.—Prepare a 2 M solution.

Hydroxyquinoline.—Dissolve 5 g. of 8-hydroxyquinoline in 2 M acetic acid.

Tannic Acid.—Prepare a fresh 10 percent solution by dissolving 5 g. of tannic acid in 50 ml. of 2 M ammonium acetate.

Thionalide.—Prepare a fresh 1 percent solution by dissolving 0.5 g. of thionalide in 50 ml. of glacial acetic acid.

Procedure.—Evaporate the soil extract (2.5 percent acetic acid or neutral ammonium acetate) to dryness on the steam bath. Destroy organic matter with hydrogen peroxide or with nitric acid. Take up the residue in dilute hydrochloric acid. If nitric acid is used to destroy organic matter, it should be removed by repeated evaporation with hydrochloric acid. Make the solution to a volume of 150 ml., containing 15 ml. of concentrated hydrochloric acid. Aluminum equivalent to about 30 mg. Al_2O_3 and iron equivalent to 2–5 mg. Fe_2O_3 must either be present or the solution must be made up to this amount at this point. The former provides the carrier for the trace element precipitates and the matrix for the spectrographic determination, whereas the latter is used as an internal standard for all elements except zinc. A solution of cadmium chloride is added to provide 0.4 mg. of cadmium as an internal standard for zinc. Fifteen ml. of 8-hydroxyquinoline solution is added and the solution adjusted with 1:1 ammonium hydroxide to the yellow to green color change which occurs at pH 1.8–1.9. The solution is stirred continuously as 30 ml. of ammonium acetate solution is added followed by 2 ml. of tannic acid solution and 2 ml. of thionalide solution. Sufficient ammonium hydroxide is then added to bring the pH to 5.1–5.2. After standing overnight, the precipitate is filtered, washed, and dried. It is then ashed in porcelain at 450°C. and allowed to reach air-dry moisture equilibrium. It is then weighed and sufficient Al_2O_3 added to make up the weight to 40 mg. The ash is ground in an agate mortar. An aliquot is taken for the photometric determination of iron. It is necessary to know the iron content because iron is used as a variable internal standard.

Determination.—A 3–4 mg. portion of concentrate is mixed with twice its weight of carbon powder and packed in a 2.8-mm. diameter carbon electrode with a boring 1.0 mm. wide and 8 mm. deep, using a blunt needle to assure uniformity of packing. The electrode is burned as a cathode in a 9-amp. d.c. arc supplied from a 250-volt source.

FLAME EMISSION SPECTROMETRY

Flame spectrometry has been used routinely for the determination of the alkali and alkaline earth cations that occur in soil extracts, particularly sodium, potassium, calcium, and magnesium. It has also been used for the determination of these elements in the total analysis of soils. Various procedures have been followed in the preparation of test solutions for flame determination. In some cases, determinations have been carried out directly in the extractant solutions.[39] The speed and simplicity of this approach are appealing, but pretreatment to remove organic matter, silica, and various cations and

---

[38] Yoe, J. H., and Koch, H. J., Trace Analysis, John Wiley and Sons, Inc., New York, 1957, pp. 398–412.

[39] Myers, et al., Soil Sci. Soc. Am. Proc., **12**, 127–130, 1947; Shaw and Veal, Soil Sci. Soc. Am. Proc., **20**, 328–333, 1956.

anions is usually recommended to prevent ion interferences and to avoid the accumulation of salt residues and the clogging action of finely divided insoluble substances.

PREPARATION OF TEST SOLUTION

TOTAL ANALYSIS[40]

Procedure.—Weigh a finely ground 0.2-g. sample into a shallow platinum dish. Digest overnight with 0.5 ml. of 1:1 sulfuric acid and 10 ml. of 48 percent hydrofluoric acid. Evaporate on the sand bath to fumes of sulfuric acid, taking care to avoid spattering. Moisten with 1:1 sulfuric acid and again heat to fumes of sulfuric acid. Cool, take up in 10 ml. of hot 1:1 hydrochloric acid, cool, and filter. Transfer the filtrate, or a suitable aliquot, to a 250-ml. beaker. Heat to boiling, neutralize to methyl red with 1:1 ammonium hydroxide, and then add 2 ml. of saturated bromine water and 1 ml. of 1:1 ammonium hydroxide. Boil for 2 min., keeping alkaline by dropwise additions of 1:1 ammonium hydroxide. Filter hot through 9-cm. Whatman No. 31 filter paper and wash with hot 2 percent ammonium chloride solution until free of chloride. Evaporate the filtrate to a volume of 20 ml. Add 10 ml. of concentrated nitric acid and continue evaporation to dryness. Bake on the hot plate for 15 min., and, when cool, add 20 ml. of 0.2 N hydrochloric acid. Filter and determine calcium, magnesium, potassium, and sodium in suitable aliquots of the filtrate.

EXCHANGEABLE AND SOLUBLE CATIONS

Procedure.—Destroy organic matter in ammonium acetate or similar extracts of soils by evaporation and treatment with aqua regia, as previously described.[41] Take up the residue in 0.2 N hydrochloric acid, filter or centrifuge to remove silica, and determine sodium, potassium, calcium, and magnesium in suitable aliquots. If sufficient phosphate is present to interfere with the flame determination of calcium and magnesium, it can be removed by precipitation with ferric chloride[42] or by passage through an anion-exchange column.[43]

DETERMINATION OF CALCIUM, MAGNESIUM, POTASSIUM, AND SODIUM

Several procedures have been given that are applicable for use with different commercially available flame photometers.[44] Interference from calcium, magnesium, and other substances in the determination of sodium and potassium in test solutions prepared as directed above is usually not a problem for most soils, but with calcium, and particularly with magnesium, interferences and conditions of determination are more critical. For most purposes, removal of organic matter and phosphate is advisable. Iron should also be removed if present in more than trace amounts in the test solution. One procedure[45] recommends isolation of magnesium by precipitation with sodium hydroxide in the presence of mannitol. The precipitate of magnesium hydroxide is dissolved in hydrochloric acid for flame determination.

[40] Fieldes, *et al.*, New Zealand J. Sci. Technol., **35**, 433–439, 1954.
[41] Welcher, F. J., Standard Methods of Chemical Analysis, 6th Ed., D. Van Nostrand Co., Inc., Princeton, N. J., Vol. II, Part B, pp. 2325–2326.
[42] Fieldes, *et al.*, Soil Sci., **72**, 219–232, 1951.
[43] Pratt and Bradford, Soil Sci., **89**, 342–346, 1960.
[44] Toth and Prince, Soil Sci., **67**, 439–445, 1949; Fieldes, *et al.*, *ibid.*, **72**, 219–232, 1951; Rich, Soil Sci. Soc. Am. Proc., **16**, 51–55, 1952.
[45] Soil Sci., **89**, 342–346, 1960.

ATOMIC ABSORPTION SPECTROMETRY[46]

Sodium, potassium, calcium, magnesium, and other elements have been determined in soil extracts by atomic absorption spectrometry. Determinations of these elements have been carried out directly in ammonium chloride and ammonium acetate extracts against standards prepared in similar solutions. The addition of strontium was reported to suppress interference by phosphate, aluminum, silicate, and sulfate in the determination of calcium and magnesium. The method appears to be of particular promise for the routine determination of magnesium for which flame emission and colorimetric methods offer some difficulty.

POLAROGRAPHY

DETERMINATION OF COPPER AND ZINC[47]

Reagent Solutions. **Dithizone-Buffer Mixture.**—Add 100 ml. of 10 percent (w/v) citric acid solution to 400 ml. of 4 N ammonium hydroxide. Add 0.1 g. of dithizone to 300 ml. of this solution. Remove copper and zinc impurity by extracting with two 10-ml. portions of redistilled carbon tetrachloride.

Ternary Acid Mixture.—Mix concentrated nitric, concentrated sulfuric, and 60 percent perchloric acids in the volume ratio of 10:1:4.

Supporting Electrolyte.—Dissolve 2.1 g. of sodium sulfite (Na_2SO_3) in 66 ml. of 0.1 N ammonium hydroxide. Prepare a fresh solution daily.

Gelatin.—Add 0.1 g. of gelatin to 100 ml. of water and dissolve by gentle heating.

Procedure.—Transfer an aliquot of soil digest or extract[48] to a separatory funnel containing 25 ml. of dithizone-buffer mixture. Add 5 ml. of redistilled carbon tetrachloride and shake for 1 min. Adjust the aqueous phase to pH 9–10 with ammonium hydroxide and hydrochloric acid using thymol blue as an external indicator. Again shake for 1 min. Transfer the organic layer to a 50-ml. conical flask. Extract with successive 2-ml. portions of carbon tetrachloride until the clear green color of the organic layer indicates complete removal of copper and zinc. Evaporate the combined extracts to dryness. Oxidize the dithizone by digestion with 2 ml. of ternary acid mixture. Evaporate the acid using a Meker-type burner to remove the last traces of sulfuric acid by cautiously heating the sides of the conical flask. Add 5.00 ml. of supporting electrolyte solution and 1 drop of gelatin solution to the residue in the flask. Dissolve the copper and zinc by swirling gently at intervals over a period of 1 hr. Pour the solution into a dry sample vial and determine copper and zinc. The half-wave potential of copper is approximately -0.5 volt and that of zinc approximately -1.2 volt.

DETERMINATION OF MANGANESE

A method for the determination of manganese in soil extracts has been suggested using sodium sulfite or sodium sulfite and sodium chloride as supporting electrolyte.[49] Cation exchange capacity has been determined by treating soil with manganese chloride solu-

---

[46] Allen, Analyst, **83**, 466–471, 1957; Spectrochim. Acta, **15**, 800–806, 1959; Analyst, **86**, 530–534, 1961; David, Analyst, **85**, 495–503, 1960; *ibid.*, **87**, 576–585, 1962.

[47] Menzel and Jackson, Anal. Chem., **23**, 1861–1863, 1951; see Soil Sci. Soc. Am. Proc., **24**, 169–171, 1960, for rapid polarographic method for determination of zinc in soil extracts without preliminary separation.

[48] See p. 1866.

[49] Jackson, M. L., Ed., Soil Chemical Analysis, Prentice-Hall, Inc., Englewood Cliffs, N. J., 1958, pp. 426–427.

tion, and then replacing the sorbed manganous ion with 1 N potassium chloride.[50] The potassium chloride solution also serves as the supporting electrolyte in the subsequent determination of manganese.

DETERMINATION OF NITRATE[51]

Reagent Solutions. Barium Chloride.—Prepare a 0.01 M solution.

Zirconyl Chloride.—Dissolve 8.58 g. of zirconyl chloride in 100 ml. of water.

Procedure.—Add 200 ml. of barium chloride solution to 50 g. of 2-mm. soil. Shake 15 min. and filter through Whatman No. 40 filter paper. Add 2.0 ml. of zirconyl chloride to a 5- or 10-ml. aliquot of clear filtrate and make to a volume of 25 ml. with water. Pass nitrogen gas through the solution for 5 min. Transfer to a polarographic cell and continue to deoxygenate for 30 sec. Determine nitrate by measuring the diffusion current at -1.16 volts. The method has the advantage over the colorimetric methods for nitrate[52] in that organic matter and chlorides do not interfere. High levels of soluble sulfate interfere by coprecipitation of nitrate with barium sulfate.

METAL ION-SENSITIVE GLASS ELECTRODES

Soil reaction (pH value) is usually determined with a glass electrode in combination with a saturated potassium chloride–calomel reference electrode and a potentiometer.[53] Glass electrodes that respond to certain monovalent cations as well as to hydrogen are now commercially available. They have been applied to the determination of sodium and potassium in soil extracts. A line-operated pH meter with expanded millivolt scale is recommended as the potentiometer.[54]

The electrodes do not respond to alkaline earth cations. The response to hydrogen ions is negligible above pH 6. Interfering amounts of potassium in the determination of sodium may be removed by precipitation of the former with calcium tetraphenylboron.[55] The interference of ammonium in the determination of exchangeable sodium or potassium is avoided by substituting neutral 1 N magnesium acetate extracting solution for ammonium acetate.

DETERMINATION OF SODIUM

A glass electrode selective for sodium has been used to determine exchangeable sodium and soluble sodium in saline and alkaline soils. The presence of potassium in concentrations equal to or lower than that of sodium does not interfere. The results agree well with those obtained by flame spectrometry.[56] The extraction of exchangeable sodium with neutral 1 N magnesium acetate follows that given for ammonium acetate.[57] The sodium electrode–reference electrode assembly is introduced and the e.m.f. is measured when

[50] Holtzinger, et al., Soil Sci., **77**, 137–142, 1954. Holt, Soil Sci., **81**, 121–124, 1956, determined cation exchange capacity using silver as the saturating ion. The sorbed silver was determined by amperometric titration with thiourea using a rotating platinum microelectrode.

[51] Skyring, et al., Soil Sci., **91**, 388–392, 1961.

[52] Welcher, F. J., Ed., Standard Methods of Chemical Analysis, 6th Ed., D. Van Nostrand Co., Inc., Princeton, N. J., Vol. II, Part B, 1963, pp. 2317–2318.

[53] Welcher, F. J., Ed., Standard Methods of Chemical Analysis, 6th Ed., D. Van Nostrand Co., Inc., Princeton, N. J., Vol. II, Part B, 1963, pp. 2328–2329.

[54] See Bower, Trans. 7th Int. Cong. Soil Sci., **II**, 16–21, 1960, for method of expanding scale so that 1 division = 1 millivolt.

[55] Soil Sci. Soc. Am. Proc., **23**, 29–31, 1959.

[56] Bower, op. cit.; see also Fehrenbacher, et. al., Soil Sci. Soc. Am. Proc., **27**, 152–153, 1963.

[57] Welcher, F. J., Ed., Standard Methods of Chemical Analysis, 6th Ed., D. Van Nostrand Co., Inc., Princeton, N. J., Vol. II, Part B, 1963, pp. 2325–2326; Soil Sci., **73**, 251–261, 1952.

readings become constant. The sodium concentration is determined by means of a calibration curve relating log sodium ion concentration to e.m.f. The sodium standards are made up by dissolving sodium chloride in 1 N magnesium acetate. The curve is linear between 10^{-1} and 10^{-3} sodium ion equivalents per liter. Between 20°–25°C., the slope of the curve is 58–59 millivolts per tenfold change in sodium concentration. The value for exchangeable sodium in saline and alkaline soils should be corrected by subtracting the value for water-soluble sodium obtained by analysis of the saturation extract.[58] A method has also been proposed for determination of cation exchange capacity by saturating the soil with sodium followed by displacement of sodium and determination with the glass electrode.[59]

DETERMINATION OF POTASSIUM[60]

Exchangeable potassium has been determined in neutral 1 N magnesium acetate extracts using a glass electrode sensitive to sodium, potassium, lithium, and ammonium. Most soils of the humid regions do not contain sufficient exchangeable sodium, lithium, or ammonium to cause interference. Determinations were made by placing the electrode assembly directly in the soil-magnesium acetate mixture. Results for exchangeable potassium agreed fairly well with those obtained by flame photometric analysis of magnesium acetate and ammonium acetate extracts. The relation between log potassium ion concentration and e.m.f. was linear between 10^{-1} and 10^{-4} potassium ion equivalents per liter with a slope of 55.3 millivolts per tenfold change in potassium concentration.

ELECTRODIALYSIS

Electrodialysis has been used to remove exchangeable cations from soils or clays. Analysis of the dialysate is simplified because it is free of salts or acids contained in other types of extracting solutions. The method has been applied to rapid, routine determinations of exchangeable cations.[61] The apparatus consists of several dialysis cells connected in parallel. These are equipped with anodes of perforated sheet platinum and cathodes of perforated sheet nickel with membranes consisting of Whatman No. 2 filter paper. Dialysis of soils in 0.05 N boric acid has been found to be more effective than water in removing exchangeable cations. Some phosphate is also removed. The contents of the anode and cathode chambers are combined for analysis at the conclusion of the dialysis period.

AUTOMATIC ANALYSIS TRAINS

DETERMINATION OF NITROGEN BY THE DUMAS METHOD[62]

Total soil nitrogen has been determined successfully using a commercially available apparatus. Positive errors obtained for some soils were found to be caused by incomplete combustion resulting in the production of methane which was measured together with the nitrogen. Modification of the manufacturer's recommended procedure[63] resulted in values that agreed well with those obtained by the Kjeldahl method[64] and apparently included nitrate nitrogen at concentrations as high as are likely to occur in soils.

[58] Welcher, F. J., Ed., Standard Methods of Chemical Analysis, D. Van Nostrand Co., Inc., Princeton, N. J., Vol. II, Part B, 1963, p. 2332.

[59] Bower, *op. cit.*

[60] Mortland, Mich. Quart. Bull., **43**, 491–498, 1961.

[61] Purvis and Hanna, Soil Sci., **67**, 47–52, 1949; N. J. Agr. Exp. Sta., Bull. 780, 1955.

[62] Stewart, *et al.*, Soil Sci. Soc. Am. Proc., **27**, 377–380, 1963; *ibid.*, **28**, 366–368, 1964.

[63] Coleman Instruments, Inc., Maywood, Ill.

[64] Welcher, F. J., Ed., Standard Methods of Chemical Analysis, 6th Ed., D. Van Nostrand Co., Inc., Princeton, N. J., Vol. II, Part B, 1963, pp. 2313–2314.

Procedure.—Soil ground to pass a 100-mesh sieve was dried overnight at 70°C. Sufficient sample to furnish 0.2–0.3 mg. nitrogen was mixed with 3 g. finely ground copper oxide and placed in the normal position in a combustion tube containing copper oxide in wire form. The purge period of the combustion cycle was extended to 2 min. The combustion furnaces were set so that the initial temperature of the cycle was 875°C. The maximum temperature reached during the cycle was about 925°C. The post-heater tube was maintained at 600°C. The portion of this tube normally filled with copper oxide was replaced with a 3:1 mixture by volume of copper oxide and a platinum reforming catalyst. The mixture was changed after about 30 determinations. The metallic copper in the other portion of the post-heater tube was changed only when it began to turn black. The used copper oxide from the combustion tubes and the used copper oxide-platinum catalyst mixture were regenerated by washing with 0.1 N acetic acid, followed by heating at 850°C. for 30 min. in a stream of oxygen.

DETERMINATION OF CARBON

The automated micro-Dumas apparatus described above has been modified to permit the determination of carbon in soil by combustion in a stream of oxygen.[65] Carbon from carbonates is included. Presumably automated analysis trains specifically designed for carbon determination could be applied to soil analysis without difficulty.

DETERMINATION OF CALCIUM, MAGNESIUM, PHOSPHORUS, AND POTASSIUM[66]

A system has been described for the simultaneous autoanalysis of several elements in soil extracts obtained by electrodialysis in boric acid solution using commercially available equipment.[67] Magnesium and phosphorus are determined photometrically, while calcium and potassium are determined by flame spectrometry. With the procedures used, statistical analysis indicated potassium interfered in the calcium determination. However, the interference was highly predictable and its magnitude was considered to be well within the tolerances required for present-day agricultural advisory purposes. One hour is required for the analysis of 40 soil extracts.

CHROMATOGRAPHY

Paper chromatography and gas chromatography have received limited application in soil analysis. Copper, cobalt, nickel, and zinc in soil extracts have been isolated as dithiazone and dimethylglyoxime complexes.[68] The metal ions were then converted to chlorides and separated on Whatman No. 54 paper strips using acetone-ethyl acetate-hydrochloric acid mixture as the solvent. The strips were air-dried, neutralized with ammonia, and sprayed with the detection reagent, a solution of rubeanic acid. Copper, cobalt, and nickel were determined directly using an automatic-recording densitometer. The zinc band was cut off, dry ashed at 450°C., and zinc determined photometrically.

A commercial automated Dumas apparatus has been modified to allow determination of nitrogen by gas chromatography.[69] Also determined are gases, such as methane, carbon monoxide, and oxides of nitrogen evolved through faulty technique. These are not soluble in 50 percent potassium hydroxide solution and their presence, if undetected, results in positive errors in the ordinary Dumas procedure.

[65] Stewart, *et al.*, Soil Sci. Soc. Am. Proc., **28**, 366–368, 1964.
[66] Flannery and Steckel, Soil Sci. Soc. Am. Proc., in press.
[67] Technicon Controls, Inc., Chauncey, N. Y.
[68] Coulson, *et al.*, Analyst, **85**, 203–207, 1960.
[69] Stewart, *et al.*, Anal. Chem., **35**, 1331–1332, 1963.

Anion-exchange resins have been used to eliminate phosphate interference in the determination of calcium and magnesium by EDTA titration or flame spectrometry.[70] The residue of soil extract containing phosphate is taken up in a minimum of hydrochloric acid and filtered. The test solution is freed of phosphorus by passage through a column containing anion exchange resin in the chloride form.

A method for determining soil salinity with a cation-exchange resin has been proposed.[71] An aliquot of saturation extract[72] was passed through a column containing the resin in the hydrogen form. In the absence of soluble carbonates and bicarbonates, titration of the effluent with standard sodium hydroxide to the bromthymol blue end point will give the hydrogen ions equivalent to the cations in the saturation extract. The presence of soluble carbonates and bicarbonates will usually be indicated by a pH value of greater than 8.3 in the saturation extract. In such cases, excess standard barium hydroxide is added and back titrated to just colorless with phenolphthalein using standard hydrochloric acid.

THERMOGRAVIMETRY[73]

A recording thermobalance of 0.1 mg. sensitivity has been applied to the determination of hygroscopic water, organic matter, and carbonates. Agreement was good between this and other methods for determining organic matter and total carbonates, but for soils there is difficulty in portioning the carbonate present between calcite and dolomite. Values for hygroscopic water were greater than those obtained by oven-drying at 105°C., but lower than those obtained by Karl Fischer titration.

[70] Adams and Rouse, Soil Sci., **83**, 305–312, 1957; Pratt and Bradford, Soil Sci., **89**, 342–346, 1960.

[71] Tabikh and Russel, Soil Sci., **91**, 70–73, 1961.

[72] Welcher, F. J., ed., Standard Methods of Chemical Analysis, 6th Ed., D. Van Nostrand Co., Inc., Princeton, N. J., Vol. II, Part B, 1963, p. 2332.

[73] Schnitzer, et al., Anal. Chem., **31**, 440–444, 1959; Wright, et al., J. Sci. Food Agr., **11**, 163–167, 1960; Hoffman, et al., ibid., **11**, 167–172, 1960.

Chapter **63**

WATER ANALYSIS

By Michael J. Taras
Department of Water Supply
Detroit, Michigan

INTRODUCTION

Concurrent with the general trend of the past half-century, water analysis has progressed from burets and Nessler tubes to the complex instrumentation of the present. Instruments now play a significant role, with each year witnessing the addition of new devices to the enterprising laboratory. Table 62-1 lists a number of the more common instrumental methods which have gained acceptance[1] and were, therefore, described in Standard Methods of Chemical Analysis, Sixth Edition, Volume II, Part B.

TABLE 63-1. INSTRUMENTAL METHODS USED IN WATER ANALYSIS

Constituent	*Instrument Needed*	*Page of Volume II Part B on Which Method Is Described*
Acidity	Potentiometric Titrator or pH Meter	2398
Alkalinity	Potentiometric Titrator or pH Meter	2399
Boron	Potentiometric Titrator or pH Meter	2405
Residual Chlorine	Amperometric Titrator	2419
Specific Conductance	Wheatstone Bridge or Conductance Meter	2425
Methane	Combustible Gas Indicator	2442
pH Value	Glass Electrode pH Meter	2462
Gross Alpha and Gross Beta Radioactivity	Internal Proportional Counter preferred, or End-Window Geiger-Muller Counter	2470

Several reasons account for the trend toward instrumentation. The purely economic or labor-saving aspects are obvious and need little elaboration. The increasing physical and chemical complexity of water samples, coupled with the interest of public health authorities in trace materials, has spurred a serious search for methods of determining minor constituents. The difficulties of determining small concentrations has led to an exploration of instrumental methods that are emerging on all sides for the solution of other problems.

[1] Am. Public Health Assn., Am. Water Works Assn., Water Pollution Control Fed., Standard Methods for the Examination of Water and Wastewater, 12th Ed., New York, 1965.

The growing adoption of instruments rests on the fact that they may give more precise and reliable results than some conventional methods, and yield clues regarding constituents that might otherwise go undetected. Illustrative of the last point is the occasionally valuable lead to an unsuspected substance that may be uncovered in polarographic waves and infrared spectrograms of polluted samples.

Finally, an instrumental approach affords a check on the questionable results that may arise during routine operations, thereby conferring confidence in a value verifiable by several independent methods.

The instrumental approach has admittedly provided valuable information, albeit not the definitive or conclusive answers. However, it would be presumptuous to expect any method, instrumental or noninstrumental, to be entirely free of interferences or limitations.

The nature and function of the laboratory dictates the number and type of instruments and equipment needed for the determinations. The emphasis in a water plant laboratory is on the production of a safe and palatable water. The principal determinations, accordingly, are designed to ascertain chemical dosages and evaluate the success of the plant treatment. In such a control situation, the chief reliance is on the simpler color indicator titrations and colorimetric measurements. Since virtually all colorimetric methods now specify a spectrophotometer or filter photometer, photometry is firmly entrenched in the larger laboratories and is invading the surviving stronghold of visual colorimetry, the small laboratory. The plant which treats a relatively high-quality raw water usually relies on fewer instruments than the installation which must contend with massive pollution.

At the other extreme, the governmental agencies charged with the enforcement of pollution control statutes often possess the greatest number of instruments. The simpler tests that may suffice for the examination of a relatively pure water yield to the instrumental methods which enable the accumulation of more dependable data. Moreover, the interference of color, turbidity, and assorted chemical ions present in a highly polluted sample may necessitate resort to more than one instrumental technique for an acceptable answer.

Frequency with Which Instrumental Methods Are Performed.—Photometric instruments (see Table 63-2) generally receive the greatest usage in the water laboratory, followed by the glass electrode method of determining pH. The subsequent order of frequency varies according to the mission of the laboratory.

Flame photometry has largely supplanted the gravimetric, titrimetric, and colorimetric methods for lithium, potassium, sodium, and strontium.

Potentiometric titrations are reserved for special situations demanding confirmatory data or unusual accuracy.

Radioactivity measurements are performed mainly in governmental laboratories. The federal and state health agencies conduct the complex determinations, while the larger water departments confine their measurements to the comparatively simple counts.

Polarography and emission spectrometry are used principally in the largest laboratories for the determination of trace elements. The same holds true with respect to gas chromatography for organic pesticide examinations.

Specialized instruments are available for a restricted number of determinations, and may be found in both small and large laboratories as circumstances warrant. In this class falls the combustible gas indicator which enables an estimate of the methane concentration in potentially hazardous ground waters. Amperometric titrators are occasionally used to differentiate the residual chlorine into its free chlorine, monochloramine, and dichloramine fractions, as well as to determine chlorine dioxide. Although several iodometric titrations may also be performed with this instrument, the visual starch-iodide modification remains popular. Despite the fact that specific conductance is a valuable preliminary measurement on an unknown water sample, conductometric titrations are seldom performed.

Continuous Monitoring Instruments.—The function of a water utility is to produce a water which is safe and pleasant to drink, and clear in appearance. Chemicals are often added to achieve this objective, the number and quantities depending on the quality of the raw water entering the treatment plant. Since raw water quality can change suddenly and dramatically, increased reliance is being placed on continuous monitoring instruments equipped with recorders and alarms. Residual chlorine analyzers represent a major means of controlling the disinfection process to assure the bacteriologic safety of a water. Turbidity monitors enable the suspended matter to be maintained at the desired level. Unfortunately, no instrument can yet augment the human palate and nose for evaluating the taste and odor acceptability of a water.

A good number of different continuous analyzers have been developed for specific applications or can be custom-made for treatment plants designed to produce special grades of industrial water. Deserving mention in this connection are the hardness, pH, and conductance monitors used in softening installations, and the dissolved oxygen, hydrazine, phosphate, silica, and sulfite analyzers found in high-pressure steam-generating plants. Some instruments are relatively simple in construction while others are complex. Many of the analyzers are based on a generally accepted colorimetric or electroanalytic method.

Commercially Available Instruments.—Most of the methods described in this chapter can be performed on commercially available instruments of either the manually or automatically operated type. The automatic instruments complete the determination after the sample has been measured, prepared, and set into place.

The circuitry and design of the instruments are outside the province of this chapter, and, consequently, a detailed description of such matters has been deliberately omitted. The concern instead is directed to the chemical pretreatment and general operations which often apply to all commercial instruments. Only in isolated instances is the manufacturer's identity revealed. This disclosure is made because the original method was developed around the specified instrument. An equivalent instrument of other manufacture may be satisfactorily substituted.

SPECTROMETRIC TECHNIQUES

VISIBLE SPECTROMETRY

Visible spectrometry surpasses by far all other instrumental methods that find general acceptance in the laboratory entrusted with the chemical analysis of water.

Table 62-2 lists a number of the determinations based on this principle. The essential conditions for these determinations can be found on the indicated pages of Volume II, Part B.

COLOR[1,2]

Most waters of potable quality are colorless. Some source waters vary from yellow to brown, enabling their easy estimation by visual comparison with yellow platinum–cobalt permanent standards. However, waters which are heavily polluted with industrial wastes occasionally defy matching with the permanent standards and may require instrumental methods for a successful determination of hue, luminance, and purity.

Two instrumental modifications are available: a rapid method which uses three color

[2] Rudolfs, W., and Hanlon, W. D., Sewage and Industrial Wastes, **23**, 1125, 1951.

Table 63-2. Photometric Methods Used in Water Analysis

Constituent	Method	Concentration Range	Wavelength of Measurement, mμ	Light Path, cm.	Page of Volume II Part B on Which Method Is Described
Aluminum	Aluminon	0.001–0.05 mg.	525	1	2401
Arsenic	Heteropoly Blue	0.005–0.04 mg.	600–820	1	2402
Boron	Carmine	0.002–0.02 mg.	585	1	2406
Cadmium	Dithizone	0.0025–0.02 mg.	515	1	2407
Residual Chlorine	Orthotolidine-Arsenite	0.01–10 mg./l.	400–490	1	2416
Chromium	Diphenylcarbazide	0.00025–0.02 mg.	540	5	2423
Copper	Cuprethol	0.0025–0.05 mg.	435	5	2426
Cyanide	Bis-pyrazolone	0.0002–0.001 mg.	620	1	2430
Fluoride	SPADNS	0.010–0.14 mg.	570	1	2431
Iron	Phenanthroline	0.010–0.10 mg.	510	5	2435
Lead	Dithizone	0.010–0.05 mg.	510–520	1	2436
Lithium	Flame Photometric	0.0001–0.0015 mg.	671	1	2438
Magnesium	Brilliant Yellow	0.1–0.8 mg.	525	1	2440
Manganese	Persulfate	0.05–0.50 mg.	525	5	2441
Ammonia Nitrogen	Nessler	0.005–0.06 mg.	400–425	5	2449
Albuminoid Nitrogen	Nessler	0.005–0.06 mg.	400–425	5	2453
Kjeldahl Nitrogen	Nessler	0.005–0.06 mg.	400–425	5	2454
Nitrate Nitrogen	{Phenoldisulfonic Acid	0.005–0.05 mg.	410	5	2445
	Brucine	0.001–0.02 mg.	410	1	2447

Nitrite Nitrogen				
Sulfanilic Acid-Naphthylamine Diazotization	0.00025–0.0025 mg.	520	5	2448
Phenols (As Phenol)				
Aminoantipyrine	0.005–0.05 mg.	460	10	2464
	0.05–0.50 mg.	510	5	2464
Phosphate				
Stannous Chloride	0.002–0.05 mg.	600–700	10	2467
Aminonaphtholsulfonic Acid	0.0025–0.05 mg.	600–700	10	2468
Potassium				
Flame Photometric	0.1–10 mg./l.	768	1	2470
Selenium				
Diaminobenzidine	0.01–0.05 mg.	420	1	2474
Silica				
Molybdosilicate	0.04–0.25 mg.	410	5	2476
Heteropoly Blue	0.004–0.02 mg.	815	5	2476
Sodium				
Flame Photometric	0.1–100 mg./l.	589		2478
Strontium				
Flame Photometric	2–75 mg./l.	460.7		2481
Sulfate				
Barium Sulfate Turbidimetric	0.25–3 mg.	380–425	1–5	2483
Sulfide				
Methylene Blue	0.05–20 mg./l.	670 and 750	1	2486
Anionic Surfactants (As Alkylbenzene-Sulfonate)				
Methylene Blue	0.01–0.20 mg.	625	1–5	2489
Carbon Adsorption-Infrared	5–25 mg.	9.0–10.5 μ		2490
Tannin and Lignin				
Phosphomolybdic Acid	0.01–0.15 mg. Tannic Acid	600–700	5	2492
	0.05–0.40 mg. Lignin	600–700	5	2492
Zinc				
Dithizone	0.01–0.04 mg.	535	1	2496
Zincon	0.001–0.05 mg.	620	1	2499

filters and a filter photometer, and the more accurate spectrophotometric method. In both cases the light transmittance data are converted to the color classification terms through the use of standards adopted by the International Commission on Illumination ("CIE"), and the selected-ordinate method.

Samples are filtered because centrifugation may not remove all turbidity in the sample and also because the materials producing color in industrial wastes are not appreciably adsorbed on the specified filter media.

The color measurements are made at a standard pH of 7.6 or 8.3, as well as at the original pH of the sample. The standard pH of 7.6 or 8.3 demonstrates the variation of color which may occur with pH.

Reagents. **Sulfuric Acid, Concentrated.**

Sodium Hydroxide Solution.—50 g. per liter.

Calcined Filter Aid.—Celite No. 505, a product of Johns-Manville, New York.

Procedure. **Sample Preparation.**—Bring two 50-ml. sample portions to room temperature. Leave one portion at the original pH value of the sample. Adjust the pH value of the second portion to 7.6 or 8.3 with concentrated sulfuric acid or sodium hydroxide solution as required. Remove excessive quantities of suspended materials by centrifuging. Treat each portion individually hereafter. Thoroughly mix 0.1 g. calcined filter aid 'in a 10-ml. portion of centrifuged sample and filter the slurry to form a precoat in the micro metallic filter crucible set-up as shown in Fig. 63-1. Direct the filtrate to the waste flask. Mix 0.04 g. filter aid in a 35-ml. portion of the centrifuged sample. While the vacuum is still in effect, filter through the precoat and pass the filtrate to the waste flask until clear; then direct the clear-filtrate flow to the clean flask by means of the three-way stopcock, and collect 25 ml. for the transmittance measurements.

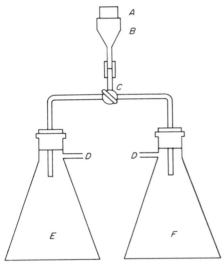

Fig. 63-1. Filtration Assembly for Color Determinations: *A*, Filter Crucible; *B*, Crucible Holder; *C*, Three-way Stopcock; *D*, Connection to Vacuum Line; *E*, Clean Flask; *F*, Waste Flask. (Reproduced with permission from Standard Methods for the Examination of Water and Wastewater, 12th Ed., The American Public Health Assn., Inc., New York, 1965.)

Determination of Light Transmittance Characteristics with a Spectrophotometer.—Determine the percent transmittance for both filtered samples at each of the visible wavelength values presented in Table 63-3, using those wavelengths marked with an asterisk for fairly accurate work, and all of the specified wavelengths for improved accuracy. Make all measurements with a narrow spectral band (preferably 10 mμ or less), a 10-mm. light path, and a distilled water blank set at 100 percent transmittance. Apply the following factors when all 30 wavelengths in each column are used: $X = 0.03269$, $Y = 0.03333$, $Z = 0.03938$. Apply the following factors when only the 10 asterisked wavelengths in each column are used: $X = 0.09806$, $Y = 0.10000$, $Z = 0.11814$.

Tabulate the transmittance values corresponding to the wavelengths shown in Col-

TABLE 63-3. SELECTED WAVELENGTHS[a] FOR SPECTROPHOTOMETRIC COLOR DETERMINATIONS[b]

Wavelength in mμ

X	Y	Z
424.4	465.9	414.1
435.5*	489.5*	422.2*
443.9	500.4	426.3
452.1	508.7	429.4
461.2*	515.2*	432.0*
474.0	520.6	434.3
531.2	525.4	436.5
544.3*	529.8*	438.6*
552.4	533.9	440.6
558.7	537.7	442.5
564.1*	541.4*	444.4*
568.9	544.9	446.3
573.2	548.4	448.2
577.4*	551.8*	450.1*
581.3	555.1	452.1
585.0	558.5	454.0
588.7*	561.9*	455.9*
592.4	565.3	457.9
596.0	568.9	459.9
599.6*	572.5*	462.0*
603.3	576.4	464.1
607.0	580.4	466.3
610.9*	584.8*	468.7*
615.0	589.6	471.4
619.4	594.8	474.3
624.2*	600.8*	477.7*
629.8	607.7	481.8
636.6	616.1	487.2
645.9*	627.3*	495.2*
663.0	647.4	511.2

[a] Measure the transmittance value (percent) at the wavelength shown in each column. Where limited accuracy is acceptable, use only the wavelengths marked with an asterisk.
[b] Reproduced with permission from Standard Methods for the Examination of Water and Wastewater, 12th Ed., The American Public Health Assn., Inc., New York, 1965.

umns X, Y, and Z in Table 63-3. Total each of the transmittance columns and multiply the totals by the appropriate factors (for 10 or 30 measurements) shown at the bottom of the table, to obtain tristimulus values X, Y, and Z. The tristimulus value Y is the percent luminance of the sample.

Calculate the trichromatic coefficients x and y from the tristimulus values X, Y, and Z by the following equations:

$$x = \frac{X}{X + Y + Z} \qquad y = \frac{Y}{X + Y + Z}$$

Locate point (x, y) on one of the chromaticity diagrams in Fig. 63-2* and determine the dominant wavelength (in mμ) and the purity (in percent) directly from the diagram. Determine the hue from the dominant-wavelength value, according to the ranges in Table 63-4.

TABLE 63-4. COLOR HUES FOR DOMINANT-WAVELENGTH RANGES[a]

Wavelength Range, mμ	Hue
400–465	Violet
465–482	Blue
482–497	Blue-green
497–530	Green
530–575	Greenish-yellow
575–580	Yellow
580–587	Yellowish-orange
587–598	Orange
598–620	Orange-red
620–700	Red
400–530c[b]	Blue-purple
530c–700	Red-purple

[a] Reproduced with permission from Standard Methods for the Examination of Water and Wastewater, 12th Ed., The American Public Health Assn., Inc., New York, 1965.
[b] The dominant wavelength of the purple region is expressed as the wavelength of the complimentary color value followed by the letter c.

Express the color characteristics (at pH 7.6 or 8.3 and at the original pH) in terms of dominant wavelength (mμ, to the nearest unit), hue (*e.g.*, "blue," "blue-green," etc.), luminance (percent, to the nearest tenth), and purity (percent, to the nearest unit). Report the type of instrument (*i.e.*, spectrophotometer), the number of wavelengths used per column (10 or 30), and the spectral band width (mμ).

Determination of Light Transmittance Characteristics with a Filter Photometer.— Equip the filter photometer with the following items or their equal: a light source consisting of a tungsten lamp at a color temperature of 3000°K. (General Electric lamp No. 1719 at 6 volts is satisfactory); photoelectric cells comparable to the General Electric photovoltaic cell, type PV-1; and three tristimulus light filters: Corning CS-3-107 (No. 1), CS-4-98 (No. 2), and CS-5-70 (No. 3). Determine the percent transmittance for both filtered samples with each of the three tristimulus light filters. Make the measurements at a 10-mm. light path against a distilled water blank set at 100 percent transmittance.

Record the luminance value as the percentage transmittance obtained with the No. 2 tristimulus filter.

Calculate the tristimulus values X, Y, and Z from the percent transmittance (T_1, T_2, T_3) for filters No. 1, 2, 3 as follows:

$$X = (T_3 \times 0.06) + (T_1 \times 0.25)$$
$$Y = T_2 \times 0.316$$
$$Z = T_3 \times 0.374$$

* Reproduced with permission from Standard Methods for the Examination of Water and Wastewater, 12th Ed., The American Public Health Assn., Inc., New York, 1965. More accurate values can be obtained from the larger charts available in Hardy, A. C., Handbook of Colorimetry, Technology Press, Massachusetts Institute of Technology, Boston, Mass., 1936.

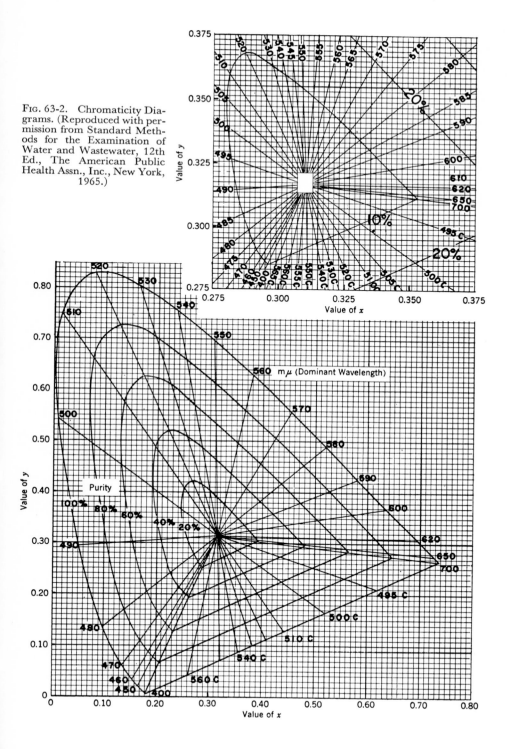

Fɪɢ. 63-2. Chromaticity Diagrams. (Reproduced with permission from Standard Methods for the Examination of Water and Wastewater, 12th Ed., The American Public Health Assn., Inc., New York, 1965.)

Compute the trichromatic coefficients x and y, and determine the dominant wavelength, hue, and purity as indicated in the spectrophotometric method. Express the results in the same manner, together with a report of the pertinent instrumental details.

ULTRAVIOLET SPECTROMETRY

NITRATE[1,3,4]

Organic matter can cause a positive but variable interference in the ultraviolet spectrometric method for nitrate. The extent of the interference depends on the nature and concentration of the organic material. One way of skirting this problem is through the accumulation of sufficient data to obtain an empirical correction factor for a given water. Obviously, this factor may be inapplicable to another water containing organic matter of a different chemical structure. Sample dilution provides another way of coping with organic interference. Interference from nitrite, chromium(VI), and surfactants can be compensated for by the preparation of individual correction curves. The interference of organic matter, chromium(VI), and surfactants demands that all apparatus be scrupulously cleaned and rinsed to remove all trace of these agents which might adhere to the interior glass surfaces. Highly colored samples should be decolorized or diluted to minimize color interference.

Reagents. Redistilled Water.—Redistill single-distilled water from an all-Pyrex still. Use the redistilled water for the preparation of all solutions and dilutions.

Standard Nitrate Solution.—(a) Dissolve 0.7218 g. potassium nitrate, dried at 105°C., in redistilled water and dilute to 1000 ml. to form a solution containing 0.100 mg. N per 1.00 ml. (b) Dilute 100 ml. stock solution to 1000 ml. with redistilled water to form a standard solution containing 0.0100 mg. N per 1.00 ml.

Hydrochloric Acid, 1 M.

Procedure. Preparation of Standard Calibration Curve.—Prepare nitrate calibration standards in the range 0–0.35 mg. nitrogen by diluting to 50 ml. the following volumes of the standard nitrate solution: 0, 1.00, 2.00, 4.00, 7.00 . . . 35.0 ml. Add to each standard 1 ml. 1 M hydrochloric acid, and mix. Transfer to a matched silica cell of 1-cm., or longer, light path, and measure the absorbance at 220 mμ in an ultraviolet spectrophotometer against a redistilled water reference. Check the standard curve periodically in the area of interest.

Sample Treatment.—Remove possible interference from suspended particles by passing the sample through a membrane filter (Millipore type HA, or equivalent) or an acid-washed, ashless, hard-finish filter paper sufficiently retentive for fine precipitates. If filter paper is used, wash the paper thoroughly with redistilled water and reject the first 25 ml. of the filtrate before collecting the remainder. To 50 ml. of the filtrate add 1 ml. 1 M hydrochloric acid to prevent interference from hydroxide or carbonate concentrations up to 1000 mg. per liter as calcium carbonate, and mix.

Spectrophotometric Measurement.—Using a redistilled water reference, read the absorbance due to nitrate at 220 mμ and the absorbance due to dissolved organic matter at 275 mμ.

Preparation of Correction Curves for Nitrite, Chromium(VI), and Surfactants.—When known to be present in the sample, prepare separate correction curves for nitrite, chromium(VI), and anionic surfactants at 2 mg. per liter intervals up to 10 mg. per liter. Use potassium nitrate, potassium dichromate, alkylbenzenesulfonate, or linear alkylate sulfonate, and redistilled water for the purpose. Measure the absorbances at 220 mμ against redistilled water.

[3] Hoather, R. C., and Rackham, R. F., Analyst, **84**, 549, 1959.
[4] Goldman, E., and Jacobs, R., J. Am. Water Works Assn., **53**, 187, 1961.

Calculation. **Correction for Dissolved Organic Matter.**—Convert the absorbance measurement at 275 mμ (a wavelength at which nitrate does not absorb) into equivalent nitrate by reading the nitrate value from the standard calibration curve prepared at 220 mμ. Multiply the value by a suitable correction factor that has been determined on a sufficient number of samples of the particular water. Deduct the organic correction from the gross nitrate result.

Correction for Nitrite, Chromium(VI), or Surfactants.—Deduct the equivalent nitrate values for each of these interfering substances from the gross nitrate result.

$$\text{Nitrate N, mg. per liter} = \frac{\text{mg. of nitrate N} \times 1000}{\text{ml. of sample}}$$

$$NO_3, \text{ mg. per liter} = \text{mg. per liter of nitrate N} \times 4.43$$

Interference Removal with Reducing Agents.—An alternate way of solving the interference dilemma is through the use of a reduced sample which serves as the reference blank in the absorbance measurement. One reducing agent is a zinc-copper couple capable of converting the nitrate to ammonia, and thus enabling the cancellation of all interferences except nitrite.[5]

The zinc-copper couple is prepared by adding 100 g. granulated zinc and 50 ml. distilled water to a 250-ml. beaker. After the addition of 5 ml. (1 + 9 v/v) sulfuric acid, the mixture is stirred until the clean surface of the zinc metal shows. The supernatant liquid is decanted and the zinc granules are washed with two or three 50-ml. portions of distilled water. Then 50 ml. distilled water and 25 ml. copper sulfate solution (5 g. $CuSO_4 \cdot 5H_2O$ per 100 ml.) are added, the mixture is stirred, and more copper sulfate is added as needed to cover all the zinc surfaces with a copper deposit. The supernatant liquid is again decanted, the coated zinc rinsed several times with distilled water, and the zinc granules allowed to air-dry.

The samples and the standard nitrate solutions are handled in exactly the same manner. Two 25.0-ml. samples and standard nitrate portions are pipetted into duplicate test tubes. One sample and one standard nitrate portion are treated with 1 g. zinc-copper couple and 1.0 ml. (1 + 9 v/v) sulfuric acid solution. The duplicate set of sample and standard nitrate portions is treated with 1.0 ml. (1 + 9 v/v) sulfuric acid solution After the reaction has proceeded for 4 hours, all solutions are filtered into clean test tubes, and absorbance measurements made at 210 mμ, using the unreduced sample and standard nitrate portions for the measurement and the counterpart reduced portions as the reference blanks. A satisfactory standard nitrate curve can be prepared from solutions containing 0.500, 1.00, 1.50, and 2.00 μg. per ml. nitrogen.

Hydrazine sulfate can also destroy the nitrate in surface and sea water samples, thereby allowing the measurement of the non-nitrate absorbance of the samples. In this instance, the absorbance is read at 230 mμ because the necessary sulfuric acid, together with the presence of chloride, causes a change in the nitrate absorption spectrum.[6]

ALKYLBENZENESULFONATES[7]

Ultraviolet spectrometry has enabled the determination of a number of alkylbenzene-sulfonates in which the alkyl group is composed of the following: (2-hexyl)-, (2-octyl)-, (2-decyl)-, (2-dodecyl)-, (3-dodecyl)-, (6-dodecyl)-, and (2-tetradecyl)-. Excellent conformity to the Beer-Lambert law prevails in the concentration ranges of 10^{-6} to 10^{-4} M, allowing determinations to be made in the interval of 0.3 to 3 mg. per liter within 0.03

[5] Navone, R., J. Am. Water Works Assn., **56**, 781, 1964.
[6] Armstrong, F. A. J., Anal. Chem., **35**, 1292, 1963.
[7] Weber, W. J., Jr., Morris, J. C., and Stumm, W., Anal. Chem., **34**, 1844, 1962.

mg. per liter. However, the numerous interferences limit the method to synthetic and simple solutions rather than complex wastes.

The procedure consists of introducing a 10.0-ml. sample into 10.0 ml. 0.02 M potassium dihydrogen phosphate in a small beaker or flask, mixing thoroughly, and measuring the absorbance at 225 mμ in a 5-cm. quartz cell against a 0.01 M potassium dihydrogen phosphate reference. Since alkylbenzenesulfonates exhibit a strong tendency to adsorb on such surfaces, all glassware needed in the determination should be rinsed with 0.01 M potassium dihydrogen phosphate prior to use.

Benzenesulfonate and p-toluenesulfonate show maximum absorbance at 215 and 220 mμ respectively.

EMISSION SPECTROMETRY

SILVER[1,8]

Sample containers should be washed with $(1 + 1 \text{ v/v})$ nitric acid and rinsed with silver-free water before use. The determination should be started as soon as possible after sample collection because of the silver loss which may occur through adsorption on the container walls. The addition of a small volume of concentrated nitric acid of known purity is desirable when sample storage time is excessive.

Reagents. Low-Silver Dilution Water.—Select a potable water of approximately 250–450 mg. per liter total residue, containing less than 0.5 μg. per liter silver for the preparation of the silver standards. Determine the silver concentration in the dilution water by a semiquantitative spectrographic method. This range of total residue enables samples of potable water with approximately 150–800 mg. per liter of total residue to be analyzed within 10 percent from the standard working curve. When markedly different types of waters are to be determined, a comparable dilution water must be used to prepare the standard working curve.

Standard Silver Solution.—(a) Dissolve 0.1260 g. silver nitrate, dried at 105°C., in distilled water and dilute to 1000 ml. to form a solution containing 0.0800 mg. Ag per 1.00 ml. (b) Dilute 5.00 ml. stock solution to 1000 ml. with distilled water to form a standard solution containing 0.400 μg. Ag per 1.00 ml. Store the standard solution overnight to allow the plating-out process to reach equilibrium. Discard this standard solution and prepare a second batch in the same flask just before use.

Palladium Internal Standard Solution.—Dissolve 0.0667 g. palladium chloride in 10 ml. 0.1 M hydrochloric acid by heating up to 60°C., and then dilute with distilled water to 1000 ml. to form a solution containing 0.040 mg. Pd per 1.0 ml.

Lithium Sulfate Spectrobuffer Solution.—Dissolve 5.5 g. $Li_2SO_4 \cdot H_2O$ in 1 liter distilled water to form a solution which yields a residue of 5.7 mg. per 1.0 ml. after evaporation at 150°C.

Cementing Solution.—Dissolve 39 g. sucrose in 300 ml. absolute methyl alcohol and 100 ml. distilled water.

Procedure. Sample Treatment.—If the total residue is outside the range of 150–800 mg. per liter, determine the total residue by evaporating 20.0 ml. water sample on a steam bath, drying to constant weight in an oven adjusted at 150°C., and weighing the residue in the platinum evaporating dish immediately after cooling to room temperature in a desiccator. Alternatively, estimate the total residue by determining the specific conductance as described in Volume II, Part B, page 2425, and multiplying the specific conductance in micromhos per cm. by a factor of 0.0124.

Select the appropriate volume of water sample according to the following schedule:

8 Uman, G. A., J. Am. Water Works Assn., **55,** 205, 1963.

20.0 ml. sample if the total residue falls in the range of 150–800 mg. per liter, and 40.0 ml. if the total residue is 75 mg. per liter. When the silver concentration exceeds 10 μg., dilute the sample appropriately with a dilution water containing less than 0.5 μg. per liter of silver. Pipet the sample into a 250-ml. tall-type electrolytic beaker, add 1.0 ml. palladium internal standard solution and 20 ml. lithium sulfate spectrobuffer solution, and evaporate to dryness in a 150°C. oven. When the volume reaches 5–10 ml., swirl the beaker lightly to redissolve the salts which have accumulated on the beaker walls and to concentrate the residue as much as possible on the bottom. Scrape the residue in the beaker loose from the glass and grind to a homogeneous powder against the side of the beaker with a small stainless-steel spatula or a silver-free monel spatula. Weigh a 5.0-mg. portion of the ground residue, transfer to the lower sample electrode (anode), add three drops of the cementing solution, and heat over a spirit lamp or a small burner until caramelized (when further heating fails to produce steam and the residue smells like caramel). If trouble occurs in the transfer of the residue to the electrode, first wet the electrode with one drop of cementing solution to ease the transfer.

Preparation of Silver Standards.—Prepare a series of four silver standards (0.01, 0.04, 0.16, and 0.50 mg. per liter) by adding 0.50, 2.00, 8.00, and 25.0 ml. standard silver solution to each of four 20-ml. aliquots of the low-silver dilution water. Treat exactly as the unknown water sample throughout the procedure.

Spectrograph Operations.—Properly adjust the electrode system and operate the spectrograph and its accessories according to the manufacturer's instructions. Handle the sample and standards in the same manner.

In the case of an Applied Research Labs., Inc. (Glendale, Calif.) Multisource Model No. 5700, 1.5-meter grating spectrograph, the following settings and conditions have given satisfactory results:

Electrode System.—An analytical gap of 5 mm. is maintained between the upper and lower sample electrodes. The lower sample electrode or anode is a $\frac{1}{4}$-inch diameter, high purity graphite preform, 30-degree angle platform with center post manufactured by United Carbon Products of Bay City, Mich., Nos. 104U and 104L; or National Carbon Co. of New York City, Nos. L3948 and L3963. A slightly smaller diameter in the upper electrode may be preferable in instances of trouble caused by arc wandering, although a $\frac{1}{4}$-inch diameter has been successfully used. The upper electrode is a high purity graphite preform with center post and $\frac{3}{16}$-inch diameter undercut.

Excitation Settings.—Voltage, 300 volts; capacitance, 62 microfarads; inductance, 460 microhenries; resistance, 20 ohms (10 + 10); average current, 13 amperes on short and 11–12 amperes during run.

Exposure Conditions.—Spectral region, 3200–3300 Angstroms; slit width, 55 microns has been found satisfactory.

Burn the sample and silver standards to completion until the platform is gone. Use filters or sectors to expose to background (7.5 percent of total light has proved satisfactory). Record the spectrum on Eastman SA No. 2 film or plates, or No. 1 film or plates, or equivalent.

Photographic Processing.—Develop and fix the film as follows: Emulsion, Eastman SA No. 2; Developer, Eastman D-19, rocked 3 minutes at 68°F.; Stop Bath, 50 ml. concentrated (glacial) acetic acid diluted to 1 liter, 10 seconds; Fixing, Eastman F-5, 3 minutes; Washing, running water, 3 minutes; Drying, blower and heater, 5 minutes.

Estimation of Silver Concentration.—Use an Applied Research Labs., Inc. (Glendale, Calif.) No. 5400 film densitometer, or equivalent, to read the transmittance of the spectral lines Ag 3280.7 Angstroms and Pd 3242.7 Angstroms. By means of a sliding scale calculating board, convert the transmittance readings to intensity ratios based on film calibration data. Prepare a standard working curve from the silver standards by plotting the silver concentration against the intensity ratio of Ag 3280.7 to Pd 3242.7 on log-log paper (2 × 2 cycles). Convert the Ag/Pd intensity ratio to milligrams per liter of silver from the standard working curve.

ELECTROMETRIC TECHNIQUES

POTENTIOMETRIC TITRATIONS

The sharp starch indicator end point has minimized the need for a potentiometric method for iodometric titrations. The same consideration applies to the complexometric titration of hardness in water where the end point is also readily apparent. The potentiometric titration is, therefore, largely reserved for situations wherein the end point color transitions are less definite and pronounced, as in the case of acidity, alkalinity, boron, and chloride. The boron titration is performed in a special manner and is described adequately in Volume II, Part B, page 2405.

The principles involved in the titration of acidity, alkalinity, and chloride are generally similar, differing only in the required electrode pairs and standard titrants. Consequently, the chloride titration alone will be presented as the model. The acidity and alkalinity can be determined potentiometrically by means of the glass electrode and mercury reference electrode which compose the normal pH meter. The data can be collected and calculated in the same way as for chloride.

CHLORIDE[1]

The potentiometric titration can be performed without preliminary sample treatment in the presence of chromium(III), iron(II), phosphate, and a number of other heavy metal ions. Iron(III) concentrations below the level of the chloride content can also be handled without preliminary treatment. Ferricyanide causes high results and must be removed. Chromate and dichromate interfere and must be reduced to the chromic state or eliminated. Minor contamination can often be combatted by the simple addition of nitric acid. Grossly contaminated samples require more extensive pretreatment. Bromide and iodide are titrated as chloride.

Reagents. Deionized Distilled Water or Redistilled Water.—Should be used for the preparation of all solutions and dilutions.

Standard Silver Nitrate Titrant, 0.0141 N.—Dissolve 2.396 g. $AgNO_3$, and dilute to 1000 ml. with water. Store in a brown bottle or in the dark. Standardize against standard 0.0141 N sodium chloride solution as described in the procedure. The equivalence of 0.0141 N silver nitrate is 0.500 mg. chloride per 1.00 ml.

Standard Sodium Chloride Solution, 0.0141 N.—Dissolve 0.8241 g. NaCl, dried at 140°C., and dilute to 1000 ml. with water. The chloride equivalence of this solution is 0.500 mg. per 1.00 ml.

Hydrogen Peroxide, 30 percent.

Nitric Acid, concentrated.

Sulfuric Acid, (1 + 1 v/v).

Sodium Hydroxide, 1 N.

Procedure. Standardization of Silver Nitrate Titrant.—Follow the manufacturer's instructions regarding the operation of the electrotitrator and the handling of the glass and silver-silver chloride electrodes. Allow sufficient time (approximately 10 minutes) for the instrument to warm up before balancing the internal electrical components at a setting of 0 millivolt, or a pH reading of 7.0 if a pH meter is used. Pipet 10.00 ml. standard 0.0141 N sodium chloride solution into a 250-ml. beaker, dilute to about 100 ml., and add 2.0 ml. concentrated nitric acid. Immerse the electrodes and the plastic-coated or glass impeller of the mechanical stirrer into the solution. Adjust the instrument to the desired range of millivolts or pH units. Start the stirrer and begin adding the standard silver nitrate titrant in relatively large increments at first. Record the scale reading and buret reading after each addition. As the end point approaches, reduce the silver nitrate increments to 0.1 or 0.2 ml. and extend the reaction time so that the exact end point can be determined. Accept as the equivalence the point at which the greatest change occurs in the meter reading per unit addition of silver nitrate. If the exact end point cannot be determined by an inspection of the data, plot the change in instrument reading for equal increments of silver nitrate against the volume of silver nitrate added, using the average of the buret readings before and after each addition.

Removal of Interference from Sample.—Pipet 100 ml. sample, or an aliquot containing less than 10 mg. chloride, into a 250-ml. beaker. In the event organic compounds, sulfite, and large amounts of iron(III), cyanide, or sulfide are present, acidify the sample with (1 + 1 v/v) sulfuric acid, using litmus paper. Remove the volatile compounds by boiling for 5 minutes, adding more sulfuric acid, if necessary, to keep the solution acidic. Add 3 ml. hydrogen peroxide and boil for 15 minutes. Maintain the solution volume above 50 ml. by adding chloride-free water. Dilute to 100 ml., add 1 N sodium hydroxide dropwise until the solution becomes alkaline to litmus, then 10 drops in excess. Boil for 5 minutes, filter into a 250-ml. beaker, and wash the precipitate and paper several times with hot chloride-free water.

Sample Titration.—Add concentrated nitric acid dropwise until the 100-ml. sample (or sample aliquot containing no more than 10 mg. chloride) becomes acidic to litmus paper, and then add 2.0 ml. in excess. Cool and dilute to 100 ml. if necessary. Immerse the stirrer and the electrodes in the sample and activate the stirrer. Complete the titration as described under "Standardization of Silver Nitrate Titrant." If an end point reading has been established from previous determinations for similar samples and conditions, titrate to this predetermined end point. Ascertain the blank titration by carrying deionized distilled water or redistilled water through the entire procedure.

$$\text{Chloride, mg. per liter} = \frac{(A - B) \times N \times 35{,}450}{\text{ml. of sample}}$$

where: A = ml. of titration for sample;
B = ml. of titration for blank; and
N = normality of silver nitrate.

POLAROGRAPHY

The complexity of industrial wastes has impelled the larger water pollution laboratories to display an interest in voltammetric methods of analysis. The possibility of rapidly scanning a sample for several ions at a time resides at the root of this interest. To date most of the work has involved voltammetry at the dropping mercury electrode (polarography). However, interest is also being directed toward voltammetry at electrodes with fixed surfaces.

DISSOLVED OXYGEN[1]

The polarographic approach is generally reserved for those highly contaminated samples which yield questionable results with the various modifications of the conventional Winkler method. In common with the Winkler modifications, however, the polarographic method may be subject to serious interferences when applied to samples containing 50 percent or more of many strong or concentrated industrial wastes. Diluting the waste to a strength between 1 and 25 percent in natural or Biochemical Oxygen Demand dilution water improves the chance for a successful determination. The polarographic method usually gives reliable results with tap, lake, river, and sea water samples, as well as sewage samples.

Although the voltage range from 0.3 to 1.0 has been proposed by various authors for the polarographic determination of dissolved oxygen, the preferred procedure is to ascertain experimentally the optimum operating voltage for the polarograph, and the samples at hand. By the same token, reliance on single readings at one potential or the difference between the current readings at two potentials as the index of dissolved oxygen concentrations is not recommended for samples containing industrial wastes because of the errors introduced by frequently occurring interferences.

Gaseous or volatile oxidants stronger than molecular oxygen interfere by virtue of their discharge at the voltage used. Their removal by the nitrogen stream prevents their diffusion current from registering in the blank reading. The free halogens fall into this class. Certain heavy metal ions as well as high concentrations of soaps or detergents distort the current-voltage relationship characteristics of dissolved oxygen, and may adversely affect the determination. These errors may be minimized or reduced by using the sample itself for determining the operating electrode voltage.

Reagents. **Potassium Chloride Solution, 0.01 *M*.**—0.75 g. per liter.

Methyl Red Solution.—0.100 g. methyl red sodium salt per 100 ml.; 1 ml. = 1.0 mg.

Nitrogen Gas.

Procedure. **Determination of Optimum Operating Voltage.** *Potassium Chloride Solution and Simple Water Samples.*—Aerate the 0.01 *M* potassium chloride solution for several minutes, complete saturation being unnecessary. Introduce the aerated potassium chloride solution into the instrument cell, add sufficient methyl red solution (0.15 ml. for each 10 ml. of potassium chloride) to bring the final methyl red concentration to 15 mg. per liter. Follow the manufacturer's instructions regarding the operation of the polarograph. Vary the voltage on the electrode in steps of 0.02 volt over the range from 0 to 2 volts. Record the current or galvanometer deflection at each voltage. Since the current increases as the mercury drop grows and abruptly decreases when the drop falls, regard the maximum deflection as the reading. Graph the data by plotting voltage as abscissa and current as the ordinate. Adopt as the optimum operating voltage the center of the plateau between the two waves, illustrated in Fig. 63-3.

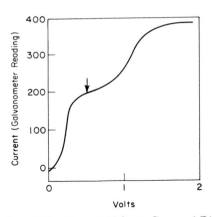

FIG. 63-3. Current-Voltage Curve of Dissolved Oxygen. (Reproduced with permission from Standard Methods for the Examination of Water and Wastewater, 12th Ed., The American Public Health Assn., Inc., New York, 1965.)

Highly Contaminated Samples.—For best results determine the optimum operating voltage of a complex sample itself. Place the aerated sample in the instrument cell and record the current readings at 0.02-volt intervals over the range from 0 to 3 volts, or until the current becomes too great to be measured. Deoxygenate the sample by bubbling a rapid stream of nitrogen through it for 5 minutes. Raise the gas tube above the level of the liquid and allow the nitrogen to flow gently over the surface of the sample while the readings are repeated over the previous voltage range. Draw a second graph of voltage *versus* current with the difference between the two readings at each voltage being the ordinate in this case. Although the curve may be distorted from the form shown in Fig. 63-3, accept for subsequent operation that voltage which lies at the midpoint of the best plateau in the curve. Avoid optimum operating voltages which are far removed from the optimum voltage used in the preparation of the standard curve unless confirmed by experimental work on the sample under examination.

Preparation of Standard Calibration Curve.—Prepare several liters of 0.01 M potassium chloride solution. Siphon off sufficient potassium chloride solution and determine the dissolved oxygen concentration of one portion by the standard iodometric method described in Volume II, Part B, page 2457. Pipet a second portion of the potassium chloride solution and determine the current before and after deaeration as described under "Sample Measurements." Change the dissolved oxygen concentration by bubbling air, oxygen, or nitrogen through the potassium chloride solution, and determine the dissolved oxygen concentration of one portion by the standard iodometric method and the diffusion current on the second portion. Repeat the process until a set of points is obtained which covers the desired range of dissolved oxygen concentration in steps of 1 mg. per liter. Calculate the corrected galvanometer reading G_s at a standard temperature t_s by means of the following equation:

$$G_s = G + KG(t_s - t)$$

where: G = galvanometer reading;
      t = temperature in degrees Centigrade; and
      K = temperature coefficient of the diffusion current at 20°C., which is 0.014 per degree Centigrade in the case of most industrial wastes, and 0.016 per degree Centigrade for less contaminated samples.

Use the corrected values for the construction of a standard curve. Prepare a new standard curve when a new capillary is installed in the polarograph.

Sample Measurements.—Execute the following steps speedily in order to minimize changes in the dissolved oxygen concentration of the sample due to atmospheric exposure. With a minimum of aeration introduce the unknown sample into the instrument cell and add 0.15 ml. methyl red solution for each 10 ml. of sample. Apply the optimum operating voltage to the electrode and note the resulting current. Since the initial galvanometer reading can be made in 30 to 40 seconds, special precautions to protect the sample from the air can be dispensed with at this stage. Insert a thermometer into the sample and read the temperature. Remove the dissolved oxygen by bubbling nitrogen gas through the sample rapidly for 5 minutes. Raise the gas tube above the sample surface and allow the nitrogen to flow gently over the surface of the sample while a second current reading is taken. Make the necessary temperature correction on the difference between the two current readings by means of the equation given in "Preparation of Standard Calibration Curve." Convert the value to dissolved oxygen concentration with the aid of the standard calibration curve.

Dissolved Oxygen Analyzers.—A number of portable analyzers are commercially available for the determination of dissolved oxygen in lakes, rivers, and treatment plants. The instruments contain polarographic electrodes, often of noble metal construction, which are separated from a plastic film cover by an intervening electrolyte solution. The dissolved oxygen diffuses first through the plastic membrane and then through the electrolyte solution to the electrode surface. A judicious selection of metals in the electrode pair enables the electrochemical potential between the metals to provide the necessary voltage for electron flow. The depolarizing effect exerted by the dissolved oxygen is recorded as a percentage of oxygen saturation on the meter. For this reason, identical instrument readings can mean different dissolved oxygen values in samples having dissimilar oxygen saturations, such as might occur in an estuary subject to saline fluctuations or in a stratified lake containing water of variable temperatures. In the case of temperature-stratified lakes, sufficient time must be allowed for the electrodes to become accommodated to the changing temperature. Calibration is performed in one of several ways: (1) by the standard iodometric method, (2) by the dropping mercury electrode polarographic method, or (3) by adjusting the instrument against atmospheric oxygen. Standardization at the temperature of field use is desirable because temperature plays a crucial role in dissolved oxygen measurements.

NITRATE

Two polarographic modifications are offered for nitrate. The simpler of the two is based on the addition of uranyl ion, while the second requires the introduction of zirconyl chloride, the removal of dissolved oxygen by bubbling nitrogen gas through the sample, and the use of ferrous ammonium sulfate.

METHOD I[1,9]

This method is designed for the nitrate nitrogen range of 0.2–35 mg. per liter, with the best results obtaining at levels above 0.5 mg. per liter. Nitrite interferes by giving readings approximately one-half those provided by equivalent concentrations of nitrate nitrogen. Phosphate concentrations greater than 4 mg. per liter as phosphorus interfere

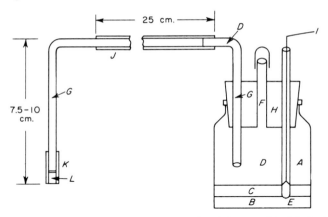

Fig. 63-4. Reference Electrode and Salt Bridge for Polarographic Method for Nitrate: A, 60-ml. (2-oz.) Wide-Mouth Bottle; B, Mercury Layer; C, Mercury-Mercurous Chloride Paste; D, Saturated Potassium Chloride Solution; E, Platinum Sealed in Glass; F, Vent and Fill Tube; G, 6.5-mm. (¼-inch) O. D. Glass Tube; H, Rubber Stopper; I, Wire Lead; J, 6.5-mm. (¼-inch) I. D. Tygon Tubing, 1.5-mm. (1/16-inch) Wall; K, Thin Wall Teflon Sleeve; L, Porous Glass Plug from Corning No. 7930 Glass or Equivalent. (Reproduced with permission from Standard Methods for the Examination of Water and Wastewater, 12th Ed., The American Public Health Assn., Inc., New York, 1965.)

in samples containing more than 20 mg. per liter nitrate nitrogen. Since phosphates interfere only in high nitrate samples, dilution often overcomes this interference. Iron(III) interferes slightly but can be minimized by allowing the iron floc to settle out of the sample before withdrawal of the portion for nitrate determination.

[9] Frazier, R. E., J. Am. Water Works Assn., **55**, 624, 1963.

A commercially available polarograph can be used for the determination. The only special item required is a low resistance reference electrode with a flexible salt bridge of the type illustrated in Fig. 63-4 that can be immersed in the sample. Since relatively large diffusion currents are involved in the procedure, voltage drops through the system should be kept at a minimum.

Reagents. Uranyl Catalyst.—Dissolve 25 ml. concentrated (glacial) acetic acid, 0.34 g. uranyl acetate, $UO_2(C_2H_3O_2)_2 \cdot H_2O$, 14.8 g. potassium chloride, and 1.7 ml. concentrated hydrochloric acid in distilled water, and dilute to 1 liter.

Standard Nitrate Solution.—(a) Dissolve 0.7218 g. potassium nitrate, dried at 105°C., in distilled water and dilute to 1000 ml. to form a solution containing 0.100 mg. nitrogen per 1.00 ml. (b) Dilute 100 ml. stock solution to 1000 ml. with distilled water to form a standard solution containing 0.0100 mg. nitrogen per 1.00 ml.

Procedure. Preparation of Sample and Standard.—Bring both the sample and the standard nitrate solution to room temperature. If necessary, dilute the sample to a nitrate nitrogen concentration below 30 mg. per liter. Measure 5.00 ml. sample, 5.00 ml. distilled water, and 5.00 ml. standard nitrate solution into separate $\frac{3}{4}$-oz. paper souffle cups or 15-ml. beakers. Add 5.00 ml. uranyl catalyst to each cup and allow to stand a few minutes.

Polarographic Measurement.—At -1.2 volts *versus* the saturated calomel electrode, zero the polarograph with the electrodes in the air. Immerse the electrodes in the blank and adjust the sensitivity to yield a reading of approximately 25 percent of full scale. Suppress this reading to zero with the zero set adjustment. Read the sample and the standard nitrate solution at these settings.

$$\text{Nitrate N, mg. per liter} = \frac{A \times 10}{B}$$

$$NO_3, \text{ mg. per liter} = \text{mg. per liter of nitrate N} \times 4.43$$

where: A = reading for sample; and
B = reading for nitrate standard.

This relation holds up to about 35 mg. per liter nitrate nitrogen. The sample should be diluted and the determination repeated when higher nitrogen concentrations are encountered.

METHOD II[1,10,11]

This method is suitable for determinations in the nitrate nitrogen range of 0.1–25 mg. per liter when performed on 10 ml. samples in a commercially available polarograph with a dropping mercury electrode and a polarographic cell volume of at least 25 ml. The zirconyl chloride solution is sufficiently acid to reduce the normal water sample pH to approximately 1.7. For this reason, samples exhibiting extremely high pH and alkalinity may have to be neutralized before the addition of the zirconyl chloride. The reduction of nitrite by iron(II) necessitates the determination of the nitrite concentration and the application of a correction factor to the total nitrate concentration. Since large amounts of organic matter are known to suppress polarographic waves, such material as slime and zoogleal suspensions must be removed by aluminum hydroxide coagulation (as described in Volume II, Part B, page 2446, "NITRATE, Removal of Color and Turbidity") before the analysis is undertaken. Sulfide and mercaptans affect the results by contaminating the mercury in the polarographic cell, and, therefore, must be absent

[10] Rand, M. C., and Heukelekian, H., Anal. Chem., **25**, 878, 1953.
[11] Lawrence, W. A., and Briggs, R. M., *Ibid.*, **25**, 965, 1953.

or removed from the sample. All glassware should be acid washed and rinsed thoroughly in nitrate- and iron-free distilled water.

Reagents. Zirconyl Chloride Solution.—17.700 g. $ZrOCl_2 \cdot 8H_2O$ per 100 ml.

Ferrous Ammonium Sulfate Reagent.—Dissolve 10.600 g. fresh $Fe(NH_4)_2(SO_4)_2 \cdot 6H_2O$ in distilled water, add 0.5 ml. concentrated sulfuric acid, and dilute to 100 ml. Add a piece of standard iron wire which has been cleaned with sandpaper and rinsed with dilute sulfuric acid.

Standard Nitrate Solution.—Prepare as described in Method I to obtain a solution containing 0.0100 mg. nitrate nitrogen per 1.00 ml. If necessary, dilute additionally to prepare a solution containing 0.00100 mg. nitrogen per 1.00 ml.

Nitrogen Gas.—Purify commercial nitrogen gas by passing through alkaline pyrogallol solution and then two bottles of deoxygenated distilled water. Prepare the alkaline pyrogallol solution by dissolving 50 g. pyrogallol and 250 g. potassium hydroxide and diluting to 1 liter with distilled water.

Triple Distilled Mercury.

Procedure.—Standardize the polarograph against the saturated calomel electrode according to the manufacturer's instructions. Regulate the mercury drop rate at one drop per three to four seconds.

Pipet 10.00 ml. sample into the polarographic cell and add 1.00 ml. zirconyl chloride solution. Place the dropping mercury electrode in the sample about one-half inch above the mercury pool. Adjust the applied potential to -1.2 volts *versus* the saturated calomel electrode. Eliminate the dissolved oxygen by bubbling nitrogen gas through the sample for five minutes. (The sample and electrolyte pH of 1.7 usually enables the simultaneous removal of sulfide at this point.) Raise the outlet of the gas tube above the sample surface and record the current reading, I_1. Add 0.50 ml. ferrous ammonium sulfate reagent, mix for five minutes with the nitrogen gas stream, and again note the current reading, I_2. Ignore the dense white precipitate which forms at this stage. The difference in current readings, $I_1 - I_2$, is directly proportional to the nitrate concentration.

Correct the second current reading, I_2, daily for the iron(III) ion interference contributed by the aging of the ferrous ammonium sulfate reagent. Prepare the first correction solution from 10.00 ml. distilled water and 1.00 ml. zirconyl chloride solution. Prepare the second correction solution from 10.00 ml. distilled water, 1.00 ml. zirconyl chloride solution, and 0.50 ml. ferrous ammonium sulfate reagent. Measure the current values of both solutions at -1.2 volts. Calculate the correction factor by subtracting the current reading of the first solution from the current reading of the second solution. Then subtract the correction factor from the I_2 value.

If nitrate is determined routinely, prepare a calibration curve of current change, ΔI, *versus* nitrate concentration which usually follows a straight line relationship up to 25.0 mg. per liter nitrate nitrogen.

In the event of infrequent nitrate determinations, prepare a standard nitrate solution approximately equal to the unknown sample, and calculate the nitrate in the unknown sample by means of the following equation:

$$\text{Nitrate N, mg. per liter} = \frac{\Delta I_u \times A}{\Delta I_s}$$

$$NO_3, \text{ mg. per liter} = \text{mg. per liter of nitrate N} \times 4.43$$

where: A = nitrate nitrogen concentration of the standard nitrate solution;
ΔI_u = current change in the unknown sample; and
ΔI_s = current change in the standard nitrate solution.

ZINC[1]

Zinc yields a good wave in an ammonia-ammonium chloride-ammonium carbonate solution. Chromium and iron are reduced in the preliminary stages of the procedure. The chromium, and most of the iron, is precipitated by the carbonate. The remaining iron, present as an ammonia complex, gives a wave which closely follows that of zinc, but the separation is sufficient to permit satisfactory readings. Copper, cadmium, and nickel are reduced at more positive potentials than zinc and yield well separated waves which precede the zinc wave, thereby enabling their determination by this procedure with about the same order of precision and sensitivity as zinc. However, cadmium, copper, and nickel should not be present in concentrations much greater than zinc if very accurate zinc results are desired. Cobalt gives a wave at the same potential as zinc and must be absent, or a correction factor derived from the determination of cobalt by an independent method should be applied. Dissolved oxygen is removed by the addition of sodium sulfite. Samples relatively free of organic matter need not be evaporated.

Reagents. Deionized Distilled Water or Redistilled Water.—Should be used for the preparation of all solutions and dilutions.

Standard Zinc Solution.—Dissolve 0.0500 g. pure zinc metal (30-mesh) in a slight excess (about 0.5 ml.) of (1 + 1 v/v) hydrochloric acid, and dilute to 1000 ml. to form a standard solution containing 0.0500 mg. per 1.00 ml.

Ammonium Carbonate Solution.—150 g. per liter.

Gelatin Solution.—Dissolve 0.1 g. gelatin in 10 ml. warm water. Prepare daily.

Nitric Acid, concentrated.

Hydrochloric Acid, concentrated.

Ammonium Hydroxide, concentrated.

Sodium Sulfite.

Procedure. Calibration of Polarograph.—When polarographic determinations are made in large numbers on a more or less daily basis, the polarograph can be calibrated at a desired temperature and temperature correction factors determined. Since polarographic response is usually linear with concentration, a periodic examination of a single zinc standard will serve to check the instrument.

A blank and one or two standards should be carried with each series of samples through all of the steps in the procedure when the determinations are made at infrequent intervals. A wise precaution is to add increments of standard zinc solution to portions of the sample for a confirmation of zinc recovery in the presence of extraneous and unknown salts.

The complete polarogram need not be recorded routinely over the voltage range of interest after a satisfactory wave form has definitely been established. Voltage points at the foot of the wave and on the plateau can be selected and readings taken at these points (−1.2 volts and −1.4 volts *versus* the saturated calomel electrode). The difference between the readings at −1.4 volts and −1.2 volts, after correction for the increase in residual current corresponding to the increase in voltage, represents the polarographic response for the sample or standard being determined. The increase in residual current is obtained from the blank readings at the selected points and automatically compensates for the zinc traces present in the reagents.

Sample Treatment. *Preliminary Removal of Organic Matter Interference.*—Place a sample volume, not exceeding 100 ml. or 0.1 mg. zinc, in a 250-ml. glass-stoppered Erlenmeyer flask, add 3 ml. concentrated nitric acid, and evaporate to dryness. If the sample contains considerable organic matter, add more acid, and evaporate again. Repeat the treatment until the organic matter is destroyed. Finally, add 2 ml. concentrated hydrochloric acid and evaporate to dryness. Treat the residue with exactly 0.50 ml. concentrated hydrochloric acid followed by 7.50 ml. zinc-free distilled water, and a few crystals of sodium sulfite. Warm the flask under a hot-water tap to dissolve all of the zinc, swirl the acid up the sides of the flask, stoppering if necessary to permit more vigorous agitation without loss of sample. Ignore the small amounts of silica that may remain undissolved.

Sample Relatively Free of Organic Matter.—Pipet up to 7.50 ml. sample containing 1 mg. per liter zinc or more into a 50-ml. Erlenmeyer flask, and make the total volume 7.5 ml. Add exactly 0.50 ml. concentrated hydrochloric acid, a few crystals of sodium sulfite, and swirl.

Treatment of All Samples.—Add successively with mixing 1 ml. concentrated ammonium hydroxide, 1 ml. ammonium carbonate solution, and 1 drop gelatin solution. Measure with a standardized scoop 0.2 g. sodium sulfite crystals, add to the flask, and swirl to dissolve. Decant into a suitable vessel (4-dram shell vials are excellent), allow to stand and settle for 30 minutes, and polarograph without removal of the precipitate.

Polarographic Measurements.—Immerse the electrodes in the clear portion of the sample and polarograph over the range -1.1 to -1.5 volts *versus* the saturated calomel electrode. Compare the polarographic response of the sample with that obtained on a distilled water blank (also called an electrolyte blank) and a standard containing 0.0500 mg. zinc which have been treated in the same manner as the sample.

$$\text{Zinc, mg. per liter} = \frac{A \times 50}{B \times C}$$

where: A = corrected reading for sample,
B = corrected reading for 0.0500 mg. zinc standard; and
C = ml. of sample taken.

POLAROGRAPHIC SCANNING FOR FIVE METALS[1,12]

The following two polarographic modifications are designed for the determination of copper, nickel, lead, cadmium, and zinc, even in the presence of large quantities of one or more of the metals. Both methods have been successfully applied in the presence of 100 mg. per liter of chromium, iron, and tartaric acid. When 100 ml. of sample has been concentrated to 10 ml., the dropping mercury electrode method is capable of detecting concentrations down to approximately 0.1 mg. per liter. In the case of the quiet mercury-pool electrode method, it is advisable to minimize interference by working at sensitivity settings which will allow determinations at the 0.01 mg. per liter level.

Reagents. **Redistilled Water.**—Redistill single-distilled water from an all-glass apparatus. Use this water for the preparation of all solutions and dilutions.

Nitric Acid, concentrated and $(1 + 1 \text{ v/v})$.

Sulfuric Acid, concentrated.

Sodium Sulfite.

Ammonium Hydroxide Solution.—Pass tank ammonia gas through a glass wool trap into chilled redistilled water until the concentration reaches about 7 M. Alternatively, place 900 ml. concentrated ammonium hydroxide in a 1500-ml. distilling flask and distill into a 1-liter polyethylene bottle containing 250 ml. chilled redistilled water until the volume of liquid in the bottle increases to 900 ml. Keep the tip of the condenser below the surface of the liquid during the distillation.

[12] Ullmann, W. W., Pfeil, B. H., Porter, J. D., and Sanderson, W. W., Anal. Chem., **34,** 213, 1962.

Ammonium Sulfate Saturated Solution.—Neutralize the preceding 7 M metal-free ammonium hydroxide solution with concentrated sulfuric acid by adding the acid slowly with extreme caution. Extract the neutralized solution with a solution of dithizone in carbon tetrachloride. Wash with carbon tetrachloride until all traces of color have been removed. Concentrate to a saturated solution by the evaporation of the excess water.

Mercury, Redistilled, National Formulary Grade.—If desired, purify used mercury with commercially available oxidizers and gold adhesion filters.

Nitrogen Gas.—Purify commercially available tank nitrogen, which is usually contaminated with traces of oxygen, by passage through a purification train consisting of a Vycor tube filled with copper turnings and heated to 450°C. in an electric furnace (E. H. Sargent & Co., of Chicago, Ill.), and then successively through a trap, a bubbler to indicate the flow rate, and finally the polarographic cell.

Additional Reagents for Dropping Mercury Electrode Method. *Disodium Ethylene-diaminetetraacetate (Disodium EDTA).*

Gelatin, U. S. P. powder.

Additional Reagent for Quiet Mercury-Pool Electrode Method. *Potassium Chloride Saturated Solution.*

Procedure. **Preliminary Treatment of Sample.**—Rinse all glassware with $(1 + 1 \text{ v/v})$ nitric acid, distilled water, and finally redistilled water.

Add 0.1 ml. concentrated sulfuric acid to 100 ml. sample in an Erlenmeyer flask and evaporate to dense white fumes. Add concentrated nitric acid dropwise to the fuming liquid until the solution clears and becomes colorless. In the case of samples whose color is impossible to remove by this procedure, add nitric acid until no further color change can be observed. Wash down the sides of the flask with redistilled water to remove the excess nitric acid, add a few crystals of sodium sulfite to reduce chromium(VI), and again bring to fumes. (Fuming also eliminates chloride interference.) Cool the flask, neutralize the solution with the ammonium hydroxide solution, using pink litmus paper to indicate the completion of neutralization. (The resultant solution is roughly 0.18 M in ammonium sulfate.) Boil off the excess ammonia as evidenced by the disappearance of the ammonia odor. Filter the solution through a sintered-glass filter, and make up to 10 ml. with redistilled water.

Measurements with the Dropping Mercury Electrode.—Transfer the prepared sample to the polarographic cell, and add about 10 mg. gelatin to suppress maxima which may interfere. Use a fritted-glass bubbler for better dispersion of the nitrogen and more complete deoxygenation. Place a small amount of purified mercury in the bottom of the cell to form the indicator electrode. Insert the dropping mercury electrode into the cell so that the tip dips into the upper part of the solution. Adjust the height of the mercury reservoir to give a drop time of 4 or 5 seconds.

Connect the cell to the polarograph (although not mandatory, automatic voltage scanning and recording are preferred), and run a polarogram from 0 to −1.67 volts at suitable sensitivity. While the polarograms are being run, remove the nitrogen bubbler from the solution and hold just over the surface to maintain an atmosphere of nitrogen over the surface of the solution and thereby prevent surface absorption of oxygen.

After suitable curves have been obtained with ammonium sulfate supporting electrolyte, add sufficient (generally 4–5 drops) ammonium hydroxide solution to make the solution about 0.4 M in ammonium hydroxide, and run another set of polarograms.

Repeat the process following the addition of approximately 300 mg. of disodium ethylenediaminetetraacetate (disodium EDTA).

Interpretation of Polarograms.—Determine by inspection or rough estimation the half-wave potentials which are at the half-way point of the rise. Ignore the correction for the current resistance (IR) drop across the resistors in the measuring circuit. Measure vertically the wave heights through the half-wave potential between the straight-line extrapolations of the sections of the polarogram immediately preceding and following the wave. Table 63-5 presents the half-wave potential and current concentration ratios

TABLE 63-5. HALF-WAVE POTENTIALS AND CURRENT CONCENTRATION RATIOS OF METALS AT THE DROPPING MERCURY ELECTRODE[a]

Metal	Supporting Electrolyte					
	0.18 M Ammonium Sulfate		0.18 M Ammonium Sulfate + 0.4 M Ammonium Hydroxide		0.18 M Ammonium Sulfate + 0.4 M Ammonium Hydroxide + EDTA	
	Half-Wave Potential in Volt	Relative Wave Height in μa. per μg. of Metal	Half-Wave Potential in Volt	Relative Wave Height in μa. per μg. of Metal	Half-Wave Potential in Volt	Relative Wave Height in μa. per μg. of Metal
Copper	0.02 to 0.05	0.0076	2 waves— 0.17 and 0.38 to 0.45	often not seen 0.0040	0.47 to 0.51	0.0050
Lead	0.37 to 0.40	0.0010	0.43 to 0.47	0.0010	1.13 to 1.17	0.0010
Cadmium	0.57 to 0.59	0.0036	0.67 to 0.74	0.0036	no wave	
Nickel	1.01 to 1.03	0.0083	0.91 to 0.95	0.0083	no wave	
Zinc	0.98	0.0083	1.19 to 1.22	0.0083	no wave	

[a] Reproduced with permission from Standard Methods for the Examination of Water and Wastewater, 12th Ed., The American Public Health Assn., Inc., New York, 1965.

of metals at the dropping mercury electrode. These values serve to identify the five metals—copper, nickel, lead, cadmium, and zinc, and suffice for semi-quantitative work. For quantitative results, a similar table should be prepared by the use of the available equipment and standard solutions of the metals of interest.

Measurements with the Quiet Mercury-Pool Electrode.—For best results, construct the polarographic cell illustrated in Fig. 63-5 with the following features. Mark permanently a test tube of 15 mm. inside diameter at the level wherein the volume from the top of the fritted-glass bubbler is 10 ml., and attach a sidearm about 15 mm. above this graduation. Use 140–200 mesh borosilicate glass powder to make the bubbler which projects upward through the bottom of the cell. Seal the bubbler tube into the bottom of the cell so that the mercury pool in the annular space around the bubbler tube occupies an area about 0.8 sq. cm., and is independent within limits of the volume of mercury added. Use a sealed-in platinum wire for electrical contact with the pool, and a three-way stopcock for admitting nitrogen either through the bubbler or over the surface of the solution. Suspend the reference electrode, consisting of a small helix of No. 24 silver wire chloridized by brief anodic treatment in 10 percent hydrochloric acid, in the U-shaped sidearm of the cell. Coat the interior surface of the cell with the silicone preparation, Desicote (a product of Beckman Instruments, Inc., Fullerton, Calif.), to prevent penetration of the sample between the glass and the mercury.

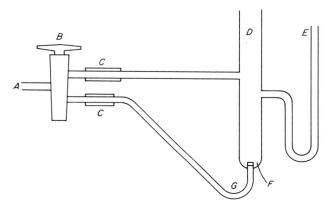

Fig. 63-5. Polarographic Cell for Use with Quiet Mercury Pool Electrode: *A*, Nitrogen Inlet; *B*, Three-Way Stopcock; *C*, Tygon Tubing; *D*, 6-Inch Pyrex Test Tube; *E*, Reference Electrode; *F*, Platinum Wire; *G*. Sintered Glass Bubbler. (Reproduced with permission from Standard Methods for the Examination of Water and Wastewater, 12th Ed., The American Public Health Assn., Inc., New York, 1965.)

Construct a deaeration apparatus from a test tube, of 15 mm. inside diameter, marked at the 10-ml. level, and with a sidearm protruding about 15 mm. above this graduation.

Rinse all glassware, including the cell, successively with concentrated nitric acid, distilled water, and twice with redistilled water.

Place a fritted bubbler into the sidearm test tube to which has been added the prepared sample. Connect the nitrogen purification train to the bubbler, and pass nitrogen through the sample for about 10 minutes before transferring to the polarographic cell.

Add saturated ammonium sulfate solution to the sidearm of the cell with a dropper to fill about half its height. Add carefully sufficient saturated potassium chloride solution to the outer end of the sidearm to force the ammonium sulfate just to the junction of the sidearm with the main body of the cell. (The less dense potassium chloride solution forms a layer above the ammonium sulfate solution.) Insert the chloridized silver wire into the potassium chloride solution to complete the silver-silver chloride reference electrode. Add redistilled water to the main section of the cell to a level just below the bottom of the sidearm juncture and add 10 drops of ammonium sulfate solution. Connect the cell to the nitrogen train and bubble nitrogen through the solution for about 5 minutes. Add sufficient mercury from a small buret to form an annular ring in the bottom of the cell surrounding the bubbler, making sure that the platinum wire is covered. Then add sufficient redistilled water to raise the level to the top of the juncture of the sidearm. (Allow the mercury to stand in the buret for at least one day before use so that certain impurities can rise to the surface.)

Bubble nitrogen through the solution for an additional 3–5 minutes, and then turn the stopcock to bypass it over the solution. Scan the voltage rapidly up and down several times manually, and then make one or two automatic voltage scans from about +0.3

to −2.0 volts. (The first voltage scan with a freshly prepared mercury pool cathode usually yields an irregular curve with a high residual current, probably due to basic salts, oxides of mercury, and traces of organic matter. The preconditioning process serves to smooth out these irregularities without affecting the peak heights in the sample runs which follow.)

Remove all of the blank solution from the cell by aspiration, taking care not to disturb the mercury surface. Transfer the sample through the sidearm of the deaeration apparatus to the cell. Maintain a good current of nitrogen while the blank is being removed and the sample is being added to prevent the entrainment of oxygen. Bubble nitrogen through the sample for about 5 minutes. Meanwhile, make a few rapid manual up-and-down scans to further precondition the mercury. Bypass the nitrogen over the solution and make at least two automatic scans from +0.2 to −1.4 volts at a rate of 0.15 volt per minute. (The multiple scans reduce the risk of mistaking an accidental and transitory peak for a significant one.) After the peaks for the various metals in the sample have been located, rescan the sample automatically as before, but hold the voltages stationary just beyond each peak until the current decays, and then allow automatic scanning to continue. (In this manner, metals whose half-peak potentials lie close together may be evaluated without interference.)

When satisfactory curves have been obtained in the ammonium sulfate medium, make the solution about 0.4 M with respect to ammonium hydroxide. Bubble nitrogen through the solution to remove any oxygen which may have been introduced during the addition of the ammonium hydroxide solution. Make at least two automatic scans from 0 to −1.4 volts at a rate of 0.15 volt per minute. After the solution has been made ammoniacal, guard against the pool electrode becoming positive and thereby forming troublesome mercury-ammonia complexes. Finally, rescan the sample, pausing just beyond each peak as previously described.

Interpretation of Polarograms.—Draw two parallel lines tangent to the curve at the

TABLE 63-6. HALF-PEAK POTENTIALS AND CURRENT CONCENTRATION RATIOS OF METALS AT THE QUIET MERCURY POOL ELECTRODE[a]

Metal	Supporting Electrolyte			
	0.18 M Ammonium Sulfate		0.18 M Ammonium Sulfate + 0.4 M Ammonium Hydroxide	
	Half-Peak Potential in Volt	Relative Peak Height in μa. per μg. of Metal	Half-Peak Potential in Volt	Relative Peak Height in μa. per μg. of Metal
Copper	+0.05 to 0	0.161 ± 0.008	−0.07 to −0.09	0.041 ± 0.005
Copper			−0.32 to −0.33	0.060 ± 0.003
Lead	−0.33 to −0.38	0.036 ± 0.006	−0.38	0.022 ± 0.005
Cadmium	−0.50 to −0.54	0.092 ± 0.006	−0.65 to −0.67	0.094 ± 0.006
Nickel	No peak		−0.88 to −0.93	0.097 ± 0.003
Zinc	−0.96 to −1.02	0.180 ± 0.010	−1.17 to −1.19	0.180 ± 0.028

[a] Reproduced with permission from Standard Methods for the Examination of Water and Wastewater, 12th Ed., The American Public Health Assn., Inc., New York, 1965.

turning points, marking the lower and upper limits of the excursion associated with the particular metal. The half-peak potential is the point on the curve lying half way between the parallel lines, while the peak height is the vertical distance between the lines.

Table 63-6 presents the half-peak potentials and current concentration ratios of metals at the quiet pool electrode. These values identify the five metals—copper, nickel, lead, cadmium, and zinc—for semi-quantitative work. Since the current concentration ratios are strictly dependent upon the rate of voltage application, any variation from the 0.15 volt per minute application rate will invalidate the reported data. The results can be made quantitative for the particular cell and equipment on hand by collecting similar data with standard solutions of the metals of interest.

NUCLEAR TECHNIQUES

Broad screening methods for the routine measurement of radioactivity appeal to the general laboratory which cannot afford the equipment, skill, or time for identifying the particular radionuclides that might be present in a water sample. Regular recourse to the method for determining gross alpha and gross beta radioactivity in water described in Volume II, Part B, page 2470, enables the early detection of radioactive contamination, and can also suggest the need for any supplemental data on the concentrations of the more hazardous radionuclides. Strontium, barium, and radium are of public health interest, with the result that these determinations are performed mainly in the large governmental laboratories.

TOTAL RADIOACTIVE STRONTIUM[1,13,14]

Four beta-emitting radioisotopes of strontium have half lives greater than two hours. Strontium-91 and -92 are eliminated from the sample by storage for three days, leaving strontium-89 and -90 as the radioisotopes likely to be found in the usual water sample. The strontium-89 and -90 isotopes are measured by direct counting of their beta radiations. The strontium carbonate precipitate should be counted within three or four hours after the final separation to avoid serious ingrowth of its daughter, yttrium-90. If the final precipitate contains only strontium-90 activity, a recount of the precipitate three weeks later will yield more than double the first count rate because of the yttrium-90 ingrowth.

Reagents. Strontium Nitrate Carrier Solution.—48.31 g. $Sr(NO_3)_2$ per 1000 ml.; 20 mg. Sr per ml. Prepare in a volumetric flask.

Barium Nitrate Carrier Solution.—42.1 g. $Ba(NO_3)_2$ per liter; 22.1 mg. Ba per ml. Prepare in a volumetric flask if radioactive barium is also determined.

Acetate Buffer Solution.—Dissolve 154 g. ammonium acetate in 700 ml. distilled water, add 57 ml. concentrated (glacial) acetic acid, and dilute to 1 liter.

Mixed Rare Earth Carrier Reagent.—Dissolve 12.8 g. cerium(III) nitrate, $Ce(NO_3)_3 \cdot 6H_2O$, 14 g. zirconyl chloride, $ZrOCl_2 \cdot 8H_2O$, and 25 g. iron(III) chloride, $FeCl_3 \cdot 6H_2O$, in 600 ml. distilled water containing 5 ml. concentrated hydrochloric acid, and dilute to 1 liter.

Sodium Carbonate Solution, 1 M.—124 g. $Na_2CO_3 \cdot H_2O$ or 106 g. Na_2CO_3 per liter.

Sodium Chromate Solution.—351 g. $Na_2CrO_4 \cdot 4H_2O$ per liter.

Phenolphthalein Indicator Solution.

Acetone, anhydrous.

Ethyl Ether.

Ethyl Alcohol, 95 percent.

[13] Hahn, R. B., and Straub, C. P., J. Am. Water Works Assn., **47**, 335, 1955.
[14] Goldin, A. S., Velten, R. J., and Frishkorn, G. W., Anal. Chem., **31**, 1490, 1959.

Nitric Acid, concentrated and 6 *M*.

Ammonium Hydroxide, concentrated and 5 *M*.

Procedure. **Concentration of Strontium Activity by Precipitation.**—Remove any suspended matter from the sample and analyze separately, if desired. Measure 4 liters filtered water sample into a beaker, add 1.0 ml. each of strontium nitrate and barium nitrate carrier solutions to precipitate the strontium and barium radionuclides, and mix. If the radioactive strontium exceeds 25 picocuries per liter, reduce the sample size proportionately. Add 5 ml. concentrated nitric acid, heat to boiling, then add 50 ml. concentrated ammonium hydroxide. Add 50 ml. sodium carbonate solution to the boiling solution to precipitate the alkaline earth carbonates and other radioactive elements. Stir and allow to simmer at 90–95°C. for about 1 hour. Set the beaker aside and let stand for 1–3 hours until the precipitate has settled. Decant and reject the clear supernatant liquid. Transfer the precipitate and the remaining solution to a 50-ml. glass centrifuge tube, and centrifuge. Discard the supernatant liquid.

Reprecipitation of Strontium Nitrate.—Dissolve the precipitate by the dropwise addition of about 2 ml. concentrated nitric acid. Heat to boiling, add 1 ml. distilled water (3 ml. distilled water if the sample hardness exceeds 250 mg. per liter as calcium carbonate), stir, and centrifuge. Discard any residue such as silica which may remain after centrifuging. Transfer the clear supernatant liquid to a clean tube. If necessary, evaporate the solution to 3 ml. or less. Add 30 ml. concentrated nitric acid, cool in an ice bath for 10 minutes with stirring to precipitate the strontium and barium nitrates, and centrifuge. Reject the supernatant liquid, and invert the tube in a beaker for about 10 minutes to drain off most of the excess nitric acid. Dissolve the precipitate in 2 ml. distilled water, add 30 ml. concentrated nitric acid, cool in an ice bath for 10 minutes with stirring, and centrifuge. Discard the supernatant liquid, and again invert the tube in a beaker for about 10 minutes to drain off most of the excess nitric acid. If the calcium content of the original water sample exceeds 200 mg., repeat the addition of 30 ml. concentrated nitric acid, cool, centrifuge, reject the supernatant liquid, and invert the tube. Add 20 ml. anhydrous acetone to dissolve any calcium nitrate which may have coprecipitated with the strontium nitrate. Stir thoroughly, cool in an ice bath, and centrifuge. Discard the supernatant liquid. Dissolve the precipitate of strontium nitrate and barium nitrate in 3 ml. distilled water and heat to boiling for about 30 seconds to remove any lingering acetone. Add 20 ml. concentrated nitric acid, cool in an ice bath, stir, and centrifuge. Discard the supernatant liquid.

Removal of Interfering Radionuclides by Hydroxide Precipitation.—Dissolve the precipitate in 10 ml. distilled water, add 1 ml. mixed rare earth carrier reagent, and precipitate the hydroxides by making the solution basic with 5 *M* ammonium hydroxide. Centrifuge and decant the supernatant liquid to a clean tube. Discard the precipitate.

Barium Precipitation.—Add 6 *M* nitric acid dropwise with stirring until the solution is neutral to (1 drop) phenolphthalein indicator. Add 5 ml. acetate buffer solution to adjust the pH to 5.5, and heat to boiling. Precipitate barium chromate by adding 1 ml. sodium chromate solution, stir for 1 minute, and centrifuge. Save the supernatant liquid by decanting to a clean centrifuge tube, and set aside the barium chromate precipitate for the additional processing described under "Radioactive Barium," page 1912.

Final Reprecipitation of Strontium.—Add 2 ml. concentrated ammonium hydroxide to the supernatant liquid and heat to boiling. Add 10 ml. sodium carbonate solution and stir. Filter by suction through a weighed 1 lter paper disk in a small Hirsch funnel or through a membrane filter. Wash with three 5-ml. portions of distilled water, three 5-ml. portions of 95 percent ethyl alcohol, and three 5-ml. portions of ethyl ether. Omit the ethyl ether wash and allow a longer period for evaporating the ethyl alcohol if a membrane filter is used because of the possible destructive action of the ether on the filter. Transfer the filter and precipitate to a 25-mm. watch glass or stainless steel counting pan (54 mm. in diameter and 7 mm. deep), dry 5 minutes at 90–100°C. in an oven, and weigh on an analytical balance.

Instrumental Measurement.—Mount and count the strontium carbonate precipitate in one of the following counting instruments: (a) an internal proportional counter of the gas flow type, with scaler, timer, and register; or (b) an end-window Geiger-Müller tube (mica) or other thin-window (Mylar) counter each equipped with the required scaler, timer, register, and amplifier.

Determination of Over-all Strontium-90 Counting Efficiency.—Obtain a standard radioactive strontium-90 solution certified by the National Bureau of Standards. Measure ascending increments of this solution into tared pans, and prepare a series of samples which will yield residues of 1–10 mg. per square centimeter over the bottom area of the counting pan. Evaporate carefully in order to obtain uniformly deposited residues, particularly in the 0–3 mg. per sq. cm. range where inconsistent results may occasionally occur. Dry at 103°C., weigh on an analytical balance, and count under geometrical conditions identical with those of the unknown sample. Calculate the ratio of counts per minute to disintegrations per minute (efficiency) for different weights of sample residue. Plot the efficiency for different weights of sample residue. Plot the efficiency as a function of sample residue, and use the resulting calibration curve to convert counts per minute to disintegrations per minute.

Calculation.—Assume that any loss in the strontium nitrate carrier causes a corresponding loss in activity. Thus, 1.0 ml. strontium nitrate carrier solution (20 mg. Sr per ml.) is equivalent to 33.6 mg. strontium carbonate. Alternatively, ascertain the strontium carrier loss by the flame photometric method described in Volume II, Part B, page 2481. Determine the strontium concentration of the original filtered water sample by flame photometry, and consider more than a trace of stable strontium in the original sample as strontium carrier, and compensate accordingly.

Compute the total radioactive strontium by means of the following equation:

$$\text{Total strontium activity in picocuries per liter} = \frac{C}{D \times E \times S \times 2.22}$$

where: A = total counts accumulated;
$\quad\quad B$ = background in counts per minute;

$\quad\quad C$ = beta activity in net counts per minute = $\dfrac{A}{t} - B$;

$\quad\quad D = \dfrac{\text{weight of final } SrCO_3 \text{ precipitate in mg.}}{33.6}$;

$\quad\quad E$ = beta counter efficiency;
$\quad\quad S$ = sample volume in liters; and
$\quad\quad t$ = time of counting in minutes.

STRONTIUM-90[1,13,14,15]

On arrival at the laboratory many environmental samples are relatively old from the standpoint of radioactivity because of the presence of strontium-90 which has been widely disseminated from nuclear test fallout. The strontium-90 in a water sample results from its half life of approximately 28 years and solubility. Most other radio-

[15] Velten, R. J., and Goldin, A. S., Anal. Chem., **33**, 128, 1961; **33**, 149, 1961.

nuclides are naturally removed by adsorption on suspended matter and subsequent sedimentation. Decay usually eliminates many interfering elements except yttrium-91 and promethium-147 in samples more than 400 days old.

Reagents.—The following reagents are needed for the determination and are described under "Total Radioactive Strontium," page 1907: Strontium Nitrate Carrier Solution, Barium Nitrate Carrier Solution, Acetate Buffer Solution, Mixed Rare Earth Carrier Reagent, Sodium Carbonate Solution, and Sodium Chromate Solution.

The following additional reagents are also required:

Ferric Nitrate Reagent.—Dissolve 36.0 g. $Fe(NO_3)_3 \cdot 9H_2O$ in 100–200 ml. distilled water containing 2 ml. concentrated hydrochloric acid, and dilute to 1 liter; 5 mg. Fe per ml.

Tributyl Phosphate, Reagent Grade.—Shake with concentrated nitric acid for 10 minutes to equilibrate.

Methyl Orange Indicator Solution.

Fuming Nitric Acid.

Nitric Acid, concentrated, 6 M, and 0.1 M.

Hydrochloric Acid.—(1 + 1 v/v).

Ammonium Hydroxide, concentrated and 5 M.

Special Reagents for the Alternate Oxalate Precipitation. *Yttrium Carrier Reagent.*— Dissolve 12.7 g. yttrium oxide (Code 118, American Potash and Chemical Corp., West Chicago, Illinois, or equivalent) in 30 ml. warm concentrated nitric acid, add 20 ml. concentrated nitric acid, and dilute to 1 liter with distilled water; 1 ml. = 34 mg. $Y_2(C_2O_4)_3 \cdot 9H_2O$.

Saturated Oxalic Acid Solution.—110 g. $H_2C_2O_4$ per liter.

Ethyl Ether.

Procedure. Concentration of Strontium-90 Activity by Precipitation.—Follow the steps described in the paragraph entitled "Concentration of Activity by Precipitation," under "Total Radioactive Strontium."

Reprecipitation of Strontium Carbonate.—Dissolve the precipitate in 2–3 ml. (1 + 1 v/v) hydrochloric acid, heat to drive off the carbon dioxide, and dilute to 15–20 ml. with distilled water. Add sufficient drops of 5 M ammonium hydroxide to reach the methyl orange end point. Add 1 ml. sodium chromate solution to remove the radiobarium, and warm in a water bath. Slowly add 5 ml. acetate buffer solution to attain a pH of 5, and digest hot for 5–10 minutes. Centrifuge, add 2–3 drops barium nitrate carrier solution, stir without disturbing the precipitate, and recentrifuge. Save the supernatant liquid. After making the supernatant liquid alkaline with 5 M ammonium hydroxide, precipitate the strontium with 10 ml. sodium carbonate solution. Centrifuge, discard the supernatant liquid, and wash the precipitate with 15–25 ml. distilled water containing 1–2 drops sodium carbonate solution.

Removal of Rare Earth and Polyvalent Metals.—Dissolve the precipitate in 2–3 ml. (1 + 1 v/v) hydrochloric acid, add 25 ml. distilled water and 2–3 drops ferric nitrate reagent, heat, and make alkaline with 5 M ammonium hydroxide. Centrifuge, add 2–3 drops ferric nitrate reagent, and recentrifuge. Decant the supernatant liquid and add to it 0.5 ml. Mixed Rare Earth Carrier Reagent. If a precipitate forms, add (1 + 1 v/v) hydrochloric acid dropwise to dissolve the precipitate; then warm, make alkaline with 5 M ammonium hydroxide, centrifuge, add 0.5 ml. Mixed Rare Earth Carrier Reagent, and recentrifuge. Decant and note the time of the last rare earth precipitation, which constitutes the start of the yttrium-90 ingrowth period. Add 10 ml. sodium carbonate solution to the supernatant liquid which contains the strontium, and centrifuge.

Storage of Strontium Carbonate Precipitate.—Store the strontium carbonate precipitate overnight or up to two weeks when strontium-90 and its daughter yttrium-90 will be in secular equilibrium. Regulate the storage period on the basis of activity:

14 days for a sample with low-level strontium activity, and diminishing to overnight standing for samples with progressively higher activity. The yttrium-90 reaches about 18 percent of final equilibrium after 18 hours and 97 percent after two weeks. Dissolve the strontium carbonate precipitate in 2 ml. 6 M nitric acid, and continue the procedure as described below under "Extraction of Yttrium-90" or under "Alternate Oxalate Precipitation."

Extraction of Yttrium-90.—Cool in an ice bath and add with stirring 10 ml. fuming nitric acid. Centrifuge and transfer the supernatant liquid to a 60-ml. separatory funnel. Dissolve the residue in 2 ml. 6 M nitric acid, again cool in an ice bath, add with stirring 10 ml. fuming nitric acid, centrifuge, and transfer the supernatant liquid to the separatory funnel. Note the time which is the end of the yttrium-90 production and the beginning of its decay. Save the residue for processing as described subsequently under "Determination of Strontium Yield." Add 6 ml. 6 M nitric acid to the combined supernatants in the separatory funnel to bring the aqueous phase to 30 ml. Add 5.0 ml. tributyl phosphate reagent and shake thoroughly for 10 minutes. Transfer the aqueous layer to another 60-ml. separatory funnel and repeat two more times the extraction with 5-ml. portions of tributyl phosphate. Combine the aqueous solution after the third organic extraction with the conserved residue. Wash the combined organic extracts three times with 5-ml. portions of concentrated nitric acid. (Merge the acid washings, the combined aqueous solution which was extracted with tributyl phosphate, and the conserved residue, and treat as described under "Determination of Strontium Yield.") Back-extract the combined organic phases with 10 ml. 0.1 M nitric acid for 10 minutes. Transfer the aqueous phase to a 50-ml. beaker and reduce its volume on a hot plate. Repeat two more times the back-extraction with 10 ml. 0.1 M nitric acid and combine the aqueous phases in the 50-ml. beaker. Evaporate the solution to about 10 ml., transfer to a stainless steel counting pan (54 mm. in diameter and 7 mm. deep), and evaporate to dryness. Wash the beaker with small portions of 0.1 M nitric acid. Add the washings to the counting pan and evaporate to dryness.

Alternate Oxalate Precipitation.—Add 1 ml. yttrium carrier reagent followed by sufficient drops of concentrated ammonium hydroxide to reach the methyl orange endpoint, and then add 5 ml. concentrated ammonium hydroxide in excess. Record the time which represents the end of the yttrium-90 production period and the start of its decay. Centrifuge and save this and subsequent supernatant liquids for a strontium yield determination. Wash the precipitate twice with 20-ml. portions of hot distilled water, likewise saving the supernate. Dissolve the precipitate with 6 M nitric acid. Again add sufficient drops of concentrated ammonium hydroxide to reach the methyl orange endpoint and then 5 ml. concentrated ammonium hydroxide in excess. Centrifuge and wash the precipitate twice with 20-ml. portions of hot distilled water, conserving the supernatant liquid and washings. Combine the supernatant liquids and washings, and treat as described under "Determination of Strontium Yield." Dissolve the precipitate with 6 M nitric acid (about 2 drops), add 25 ml. distilled water, and heat in a water bath at 90°C. Gradually add 15–20 drops of saturated oxalic acid solution with stirring, followed by 2–3 drops concentrated ammonium hydroxide to adjust the pH at 2.0–3.0. Digest the precipitate for 5 minutes, then cool in an ice bath with occasional stirring. Collect the precipitate on a weighed glass fiber filter (H. Reeve Angel & Co. No. 934-AH, 2.4-cm. diameter, or equivalent) supported on a two-piece suction funnel. After the precipitate has settled by gravity, apply suction, and wash the precipitate successively with hot distilled water, three times with 95 percent ethyl alcohol, and finally three times with ethyl ether. Air dry the precipitate with suction for 2 minutes, and weigh.

Instrumental Measurement.—Mount the extracted residue or the oxalate precipitate and count the beta emissions in one of the following counting instruments: (a) an internal porportional counter of the gas flow type, with scaler, timer, and register; or (b) an end-window Geiger-Müller tube (mica) or other thin-window (Mylar) counter each equipped with the required scaler, timer, register, and amplifier.

Determination of Strontium Yield.—Make the combined aqueous solution, acid washings, and residue, alkaline with ammonium hydroxide, and precipitate strontium carbonate with 10 ml. sodium carbonate solution. Centrifuge, discard the supernate, and wash the precipitate with 15–25 ml. distilled water containing 1–2 drops 5 M ammonium hydroxide. Transfer the precipitate to a tared dish, dry at 120°C., and weigh on an analytical balance to determine the strontium yield. Alternatively, determine the strontium yield by the flame photometric method described in Volume II, Part B, page 2481, or with a strontium-85 tracer. The tracer technique overcomes the fictitious yield from samples high in stable strontium.

Determination of Over-all Strontium-90 Counting Efficiency.—Determine as described under "Determination of Over-all Strontium-90 Counting Efficiency," "Total Radioactive Strontium," page 1909.

Calculation.—Assume that any loss in the added strontium nitrate carrier causes a corresponding loss in radioactivity. Determine the strontium concentration of the original filtered water sample by the flame photometric method, and consider more than a trace of stable strontium in the original sample as strontium carrier, and compensate accordingly.

Compute the strontium-90 activity by means of the following equation:

$$\text{Strontium-90 activity in picocuries per liter} = \frac{M}{R \times S \times V \times W \times Y \times Z \times 2.22}$$

where: M = beta activity in net counts per minute = $\dfrac{N}{P} - Q$;

N = total counts accumulated;
P = time of counting in minutes;
Q = background in counts per minute;
R = chemical yield of strontium determined gravimetrically or by flame photometry (may vary from 70 to 100 percent with a mean of approximately 85 percent);
S = sample volume in liters;
V = beta counter efficiency;
W = chemical yield of extracting or precipitating yttrium-90;
Z = yttrium-90 ingrowth correction factor if not in secular equilibrium; and
Y = yttrium-90 decay factor, which is calculated by the following equation:

$A = A_0 e^{-\lambda t}$ in which A is the activity remaining after the time interval, t, in hours, between separation and counting; A_0 is the activity of the sample at time zero; e is the natural logarithm base; and $\lambda = 0.693/64.2$, or the half life of yttrium-90 in hours.

RADIOACTIVE BARIUM[13]

Barium 140—lanthanum 140 and cesium 137—barium 137 are hazardous fission-product isotopes. Although radiobarium does not represent the same long-term hazard as strontium-90, it is conveniently separated and measured during the radiostrontium determination. The half lives of barium-140, lanthanum-140, and barium-139 are 12.8 days, 40.2 hours, and 85 minutes, respectively.

Radioactive barium and strontium are concentrated and handled similarly up to the final separatory steps. Therefore, the entire writeup, "Total Radioactive Strontium," page 1907, should be studied before the barium activity is determined. Approximately 400 picocuries per liter of barium activity can be detected with the following method.

Reagents.—All the reagents for the "Total Radioactive Strontium" determination are needed for the barium determination. The following additional reagents are also required.

Hydrochloric Acid, concentrated and 6 *M*.

Ethyl Ether.

Hydrochloric Acid-Ether Mixture.—Add 500 ml. cold concentrated hydrochloric acid to 100 ml. ethyl ether.

Ethyl Alcohol, absolute.

Procedure.—Follow the procedure described under "Total Radioactive Strontium" from the beginning through the "Barium Precipitation" step.

Wash the barium chromate precipitate with 10 ml. hot distilled water. Centrifuge and discard the supernatant liquid. Add 2 ml. 6 *M* hydrochloric acid and heat to boiling to dissolve the precipitate. Cool and add 15 ml. hydrochloric acid-ether mixture. Chill, stir for 1–2 minutes, and then centrifuge. Reject the supernatant liquid. Dissolve the precipitate in 1 ml. distilled water, then add 15 ml. hydrochloric acid-ether mixture. Chill, stir, centrifuge, and discard the supernatant liquid. Transfer the precipitate to a weighed filter paper disk in a Hirsch funnel with three 5-ml. portions of absolute ethyl alcohol, using suction for filtration. Wash with three 5-ml. portions of ethyl ether. Transfer the precipitate to a watch glass. Dry 5 minutes at 80–90°C., weigh, mount, and count the $BaCl_2 \cdot H_2O$ precipitate.

Calculation.—Assume that any loss in the barium nitrate carrier causes a corresponding loss in activity. Compute the radioactive barium by means of the following equation:

$$\text{Barium activity in picocuries per liter} = \frac{C}{D \times E \times S \times 2.22}$$

where: A = total counts accumulated;
$\quad\quad B$ = background in counts per minute;
$\quad\quad C$ = beta activity in net counts per minute = $\dfrac{A}{t} - B$;
$\quad\quad D$ = chemical yield of final $BaCl_2 \cdot H_2O$ precipitate;
$\quad\quad E$ = beta counter efficiency;
$\quad\quad S$ = sample volume in liters; and
$\quad\quad t$ = time of counting in minutes.

RADIUM

Four radium nuclides occur naturally: 1620-year radium-226, 6.7-year radium-228 (a beta emitter), 11.6-day radium-223, and 3.6-day radium-224. Except for radium-226, each of these radium nuclides gives rise to a family of relatively short-lived daughter products. Because of the different half lives the radium nuclides in these series can be identified isotopically by the rate of ingrowth and decay of the alpha-emitting daughters in a barium sulfate precipitate. Since the other radium nuclides are less important in causing internal radiation exposure, the U. S. Public Health Service Drinking Water Standards single out and impose an upper limit on the tolerable radium-226 activity.

The precipitation method is suitable for screening samples for total radium nuclides, while the emanation method is specific for radium-226. A sample approaching 3 picocuries per liter in total radium activity should be checked by the emanation method.

TOTAL RADIUM[1,16]

Reagents. Barium Chloride Carrier Solution.—11.9 g. $BaCl_2 \cdot 2H_2O$ per liter; 6.7 mg. Ba per ml.

Lead Nitrate Carrier Solution.—160 g. per liter; 100 mg. Pb per ml.

Disodium Ethylenediaminetetraacetate (Disodium EDTA), 0.25 M.—93 g. per liter.

Methyl Orange Indicator Solution.

Citric Acid Solution, 1 M.—210 g. $H_3C_6H_5O_7 \cdot H_2O$ per liter.

Acetic Acid, concentrated (glacial).

Nitric Acid, concentrated.

Sulfuric Acid, 18 N.

Ammonium Hydroxide, concentrated and 5 N.

Ethyl Alcohol, 95 percent.

Acetone.

Lucite Solution.—0.5 g. Lucite per 100 ml. acetone.

Procedure.—Measure 1 liter filtered sample into a 1500-ml. beaker and add 5 ml. 1 M citric acid solution, 2.5 ml. concentrated ammonium hydroxide, 2 ml. lead nitrate carrier solution, and 1.0 ml. barium chloride carrier solution. Heat to boiling, add 10 drops methyl orange indicator solution, and slowly add, with stirring, 18 N sulfuric acid until the indicator changes to a permanent pink color. After adding 0.25 ml. 18 N sulfuric acid more, boil the sample gently for 5 to 10 minutes, then set the beaker aside so that the radium-barium-lead sulfate precipitate can settle for 3 to 5 hours or more. Decant and reject the clear supernatant liquid. Transfer the precipitate to a 50-ml. (or larger) centrifuge tube and centrifuge. Decant and discard the supernatant liquid. Wash the precipitate three times with 10-ml. portions of concentrated nitric acid, discarding the washings. Dissolve the precipitate in the centrifuge tube with 10 ml. distilled water, 10 ml. 0.25 M EDTA solution, and 3 ml. 5 N ammonium hydroxide. Clear the solution by warming in a steam bath, and add 2 ml. glacial acetic acid dropwise. (The acetic acid volume is approximately double the amount needed to neutralize the ammonium hydroxide and yield a pH of 4.5 which will destroy the barium-EDTA complex but not the soluble lead-EDTA.) Digest for 5–10 minutes, cool to room temperature, centrifuge, and discard the supernatant liquid. Wash the barium-radium sulfate with distilled water and mount the precipitate for counting in one of the following ways.

(a) Transfer the barium-radium sulfate with a minimum of 95 percent ethyl alcohol to a tared stainless steel planchet. Add 2 ml. acetone, 2 drops Lucite solution, disperse the precipitate evenly, and evaporate under an infrared lamp. Dry in an oven at 110°C., weigh on an analytical balance, and determine the alpha activity in an internal proportional counter of the gas flow type with scaler, timer, and register.

(b) Collect the precipitate on a tared membrane filter in a holder. Wash the precipitate with 15–25 ml. distilled water. Place the membrane filter in a counting dish with a glass ring weight and dry at 110°C. Weigh on an analytical balance and count in an internal proportional counter or an alpha zinc sulfide scintillation phototube counter.

(c) Add 20 ml. distilled water to the barium-radium sulfate precipitate and allow to settle in a steam bath. Cool to room temperature. Transfer the precipitate into a stainless steel two-piece funnel (Tracerlab, Inc., Waltham, Mass.) containing a tared glass fiber filter. Dry the precipitate in an oven at 110°C. to constant weight. Mount the precipitate on a Nylon disc and ring with an alpha phosphor on Mylar, and count with a bare phototube on an alpha scintillation counter.

[16] Goldin, A. S., Anal. Chem., **33**, 406, 1961.

Calculation.—Assume that any loss in the added barium nitrate carrier causes a corresponding loss in radium activity.

$$\text{Total radium activity in picocuries per liter} = \frac{C}{D \times E \times F \times G \times S \times 2.22}$$

where: A = total counts accumulated;

B = background in counts per minute;

C = alpha activity in net counts per minute = $\dfrac{A}{t} - B$;

D = chemical yield of barium;

E = alpha counting efficiency;

F = self-absorption factor;

S = sample volume in liters;

t = time of counting in minutes; and

G = ingrowth factor based on the assumption that the total radium is radium-226, according to the following table:

Ingrowth in Hours	Alpha Activity from Radium-226
0	1.0000
1	1.0160
2	1.0363
3	1.0580
4	1.0798
5	1.1021
6	1.1238
24	1.4892
48	1.9054
72	2.2525

RADIUM-226[1,17,18]

Radium-226 decays to form radon-222, a gas which is withdrawn from the solution by aeration. For this reason, the gaseous alpha-emitting radionuclides radon-219 (actinon) and radon-220 (thoron) may interfere with the determination. Since these short-lived radon isotopes, with half lives of 3.92 seconds and 54.5 seconds, respectively, decay before the radon-222 is counted, it is their alpha-emitting decay products which can contribute a possible interference. Such interference is very rare in water samples, being confined to certain uranium mill effluents. The stable chemical interferences present in water are limited because relatively few substances significantly contaminate barium sulfate precipitated from acid solution. The small amounts of calcium, lead, and strontium collected by the barium sulfate do not interfere, even though lead may attack the platinum ware. Calcium concentrations of 300 mg. per liter cause no difficulty. Total filtrable residue up to 269,000 mg. per liter of brine is without effect on the recovery of radium. The suspended matter and a small flocculent precipitate of zirconyl phosphate that may occur in the final solution do not prevent the removal of the radon when the amount of carrier is that specified. The small orange-yellow precipitate, probably chloroplatinate, that sometimes appears in the final solution exerts no adverse effect.

[17] Hursh, J. B., J. Am. Water Works Assn., **46**, 43, 1954.

[18] Rushing, D. E., Garcia, W. J., and Clark, D. A., The Analysis of Effluents and Environmental Samples from Uranium Mills and of Biological Samples for Radium, Polonium, and Uranium, Radiological Health and Safety in Mining and Milling of Nuclear Materials, Vol. II, International Atomic Energy Agency, Vienna, Austria, 1964, p. 187.

Without reagent purification, the over-all blank is about 0.03 to 0.05 picogram radium-226. A 1-liter sample of water enables a minimum detectable concentration of about 0.04 pg. radium-226 per liter. Enlarging the sample volume, prolonging the counting times, and purification of the reagents will result in a lower minimum detectable concentration.

All glassware, unless new, must be decontaminated of radium-barium sulfate by heating for one hour in a solution containing 10 g. of tetrasodium ethylenediaminetetraacetate (tetrasodium EDTA) and 10 g. sodium carbonate per liter at 90 − 100°C., followed by rinsing first with water, then with (1 + 9 v/v) hydrochloric acid, and finally with distilled water. Platinum ware should be cleaned by immersion and rotation in a molten bath of potassium pyrosulfate, cooling, rinsing in hot tap water, digesting in hot (1 + 1 v/v) hydrochloric acid, rinsing in distilled water, and igniting over a burner.

Reagents. Barium Chloride Carrier Solutions. (a) *Stock Solution.*—35.6 g. $BaCl_2 \cdot 2H_2O$ per liter; 20 mg. Ba per ml. Store in a polyethylene bottle for prolonged periods.

(b) *Dilute Solution.*—Dilute 100 ml. stock solution to 1000 ml. as needed; 2 mg. Ba per ml.

Acid Barium Chloride Solution.—Dilute 100 ml. stock barium chloride carrier solution to 1980 ml. After standing overnight, filter through a membrane filter, add 20 ml. concentrated hydrochloric acid, and mix; 1 mg. Ba per ml.

Ammonium Sulfate Solution.—10 g. per 100 ml.

Tetrasodium Ethylenediaminetetraacetate-Sodium Carbonate Decontaminating Solution.—Prepare a large volume of this solution from 10 g. of each reagent per liter. Store after each use.

Dilute Hydrogen Peroxide Solution.—Dilute one volume 30 percent hydrogen peroxide with nine volumes of distilled water.

Ascarite, 8–20 mesh.

Magnesium Perchlorate, anhydrous desiccant.

Hydrofluoric Acid, 48 percent.

Phosphoric Acid, concentrated, 85 percent.

Hydrochloric Acid, concentrated, (1 + 3 v/v), (1 + 100 v/v), and 1 M.

Sulfuric Acid, concentrated and (1 + 200 v/v).

Flux Required for Total Radium-226 Determination.—Place 30 mg. barium sulfate, 65.8 g. potassium carbonate, 50.5 g. sodium carbonate, and 33.7 g. sodium borate, $Na_2B_4O_7 \cdot 10H_2O$, in a large platinum dish of 500 ml. capacity. Heat the well-mixed salts cautiously until the water is expelled; then fuse and mix thoroughly by swirling the melt. Grind the cooled flux in a porcelain mortar to pass a 10-mesh, or finer, screen. Store in an air-tight bottle. If desired, prepare smaller batches of flux in smaller dishes.

Procedure. Calibration with Standard Radium-226.—Secure an ampoule of National Bureau of Standards radium gamma-ray standard containing 0.1 μg. radium-226. Treat this standard with the utmost caution because the very high activity can contaminate the equipment and the work area. Place the ampoule in a 600-ml. beaker, cover with 300 ml. acid barium chloride solution, and break the ampoule neck with a stout rod. Chip the ampoule until it is broken or until the hole is large enough to allow effective mixing and rinsing. Mix, transfer the solution to a 1-liter volumetric flask, dilute to the mark with the acid barium chloride solution, and mix. Dilute 100 ml. of the stock radium solution to 1000 ml. in a second 1-liter volumetric flask with the acid barium chloride solution to obtain an intermediate solution containing 10 pg. radium-226 per ml. Add 30.0 ml. of the intermediate solution to a 100-ml. volumetric flask, dilute to the mark with acid barium chloride solution, and mix. Correct for the decay of radium-226 since its standardization by the National Bureau of Standards.

Add 1 ml. stock barium chloride carrier solution (a), 10.0 ml. (30 pg.) final standard radium-226 solution, and sufficient acid barium chloride solution to fill the radon bubbler three-fourths full. Seal and close the bubbler. Store the excess radium solutions in pyrex bottles and seal the stoppers with paraffin. Continue the procedure as described under "Operations Involving Radon Bubbler," below beginning with the sentence "Dry the joint with lint-free paper or cloth."

Perform the calibration by de-emanating the standard bubbler with the scintillation cell before the analysis of the samples is undertaken. The calibration remains essentially unchanged for years unless the scintillation cell is damaged physically. A 16-hour in-growth of radon in the standard bubbler produces about 5 picocuries (pc.) radon, which is a suitable amount of radon for the calibration of the cell, if an overnight count of 12 hours or more is taken. The standard bubbler may be kept indefinitely.

Dissolved Radium-226 in Water.—Filter the water sample through membrane filters as soon as possible after collection. If desired, save the filters for the analysis of the radium-226 in the suspended matter. Immediately acidify the filtered sample with a volume of 20 ml. concentrated hydrochloric acid for each liter of sample, and store in polyethylene bottles until the determination can be started. In the case of uranium mill effluents, begin the analysis immediately after filtration to prevent precipitation during storage. Measure 1020 ml. of the acidified sample into a 1500-ml. beaker and continue the analysis as described in the paragraph entitled "Precipitation of Radium-Barium Sulfate."

Precipitation of Radium-Barium Sulfate.—Prepare a reagent blank of distilled water containing the same volume of concentrated hydrochloric acid present in the sample aliquot taken for analysis. Treat the blank and the sample identically throughout the procedure. Add with vigorous stirring 50 ml. dilute barium chloride carrier solution (b). Add slowly and with vigorous stirring 20 ml. concentrated sulfuric acid for each liter of sample aliquot taken. Cover the beaker and let stand overnight at room temperature. Pass the supernatant liquid through a membrane filter, transfer the precipitate quantitatively to the filter with (1 + 200 v/v) sulfuric acid, and wash the filter twice with (1 + 200 v/v) sulfuric acid. Place the membrane filter with its precipitate in a 20–30 ml. platinum crucible or a small 50–75 ml. platinum dish. By means of a fine jet of distilled water transfer any precipitate which adheres to the filtration apparatus to the platinum container. Add 0.5 ml. 48 percent hydrofluoric acid and 0.15 ml. ammonium sulfate solution, and evaporate to dryness. Cautiously ignite over a Bunsen burner until the organic matter has been burned off, then cool to room temperature. After adding 1.0 ml. concentrated phosphoric acid from a calibrated dropper, heat on a hot plate at 200°C., gradually raise the temperature to 300–400°C., and maintain at that temperature for 30 minutes. Hold the platinum container with a platinum-tipped tongs over a low flame, and adjust the heating rate to avoid spattering. Swirl the container so that the walls are covered with hot phosphoric acid. Continue heating until the barium sulfate dissolves to yield a clear glassy melt which occurs just below redness. Heat one more minute to insure the removal of sulfur trioxide. Cool the platinum vessel and fill half-full with (1 + 3 v/v) hydrochloric acid. Place the platinum vessel over live steam and finish filling the container to within 2 mm. of the top with (1 + 3 v/v) hydrochloric acid. Evaporate on a steam bath until barium chloride crystals, phosphoric acid, and a trace of hydrochloric acid remain, as evidenced by a cessation of vapors. Add 6 ml. 1 M hydrochloric acid, swirl, and warm to dissolve the barium chloride crystals.

Operations Involving Radon Bubbler.—Use the radon bubbler illustrated in Fig. 63-6. A suitable apparatus with a total volume of 18 to 25 ml. from the fritted glass disk to the stopper is available from Corning Glass Works, Special Apparatus Division. Reserve one bubbler for the standard radium solution and another for the sample. Close the inlet stopcock and wet the disk with a drop of distilled water. Transfer the soluble

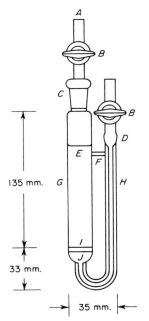

FIG. 63-6. Radon Bubbler: *A*, 7-mm. O. D. Side Arm; *B*, Stopcock (Corning No. 2 or Equivalent); *C*, Ground Glass Joints Standard Taper No. 10/30; *D*, 7-mm. I. D. Bubble Trap; *E*, Liquid Level; *F*, Rigidity Brace; *G*, 17-mm. O. D. Body; *H*, 7-mm. Capillary Tubing, 1½-mm. I. D.; *I*, Fritted Glass Disc, 10–15-micron Pores; *J*, Volume to be Kept at Minimum. (Reproduced with permission from Standard Methods for the Examination of Water and Wastewater, 12th Ed., The American Public Health Assn., Inc., New York, 1965.)

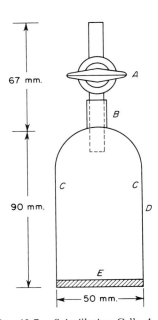

FIG. 63-7. Scintillation Cell: *A*, Stopcock (Corning No. 2 or Equivalent); *B*, Brass Collar; *C*, Phosphor Coating; *D*, Kovar Metal; *E*, Clear Silica Window. (Reproduced with permission from Standard Methods for the Examination of Water and Wastewater, 12th Ed., The American Public Health Assn., Inc., New York, 1965.)

radium-barium phosphate and chloride sample concentrate to the bubbler with a medicine dropper. Rinse the dropper and platinum container with three 2-ml. portions of distilled water. Be certain to rinse the phosphoric acid from the waxed ground glass joint of the bubbler stopper.

Dry the joint with lint-free paper or cloth. Gently warm the male and female joints of the waxed bubbler ground glass joint stopper. Insert the stopper with a twisting motion in order to spread.the "Pyseal," low-melting sealing wax uniformly in the ground glass joint, then allow the joint to cool.

Close both stopcocks on the bubbler and invert several times to mix. Open the outlet cock and force the droplet out of the stopper by the application of external pressure with a rubber bulb. Leave the cock open. Adjust the two-stage gas pressure regulator so that a very slow stream of compressed air (aged 30 days in the cylinder to allow the decay of the radon) will flow with the needle valve open. Connect the valve to the inlet stopcock of the bubbler by means of a hose. Open the inlet cock and cautiously raise the pressure by adjusting the regulator valve, not the needle valve, until bubbles pass through the fritted glass disk at a rate which will produce a froth a few mm. deep at the surface of the solution. Continue the aeration (de-emanation) for 20 minutes. In quick succession, close the inlet cock, remove the air hose connection, and close the outlet cock. Record the date and time. Set the bubbler aside and allow radon ingrowth to proceed for a few days to a few (3) weeks, depending on the suspected radium content.

Operations Involving Scintillation Cell.—Use the Lucas-type scintillation cell[19] illustrated in Fig. 63-7. A suitable apparatus, having a volume of 95 to 140 ml., is available from William H. Johnston Laboratories, Inc., 3617 Woodland Ave, Baltimore, Md. 21215. Evacuate the calibrated scintillation cell whose background has been determined when filled with aged compressed air. Connect the scintillation cell, the bubbler containing the treated sample, and the de-emanation assembly as shown in Fig. 63-8. Adjust the gas regulator valve to give a very slight flow and pressure when the needle valve is open. Attach the air hose from the needle valve to the inlet stopcock of the bubbler, and open the needle valve. Open the stopcock on the scintillation cell and observe the manometer reading. Again check the manometer reading one minute later. If no leak is evident, note the time. With extreme care partially open the outlet stopcock of the bubbler, whereupon considerable bubbling will take place because of the lowered pressure. After the bubbling abates, open the cock a little more, repeating these steps until the cock is completely open and vigorous bubbling has stopped. Close the outlet stopcock of the bubbler. In very gradual stages partially open the inlet stopcock of the bubbler, so that the rate of movement of the bubbles in the capillary inlet tube is slow enough to avert the loss of liquid. Open the stopcock completely after the bubbling subsides. Carefully open the outlet stopcock in very gradual stages in order to dissipate the bubbling. When both stopcocks are fully open and the bubbling has subsided, raise the air pressure gradually by means of the pressure regulator, making certain at all times that the movement of the bubbles in the capillary inlet tube proceeds at a sufficiently slow rate to avoid the loss of liquid. Continue

[19] Lucas, H. F., Rev. Sci. Instruments, **28**, 680, 1957.

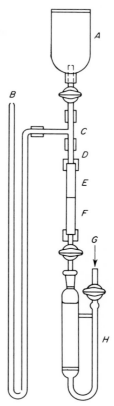

Fig. 63-8. De-emanation Assembly: *A*, Scintillation Cell; *B*, Open End Manometer, 1.5-mm. I. D.; *C*, Capillary T-tube; *D*, Thermometer Capillary; *E*, Anhydrous Magnesium Perchlorate Layer; *F*, Ascarite Layer; *G*, Air from Compressed Air Regulator; *H*, Radon Bubbler. (Reproduced with permission from Standard Methods for the Examination of Water and Wastewater, 12th Ed., The American Public Health Assn., Inc., New York, 1965.)

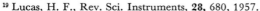

raising the pressure until the manometer indicates atmospheric pressure within the system. Note the time. The elapsed time for the de-emanation should be at least 15 minutes. Promptly close the following stopcocks in the order mentioned: the cock on the scintillation cell, and the inlet and outlet cocks on the bubbler. After closing the needle valve, disconnect the compressed air hose, and set the bubbler aside for a possible second de-emanation.

Instrumental Measurement.—If the scintillation counter is free and available, place the scintillation cell on the photomultiplier tube, and cover both with the light-tight cover. After the radon has been in the cell for four hours, turn on the high voltage, and start counting.

If the counter is in use, allow the radon to age in the scintillation cell for 4 hours by storing in dark or subdued light. Place in the counter, wait 10 minutes, turn on the high voltage, and start counting.

Conduct the measurements in a complete scintillation counter with a two-inch, or larger, photomultiplier tube mounted vertically with its face up in a light-tight housing which is large enough to contain the Lucas-type scintillation cell.

Total Radium-226 in Water.—Immediately acidify the collected water sample with a volume of 20 ml. concentrated hydrochloric acid for each liter of sample, and store in polyethylene bottles until the determination can be started. Thoroughly mix the acidified sample before withdrawing an aliquot for analysis. Select an aliquot of 1020 ml. when such a volume contains 1 g., or less, of inorganic suspended matter. Otherwise, measure an aliquot which will contribute no more than 1 g. of suspended matter. Measure the acidified sample into a 1500-ml. beaker, and continue the analysis as described in the paragraph entitled "Precipitation of Radium-Barium Sulfate," page 1917.

Follow the procedure for "Dissolved Radium-226 in Water" with the following exceptions. Weigh the platinum crucible or dish before the addition of the barium sulfate precipitate and after the ignition of the organic matter. Omit the hydrofluoric acid addition. Calculate the approximate weight of the ashed inorganic suspended matter.

Add 8 g. flux for each 1 g. residue, but never use less than 2 g. flux. Since the volumes of reagents and solutions prescribed in the succeeding steps are based on 8 g. flux, reduce proportionately the reagent and solution volumes when a smaller weight of flux will suffice. Mix the flux and sample residue with a glass rod, and heat over a burner until fusion and bubbling begins. Continue to heat at a rate which averts spattering. After bubbling ceases, heat over a Meker burner for an additional 20 minutes, occasionally swirling the platinum vessel with platinum-tipped tongs so that the entire sample residue is entirely fused and decomposition is complete. Only the melt of high silica or very small samples becomes clear at the end. As the melt cools, rotate the platinum vessel to allow the melt to spread and solidify in a thin layer on the wall. Place the vessel in a covered beaker containing 120 ml. distilled water, 20 ml. concentrated sulfuric acid, and 5 ml. dilute hydrogen peroxide solution. Ignore the yellow color produced by titanium. After the melt dissolves in a few minutes, remove and rinse the platinum vessel, and set the platinum vessel aside momentarily. Add 50 ml. distilled water and digest the solution on a steam bath until the radium-barium sulfate is filterable. Add 1 ml. dilute hydrogen peroxide solution to the beaker. If the yellow color deepens, add more dilute hydrogen peroxide solution until further change ceases. Continue the analysis as described under "Dissolved Radium-226 in Water," "Precipitation of Radium-Barium Sulfate," beginning with the sentence "Pass the supernatant liquid through a membrane filter, transfer the precipitate quantitatively to the filter with $(1 + 200 \text{ v/v})$ sulfuric acid, and wash the filter twice with $(1 + 200 \text{ v/v})$ sulfuric acid." Place the filter and precipitate in the rinsed platinum vessel used for the fusion.

Calculation.—The direct calibration of the scintillation cell by means of an essentially stable radium-226 standard enables the usual corrections for geometry, backscatter, and self-absorption to be dispensed with. As a result, the radium-226 in the sampler bubbler and the reagent blank bubbler can be computed by the following equation:

$$\text{pc. Ra-226} = \frac{(X - Y)}{Z} \times \frac{1}{1 - e^{-\lambda t_1}} \times \frac{1}{e^{-\lambda t_2}} \times \frac{\lambda t_3}{1 - e^{-\lambda t_3}}$$

where: X = observed counting rate of sample in scintillation cell in counts per hour;

Y = previously observed background counting rate of scintillation cell with compressed air in counts per hour;

Z = calibration constant of scintillation cell in counts per hour per pc. of radon-222 plus decay products;

t_1 = time interval allowed for ingrowth of radon-222;

t_2 = time interval between de-emanation and counting;

t_3 = time interval of counting;

e = natural logarithm base; and

λ = decay constant for radon-222 = 0.00755 per hour.

The correction factors are obtained from Table 63-7. The values of $e^{-\lambda t_2}$ are calculated from entries under columns A in the table, making use of the identity $e^{-\lambda t_2} = e^{-\lambda t_{2a}} \times e^{-\lambda t_{2b}} \times e^{-\lambda t_{2c}}$ where $t_2 = t_{2a} + t_{2b} + t_{2c}$ and t_{2a}, t_{2b}, and t_{2c} are time entries in the table. Values of $1 - e^{-\lambda t_1}$ are found by calculating $e^{-\lambda t_1}$ and subtracting from 1. The tabular entries of $1 - e^{-\lambda t}$, under column B, are for estimates of radon ingrowth; the time intervals are generally too large for accurate interpolation. On the other hand, interpolation can be used to determine intermediate values of $\lambda t/(1 - e^{-\lambda t})$ in column C. Examples will serve to illustrate the use of the table. If the radon decayed for 1 day 4 hours 15 minutes, the decay factor would equal the product of the factors drawn from column A for these individual periods, or $0.8343 \times 0.9703 \times 0.9981 = 0.8080$. If the radon grew for 7 days 14 hours 17 minutes, the ingrowth factor would be calculated by the equation $(1 - e^{-\lambda t})$, or $1 - (0.2813 \times 0.8997 \times 0.9979) = 0.7474$.

When the correction factors are drawn from columns A, B, and C of Table 63-7, the fundamental equation can be written in the following abbreviated form:

$$\text{Radium-229 in picocuries} = \frac{(X - Y)}{Z} \times \frac{C}{AB}$$

In calculating cell calibration constants, the same equation is used. Since the picocuries of radium-226 is known, Z becomes the unknown, and the two terms can be interchanged in the equation.

For all practical purposes, 1 gram of radium-226 equals 1 curie. Therefore,

$$\text{Radium-226 in picograms per liter} = \frac{(D - E) \times 1000}{\text{milliliters of sample}}$$

where: D = picocuries of radium-226 found in sample; and

E = picocuries of radium-226 found in the reagent blank.

Cleaning and Handling of Special Apparatus. Scintillation Cell.—After the sample has been counted, remove the radon from the cell, taking the necessary precautions to protect the phosphor. Evacuate the cell and admit air slowly by gradually opening

TABLE 63-7. CORRECTION FACTORS FOR DETERMINATION OF RADIUM-226*

Time	A Decay of Radon, $e^{-\lambda t}$			B Growth of Radon from Radium, $1 - e^{-\lambda t}$	C Multiplicative Factor for Correction of Radon Activity for Decay During Counting, $\lambda t/(1 - e^{-\lambda t})$
	Minutes	Hours	Days	Days	Hours
0	1.0000	1.0000	1.0000	0.0000	1.0000
1	0.9999	0.9925	0.8343	0.1657	1.0037
2	0.9998	0.9850	0.6960	0.3040	1.0075
3	0.9996	0.9776	0.5807	0.4194	1.0114
4	0.9995	0.9703	0.4844	0.5156	1.0152
5	0.9994	0.9630	0.4041	0.5959	1.0190
6	0.9993	0.9557	0.3372	0.6628	1.0228
7	0.9991	0.9485	0.2813	0.7187	1.0267
8	0.9990	0.9414	0.2347	0.7653	1.0305
9	0.9989	0.9343	0.1958	0.8042	1.0344
10	0.9987	0.9273	0.1633	0.8367	1.0382
11	0.9986	0.9203	0.1363	0.8637	1.0421
12	0.9985	0.9134	0.1137	0.8863	1.0460
13	0.9984	0.9065	0.0948	0.9052	1.0500
14	0.9982	0.8997	0.0791	0.9209	1.0538
15	0.9981	0.8929	0.0660	0.9340	1.0577
16	0.9980	0.8862	0.0551	0.9449	1.0616
17	0.9979	0.8796	0.0459	0.9541	1.0655
18	0.9977	0.8729	0.0383	0.9617	1.0695
19	0.9976	0.8664	0.0320	0.9680	1.0734
20	0.9975	0.8599	0.0267	0.9733	1.0774
21	0.9974	0.8534	0.0223	0.9778	1.0814
22	0.9972	0.8470	0.0186	0.9814	1.0854
23	0.9971	0.8406	0.0155	0.9845	1.0893
24	0.9970	0.8343	0.0129	0.9871	1.0933
25	0.9969	0.8280	0.0108	0.9892	1.0973
26	0.9967	0.8218	0.0090	0.9910	1.1014
27	0.9966	0.8156	0.0075	0.9925	1.1054
28	0.9965	0.8095	0.0063	0.9937	1.1094
29	0.9964	0.8034	0.0052	0.9948	1.1135
30	0.9962	0.7973	0.0044	0.9956	1.1175
31	0.9961	0.7913	0.0036	0.9964	1.1216
32	0.9960	0.7854	0.0030	0.9970	1.1257
33	0.9959	0.7795	0.0025	0.9975	1.1297
34	0.9957	0.7736	0.0021	0.9979	1.1338
35	0.9956	0.7678	0.0018	0.9982	1.1379
36	0.9955	0.7620	0.0015	0.9985	1.1421
37	0.9954	0.7563	0.0012	0.9988	1.1462
38	0.9952	0.7506	0.0010	0.9990	1.1503
39	0.9951	0.7449	0.0009	0.9992	1.1544
40	0.9950	0.7393	0.0007	0.9993	1.1586

Table 63-7 (cont.)

Time	A Decay of Radon, $e^{-\lambda t}$			B Growth of Radon from Radium, $1 - e^{-\lambda t}$	C Multiplicative Factor for Correction of Radon Activity for Decay During Counting, $\lambda t/(1 - e^{-\lambda t})$
	Minutes	*Hours*	*Days*	*Days*	*Hours*
41	0.9949	0.7338	0.0006	0.9994	1.1628
42	0.9947	0.7283	0.0005	0.9995	1.1669
43	0.9946	0.7228	0.0004	0.9996	1.1711
44	0.9945	0.7173	0.0003	0.9997	1.1753
45	0.9944	0.7120	0.0003	0.9997	1.1795
46	0.9942	0.7066	0.0002	0.9998	1.1837
47	0.9941	0.7013	0.0002	0.9998	1.1879
48	0.9940	0.6960	0.0002	0.9998	1.1921
49	0.9939	0.6908	0.0001	0.9999	1.1964
50	0.9937	0.6856	0.0001	0.9999	1.2006
51	0.9936	0.6804	0.0001	0.9999	1.2049
52	0.9935	0.6753	0.0001	0.9999	1.2091
53	0.9934	0.6702	0.0001	0.9999	1.2134
54	0.9932	0.6652	0.0001	0.9999	1.2177
55	0.9931	0.6602	0.0001	1.0000	1.2220
56	0.9930	0.6552	0.0000	1.0000	1.2263
57	0.9929	0.6503	0.0000	1.0000	1.2306
58	0.9927	0.6454	0.0000	1.0000	1.2349
59	0.9926	0.6405	0.0000	1.0000	1.2392
60	0.9925	0.6357	0.0000	1.0000	1.2435

* Based on 3.825 days as the half life of radon.

Rushing, D. E., Garcia, W. J., and Clark, D. A., The Analysis of Effluents and Environmental Samples from Uranium Mills and of Biological Samples for Radium, Polonium, and Uranium, Radiological Health and Safety in Mining and Milling of Nuclear Materials, International Atomic Energy Agency, Vienna, Austria, Vol. II, p. 187, 1964. Reprinted with permission of the copyright owners.

the stopcock over a period of 15 seconds. Attach the cell to a good vacuum pump with heavy-walled tubing and evacuate for 5 to 10 minutes. Remove, admit air, and evacuate again for 10 minutes. Repeat if the radon content was high.

Under ordinary circumstances use a cell once a day because the approximately 30-minute half life of the decay products of radon-222 enables the cell to be ready for another sample or for a background determination within that time.

Bubbler.—Unless a check of the analysis is required by a second de-emanation, discard the sample concentrate from the bubbler.

If the bubbler contained no more than 10 pg. radium-226, thoroughly rinse with $(1 + 100$ v/v) hydrochloric acid by the following procedure. Connect the outlet stopcock to a suction flask by means of Tygon tubing. Attach another length of Tygon tubing to the inlet stopcock. Invert the bubbler and clamp onto a ring stand. Dip the free end of the tubing into 100 ml. $(1 + 100$ v/v) hydrochloric acid. Turn on the vacuum and open the outlet cock to empty the bubbler. Open the inlet cock to rinse the fritted glass disk and bubbler. After a few ml. have passed through, close the outlet cock and allow the rinse solution to accumulate in the bubbler until three-fourths full. Open the outlet cock. Repeat the process until the rinse solution is exhausted. Place the bubbler in an upright position and allow to drain for a few minutes. Use a vacuum to draw out most of the solution through the inlet capillary tube. Gently warm the stopcock until the "Pyseal" wax melts, and remove the stopper with a twisting motion. After the stopper and joint cool, add the next sample to the bubbler.

If the bubbler contained more than 10 pg. radium-226, follow the $(1 + 100 \text{ v/v})$ hydrochloric acid rinsing procedure described above. Disassemble the bubbler and remove most of the stopcock grease and sealing wax mechanically or by cloth or swabs moistened with organic solvents (kerosene for grease and benzene for wax). Immerse for one hour in hot (90—100°C.) EDTA-sodium carbonate solution, taking the precaution to preheat the bubbler gradually in order to avert thermal shock to the disk. Also draw a few ml. of the solution through the disk. Remove the bubbler, cool to room temperature, and rinse with distilled water through the application of suction. Immerse in $1 M$ hydrochloric acid and warm for 30 minutes. Remove, cool, and rinse with distilled water. Dry in an oven or by overnight exposure to the air. Regrease the stopcocks and rewax the stopper with an adequate but non-excessive amount of grease and wax.

Should the occasion demand, use the following more drastic cleaning methods: hot kerosene or hot alcoholic potassium hydroxide (10 g. KOH + 90 ml. alcohol) to remove the grease, or hot concentrated nitric acid to remove most organic matter except stopcock grease. In such case, avoid prolonged contact of the disk with alcoholic potassium hydroxide which is very corrosive, and avoid the use of sulfuric acid in the bubbler.

GAS CHROMATOGRAPHY

At the present time gas chromatography shows considerable promise for the estimation of the trace organic pesticide concentrations likely to occur in water supplies. However, the application to water analysis is in an infant stage of development. The trend is apparent, but the refined details for generally accepted methods remain to be worked out.

The prior separation of pesticides by means of thin-layer chromatography supplemented by subsequent gas chromatography based on an electron capture detection system and microcoulometric titration gas chromatography is making feasible the determination of small amounts of halogenated pesticides and organophosphate insecticides containing sulfur.

ORGANIC PESTICIDES[20]

The following organic pesticides may be detected and determined by the microcoulometric gas chromatograph in the 50 to 100 nanogram per liter range, enabling this system to be used for monitoring 1-liter water samples without cleanup of the extract:

Aldrin—1,2,3,4,10,10-hexachloro-1,4,4a,5,8,8a-hexahydro-1,4-endo,exo-5,8-dimethanonaphthalene
BHC (Benzene hexachloride)—a mixture of hexachlorocyclohexane isomers
Diazinon—O,O-diethyl O-(2-isopropyl-4-methyl-1-6-pyrimidyl)phosphorothioate.
DDT—1,1,1-trichloro-2,2-bis(p-chlorophenyl)ethane
Dieldrin—1,2,3,4,10,10-hexachloro-exo-6,7-epoxy-1,4,4a,5,6,7,8,8a-octahydro-1,4-endo-exo-5,8-dimethanonaphthalene
Parathion—O,O-diethyl-O-p-nitrophenylphosphorothioate
Toxaphene—octachlorocamphenes

[20] Teasley, J. I., and Cox, W. S., J. Am. Water Works Assn., 55, 1093, 1963.

Reagents.—Redistill the following ACS grade organic reagents prior to use.

Ethyl Ether.

Petroleum Ether.

Chloroform.

Benzene.

Ethyl Ether-Petroleum Ether Mixture.—Mix one volume of redistilled ethyl ether with one volume of redistilled petroleum ether.

Pesticide Standard Solutions.—Prepare the pesticide standards in the desired concentration range by dissolution in acetone and further dilution with acetone, so that small aliquots of these solutions can be made up to 4 liters with water without precipitation of the pesticides.

Sodium Sulfate, Anhydrous.

Procedure.—Collect the water sample in a glass container because some plastic containers readily adsorb some pesticides from water.

Extract 1-liter of sample repetitively with 100, 50, 50, 50, and 50 ml. of redistilled solvent (ethyl ether—petroleum ether mixture, or chloroform) in 2-liter separatory funnels. Shake the separatory funnel vigorously for at least 1 minute each time. Combine the extracts and dry on a 2-inch column of anhydrous sodium sulfate. When all the extract has passed through, wash the column with three 5-ml. portions of petroleum ether. Evaporate the combined dried extracts to 5 ml. in a water bath held at 40°C. Transfer the concentrate to a 15-ml. conical centrifuge tube (use three 3-ml. rinses of petroleum ether to insure quantitative transfer). With a slow stream of dry air, evaporate just to apparent dryness, rinse down the walls of the tube with 0.5 ml. ethyl ether, and again evaporate to apparent dryness. Take up the residue in 50 or 100 μl. benzene. With a calibrated microsyringe, withdraw a 50 to 75 percent aliquot for injection into the gas chromatograph according to the following schedule:

Pesticide	*Original Sample Concentration, ng. per liter*	*Portion of Extract to Be Injected, percent*
Aldrin	50	70
BHC	50	70
Diazinon	100	75
DDT	100	50
Dieldrin	50	70
Parathion	100	75
Toxaphene	100	75

Dohrmann microcoulometric gas chromatograph operating conditions: maximum sensitivity (512-ohm setting); damping position 4 (with a 22-megohm resistor placed across damping switch); nitrogen carrier gas flow 100 ml. per minute; column temperature 195°C.; aluminum column, $\frac{1}{4}$ inch O.D. by 6 ft. long, packed with 60–80 mesh acid-washed Chromosorb P (a product of Johns-Manville, New York) and coated with 5 percent DIC 200 oil (a product of Dow Corning, Midland, Mich.).

Results.—For those pesticides that show sharp, well-defined peaks, such as Aldrin, BHC, and Diazinon, as little as 25 ng. per liter is detectable in the original 1-liter sample at the maximum sensitivity of the detection system. For those pesticides that are relatively low in chlorine or sulfur content, or that do not produce sharp, well-defined peaks, such as Chlordane, DDT, and Toxaphene, about 50 ng. per liter is the apparent lower limit of detectable concentration at maximum sensitivity in this sample volume. The extraction of larger sample volumes permits the estimation of lower concentrations.

CHLORINATED HYDROCARBON PESTICIDES[21]

Organic pesticides may be detected in water by passing the sample through an activated carbon filter and removing the organic materials by adsorption. The organic materials are recovered from the carbon by extraction with chloroform. The extracted organic materials are percolated through a mixture of magnesium oxide and silicon dioxide (Activated Florosil, a product of Floridin Co., Tallahassee, Fla.). The resulting common chlorinated hydrocarbon pesticides are generally sufficiently free of interferences for analysis by the argon and electron capture ionization detectors of the gas chromatograph model 10 manufactured by Barber-Colman Co., Rockford, Ill.

The argon detector operates as an electron capture detector for gamma benzene hexachloride (BHC) at voltages below approximately 500 volts. The voltage for electron capture measurement varies with the chlorine content of the pesticide.

Gamma BHC dissolved in chloroform yields a linear response in the range from 0.4 to 2.4 μg. with the argon detector operating at 1000 volts. The sensitivity of detection improves as the voltage falls from 1000 to 50 volts. Moreover, larger samples can be injected in the lower-voltage electron capture range without obscuring the pesticide peak. The gamma BHC may also be dissolved in o-xylene prior to injection into the chromatograph.

AQUATIC HERBICIDE[22]

Electron affinity gas chromatography has also been recommended for the determination of 2-(2,4,5-trichlorophenoxy)propionic acid, an aquatic herbicide commercially known as Silvex. The method is sensitive to 0.05 mg. per liter Silvex in a 25-ml. water sample.

Procedure.—The procedure consists of adding sufficient sodium sulfate to saturate 25 ml. of filtered water sample, followed by 1 ml. (1 + 1v/v) sulfuric acid and exactly 5.0 ml. ethyl ether. After the volume has been brought to the mark of a 50-ml. volumetric flask with saturated sodium sulfate solution and the contents shaken vigorously for 1 minute, up to 3 ml. of the ether layer are transferred to a 10-ml. volumetric flask. The ether layer is evaporated to dryness with air and 1.0 ml. boron trifluoride-methanol solution (125 mg. per ml.) is pipetted into the flask. The flask is held in a boiling water bath for 2 minutes with frequent swirling and then cooled. Exactly 1.00 ml. hexane is pipetted into the flask, the volume diluted to the mark with 2 percent sodium sulfate, and the flask is well shaken. Up to 10 μl. of the upper hexane layer is injected into the gas chromatographic column.

The standard working curve is prepared by pipetting 0, 0.20, 0.40, 0.60, 0.80, and 1.00 ml. Silvex (0.1 mg. per liter in acetone) into a series of 10-ml. volumetric flasks, evaporating the acetone with air, and proceeding with the methylation and the remaining steps as in the water sample analysis. The peak height in centimeters is plotted against micrograms of Silvex.

The following settings and conditions were used with the Barber-Colman Model 10 gas chromatograph. The battery operated, 6-c.c. detector containing 56 microcuries of radium-226, was operated at 9 volts, which was found to be optimum for electron capture by chlorinated compounds. The borosilicate glass column was U-shaped, 9 mm. in outer diameter, and 6 ft. long. The packing was 5 percent ethyl acetate-fractionated high-vacuum silicone grease on 80–100 Chromosorb W (Johns-Manville of New York City). The operating temperatures for the column, flash heater, and detector were

[21] Skrinde, R. T., Caskey, J. W., and Gillespie, C. K., J. Am. Water Works Assn., **54**, 1407, 1962.
[22] Gutenmann, W. H., and Lisk, D. J., J. Am. Water Works Assn., **56**, 189, 1964.

200°, 265°, and 235°C., respectively. Nitrogen at 60 ml. per minute constituted the carrier gas. The electrometer was operated at a gain setting of 3000. A Wheelco recorder (Wheelco Instruments Division, Barber-Colman Co. of Rockford, Ill.), 0–50 millivolts, and equipped with 10-inch chart paper, was run at 10 inches per hour.

MICROELECTROPHORESIS

New instruments are constantly being applied to the study of water and its treatment. Among the approaches exciting a growing interest is the field of microelectrophoresis. The applications to date have centered on the coagulation of turbidity and the removal of color. The results reported by several investigators are conflicting. Proponents contend that microelectrophoresis is valuable for the determination of the chemical dose needed to coagulate a water properly. Others dispute this claim. Despite the controversy, microelectrophoresis continues to command attention. For this reason, two of the more widespread techniques are presented in this volume.

METHOD I[23]

Apparatus.—The following special apparatus, illustrated in Fig. 63-9, must be assembled for the measurement of electrophoretic mobility.

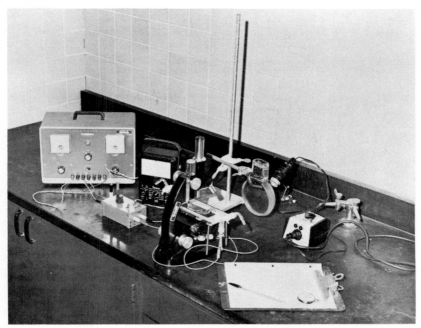

FIG. 63-9. Complete Microelectrophoresis Assembly When Direct Current Power Supply is Used. (Photograph Courtesy of Dr. A. P. Black and Mrs. A. L. Smith.)

Microelectrophoresis Cell.—This cell should be of flat construction and should contain the necessary platinum wire and mercury-mercuric nitrate electrode connec-

[23] Black, A. P., and Smith, A. L., J. Am. Water Works Assn., **54,** 926, 1962; also private communication.

tions designed by Briggs.[24] The following cell modifications improve operations:[23] a thin line etched in the center of the inside bottom of the cell provides a permanent reference point for locating the bottom of the cell (Fig. 63-10). Teflon stopcocks permit easier manipulation during the flushing phase than the original Pyrex stopcocks. The improved cell is available from Mr. James D. Graham, Jr., Room 127, University of Pennsylvania Medical School, 36 and Hamilton Walk, Philadelphia, Pa.

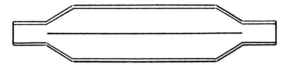

FIG. 63-10. Etched Line on Inside Bottom of Flat Part of Microelectrophoresis Cell, as Seen Through Microscope. (Diagram courtesy of Dr. A. P. Black and Mrs. A. L. Smith.)

Metal Cell Support.—The support should have a $3\frac{1}{2} \times 7\frac{1}{2}$ inch metal frame which permits the microelectrophoresis cell to be mounted on the microscope stage, and serves as a stand for the cell when it is removed from the stage for cleaning or storage purposes. The addition of a small piece of metal to the top of the cell support extending over the mounting frame (Fig. 63-11) creates a "stop" for improving the reproducibility of

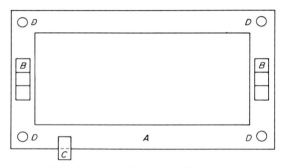

FIG. 63-11. Plan View of Metal Support Frame for Microelectrophoresis Cell with Coordinate System "Stop" in Position: A, Metal Frame for Support of Cell; B, Mounting Yokes for Holding Cell in Place With Plastic Wood; C, Metallic Extension Which Serves as "Stop"; D, Openings for Inserting Legs of the Frame. (Diagram courtesy of Dr. A. P. Black and Mrs. A. L. Smith.)

mobility measurements. Coordinated with the stage micrometer, the "stop" enables the placement of the cell in such a position that the focus can be made in the same section for each measurement. Attachment of the cell support frame to the microscope stage with a pair of small C-clamps prevents misalignment of the cell during determinations. The support is not available commercially and must be made by a local machine shop.

Microscope and Accessories.—(a) A monocular dynoptic microscope should be selected which is linear over the necessary fine adjustment range and which gives the proper focal length at the desired magnification. The linearity of the fine adjustment on the microscope is a critical factor in the determination of the stationary level or

[24] Briggs, D. R., Anal. Chem., **12**, 703, 1940.

layer. For this reason, older microscopes which have had a great deal of use may be unsuitable by virtue of their nonlinearity. Model CGR-8 available from Bausch and Lomb, Rochester, N. Y., has proved satisfactory, although other makes doubtless can serve equally well.

(b) The dark field condenser assembly should disperse sufficient light from the microscope illuminator for viewing the transparent-like colloidal particles.

(c) Apochromatic objective, $10\times$, and compensating eyepiece, $25\times$. Although other magnifications are optional, $250\times$ has proved to be convenient for most coagulation studies.

(d) The Howard count disk, fitted in the eyepiece, should contain squares of calibrated width which can be used to accurately determine the distance a particle travels in a given time.

(e) The stage micrometer, graduated in microns, enables the calibration of the distance across a square of the Howard counter at a given magnification.

(f) The microscope illuminator should be focussed on the mirror and the light reflected through the dark-field condenser into the microelectrophoresis cell. The unit available from American Optical Co., Buffalo, N. Y., has proved satisfactory.

(g) A standard thickness cover slip is needed for checking the linearity of the fine adjustment on the microscope.

Source of Direct Current.—Although a line source is more versatile and easier to manipulate, batteries may also be used for coagulation studies. The variable-voltage (0–400 volts) regulated power supply, Heathkit IP-32, of Heath Co., Benton Harbor, Mich., can be wired to the assembly according to the circuit diagram given in Fig. 63-12. Alternatively, B batteries of 22.5 volts, sufficient to give a total of 135–270 volts, are wired in series with the milliammeter and the microelectrophoresis cell according to the circuit diagram given in Fig. 63-13. The deterioration of the batteries necessitates their periodic replacement.

Control Box.—The control box is for controlling the voltage through the cell by means of a potentiometer arrangement with both an "on-off" switch (optional for the direct current power supply but necessary when batteries are used) and a polarizing switch in order that the electrical field may be conveniently reversed in the cell. The single-pole, single-throw switch ("on-off") can be eliminated in the case of the recommended power supply which contains a "stand-by" switch. The circuit diagram in Fig. 63-12 applies to the recommended power supply, and Fig. 63-13 when batteries are used. Plastic coated alligator clips (Safe-T-Klips, made by Industrial Devices, Inc., of Edgewater, N. J.) on the leads from the control box to the cell are a desirable safety measure.

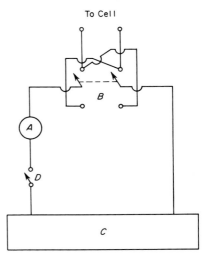

Fig. 63-12. Circuit Diagram for Mobility Determinations When Direct Current Power Supply is Used: A, Milliammeter; B, Double-pole, Double-throw Switch; C, Direct Current Power Supply; D, Single-pole, Single-throw Switch. (Diagram courtesy of Dr. A. P. Black and Mrs. A. L. Smith.)

Volt-Ohm Ammeter.—Multiple range, a.c.-d.c., for reading the current through the cell; wired in series with the microelectrophoresis cell and the direct current power supply or the batteries. A Simpson Model 260, available from E. H. Sargent and Co. of Chicago, Ill., has proved satisfactory.

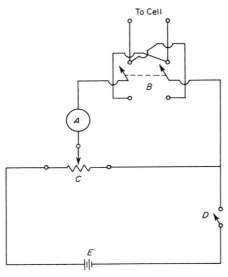

To Cell

Impedance Bridge.—This is for reading the resistance values of the solutions to be observed in the microelectrophoresis cell. The recommended instrument is the Heathkit Model 1B-2A manufactured by the Heath Co. of Benton Harbor, Mich. More reliable data can be obtained with a direct-reading impedance bridge than the conventional conductivity bridge based on an "eye" opening adjustment.

Conductance Cell.—Pipet type having platinized electrodes, for use with the impedance bridge. A cell constant of 1 is generally adequate for solutions of moderate conductance.

Stop Watch, graduated in 0.1-second intervals.

Reagents. **Deionized Distilled Water.** —This water should be used for the preparation of reagents and as dilution water.

Reagents for Cleaning the Microelectrophoresis Cell and the Electrodes. *Nitric Acid,* concentrated.

Hydrochloric Acid, 6 M (1 + 1 v/v.).

Reagents for Electrode Preparation. *Mercuric Nitrate Solution.*—150 g. $Hg(NO_3)_2$ per liter. Add a few drops of concentrated nitric acid and mix for a prolonged time

Fig. 63-13. Circuit Diagram for Mobility Determinations When Batteries Are Used: *A,* Milliammeter; *B,* Double-pole, Double-throw Switch; *C,* 10 K ohms, *D,* Single-pole, Single-throw Switch; *E,* 22.5-volt Batteries Wired in Series to Provide 135–270 Volts. (Black, A. P., and Smith, A. L., J. Am. Water Works Assn., **54**, 926, 1962. Copyright 1962 by the American Water Works Assn., Inc., and reprinted with permission of the copyright owner.)

to aid in dissolving the mercuric nitrate.

Potassium Nitrate Solution.—170 g. per liter.

Mercury.—Instrument grade, triple distilled.

Heat-Absorbing Copper Sulfate Solution, saturated.

Buffer Solutions for Blood Cell Calibration. *Disodium Hydrogen Phosphate Solution.*— 9.47 g. Na_2HPO_4 or 23.88 g. $Na_2HPO_4 \cdot 12H_2O$ per liter.

Potassium Dihydrogen Phosphate Solution.—9.08 g. per liter.

Phosphate Buffer Solution, pH 7.40.—Mix 80.4 ml. disodium hydrogen phosphate solution with 19.6 ml. potassium dihydrogen phosphate solution.

Immersion Oil.

Ethyl Alcohol.

Procedure. **Precautions for Minimizing Errors.**—Avoid in the following manner any mechanical displacement of liquid in the microelectrophoresis cell not due to the electric field when electrophoretic migration is being observed. Use a Kolle culture flask or other vessel with parallel sides and 1 inch thickness for holding the heat-absorbing copper sulfate solution between the light source and the cell in order to prevent unequal temperature due to heating of the liquid by the microscope illuminator. Use a water aspirator to produce the necessary suction for properly filling the microelectrophoresis cell in order to forestall the entrance of an air bubble into the cell during the filling process. Scrupulously clean the electrode vessels and use mercury-mercuric nitrate electrodes to minimize gassing of the electrodes. Guard against vibrations by using a cell support on the microscope and a rigid bench for the apparatus setup. Compensate for electroosmotic streaming by mobility determinations made at the stationary layer.

Check of Linearity of Fine Adjustment on Microscope.—Calibrate the fine adjustment on the microscope against a standard-thickness cover slip by using different segments of the fine adjustment range to measure the thickness of the cover slip. Since the stationary levels are relative to the total cell depth, use any linear portion of the fine adjustment range for finding the stationary levels.

Mounting of Microelectrophoresis Cell on Support.—Mount the microelectrophoresis cell on the metal support frame in a "yoke arrangement." Place a "spirit level" on the microscope stage to make certain that the microscope is in a level position. Clamp the mount on the stage and support the cell by the equal numbers of cover glass slips until the desired height above the mounting is reached. (The height to which the cell is raised will be governed by the height to which the dark field condenser of the microscope is raised. The bottom of a properly mounted cell will touch the condenser.) Mount the cell so that it is parallel to the horizontal plane of the microscope stage. Hold the cell in the mounting yoke with Plastic Wood, a product of Boyle-Midway, Chamblee, Ga. Should a change in the mounting of the cell become necessary, dissolve the Plastic Wood with acetone.

Cleaning of Cell and Electrodes.—Close the electrode cavities with ground glass stoppers and fill the cell with concentrated nitric acid. Allow the acid to stand in the cell for 15 minutes after which time thoroughly rinse the cell with deionized distilled water. Use a water aspirator for conveniently drawing high purity distilled water through the cell. Clean the electrodes by successive washings with 6 M hydrochloric acid and deionized distilled water until the surface of the glass is free of visible particles. Thoroughly rinse the electrodes with deionized distilled water and allow to dry before use.

Cell Calibration.—Calibrate each cell at 25°C. with the same microscope on which the mobility values are to be determined.

Determine the inside depth of the empty cell by focussing on the line etched on the inside bottom of the cell and counting the number of divisions necessary to reach a focus at the inside top of the cell. If difficulty arises in distinguishing the upper inner surfaces of the cell, blow some talcum powder or finely powdered clay into the cell. Make at least three measurements at different points on the cell to check for uniformity. For example,

$$\text{depth} = 1000 \text{ divisions} \times 0.001 \text{ mm. per division} = 0.100 \text{ cm.}$$

The mm. per division will vary with the particular microscope employed.

Measure the inside width of the cell by focussing on one edge and moving across the cell to a focus on the other side through the use of the horizontal mechanical stage adjustment. Repeat at several places to check for uniformity. For example, if the width is 1.73 cm., the cross-sectional area in depth times width is 0.100 cm. $\times$ 1.73 cm., or 0.173 sq. cm.

Use a micrometer slide to determine the microns per square of the Howard counter for the optical system employed. For example, at 250 magnifications, the distance across a square is 49 microns.

Rotate the fine adjustment of the microscope the necessary units to come up 19.9 percent of the total cell depth. The reason is that the stationary levels fall at 19.9 percent and 80.1 percent of the whole cell depth for this width/thickness ratio.[25] Observations are more conveniently made at the bottom stationary level because the lighting is better and the microscope is more easily focussed on the bottom of the cell. Example of calculation:

$$\text{apparent depth of cell} = \frac{\text{depth of cell}}{\text{index of refraction of water}} = \frac{1000 \text{ units}}{1.333} = 750$$

bottom stationary layer
$$= 0.199 \times 750 = 149 \text{ units up on the fine adjustment of the microscope.}$$

Check the complete setup and calibration by measuring the mobility of human erythrocytes in pH 7.40 phosphate buffer solution. Abramson[26] reports the mean value for the mobility of human red blood cells to be -1.31 μ/sec./volt/cm. at 25°C., whereas Briggs[24] assigns a value of -1.33 μ/sec./volt/cm. at 25°C. for his cell. Considerable experience in microelectrophoresis technique is needed to reproduce the Abramson and Briggs values because of the difficulties which beset the behavior of the blood sample. Blood coagulates very easily and the erythrocytes settle rapidly to the bottom of the cell, conditions which interfere with their viewing, tracking, and timing. Research is currently underway in an attempt to replace blood as a standard for the calibration of the microelectrophoresis cell. If the research succeeds, the results will promptly be reported in the Journal of the American Water Works Assn.

Preparation of Electrodes.—Add sufficient mercury to cover the platinum wire completely. By means of a dropper with a tip that extends into the neck of the electrode, add sufficient mercuric nitrate solution to fill the bulb portion of the electrode above the mercury. Then add potassium nitrate solution with a dropper to fill the electrode from the neck portion to the top. Bend downward the platinum wire inside the electrode to reduce the mercury required to cover it, if the wire extends over half the height of the bulb portion. Take care to exclude any air bubbles during the filling process.

Preparation of Blood Cells.—Swab the finger with alcohol and puncture with a sterile hemolet. Add the drops of blood to the pH 7.40 phosphate buffer solution until the suspension appears moderately colored with the red cells. Determine the mobility values by the usual mobility procedure. Determine the blood sample immediately after transfer to the buffer solution, before the blood cells precipitate or coagulate in the cell. Flush some sample through the cell after the stationary level is found.

Use of Cell.—To improve the visibility of the particles, perform the determination in a darkened room where the sole illumination is that of the microscope light. Fit the clean cell with the filled electrode vessels. Place in the cell the sample whose mobility is to be determined. Apply suction lines from a water aspirator to the ends of the cell to draw the sample in both directions from the filling funnel until all air bubbles are removed. Cover the dark field condenser lens with immersion oil and lower below the level of the stage. Mount the cell in the holder designed to keep it level and place the assembly on the microscope stage. Attach the electrode leads to the platinum wires extending from the bottom of the electrode vessels. Raise the dark field condenser until a round bubble appears on the bottom of the cell. Make sure that the cell is flat on the microscope stage and is not moved by raising the condenser too far. Adjust the light source and the microscope mirror for proper illumination. Pass the light beam through the copper sulfate solution to absorb the heat and to prevent convection cur-

[25] Bier, M., Electrophoresis, Academic Press, New York, 1959, p. 444. Consult this reference for the theory of stationary levels and width/thickness ratio.
[26] Abramson, H. A., Electrokinetic Phenomena and Their Application to Biology and Medicine, Chemical Catalog, Inc. (now Reinhold Pub. Co.), New York, 1934, p. 237.

rents in the cell. Focus the microscope on the bottom of the cell, using the proper illumination. Rotate the fine adjustment on the microscope the calculated number of divisions necessary to come up to the bottom stationary layer—for example, from the previous calculation 149 counts. Turn on the switch of the control box, and by means of the potentiometer adjust the resistance until the speed of the particles can be easily timed. (Avoid touching both electrodes simultaneously when the current is on because sufficient voltage is present to give a shock.) Record the milliammeter reading and keep constant throughout each individual sample. With a stop watch graduated in 0.1-second intervals, time the particles as they travel a known distance on the cross hatch. Consider only the movement in a horizontal direction from one electrode to another. Time approximately 10 particles going in each direction. Alter the direction of movement after each observation by using the polarizing switch. There should be agreement in these readings in each direction if the stationary layer is properly obtained and there are no leaks in the system. If the electrodes gas during a determination, or if there appears to be a leak in the system—particles moving when the current is off—dismantle and clean the cell, and use new electrodes in subsequent determinations. Since the field strength (volts per centimeter) within the cell must be determined by the use of Ohm's law, measure with an impedance bridge and a calibrated conductance cell the resistance on the portion of the suspension which has not been in the cell. Since the pH is closely related to particle mobility, measure the pH of each sample as described in Volume II, Part B, page 2462.

Calculation.—Calculate the mobility by means of the following equation:

$$\text{Electrophoretic mobility} = \frac{dX}{tIR_s}$$

where: d is the distance across a square of the Howard counter at a given magnification;

X is the cross-sectional area of the cell in square centimeters;

t is the time in seconds;

I is the current in amperes; and

R_s is the specific resistance of the suspension in ohm-centimeters.

The experimental results are thus expressed in velocity per unit field strength (microns/second/volt/centimeter).

A typical calculation of mobility follows:

Given: $d = 49\ \mu$

$X = 1.73$ cm. $\times$ 0.100 cm. $= 0.173$ sq. cm.

$t = 7.8$ seconds (average)

$I = 4.0 \times 10^{-4}$ amp.

$R = 4450$ ohms

$R_s = 4450/1.0 = 4450$ ohm-cm.

Then, electrophoretic mobility $= \dfrac{(49)(0.173)}{(7.8)(4.0 \times 10^{-4})(4450)} = 0.61\ \mu/\text{sec.}/\text{v.}/\text{cm.}$

Express mobility values as positive ($+$) for those particles which migrate toward the negative pole of the cell, and as negative ($-$) for those that migrate toward the positive pole. It should be noted that the apparent direction of movement is reversed as the particles are viewed through a non-erecting microscope.

Report the pH of the water sample whose mobility values were determined.

METHOD II[27,28]

A complete apparatus assembly for determining electrophoretic mobility is available from Zeta-Meter, Inc., of New York City. The assembly consists of the following components.

The special tube type cell is made of clear plastic and fitted with removable platinum iridium electrodes. The 4.4-mm. diameter of the cell tube permits the tracking of small floc particles. The cell chamber connects directly with the cell tube, enabling the measurement of specific conductance from 0.1 to 100,000 micromhos per cm. Since there is no significant voltage drop except in the cell tube, and the cell tube has a length of 10.0 cm., the volts per cm. equals the applied voltage divided by 10.

A mirrored cell holder which reflects light through the cell at an angle approximating 50° allows dark-field illumination.

An illuminator provides a thin beam of intense blue-white light.

A specially designed stereoscopic microscope accommodates the mirrored cell holder and is equipped with 4, 6, and 8 X objectives, together with paired 15 X widefield eyepieces. One eyepiece is fitted with an ocular micrometer ruled horizontally so that when the top line of the micrometer is focussed on the front wall of the cell, the tracking lines (4, 6, or 8 X) are properly positioned at a distance from the front wall of 14.7 percent of tube diameter, the plane of zero electroosmotic flow.

Procedure.—The determination of the zeta potential with the Zeta-Meter consists essentially of introducing the sample into the cell, setting the cell on the cellholder, and placing the cellholder on the mechanical stage of the microscope. The lamp is positioned to illuminate the tube of the cell, and the output cables of the power supply are connected to the electrodes. The mechanical stage and the stereoscopic microscope are then adjusted so that the front wall of the cell (at its middepth) is seen as two bright lines. A voltage of 100, 200, or 300 volts is applied, and the rate of migration of the colloid is determined by timing the passage of about ten particles between the horizontal division lines of the ocular micrometer. The average time in seconds is inserted into a graph yielding the electrophoretic mobility directly in microns per second per volt per cm. Another graph which takes temperature into account converts electrophoretic mobility directly to zeta potential.

The time required for determining the zeta potential is said to approximate 3 to 5 minutes. With an assistant to read the timer, a particle charge distribution curve representing 50 determinations may be prepared in 30 minutes.

The cell is readily cleaned with a pipe cleaner and soap or a detergent. No standardization is required.

[27] Riddick, T. M., J. Am. Water Works Assn., **53**, 1007, 1961.
[28] Bean, E. L., Campbell, S. J., and Anspach, F. R., J. Am. Water Works Assn., **56**, 214, 1964.

Chapter 64

DETERMINATION OF WATER

By John Mitchell, Jr.

Plastics Department
E. I. du Pont de Nemours & Co.
Wilmington, Delaware

INTRODUCTION

In Volume II, Part A, of Standard Methods of Chemical Analysis, Chapter 21 established and described conventional methods for the determination of water. Among the methods emphasized were the Karl Fischer reagent titration, oven drying, Penfield, absorption, and distillation procedures. These represented reasonably well defined techniques for which generalized procedural information could be provided. Other techniques mentioned briefly were those based on some electrical property, dew point, hygrometry, infrared and nuclear magnetic resonance spectrometry, neutron scattering, and gas chromatography. Most of this latter group can be classified appropriately as instrumental and, therefore, properly form a part of this present chapter.

In discussing the more generally useful instrumental methods for determining water, it is assumed that background information is available to the reader from other sources. Basic principles for many of the techniques are described in Part 1 of this volume. In most areas instruments suitable for each type of measurement may be purchased from several different commercial sources. Operating instructions vary from one model to another. Consequently, only general statements on procedure will be made in this chapter. Rather, emphasis will be placed on applicability and, where available, precision, accuracy, and sensitivity. Most of the methods described are broadly applicable to a variety of materials. A few systems are mentioned also which have been used in limited areas but which have wider potential utility.

INFRARED SPECTROMETRY

The infrared method is broadly useful for determining water in the gas, liquid, or solid phase. Several absorption bands in the near and fundamental regions can be used for analysis. Most of these bands are associated with —OH group vibrations and, therefore, may not be specific for water. Because of its polar nature, water tends to form hydrogen bonds with itself or with other molecules having some measure of polar attraction. The exact location of the absorption maximum is associated with the type and extent of bonding. Usually, therefore, each system needs to be calibrated after an appropriate analytical wavelength has been chosen.

The most useful absorption bands are those in the near infrared at about 1.9 microns (μ) and in the fundamental region at about 2.7 and 6 μ. Other bands which have been used include those at about 1 and 1.4 μ. Suitable instruments are available commercially for the near infrared as well as the fundamental region. The latter usually have a lower limit of near 2 μ, and normally cover the sodium chloride region from 2 to 15 μ.

1935

Typical applications are given in Table 64-1. In addition to reviews by Kaye[1] and Wheeler,[2] the report by Keyworth[3] provides useful information on the near infrared

TABLE 64-1. APPLICATIONS OF INFRARED METHOD TO DETERMINATION OF WATER

Material	Wavelength, μ	Range Studied, wt. %
Hydrocarbons................	1.4	tenths[a]
Nitric acid, fuming...........	1.423	0.1 to 6[b]
Alcohols....................	1.9	tenths to several[c,d]
Amines.....................	1.9	several[e]
Glycerol, glycols.............	1.9	tenths to several[c,d,f]
Hydrocarbons................	1.9	high p.p.m.[a]
Hydrogen fluoride............	1.9	0 to 50[g]
"Freon" fluorine refrigerants...	2.67	0 to 100 p.p.m.[h]
Sulfur dioxide................	2.67	tenths[i]
Hydrocarbons................	2.71	p.p.m.[j]
Mercaptans..................	2.8	0 to 0.2[k]
Gases......................	5.5–7.5	0 to 2 vol.[l]
Chlorine (liquid).............	6.1	p.p.m.[m]

[a] Kaye, W., Spectrochim. Acta, **6**, 257, 1954.
[b] White, L., Jr., and Barrett, W. J., Anal. Chem., **28**, 1538, 1956.
[c] Keyworth, D. A., Talanta, **8**, 461, 1961.
[d] Wiegel, E., and Kirchner, H. H., Z. anal. Chem., **195**, 97, 1963.
[e] Streim, H. G., Boyce, E. A., and Smith, J. R., Anal. Chem., **33**, 85, 1961.
[f] Chapman, D., and Nacey, J. F., Analyst, **83**, 377, 1958.
[g] Hyman, H. H., Kilpatrick, M., and Katz, J. J., J. Am. Chem. Soc., **79**, 3668, 1957.
[h] Diamond, W. J., Appl. Spectroscopy, **12**, 10, 1958; *Ibid.*, **13**, 77, 1959.
[i] Karasek, F. W., and Miller, E. C., Ind. Eng. Chem., **46**, 1374, 1954.
[j] Forbes, J. W., Anal. Chem., **34**, 1125, 1962.
[k] Matsuyama, G., Anal. Chem., **29**, 196, 1957.
[l] Luft, K. F., and Guérin, R., Chim. Anal., **37**, 100, 1955.
[m] Pross, A. W., Can. J. Chem., **32**, 956, 1954.

with respect to instrumentation, technique, and applications. For the determination of water in hydroxyl-containing compounds, he recommended absorption measurements at 1.9 μ, using a differential approach. In this case net absorbance of the wet substance was obtained by reference to the anhydrous substance to the substance containing a known amount of water, or to a screen attenuator for adjusting light energy. With methanol, for example, Keyworth determined water in the range from 0.1 to 2.5 percent in 1-cm. cells, using the dry alcohol as reference. For samples containing higher concentrations of water, he diluted with dry methanol. A straight line relationship was obtained between absorbance and weight percent water up to 2.5 percent. Amount of water in methanol was calculated from the relation

$$\text{wt. \% } H_2O = \frac{(A)(\text{dilution wt.})}{(0.47)(\text{sample wt.})}$$

where 0.47 was the proportionality constant. Similarly, water in glycol-base antifreeze compositions was determined, using ethylene glycol of known water content in the ref-

[1] Kaye, W., Spectrochim. Acta, **6**, 257, 1954; **7**, 181, 1955.
[2] Wheeler, O. H., Chemical Reviews, **59**, 629, 1959.
[3] Keyworth, D. A., Talanta, **8**, 461, 1961.

erence beam of the spectrophotometer. Results on different antifreezes were compared with ASTM method D1123 (Karl Fischer reagent titration) and a gas-liquid chromatographic (G-LC) method using polyethylene glycol 400 on Fluoropak 80 in the column. Typical data were:

Water, wt. %

Sample No.	Near IR	ASTM	G-LC
1	2.3	2.2	2.1
2	3.5	3.4	3.3
3	4.9	5.0	4.9

For routine work chloroform was suggested as a reference material. In this case a wavelength associated with chloroform but unaffected by water was chosen for reproducible adjustment of the spectrophotometer from day to day. A screen attenuator was used to adjust the energy level, based on a constant absorbance of the C–H overtone at 1.69 μ. Analyses of methanol containing from 0.03 to 4 percent water gave an accuracy of from 0.01 to 0.1 percent absolute with a precision of about 5 percent, relative. Precision and accuracy on analyses for from 1 to 5 percent water in fuming nitric acid[4] and in amines[5] was about ± 0.1 percent.

Since the exact location of the absorption band is associated with bonding, the infrared method can be used often to discriminate between "free" and "bound" water. Bands for several hydrated chlorides and sulfates[6] and carbonates[7] have been reported. In most cases excess water can be measured in the presence of the water of hydration and vice versa.

NUCLEAR MAGNETIC RESONANCE (NMR) SPECTROMETRY

Hydrogen, as well as certain other atoms whose nuclei have net magnetic moments, is measurable by the technique of NMR spectrometry. "High-" and "low-resolution" equipment has been used in studies of protons in liquids and solids. The former provides a means for differentiating among protons associated with different groups. For example, with a 60 Mc. spectrometer having a magnetic field of 14,100 gauss, the resonance line for protons of the water molecules is clearly resolved from those of other molecules such as alcohols or acids. The latter type of apparatus responds to protons in the liquid phase regardless of the molecule; consequently, proton signals from water, on the one hand, and from liquid alcohols, hydrocarbons, etc., on the other, are indistinguishable. Commonly used "low-resolution" instruments have employed a fixed magnetic field of 6300 gauss at a frequency of 27 Mc.[8] or of 1750 gauss at about 7.5 Mc.[9] These have been designed especially for water determinations and are considerably less expensive than the more broadly applicable but more complex "high-resolution" units. The basic instrument requires a magnet, a fixed radio frequency probe, and a detector. For solid samples, where water is the only liquid component, a signal is recorded which is proportional to its concentration. Protons from liquid water give a sharp signal superimposed on a broad signal from the less mobile protons in the solid as indicated in the absorption

[4] Wiegel, E., and Kirchner, H. H., Z. Anal. Chem., **195,** 97, 1963.
[5] Streim, H. G., Boyce, E. A., and Smith, J. R., Anal. Chem., **33,** 85, 1961.
[6] Gamo, I., Bull. Chem. Soc. Japan, **34,** 760, 1961.
[7] Buijs, K., and Schutte, C. J. H., Spectrochim. Acta, **17,** 917, 1961.
[8] Shaw, T. M., Elsken, R. H., and Kunsman, C. H., J. Assoc. Official Agr. Chemists, **36,** 1070, 1953.
[9] Rubin, H., ISA J., **5,** 64, 1958.

curve in Fig. 64-1 (H_0 represents the strength of the applied magnetic field). Quantitative data can be taken from the first derivative plot based either on peak-to-peak amplitude or on line width δf.[8] Determinations of 1 percent or more of water can be made quickly with a precision of about ±0.2 percent. Among the reports describing the technique as applied to determinations of water are those of Shaw and coworkers,[8] Rubin,[9] and Conway and Smith.[10]

Where applicable, the NMR technique provides a rapid, nondestructive method of analysis for water in a variety of solids. With "low-resolution" equipment, each system must be calibrated and examined to assure that no significant amount of other hydrogen-containing compound is present in the liquid phase. Interference could be due to other liquids or to solids in solution. In special cases the extent of interference might be ascertained and the method modified accordingly. For some systems the signal might be measured from the sample as received and again after freezing out the water or other liquid component; then water content might be determined by difference. An empirical correction could be applied for some materials. For example, Elsken and Kunsman[11] determined water in apples by making a correction for the small amount of sugar dissolved in the liquid; corrected results gave a standard deviation of about 1.3 percent in the range from 80 to 86 percent and usually were within 1 percent of results by conventional vacuum oven drying.

The technique has been applied to the determination of "free" water in a variety of materials, such as noted in Table 64-2.

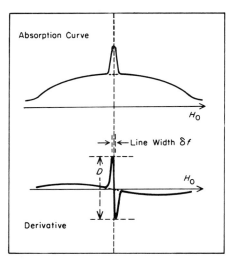

FIG. 64-1.   Proton Absorption and Derivative Curves for Water in a Solid.

COLORIMETRIC METHODS

Most procedures based on colorimetry have employed cobaltous chloride or bromide as reagent. The anhydrous chloride is blue and, upon addition of water, a color change occurs through violet to red as increasing degrees of hydration occur. The anhydrous bromide is green and fully hydrated salt is red. These salts are used widely as relative humidity indicators.

Ferguson and Coulter[12] studied several variables in establishing conditions for a fairly general method of analysis for water. Cobalt chloride in ethyl alcohol gave an absorption maximum at 671 mμ. With increasing water content, the peak position tended to shift toward a longer wavelength. However, by carefully controlling concentration and conditions, a reproducible method was developed for water concentrations of from a few tenths to several percent in solids insoluble in ethyl alcohol. Anhydrous alcohol was used to extract water from the solid sample. Results on such materials as

[10] Conway, T. F., and Smith, R. J., Electronics, Eng. Ed., **31**, 51, 1958.
[11] Elsken, R. H., and Kunsman, C. H., J. Assoc. Official Agr. Chemists, **39**, 434, 1956.
[12] Ferguson, B. L., and Coulter, N. M., Proc. Indiana Acad. Sci., **63**, 124, 1953.

TABLE 64-2. ANALYTICAL DATA FOR WATER BY NMR SPECTROMETRY

Material	Optimum Range, wt. % Water	Precision, %
Chicle	6–24[a]	
Corn sirup	13–25[a]	
Cotton	10–17[a]	
Egg albumin	7–17	0.2[b]
Paperboard pulp	7–>20[c]	
Pectin	7–20	0.2[d]
Potato	8–16	1[e]
Potato	20–85	2[d]
Starch	7–20	0.2[d]
Starch	8–>16	0.1[c]
Starch suspensions	63–92	2[b]
Sucrose	20–90	2[e]
Vegetables	80–92	2[e]
Wheat, wheat products	10–20	0.1[f]
Wood	7–>20[c]	

[a] Conway, T. F., and Smith, R. J., Electronics, Eng. Ed., **31**, 51, 1958.
[b] Shaw, T. M., and Elsken, R. H., Anal. Chem., **27**, 1983, 1955; J. Chem. Phys., **21**, 565, 1953.
[c] Rubin, H., ISA J., **5**, 64, 1958.
[d] Shaw, T. M., Elsken, R. H., and Kunsman, C. H., J. Assoc. Official Agr. Chemists, **36**, 1070, 1953.
[e] Elsken, R. H., and Kunsman, C. H., J. Assoc. Official Agr. Chemists, **39**, 434, 1956.
[f] Miller, B. S., and Kaslow, H. D., Food Tech. (Champaign), **17**, 142, 1963.

bauxite, cereals, sawdust, and soybean mash usually checked within 0.1 percent of those from Karl Fischer reagent titration.

Procedure.—Weigh 1 to 5 g. of sample into a glass-stoppered (g.s.) flask, and add exactly 50 ml. of dry ethyl alcohol ($\geq$99.98 percent). Shake the mixture vigorously for 5–10 minutes and then allow the solids to settle, centrifuging if necessary. Pipet a portion of the clear extract into a 50-ml. g.s. volumetric flask. Add sufficient cobaltous chloride in ethyl alcohol reagent such that when the solution is diluted to 50 ml., the cobalt concentration will be 300 p.p.m. Then add absolute alcohol almost to volume and place the flask in a bath at 25 $\pm$ 0.1°C., finally adjusting to the mark with alcohol. Measure the absorbance of the solution at 671 mμ against the absolute ethyl alcohol solvent, preferably in a double beam spectrometer. Determine water content after reference to a calibration curve prepared from alcohol solutions containing known amounts of water.

Other substances which have found specific uses as colorimetric reagents have been methylene blue for traces of water in jet fuels, halides, ketones, and hydrocarbons,[13] cobalt bromide impregnated strips for testing halogenated refrigerants, gasoline and oils,[14] fuchsine for estimating water in granulated sugar and refinery pastes,[15] lithium chloride-cupric perchlorate for acetone,[16] and chloranilic acid for miscellaneous organic solvents except those containing amino-nitrogen.[17] In this last case an ethyl alcohol

[13] Nesh, F., U. S. Patent 3,106,836, October 15, 1963.
[14] Line, R. A., and Hoftiezer, H., Brit. Patent 805,012, November 26, 1958.
[15] Lysyanskiĭ, E. B., Sakharn. Prom., **1961** (12), 40–1; Ref. Zhur. Khim., VIII, 1962 (12) Abstr. No. 12N308; Anal. Abstr., **10**, #1181, 1963.
[16] Jackwerth, E., and Specker, H., Z. Anal. Chem., **171**, 270, 1959.
[17] Barreto, R. C. R., and Barreto, H. S. R., Anal. Chim. Acta, **26**, 494, 1962.

solution containing 2 millimoles of chloranilic acid was added to 5 ml. of an alcohol solution of the sample. Absorbance was measured at 520 mμ against a reagent blank and the amount of water taken from a calibration curve. A standard deviation of 1.5 percent was reported for samples containing more than 2 percent water.

For certain gases acetylene formed from the reaction of moisture with calcium carbide

$$CaC_2 + 2H_2O \rightarrow Ca(OH)_2 + C_2H_2 \tag{1}$$

was determined as the red-colored cuprous acetylide[18] or ammonia from reaction with magnesium nitride

$$Mg_3N_2 + 6H_2O \rightarrow 3Mg(OH)_2 + 2NH_3 \tag{2}$$

was estimated using Nessler's reagent, measuring absorbance at 470 mμ.[19]

Moisture, plus other compounds containing active hydrogen, was determined in liquid systems containing metal alkyls by a colorimetric procedure. The amount of bleaching of the red-colored diethylaluminum hydride-2-isoquinoline complex was proportional to total activity.[20] Absorbance was measured at 460 mμ. Dissolved oxygen interfered reproducibly and a colorimetric method was given for its estimation.

NEUTRON SCATTERING AND OTHER RADIOCHEMICAL METHODS

Neutron scattering was shown by Gardner and Kirkham[21] to be a particularly effective means for determining moisture in soil. Hydrogen is more capable than other elements of slowing and scattering fast neutrons. A unit consisting of a fast neutron source, such as provided by polonium and beryllium, with a slow neutron counter, such as boron trifluoride, was devised for determining *volume* percent hydrogen in soil. Based on results from five mineral soils, a precision of about 2 percent was found. No effects were observed from temperature, texture, or compaction of the soil.

The procedure measures hydrogen level. Therefore, other hydrogen-containing materials will respond to the method. Soils high in organic matter, *e.g.*, humus, may interfere unless the level is reasonably constant, permitting a correction. (Hydrogen content of humus averages about 5 weight percent; of water, about 11 percent.) An interesting feature of the method is its use *in situ*. A hole may be drilled in the soil and the instrument inserted for the direct analysis.

Carver[22] combined a fast neutron source with a gamma ray source for providing results on a weight percent basis. The reflection of the γ-rays provided by a cesium-137 source, was inversely proportional to density of the solid material. He described an instrument, available commercially, which fed the signals from the neutron and γ-ray detectors to a computer, which calculated results as weight percent water. For solids, such as soil and cement, an accuracy of about 0.2 percent was claimed for the range 2 to 80 percent moisture in samples containing significant amounts of hydrogen-containing substances. Results of extensive testing studies were reported in a symposium sponsored by the ASTM.[23]

[18] Boller, W., Chemiker-Ztg., **50,** 537, 1926.
[19] Šingliar, M., and Zubák, J., Chem. Průmysl, **6,** 426, 1956.
[20] Mungall, T. G., and Mitchen, J. H., Anal. Chem., **33,** 1330, 1961.
[21] Gardner, W., and Kirkham, D., Soil Science, **73,** 391, 1952.
[22] Carver, R. L., Instrum. & Control Systems, **36** (5), 106, 1963.
[23] American Society for Testing and Materials, ASTM Special Technical Publication No. 293, "Symposium on Nuclear Methods for Measuring Soil Density and Moisture," Philadelphia, 1961.

Beta- and gamma-ray counting have been used for special applications. Friedman, Zisman and Sullivan[24] employed β-rays for determining water continuously in fuels. A source was placed on one side of the line carrying the fuel. Rays passing through a radiation permeable plug on the opposite side were measured with a Geiger-Müller counter.

Gamma radiation formed the basis for a nuclear density gauge for estimating water in cement slurries passing through pipes. Cesium-137 served as a source. The γ-rays emitted by the cesium were absorbed by the pipe carrying the slurry. The β-rays, on the other hand, having considerably greater penetrating power, passed through the two thicknesses of pipe plus slurry and were detected in an ionization chamber. This method depended on the fact that differing densities of materials reduce nuclear radiation intensity by different amounts. In this system the intensity of the rays passing through the flowing slurry was related to density or specific gravity. By suitable calibration, the percentage of water or solids could be recorded. In the 30 to 40 percent water range the accuracy was reported to be ±0.2 percent water when a 12-second time constant was used or ±0.3 percent, with a 6-second time constant.[25]

Solubility of water in hydrocarbons was determined conveniently by use of tritiated water in conjunction with a liquid scintillation counter.[26,27] The former investigators used tritium concentrated to a level of about 10^{-12} mole/mole of deuterium oxide; it was present primarily as TDO. After equilibration with the hydrocarbon, the radioactive water was absorbed by calcium oxide. Hydrocarbon was removed by vacuum distillation, and the tritium was extracted for counting through an exchange reaction with ethyl alcohol vapor. Activity was measured by a Geiger-Müller counter after adjustment of the pressure with argon. Through application of known relative solubility data, the results were calculated in terms of normal water. Data were reported for benzene (0.030 g. H_2O/100 g. at 100°C., 0.054 g./100 g. at 26°C.), cyclohexane (0.010 g./100 g. at 20°C.), plus 13 C_4 to C_8 saturated and unsaturated aliphatic hydrocarbons. This procedure required only small amounts of sample. Jones and Monk[27] used a simpler approach. Hydrocarbon or halide was shaken with TDO. After equilibration was achieved, the solvent was separated, and a measured volume was shaken with inactive water. Samples of this mixture were assayed by a liquid scintillation counter. The same technique involving tritium exchange was used effectively for determining water in halogenated oils[28] and for measuring moisture permeability of synthetic materials using tritiated water vapor.[29]

MASS SPECTROMETRY

Mass spectrometry is not often considered as a technique for use in the quantitative determination of water. Actually it is capable of giving fairly reliable results over a wide concentration range, being particularly valuable in estimating water as part of the complete analysis of complex mixtures of gases or volatile liquids. Only small samples are required, about 0.1 cc. of gas at S.T.P. or a few microliters of liquid.

The spectrum of water consists primarily of the mass 18 peak due to $HO^{16}H^+$ ions, commonly referred to as the parent mass. Actually many ions are produced by direct bombardment and by secondary collisions of some of these ions with neutral molecules.

[24] Friedman, L., Zisman, W. A., and Sullivan, M. V., U. S. Patent 2,487,797, 1949.
[25] Minneapolis-Honeywell Regulator Co., Instrumentation Data Sheet No. 1.1-4, October 1957.
[26] Joris, G. G., and Taylor, H. S., J. Chem. Phys., **16**, 45, 1948.
[27] Jones, J. R., and Monk, C. B., J. Chem. Soc., 2633, 1963.
[28] Cameron, J. F., Boyce, I. S., and Glaister, R. M., Brit. J. Appl. Phys., **10**, 463, 1959.
[29] Finkel, E. E., and Chmutov, K. V., Zhur. Fiz. Khim., **33**, 943, 1959.

Washburn, Berry, and Hall[30] reported the following, exclusive of deuterium and tritium: H^+, O^{16+}, $O^{16}H^+$, O^{17+}, $HO^{16}H^+$, $O^{17}H^+$, O^{18+}, $HO^{17}H^+$, $O^{18}H^+$, $HO^{18}H^+$ In the range of mass 16, 17, and 18, the relative intensities are 2.3, 24.5 and 100.0, respectively.[31] Calculations based on mass 18 are best suited for determining water. Usually contributions by other compounds to this mass are relatively small.

Water may be adsorbed to a serious extent on the walls of the mass spectrometer inlet system. The sorption problem may lead to a variable background, limiting the lower level for which reliable analyses for water can be made. Usually an accuracy and precision of about 0.2 percent absolute or 1 percent relative can be expected, whichever is the larger.

THERMOGRAVIMETRY

Thermogravimetric analysis (TGA) is a technique for determining weight loss as a function of temperature or time. These measurements are usually accomplished using apparatus which provides temperature programming and continuous recording of weight loss during drying or decomposition. (Such equipment differs from ovens with built-in balances used widely for conventional total weight loss measurements as a function of time at constant temperature.) TGA often permits selective measurement of free and bound water as evidenced by weight loss curves showing inflections at various stages representing changes in composition.

The technique of TGA, instrumentation, and applications to inorganic analysis were discussed in detail by Duval.[32] TGA is a dynamic technique; consequently, high precision of measurement is dependent on careful control of several factors: furnace design; air buoyancy and convection effects; atmosphere; heating rate; heat of reaction; physical form; amount and depth of sample in its container; and location of the temperature measuring device.[33,34,35,36,37] The initial temperature indicating the onset of loss of water or of decomposition is so dependent on conditions that it has been recommended that this be defined as *procedural decomposition temperature*.[36] Simons and Newkirk[37] illustrated these phenomena in their studies of calcium oxalate monohydrate. Figure 64-2 shows the thermogram from 500 mg. of the monohydrate heated in a porcelain crucible in air at a rate of 5° per minute. Variations of several degrees were observed under slightly different conditions, although the differences were much greater at the decomposition temperature of the anhydrous salt and its products. In reference to the use of TGA in analyses for water, Duval[38] noted that under carefully controlled conditions bound water can be distinguished as: (1) water of constitution; (2) water of crystallization; (3) imbibed or zeolitic water; (4) deeply adsorbed water; and (5) physiologically bound water. He reported results on a variety of grains as well as on many inorganic hydrates.

[30] Washburn, H. W., Berry, C. E., and Hall, L. G., Anal. Chem., **25**, 130, 1953.
[31] Taylor, R. C., Brown, R. A., Young, W. S., and Headington, C. E., Anal. Chem., **20**, 396, 1948.
[32] Duval, C., Inorganic Thermogravimetric Analysis, 2nd Ed., Elsevier, Amsterdam-London-New York, 1963.
[33] Garn, P. D., and Kessler, J. E., Anal. Chem., **32**, 1563, 1960.
[34] Gordon, S., and Campbell, C., Anal. Chem., **32**, 271R, 1960.
[35] Murphy, C. B., Anal. Chem., **32**, 168R, 1960; **34**, 298R, 1962; **36**, 347R, 1964.
[36] Newkirk, A. E., Anal. Chem., **32**, 1558, 1960.
[37] Simons, E. L., and Newkirk, A. E., Talanta, **11**, 549, 1964.
[38] Duval, C., Chim. Anal., **36**, 61, 1954; **44**, 102, 1962.

The combination of TGA and DTA often aids in establishing the nature of dehydration or decomposition steps as a substance is heated.

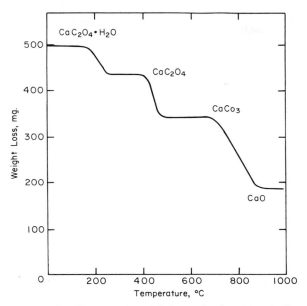

FIG. 64-2. TGA Thermogram of Calcium Oxalate Monohydrate.

DIFFERENTIAL THERMAL ANALYSIS

Differential thermal analysis (DTA) is becoming increasingly valuable for determining transitions in solids and liquids. In this method sample and inert reference material are heated in a common environment. The temperature of sample and reference remain essentially the same until a thermally induced transition occurs. This leads to a difference in temperature between sample and reference which is proportional to the amount of heat adsorbed by or evolved from the sample, *i.e.*; endothermic or exothermic activity. A plot of ΔT *vs.* T gives a thermogram such as shown in Fig. 64-3. Theoretical and experimental aspects of DTA were discussed by Smothers and Chiang.[39] Recent developments were reviewed by Murphy.[35]

Application to determinations of melting and boiling points is obvious. In addition, with apparatus of adequate sensitivity, the technique is capable of recording such changes as loss of free water, breaking of hydrate bonds followed by vaporization of the water, and decomposition reactions. Areas under peaks in the thermogram are proportional to the amount of heat required to effect the transitions. By suitable calibration with known substances, quantitative results can be obtained.

Suitable equipment is available commercially for DTA, and the manufacturer provides operating instructions for his apparatus. Illustrations of the type of information

[39] Smothers, W. J., and Chiang, Y., DTA: Theory and Practice, Chemical Publishing Co., New York, 1959.

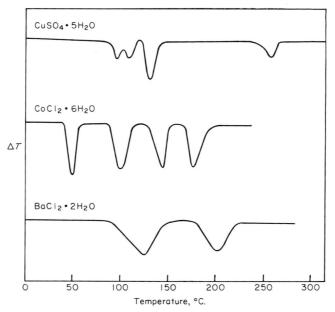

ΔT

CuSO$_4$·5H$_2$O

CoCl$_2$·6H$_2$O

BaCl$_2$·2H$_2$O

Temperature, °C.

FIG. 64-3.   DTA Thermograms of Inorganic Hydrates.

that can be obtained are given in Fig. 64-3, which is a plot of some data reported by Borchardt and Daniels.[40] The sequences of endothermic reactions indicated in the figure were reported as:

$$CuSO_4 \cdot 5H_2O \ (s) \xrightarrow{\sim 95°C.} CuSO_4 \cdot 3H_2O \ (s) + 2H_2O \ (l)$$

$$2H_2O \ (l) \xrightarrow{\sim 108°} 2H_2O \ (g)$$

$$CuSO_4 \cdot 3H_2O \ (s) \xrightarrow{\sim 135°} CuSO_4 \cdot H_2O \ (s) + 2H_2O \ (g)$$

$$CuSO_4 \cdot H_2O \ (s) \xrightarrow{\sim 260°} CuSO_4 \ (s) + H_2O \ (g)$$

$$CoCl_2 \cdot 6H_2O \ (s) \xrightarrow{\sim 49°C.} CoCl_2 \cdot 2H_2O \ (s) + 4H_2O \ (l)$$

$$4H_2O \ (l) \xrightarrow{\sim 99°} 4H_2O \ (g)$$

$$CoCl_2 \cdot 2H_2O \ (s) \xrightarrow{\sim 137°} CoCl_2 \cdot H_2O \ (s) + H_2O \ (g)$$

$$CoCl_2 \cdot H_2O \ (s) \xrightarrow{\sim 175°} CoCl_2 \ (s) + H_2O \ (g)$$

$$BaCl_2 \cdot 2H_2O \ (s) \xrightarrow{\sim 125°C.} BaCl_2 \cdot H_2O \ (s) + H_2O \ (g)$$

$$BaCl_2 \cdot H_2O \ (s) \xrightarrow{\sim 200°} BaCl_2 \ (s) + H_2O \ (g)$$

[40] Borchardt, H. J., and Daniels, F. J., Phys. Chem., **61**, 917, 1957.

Thus, with $CuSO_4 \cdot 5H_2O$ and $CoCl_2 \cdot 6H_2O$, the first stage of the dehydration sequence below 100° represented heat required to form the next lower hydrate, and the second peak represented the heat necessary to vaporize the water released. When the initial dehydration step was well above 100°, as with $BaCl_2 \cdot 2H_2O$, both processes occurred simultaneously, and a single peak resulted.

An example of a unique application of DTA is in the following dehydration of calcium sulfate dihydrate (gypsum). Kuntze[41] diluted 100-mg. samples, 325 mesh, with an equal weight of aluminum oxide. The sample-alumina mixture and a reference of alumina alone were heated in an atmosphere saturated with water vapor at a rate less than 6°/minute. A major endotherm at 130°C. represented dehydration to the hemihydrate and a second endotherm at about 195°C., to soluble β-anhydrite. After suitable calibrations, as little as 0.1 percent dihydrate was determined in hemihydrate.

GAS CHROMATOGRAPHY

Direct and indirect gas chromatographic methods have been employed for estimating water in mixtures. Usually the direct methods have been less precise for water than for other compounds because of the broad, unsymmetrical peaks resulting from either gas-liquid or gas-solid chromatography. Consequently, the direct approach was best suited for several tenths of a percent or more of water. Elvidge and Proctor[42] used the technique successfully for determining water in a variety of pastes, ointments, creams, and emulsions. A special injection system to trap nonvolatile components was connected to the column: 5-foot column packed with 20 percent "Carbowax" 1500 on 36–85 mesh "Chromosorb" at 117°C. A hydrogen-nitrogen carrier gas was used at a flow rate of 100 cc./min. and a thermal conductivity detector analyzed the effluent gas. Peak height ratios were calculated between water and n-pentyl alcohol added as an internal standard. To carry out an analysis, weighed samples were shaken vigorously with a known volume of acetone and 2 percent pentyl alcohol added. A 30-μl. sample was used. Results on several creams, containing from 30 to 80 percent water, usually gave a precision and accuracy of about 1 percent as compared to azeotropic distillation.

Small amounts, p.p.m. levels, of moisture were determined successfully by means of a concentration step prior to separation. Carlstrom and coworkers[43] analyzed for water in butane gas by scrubbing the gaseous sample through a U-tube packed with 30 percent polyethylene glycol (M. W. ca. 200) at 10°C. on 20–30 mesh firebrick. To displace the water, the temperature of the trap was raised to 90°, and helium was passed through countercurrent to the flow of butane during sampling and then into a 2-foot column at 80°, packed with the same materials as the trap. A thermal conductivity detector was used. A standard deviation of 26 p.p.m. was observed on 0.5-liter samples of butane averaging 166 p.p.m. moisture and 2.8 p.p.m. on 3-liter portions averaging 15.4 p.p.m. Estimates indicated that the limit of detection was about 0.2 p.p.m. water on a 10-liter sample. A similar technique was used for water in lithium chlorate. Evolved oxygen and water from the heated sample were condensed into a liquid nitrogen trap. After warming to 0°, the trap contents were diluted with dry ethyl alcohol, and the resulting solution was analyzed by gas chromatography.[44]

An alternate technique, involving reaction with calcium carbide, Eq. (1), prior to separation, was applied to a number of hydrocarbons and combustion products. The resulting acetylene was readily separated through a column packed with 13 g. of dimethyl

[41] Kuntze, R. A., Materials Res. & Stds. (ASTM), **2**, 640, 1962; Nature, **193**, 772, 1962.
[42] Elvidge, D. A., and Proctor, K. A., Analyst, **84**, 461, 1959.
[43] Carlstrom, A. A., Spencer, C. F., and Johnson, J. F., Anal. Chem., **32**, 1056, 1960.
[44] Campbell, A. N., Kartzmark, E. M., and Williams, D. F., Can. J. Chem., **40**, 890, 1962.

sulfolane and 17 g. of squalane per 100 g. of crushed firebrick.[45] Using a flame ionization detector, as little as 1 p.p.m. of acetylene was determined in 0.5 cc. of light hydrocarbon vapor. A standard deviation of 1 3 p.p.m. was found on a butadiene sample, analyzing 22 p.p.m. water, as compared to 25 p.p.m. by Karl Fischer reagent titration.

ELECTRICAL METHODS

Water has several unique electrical properties which can be applied to its analysis in a variety of fairly uniform solids, liquids, and gases. A number of instruments have been developed for the determination of water by electrical means. These usually are relatively small, compact units which employ measurement of conductivity, dielectric constant, or capacitance, or are based on electrolysis. When once standardized, they serve as rapid means for routine analyses in the plant, laboratory, or field.

Conductivity, Resistance.—Among the electrical techniques, those based on conductivity measurements are most widely used. Applications have been reported for analyses of solids, liquids, and gases. The technique requires that an electrolyte be present, and that other components in the sample be essentially nonconducting. Under these conditions, when electrodes at a fixed potential are placed in the sample, the current is proportional to water content. Analyses are made either directly on a measured amount of the sample or indirectly on an inert water-miscible liquid used to extract water from the sample. The former method requires rather simple, compact apparatus and is well suited for rapid analyses of solid materials containing several percent water. Each system must be calibrated, however, since the physical form and density of the material may affect the results. Instruments have been described for direct determination of water in grains,[46,47] paper,[48] textiles,[49,50] jute,[51] plastics,[52] tobacco,[52] sand,[53] concrete mix,[53] wood,[54] leather,[55] soils,[56] petroleum products,[57] and aliphatic amines.[58]

Ukazi and Kageyama[59] used direct resistance measurements at −15°C. for determining from 0.1 to 5 percent water in hydrogen fluoride. The sample was collected in a polychlorotrifluoroethylene cell at −15°. Platinum black electrodes were inserted and specific resistance, R in ohms/cm., was measured via a Kohlrausch bridge. Water content, X weight percent, was calculated from the relation

$$\log x = 1.808 - 1.528 \log R$$

The cell constant was determined using known concentrations of potassium chloride in water. Correction to the resistance was determined for samples containing up to 5 percent sulfuric acid at −15°

[45] Knight, H. S., and Weiss, F. T., Anal. Chem., **34**, 749, 1962.
[46] Hlynka, I., Martens, V., and Anderson, J. A., Can. J. Res., **27F**, 382, 1949.
[47] Shufflebottom, K., Brit. Pat. 885,306, February 9, 1960.
[48] Kotilainen, P., Can. Pat. 656,158, 1963.
[49] Toner, R. K., Bowen, C. F., and Whitwell, J. C., Text. Res. J., **18**, 526, 1948.
[50] Hearle, J. W. S., in Moisture in Textiles, J. W. S. Hearle and R. H. Peters, Eds., Butterworths Publications, London, and Textile Book Publishers, New York, 1960, p. 123.
[51] Banerjee, B. L., and Sen, M. K., J. Sci. Ind. Res., A, India, **15**, 24, 1856.
[52] Eicken, H., Brit. Pat. 737,145, July 8, 1963.
[53] Glegg, G. L., Brit. Pat. 645,998, July 28, 1948.
[54] Anon., Holztech, **28**, 201, 1948.
[55] Stubbings, R., and Ambrose, L., J. Am. Leather Chemists' Assoc., **56**, 148, 1961.
[56] Boujoucos, G. J., and Mick, A. H., Soil Sci., **66**, 217, 1948.
[57] Delgass, E. B., Brooks, J. M., Kleinheksel, S., and Traver, A. E., Ind. Eng. Chem., **46**, 1418, 1954.
[58] Pouyet, B., Compt. Rend., **256**, 2834, 1963.
[59] Ukazi, R., and Kageyama, I., Japan Analyst, **9**, 604, 1960.

$$\log R = \log (15.2 - 0.43 \text{ wt. } \% \text{ H}_2\text{SO}_4) - 0.65 \log x$$

A similar relationship was observed in correcting for fluosilicic acid in samples.

Radio frequency power absorption has been employed in rapid, accurate non-destructive analyses for free water in certain solids, liquids, and pastes. With this power source for use with conductance measurements, lower moisture levels often can be determined and broad moisture gradients can be tolerated. Applications were reported to such diverse materials as inorganic salts, corn starch, and glycerol, containing from 0 to 80 percent water with an accuracy of 0.001 to 0.5 percent.[60] Commercial instrumentation is available.

The indirect approach, using an inert liquid, gives more versatility provided the water can be extracted reproducibly. Acetone and methyl and ethyl alcohols have been used as extractants. Oxalic acid, sodium chloride, and lower fatty acids are typical of electrolytes which have been added when necessary. Indirect methods have been used in analyses for moisture in gases and soils.[61]

Electrical conductivity measurements on solid or liquid absorbants can be used directly and indirectly for determining water in gases. Thus, lithium salts have been employed for measuring the relative humidity of gases above 5 percent. A mixture of sulfuric and phosphoric acids has been a suitable absorbant in rapid determinations of low concentrations of water in small samples. Weaver and coworkers[62,63] actually measured water content by balancing pressure (designated "comparison pressure") between a standard and the unknown until the electrical resistance was constant. A pressure gauge actually served as the measuring instrument, and approximate water content, W, was calculated from the relation

$$W = C \frac{P_w}{P_x} = \frac{SP_c P_w}{P_s P_x}$$

where: C = water content of the standard at the "comparison pressure";
$\quad P_w$ = absolute pressure at which water content of unknown is desired;
$\quad P_c$ = "comparison pressure" at which the standard is balanced with the electrical resistance produced by the unknown at pressure P_x; and
$\quad P_s$ = pressure at which the standard contains a known concentration of water vapor, S.

In preparation for moisture in compressed gases, air, oxygen, or nitrogen saturated at about 36 atmospheres and expanded to 1 atmosphere were recommended as standards. Where the water content of the unknown was desired at 1 atmosphere, the above equation reduced to,

$$W_x = \frac{S}{P_s P_x}$$

where: S = concentration of water in a vapor space in equilibrium with liquid water. S and W may be expressed in weight per unit volume, relative humidity, or other desired unit.

Actually, these equations assume that all components, including water vapor, behave as ideal gases. Ideally, where a dry, inert gas is used to equilibrate with a liquid or solid

[60] Miller, P. S., and Jones, J. J., Proc. Scientific Sect. Toilet Goods Assoc., No. 31, May 1959.

[61] Hancock, C. K., and Hudgins, C. M., Jr., Anal. Chem., 26, 1738, 1954.

[62] Weaver, E. R., Anal. Chem., 23, 1076, 1951.

[63] Weaver, E. R., Hughes, E. E., and Diniak, A. W., J. Research Natl. Bur. Stds., 60, 489, 1958.

sample, the mass of water vapor in equilibrium with liquid water is independent of the presence of other gases. Deviations from ideality, of course, are common, and are best explained on the basis of fugacity, *i.e.*, the tendency for a substance to escape from one phase into another. For best accuracy, the relation between fugacity and pressure must be established by experiment, and the equation must be modified to account for deviations from ideality. Necessary constants for oxygen, air, and nitrogen are essentially the same, and a more exact relation has been presented, together with a hand computer in the form of a circular slide rule to assist in handling this calculation.[63]

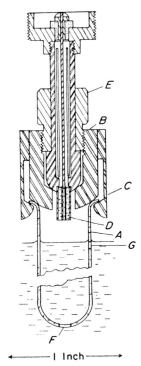

FIG. 64-4. Detector for Determination of Water Vapor in Equilibrium with a Liquid.

Figure 64-4 shows a convenient arrangement of the detector for determining water vapor in equilibrium with a liquid.[63] A glass tube, *A*, having openings at the bottom, *F*, and one side, *G*, is dipped into the liquid. (For small samples capillary tubes with flared tops can be used.) The detector, *D*, is connected as shown in the figure. Block *B* and spring *C* provide a tight fit with the top of the tube, and nut *E* serves as a rigid connector for the detector. Only a fraction of a cubic centimeter of space is necessary for measuring relative humidities in a static system.

The procedure has been applied to determinations of moisture in such gases as air, oxygen, nitrogen, and natural gas. Equipment is available from commercial sources.

The method also can be used for determining water in liquids and solids; a dry inert gas is used to elute the water. Alternatively the water content of air in equilibrium with a liquid sample may serve as a measure of water in the sample. This approach was reliable for ether but not for alcohol.

The technique has proved particularly sensitive for determining water in liquids having limited solubility for water, such as hydrocarbons, ethers, and ketones. It has been less reliable for water-miscible substances such as alcohols and mineral acids. Since the quantitative significance of the fugacity in terms of water content differs for each liquid, application to each system must be established empirically. Water in solids has been determined after extraction into a suitable liquid.

The sensitivity of measurement, *i.e.*, the change in concentration of water that can be observed with the instrument approaches 0.3 µg./liter or 0.1 percent, whichever is greater.

Dielectric methods usually are not well suited to analyses of samples in which the conductivity increases markedly with increase in water content. This is particularly critical in samples containing relatively high concentrations of electrolytes. In these cases high frequency systems may be used for conductivity measurements. Jensen and coworkers[64] used this approach in analyses for water in sodium chloride and ammonium nitrate. A dioxane-methyl alcohol solution was used to extract the moisture for analysis in a 9.45 Mc./sec. unit. A precision of 0.02 percent was found for water

[64] Jensen, F. W., Kelly, D. J., and Burton, M. B., Jr., Anal. Chem., **26**, 1716, 1954.

contents in the range of 0.3 to 2.5 percent. Binary mixtures of water in several alcohols were analyzed successfully.[65] At the 1-percent water level, the precision and accuracy were about 0.05 percent and 0.2 percent, respectively.

Dielectric Techniques.—Dielectric methods may employ measurement of dielectric constant, dielectric loss, or capacitance. Direct determination of dielectric constant is usually the most reliable because of the high constant for water, 78.5 at 25°C., as compared to other materials. Most solids, for example, have dielectric constants from about 2 to 5. Many liquids, however, have considerably higher constants, e.g., 32.6 for methyl alcohol at 25°. Some instruments which presumably determine the constant, actually measure the capacitance of a condenser using the sample as the dielectric.[66,67] In these cases the capacitance of a condenser filled with the sample is compared with that of the same condenser when empty. The capacitance of a parallel plate condenser is proportional to the area of the plates and the dielectric constant of the sample between the plates, and inversely proportional to the distance between the plates. Consequently, results usually depend on the thickness and density of the sample as well as water content.

Theoretically, the dielectric constant of a binary mixture, ϵ_m, can be calculated from a linear relation

$$\epsilon_m = \epsilon_1 p_1 + \epsilon_2 p_2$$

where p_m and p_2 are the relative concentrations of each component. Oehme[68] found, however, that most systems did not behave ideally, and calibration curves were required for each system to be analyzed.

Oehme applied high frequency techniques for dielectric measurements, using a single stage quartz oscillator with a working frequency of 7 Mc./sec. ("DK meter"). Probably the most rapid measurement was that of grid current. However, if damping due to the sample varied widely, measurements by the grid current method could be in serious error.

The dielectric methods have been applied to determinations of water in liquids and solids. The sample is placed reproducibly in a suitable cell of fixed dimensions. The instrument is tuned and a reading is taken. Equipment and type of measurement have varied with the nature of the material to be analyzed. Oehme applied variations of the grid current method to determinations of certain levels of water in alcohols, acids, uniform emulsions, powders, cellulose, tobacco, and ceramics. For determining water directly in leather, Kremen[69] used an oscillator circuit operating at about 11 Mc./sec. With the measuring condenser, C_m, empty, the tuning condenser, C_t, was adjusted to give a minimum reading on the tuning meter. Insertion of the sample between the plates of C_m required a reduction in C_t proportional to the water content. Calibration curves were needed for various thicknesses. For calf leather an accuracy of about 3 percent (as compared to oven drying) was observed in the optimum range of 15 to 50 percent water.

Analysis of extracts from solids often has been preferable to direct analysis, particularly on materials which are difficult to pack uniformly or on which the water may be distributed unevenly. Dioxane is one of the most useful extraction solvents because of its low dielectric constant (2.2 at 25°) and complete miscibility with water. Oehme[68] set the following restrictions on the use of dioxane for most dielectric measurements: (1) the dioxane must not dissolve any material other than water; (2) the water must be extracted completely from the solid; and (3) the volume used should be selected such that the

[65] West, P. W., Senise, P., and Burkhalter, T. S., Anal. Chem., **24**, 1250, 1952.
[66] Fairbrother, T. H., and Wood, R. J., Industrial Chemist, **6**, 442, 1930.
[67] Fischer, R. B., Anal. Chem., **19**, 835, 1947.
[68] Oehme, F., Angew. Chem., **68**, 457, 1956.
[69] Kremen, S. S., J. Am. Leather Chemists' Assoc., **44**, 774, 1949.

dioxane will contain no more than 1 percent water. This final restriction is made to assure minimum extraction of electrolytes. Some solids may be completely soluble in dioxane. However, the method still may be useful as long as the composition of the substance remains essentially constant, *e.g.*, aminocaprolactam. Satisfactory analyses were made on the lactam containing up to 1 percent water, after proper calibration curves had been prepared.[68] For extraction of some materials, *e.g.*, meats, a mixture of dioxane and ethyl glycol was found superior to dioxane alone.[70]

Dielectric techniques have been used for rapid, routine determinations of water in paper, textiles,[50,71,72] powders,[73] meat products,[70] salts,[68] and soil.[74]

Improved precision for water added to solvents was achieved by a differential dielectric measurement.[75] This was particularly useful for analyses in which dioxane or diethylene glycol diethyl ether was used to extract water from a solid. The difference in dielectric constant between solvent before and after extraction was directly proportional to water removed from the sample. The relation was not strictly linear, however, requiring the use of calibration curves.

Electrolysis.—Of the electrical methods available for determining water in gases, that based on electrolysis probably is the most versatile. Keidel[76] devised a unique system based on quantitative absorption of water in a suitable hygroscopic material followed by electrolysis of the water to oxygen and hydrogen. The electrolysis current served as a direct indication of water content. The technique has been particularly well suited for continuous determination of less than 1 to 1000 p.p.m. moisture in gases. It also serves as a batch analyzer.

Analysis is accomplished in a special cell which combines absorption with electrolysis. The absorbant is distributed as a thin viscous film in contact with two platinum electrodes which may be coiled inside a tube of Teflon® TFE-fluorocarbon resin. Water vapor in the gas flowing through the cell is absorbed by the hygroscopic electrolyte. The absorbed water is electrolyzed quantitatively at the electrodes by application of a d.c. voltage greater than the decomposition potential of water. According to Faraday's law, the electrolysis of 0.5 gram-mole of water requires 96,500 coulombs. The electrolysis current is proportional to the number of moles of water absorbed per unit time. This not only provides a continuous measure of water concentration, but also maintains the film in an active condition. Usually a flow rate of 100 cc. of gas per minute is suitable. Under these conditions the electrolysis current is 13.2 μa./p.p.m. by volume. A schematic diagram is shown in Fig. 64-5.[76]

The choice of absorbing material is critical. Requirements include: (1) ability to remove very small quantities of water from a flowing gas stream; (2) stability in the electrical system, *i.e.*, current flow from application of the d.c. potential must result only from electrolysis of water; and (3) inertness toward other components in the gas stream.[76] Partially hydrated phosphorous pentoxide has been found to be satisfactory, particularly for low concentrations of water.

The method has been applied successfully to determinations of water in gases such as air, nitrogen, hydrogen, carbon dioxide, argon, helium, hydrocarbons, Freon fluorinated refrigerants, and propellants. Successful applications also have been made to analyses for water in many liquids. Materials boiling below 100°C. often can be handled as vapors. Others in which water is only slightly soluble have been analyzed indirectly by sparging

[70] Mohler, K., and Slevogt, K., Fette u. Seifen, **56,** 46, 1954.
[71] McMaster, E. A., Textile World, **98,** 141, 201, 1948.
[72] Pande, A., Instrum. Practice, **15,** 432, 1961.
[73] Gur'yanova, E. N., Zavodskaya Lab., **13,** 163, 1947.
[74] van der Marel, H. W., Soil Sci., **87,** 105, 1959.
[75] Wolfe, W. C., Anal. Chem., **35,** 1884, 1963.
[76] Keidel, F. A., U. S. Patent 2,830,945, 1958; Anal. Chem., **31,** 2043, 1959.

with a stream of dry, inert gas, such as air or nitrogen. Czuha and Gardiner,[77] for example, used counter current scrubbing with nitrogen for determining moisture in jet fuels. Chastagner[78] swept moisture from fused uranium oxide at 300° into an electrolytic analyzer. He reported a sensitivity of 0.2 μg. of water equivalent to 0.04 p.p.m. in a 5-g.

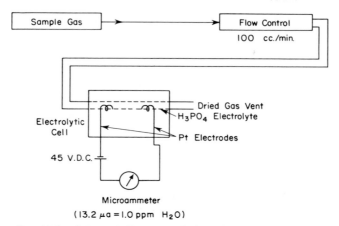

FIG. 64-5. Schematic Diagram of Electrolytic Water Analyzer.

sample. A standard deviation of ±20 percent was estimated for 100 μg. of water. A direct pressure measurement of the evolved water vapor also was made, using a Pirani gauge. Results by the two procedures compared favorably, *e.g.*, 16 p.p.m. and 18 p.p.m. water by the electrolytic and manometric method, respectively.

Compounds which interfere include hydrogen fluoride, ammonia, and other basic materials, and high concentrations of alcohols or acetone. The basic substances react with the phosphoric acid electrolyte. In many cases potassium carbonate or hydroxide can be substituted for the phosphorus pentoxide absorbent in analyses for several hundred parts per million of water in volatile bases. Olefins, particularly diolefins, may interfere through polymerization and ultimate plugging of the cell.[79]

Units based on direct electrolysis are available from several commercial sources. Usually at least 1 liter of gas sample is required for an analysis. A maximum error of 5 percent in the reading has been achieved easily using commercially available components.

In a special case, Klingelhoefer[80] devised a coulometric method for water in liquid ammonia. The sample was passed through a tube packed with KCl into a glass electrolysis cell containing a platinum cathode and graphite anode, and having a fritted glass partition. (The solubility of KCl in liquid ammonia at 0°C. was reported to be 0.132 wt.%.) Potassium formed at the cathode reacted with water. The end point was indicated by an increase in electrical conductivity of the solution as measured with platinum electrodes; this change was used to stop the electrolysis. Water concentration was calculated from the relation

[77] Czuha, M., and Gardiner, K. W., Instrum. & Control Systems, **34**, 2074, 1961.
[78] Chastagner, P. J. P., AEC R&D Rept. DP-766, September 1962.
[79] Knight, H. S., and Weiss, F. T., Anal. Chem., **34**, 749, 1962.
[80] Klingelhoefer, W. C., Anal. Chem., **34**, 1751, 1962.

$$H_2O \text{ (p.p.m., uncorr.)} = \frac{18}{96,500} \cdot \frac{it}{Vd} \cdot 10^6$$

where: 18 = molecular weight of water;
$96,500$ = Faraday;
i = electrolysis current (amp.);
t = time for electrolysis (sec.);
V = cc. sample in cathode section; and
d = density of liquid ammonia at operating temperature ($-40°C$.).

A small correction was necessary for the tiny bubble of hydrogen remaining near the cathode. This gas displaced a portion of the sample through the separator, giving low results. The correction varied from $+1$ at the 40-p.p.m. water level to $+7$ at the 100-p.p.m. level. The method was capable of detecting less than 1 p.p.m. water and suitable for use to about 100 p.p.m. The upper level appeared to be set by the solubility of KCl in liquid ammonia.

MISCELLANEOUS INSTRUMENTAL METHODS

Traces of moisture in such gases as nitrogen, hydrogen, oxygen, and carbon dioxide have been estimated from absorption in the far ultraviolet region of the spectrum near 1220 A. Garton and coworkers[81] devised equipment utilizing an r.f. discharge in hydrogen for continuous monitoring of gas streams. The equipment consisted of: (1) a silica lamp containing hydrogen at low pressure which was excited by a radio-frequency oscillator at a frequency of 16 to 20 Mc./sec.; (2) absorption tubes, having lengths of 1, 42, and 82 cm., with lithium fluoride windows (transparent down to 1050 A); and (3) a photomultiplier and recorder. The light was allowed to pass down one of the absorption tubes containing the gaseous sample. The decrease in intensity of the radiation was found to be due to absorption by the 1220 A band of water. Calibration with nitrogen samples containing known amounts of water gave a linear relationship between concentration and cell response between 0 to 10 p.p.m. and 10 to 700 p.p.m. As little as 0.1 p.p.m. water was detected in nitrogen. At the 1-p.p.m. level, the standard deviation was 0.23, and at 10 p.p.m., 1.96 p.p.m. Oxygen and carbon dioxide absorbed slightly in the 1200 A region, raising the limit of detection in the presence of these gases to 10 and 100 p.p.m., respectively.

Microwaves also have been used for continuous determination of water in solids. Equipment has been designed which provides various microwave signals. For a particular signal system a frequency is chosen which is absorbed by water. The signal is projected from a generator along the surface of the material to be analyzed, e.g., paper. A sensing element is used which measures the amount of energy absorbed. This is correlated with water content based on prior calibration by an independent method of analysis.[82,83]

X-ray diffraction provides a convenient and reliable means for identification and semiquantitative analysis of crystalline substances. Patterns for crystalline hydrates are unique and often permit determination of various forms. The technique, like other physical methods, is a comparison method and requires a file of reference data on known materials. Such reference data are available from sources such as the American Society

[81] Garton, W. R. S., Webb, M. S. W., and Wildy, P. C., J. Sci. Instrum., **34**, 496, 1957.
[82] Beloit Iron Works, Brit. Pat. 887,556, 1961.
[83] Anon., Process Control Automation, **10**, 329, 1963.

for Testing and Materials. Illustrative of unique applications of the x-ray method are studies of the dehydration of calcium sulfate dihydrate and identification of the alpha- and beta-forms of the hemihydrate[84] and of the complexing of clays with organic substances, *e.g.*, bentonite and α-picoline.[85]

[84] Morris, R. J., Nature, **198,** 1298, 1963.
[85] Van Olphen, H., and Deeds, C. T., Nature, **194,** 176, 1962.

INDEX

Abbe equation, 245
  refractometer, 250
Abietic acid derivatives, determination of, 963–5
Absolute retention, 720
Absorbance, definition of, 6
Absorption cells,
  ultraviolet spectrometry, 28
  visible spectrometry, 9
Absorption edge absorptiometry, 170, 181
Absorption flame photometry. *See* Atomic absorption spectrometry.
Absorption spectrometry, analysis of functional groups, 1162
Absorption-thin-layer chromatography. *See* Thin-layer chromatography.
Absorptivity, definition of, 6
Accelerator targets for neutron production, table of, 1536
Accelerators,
  in activation analysis, 1534
  in rubber. *See* Rubber accelerators.
Acetate, microtest for, 221
Acetic acid,
  determination of, 1179
  glacial, analysis of, for water, 242
Acetic anhydride,
  analysis of, for acetic acid, 1179
  determination of, 35
Acetone, determination of, 35
Acetophenone, determination of, 103
Acetylenes. *See* Alkynes.
Acetyl tributyl citrate, determination of in polymer extracts, 1656
Acid Alizarin Garnet R, fluorometric reagent, 99
Acid-base titrations, potentiometry, 290
Acid chlorides. *See* Acyl halides.
Acid phosphatase, determination of, 981–4
Acids. *See individual acids.*
Acids, amino. *See* Amino acids.
  carboxylic. *See* Fatty acids *and* Carboxylic acids.
  conductometric titration of, 309–17
  dibasic, determination of in alkyd resins, 1319
  fatty. *See* Fatty acids.
Acrylic monomers, determination of in polymers, 1308
Acrylic polymers, analysis of, 1317–8
Acrylonitrile-butadiene copolymer, identification of, 1670, 1673–5
Acrylonitrile content, determination of,
  in NBR-phenolic blends, 1693
  in polymers, 1611
Activation analysis, 555
  accelerator targets for neutron production, 1536

Activation analysis (Cont.)
  analysis of,
    cracking catalysts, 1537
    dehydrosulfurization catalysts, 1537
    ferroalloys, 865
    ferrous materials, 864, 865
    gallium, 1791
    gallium arsenide, 1791
    germanium, 1790
    iron and steel, 864, 865
    meteorites, 864
    nonferrous metals, 950–2
    organic compounds, 1537
    petroleum and petroleum products, 1535–8
    polymers, 1537
    reforming catalysts, 1537
    semiconductor materials, 1789, 1791
    silicon, 1790, 1791, 1792–1800
    sulfuric acid, 1537
  applications of, 573, 581
  detection limits, table of, 574
  determination of,
    aluminum, 864, 1537
    antimony, 864, 1792–1800
    arsenic, 864, 1790, 1792–1800
    bismuth, 1792–1800
    boron, 1791
    bromine, 1537
    chlorine, 1537
    chromium, 864
    cobalt, 864, 1792–1800
    copper, 864, 1790, 1792–1800
    gallium, 1792–1800
    gold, 1792–1800
    indium, 1791, 1792–1800
    magnesium, 1537, 1791
    manganese, 864, 1537
    molybdenum, 865, 1537
    nickel, 865
    nonmetallic compounds, 865
    oxygen, 865, 950–2, 1791
    phosphorus, 865, 1790
    platinum, 1537
    selenium, 1791
    silicon, 865, 1791
    sodium, 1537
    sulfur, 865, 1791
    tantalum, 865
    tellurium, 1791
    tin, 865
    titanium, 865
    tungsten, 1537
    zinc, 1791
  elements detected by, table of, 1538
  elements determined by, table of, 575–7, 1535

Activation analysis (Cont.)
　methods of, 565
　　charged-particle method, 1531
　　fast-neutron method, 1531, 1537
　　photon activation analysis, 1532
　　prompt-gamma ray method, 1533
　　thermal-neutron method, 1530, 1535
　neutron activation sensitivities, table of, 1537
　principles of, 1528–30
　selectivity in, methods for achieving, 1529
　sensitivity of, 565, 1538
　sources,
　　accelerators, 1534
　　isotopic neutron sources, 1534
　　nuclear reactors, 1533
Activation energy of thermal degradation of polymers, 1634–7
Active chlorine. See Chlorine, active.
Acyclic compounds, identification of, 679
Acyl halides, analysis of, for fatty acids, 1171
　determination of, 1171–2
Added water. See Water, added.
Additives in polymers. See Polymer additives.
Adrenaline, determination of, 1033
Agar salt bridge for polarography, 358
Air,
　analysis by,
　　conductometry, 847, 1947–8
　　coulometry, 848, 849
　　emission spectrometry, 839
　　gas chromatography, 840
　　infrared spectrometry, 838, 850
　　ionization analysis, 851
　　nephelometry, 842
　　radiometric method, 556
　　turbidimetry, 842
　　ultraviolet spectrometry, 843
　　visible spectrometry, 845–6
　analysis for,
　　carbon monoxide, 850
　　hydrocarbons, 838, 840, 851
　　mercury vapor, 556
　　metals, 839
　　oxidants, 843
　　oxides of nitrogen, 845–6
　　ozone, 843, 848, 849
　　sulfate, 842
　　sulfur compounds, 1211
　　sulfur dioxide, 847, 1211
　　water, by conductivity, 1947–8
Air pollutants, analysis for, 837
Air resistance of paper, 1452–4
Air spectrometer, in analysis of iron and steel, 857
Albumens, determination of, 256
Albumin, determination of, 1007–9
Alcoholic beverages, analysis of, 736
Alcohols,
　analysis of, for water, 1936, 1949
　determination of, 1172–4, 1177, 1180, 1194–5
　microtest for, 224
Aldehyde-amine accelerators, identification of, 1699–1701

Aldehydes, determination of,
　amperometric titration, 399
　gas chromatography, 1194
　infrared spectrometry, 1171–2, 1177–9
　near infrared spectrometry, 1179
　nuclear magnetic resonance spectrometry, 1202
Aldrin, 1464, 1478, 1484, 1493, 1496
　determination of, 1924–5
Alexander's stain, in paper analysis, 1382, 1388
Alkali metals. See also individual metals.
　detection of, 213
　determination of, 1294
　separation of, 714
Alkaline earth metals. See also individual metals.
　determination of, 132, 561, 1226, 1228
　separation of, 714
Alkaline phosphatase, determination of, 984–7
Alkaloids,
　analysis of, by thin-layer chromatography, 754–60
　chemical tests for, table of, 236
　determination of, 399
　microtests for, 235
　properties of, table, 237
Alkanes. See also Hydrocarbons.
　analysis of, by gas chromatography, 1192, 1568–70
　characterization of, 1546
　infrared absorption of, 1165
Alkenes. See also Hydrocarbons.
　characterization of, 1547
　determination of,
　　by gas chromatography, 1192–3
　　by ultraviolet spectrometry, 1182
　　terminal unsaturation, 1178
　infrared absorption of, 1167
　Raman spectra of, 77
Alkoxyl determination, for analysis of acrylic polymers, 1318
Alkyd esters, analysis of, for phthalic acid isomers, 1274–6
Alkyd resins, analysis for,
　benzoic acid, 1274–6
　fatty acids, 1320
　phthalic acid content, 1319
　phthalic acid isomers, 1274–6
　phthalic anhydride, 1272
　polyols, 1321
　polyunsaturated acids, 1278
　p-tert.-butylbenzoic acid, 1278
Alkyd resins, oil modified, analysis of, for fatty acids, 1277
Alkyd resins, styrenated, analysis of, 1597
Alkyl benzene sufonates,
　analysis of, for chain branching, 1166, 1833–6
　determination of,
　　by ultraviolet spectrometry, 35
　　in detergents, 1821–3
　　in sewage, 1833–6
　　in water, 1891
Alkyl halides, determination of, 1197

Alkyl phenol ethoxylates, analysis of, 1173
Alkyl phenoxypolyoxythylene ethanol detergents, determination of, 1828
Alkylates,
  branched chain, determination of, 1845
  linear, determination of, 1845
Alkynes. *See also* Hydrocarbons.
  determination of, 1184, 1193
  infrared absorption of, 1168
Alloys. *See individual alloys and components.*
Alpha particle, 542
Alpha-particle emission, 542
Alpine air jet sieve, 802
Alternating current polarography, 350
Aluminum,
  determination by, 575, 864, 1537
    activation analysis, 575, 1537
    amperometric titration, 390
    atomic absorption spectrometry, 864
    colorimetry, 1865
    electrogravimetry, 448, 449
    emission spectrometry, 864, 900–5, 1772–5, 1778–80, 1780–2
    flame spectrometry, 132, 136, 138, 967–8, 1228
    fluorometric analysis, 100
    polarography, 943, 1235
    ultraviolet spectrometry, 32
    visble spectrometry, 1865
    x-ray spectrometry, 864, 969–73, 1248
  determination of,
    in alloy steel, 390
    in bronze, 390, 943
    in cement, 967–8, 969–73
    in cracking catalysts, 1537
    in glass, 132, 1235, 1248
    in graphite, 575
    in magnesium alloys, 900–5
    in magnesium-base alloys, 138
    in metals, 575
    in minerals, 575
    in reforming catalysts, 1537
    in rocks, 575
    in sea sediments, 575
    in semiconductor materials, 1772–5, 1778–80, 1780–2
    in silicates, 1228
    in soil, 1865, 1873
    in steel, 100, 448, 864
    in zinc-base alloys, 449
  reagents for, fluorometric, 98–100
Aluminum alloys,
  analysis by,
    atomic absorption spectrometry, 923
    flame spectrometry, 135, 136
    polarography, 937–43
  analysis for,
    copper, 136, 923, 937–43
    iron, 136
    lead, 937–43
    magnesium, 923
    manganese, 136
    nickel, 937–43
    sodium, 135
    zinc, 937–43

Aluminum-base alloys,
  analysis of, by emission spectrometry, 884–9, 892–900
  analysis for,
    copper, 137, 875–9
    zinc, 916–20
Aluminum chelates, fluorescent, 98, 99
Aluminum-copper-zinc alloys, analysis of, 943, 947
Aluminum metal, analysis for,
    cadmium, 944
    gallium, 575
    hydrogen, 951
    lithium, 135
    magnesium, 923
    oxygen, 951
    sodium, 135
    tin, 947
    titanium, 947
    vanadium, 577
Aluminum oxide, determination of, in iron ore, 449
Amalgams, analysis of, 423
Amides, determination of, 1174, 1846
  microtests for, 227
Aminco-Bowman spectrofluorometer, 92, 94
Amine antioxidants. *See* Antioxidants, amine.
Amine hydrochlorides, x-ray diffraction data, table of, 1710–2
Amines,
  analysis for, water, 1936, 1946
  determination by,
    gas chromatography, 1196
    infrared spectrometry, 1174, 1177, 1180
    nuclear magnetic resonance spectrometry, 1202
    potentiometric titration, 292
    ultraviolet spectrometry, 1188
  identification of,
    by chemical microscopy, 225
    by x-ray diffraction, 1706–12
  microtest for, 225
  Raman spectra of, 77
Amino acids,
  analysis by, 953
    gas chromatography, 960–1
    paper chromatography, 954–8
    thin-layer chromatography, 757, 760, 958–60
  configuration, determination of, 275
  determination of,
    by potentiometric titration, 291
    by ultraviolet spectrometry, 35
    in urine, 1038
  esterfication of, for gas chromatography, 961
  migration characteristics in paper chromatography, table of, 956
  trifluoroacetylation of, for gas chromatography, 961
1-Amino-4-hydroxyanthraquinone, fluorometric reagent, 99
Ammonia. *See also* Nitrogen ammonia.
  determination of, 33
  liquid, analysis of, for water, 1951

Ammoniacal nitrogen. *See* Nitrogen ammonia.
Ammonium ion, determination of, 395
  microtest for, 213
Amorphous polymers, 1617
Amperometric coulometry, 849
Amperometric titration, 377
  analysis of,
    alloy steel, 390
    alloys, 391, 392
    anodic sludge, 396
    black copper, 390
    brass-plating salts, 395
    bronze, 390, 395
    cadmium, 397
    electrolytes, 391
    electroplating baths, 390, 398
    ferrotungsten, 397
    ferrous materials, 864, 865
    fly dust, 396, 398
    glass, 390, 1236
    iron raw materials, 390
    lead, 391
    lead concentrates, 390
    minerals, 393
    mineral water, 390
    monazite melt, 396
    ores, 390, 392, 398
    organic compounds, 393, 395, 396, 399
    pharmaceuticals, 390, 391, 399
    rubber, 1695, 1742–3
    silicates, 394
    sphalerite, 393
    steel, 395, 397, 562
    water, 392, 393
  applications of, 389
  determination of,
    accelerators in rubber, 1695
    aldehydes, 399
    alkaloids, 399
    aluminum, 390
    ammonium ion, 395
    antimony, 396
    arsenic, 390
    barbiturates, 399
    barium, 390
    beryllium, 391
    bismuth, 391
    bromide, 391
    boron, 390
    cadmium, 391
    calcium, 391
    carbonyl group, 399
    cerium, 392
    chloride, 392
    chlorine, active in water, 392
    cobalt, 392, 864
    copper, 392
    dichromate, 392
    fluoride, 393
    gold, 390
    indium, 393
    inorganic substances, table of, 390–8
    iodide, 394
    iodine, 394
    iodine number, 399

Amperometric titration, determination of (Cont.)
    iridium, 394
    iron, 393
    ketones, 399
    lead, 395
    magnesium, 394
    manganese, 394
    mercaptobenzothiazole, 1742–3
    mercury, 393
    molybdenum, 395
    nickel, 395
    organic bases, 399
    organic substances, table of, 399
    palladium, 395
    permanganate, 394
    phosphorus, 395
    potassium, 394, 1236
    selenium, 396
    silver, 390, 391
    styrene, 399
    sulfate, 396
    sulfide, 394
    sulfur, in organic substances, 396
    tellurium, 396
    thallium, 397
    thiols, 399
    thorium, 396
    tin, 396
    titanium, 397
    α-tocopherol, 399
    tungsten, 397
    unsaturation, 399
    uranium, 397
    vanadium, 397, 562, 865
    zinc, 398
    zirconium, 398
  end point determination, 379
  instrumentation,
    electrical circuit, 384
    indicator electrodes, 384
    reference electrodes, 385
  linear-scan polarography, 347
  principles of, 378
  procedure, 386–9
  titration curves, 379–84
Amperostatic coulometry, 474. *See* Coulometric titrations.
Amplifiers, infrared spectrometry, 42
Amprolium, determination of, in food, 1116
Analytical electrode, 463
Analyzer crystals, for x-ray spectrometry, table of, 175
Anatase, determination of, in titanium dioxide pigments, 1303
Angle-of-contact method, 1449
Anhydrides, determination by,
  gas chromatography, 1194
  infrared spectrometry, 1171–2
  ultraviolet spectrometry, 1187
Aniline point, 674
Aniline sulfate stain, in paper analysis, 1389
Animal tissue. *See* Tissue.
Anionic surfactants. *See* Detergents.
Anions, microtests for, 217
Anisotropic crystals, 223

Anodic chronopotentiometric analysis, 423, 425
Anodic deposition, 454
Anodic sludge, analysis of, for tellurium, 396
Anodic stripping coulometry, 489
Anodic stripping polarography, 349
Anthracene,
  analysis for phenanthrene, 1186
  determination by electron spin resonance spectrometry, 633
Anthraquinone, determination by polarography, 1206
Antiferromagnetism, 588
Antimony,
  determination by,
    activation analysis, 575, 1792–1800
    amperometric titration, 396
    atomic absorption spectrometry, 110
    electrogravimetry, 458
    emission spectrometry, 864, 1780–2
    isotope dilution, 561
    polarography, 864, 943, 1232, 1802
    ultraviolet spectrometry, 33
    x-ray emission spectrometry, 1248
  determination of,
    in blood, 575
    in gallium, 1802
    in glass, 1233, 1248
    in iron and steel, 864
    in lead, 561, 943
    in metals, 575
    in metals, nonferrous, 110
    in selenium, 575
    in semiconductor materials, 1780–2
    in silicon, 575, 1792–1800
    in steel, 575
Antimony alloys, analysis of, for copper, 944
Antimony electrode, for pH measurements, 524
Antimony metal, analysis of,
  by emission spectrometry, 1772–5
  by radiochemical methods, 1791
  for tin, 1801
Antioxidants,
  analysis by,
    chromatography, 1695
    differential thermal analysis, 1647
    fluorometry, 1695
    infrared spectrometry, 1599
    gas chromatography, 1738–40
    polarography, 1308, 1695
    potentiometric titration, 1695
    thin-layer chromatography, 763
    ultraviolet spectrometry, 1596–7, 1695, 1713–7, 1733–5
    visible spectrometry, 1717–9, 1733, 1734, 1735–8
    x-ray diffraction, 1713–7
  determination of,
    in fats, 1057
    in hydrocarbon thinners, 1308
    in polymers, 1596–7, 1599
    in rubber, 1695, 1715, 1733–5, 1735–8, 1738–40
  effectiveness of, determination, 1647

Antioxidants (Cont.)
  identification of, in rubber,
    by chromatography, 1695
    by colorimetry, 1717–9
    by fluorometry, 1695
    by ultraviolet spectrometry, 1695, 1713–7
    by x-ray diffraction, 1713–7
Antioxidants, amine,
  determination of, 1735–8, 1738–40
  identification of, 1713–7, 1717–9
  ultraviolet absorption characteristics of, table, 1715
Antioxidants, phenolic,
  absorptivity data, visible, table of, 1734
  determination of, 1733, 1733–5
Antiozonants in polymers, determination of, 1596
Antipyrine-pyramidon mixtures, analysis of, 239
Apparatus. See Instrumentation.
Aqueous solutions, Raman spectra of, 77
Aromatic hydrocarbons. See also Hydrocarbons.
  analysis by, gas chromatography, 1569–72
  characterization of, 1549
  determination of,
    by gas chromatography, 1193
    by ultraviolet spectrometry, 1185
  infrared absorption of, 1169
Arsenate, microtest for, 220
Arsenic,
  analysis of, by emission spectrometry, 1778–80
  analysis for,
    copper, 1800–2
    iron, 1800
    lead, 1802
  determination by,
    activation analysis, 575, 864, 1790, 1792–1800
    amperometric titration, 390
    chronopotentiometry, 422
    electrogravimetry, 457
    emission spectrometry, 1780–2
    isotope dilution, 561
    polarography, 864, 1802
    potentiometric titration, 1237
    ultraviolet spectrometry, 32
    x-ray fluorescence, 864
    x-ray spectrometry, 1250
  determination of,
    in biological materials, 575
    in ferrous materials, 864
    in foods, 1128
    in gallium, 1802
    in germanium, 1790
    in glass, 390, 1237, 1250
    in meteorites, 864
    in mineral water, 390
    in nonmetals, 575
    in pharmaceuticals, 390
    in semiconductor materials, 1780–2
    in silicon, 1792–1800
    in steel, 575

Arsenic, determination of (Cont.)
  in sulfuric acid, 1537
  in zinc, 561
Arsenite, microtest for, 221
Aryl halides, determination of, 1197
Ascorbic acid. *See also* Vitamin C.
  determination of, 35
Aspirin, determination of,
  by nuclear magnetic resonance, 1204
  in blood serum, 103
ASTM
  index of powder diffraction patterns, 203
  proceedings, methods of infrared spectrometry, 54
Atactic polymers, 1618
Atomic absorption spectrometry, 105
  accuracy of, 111
  advantages, 111
  analysis of,
    alloys, nonferrous, 913–24
    aluminum, 923
    aluminum alloys, 923
    biological materials, 1228
    bronze, 923
    cast iron, 864
    cement, 965
    copper, electrolytic, 922–3
    copper-base alloys, 916–20
    ferrous materials, 864, 865
    fertilizers, 1105, 1106, 1107
    gas oil fraction of crude petroleum, 1511
    glass, 1213–28
    gun metal, 923
    light oil, 1511
    nickel, 920–3
    nickel alloys, 920–3
    petroleum and petroleum products, 1507–17
    slags, 864
    soil, 1228, 1876
    steel, 864
    steels, low alloy, 864
    white metal, 923
    zirconium alloys, 923
    zirconium-base alloys, 916–20
  applications, 108
  applications of, in analysis of nonferrous alloys, table of, 914
  detection limits of elements, 1514
  determination of,
    aluminum, 864
    cadmium, 923
    calcium, 1107, 1228, 1876
    chromium, 864
    cobalt, 864, 1106
    copper, 864, 923, 1105, 1511
    iron, 1106, 1511
    lead, 864, 923
    magnesium, 864, 920–3, 1107, 1228, 1876
    manganese, 1106
    metals, sensitivities of, table, 109, 110
    molybdenum, 1106
    nickel, 1511
    potassium, 1228, 1876
    sodium, 1228, 1876

Atomic absorbtion spectrometry, determination of (Cont.)
    strontium, 1228
    zinc, 865, 916–20, 922–3, 1106
  elements determined by, in glass, table, 1216–7
  instrumentation, 106, 1214, 1508–10
    detectors, 108
    double-beam operation, 108
    flame, 107
    light sources, 107
    monochromators, 108
    single-beam operation, 108
  interferences, 110, 1513–14
  principles, 105
  procedure, 112
  quantitative analysis by, 1510
  sample preparation, 112
  sensitivities of various elements, table of, 915
  sensitivity, 111
  limitations of, 108, 111
  precision, 111
Atomic susceptibility, 585
  additivity of, 587
  constants, table of, 589
ATR. *See* Attenuated total reflectance.
Attenuated total reflectance, 1283
  analysis of plastics, 1626–30
  in infrared spectrometry, 1164
  instrumentation for, 1627
    reflective crystals, 1627, 1629
  theory of, 1626
Autoanalyzer, 1159, 1863
  analysis of fertilizers, 1103
  in clinical medicine, 975–8

Bacterial examination,
  of paper, 1437–40
  of process water, 1458–60
  of slush pulp, 1458–60
Barbiturates,
  determination of,
    by amperometric titration, 399
    by ultraviolet spectrometry, 35
    in serum, 1039
  identification of, 233, 234
  microtest for, 233
Barium. *See also* Alkaline earth metals.
  determination by,
    amperometric titration, 390
    atomic absorption spectrometry, 110, 1516, 1517
    emission spectrometry, 900–5
    flame spectrometry, 135, 967–8, 1295
    isotope dilution, 561
    polarography, 1235
    potentiometric titration, 293
    x-ray spectrometry, 1250, 1543
  determination of,
    in cement, 967–8
    in glass, 1235, 1250, 1295
    in lubricating oils, 135, 1543
    in magnesium alloys, 900–5
    in ores, 390
    in petroleum and petroleum products, 110

Barium, determination of (Cont.)
   in phosphors, 561
   in worn lube oils, 1516, 1517
Barium chloride, reagent for sulfate, 220
Barium, radioactive, determination of, 1912
Barlow's method for estrogens, 1033–6
Bases,
   conductometric titration of, 309–17
   organic, determination of, 399
Basis weight of paper, 1398–1400
Bausch and Lomb Opacimeter, 1415
Bauxite, analysis of, for water, 1939
Beater method for laboratory processing of pulp, 1332–7
Becke line in chemical microscopy, 224
Beckman DU Spectrophotometer, 25, 26
Beer's law, 5–6
Bendix polarimeter, photoelectric, 263
Bendix spectropolarimeter, Model 460 C, 271
Benzaldehyde, determination of, 35
Benzene,
   analysis of, for carbon disulfide, 1190
   determination of,
      by Raman spectrometry, 77
      in poly(methyl vinyl ether-maleic anhydride), 1186
Benzene, substituted, determination of, 77
Benzenehexachloride. See BHC pesticide.
Benzoic acid, determination of,
   by ultraviolet spectrometry, 35
   in alkyd resins, 1274–6
   in cement, 963–5
   in foods, 1111
Benzoin, fluorometric reagent, 99
Benzophenone, determination of, 103
Beryllium,
   determination by,
      activation analysis, 575
      amperometric titration, 391
      emission spectrometry, 900–5, 1772–5, 1778–80, 1780–2
      fluorometric analysis, 101
      ultraviolet spectrometry, 32
   determination of,
      in electrolytes, 391
      in magnesium alloys, 900–5
      in ores and minerals, 575
      in semiconductor materials, 1772–5, 1778–80, 1780–2
      in silicates, 101
   fluorometric reagents for, 98, 99, 101
Beryllium chelates, fluorescent, 98, 99
Beryllium metal, analysis of, 576, 951
B.E.T. method of measuring surface area, 830
Beta particle, 542
Beta-particle emission, 542
BHA. See Antioxidants and Butylated hydroxyanisole.
BHC pesticide, 1464
   determination of, in water, 1924–5
BHT. See Antioxidants and Butylated hydroxytoluene.
Biacetyl, Raman spectra of, 66
Biamperometric end point titrations, 378

Bilirubin, determination of, 987–90
Biodegradability of surfactants, 1819–21
Biological fluids. See also Urine, Blood, Blood serum, and Plasma.
   analysis by,
      coulometric titration, 1019–23
      flame spectrometry, 134
   analysis for,
      calcium, 990–2
      chloride, 994–6, 1019–23
      glucose, 978–81
      inorganic phosphate, 1003–5
      potassium, 134
      sodium, 134
      uric acid, 1015–9
Biological materials. See also Blood, Blood serum, Plasma, Tissue, and Feces.
   analysis by,
      activation analysis, 575–7
      atomic absorption spectrometry, 1228
      electrophoresis, 709
      flame spectrometry, 133, 134, 1009–11
      isotope dilution, 561
      radiometric methods, 556
   analysis for,
      arsenic, 575
      bismuth, 556
      cadmium, 575
      calcium, 134, 575
      cesium, 575
      chloride, 561
      chlorine, 575
      copper, 575
      gold, 575
      iodine, 576
      lead, 556
      manganese, 576
      mercury, 576
      oxygen, 576
      phosphorus, 556, 576
      potassium, 1009–11
      sodium, 576, 1009–11
      strontium, 577, 1228
      uranium, 577
   fractionation by electrophoresis, 709
Bismuth,
   determination by,
      activation analysis, 575, 1792–1800
      amperometric titration, 391
      atomic absorption spectrometry, 110
      electrogravimetry, 453, 457
      emission spectrometry, 864, 1772–5, 1778–80, 1780–2, 1873
      polarography, 864, 943, 944, 1800, 1801, 1802–7
      potentiometric titration, 293
      ultraviolet spectrometry, 32
   determination of,
      in aluminum-copper-zinc alloys, 943
      in biological materials, 556
      in cadmium, 944
      in ferrous materials, 864
      in gallium arsenide, 1801, 1802–7
      in germanium, 1802–7
      in indium, 1800, 1801, 1802–7
      in indium antimonide, 1802–7

Bismuth, determination of (Cont.)
   in indium arsenide, 1802–7
   in lead, 391
   in lead bullion, 453
   in nonferrous metals, 110
   in semiconductor metals, 1772–5, 1778–
     80, 1780–2
   in silicon, 1792–1800, 1802–7
   in soil, 1873
   in steel, 575
Black copper, analysis of, for silver, 390
Blood. *See also* Biological fluids.
   analysis by,
     activation analysis, 575–7
     analysis, fluorometric 1036–7
     gas chromatography, 1043, 1045–6
     isotope dilution, 561
   analysis for,
     antimony, 575
     carbon, 561
     carbon dioxide, 1043
     chromium, 561
     cobalt, 561
     hemoglobin, 1003
     iodine, 561
     iron, 576
     magnesium, 576
     oxygen, 1043
     potassium, 576
     pregnanediol, 1045–6
     serotonin, 1036–7
     zinc, 577
Blood serum. *See also* Biological fluids.
   analysis by,
     atomic absorption spectrometry, 109, 114
     phosphorimetry, 103
   analysis for,
     aspirin, 103
     cadmium, 109
     calcium, 109, 114
     copper, 109
     iron, 109
     lead, 109
     magnesium, 109
     mercury, 109
     nickel, 109
     potassium, 109
     sodium, 109
     zinc, 109
Bohr magneton, 583, 616
Bohr magneton numbers, table of, 592
Boiler cap in emission spectrometry, 1771,
    1777
Boiler deposits, analysis of, 110
Boric acid, determination of, 1111
Boron,
   determination by,
     activation analysis, 575, 1791
     amperometric titration, 390
     colorimetry, 1866
     emission spectrometry, 900–5, 1772–5,
      1778–80, 1780–2
     flame spectrometry, 132, 135, 136
     ultraviolet spectrometry, 32
   determination of,
     in glass, 132

Boron, determination of (Cont.)
   in lubricating oils, 135
   in magnesium alloys, 900–5
   in minerals, 575
   in nickel-plating baths, 136
   in semiconductor materials, 1772–5,
     1778–80, 1780–2
   in silicon, 1791
   in soil, 1866
   in steel, 575
   reagents, fluorometric, 99
Boron chelates, fluorescent, 99
Brass. *See also* Bronze.
   analysis for,
     copper, 400, 879–80
     lead, 440, 946
     nickel, 946
     tin, 440
     zinc, 946, 948
Brass-plating salts, analysis of, 395
Bremsstrahlung, 1535
Brice-Phoenix photometer, 280
Brightness of paper, 1440–6
Bromide,
   determination by,
     amperometric titration, 391
     coulometric analysis, 491
     electrogravimetry, 458
     radiometric titration, 559
     radioreagent method, 553
   microtest for, 218
Bromine, determination by,
   activation analysis, 575, 1537
   ultraviolet spectrometry, 32
   x-ray spectrometry, 181, 1541
4-Bromoisoquinoline, reagent for platinum,
    217
Bronze. *See also* Brass.
   analysis for,
     aluminum, 390, 943
     copper, 440, 879–80
     lead, 395, 440, 923, 946
     nickel, 946
     tin, 440
     zinc, 923, 946
Bulking thickness of paper, 1419–21
Buna N, identification of, 1668, 1672
Bursting strength of paper, 1392–5
Butadiene, determination of, 35
Butadiene-isoprene copolymers, structural
    characteristics of, 1648
Butane-butylene mixtures, analysis of, 1211
1,4-Butanediol, determination of, 1323–4
Butane gas, analysis of, for water, 1945
2-Butene-1,4-diol, analysis of, for 2-butyne-
    1,4-diol, 1168
Butter fat, analysis of, for butyric acid,
    1087–9
Butyl rubber, identification of, 1668, 1670,
    1671
Butylated hydroxyanisole, determination of,
    1117–9
Butylated hydroxytoluene, determination
    of, 1117–9
p-tert.-butylbenzoic acid, determination of,
    1278

2-Butyne-1,4-diol, determination of, in 2-
  butene-1,4-diol, 1168
Butyrate, microtest for, 221
Butyric acid, determination of, 1087–9

"C" stain, in paper analysis, 1380–1, 1386
Cadmium,
  determination by,
    activation analysis, 575
    amperometric titration, 391
    atomic absorption spectrometry, 109,
      110, 923, 1513
    chronopotentiometry, 422, 423
    coulogravimetry, 491
    electrogravimetry, 456
    emission spectrometry, 1772–5, 1778–
      80, 1780–2, 1783
    polarography, 864, 944, 1234, 1800,
      1801, 1802–7, 1902–7
    potentiometric titration, 293
    radiometric titration, 559
    ultraviolet spectrometry, 32
  determination of,
    in aluminum, 944
    in biological materials, 575
    in blood serum, 109
    in electroplating solution, 110
    in gallium arsenide, 1801, 1802–7
    in germanium, 1802–7
    in glass, 1234
    in gold, 1800
    in indium, 1800, 1801, 1802–7
    in indium antimonide, 1802–7
    in indium arsenide, 1802–7
    in nonferrous metals, 110
    in semiconductor materials, 1772–5,
      1778–80, 1780–2
    in silicon, 1802–7
    in soil, 1873
    in stainless steel, 864
    in tissue, 109
    in urine, 109
    in water, 1902–7
    in zinc, 844
    in zirconium alloys, 923
  microtest for, 214
Cadmium metal, analysis of, 397, 944
Caffeine, determination by,
  nuclear magnetic resonance, 1204
  ultraviolet spectrometry, 35
Calcium. See also Alkaline earth metals.
  determination by,
    activation analysis, 575
    amperometric titration, 391
    atomic absorption spectrometry, 109,
      110, 114, 135, 1107, 1228, 1513, 1516,
      1517, 1876
    emission spectrometry, 900–5, 1772–5,
      1873
    flame spectrometry, 133, 134, 135, 864,
      967–8, 1295, 1296, 1875, 1879
    ion exchange, 1880
    isotope dilution, 561
    polarography, 864
    potentiometric titration, 293, 973
    radiometric titration, 559

Calcium, determination by (Cont.)
  ultraviolet spectrometry, 32
  x-ray spectrometry, 969–73, 1251, 1543
  determination of,
    in biological fluids, 990–2
    in biological materials, 134, 575
    in blood serum, 109, 114
    in boiler deposits, 110
    in cement, 867–8, 969–73
    in coal ash, 110
    in ferrous materials, 864
    in fertilizers, 109, 133, 1107
    in flour, 1110
    in glass, 1251, 1295
    in lubricating oils, 1516, 1517, 1543
    in magnesium alloys, 900–5
    in paint driers, 1296
    in petroleum and petroleum products,
      110, 135
    in phosphors, 561
    in phosphorus, 135
    in plant materials, 109
    in semiconductor materials, 1772–5
    in slags, 864
    in soils, 109, 561, 1228, 1873, 1875, 1876,
      1879, 1880
    in steel, 575
    in tissue, 109
    in urine, 109
Calcium disodium EDTA, determination
  of, in foods, 1119–20
Calcium pantothenate, determination of,
  265
Calomel electrode, 358
  for pH measurements, 527
Calorimeter, for thermal analysis, 648
Camphor, determination of, 241
Capillary for dropping mercury electrode,
  354
  calibration of, 356
Captan, 1479, 1484
Carbohydrates, analysis of, 760
Carbon,
  determination by,
    activation analysis, 575
    conductometry, 864
    emission spectrometry, 864
    high temperature oxidation, 864
    infrared spectrometry, 864
    isotope dilution, 561
    radiometric method, 556
  determination of,
    in blood, 561
    in ferrous materials, 864
    in metals, 575
    in nonferrous metals, 950
    in soil, 1879
    in steel, 556, 575
Carbon black, determination of, in rubber,
  1695, 1731–3
Carbon dioxide, determination of,
  in blood, 1043
  in plasma, 992–4
  in serum, 992–4
Carbon disulfide, determination of, in benzene, 1190

Carbon monoxide, determination of, in air, 850
Carbon steel, analysis of, for copper, 453
Carbonate, determination of, in soil, 1880
Carbonyl compounds,
analysis of, by gas chromatography, 1194
infrared absorption of, 1171
Carbonyl group, determination of,
by amperometric titration, 399
by ultraviolet spectrometry, 1187
in polyethylene, 1613
Carboxyl group, determination of, in cellulose, 555
Carboxylic acids. *See also* Fatty acids.
determination by,
gas chromatography, 1194
infrared spectrometry, 1171–2
ultraviolet spectrometry, 1187
Carboxymethyl cellulose, determination of, in synthetic detergents, 1815
Carburated water gas, analysis of, 1524
Carotenoids, analysis of, 754, 761
Cary Model 60 Spectropolarimeter, 270
Cast iron. *See also* Iron, Steel, Iron and Steel, *and* Ferrous materials.
analysis for,
chromium, 864
lithium, 135
magnesium, 864
silicon, 865
sodium, 135
Castor oil, blown, absorptivity value, 1289
Castor oil, dehydrated,
absorptivity value, 1289
analysis for,
conjugated dienoic acid, 1071
diene value, 1277
Castor oil, fatty acid composition of, 1322
Catalysts. *See special catalysts, such as* Cracking *and* Reforming *catalysts, and also* Metallurgical products.
Catalytic currents, 335, 336
Catecholamines, determination of, 1032–3
Cathode layer excitation, 155
Cathode ray polarography, 348
Cathodic chronopotentiometric analysis, 423
Cathodic stripping coulometry, 489
Cations, microtests for, 213
CD. *See* Circular dichroism.
Cells,
for amperostatic coulometry, 477
for conductometric titrations, 308
for electrolysis, 431
for polarography,
controlled potential, 358
single-compartment, 356
three-electrode, 358
two-compartment, 357
for potentiostatic coulometry, 463
Cellulose, analysis of, for carboxyl group, 555
Cellulose acetate, characterization of, 1317
Cellulose butyrate, characterization of, 1317
Cellulose nitrate, determination of, 1271, 1289–92

Cement, 962
analysis by,
atomic absorption spectrometry, 965
differential thermal analysis, 974
emission spectrometry, 968–9
flame spectrometry, 132, 133, 137, 965–7, 967–8
infrared spectrometry, 963–5, 965–7
potentiometric titration, 973
x-ray spectrometry, 969–73
analysis for,
abietic acid derivatives, 963–5
aluminum, 967–8, 969–73
barium, 967–8
benzoic acid, 963–5
calcium, 967–8, 969–73, 973
chloride, 973
dodecyl benzene sodium sulfonate, 963–5
hydroxylamine-sulfonated hydrocarbon, 963–5
iron, 967–8, 969–73
lignosulfonates, 963–5
lithium, 967–8
magnesium, 133, 965–7, 969–73, 973
manganese, 137, 965–7, 969–73
oleic acid, 963–5
polyvinyl acetate, 963–5
potassium, 132, 137, 965–7, 969–73
silicon, 969–73
sodium, 132, 137, 965–7
stearic acid, 963–5
strontium, 133, 967–8
sulfur, 969–73
water, 1941
Centrifuge, Kaye disc, 819
Slater and Cohen disc, 819
Cereals, analysis for, 1108
butylated hydroxyanisole, 1117–9
butylated hydroxytoluene, 1117–9
starch, 1109
sugars, 1109
water, 1939
Cerium, determination by,
amperometric titration, 392
chronopotentiometry, 422
emission spectrometry, 451
isotope dilution, 561
potentiometric titration, 294
ultraviolet spectrometry, 32
Cesium, determination by,
activation analysis, 575
flame spectrometry, 132, 1219–26, 1227
Charged-particle activation analysis, 1531
Charging current, 469
Chelates, fluorescent, 98
Chemical contact printing, 500
Chemical microscopy, 212
analysis of,
antipyrine-pyramidon mixtures, 239
DDT-gammexane mixtures, 238
proponal-sandoptal mixtures, 239
detection of,
anions, 217
cations, 213

Chemical microscopy, detection of (Cont.)
  organic compounds, 222
  determination of,
    camphor in camphorated oil, 241
    critical solution temperature, 240
    eutectic temperatures, 224
    hydrogen peroxide, 242
    melting points, 224
    refractive index of fused compounds, 224
    water in glacial acetic acid, 242
  identification of,
    alcohols, 224, 225
    alkaloids, 235
    amides, 227
    amines, aliphatic, 225
    amines, aromatic, 227
    barbiturates, 233
    sugars, 230
  qualitative analysis, 212
  quantitative analysis, 238
Chlorate, microtest for, 219
Chlorbenside, 1464, 1479, 1484
Chlordane, 1464, 1479, 1484, 1485, 1493
Chloride, determination by,
  amperometric titration, 392
  amperostatic coulometry, 487
  coulogravimetry, 491
  coulometric titration, 487–8, 1019–23
  electrogravimetry, 458
  isotope dilution, 561
  potentiometric titration, 973, 1894–5
  radiometric titration, 559
  ultraviolet spectrometry, 32
  visible spectrometry, 994–6
Chloride, microtest for, 217
Chlorinated hydrocarbon pesticides, determination of, 1926
Chlorinated insecticides, determination of, 1141-4
Chlorinated organic pesticides. See Pesticides, Chlorinated.
Chlorine,
  determination by,
    activation analysis, 575, 1537
    ultraviolet spectrometry, 32
    x-ray spectrometry, 1251, 1541
  determination of,
    in biological materials, 575
    in glass, 1251
    in petroleum hydrocarbons, 1541
    in polymers, 1537
    in reforming catalysts, 1537
Chlorine, active, determination of, in water, 392
Chlorine, liquid, analysis of, for water, 1936
Chloroform, determination of, 35
Chlorophenoxy acid esters, 1469–72
Chlorophenoxy acids, 1469–72
Chlorophyll, determination of, 1065
Chloroplatinic acid reagent, microtests, 213–4
Chlorothion, 1478, 1485
Cholesterol, total, determination of, in serum, 997–1000
Chromatography,
  column, see Elution chromatography

Chromatography (Cont.)
  determination of,
    accelerators in rubber, 1695
    antioxidants in rubber, 1695
    processing oils in rubber, 1695
    rubber extenders, 1695
  elution, see Elution chromatography
  gas, see Gas chromatography
  gas-liquid, see Gas chromatography
  gas-permeation, see Gel-permeation chromatography
  gas-solid, see Gas chromatography
  identification of,
    dithiocarbamate accelerators, 1696–9
    rubber accelerators, 1695–9, 1701–6
    rubber antioxidants, 1695
  paper, see Paper chromatography
  partition-thin-layer, see Partition-thin-layer chromatography
  principles of, 739
  pyrolysis-gas, see Pyrolysis-gas chromatography
  techniques of, 739
  thin-layer, see Thin-layer chromatography
Chromite minerals, analysis for iron, 393
Chromium,
  determination by,
    activation analysis, 575, 864
    atomic absorption spectrometry, 110, 115, 864, 1516, 1517
    chromopotentiometry, 422
    emission spectrometry, 1772–5, 1778–80, 1780–2, 1873
    isotope dilution, 561
    polarography, 864, 940–3
    potentiometric titration, 294
    radiometric method, 556
    x-ray spectrometry, 864, 1252
  determination of,
    in alloy steels, 864
    in blood, 561
    in cast iron, 864
    in feces, 556
    in gallium arsenide, 575
    in glass, 1252
    in iron and steel, 110
    in low alloy steels, 864
    in metals, 575
    in nonferrous metals, 110
    in petroleum and petroleum products, 110
    in rocks, 575
    in semiconductor materials, 1772–5, 1778–80, 1780–2
    in soil, 1873
    in steel, 115, 575, 864
    in titanium alloy, 940–3
    in worn lube oils, 1516, 1517
Chromophoric groups in ultraviolet spectrometry, 31
  table of, 31
Chronopotentiograms, 404, 417
Chronopotentiometric analysis,
  anodic, 423, 425
  cathodic, 423

Chronopotentiometric wave,
  equation for, 407
  irreversible, 408
Chronopotentiometry, 404
  analysis of,
    amalgams, 423
    liquid alloys, 423
    mixtures, 425
    molten salts, 422
  applications of, 422
  concentration limits, 421
  determination of,
    arsenic, 422
    cadmium, 422, 423
    cerium, 422
    chromium, 422
    electrode reactions, 426
    end points in EDTA titrations, 426
    ferricyanide, 422
    ferrocyanide, 422
    gallium, 422
    hydrazine, 425
    hydroxylamine, 425
    iodide, 422
    iron, 422
    lead, 422, 423
    organic compounds, 422
    permanganate, 422
    thallium, 422, 423
    thickness of oxide and tarnish films on
      metals, 424
    uranium, 422
    zinc, 422
  instrumentation for, 410
    cells, 414
    constant current source, 416
    electrodes, auxiliary, 413
    electrodes, reference, 413
    electrodes, working, 410
  principle of, 404
  theory of, 406
    chronopotentiometric wave, 407, 408
    current-reversal, 409
    quarter-wave potential, 407
    Sand equation, 406, 409
    transition potential, 419
    transition time, 406, 417, 420
Circular dichroism, 258, 275
Cis-1,4-content, determination of, in rub-
  ber, 1599
Cis-trans-isomers, separation of, 757
Citrus fruits, analysis of, for coumarone-
  indene resins, 1120
Clerget constant, 267
Cloud point, of detergents, determination
  of, 1839
Coagulation timer, 1013
Coal ash, analysis of, 110
Coal tar products, analysis of, 736
Coatings, determination of pores in, 512, 518
Coatings on metals, determination of, 489
Cobalamines, determination of, 564
Cobalt,
  determination by,
    activation analysis, 575, 864, 1792
    amperometric titration, 392, 864

Cobalt, determination by (Cont.)
  atomic absorption spectrometry, 110,
    864, 1106
  electrogravimetry, 435, 454, 455
  emission spectrometry, 1772–5, 1778–
    80, 1780–2
  flame spectrometry, 1296
  isotope dilution, 561, 864
  paper chromatography, 1879
  polarography, 864, 937–43
  potentiometric titration, 293
  radiometric titration, 559
  ultraviolet spectrometry, 32
  visible spectrometry, 1866–8
  x-ray spectrometry, 1252, 1541
  determination of,
    in alloys, 392
    in aluminum alloys, 937–43
    in blood, 561
    in ferrous materials, 864
    in fertilizers, 1106
    in glass, 1252
    in iron and steel, 110
    in metals, 575
    in nonferrous metals, 110
    in ores and concentrates, 110
    in organic matrices, 1541
    in paint driers, 1296
    in semiconductors, 1772–5, 1778–80,
      1780–2
    in silicon, 1792–1800
    in soil, 1866–8, 1873, 1879
    in steel, 575
    in titanium alloy, 940–3
  microtest for, 215
Cobalt mattes, analysis of, for iron, 136
Cobalt metal, analysis of, for nickel, 946
Cobb test, 1427
Coblentz Society, methods of infrared spectrometry, 54
Cockcroft-Walton accelerators, 1535
Coconut oil,
  absorptivity value, 1289
  fatty acid composition of, 1322
Collective magnetism, 586
Color, determination of,
  in detergents, 1861–3
  in natural fat, 1064
  in paper, 1429–32
  in pulp, 1348–51
  in water, 1883–90
Color additives in foods, 1113
  identification of, 1113–4
Color filters, table of, 9
Column chromatography. See Elution chro-
  matography.
Complexometric titrations,
  conductometric, 318
  potentiometric, 293
Concentration overpotential, 432
Concrete. See Cement.
Concrete mix, analysis of, for water, 1946
Conductance. See also Conductometry.
  definition of, 297
  relation to solution composition, 298
Conductivity. See Conductometry.

Conductometric titrations, 297
  alternating current methods, 301
  applications, 319
    table of, 320–1
  automatic, 305
  determination of alkalinity, 305
  direct current methods, 303
    constant current measurements, 303
    high applied voltage measurements, 303
  instrumentation, 299, 306
    burets, 309
    cells, 308
    commercial instruments, table of, 306
    direct-reading instruments, 301
    electrodes, 307
    temperature control, 309
    Wheatstone bridge, 302
  magnetic induction methods, 304
  technique, 307
  titration curves, 309
    complexometric, 318
    mixture of acids, 315
    nonaqueous acid-base, 317
    oxidation-reduction, 318
    polybasic acids, 315
    precipitation, 317
    replacement, 317
    strong acid-strong base, 309
    weak acid-strong base, 311
    weak acid-weak base, 315
    weak base-strong acid, 313
  types of,
    complexometric, 318
    mixtures of acids, 315
    nonaqueous acid-base, 317
    oxidation-reduction, 318
    polybasic acids, 315
    precipitation, 317
    replacement, 317
    strong acid-strong base, 309
    weak acid-strong base, 311
    weak acid-weak base, 315
    weak base-strong acid, 313
Conductometry,
  analysis of,
    air pollutants, 847
    ferrous materials, 864
    latex, 1756
    natural fats, 1080
    rubber, 1695
    semiconductors, 1767
  determination of,
    accelerators in rubber, 1695
    carbon in ferrous materials, 864
    soap in latex, 1756
    water, 1946–9
Configuration, determination of, 285
Conformational analysis, 273
Conjugate solutions, 669
Conjugated dienoic acid, determination of,
    in dehydrated castor oil, 1071
Conjugated polyunsaturated fatty acids.
    See Polyunsaturated fatty acids.
Consolute temperature, 669
Constant current electrolysis, 433
Continuous faradaic current, 469

Contrast gloss of paper, 1411
Controlled electrode, 463
Controlled potential electrolysis, 436
Copper,
  determination by,
    activation analysis, 575, 864, 1790,
      1792–80
    amperometric titration, 392
    atomic absorption spectrometry, 109,
      110, 116, 864, 923, 1105, 1511, 1513,
      1516, 1517
    electrogravimetry, 434, 440, 443, 453,
      455
    emission spectrometry, 1074, 1772–5,
      1778–80, 1780–2, 1873
    flame spectrometry, 136, 137, 875–9,
      879–80
    isotope dilution, 561
    paper chromatography, 1879
    polarography, 864, 940–3, 944, 945,
      1800, 1801, 1802–7, 1876, 1902–7
    potentiometric titration, 293
    radiometric titration, 32, 559
    visible spectrometry, 1056, 1129, 1816–
      7, 1866–7
    x-ray spectrometry, 908, 1252
  determination of,
    in aluminum alloys, 136, 923
    in aluminum-base alloys, 137, 875–9
    in antimony alloys, 944
    in arsenic, 1800–1802
    in biological materials, 575
    in blood serum, 109
    in brass, 440, 879–80
    in bronze, 440, 879–80
    in carbon steel, 453
    in copper alloys, 944
    in copper-nickel alloys, 879–80
    in crude oil, 1516, 1517
    in dairy products, 109
    in diamonds, 575
    in electroplating solution, 110
    in fats and oils, 1056, 1074
    in ferrous alloys, 136
    in ferrous materials, 864
    in fertilizers, 109, 1105
    in foods, 1129
    in gallium arsenide, 575, 1801, 1802–7
    in gas oil fraction of crude petroleum,
      1511
    in germanium, 1790, 1801, 1802–7
    in glass, 1252
    in gold, 1800
    in indium, 1800, 1801, 1802–7
    in indium antimonide, 1802–7
    in indium arsenide, 1801, 1802–7
    in lead alloys, 944
    in lead bullion, 453
    in lubricating oil, 116
    in magnesium, 945
    in manganese bronze, 879–80
    in metals, 575
    in minerals, 575
    in nickel bronzes, 443
    in nonferrous alloys, 136
    in ores and concentrates, 110, 392

Copper, determination of (Cont.)
in petroleum products, 110, 1516, 1517
in plant materials, 109
in rocks, 110, 575
in selenium, 575
in semiconductor materials, 1772–5, 1778–80, 1780–2
in silicon, 575, 1792–1800, 1802–7
in silicon carbide, 1800
in soap, 1816–7
in soils, 109, 1866–7, 1873, 1876, 1879
in steel, 864
in tin alloys, 944
in tin-base alloys, 875–9
in tissue, 109
in titanium alloys, 940–3
in uranium, 908
in urine, 109
in water, 1902–7
in white metal, 923
in wines, 109
in worn lube oils, 1516, 1517
in zinc-base alloys, 137, 875–9
diffusion in titanium, determination of, 911
microtest for, 214, 215
Copper alloys, analysis of, 391, 944
Copper-base alloys, analysis of,
by emission spectrometry, 884–9
for hydrogen, 951
for oxygen, 951
for zinc, 916–20
Copper, electrolytic, analysis of, for zinc, 922–3
Copper metal, analysis of, 951
Co-Ral pesticide, 1480, 1485, 1486, 1492, 1497, 1499
Cord, analysis of, 1263
Corticosteroids, determination of, 1032
Corticosterone, determination of, 564
Cosmetics, analysis of, by gas chromatography, 735
Cotton,
analysis of, for water, 1939
characterization of, 1317
Cotton effect, 259, 272, 274, 275
Cottonseed oil,
absorptivity value, 1289
fatty acid composition of, 1322
Coulograms, 467, 473
Coulogravimetry, determination of,
bromide, 491
cadmium, 491
chloride, 491
lead, 491
thallium, 491
zinc, 491
Coulomb's law, 583
Coulometric internal electrolysis, 490, 849
Coulometric methods, 459. See also Coulometric titrations and Coulometry at controlled potential.
characteristics of, 460
at controlled current, 460
at controlled potential, 459
coulometric internal electrolysis, 490, 848

Coulometric methods (Cont.)
definition of, 459
determination of,
coatings, 489
dinitrophenol, 491
films on metals, 489
ozone in air, 848–50
picric acid, 491
water, 1950, 1951
stripping coulometry, 489
techniques of, 459
voltage-scanning coulometry, 490
Coulometric titrations, 460, 474
accuracy of, 486
applications of, 488
determination of chloride, 487–8, 1019–23
end point detection,
amperometry, 482
conductometry, 483
optical methods, 480
potentiometry, 481
experimental conditions, 484
instrumentation for, 477
precision of, 486
principles of, 474
sensitivity of, 486
titrant, generation of, 484
Coulometry at controlled current. See Coulometric titration.
Coulometry at controlled potential, 459, 461. See also Coulometric methods.
accuracy, 471
applications of,
analytical, 473
formal potential, determination of, 473
n-values, determination of, 473
reaction kinetics, 473
reaction mechanisms, 473
background current, 469
charging current, 469
continuous faradaic current, 469
impurity, faradaic current, 469
induced background current, 470
kinetic background current, 470
current efficiency, 469
determination of,
ozone in air, 849
uranium, 471
experimental conditions, 467
instrumentation for, 463
precision of, 471
principles of, 461
sensitivity of, 471
Coulter counter, 825
Coumarins, analysis of, 763
Coumarone-indene resins, determination of, in citrus fruits, 1120
Counter electrode, 463
Cracking catalysts,
analysis by,
activation analysis, 1537
x-ray emission spectrometry, 1543
analysis for,
aluminum, 1537
iron, 1543
magnesium, 1537

Cracking catalysts, analysis for (Cont.)
nickel, 1543
vanadium, 1543
Creatinine, determination of, 1000–2
Critical solution temperatures, 669
analysis of,
camphorated oil, 241
fats and oils, 683
liquid mixtures, 682
petroleum products, 683
solutions, 682
applications of, 672
characterization of,
acrylic compounds, 679
cyclic compounds, 680
essential oils, 684
fats, 671
hydrocarbons, 671
positional isomers, 680
unsaturated compounds, 680
determination of, 240, 675–9
equipment for, 675–7
experimental techniques,
aniline point, 674
solubility studies, 673
factors affecting, 672
lower critical temperature, 670
micromethod, 679
standards used, 678
requirements for, 678
tables of,
for aliphatic compounds, 680
for cholesteryl esters, 682
for cyclic compounds, 682
for esters, 681
for standard substances, 678
upper critical solution temperature, 669
Crude oil. See Petroleum and petroleum
products.
Cryoscopy, 1134–6, 1136–7
Cryptogenin, determination of, 272
Crystalline melting point of polymers, de-
determination of, 1593
Crystalline polymers, 1617
Crystallinity of polymers. See Polymers, crystallinity of.
Crystals,
anisotropic, 223
dichroic, 223
isotropic, 223
pleochroic, 223
CST. See Critical solution temperatures.
Curie, 544
Curie law, 586
Curie point, 588
Curie-Weiss law, 586
Current-reversal chronopotentiometry, 409
Curtain electrophoresis, 694
Cyanide, determination of, 553, 559
microtest for, 219
Cyanide liquors, analysis of, for gold, 110
Cyanides, organic. See Nitriles.
2-Cyanopyridine, reagent for palladium, 216
Cyclic compounds, characterization of, 680
Cyclic potentiometry, 427
Cycloalkanes, characterization of, 1546

Cycloparaffins. See Cycloalkanes.

2,4-D herbicide, 1469–72, 1501
Dairy products, analysis of, for copper, 109
Darex. See Hydroxylamine-sulfonated hy-
drocarbon.
2,4-DB herbicide, 1470, 1501
DDD pesticide, 1464, 1479, 1484, 1493, 1496
DDE pesticide, 1464, 1479, 1484, 1493, 1496
DDT-Gammexane mixtures, analysis of, 238
DDT pesticide, 1464, 1479, 1483, 1485, 1493,
1496, 1500
determination of, 559, 1924–5
Dead-stop end point titration, 378, 483
de Broglie equation, 244
Debye-Scheerer x-ray diffraction camera,
199
Decay constant, radioactivity, 543
Degree of crystallinity, of polymers, 1644
Degree of curl of paper, 1454–6
Degree of sizing of paper, 1454–6
Dehydrosulfurization catalysts, analysis of,
for tungsten, 1537
Delnav, 1497, 1499
Densitometry in emission spectrometry, 159
Derivative d. c. polarography, 343
Detectors,
atomic absorption spectrometry, 108
flame emission spectrometry, 121
infrared spectrometry, 41
Raman spectrometry, 74
ultraviolet spectrometry, 28
x-ray emission and absorption, 176
Detergents,
analysis by,
flame spectrometry, 1837
gas chromatography, 1857–60, 1860–1
infrared spectrometry, 1829, 1831
ion exchange, 1845, 1846–54
mass spectrometry, 1844
potentiometric titration, 1840
radiochemical method, 553
thin-layer chromatography, 757, 760
turbidimetry, 1839
ultraviolet spectrometry, 1821–3, 1823–
5, 1825–6, 1826–8
visible spectrometry, 1815, 1817–9
x-ray diffraction, 1838–9
analysis for,
alkyl benzene sulfonic acid, sodium
salt, 1821–3
cloud point, 1839
color, 1861–3
fatty acids, 1857–60
germicides, 1826–8
insoluble materials, 1838–9
iron, 1817–9
nonionics, 1828, 1845
phosphates, 1846–54
phosphorus, 553, 1863–4
polyphosphates, 1846–54
potassium, 1837
sodium, 1837
sodium caboxymethylcellulose, 1815
sulfuric acid, 1840
toluene sulfonic acid, sodium salt, 1823–5

Detergents, analysis for (Cont.)
  xylene sulfonic acid, sodium salt, 1825–6
  anionic, determination of, 1819–20
  identification of, 1829–31
  infrared absorption data, 1832
  liquid, analysis for ethyl alcohol, 1860–1
  nonionic, determination of, 1828
  sampling of, 1812
  separation of, 1813–4
  sulfates, identification of, 1831
  sulfonates, identification of, 1831
Deuterium arc, in fluorometric analysis, 86
Devarda method for nitrate, 1104
Diamagnetism, 586
  Langevin's equation, 589
  Van Vleck's equation, 589
Diamines, Raman spectra of, 77
Diamonds, analysis for copper, 575
Diamperometric end point titrations, 378
Diazinon, 1492, 1497, 1503
  determination of, in water, 1924–5
Dibasic acids. See Acids, dibasic.
2,6-di-*tert*.-butyl-*p*-cresol, determination of, in polyethylene, 1616
Dibutyl sebacate, determination of, in polymer extracts, 1656
Dichograph, 275
Dichroic crystals, 223
Dichroic ratio of polymers, 1625
Dichromate. See also Chromium.
  determination of, 392
Dieldrin, 1464, 1479, 1484, 1493, 1496
  determination of, in water, 1924–5
Dielectric constant, determination of, 498
Dielectric techniques,
  determination of,
    fat content of fats, 1100
    water, 1949–50
Diene value, determination of, in castor oil, dehydrated, 1277
Diethyl malonate, NMR spectrum of, 601
Diethylene glycol, determination of, 1323–4
Differential cathode ray polarograph, 364
Differential electrolytic potentiometry, 290
Differential polarography, 345
Differential process refractometers, 251
Differential thermal analysis, 650
  analysis of,
    cement, 974
    fats, 1083
    paints, 1308
    plastics, 1637–47
    polymers, 1308
    steel, 865
  applications of, 656, 660
  characterization of,
    polyethylene blends, 1645
    polymers, 1642
    rare earth chloride hydrates, 659
  detection of, in polymers,
    chemical changes, 1639–42
    glass transition temperature, 1643
    physical changes, 1639–42
  determination of,
    degree of crystallinity of polymers, 1644

Differential thermal analysis, determination of (Cont.)
  effect of radiation on substances, 658
  effectiveness of antioxidants in polymers, 1647
  fat crystallizing characteristics, 1083
  glass transition temperatures of ethylene-propylene polymers, 1643
  heat of fusion of polymers, 1644
  hydrocarbons in petroleum, 1553
  internal structures of rubber polymers, 1667
  linear polymer content of polyethylene, 656
  moisture content of powdered substances, 656
  nonmetallic compounds in steel, 865
  organic derivative-forming reactions, 658
  thermal decomposition of polymers, 1646
  water, 1943
  factors affecting results, 655
  identification of plastics, 1642
  instrumentation, 652
  qualitative analysis, 651
  theory of, 652
Diffractometer, x-ray, 202
Diffusion current, 331, 364–7, 378
  constant, 332
  calculation of concentration from, 364
  departures from, 334
  factors affecting, 333
  measurement of, 361–7
  relationship of concentration to, 364–7
1,4-Dihydroxyanthraquinone, fluorometric reagent, 99
2,2′-Dihydroxyazobenzene, fluorometric reagent, 99
Dilatometry, determination of solid fat index, 1096–8
Dimethylanthracene, determination of, 633
Dimethylglyoxime, reagent for nickel, 215
Dinitrophenol, determination of, 491
2,4-Dinitrophenylhydrazine, reagent for sugars, 232
Diosgenin, analysis of, for cryptogenin, 272
Diphenylamine, determination of,
  by phosphorimetry, 103
  in vinyl acetate, 1280
1,1-Diphenylhydrazine, reagent for sugars, 232
Dipping refractometer. See Immersion refractometer.
Dipropylene glycol, determination of, 1323–4
Direct method of polarization, 266
Disodium EDTA, determination of, in salad dressing, 1121
Dispersion of a liquid, 252
Dissolved oxygen. See Oxygen, dissolved.
Dithiocarbamate accelerators,
  determination of, 1740–2
  identification of, 1696–9, 1699–1701
Diuron, 1478, 1483
Divinyl sulfone, determination of, 1190
DME. See Dropping mercury electrode.

Dodecylbenzene sodium sulfonate, determination of, 963–5
Dopants in semiconductors, controlled addition of, 1766
Double bond. *See* Unsaturation.
Double isotope dilution, 554
Double polarization, 266
Drainage factor for pulp, 1363–6
Drainage time for pulp, 1363–5
Driers. *See* Paint driers.
Dropping mercury electrode, 327, 384, 411
  amperometric titration, 384
  capillary for, 354
  charging current, 328
  chronopotentiometry, 411
  mercury, purification for, 355
  mercury reservoir assembly, 355
  polarographic maxima, 334
  voltage range, 328
Dropping mercury electrode polarography, 327
  rapid, 348
DTA. *See* Differential thermal analysis.
Dumas method,
  for carbon in soil, 1879
  for nitrogen in soil, 1878
Durrum-Jasco ORD-5 spectropolarimeter, 270
Dyes, analysis of, 755, 760, 761
Dyna-cath electrolysis apparatus, 445, 448–51

EC, 542
Edge tearing resistance of paper, 1456
EDTA. *See also* Disodium *and* Calcium salts.
  determination of, in foods, 1119, 1121
EDTA, titrant for metals, 293
  conductometric titrations, 318
  potentiometric titrations, 293
  radiometric titrations, 559–60
Ehrlich's reagent, 1269
Elastomers, characterization of, 1317
Electrocapillary maximum, 330
Electrode(s),
  dropping mercury, 384, 411
  for amperometric titration,
    dropping mercury electrode, 384
    rotating platinum electrode, 384
    vibrating platinum electrode, 385
  for chronopotentiometry,
    dropping mercury electrode, 411
    hanging mercury drop electrode, 411
    mercury-film electrode, 411
    mercury pool electrode, 411
    working electrode, 410
  for conductometric titrations, 307
  for coulometric titration, 476
  for electrophoresis, 693
  for emission spectrometry, 152
  for high frequency methods, 494
  for pH measurement,
    antimony electrode, 525
    glass electrode, 522, 525
    hydrogen electrode, 522, 528
    quinhydrone electrode, 524
    reference electrode, 527

Electrode(s) (Cont.)
  for potentiostatic coulometry,
    analytical electrode, 463
    auxiliary electrode, 463
    controlled electrode, 463
    counter electrode, 463
    separated electrode, 463
    working electrode, 463
  hydrogen ion responsive, 522
Electrode potentials, 428
Electrode reactions, identification of, 426
Electrodialysis, analysis of soil, 1878
Electrography, 500, 512
  applications, 518–20
    anions-corrosion films, 515
    conducting minerals, 515
    inclusions, 515
    pores and discontinuities in protective coatings, 512, 518
    printing of structural patterns, 514, 519
    transfer between metal surfaces, 515
  electrolyte used, 506
  instrumentation for, 501
  transfer medium, 503
Electrogravimetric analysis, 428
  analysis of,
    brass, 440
    bronze, 440
    iron ore, 449
    lead bullion, 453
    nickel bronze, 443
    steel, 448, 450, 453
    zinc-base alloys, 449
  applications, 454
  determination of,
    aluminum, 448, 449
    aluminum oxide, 449
    antimony, 458
    arsenic, 457
    bismuth, 453, 457
    bromide, 458
    cadmium, 456
    chloride, 458
    cobalt, 435, 455
    copper, 434, 440, 443, 453, 455
    gold, 456
    iron, 455
    lead, 440, 455, 457
    magnesium, 449
    manganese, 455
    mercury, 456
    nickel, 443, 455
    silver, 455, 456
    thallium, 457
    tin, 440, 455, 457
    vanadium, 450
    zinc, 455, 456
    zirconium, 450
  instrumentation for, 433, 436–40, 444–8, 451
    Dyna-cath electrolysis apparatus, 445
    Melaven cell, 444
  semiquantitative analysis, 519
  types of,
    anodic deposition, 454
    internal electrolysis, 451
    mercury cathode electrolysis, 444

Electrolytes, analysis of, for beryllium, 391
Electrolytic cells, 431
Electron-capture detector, 1480
Electron, configuration of neutral atoms, table of, 620
Electronic magnetic susceptibility, 584
Electron magnetic resonance, 616
Electron microscope, 246
    resolution limit, 245
Electron microscopy, 244
    applications of, 248
        polymers, 1592
        rubber, 1761
    instrumentation, 246, 247
    principles of, 244
Electron paramagnetic resonance, 616
Electron probe x-ray microanalyzer, 186
    applications, 194
        glass, 1229–32
        iron and steel, 863
        nonferrous alloys, 912
    instrumentation, 186
        electron optics, 187
        specimen chamber, 189
        x-ray optics, 189
    sample preparation, 193
Electron spin resonance, 616
    analysis by, 627
    applications, 620, 632
    catalyst contamination monitoring, 635
    continuous process analyzers, 634
    determination of,
        oxygen, 633
        polynuclear hydrocarbons, 633
        vanadium in petroleum oils, 632, 634
    hyperfine interaction, 627
    identification of free radicals, 621
    instrumentation, 619, 621–7
        spectrometers, 619, 624–7
    quantitative analysis,
        calibration, 630
        intensity measurements, 630
        sensitivity, 632
        standards, 630
Electrons, wave nature of, 244
Electron volt, 542
Electroosmosis, 701
Electrophoresis, 685. See also Microelectrophoresis.
    applications of, 709–14
    factors affecting,
        diffusion, 704
        electrolysis, 695–7
        electroosmosis, 701
        heat, 702–4
        interaction with supporting medium, 702
        ionic strength, 697–9
        pH, 699–701
    instrumentation, 685, 690–5
    particle mobility, 685–7
    separation of,
        alkali metals, 714
        alkaline earth metals, 714
        inorganic substances, 714
        isotopes, 714

Electrophoresis, separation of (Cont.)
        rare earths, 714
        serum proteins, 710
    technique used,
        on cellulose acetate, 706
        filter paper electrophoresis, 704–6
            two-dimensional, 706
        in gels, 707–9
        in powders, 709
        thin-layer electrophoresis, 709
    types of,
        curtain electrophoresis, 694
        free-solution electrophoresis, 687
            density gradient, 688
            moving boundary, 688
        high voltage electrophoresis, 690
        immunoelectrophoresis, 689
        preparative electrophoresis, 689
        zone electrophoresis, 688
Electroplating solutions. See also Special solutions.
    analysis of, 110, 390
Electrospot testing, 500
    alloys, 509
    applications, 517, 518–20
    electrolyte used, 506
    electrotransfer recognition, 508
    examination of electrospots, table, 511
    fixed reagent papers, table of, 510
    instrumentation for, 501
    separations, 509
    single metal surfaces, 508
    technique, 504
    transfer medium, 503
Electrotransfer, 500
    electrolyte used, 506
Eleostearic acid, determination of in tung oil, 1071
Elmendorf tearing-strength tester, 1403
Elution chromatography,
    analysis of,
        fats, 1085
        plastics, 1647–50
    determination of,
        butyric acid in butter fat, 1087–9
        neutral oil in crude soybean oil, 1085–7
        saturated hydrocarbons, in fats, 1089
        structural composition of rubber polymers, 1667
    fractionation of,
        hydrocarbons, 1552
        polymers, 1647
        polypropylene, 1648
        polystyrene, 1647
        silicon polymers, 1647
Emission spectrometry, 141
    analysis of,
        air pollutants, 839
        aluminum-base alloys, 884–9, 892–900
        antimony, 1772–5
        cement, 968–9
        copper-base alloys, 884–9
        fats, 1074
        ferromanganese, 865
        ferrotungsten, 865
        ferrous materials, 864–5

Emission spectrometry, analysis of (Cont.)
  gallium arsenide, 1771–5
  indium, 1772–5
  indium antimonide, 1772–5
  indium arsenide, 1772–5
  iron, 856, 864–5
  lead-tin base alloys, 884–9
  magnesium, 900–5
  magnesium alloys, 900–5
  nonferrous alloys, 884–905, 950
  paints, 1298
  semiconductors, 1770–1
  silicomanganese, 865
  soils, 864, 1872–3
  stainless steel, 451
  steel, 856, 864
  tantalum, 889–91
  tantalum oxide, 889–91
  water, 1892–4
  boiler cap technique, 1771, 1777
  determination of,
    aluminum, 864, 900–5, 1873
    antimony, 864
    barium, 900–5
    beryllium, 900–5
    bismuth, 864, 1873
    boron, 900–5
    cadmium, 1873
    calcium, 900–5, 1873
    carbon, 864
    cerium, 451
    chromium, 1873
    cobalt, 1873
    copper, 1074, 1873
    gallium, 1873
    hydrogen, 864, 950
    iron, 1074, 1873
    lanthanum, 451
    lead, 1873
    lithium, 900–5
    magnesium, 864, 1873
    metals, 839, 1874
    molybdenum, 1873
    nickel, 1873
    nitrogen, 950
    oxygen, 950
    phosphorus, 865
    potassium, 1873
    rare earth elements, 865, 900–5
    silicon, 865, 1771
    silicon carbide, 1771
    silver, 1892–4
    strontium, 1873
    sulfur, 865
    thorium, 562
    tin, 865, 1873
    titanium, 1873
    trace elements, 900–5
    uranium, 562
    vanadium, 1873
    zinc, 1873
  electrodes, 152
  instrumentation, 142
    excitation sources, 147, 148
    excitation stands, 152
    gaseous discharge tubes, 151

Emission spectrometry, instrumentation
    (Cont.)
    illumination systems, 146
    spark discharges, 148
    spectrometers, 142
  qualitative analysis, 155
    methods, 157
    principle, 155
  quantitative analysis,
    analytical curves, 163
    intensity measurements, 159, 162
    principle, 158
    standards, 158, 162
  sample polarity, 155
  sample preparation,
    ferrous materials, 859
    metals, 153
    powders, 153
    solutions, 154
  semiquantitative analysis, 164
  units used, 142
EMR, electron magnetic resonance, 616
End point detection,
  amperometric titrations, 388
  conductometric titrations, 309, 314
  coulometric titrations, 480
    amperometry, 482
    conductometry, 483
    optical methods, 480
    potentiometry, 481
  EDTA titrations, by chronopotentiometry,
    426
  potentiometric titrations, 287–90
Endrin, 1479, 1484, 1493, 1496
Enthalpimetric sensitivity index, 638
Enzyme assay, by polarimetry, 268
Enzymes, detection of, 714
EPN pesticide, 1486, 1492, 1497
α-epoxides, determination of, in epoxy res-
    ins, 1600–2
Epoxy resins,
  analysis of, for α-epoxides, 1600–2
  determination of, 1271
EPR. See Electron paramagnetic resonance,
    616
Equivalent conductance, 298
Equivalent ionic conductance, 299
ESI. See Enthalpimetric sensitivity index,
    638.
ESR. See Electron spin resonance.
Essential oils, analysis by,
  critical solution temperatures, 684
  thin-layer chromatography, 754
Esters, determination of,
  by gas chromatography, 1194
  by infrared spectrometry, 1171–2
  by ultraviolet spectrometry, 1187
  in fatty acid ethanolamide, 1831–3
Esters, high-boiling,
  determination of, in polymer extracts,
    1656
Estradiol benzoate, determination of, 265
Estrogens, determination of, 1033–6, 1047–8
Ethers, determination by,
  gas chromatography, 1195
  infrared spectrometry, 1172–4

Ethers, determination by (Cont.)
nuclear magnetic resonance spectrometry, 1202
Ethion, 1492, 1497
Ethyl acrylate, determination of, in copolymer with methyl methacrylate, 1581
Ethyl alcohol, determination of, in liquid detergents, 1860-1
Ethylene, combined, determination of, in polymers, 1588
Ethylenediaminetetraacetic acid. *See* EDTA.
Ethylene glycol, determination of, 1323-4
Ethylene homopolymers, analysis for chain branching, 1580
Ethylene oxide chain length, determination of in alkylphenol ethoxylates, 1173
Ethylene-propylene copolymers,
analysis by,
infrared spectrometry, 1165
mass spectrometry, 1663
radiochemical method, 1588
analysis for,
monomer content, 1687
propylene content, 1686, 1689
Ethylene-propylene rubbers, analysis of, for glass transition temperatures, 1643
Eutectic temperatures, 224
e.v., 542
Exchangeable magnesium, *See* Magnesium, exchangeable.
Excitation sources,
for emission spectrometry, 147
arc discharges, 148
flames, 148
gaseous discharge tubes, 151
spark discharges, 148
for x-ray emission and absorption analysis, 172
Extenders, identification of, in paints, 1286
Extenders, rubber, determination of, 1695
Extractables from resinous and polymeric coatings from packaging materials, determination of, in foods, 1123-5

Faraday balance, magnetic studies, 594
Faraday method, magnetic susceptibility, 593
Faraday's law, 459
Faraday-type helical spring microbalance, magnetic studies, 594
Fast-neutron activation analysis, 1531
petroleum and petroleum products, 1537
Fat content, determination of, 1100
Fat stability, determination of, 1098-1100
Fats, 1054
analysis by,
critical solution temperatures, 671, 683
dielectrometry, 1100
differential thermal analysis, 1083
dilatometry, 1096-8
emission spectrometry, 1074
gas chromatography, 1090-2
infrared spectrometry, 1072-3
ion exchange, 1085, 1087, 1089
manometry, 1098-1100

Fats, analysis by (Cont.)
nuclear magnetic resonance, 1082, 1202, 1306
paper chromatography, 1094-6
polarography, 1081
refractometry, 256, 1075-7
thin-layer chromatography, 754, 761
ultraviolet spectrometry, 1066-71
visible spectrometry, 1054-66
x-ray diffraction, 1075
analysis for,
antioxidants, 1057
butyric acid, 1087
chlorophyll, 1065
color, 1064
consistency, 1101
copper, 1056, 1074
crystal forms, 1075
crystallizing characteristics, 1083
fat content, 1100
fat stability, 1098-1100
fatty acids, 1090-2
gossypol, 1062-4, 1094-6
iron, 1055, 1074
isolated *trans*-isomers, 1072-3
lactated compounds, 1060
metals, 1074
molecular weight, average, 1202, 1306
nickel, 1054
phosphorus, 1056
polyunsaturated, 1066-71
propylgallate, 1057-8
rancidity, 1059
saturated hydrocarbons, 1089
sesamin, 1060
sesamol, 1060
solid fat content, 1082
solid fat index, 1096-8
tin, 1081
tocopherols, 1062, 1096
unsaturation, 1202, 1306
characterization of, 671
refractive index, table of, 1075
Fatty acid alkanolamides, analysis of,
for amide content, 1846
for ester, 1831-3
Fatty acid esters, R_F values of, 1093
Fatty acids. *See also* Carboxylic acids.
analysis of, 733
determination by,
gas chromatography, 1090-2, 1320, 1857-60
infrared spectrometry, 1171, 1857-60
paper chromatography, 1092
thin-layer chromatography, 757
ultraviolet spectrometry, 1066-71, 1277
determination of,
in acid chlorides, 1171
in alkyd resins, 1320
in detergent products, 1857-60
in fats, 1090-2
in oil modified alkyd resins, 1277
in oils, 1277
separation of, 757
from fats, 1092

Fatty acids, polyunsaturated. *See* Polyunsaturated fatty acids.
Feces, analysis of, 556
Feeds, analysis of, for, selenium, 576
Feed stocks. *See* Petroleum and petroleum products.
Fehling's solution, 222
Feret's diameter, 797–8
Ferricyanide, determination of, 422
Ferrimagnetism, 588
Ferroalloys. *See also* Ferrous materials.
  analysis for,
    copper, 136
    tantalum, 865
  reference materials, 854–5
  sampling of, 853–4
  techniques, 855
Ferrocyanide, determination of, 422
Ferromagnetism, 586
Ferromanganese, analysis for,
  copper, 864
  manganese, 864
  silicon, 865
  zinc, 865
Ferrotungsten, analysis for,
  silicon, 865
  tin, 865
Ferrous materials. *See also* Ferroalloys, Iron, Iron and steel, *and* Steel.
  analysis by,
    activation analysis, 864, 865
    amperometric titration, 864, 865
    atomic absorption spectrometry, 864, 865
    conductometry, 864
    emission spectrometry, 864, 865
    flame spectrometry, 865
    fluorometry, 865
    high-temperature oxidation, 864
    infrared spectrometry, 864
    isotope dilution, 864
    polarography, 864, 865
    potentiometric titration, 865
    radiometric methods, 865
    x-ray spectrometry, 864, 865
  analysis for,
    bismuth, 864
    calcium, 864
    carbon, 864
    cobalt, 864
    copper, 864
    lead, 864
    manganese, 864
    molybdenum, 865
    nickel, 865
    nonmetallic compounds, 865
    phosphorus, 865
    rare earth metals, 865
    silicon, 865
    sulfur, 865
    tin, 865
    titanium, 865
    uranium, 865
    vanadium, 865
    zinc, 865
Fertilizers, 1102

Fertilizers (Cont.).
  analysis by
    activation analysis, 576
    atomic absorption spectrometry, 104, 109, 1105, 1106, 1107
    flame spectrometry, 133, 1104
    gas chromatography, 736
    visible spectrometry, 1103–4
    x-ray emission spectrometry, 1102
  analysis for,
    calcium, 109, 1107
    cobalt, 1106
    copper, 109, 1105
    iron, 109, 1106
    magnesium, 109, 133, 1107
    manganese, 109, 1106
    molybdenum, 109, 1106
    nitrate, 1104
    nitrogen, ammoniacal, 1104
    phosphorus, total, 1103
    phosphorus, water-soluble, 1103
    potassium, 109, 133, 1104
    selenium, 576
    sodium, 109
    strontium, 109
    zinc, 109, 1106
Fiber analysis of paper and paperboard, 1378–92
Fick's law, 326
Fillers, in polymers, determination of, 1606–10
Fillers, in rubber,
  determination of, 1695
  dispersion of, 1757
  identification of, 1695, 1719
Film, analysis of, for silver, 553
Films on metals, determination of, 489
Filter paper electrophoresis, 704–6
Filters, visible spectrometry, 7
Finch method, 1456
FINK index of powder diffraction patterns, 203
First-order transition temperature of polymers, determination of, 1593
Fish oil, blown, absorptivity value, 1289
Flame spectra of elements, table of, 125
Flame spectrometers, 118, 121
Flame spectrometry, 118
  analysis of,
    biological materials, 1009–11
    cement, 967–8
    detergents, 1837
    fats, 1073–4
    ferrous materials, 865
    glass, 1213–28, 1295
    nonferrous alloys, 870–84
    oils, 1073–4
    paint driers, 1296
    paints, 1294–6
    rocks, 1228
    serum, 1027–31
    silicates, 1228
    slags, 864
    soap, 1837
    soil, 1874–5, 1879
    urine, 1027–31

Flame spectrometry (Cont.)
  applications, 124, 131
  determination of,
    alkaline earth metals, 1226, 1228
    aluminum, 967–8, 1228
    barium, 967–8, 1295
    calcium, 864, 967–8, 1295, 1296, 1875, 1879
    cesium, 1219–26, 1227
    cobalt, 1296
    iron, 864, 967–8, 1228
    lanthanum, 125, 131
    lead, 1296
    lithium, 967–8, 1219–26, 1227
    magnesium, 965–7, 1295, 1875
    manganese, 965–7, 1228, 1296
    metals, 1295
    nickel, 865
    potassium, 965–7, 1009–11, 1027–31, 1219–26, 1227, 1294, 1837, 1875, 1879
    rubidium, 1219–26, 1227
    sodium, 965–7, 1009–11, 1027–31, 1073–4, 1219–26, 1227, 1294, 1837, 1875
    strontium, 967–8
  elements determined, 131
  elements determined by, 131
    table of, 872–3
  elements determined by, in glass, table of, 1216–7
  evaluation methods, 128
  instrumentation, 118, 1214
    clinical, 1025–7
    detectors, 121
    double-beam instruments, 122
    light source, 119
    monochromators, 119
    single-beam instruments, 121
  interferences, 127, 875
    by anions, table of, 874
  principles,
    flame background, 123, 126
    metallic spectra, 122
    variation of emission intensity within the flame, 123
    radiation buffers, 127
  sample preparation, 134
    glass, 132
    water, 132
  sensitivity of, 125
  solvents used, 124
  working conditions, selection of, 126
Flammability of treated paper, 1454
Flavone glycosides, analysis of, 763
Flavonol, fluorometric reagent, 99, 102
Flaxseed, analysis of, for oil content, 1076
Flour, analysis of, 1108, 1110
Fluorescence,
  intensity of,
    concentration effect, 82
    linearity, 83, 84
  measurement of, 86
  of organic reagents, 81
  spectra, reporting of, 96
  and structure, 80
  theory of, 81
Fluoride,
  determination of, in water, 393
  microtest for, 218
Fluorine, determination of,
  in minerals, 575
  in rubber, 1752–6
  in teflon, 575
Fluorometers, 87
Fluorometric reagents, 98–100
Fluorometry, 78
  analysis by,
    advantages of, 78
    applications of, 100–102
    calculation of results, 84
    calibration curves, 84
    excitation wavelength, selection of, 97
    instrumentation, 85, 86, 92, 94
    limitations of, 79
    metal chelates, 98
    precautions in, 97
    radiation involved, 85
    sources of exciting radiation, 85
    theory of, 80
  analysis of,
    blood, 1036–7
    clinical materials, 1031
    ferrous materials, 865
    food products, 1116, 1152–4, 1154–5
    plasma, 1032
    rubber, 1695
    silicates, 101
    steel, 100
    urine, 1032–3, 1033–6
  determination of,
    adrenaline, 1033
    aluminum, 100
    amprolium, 1116
    beryllium, 101
    catecholamines, 1032–3
    corticosteroids, 1032
    estrogens, 1033–6
    riboflavin, 1154–5
    serotonin, 1036–7
    thiamine, 1152–4
    uranium, 562, 865
  identification of rubber antioxidants, 1695
Flux density, 583
Fluxes, sampling of, 853–4
Fly-dust, analysis for,
  tellurium, 396
  zinc, 398
Folding endurance of paper, 1407–11
Folin-Wu method, for lactose, 1133
Food additives, 1114
  tolerances for, table of, 1122
Foods, 1108. See also individual foods.
  analysis by,
    activation analysis, 575, 576
    electrical methods, 1161
    fluorometry, 1116, 1152–4, 1154–5
    gas chromatography, 732, 1141–4
    infrared spectrometry, 1113–4
    nuclear magnetic resonance, 1938–9
    polarimetry, 1145
    radiochemical methods, 553
    refractometry, 1148

Foods, analysis by (Cont.)
  ultraviolet spectrometry, 1111–2
  visible spectrometry, 1111, 1112, 1119–20, 1121, 1129, 1130–1, 1148–52, 1155
  analysis for,
    amprolium, 1116
    arsenic, 1128
    benzoic acid, 1111
    boric acid, 1111
    bromine, 575
    calcium disodium EDTA, 1119–20
    chemical preservatives, 1111
    chlorinated insecticides, 1141–4
    color additives, 1113–4
    copper, 1129
    EDTA, 1119, 1121
    extractables from resinous and polymeric coatings from packaging materials, 1123–5
    glucose, 1147
    lead, 1130–1
    moisture, 1161
    niacin, 1156–7
    nitrogen, 1157
    nitrogen content, 1157–9
    parathion, 1144
    pesticides, 1139
    phosphorus, 553, 576
    riboflavin, 1154–5
    sorbic acid, 1112
    sugar, 1145, 1146, 1148
    sulfur dioxide, 1112
    thiamine, 1152–4
    Vitamin A, 1148–52
    Vitamin C, 1155
    water, 1159–61, 1938, 1939
Formaldehyde,
  analysis of, for iron, 1267
  determination of,
    in maple syrup, 1121
    in phenolic resins, 1316–7
Formal potentials, determination of, 473
Formates, determination of, 1178
Formula, molecular determination of, 536
Freeness of pulp, 1366–74
Freeness test for pulp, 1366–74
Free-solution electrophoresis, 687
Freon, analysis of, for water, 1936
Fruits, citrus. See Citrus fruits.
Fruits, dried, analysis of, for sulfur dioxide, 1112
Frustrated multiple internal reflectance, 1283
Fuels, analysis of, for water, 1941
Fuels, jet. See Jet fuels.
Functional groups,
  determination by,
    gas chromatography, 1191–8
    infrared spectrometry, 1164–82
    mass spectrometry, 1198
    nuclear magnetic resonance spectrometry, 1200–5
    optical rotatory dispersion, 1207
    polarography, 1205
    Raman spectrometry, 1208
    ultraviolet spectrometry, 1182–91
  identification of, 272

Functional groups (Cont.)
    polarographically active, 376
    position, determination of, 272
Furfural, determination of, 35

Gallic acid esters, analysis of, 763
Gallium,
  determination by,
    activation analysis, 575, 1792–1800
    chronopotentiometry, 422
    emission spectrometry, 1780–2, 1873
  determination of,
    in aluminum, 575
    in minerals, 575
    in rocks, 575
    in semiconductor materials, 1780–2
    in silicon, 1792–1800
    in soil, 1873
Gallium, reagents for, fluorometric, 98–9
Gallium arsenide,
  analysis by,
    activation analysis, 575–7, 1791
    emission spectrometry, 1771, 1772–5
    mass spectrometry, 1784–8
    polarography, 1801, 1802–7
  analysis for,
    bismuth, 1801, 1802–7
    cadmium, 1801, 1802–7
    chromium, 575
    copper, 575, 1801, 1802–7
    gold, 575
    indium, 1801, 1802–7
    lead, 1802–7
    oxygen, 576, 1791
    selenium, 1791
    silicon, 576
    sulfur, 1791
    tellurium, 1791
    thallium, 1802–7
    tin, 1802–7
    zinc, 577, 1802–7
Gallium chelates, fluorescent, 98, 99
Gallium metal,
  analysis by,
    activation analysis, 1791
    isotope dilution, 562
    mass spectrometry, 1788
    polarography, 1082
  analysis for,
    antimony, 1802
    arsenic, 1802
    indium, 1791
    lead, 1802
    zinc, 562
Galvanic coulometry. See Coulometric internal electrolysis.
Gamma, 582
Gamma-ray scintillation spectrometry, 546
Gammexane-DDT mixtures, analysis of, 238
Gas(es). See also Natural gas and special gases.
  analysis by,
    gas chromatography, 1210, 1562–3
    mass spectrometry, 1210, 1523
  analysis for,
    water, 1936, 1947, 1950, 1952
Gas, reformed. See Reformed gas.

1978 INDEX

Gas chromatography, 716. *See also* Pyrolysis-gas chromatography.
  analysis of,
    air pollutants, 840
    alkanes, 1192, 1568–70
    amino acids, 960–1
    butane-butylene mixtures, 1211
    clinical materials, 1041, 1043, 1044, 1045–6, 1047–8, 1048–9
    coal tar products, 736
    cosmetics, 735
    detergents, 1857–60, 1860–1
    fats, 1090–2
    fatty acids, 733
    fertilizers, 736
    foods, 732, 1115, 1144
    functional groups, 1191–8
    gases, 1210, 1211, 1562–3, 1945
    hydrocarbons, 1945, 1563–74
    hydrocarbons, aromatic, 1193, 1569–72
    latex, 1316
    naphthalenes, 1572
    naphthenes, 1569–71
    natural gas, 1211
    octenes, 1567
    paints, 735, 1309–23
    perfumes, 735
    pesticides and herbicides, 734, 1472, 1477, 1488–92
    petroleum and petroleum products, 731, 1551, 1554–78
    petroleum gas, liquefied, 1211
    pharmaceuticals, 735, 1945
    plastics, 736, 1653–60
    polymer extracts, 1656
    polymers, 1314, 1315, 1316–7, 1319, 1320, 1321
    polymers, acrylic, 1317, 1318
    polymers, rubber, 1667
    polymers, styrene, 1658
    reformed gas, 1211
    rubber, 1667, 1738–40
    soil, 1879
    steroids, 733
    water, 1924–5, 1926
  chromatographic peaks, 722–4, 726, 1556–60
    factors affecting shape of, table of, 1558
  columns,
    capillary, 717, 1564, 1573–4, 1575
    efficiency of, 722, 724
    packed columns, preparation of, 1561–4
    partition coefficient, 721
    partition ratio, 717, 720
    programmed temperature operation of, 730
    temperatures, table of, 1561
  description of, 717
  determination of,
    acetyl tributyl citrate, 1656
    alcohols, 1194–5
    aldehydes, 1194
    aldrin in water, 1924–5
    alkanes, 1192
    alkenes, 1192–3
    alkoxyl, acrylic polymers, 1318

Gas chromatography, determination of (Cont.)
    alkyl halides, 1197
    alkynes, 1193
    amines, 1196
    anhydrides, 1194
    antioxidants, amine, 1738–40
    aryl halides, 1197
    BHC, in water, 1924–5
    carbon dioxide, 1043
    carbonyl compounds, 1194
    carboxylic acids, 1194
    copolymer composition of rubber polymers, 1667
    DDT in water, 1924–5
    Diazinon in water, 1924–5
    dibutyl sebacate in polymer extracts, 1656
    Dieldrin, 1924–5
    esters, 1194
    esters, high-boiling, in polymer extracts, 1656
    estrogens, 1047–8
    ethers, 1195
    ethyl alcohol, in liquid detergents, 1860–1
    fatty acids, 1090–2, 1320, 1857–60
    formaldehyde, in phenolic resins, 1316–7
    herbicide, aquatic, 1926
    homovanillic acid, 1044
    hydrocarbons, 840, 1192–4
    hydrocarbons, aromatic, 1193
    17-hydroxy corticosteroids, 1048–9
    ketones, 1194
    17-ketosteroids, 1046–7
    lactones, 1194
    3-methoxy-4-hydroxy mandelic acid, 1044
    3-methoxy-4-hydroxyphenyl acetic acid, 1044
    monomer, free in polymers, 1314
    nitrites, 1196
    nitrogen, 1879
    oxygen, 1043
    paint solvents, 1309–14
    Parathion, 1144, 1924–5
    pesticides, 1141–4, 1477–80, 1480–5, 1485–7, 1488–92, 1924–5, 1926
    pesticides, organophosphate, 1488–92
    phenol, in phenolic resins, 1316–7
    phenols, 1195
    phthalic acid content, of alkyd resin, 1319
    piperazine, 1196
    polymer additives, 1655
    polymer plasticizers, 1655
    polyols, in alkyd resins, 1321
    pregnanediol, 1045–6
    pyrrolidine, 1196
    residual solvents in spice oleoresins, 1115
    silanes, 1197
    Silvex, 1926
    styrene monomer, in polymers, 1315
    styrene monomer, residual in styrene polymers, 1658
    sulfides, organic, 1197

Gas chromatography, determination of (Cont.)
thiols, 1197
thiopesticides, 1485–7
toluene diisocyanate monomer, in polymers, 1316
Toxaphene, 1924–5
vanilmandelic acid, 1044
vinyl toluene, in polymers, 1315
water, 1945
fraction collection, 1659
identification of,
plastics, 1654
rubber polymers, 1667
instrumentation for, 718, 961, 1554–6
electron capture detector, 1480
fraction collection, 1659
mass spectrometer detector, 538
microcoulometric detector, 1481
sodium thermionic detector, 1888
qualitative analysis by, 1556
quantitative analysis by, 1556–60
resolution, 726–7
retention,
absolute, 720
relative, 722
specific, 721
temperature, 731
temperature dependence of, 727–9
volume, 720
separation of hydrocarbons, 1551
Gas-liquid chromatography. See Gas chromatography.
Gasoline. See also Petroleum and petroleum products.
analysis for,
lead, 1542
pyridine, 1189
quinoline, 1189
water, 1939
Gas overvoltage, 432
Gauss, 582
Gauss's law, 584
GC. See Gas chromatography.
Geiger detector, 176
Geiger-Müller counter, radioactivity, 545
Gel-permeation chromatography, 1323
characterization of paint vehicles, 1323–4
characterization of varnishes, 1323–4
determination of molecular size of polymers, 1324
Generator electrode, 476
coulometry, 476
Georgi system, 585
Germanium,
analysis by,
activation analysis, 1790
emission spectrometry, 1780–2
mass spectrometry, 1784–8
polarography, 1801, 1802–7
vacuum fusion, 1808
analysis for,
arsenic, 1790
bismuth, 1802–7
cadmium, 1802–7
copper, 1790, 1801, 1802–7

Germanium, analysis for (Cont.)
indium, 1802–7
iron, 1801
lead, 1801, 1802–7
nickel, 1801
oxygen, 1808, 1811
phosphorus, 1790
silver, 1801
thallium, 1802–7
tin, 1802–7
zinc, 1801, 1802–7
determination of, in semiconductor materials, 1780–2
Germanium, reagents for, fluorometric, 99
Germicides, determination of,
in detergents, 1826–8
in soaps, 1826–8
g-factor, 616
Gilbert, unit, 583
Glacial acetic acid. See Acetic acid, glacial.
Glass, 1212
analysis by,
amperometric titration, 390, 1236
atomic absorption spectrometry, 1213
electron microprobe, 1229–32
flame spectrometry, 132, 1213–28, 1295
polarography, 1233–5
potentiometric titration, 1237, 1238–42
x-ray spectrometry, 1243–57
analysis for,
alkaline earth metals, 132, 1226, 1228
aluminum, 132, 1235, 1248
antimony, 1233, 1248
arsenic, 390, 1237, 1250
barium, 1235, 1250, 1295
boron, 132
cadmium, 1234
calcium, 1251, 1295
cesium, 1219–26, 1227
chlorine, 1251
chromium, 1252
cobalt, 1252
copper, 1252
iron, 1238–42, 1252
lead, 1235
lithium, 1219–26, 1227
magnesium, 132, 1252, 1295
manganese, 1252
nickel, 1252
potassium, 132, 1219–26, 1227, 1235, 1236, 1253
rubidium, 1219–26, 1227
selenium, 1234
silicon, 1253
sodium, 132, 1219–26, 1227, 1235, 1255
strontium, 1256
sulfur, 1256
thin films, 1264
titanium, 1250
zinc, 1235, 1252
zirconium, 1256
elements determined in,
by atomic absorption spectrometry, table of, 1216–7
by flame spectrometry, table of, 1216–7
sample preparation, 1258–60

Glass, sample preparation (Cont.)
  briquet methods, 1259
  fusion methods, 1258
  physical concentration methods, 1259
  sample preparation for,
    atomic absorption spectrometry, 1218
    electron microprobe, 1229–30
    flame spectrometry, 1218
    x-ray emission spectrometry, 1247
    standards for x-ray spectrometry, 1247
Glass electrodes, 285
  for determination of,
    pH, 522, 525
    potassium, 1878
    sodium, 1877
Glass transition temperature of polymers,
    detection of, 1643
GLC, 716. See Gas-liquid chromatography.
Globulins, determination of, 256
Glucose, determination of,
  in biological fluids, 978–81
  in foods, 1147
Glycerol, analysis of, for water, 1936
Glycerol, determination of, 1323–4
Glycols, analysis of, for water, 1936
Glycosides, analysis of, 760
Gold,
  determination by,
    activation analysis, 575, 1792–1800
    amperometric titration, 390
    atomic absorption spectrometry, 110,
      1513
    electrogravimetry, 456
    emission spectrometry, 1772–5, 1778–
      80, 1780–2
    ultraviolet spectrometry, 32
  determination of,
    in alloys, 575
    in biological materials, 575
    in cyanide liquors, 110
    in electroplating baths, 390
    in gallium arsenide, 575
    in minerals, 575
    in noble metals, 110
    in semiconductor materials, 1772–5,
      1778–80, 1780–2
    in silicon, 575, 1792–1800
  microtest for, 216
Gold metal, analysis of, 1800
Gossypol, determination of, 1062–4, 1094–
  6
Gouy method, magnetic susceptibility, 593
Grain, analysis of, for water, 1946
Granite, analysis for thorium, 562
Graphite, analysis for,
  aluminum, 575
  mercuric chloride, 561
  rare earths, 576
  uranium, 577
  vanadium, 577
Grating spectrometer for emission spectrom-
  etry, 143
Griess-Illosvay reaction for nitrites, 845
GSC. See Gas chromatography.
Guanidine accelerators, identification of,
  1699–1701

Guanidines, x-ray diffraction data, table of,
  1716
Guinier x-ray diffraction camera, 201
Gunmetal, analysis for zinc, 923
Guthion, 1486, 1497, 1499
Gyromagnetic ratio, 616

Hafnium, determination of, 561, 576
Hafnium metal, analysis for oxygen, 951
Hafnium-zirconium alloys, analysis of, 906–
  8
Half-life, radioactive disintegration, 543
Half-wave potential(s), 339
  table of, 370–3, 926–9
Halides, alkyl. See Alkyl halides.
Halides, aryl. See Aryl halides.
Halides, detection of, 217
Hall coefficient, 1767
Halogens. See Fluorine, Chlorine, Bromine,
  and Iodine.
Hanawalt index, 1839
Hanging mercury drop electrode, chrono-
  potentiometry, 411
HCH. See Gammexane.
Heat of fusion, determination of, of poly-
  mers, 1644
Heavy oils, analysis of, 1511
Hecogenin, analysis of, for tigogenin, 1208
Heinrich probe, 1259
Hellige turbidimeter, 279
Hemoglobin, determination of, in blood,
  1003
Heptachlor, 1464, 1478, 1484, 1493, 1496
Heptachlor epoxide, 1464, 1479, 1484, 1493,
  1496
Herbicides. See also Pesticides and individual
    herbicides.
  analysis of, by gas chromatography, 734
  aquatic, determination of, 1926
  extraction and purification,
    chlorophenoxy acids and their esters,
      1469–72
Herzberg stain, in paper analysis, 1381, 1387
Heterotactic structures, 1580
Hexachlorobenzene, 1478, 1483
Hexachlorocyclohexane. See Gammexane.
High frequency methods,
  applications, 497
  instrumentation for, 496
  principles, 493
  with immersed electrodes, 494
  with nonimmersed electrodes, 494
High temperature oxidation, determination
  of carbon, 864
Homovanillic acid, determination of, 1044
Hydrazine, determination of, 425
Hydrazone derivatives of sugars, 230
Hydrocarbons. See also individual hydrocarbons,
    Alkanes, Alkenes, Alkynes, Aromatic
    hydrocarbons, Cycloalkanes, Satu-
    rated hydrocarbons, and Polynuclear
    hydrocarbons.
  analysis, 1545
  analysis by,
    differential thermal analysis, 1553
    elution chromatography, 1552

Hydrocarbons, analysis by (Cont.)
  gas chromatography, 1192–4, 1551, 1563–74
  mass spectrometry, 1576
  ultraviolet spectrometry, 1182–7
 analysis of, for water, 1936, 1939, 1941, 1945
 characterization of, by critical solution temperature, 671
 determination by,
  electron spin resonance, 633
  elution chromatography, 1089
  gas chromatography, 840, 1193
  infrared spectrometry, 838, 1165–70, 1177–8
  mass spectrometry, 1522–6
  nuclear magnetic resonance, 1201
  ultraviolet spectrometry, 1185
 determination of,
  in air, 838, 840, 851
  in fats, 1089
  in petroleum and petroleum products, 1522–6
 mass spectra of, 1518
 Raman spectra of, 76
 separation of,
  by elution chromatography, 1552
  by gas chromatography, 1551
Hydrodesulfurization catalysts, analysis of, for molybdenum, 1537
Hydrogen,
 determination by,
  emission spectrometry, 850, 864
  inert gas fusion, 949
  isotope dilution, 561, 949
  nuclear magnetic resonance, 611
  vacuum extraction, 949–52
  vacuum fusion, 862, 949, 1807
 determination of,
  in aluminum, 951
  in copper, 951
  in copper-base alloys, 951
  in ferrous materials, 864
  in iron and steel, 862
  in metals, 561
  in nonferrous metals, 949–52
  in semiconductor materials, 1807
  in titanium, 951
  in zirconium, 951
Hydrogen arc, in fluorometric analysis, 86
Hydrogen electrode, for pH measurements, 522–3
Hydrogen fluoride, analysis of, for water, 1946
Hydrogen ion-responsive electrodes, 522
Hydrogen peroxide, determination of, 242
Hydroperoxides, determination of, 633
Hydroquinone, determination of, in vinyl monomers, 1280
17-Hydroxycorticosteroids, determination of, 1048–9
3-Hydroxyflavone. See Flavonol.
Hydroxyl group, determination of, 1172–4, 1177, 1180, 1181
Hydroxyl number, determination of, in polymers, 1599

Hydroxylamine, determination, 425
Hydroxylamine-sulfonated hydrocarbon, determination of, 963–5
2-Hydroxy-3-naphthoic acid, fluorometric reagent, 99
8-Hydroxyquinoline, fluorometric reagent, 98
5-Hydroxytryptamine. See Serotonin.
Hyperfine coupling constant, ESR, 627
Hyperfine interaction, ESR, 627
Hypobromite, determination of, 32
HVA. See Homovanillic acid.

Ilkovic equation, 332
Illumination systems for emission spectrometry, 146
Immersion refractometer, 251
Immunoelectrophoresis, 689
Impurity faradaic current, 469
Inconel-x, analysis by electron probe x-ray microanalyzer, 194
Index of refraction. See Refractive index.
Indicator electrodes, for amperometric titrations, 384, 385
Indium,
 determination by,
  activation analysis, 1791, 1792–1800
  amperometric titration, 393
  emission spectrometry, 1780–2
  flame spectrometry, 880–4
  polarography, 945, 1801, 1802–7
 determination of,
  in gallium, 1791
  in gallium arsenide, 1801, 1802–7
  in germanium, 1802–7
  in indium antimonide, 1802–7
  in indium arsenide, 1802–7
  in magnesium-base alloys, 880–4
  in semiconductor materials, 1780–2
  in silicon, 1792–1800, 1802–7
  in sphalerite, 393
  in zinc, 945
Indium metal,
 analysis by,
  emission spectrometry, 1772–5
  mass spectrometry, 1784–8
  polarography, 933–6, 1800, 1801, 1802–7
 analysis of, 933–6, 1800, 1801, 1802–7
Indium antimonide,
 analysis by,
  emission spectrometry, 1772–5
  mass spectrometry, 1784–8
  polarography, 1802–7
 analysis of, 1802–7
Indium arsenide,
 analysis by,
  emission spectrometry, 1772–5
  mass spectrometry, 1784–8
  polarography, 1802–7
 analysis of, 1802–7
Induced background current, 470
Inert gas fusion, determination of,
 hydrogen, 949
 oxygen, 949–52
 nitrogen, 949

Infrared. *See also* Near-infrared.
Infrared absorption data for,
  alkanes, 1165
  alkenes, 1167
  alkynes, 1168
  aromatic hydrocarbons, 1169
  carbonyl compounds, 1171
  functional groups, 1176
    nitrogen-containing, 1174
  oxygen compounds, noncarbonyl, 1172
  polyurethane rubbers, table of, 1680
  silicones, substituted, table of, 1683
  sulfate detergents, table, 1832
  sulfonate detergents, table of, 1832
Infrared spectra, 38
  of phenolic resins, 1282
  of plasticizers, 1281
  of plastics, 1281
  of polysiloxanes, 1682
  of resins, 1281
  of silicone resins, 1683
  origin of, 38, 59, 61
Infrared spectrometry, 38
  advantages of, 75
  analysis of,
    air pollutants, 838, 850
    cement, 962–5
    detergents, 1166, 1829, 1831, 1833–6
    ethylene-propylene copolymers, 1165
    fats, 1072–3
    ferrous materials, 864
    foods, 1113–4
    functional groups, 1164, 1177
    iron and steel, 860, 861
    lacquers, 1289–92
    methyl vinyl ether-maleic anhydride co-
      polymer, hydrolysis product, 1172
    paint, 1281–6, 1286–94
    plastics, 1599, 1605, 1606, 1630
    polymers, 1287, 1583, 1611–4, 1616,
      1621–2, 1692–3
    poly(vinyl chloride), 1606
    rubber, 1667, 1669–70, 1671, 1679–81,
      1681–3, 1692, 1695, 1706, 1719
    semiconductor materials, 1809–11
    varnishes, 1288
    xylenes, isomeric, 1170
  applications, 51
  attenuated total reflectance, 1164
  characterization of,
    aromatic hydrocarbons, 1549
    polybutadiene, 1618
    saturated hydrocarbons, 1546
  determination of,
    abietic acid derivatives, 963–5
    acrylonitrile content, 1611, 1693
    acyl halides, 1171–2
    additives in polymers, 1614
    alcohols, 1172–4, 1177, 1180
    aldehydes, 1171–2, 1177–9
    alkyl benzene sulfonates, 1833–6
    amides, 1174
    amines, 1174, 1177, 1180
    anhydrides, 1171–2
    benzoic acid, 963–5

Infrared spectrometry, determination of
    (Cont.)
  2-butyne-1,4-diol, 1168
  carbon in ferrous materials, 864
  carbonyl group in polyethylene, 1613
  carboxylic acids, 1171–2
  cellulose nitrate, 1289–92
  chain branching of alkyl benzene sul-
    fonates, 1166, 1833–6
  crystallinity of polymers, 1583
  2,6-di-*tert.*-butyl-*p*-cresol in polyethyl-
    ene, 1616
  dodecyl benzene sodium sulfonate, 963–5
  esters, 1171–2, 1831–3
  ethers, 1172–4
  ethylene oxide chain length in alkyl-
    phenol ethoxylates, 1173
  fatty acids in acid chlorides, 1171
  functional groups, 1164–82
  hydrocarbons, 838, 1165–70, 1177–8
  hydroxylamine-sulfonated hydrocarbon,
    963–5
  hydroxyl group, 1172–4, 1177, 1180,
    1181
  isocyanate in urethane intermediate,
    1292–4
  isolated *trans*-isomers in fats, 1072–3
  ketones, 1171–2
  lignosulfonates, 963–5
  methyl groups in polyethylene, 1612
  mineral oil in polystyrene, 1614–6
  moisture in *N*-methylpyrrolidone, 1173
  natural rubber in natural rubber-SBR
    mixtures, 1692
  nitriles, 1174
  nonylphenoxypropionitrile, 1175
  9-octadecenamide in polyethylene, 1616
  oil content of resin modified oil var-
    nishes, 1288
  oleic acid, 963–5
  oxidation products in polymers, 1622
  oxygen, 1810, 1811
  phenolic resin content of NBR-phenolic
    blends, 1693
  phenols, 1172–4, 1177
  poly(vinyl acetate), 963–5, 1287
  propargyl alcohol, 1173
  2-pyrrolidone in *N*-vinylpyrrolidone,
    1175
  soap in oil, 1073–4
  stearic acid, 963–5
  structural characteristics, 1667, 1669–70,
    1679–81, 1681–3
  styrene content of copolymers, 1611
  2,4-toluene diisocyanate, 1175
  2,6-toluene diisocyanate, 1175
  unsaturation in polybutadienes, 1621–2
  unsaturation in polyethylene, 1613
  N-vinylpyrrolidone in 2-pyrrolidone,
    1168
  water, 1181, 1935–7
identification of,
  color additives in foods, 1113–4
  detergents, 1829–31
  fillers, inorganic, in rubber, 1695, 1719
  oil in paints, 1285

Infrared spectrometry, identification of (Cont.)
  pigments and extenders in paints, 1286
  polymers in paints, 1285
  resins in paint, 1285
  rubber accelerators, 1706
  rubber polymers, 1667, 1671
  sulfate detergents, 1831
  sulfonate detergents, 1831
  study of, polymerization reactions, 1622–4
instrumentation, 40
  amplifiers, 42
  detectors, 41
  double-beam instrument, 43, 44
  infrared sources, 41
  monochromators, 41
  single-beam instrument, 43, 44
instrument operation, 44
limitations of, 75
Luft principle, 850
methods analysis,
  ASTM proceedings, 54
  Coblentz Society, 54
nondispersive, 850
polarized infrared radiation spectrometry, 1624
qualitative analysis, 51
quantitative analysis, 51
sample handling, 45
  cell materials used, table of, 46
  liquid phase, 46
  solids, 48
  solutions, 46
  vapor phase, 45
sample preparation for,
  by potassium bromide method, 1284
  for internal reflectance, 1283
  for plastics, 1602–4, 1606
solvents used, 67
theory, 38
uncertainties in, 54
Inhibitors, determination of,
  by ultraviolet spectrometry, 1280
  in vinyl monomers, 1268
Ink absorption of blotting paper, 1421
Insecticides. See also Pesticides.
  analysis of, by thin-layer chromatography, 755
Insecticides, chlorinated. See Chlorinated insecticides.
Instrumentation,
  for amperometric titration, 384
  for atomic absorption spectrometry, 1214, 1508–10
  for attenuated total reflection, 1627
  for chronopotentiometry, 410
  for conductometric titration, 299
  for coulometric analysis, 463
  for coulometry at controlled current, 477
  for differential thermal analysis, 652
  for electrography, 501
  for electrogravimetric analysis, 433, 436–40, 444–8, 451
  for electron microscopy, 246, 247
  for electron probe x-ray analyzer, 186

Instrumentation (Cont.)
  for electron spin resonance, 619, 621–7
  for electrophoresis, 690–5
  for electrospot testing, 501
  for emission spectrometry, 142
  flame spectrometry, 118, 1025–7, 1214
  for fluorometric analysis, 85
  for gas chromatography, 961, 1554–6
    electron capture detector, 1480
    fraction collection, 1659
    microcoulometric detector, 1481
    sodium thermionic detector, 1488
  for high frequency methods of analysis, 496
  for infrared spectrometry, 40
  for magnetic susceptibility, 593, 594
  for mass spectrometry, 534
  for nephelometry, 279
  for nuclear magnetic resonance, 599
  for pH determination, 528
  for polarimetry, 261
  for polarography, 342
  for potentiostatic coulometry, 463
  for Raman spectrometry, 65
  for refractometry, 250
  for spectropolarimetry, 269
  for thermal analysis, 645
  for thermogravimetric analysis, 663
  for thermometric titrimetry, 638–40
  for turbidimetry, 279
  for ultraviolet spectrometry, 25
  for visible spectrometry, 7
  for x-ray diffraction, 199
  for x-ray spectrometry, 171, 1243, 1539
    analyzing crystals, 1261
    small area masks, 1260
    small area probes, 1259
    ultra-thin-window counter tubes, 1261
Insulin, determination of, 564
Intensity of magnetization, 584
Internal electrolysis, 451
Internal tearing resistance of paper, 1402–7
International tables for crystallography, 199
International tables for x-ray crystallography, 206
Inverse polarography, 349
Iodide,
  determination by,
    amperometric titration, 394
    chronopotentiometry, 422
    radiometric titration, 559
    ultraviolet spectrometry, 32
  microtest for, 218
Iodine,
  determination by,
    activation analysis, 576
    amperometric titration, 394
    isotope dilution, 561
    radiometric method, 556
    x-ray spectrometry, 1541
  determination of,
    in biological materials, 576
    in blood, 561
    in feces, 556
    in petroleum hydrocarbons, 1541

Iodine number, determination of, 399
Iodoform test, micromethod for alcohols, 225
Ion exchange,
    determination of,
        amide content of fatty acid alkanol-
            amide, 1846
        calcium in soil, 1880
        magnesium in soil, 1880
        nonionic detergents, 1845
        phosphates in detergent products, 1846–
            54
        polyphosphates in detergent products,
            1846–54
        soil salinity, 1880
Ion exchange-thin-layer chromatography.
    See Thin-layer chromatography.
Ionic equivalent conductance, 299
Ionic susceptibility, 585
    additivity of, 587
Ionization analysis,
    for air pollutants, 851
    for hydrocarbons in air, 851
Ionization chamber, radioactivity, 545
IR drop, 432
Iridium, determination by,
    amperometric titration, 394
    ultraviolet spectrometry, 32
Iron,
    determination by,
        activation analysis, 109, 110, 576
        amperometric titration, 393
        atomic absorption spectrometry, 109,
            110, 1106, 1511, 1516, 1517
        chronopotentiometry, 422
        electrogravimetry, 455
        emission spectrometry, 1074, 1772–5,
            1778–80, 1780–2
        flame spectrometry, 136, 138, 864, 967–
            8, 1228
        isotope dilution, 561
        polarography, 945, 1800, 1801
        potentiometric titration, 1238–42
        radiometric methods, 556
        reflected β-radiation, 864
        ultraviolet spectrometry, 32
        visible spectrometry, 1055, 1110, 1266,
            1267, 1817–9, 1868
        x-ray spectrometry, 864, 967–73, 1252,
            1541, 1543
    determination of,
        in aluminum alloys, 136
        in arsenic, 1800
        in beryllium, 576
        in blood, 576
        in blood serum, 109
        in boiler deposits, 110
        in cement, 967–8, 969–73
        in chromite minerals, 393
        in coal ash, 110
        in cobalt mattes, 136
        in cracking catalysts, 1543
        in detergents, 1817–9
        in electroplating solutions, 110
        in fats, 1055, 1074
        in feces, 556

Iron, determination of (Cont.)
        in feed stocks (petroleum), 1516, 1517
        in fertilizers, 109, 1106
        in flour, 1110
        in formaldehyde, 1267
        in gas oil fraction of crude petroleum,
            1511
        in germanium, 1801
        in glass, 1238–42, 1252
        in indium, 1801
        in lead, 576
        in nickel-molybdenum-iron alloys, 945
        in nonferrous alloys, 136, 138, 945
        in ores and concentrates, 110, 864
        in organic matrices, 1541
        in petroleum catalysts, 1516, 1517
        in petroleum and petroleum products,
            110
        in plant materials, 109
        in rosin, 1266
        in semiconductor materials, 1772–5,
            1778–80, 1780–2
        in siliceous materials, 1228
        in silicon carbide, 1800
        in slags, 864
        in soils, 109, 1868, 1873
        in tissue, 109
        in urine, 109
        in wines, 109
        in worn lube oils, 1516, 1517
Iron metal. See Iron and steel and Ferrous
        materials.
Iron ore, analysis for aluminum oxide, 449
Iron raw materials, analysis for silver, 390
Iron and steel, 853
    analysis by,
        activation analysis, 862, 864
        atomic absorption spectrometry, 110,
            115
        electron probe microanalyzer, 863
        emission spectrometry, 856, 859, 864,
            865
        high temperature oxidation, 861
        high temperature reduction, 861
        mass spectrometry, 864
        polarography, 864
        vacuum fusion, 862
        x-ray spectrometry, 859
    analysis for,
        antimony, 864
        arsenic, 864
        chromium, 110, 115
        cobalt, 110
        hydrogen, 862
        lead, 110
        magnesium, 110
        manganese, 110
        oxygen, 862
        tin, 865
        zinc, 110
    reference materials, 854–5
    techniques, 855
Irreversible waves, polarographic, 341
Isocyanate group, determination of, in bond-
        ing agents (rubber), 1761–3

Isocyanates, determination of,
by infrared spectrometry, 1174, 1292–4
in urethane intermediates, 1292–4
Isomeric transition, 542
Isophthalic acid. *See* Phthalic acid isomers.
Isoprene, identification of, 1670, 1674
Isoquinoline, reagent, 215
microtest, 215
Isotactic polymers, 1618
Isotactic structures, 1580
Isotope dilution, 552
applications of, 581
determination of,
cobalt in ferrous materials, 864
elements, table of, 561
hydrogen in nonferrous metals, 949
nitrogen in nonferrous metals, 949
organic compounds, table of, 564
oxygen in nonferrous metals, 949
tungsten in high-alloy steels, 865
zinc in semiconductor materials, 1791
Isotope dilution, double, 554
Isotope dilution, reverse, 554
Isotopes, separation of, 714
Isotopic neutron sources, 1534
Isotropic crystals, 223
IT, 542

Jet fuels, analysis of, for water, 1939
Jute, analysis of, for water, 1946

K_α radiation, 199
K_β radiation, 199
Kantrowitz-Simmons stain, in paper analysis, 1388
Kappelmeir saponification, 1275, 1319
Karl Fischer method, for water,
in food, 1159–61
in soaps and detergents, 1841
Kaye disc centrifuge, 819
Kayser unit, 142
K-capture, 542
Kelthane, 1464, 1478, 1484, 1493, 1496
5-Ketogluconate, determination of, 35
Ketones,
analysis for water, 1939
determination by,
amperometric titration, 399
gas chromatography, 1194
infrared spectrometry, 1171–2
nuclear magnetic resonance, 1202
ultraviolet spectrometry, 1187
17-Ketosteroids, determination of, in urine, 1046–7
K.e.V., 542
Kiloelectron volts, 542
Kinetic background current, 470
Kinetic currents, 335, 336
Kinetic polarimetry, 268
King-Armstrong units, 983, 987
Klystrons, for ESR, 621
Kofler, eutectic temperatures, 224
Kozeny equation, 826
Kozeny-Carman equation, 725, 826
K spectra, 198

KX units for x-rays, 199

Lacquers. *See also* Paint.
analysis of, for cellulose nitrate, 1271, 1289–92
Lactated compounds, determination of, in natural fats, 1060
Lactic acid, determination of, in milk, 1138
Lactones, determination of, 1194
Lactose, determination of,
by polarimetry, 265, 1131–3
in milk, 1131–3, 1133
Langevin's equation,
for diamagnetism, 589
for molar paramagnetism, 589
Lanthanum, determination of,
by flame emission spectrometry, 125, 131
by potentiometric titration, 293
in stainless steel, 451
Lard, bleached and unbleached, differentiation of, 1071
LAS, linear alkylate sulfonate, 1833
Latex, analysis of,
for monomers, 1316
for soap, 1756
Lattice parameter measurement, 208
Lead,
determination by,
amperometric titration, 395
atomic absorption spectrometry, 109, 110, 115, 864, 923, 1513, 1516, 1517
chronopotentiometry, 422–3
coulometric analysis, 491
electrogravimetry, 440, 455, 457
emission spectrometry, 1772–5, 1778–80, 1780–2, 1873
flame spectrometry, 1296
isotope dilution, 561
polarography, 933–6, 937–43, 946, 947, 1235, 1800, 1801, 1802–7, 1901–7
potentiometric titration, 293
radiometric methods, 556, 559
ultraviolet spectrometry, 33, 1748
visible spectrometry, 1130–1
x-ray spectrometry, 864, 1542
determination of,
in alluminum alloys, 937–43
in arsenic, 1802
in biological material, 556
in blood serum, 109
in brass, 440, 946
in bronze, 395, 440, 923, 946
in ferrous materials, 864
in foods, 1130–1
in gallium, 1802
in gallium arsenide, 1802–7
in gasoline, 1516, 1517, 1542
in germanium, 1801, 1802–7
in glass, 1235
in indium, 933–6, 1800, 1801, 1802–7
in indium antimonide, 1802–7
in indium arsenide, 1801, 1802–7
in iron and steel, 110
in lube oils, 1516, 1517
in minerals, 561

Lead, determination of (Cont.)
  in nonferrous metals, 110
  in ores and concentrates, 110
  in paint driers, 1296
  in petroleum and petroleum products,
    110, 1513, 1516–7
  in rubber, 1748
  in semiconductor materials, 1772–5,
    1778–80, 1780–2
  in silicon, 1802–7
  in soil, 1873
  in tissue, 109
  in urine, 109, 115
  in water, 1901–7
  in wines, 109
  in zinc, 947
  in zinc oxide, 1748
  in zirconium alloys, 923
Lead alloys, analysis of, for copper, 944
Lead bullion, analysis of, 453
Lead concentrates, analysis of, for silver,
    116, 390
Lead metal, analysis for,
  antimony, 561, 943
  bismuth, 391
  iron, 576
Lead-tin-base alloys, analysis of, 884–9
Leather, analysis of, for water, 1946, 1949
Lemon extracts, assay of, 265
Lenz law, 602
Light oils, analysis of, 1511
Light source,
  for atomic absorption spectrometry, 107
  for flame emission spectrometry, 119
Light stabilizers in polymers, determination
    of, 1596
Lignosulfonates, determination of, in cement,
    963–5
Limestone, analysis for,
  manganese, 137
  potassium, 137
  sodium, 137
Lindane, 1464, 1478, 1483, 1493, 1496
Linear alkylates, determination of, in deter-
    gents, 1845
Linseed oil,
  absorptivity value, 1289
  fatty acid composition of, 1322
Lipids, determination of, in serum, 1039–
    41
Liquid scintillation counter, radioactivity,
    545
Lithium,
  determination by,
    emission spectrometry, 900–5, 1772
    flame spectrometry, 135, 967–8, 1219–
      26, 1227
Lithium metal, analysis of, for sodium, 135
Lofton-Merritt stain, in paper analysis,
    1388
Lorenz-Lorentz equation, 252
Low level surfactants, determination of,
    1819–20
Lube oils. See Petroleum and petroleum prod-
    ucts.

Lubricating oil. See also Petroleum and pe-
    troleum products.
Lubricating oil, analysis of, for copper, 116
Luft principle of infrared analysis, 850

Magnesia mixture, 220
Magnesium,
  determination by,
    activation analysis, 576, 1537, 1791
    amperometric titration, 394
    atomic absorption spectrometry, 109,
      110, 114, 864, 923, 1107, 1228, 1513,
      1876
    electrogravimetry, 449
    emission spectrometry, 864, 1772–5,
      1778–80, 1780–2, 1873
    flame spectrometry, 132, 133, 965–7,
      1295, 1875
    ion exchange, 1880
    potentiometric titration, 293, 973
    ultraviolet spectrometry, 33
    visible spectrometry, 1868, 1879
    x-ray spectrometry, 864, 969–73, 1252
  determination of,
    in aluminum, 923
    in aluminum alloys, 923
    in blood, 576
    in blood serum, 109
    in boiler deposits, 110
    in cast iron, 864
    in cement, 133, 965–7, 969–73
    in coal ash, 110
    in cracking catalysts, 1537
    in fertilizers, 109, 133, 1107
    in glass, 132, 1252, 1295
    in iron and steel, 110
    in nickel, 920–3
    in nickel alloys, 920–3
    in nodular cast iron, 864
    in nonferrous metals, 110
    in plant materials, 109
    in sea sediments, 576
    in semiconductor materials, 1772–5,
      1778–80, 1780–2, 1791
    in slags, 864
    in soil, 109, 114, 1228, 1868, 1873, 1875,
      1876, 1879, 1880
    in tissue, 109
    in urine, 109
    in zinc-base alloys, 449
  reagents for, fluorometric, 98
Magnesium, exchangeable, determination of,
    in soil, 114
Magnesium alloys,
  analysis of, by emission spectrometry, 900–
    5
  analysis for,
    aluminum, 900–5
    barium, 900–5
    beryllium, 900–5
    boron, 900–5
    calcium, 900–5
    lithium, 900–5
    rare earths, 900–5
Magnesium-base alloys,

Magnesium-Base alloys (Cont.)
  analysis by flame spectrometry, 138
  analysis for,
    aluminum, 138
    indium, 880–4
    silver, 880–4
Magnesium carbonate, identification of, in
    rubber, 1719–22
Magnesium metal, analysis for,
  copper, 945
  trace elements, 900–5
Magnesium oxide, identification of, in rub-
    ber, 1719–22
Magnesium oxide, standard, for spectral re-
    flectivity (paper), 1460–2
Magnetic behavior, types of, table, 586, 588
Magnetic dipole, 582
Magnetic field, strength of, 582
Magnetic flux, 583
Magnetic induction, 584
Magnetic moment, 583
Magnetic permeability, 583, 585
Magnetic susceptibility, 582, 585
  applications of, 595
  calculation of, 587
  correction constants, table of, 590
  definitions, 582
  experimental techniques, 591
    table of, 593
  instrumentation for, 593, 594
  methods of measuring, 593
  of oxygen, 595
Magnetism, types of, 586
Magnetization, intensity of, 584–5
Maleic acid, determination of, 1308
Maleic anhydride, determination of, 1205
Malathion, 1485, 1492, 1497, 1499
Manganese,
  determination by,
    activation analysis, 576, 864, 1537
    amperometric titration, 394
    atomic absorption spectrometry, 109,
      110, 1106, 1514
    electrogravimetry, 454
    emission spectrometry, 1772–5, 1778–80,
      1780–2
    flame spectrometry, 134, 136, 137, 965–
      7, 1228, 1296
    polarography, 946, 1876
    potentiometric titration, 293–4
    reflected β-radiation, 864
    visible spectrometry, 1869
    x-ray spectrometry, 864, 969–73, 1252
  determination of,
    in aluminum alloys, 136
    in biological materials, 576
    in cement, 137, 965–7, 969–73, 1252
    in ferromanganese, 864
    in ferrous materials, 864
    in fertilizers, 109, 1106.
    in gasoline, 134
    in iron and steel, 110
    in limestone, 137
    in monel metal, 946
    in nickel, 946

Manganese, determination of (Cont.)
  in nonferrous metals, 110
  in ores, 864
  in paint driers, 1296
  in plant materials, 109
  in quartz, 576
  in rocks, 1228
  in sea water, 576
  in semiconductor materials, 1772–5,
    1778–80, 1780–2
  in soils, 109, 1869, 1876
  in steel, 576
  in sulfuric acid, 1537
Manganese bronze, analysis of, for copper,
    879–80
Mannitol, determination of, 1323–4
Manometry, determination of fat stability,
    1098–1100
Manure, analysis of, for phosphorus, 553
Maple syrup, analysis of, for formaldehyde,
    1121
Marme's reagent, for alkaloids, 237
Martin's diameter, 797–8
Mass spectra, of hydrocarbons, 1518
Mass spectrometers, 533, 534
  resolution of, 534
  types of, 535
Mass spectrometry, 533
  analysis of,
    carburated water gas, 1524
    detergents, 1845
    functional groups, 1198
    gallium, 1788
    gallium arsenide, 1784–8
    gases, 1210, 1523
    germanium, 1784–8
    hydrocarbons, 1522–6, 1546, 1547, 1549,
      1576
    indium, 1784–8
    indium antimonide, 1784–8
    indium arsenide, 1784–8
    iron and steel, 862
    natural gas, 1524
    petroleum and petroleum products,
      1518–27
    plastics, 1662
    polymers, 1673–5, 1689
    rubber, 1673–5
    semiconductor materials, 1782–9
    silicon, 1784–8
    soap and detergents, 1844
  applications of, 539
    as detectors in gas chromatography, 538
    in molecular formula determination,
      536
    in molecular weight determination, 535
    in structure determination, 537
    in thermal analysis, 538
  characterization of,
    aromatic hydrocarbons, 1549
    olefins, 1547
    saturated hydrocarbons, 1546
  determination of,
    chain branching of alkylate detergents,
      1845

Mass spectrometry, determination of (Cont.)
  hydrocarbons, in petroleum and petroleum products, 1522–6
  propylene content of ethylene-propylene copolymers, 1689
  silanes, 1199
  water, 1941
  identification of rubber polymers, 1673–5
  instrumentation, 534
  principles of, 533, 1520–3
  sample requirements, 538
Mass spectrum, 533, 534, 537
Mass susceptibility, 585
  Wiedemann's additivity law, 587
Matthews index of powder diffraction patterns, 204
Maxwell, unit, 583
MBT. See Mercaptobenzothiazole.
MCP herbicide, 1501
MCPA herbicide, 1470
Meat and meat products,
  analysis for, 1125–8
    nitrate, 1127
    nitrite, 1127
    sodium chloride, 1127
    water, 1950
Melamine, determination of, in nitrogen resins, 1278
Melamine resins, analysis of, for urea, 1269
Melaven cell, 444
Melting point determination, 224
Menhaden oil, fatty acid composition of, 1322
Mercaptans. See Thiols.
Mercaptobenzothiazol, determination of, 1190, 1742–3
Mercury,
  determination by,
    activation analysis, 576
    amperometric titration, 393
    atomic absorption spectrometry, 109
    electrogravimetry, 456
    emission spectrometry, 1777–8, 1778–80, 1780–2
    isotope dilution, 561
    potentiometric titration, 293
    radiometric method, 556, 559
    ultraviolet spectrometry, 32
    x-ray spectrometry, 909
  determination of,
    in air, 556
    in biological materials, 576
    in blood serum, 109
    in graphite, 561
    in organic compounds, 393
    in semiconductor materials, 1777–8, 1778–80, 1780–2
    in tissue, 109
    in urine, 109
    in water, 576
    in zinc, 909
  purification of, 355
Mercury cathode electrolysis, 444
Mercury-film electrode, chronopotentiometry, 411

Mercury (I) nitrate,
  reagent for n-butyrate, 221
  reagent for propionate, 221
Mercury pool electrodes, chronopotentiometry, 411
Mercury vapor lamps, 85, 97
Metal additives, determination of, in lubricating oils, 135
Metal chelates, fluorescent, 98
Metals. See also individual metals, Noble metals, Metals nonferrous, and Alloys.
  analysis by,
    activation analysis, 575–7
    isotope dilution, 561
  determination of,
    in air, 839
    in fats and oils, 1074
    in paint vehicles, 1295
Metals, identification of, by electrospot testing, 519
Metals, nonferrous. See also individual metals.
  analysis of, by atomic absorption spectrometry, 110
Metamagnetism, 588
Meteorites, analysis for,
  arsenic, 864
  zirconium, 577
Methoxychlor, 1464, 1479, 1483, 1485, 1493, 1496
3-Methoxy-4-hydroxymandelic acid, determination of, 1044
3-Methoxy-4-hydroxyphenalacetic acid, determination of, 1044
2,2-Methylene bis(3,4,6-trichlorophenol) determination of, in soaps and detergents, 1826
Methyl groups, determination of, in polyethylene, 1612
Methylisopropenyl ketone, determination of, in polymers, 1597
Methyl methacrylate, determination of, in copolymer with ethyl acrylate, 1581
Methyl parathion, 1485, 1492, 1497, 1499
N-methylpyrrolidone, analysis of, for moisture, 1173
Methylstyrene, characterization of, 1317
Methyl vinyl ether-maleic anhydride copolymers, analysis of hydrolysis products, 1172
M.e.V., 542
Microcoulometric detector, 1481
Microcurie, 544
Microelectrophoresis, analysis by, of water, 1927–34
Microscope,
  polarizing, 223
  use of, in particle size analysis, 795
Microscopy,
  analysis of,
    plastics, 1591–5
    polymers, 1591
    rubber, 1757–8
  determination of,
    dispersion of fillers in rubber, 1757

Microscopy, determination of (Cont.)
spherulitic crystallization of polymers, 1591
polarizing light, 1593
Milk and milk products,
analysis of, 1131–9
for lactic acid, 1138
for lactose, 1131–3
for water added, 1134–6, 1136–7
pasteurization of, test for, 1137
Millicurie, 544
Million electron volts, 542
Mineral oils. *See also* Petroleum and petroleum products.
analysis of, by refractometry, 254
determination of, in polystyrene, 1614–6
structional group analysis, 254
Mineral water. *See also* Water.
analysis of, for arsenic, 390
Minerals. *See also* Ores.
analysis by,
activation analysis, 575–7
amperometric titration, 393
isotope dilution, 561
identification of, by electrospot testing, 519
M.I.T. folding endurance of paper, 1409
Modified bright stain, in paper analysis, 1388
Moisture. *See also* Water.
determination of,
in foods, 1161
in *N*-methylpyrrolidone, 1173
in pulpwood, 1326–32
in test sheets of pulp, 1361
Moisture content, of powdered substances, by differential thermal analysis, 656
Molar absorptivity, definition of, 6
Molar paramagnetism, Langevin's equation for, 589
Molar susceptibility, 585
Molecular formula, determination of, by mass spectrometry, 536
Molecular refractivity, 252
Molecular rotation, 260
Molecular size, by gel-permeation chromatography, 1324
Molecular weights, determination of,
by mass spectrometry, 535
of fats, 1306
of polymers,
by light scattering, 1660
by osometry, 1661
by ultracentrifugation, 1661
by ultraviolet spectrometry, 1597
Molten salts, analysis of, 422
Molybdate. *See also* Molybdenum.
determination of, 395
Molybdenum,
determination by,
activation analysis, 576, 865, 1537
amperometric titration, 395
atomic absorption spectrometry, 109, 110, 1106, 1514, 1516, 1517
emission spectrometry, 1873

Molybdenum, determination by (Cont.)
isotope dilution, 561
polarography, 865
ultraviolet spectrometry, 33
visible spectrometry, 1869–71
determination of,
in ferrous materials, 865
in fertilizers, 109, 1106
in hydrodesulfurization catalysts, 1537
in nonferrous metals, 110
in petroleum catalysts, 1516, 1517
in plant materials, 109
in rocks, 576
in sea water, 576
in soils, 109, 1869–71, 1873
in steel, 561, 576, 865
Molybdenum metals, analysis of, for oxygen, 951
Monazite, analysis of, for thorium, 396
Monel metal, analysis of, for manganese, 946
Monochromatic absorptiometry, 171
Monochromators,
for atomic absorption spectrometry, 108
for flame emission spectrometry, 119
for infrared spectrometry, 41
for Raman spectrometry, 65, 74
for ultraviolet spectrometry, 25
for visible spectrometry, 7
Monomer, free, determination of, in polymers, 1314
Monuron, 1478, 1483
Morin, fluorometric reagent, 99, 101
Mortar. *See* Cement.
Moseley's law, 169
Multiple internal reflection, 1283

NaCMC. *See* Carboxymethyl cellulose.
Naphthacene, determination of, 633
Naphthalenes, analysis of, 1572
Naphthenes, analysis of, 1569–71
Natural fats. *See* Fats.
Natural gas, analysis of,
by gas chromatography, 1211
by mass spectrometry, 1524
for water, 1947–8
Natural rubber,
determination of, in natural rubber-SBR mixtures, 1692
identification of, 1668–9, 1670, 1674–5
Natural rubber-SBR mixture, analysis of, for natural rubber content, 1692
NBR. Acrylonitrile-butadiene copolymer.
NBR-phenolic blend, analysis of,
for acrylonitrile content, 1693
for phenolic resin content, 1693
NDGA. *See* Antioxidants.
n-d-m method for ring analysis, 254
Near-infrared. *See also* Infrared.
analysis of, functional groups, 1177
plastics, 1599–1602
characteristic absorptions, 1177
determination of,
acetic acid in acetic anhydride, 1179
alkyl formates, 1178
aromatic aldehydes, 1179

Near-infrared, determination of (Cont.)
  cis-1,4-content of polyisoprene, 1690
  cis-1,4-content of rubber, 1599
  α-epoxides in epoxy resins, 1600–2
  hydroxyl number of polymers, 1599
  phenolic antioxidants in polymers, 1599
  terminal unsaturation in alkenes, 1178
Neburon, 1478, 1483
Neel temperature, 588
Neopentyl glycol, determination of, 1323–4
Neoprene, identification of, 1668, 1670, 1672
Nephelometry, 277
  analysis of air pollutants, 842
  applications, 280
  determination of,
    fillers, inorganic, in rubber, 1695
    sulfate in air, 842
  instrumentation, 279
Neptunium, determination of, 561
Nernst diffusion layer, 326
Nernst equation, 428, 461
Neutral oil, determination of, in crude soybean oil, 1085–7
Neutron activation,
  analysis by, 558
  applications of, 573, 862
  detection limits, table of, 574
  sensitivities of elements, table of, 1537
Neutron-induced radionuclides,
  gamma-ray energies of, table, 570–2
  table of, 566–9
Niacin, determination of, in foods, 1156–7
Nickel,
  determination by,
    activation analysis, 576, 865
    amperometric titration, 395
    atomic absorption spectrometry, 109,
      110, 1511, 1516
    electrogravimetry, 443, 455
    emission spectrometry, 1772–5, 1778–80,
      1780–2, 1873
    flame spectrometry, 865
    paper chromatography, 1879
    polarography, 801, 865, 937–43, 946,
      1902–7
    potentiometric titration, 293, 865
    radiometric titration, 560
    ultraviolet spectrometry, 33
    visible spectrometry, 1054
    x-ray spectrometry, 1252, 1543
  determination of,
    in aluminum alloys, 937–43
    in blood serum, 109
    in brass, 946
    in bronze, 946
    in cobalt, 946
    in cracking catalysts, 1543
    in electroplating solutions, 110
    in fats, 1054
    in feed stocks, 1516
    in ferrous materials, 865
    in gas oil fraction of crude petroleum,
      1511
    in germanium, 1801
    in glass, 1252

Nickel, determination of (Cont.)
  in nickel bronzes, 443
  in nonferrous metals, 110
  in ores and concentrates, 110
  in petroleum and petroleum products,
    110, 1516
  in sea sediments, 576
  in semiconductor materials, 1772–5,
    1778–80, 1780–2
  in soil, 1873, 1879
  in steel, 576, 865
  in tissue, 109
  in titanium alloy, 940–3
  in urine, 109
  in water, 1902–7
  microtest for, 215
Nickel alloys, analysis of, for magnesium,
  920–3
Nickel bronzes, analysis of, 443
Nickel metal, analysis of,
  for magnesium, 920–3
  for manganese, 946
Nickel-molybdenum-iron alloys, analysis of,
  for iron, 945
Nickel-plating baths, analysis of,
  for boron, 136
  for zinc, 398
Ninhydrin reagent, for amino acids, 956
Niobium, determination of,
  by isotope dilution, 561
  by ultraviolet spectrometry, 33
  in high alloy steel, 865
  in ores, 576
Niobium metal, analysis of, for oxygen, 951
Nitrate,
  determination of,
    by polarography, 1877, 1898–1900
    by ultraviolet spectrometry, 33, 1890–1
    by visible spectrometry, 1871
    in fertilizers, 1104
    in meat and meat products, 1127
    in soil, 1871, 1877
    in water, 1890–1, 1898–1900
  microtest for, 219
Nitric acid, fuming, analysis of, for water,
  1936
Nitriles, determination of,
  by gas chromatography, 1196
  by infrared spectrometry, 1174
Nitrite, determination of,
  by ultraviolet spectrometry, 33
  in meat and meat products, 1127
m-nitroaniline, determination of, 1188
Nitrobarbiturates of amines, optical properties, table of, 227, 228
Nitrobarbituric acid reagent, for amines, 225
Nitrocellulose. *See* Cellulose nitrate.
Nitrogen,
  analysis of, for water, 1947–8
  determination of,
    in foods, 1157–9
    in nonferrous metals, 949–50
    in soil, 1878–9
Nitrogen, ammonia, determination of, in
  fertilizers, 1104

Nitrogen, nitrate. *See* Nitrate.
Nitrogen, urea, determination of, 1014–5
Nitrogen-containing functional groups, infrared absorption of, 1174
Nitrogen oxides, determination of, in air, 845–6
Nitrogen resins. *See* Resins, nitrogen.
Nitron reagent, for nitrate, 219
NMR. *See* Nuclear magnetic resonance spectrometry.
Noble metals, analysis for,
  gold, 110
  palladium, 110
  platinum, 110
  silver, 110
Nodular iron, analysis of, 135
Nonalbuminous constituents of serum, determination of, 256
Nonaqueous titrations,
  conductometric, 317
  potentiometric, acid-base, 291
  thermometric, 641
Nonconjugated unsaturated fatty acids. *See* Polyunsaturated fatty acids.
Nondispersive infrared photometry, 850
Nonferrous alloys. *See individual alloys and components.*
Nonferrous metals. *See* Metals, nonferrous *and also individual metals.*
Nonionic detergents. *See* Detergents, nonionic.
Nonionic detergents, determination of, 1845
Nonmetals, analysis of, for arsenic, 575
Nonylcyclohexanol, analysis of, for nonylphenol, 1188
Nonylphenol,
  analysis of, for nonylphenoxypropionitrile, 1175
  determination of, in nonylcyclohexanol, 1188
Nonylphenoxypropionitrile, determination of, in nonylphenol, 1175
Nuclear magnetic resonance spectrometry, 598
  analysis of,
    paints, 1305
    plastics, 1579–82
  applications, 608–10, 615
  characterization of,
    hydrocarbons, aromatic, 1550
    hydrocarbons, olefin, 1548
    hydrocarbons, saturated, 1546
  determination of,
    aldehydes, 1202
    amines, 1202
    aspirin, 1204
    caffeine, 1204
    chain branching in ethylene homopolymers, 1580
    ethers, 1202
    ethyl acrylate-methyl methacrylate ratio in copolymers, 1581
    functional groups, 1200–5
    hydrocarbons, 1201

Nuclear magnetic resonance spectrometry, determination of (Cont.)
    ketones, 1202
    molecular weights, average, of fats, 1202, 1306
    oil content of oilseeds, 1083
    phenacetin, 1204
    solid fat content of plastic fats, 1082
    stereochemistry of polymers, 1306
    structural characteristics of butadiene-isoprene copolymers, 1684
    structural composition of rubber polymers, 1667
    structure of poly(vinylidene fluoride), 1580
    thiols, 1202
    unsaturation in fats, 1202, 1306
    water, 1937, 1939
  identification of polyester resins, 1306
  instrumentation, 599
  limitations of, 614
  method, 601
  nuclei other than protons, 614
  problems of,
    exchange, 613
    hydrogen bonding, 613
    overlap, 612
    solvent effects, 613
  quantitative analysis, 610
  reference resonance frequencies, 602–3
  samples used, 612
  spectrometers, 600
  tetramethylsilane, internal standard for, 603
Nuclear magnetic resonance spectrum,
  characteristics of,
    chemical shifts, 602–5
    intensity, 607
    spin-spin coupling, 605–7
  of diethyl malonate, 601
  of substituted indane, 609
  of *trans*-crotonaldehyde, 608
  origin of, 599
  significance of, 601
Nuclear magnetic susceptibility, 584
Nuclear reactors, 1533
Nucleic acids, separation of, 783
Nucleotides, analysis of, 757
Nylon 6, characterization of, 1317
Nylon 66, characterization of, 1317
n-values, 421, 426
  determination of, 473

O. C. Rudolph and Sons photoelectric polarimeter, 262
9-Octadecenamide, determination of, in polyethylene, 1616
Octenes, analysis of, 1567
Oersted, unit, 582
Ohm's law, 302
Oils. *See also* Fats *and individual oils.*
  analysis by,
    conductivity methods, 1080
    critical solution temperatures, 683
    flame spectrometry, 1073–4

Oil's, analysis by (Cont.)
    polarography, 1308
    ultraviolet spectrometry, 1277
    visible spectrometry, 1939
analysis for,
    fatty acids, 1277
    peroxides, 1308
    soap, 1073–4, 1080
    sodium, 1073–4
    water, 1939
determination of, in resin modified oil varnishes, 1288
identification of, in paint, 1285
Oils, drying, analysis of, for polyunsaturated acids, 1278
Oils, heavy. *See* Heavy oils.
Oils, light. *See* Light oils.
Oils, processing, in rubber, determination of, 1695
Oils, vegetable. *See* Vegetable oils.
Oilseeds, analysis of, for oil content, 1083
Oiticica oil, absorptivity value, 1289
    fatty acid composition of, 1322
Oleamide. *See* 9-Octadecenamide.
Oleic acid, determination of, 963–5
Olefin hydrocarbons. *See* Alkenes.
Opacimeter, Bausch and Lomb, 1415
Opacity meter, for paper analysis, 1412
Opacity of paper, 1412–9
Optical activity, 259
    recognition of, 271
Optical rotation, 259
Optical rotatory dispersion, 258, 268
    analysis of functional groups, 1207
    determination of tigogenin in hecogenin, 1208
Optical systems, x-ray spectrometric, 174
Orange extracts, assay of, 265
ORD. *See* Optical rotatory dispersion.
Ores,
    analysis by,
        activation analysis, 575–7
        amperometric titration, 390, 392, 398
        atomic absorption spectrometry, 110, 116
        reflected β-radiation, 864
        x-ray spectrometry, 860
    analysis for,
        barium, 390
        beryllium, 575
        cobalt, 110
        copper, 110, 392
        iron, 110, 864
        lead, 110
        manganese, 864
        nickel, 110
        niobium, 576
        silver, 110, 116
        zinc, 110, 398, 577
        zirconium, 398
    sampling of, 853–4
Organic acids. *See also* Carboxylic acids *and* Fatty acids.
    determination of, in rubber, 1749–52
Organic bases. *See* Bases, organic.

Organic compounds,
    analysis for,
        bromine, 1537
        mercury, 393
        phosphorus, 395
        sulfur, 396
    characterization of, 679
        position isomers, 680
    derivatives of, 658
    detection of, 222
    determination of, by chronopotentiometry, 422
Organic functional groups, analysis for, 1162
    polarographically active, 376
Organic matter, determination of, in soil, 1880
Organophosphate pesticides,
    determination by,
        gas chromatography, 1488–92
        paper chromatography, 1502–5
        thin-layer chromatography, 1497–9
        relative retention times, table of, 1492
Oscillometer, Sargent, 497
Osmium, microtest for, 216
Osmometers, 1661–2
Osmometry, determination of molecular weights, 1661
Oxidants, determination of, in air, 843
Oxidation-reduction titrations,
    conductometric, 318
    potentiometric, 294
Oxidative stability of polymers, determination of, 1646
Oxide films of metals, measurement of thickness of, 424
Oxine. *See* 8-Hydroxyquinoline.
Oxygen,
    determination by,
        activation analysis, 576, 865, 950–2, 1791
        conductivity, 1947–8
        electrochemical methods, 862
        electron-spin resonance, 633
        emission spectrometry, 950
        gas chromatography, 1043
        high temperature reduction, 862
        inert gas fusion, 949–52
        infrared spectrometry, 1810, 1811
        isotope dilution, 949
        polarography, 1895–8
        vacuum extraction, 949–52
        vacuum fusion, 949–52, 1807, 1808
    determination of,
        in aluminum, 951
        in beryllium, 951
        in biological materials, 576
        in blood, 1043
        in copper, 951
        in copper-base alloys, 951
        in ferrous materials, 865
        in gallium arsenide, 576, 1791
        in germanium, 1808, 1811
        in hafnium, 951
        in iron and steel, 862
        in metals, 576

Oxygen, determination of (Cont.)
   in molybdenum, 951
   in niobium, 951
   in nonferrous metals, 949–52
   in polymers, 576
   in rocks, 576
   in semiconductor materials, 1791, 1807
   in silicon, 1807, 1810
   in tantalum, 951
   in titanium, 951
   in tungsten, 951
   in vanadium, 951
   in water, 1895–8, 1947–8
   in zirconium, 951
  magnetic susceptibility of, 595
Overvoltage, 432
Ovex, 1479, 1484
Ozone, determination of, in air, 843, 848,
   849

Paint,
  analysis by, 1265
   differential thermal analysis, 1308
   emission spectrometry, 1298
   flame spectrometry, 1294–6
   gas chromatography, 735, 1309–23
   gel-permeation chromatography, 1323–
    4
   infrared spectrometry, 1281–94
   nuclear magnetic resonance spectrom-
    etry, 1305
   polarography, 1307
   reflectance spectrometry, 1271
   ultraviolet spectrometry, 1272–81
   x-ray diffraction, 1303–5
   x-ray emission spectrometry, 1299–1302
  analysis for,
   elements, 1295
   iron, 1266
   oils, 1285
   pigments and extenders, 1286
   polymers, 1285
   potassium, 1294
   resins, 1285
   sodium, 1294
   titanium, in pigments, 1270
  identification scheme, 1284–6
  qualitative analysis of, 1281–6
  quantitative analysis of, 1286–94
  sample preparation for infrared spectrometry, 1283
Paint driers, analysis for,
  calcium, 1296
  cobalt, 1296
  lead, 1296
  manganese, 1296
  metals, 1301
Paint pigments, analysis of, 1300
Paint plasticizers, infrared spectra of, 1281
Paint vehicles,
  analysis for,
   metals, 1295
   paint driers, 1301
   characterization of, 1323–4

Palladium,
  determination of,
   by amperometric titration, 395
   by atomic absorption spectrometry, 110,
    1514
   by radiometric titration, 560
   in noble metals, 110
  microtest for, 216
Paper, analysis for, 1378–1462
  air resistance, 1452–4
  bacteriological examination, 1437–40
  basis weight, 1398–1400
  brightness, 1440–6
  bulking thickness, 1419–21
  bursting strength of, 1392–5
  color, 1429–32
  contrast gloss, 1411
  degree of curl and sizing, 1454–6
  density, 1400–2
  edge tearing resistance, 1456
  fiber analysis, 1378–92
  flammability of treated paper, 1454
  folding endurance, 1407–11
  ink absorption of blotting paper, 1421
  internal tearing resistance, 1402–7
  opacity, 1412–9
  silver-tarnishing test, 1432–3
  spectral reflectivity, 1429–32
   magnesium oxide standard for, 1460–2
  stains used,
   Alexander's stain, 1382, 1388
   aniline sulfate, 1389
   "C" stain, 1380–1, 1386
   Herzberg stain, 1381, 1387
   Kantrowitz-Simmons stain, 1388
   Lofton-Merritt stain, 1388
   modified bright stain, 1388
   phloroglucinol stain, 1389
   Selleger's stain, 1382, 1387
   Wilson's stain, 1382, 1387
  stretch, 1446–9
  surface wettability, 1449–51
  tensile breaking strength, 1395–8
  thickness, 1400–2
  water, 1946, 1950
  water absorption of bibulous paper, 1422
  water absorptiveness of nonbibulous paper, 1427–9
  water resistance, 1423–7
  water vapor permeability, 1434–6
Paperboard pulp, analysis of, for water, 1939
Paper chromatography,
  analysis of,
   amino acids, 954–8
   fats, 1092, 1094–6
   pesticides, 1499–1505
   polyphosphates, 1854–7
   soil, 1879
  determination of,
   chlorinated pesticides, 1500
   cobalt, 1879
   copper, 1879
   gossypol, 1094–6
   nickel, 1879
   organophosphate pesticides, 1502–5

Paper chromatography, determination of (Cont.)
tocopherols, 1096
zinc, 1879
identification of rubber polymers, 1667
separation of fats and fatty acids, 1092
Paper electrophoresis, 704–6
Paraffins. *See* Alkanes *and* Saturated hydrocarbons.
Paramagnetism, 586
Pauli (free-electron), 588
temperature-independence (Van Vleck), 590
Van Vleck's equation for, 590
Paramagnetism, molar,
Langevin's equation for, 589
Parathion, 1478, 1485, 1492, 1497, 1499
determination of, 35
in foods, 1144
in water, 1924–5
Parr turbidimeter, 279
Particle size analysis, 794
by electron microscopy, 248
by elutriation techniques, 821–3
by microscope examination, 796
double image microscopy, 798
by sedimentation methods, 803
centrifugal sedimentation techniques, 818–21
cumulative-homogeneous suspensions, 813–16
cumulative two-layer systems, 816–18
incremental-homogeneous methods, 805–13
theory of, 803
by sieve methods, 799
experimental procedures, 801
by stream methods, 823–5
by surface area determinations,
gas absorption methods, 829–34
permeability techniques, 825–9
pressure differential techniques, 833
Partition-thin-layer chromatography. *See* Thin-layer chromatography.
Paste. *See* Cement.
Pasteurization of milk, 1137
PBD. *See* Polybutadiene.
PBNA, analysis of, for antioxidant, amine, 1737
PCNB pesticide, 1464, 1478, 1483
PCP herbicide, 1470
Penescope, 1426
Penicillin G, determination of, 35
Penicillins, determination of, 564
Pentaerythritol, determination of, 1323–4
2′,3,4′,5,7-Pentahydroxyflavone. *See* Morin.
3,3′,4′,5,7-Pentahydroxyflavone. *See* Quercetin.
Peptides, analysis of, 760
determination of, 35
Perchlorate, determination of, in sea water, 561
microtest for, 219
Perfumes, analysis of, 735
Perilla oil, fatty acid composition of, 1322

Perkin-Elmer Model 141 photoelectric polarimeter, 263
Permanganate. *See also* Manganese.
determination of, 394, 422
Peroxides, determination of, in oil, 1308
Perthane, 1464, 1479, 1484, 1493, 1496
Perylene, determination of, 633
Pesticides. *See also individual pesticides.*
analysis by, 1463
gas chromatography, 734, 1472–80
paper chromatography, 1499–1505
thin-layer chromatography, 1492–9
determination of,
in foods, 1139–40
in water, 1924
qualitative analysis of, 1477
quantitative analysis of, 1477
Pesticides, chlorinated,
determination by,
gas chromatography, 1477–80, 1480–5
paper chromatography, 1500
thin-layer chromatography, 1493–7
extraction and purification, 1464–8
relative retention times, table of, 1478–80, 1483–5
Pesticides, organophosphates,
determination by,
gas chromatography, 1488–92
paper chromatography, 1502–5
extraction and purification, 1468–9
Pesticides, organothiophosphates, determination of, 1497–9
Pesticides, thiopesticides, relative retention time, table of, 1485–6
Petroleum gas, liquified, analysis of, 1211
Petroleum heavy oils, analysis of, 1511
Petroleum light oils, analysis of, 1511
Petroleum and petroleum products. *See also* Catalysts *and special products.*
analysis by, 1506
activation analysis, 577, 1535–8
atomic absorption spectrometry, 110, 116, 135, 1507–17
conductivity, 1946
critical solution temperatures, 683
detection limits of elements, 1514
differential thermal analysis, 1553
electron-spin resonance, 632, 634
elution chromatography, 1552
flame spectrometry, 134, 135
gas chromatography, 731, 1551–2, 1554–78
infrared spectrometry, 1548, 1549
mass spectrometry, 1518–27, 1547, 1549
nuclear magnetic resonance, 1550
refractometry, 254
thin-layer chromatography, 754, 761
x-ray emission spectrometry, 1539–44
analysis for,
barium, 110, 135, 1516, 1517, 1543
boron, 135
bromine, 1541
calcium, 110, 135, 1516, 1517, 1543
chlorine, 1541
chromium, 110, 1516, 1517

Petroleum and petroleum products, analysis for (Cont.)
  cobalt, 1541
  copper, 110, 116, 1516, 1517
  gases, 1523
  hydrocarbons, 1522–6, 1551, 1552, 1553
  iodine, 1541
  iron, 110, 1516, 1517, 1541
  lead, 110, 1516, 1517
  lithium, 135
  manganese, 134
  molybdenum, 1516, 1517
  nickel, 110, 1516
  platinum, 1516, 1517
  potassium, 135, 1516, 1517
  silver, 110
  sodium, 110, 1516, 1517
  strontium, 135
  sulfur, 1540
  tetraethyllead, 134
  vanadium, 577, 632, 634
  water, 1946
  zinc, 1516, 1517
  characterization of,
    aromatic hydrocarbons, 1549, 1550
    olefin hydrocarbons, 1547, 1548
    saturated hydrocarbons, 1546
pH, definition of, 521–2
pH, measurement of,
  accuracy, 531
  applications of, 532
  electrodes used, hydrogen ion responsive, 522
    antimony electrode, 524
    glass electrode, 522, 525
    hydrogen electrode, 522, 523
    quinhydrone electrode, 524
  electrodes used, reference,
    calomel electrode, 527
    silver-silver chloride electrode, 527, 528
    thallium amalgam-thallous chloride electrode, 527, 528
  instrumentation for, 528
  interpretations of, 531
  methods of, 521, 530
  precision of, 531
  primary standards for, 523
  standard reference values, 522
pH meters, 528
Pharmaceutical products, analysis of,
  by gas chromatography, 735
  for arsenic, 390
  for bromide, 391
  for water, 1945
Phase-contrast microscopy, analysis of plastics, 1592
Phenacetin, determination of, 1204
Phenanthrene, determination of, in anthracene, 1186
Phenol, determination of, in phenolic resins, 1316–7
Phenolic antioxidants. See Antioxidants, phenolic.
Phenolic resin content, determination of, in NBR-phenolic blends, 1693

Phenolic resins,
  analysis of, 1316–7
  characterization of, 1317
  infrared spectra of, 1282
Phenols,
  determination by,
    gas chromatography, 1195
    infrared spectrometry, 1172–4, 1177
    ultraviolet spectrometry, 35, 1187
  identification of, 675.
m-Phenylenediamine, determination of, 1188
  reagent for bromide, 218
Phenylisocyanate reagent, for alcohols, 224
Phenylurethane derivatives,
  microtest for alcohols, 224
  optical properties, table of, 226
Phloroglucinal stain, in paper analysis, 1389
Phosphatase, acid. See Acid phosphatase.
Phosphatase, alkaline. See Alkaline phosphatase.
Phosphate. See also Phosphorus.
  determination of,
    by ultraviolet spectrometry, 33
    in detergent products, 1846–54
    in polyphosphates, 1854–7
    in soils, 561
    in water, 553
  microtest for, 220
Phosphate, inorganic, determination of, 1003–5
Phosphate rock, analysis of, 1102
Phosphorimeter, 92, 93
Phosphorimetry, 103
Phosphors, analysis of, 561, 562
Phosphorus. See also Phosphate and Polyphosphate.
  analysis of, 135
  determination by,
    activation analysis, 576, 865, 1790
    amperometric titration, 395
    emission spectrometry, 865, 1777–8, 1778–80, 1780–2
    isotope dilution, 561
    radiometric methods, 553, 556
    ultraviolet spectrometry, 33
    visible spectrometry, 1056, 1271, 1863–4
  determination of,
    in alloys, 576
    in biological materials, 556, 576
    in detergents, 553, 1863–4
    in fats, 1056
    in ferrous materials, 865
    in food, 553, 576
    in germanium, 1790
    in manure, 553
    in organic substance, 395
    in rocks, 561
    in semiconductor materials, 1777–8, 1778–80, 1780–2
    in silicon, 1790
    in slag, 556
    in soil, 1871–2, 1879
    in steel, 395, 556, 576
    in uranium compounds, 561

Phosphorus, determination of (Cont.)
  in vegetable oils, 1271
  spectrophotometric methods, comparison
    of, table, 19
Phosphorus, total, determination of, in ferti-
    lizers, 1103
Phosphorus, water-soluble, determination of,
    in fertilizers, 1103
Photographic emulsions, analysis of, for sil-
    ver, 576
Photometers for visible spectrometry, 10
  calibration of, 12
  instrument design, 10
Photon activation analysis, 1532
Phototubes for fluorescence measurements,
    86
Phthalic acid content, determination of, in
    alkyd resins, 1319
Phthalic acid isomers, determination of, in
    alkyd resins and esters, 1274–6
Phthalic anhydride, determination of,
  by ultraviolet spectrometry, 35
  in alkyd resins, 1272
Physical separation techniques, 253
Picric acid, determination of, 491
  reagent for gold, 216
Pi electrons, 82
Pi electrons and fluorescence, 83
Pigments. See also Paint pigments.
  identification of, in paints, 1286
Pinkhof-Treadwell method of end point loca-
    tion, 289
Piperazine, determination of, 1196
Plant materials,
  analysis by,
    activation analysis, 576
    atomic absorption spectroscopy, 109
    flame spectrometry, 133
  analysis for,
    calcium, 109
    copper, 109
    iron, 109
    magnesium, 109
    manganese, 109
    molybdenum, 109
    potassium, 109
    selenium, 576
    sodium, 109
    strontium, 109
    zinc, 109
Plasma. See also Biological fluids.
  analysis for,
    albumin, 1007–9
    carbon dioxide, 992–4
    coagulation time, 1023–5
    corticosteroids, 1032
    corticosterone, 564
    protein, total, 1004–7
Plasticizers, polymer. See Polymer plastici-
    zers.
Plastics. See also Polymers.
  analysis by,
    attenuated total reflectance, 1626–30
    conductivity, 1946
    differential thermal analysis, 1637–47

Plastics, analysis by (Cont.)
    elution chromatography, 1647–50
    gas chromatography, 736, 1653–60
    mass spectrometry, 1662
    microscopy, 1591–5
    nuclear magnetic resonance spectrom-
      etry, 1579–82
    polarized infrared radiation spectrom-
      etry, 1624–6
    radiochemical methods, 1588
    thermogravimetry, 1630–7
    thin-layer chromatography, 1650–3
    ultraviolet spectrometry, 1595–9
    x-ray diffraction, 1582–6
    x-ray fluorescence, 1586–7
  analysis for,
    ethyl acrylate, 1581
    ethylene, combined, 1588
    methyl methacrylate, 1581
    propylene, combined, 1588
    tris(nonylated phenyl) phosphite, 1597
    water, 1946
    zinc stearate, 1587
  detection of, by differential thermal anal-
    ysis, 1642
  examination of, by phase-contrast micros-
    copy, 1592
  identification of, by gas chromatography,
    1654
  infrared spectra of, 1281
  pyrolisis products of, analysis of, 1662
  qualitative analysis of, 1605
  quantitative analysis of, 1605
  sample preparation of, for infrared spec-
    trometry, 1602–4, 1606
Platinum,
  determination of,
    by atomic absorption spectrometry,
      1514, 1516, 1517
    in noble metals, 110
    in petroleum catalysts, 1516, 1517
    in reforming catalysts, 1537
  microtest for, 217
Pleochroic crystals, 223
Plutonium, determination of, in process wa-
    ter, 556
Polarimeters, photoelectric,
  Bendix, 263
  O. C. Rudolph & Sons, 262
  Perkin-Elmer Model 141, 263
  Zeiss, 263
Polarimeters, visual, 261
Polarimetry, 258, 260
  assay of,
    enzymes, 268
    lemon extracts, 265
    orange extracts, 265
  determination of,
    calcium pantothenate, 265
    estradiol benzoate, 265
    lactose, 265, 1131–3
    starch, 1108
    sugar, 1145
  instrumentation, 261
  quantitative analysis, 263

Polarimetry, quantitative analysis (Cont.)
Polariscope, 266
Polarization current titrations, 378
Polarized indicator electrodes, 290
Polarized infrared radiation spectrometry, 1624
  analysis of plastics, 1624–6
  determination of,
    distribution of crystallinity in polymers, 1625
    orientation of molecular groups in polymers, 1625
Polarized infrared spectra of polypropylene, 1625
Polarizing light microscopy, analysis of plastics, 1593
Polarizing microscope, 223
Polarograms,
  anodic stripping, 350
  cathode ray, 349
  derivative, 345, 347
  linear scan, 347
  pulse, 352
  regular, 345
  square wave, 352
Polarographic maxima, 334
Polarographic titrations, 377, 381
Polarographs,
  for derivative d. c. polarography, 344–5
  differential cathode ray polarograph, 364
  manual, 343
  univector, 364
Polarography,
  analysis of,
    aluminum, 944, 947
    aluminum alloys, 937–43
    aluminum-copper-zinc alloys, 943
    antimony, 1801
    antimony alloys, 944
    arsenic, 1800, 1802
    brass, 946, 948
    bronze, 943, 946
    cadmium, 944
    cast iron, 864
    cobalt, 946
    copper alloys, 944
    fats, 1081–3
    ferromanganese, 865
    ferrotungsten, 865
    ferrous materials, 864–5
    functional groups, 376, 1205
    gallium, 1802
    gallium arsenide, 1801, 1802–7
    germanium, 1801, 1802–7
    glass, 1233–5
    gold, 1800
    high alloy steel, 865
    hydrocarbon thinners in paints, 1308
    indium, 1800, 1801, 1802–7
    indium antimonide, 1802–7
    indium arsenide, 1802–7
    iron and steel, 864
    lead, 943
    lead alloys, 944
    magnesium, 945

Polarography, analysis of (Cont.)
    monel metal, 946
    nickel, 946
    nickel-molybdenum-iron alloys, 946
    nonferrous alloys, 924–48
    oils, 1308
    paints, 1307
    polymers, 1308
    rubber, 1695, 1729, 1746
    semiconductor materials, 1800–7
    silicon, 1802–7
    silicon carbide, 1800
    soil, 1876–7
    stainless steel, 864
    steel, 865
    tin alloys, 944
    titanium alloys, 940–3
    water, 1895–8, 1898–1900, 1902–7
    zinc, 944–5, 947
  applications of,
    inorganic substances, 367, 374–5
    organic substances, 367, 376
  current-voltage relationships, 324–7
  data for, 367
  determination of,
    accelerators in rubber, 1695
    acrylic monomers in polymers, 1308
    aluminum, 943, 1235
    anthraquinone, 1206
    antimony, 864, 943, 1233, 1802
    antioxidants, 1308, 1695
    arsenic, 864, 1802
    barium, 1235
    bismuth, 864, 943, 944, 1800, 1801, 1802–7
    cadmium, 864, 944, 1234, 1800, 1801, 1802–7, 1902–7
    calcium, 864
    chromium, 864, 940–3
    cobalt, 864, 940–3
    copper, 864, 937–43, 944, 945, 1800, 1801, 1802–7, 1876, 1902–7
    elements, polarographic characteristics, 370–3
    indium, 945, 1801, 1802–7
    iron, 945, 1800, 1801
    lead, 933–6, 937–43, 946, 947, 1235, 1800, 1801, 1802–7, 1902–7
    maleic acid, 1308
    maleic anhydride, 1205
    manganese, 946, 1876
    molybdenum, 865
    nickel, 865, 937–43, 946, 1801, 1902–7
    niobium, 865
    nitrate, 1877, 1898–1900
    oxygen, dissolved, 1895–8
    peroxide, 1308
    potassium, 1235
    selenium, 1234
    silver, 1801
    sodium, 1235
    styrene, 1308
    sulfur in rubber, 1695
    sulfur, free, in rubber, 1729
    thallium, 1801, 1802–7

Polarography, determination of (Cont.)
tin, 865, 947, 1801, 1802–7
titanium, 865, 947
zinc, 865, 937–43, 946, 947, 948, 1235, 1746, 1800, 1801, 1802–7, 1901–7
diffusion current, 331–7
constant, 332
factors affecting, 333
measurement of, 361, 367
diffusion-limited currents, departures from, 334
catalytic currents, 335, 336
kinetic currents, 335, 336
mixed currents, 335
nonadditive currents, 335
polarographic maxima, 334
dropping mercury electrode, 327–31
charging current, 329
voltage range, 328
half-wave potential, 339
table of, 926–9
instrumentation, 342
agar salt bridge, 358
calomel electrodes, 358
capillary, 354, 356
cells for, 356, 357, 358
mercury reservoir, assembly, 355
oxygen removal, 357
rapid dropping mercury electrode, 348
reference electrodes, 358
stationary electrode, 346
instrumentation for,
alternating current, polarography, 350
anodic stripping, polarography, 349
automatic compensation or residual current, 363
cathode ray polarography, 348
conventional polarography, 342
derivative d. c. polarography, 343, 344–5
inverse polarography, 349
pulse polarography, 350
rapid linear scan polarography, 348
slow linear scan polarography, 346
square wave polarography, 350
polarographic waves, 328
equations for, 337–41, 341–2
irreversible, 341
reversible, 337–41
theory of, 331–42
wave height, 328, 361–4, 364–7
quantitative analysis, 360–7
supporting electrolytes, table of, 925–9
types of,
alternating current, 350–4, 1801
anodic stripping, 349–50
cathode ray, 348–9, 1801
derivative d. c., 343–6
inverse, 349–50
oscillographic, 1801
pulse, 350–4
rapid dropping mercury, 348
rapid linear scan, 348–9
slow linear scan, 346–8
square wave, 350–4, 1801

Polarography, types of (Cont.)
stationary electrode, 346–8
stripping, 1801
Polarometric titrations, 377
Pole strength, 582
Polybutadiene, characterization of, 1618
identification of, 1673–5
determination of unsaturation, 1621–2
Polybutylene, characterization of, 1317
Polychromatic absorptiometry, 171
Polyester resins, identification of, 1306
Polyethylene,
analysis for,
carbonyl group, 1613
crystallinity, 1584–6
2,6-di-*tert*.-butyl-*p*-cresol, 1616
linear polymer content of, 657
methyl groups, 1612
9-octadienamide, 1616
unsaturation, 1613
characterization of, 1317
Polyethylene blends, characterization of, 1645
Poly(ethylene-ethyl acrylate), characterization of, 1317
Poly(ethylene-vinyl acetate), characterization of, 1317
Polyisoprene, analysis of, for *cis*-1,4-content, 1690
Polymer additives,
determination by,
gas chromatography, 1655
infrared spectrometry, 1614
ultraviolet spectrometry, 1596
separation of, 1650
Polymerization reactions, study of, 1622–4
Polymer plasticizers, determination of,
by gas chromatography, 1655
in poly(vinyl chloride), 1606–9
Polymers. *See also* Plastics and Rubber polymers.
analysis by,
activation analysis, 576, 1537
differential thermal analysis, 1308, 1639–42, 1644, 1646
elution chromatography, 1647
gas chromatography, 1314–6, 1656
gel-permeation chromatography, 1324
infrared spectrometry, 1285, 1583, 1614, 1622
microscopy, 1591
near infrared spectrometry, 1599
nuclear magnetic resonance, 1306
polarized infrared radiation spectrometry, 1625
polarography, 1308
radiochemical methods, 1588
thermogravimetry, 1630
ultraviolet spectrometry, 1596–7
x-ray diffraction, 1584
x-ray fluorescence, 1787
analysis for,
acetyl tributyl citrate, 1656
acrylic monomers in polymers, 1308
activation energy of thermal degrada-

Polymers, analysis for (Cont.)
  tion, 1634–7
  additives, 1596, 1614
  antioxidants, 1596–7
  antioxidants, phenolic, 1599
  antiozonants, 1596
  chlorine, 1537
  dibutyl sebacate, 1656
  ethylene, combined, 1588
  heat of fusion, 1644
  hydroxyl number, 1599
  light stabilizers, 1596
  methylisopropenyl ketone, 1597
  molecular size, 1324
  monomer, free, 1314
  orientation of molecular groups, 1625
  oxidation products, 1622
  oxygen, 576
  propylene, combined, 1588
  styrene, 1308
  styrene, combined, 1597
  styrene monomer, 1315
  thermal decomposition, 1646
  toluene diisocyanate monomer, 1316
  vinyl toluene, 1315
  zinc stearate, 1587
  characterization of, 1642
  chemical changes in, detection of, 1639–42
  crystallinity of, determination by, 1582
    density measurement, 1583
    differential solubility, 1583
    differential thermal analysis, 1644
    heat of fusion, 1584
    infrared spectrometry, 1583
    x-ray diffraction, 1584
  crystallinity of, distribution, 1625
  crystallinity, spherulitic, 1591
  fractionation of, 1647
  identification of, in paints, 1285
  molecular weight distribution, 1306
  molecular weights of, determination by,
    light scattering, 1660
    osmometry, 1661
    ultracentrifugation, 1661
    ultraviolet spectrometry, 1597
  physical changes in, detection of, 1639–
    42
  separation of, 1647
  stereochemistry of, 1306
  thermal degradation, determination of,
    1630
Polymers, types of,
  amorphous, 1617–21
  atactic, 1618
  crystalline, 1617–21
  isotactic, 1618
  stereoregular, 1617–21
  syndiotactic, 1618
Poly(methylvinyl ether), analysis of, for tolu-
    ene, 1186
Poly(methylvinyl ether-maleic anhydride),
    analysis of, for benzene, 1186
Polynuclear hydrocarbons, determination of,
    633
Polyols, determination of,

Polyols, determination of (Cont.)
  in alkyd resins, 1321
  retention times, 1324
Polypeptides, conformation, determination
    of, 274
Polyphosphates,
  analysis of,
    by paper chromatography, 1854–7
    for orthophosphate, 1854–7
  determination of,
    by isotope dilution, 562
    in detergents, 1846–54, 1854–7
Polypropylene, characterization of, 1317
  fractionation of, 1648
Polysiloxanes. See also Silicone rubbers.
  infrared spectra of, 1682
Polystyrene, analysis of, for mineral oil,
    1614–6
  attenuated total reflectance spectrum,
    1629
  fractionation of, 1647
Polythionates, determination of, 553
  by ultraviolet spectrometry, 1066–71,
    1183, 1278
  in alkyd resins, 1278
  in drying oils, 1278
  in fats and oils, 1066–71
Polyunsaturated fatty acids, determination
    of, 1066–71
Polyurethane, characterization of, 1317
Polyurethane rubbers, structural character-
    istics of, 1679–81
Poly(vinyl acetate),
  characterization of, 1317
  determination of, 963–5, 1287
Poly(vinyl chloride), analysis of,
  by infrared spectrometry, 1606
  for fillers, 1606–10
  for plasticizers, 1606–9
  for resin, 1606–10
  for stabilizers, 1606–10
  characterization of, 1317
Poly(vinylidene fluoride), structure of,
    1580
Pontachrome BBR, fluorometric reagent, 99,
    100
Pontachrome Violet SW, fluorometric re-
    agent, 99
Portland Cement. See Cement.
Positron emission, 542
Potassium,
  determination by,
    activation analysis, 576
    amperometric titration, 394, 1236
    atomic absorption spectrometry, 109,
      110, 1228, 1514, 1516–7, 1876
    emission spectrometry, 1772–5, 1873
    flame spectrometry, 132–5, 137, 965–7,
      1009–11, 1027–31, 1104, 1294, 1837,
      1879
    glass electrode, 1878
    isotope dilution, 562
    polarography, 1235
    ultraviolet spectrometry, 32
    x-ray spectrometry, 969–73, 1253

Potassium (Cont.)
  determination of,
    in biological materials, 134, 1009–11
    in blood, 576
    in boiler deposits, 110
    in cement, 132, 137, 965–7, 969–73
    in coal ash, 110
    in detergents, 1837
    in fertilizers, 109, 133, 1104
    in glass, 132, 1219–26, 1227, 1235, 1236, 1253
    in limestone, 137
    in lubricating oils, 135, 1516, 1517
    in minerals, 576
    in paint, 1294
    in phosphorus, 135, 562
    in plant materials, 109
    in semiconductor materials, 1772–5
    in silicates, 394
    in soaps, 1837
    in soils, 109, 1228, 1873, 1875, 1876, 1878, 1879
    in tissue, 109
    in tungsten metal, 135
    in urine, 109, 1027–31
  microtest for, 214
Potassium bromide pellet, for infrared spectrometry, 49–50, 1604
Potassium mercuric thiocyanate reagent, 214
Potentiometric titrations, 283
  analysis of,
    cement, 973
    detergents, 1840, 1841, 1843–4
    fats, 1077
    ferrous materials, 865
    glass, 1237, 1238–42
    meat and meat products, 1127
    rubber, 1695, 1761–3
    soap, 1841, 1843–4
    water, 1894–5
  applications, 287
  automatic titrations, 287
  determination of,
    amines, 292
    amino acids, 291
    antioxidants in rubber, 1695
    arsenic, 1237
    calcium, 973
    cerium, 294
    chloride, 973, 1894–5
    chromium, 294
    iron, 1238–42
    isocyanate group in bonding agents (rubber), 1761–3
    magnesium, 973
    manganese, 294
    nickel, 865
    soap, 1843–4
    sodium chloride, 1127
    sulfuric acid, 1840
    water, 1841
    zinc, 292
  end point location,
    differential titrations, 289
    graphical determination, 288

Potentiometric titrations, end point locations (Cont.)
    Pinkhof-Treadwell method, 289
    polarized indicator electrodes, use of, 290
    titration to equivalence point potential, 288
  instrumentation, 284
    electrode systems, 284, 285
  principles of, 283
  types of,
    acid-base, 290, 291
    complexometric, 293
    with EDTA, 293
    oxidation-reduction, 294
    precipitation, 292
Potentiostatic coulometry. See Coulometry at controlled potential.
Precipitation titrations, potentiometric, 292
Pregnanediol, determination of, 1045–6
Preservatives, chemical, determination of, 1111
Primary standards for pH measurements, table of, 523
Principal line powder, 157
Prism spectrometer, for emission spectrometry, 143
Probes, small area, for x-ray analysis, 1259
Process water (paper), bacteriological examination of, 1458–60
Prompt-gamma ray activation analysis, 1533
Propargyl alcohol, determination of, in propargyl halides, 1173
Propargyl halides, analysis of, for propargyl alcohol, 1173
Propionate, microtest for, 221
Proponal-sandoptal mixtures, analysis of, 239
Propylene, combined, determination of, in polymers, 1588
Propylene glycol, determination of, 1323–4
Propyl gallate, determination of, 1057–8
Protein content, determination of, in foods, 1157–9
Proteins, conformation, determination of, 274
Protein, total, determination of, 1004–7
Proton nuclear magnetic resonance. See Nuclear magnetic resonance.
Pulfrich refractometer, 251
Pulp, analysis, 1326–78
  analysis for,
    brightness, 1351–7
    color, 1348–61
  bacteriological examination of, 1375
  determination of,
    drainage factor, 1363–6
    drainage time, 1363–5
  freeness test for, 1366–74
  handsheets, forming of,
    for optical tests, 1357–9
    for physical tests, 1337–48
  laboratory processing of, 1332–7
  physical testing of handsheet,
    basis weight, 1359

Pulp, analysis, physical testing of handsheet (Cont.)
  bursting strength, 1361
  folding endurance, 1361
  moisture, 1361
  tearing strength, 1361
  tensile strength and stretch, 1360
  thickness, 1359
  spectral reflectivity of, 1348–51
Pulpwood, analysis for,
  moisture content, 1326–32
  specific gravity (density), 1326–32
Pulse polarography, 350
PVC. *See* Poly(vinyl chloride).
Pyramidon-antipyrine, analysis of, 239
Pyridine, determination of, 77, 1189
Pyrolysis-gas chromatography. *See also* Gas chromatography.
  characterization of,
    cellulose acetate, 1317
    cellulose butyrate, 1317
    cotton, 1317
    elastomers, 1317
    methylstyrene, 1317
    nylon 6, 1317
    nylon 66, 1317
    phenolic resins, 1317
    polybutylene, 1317
    polyethylene, 1317
    poly(ethylene-ethyl acrylate), 1317
    poly(ethylene-vinyl acetate), 1317
    polypropylene, 1317
    polyurethane, 1317
    poly(vinyl acetate), 1317
    poly(vinyl chloride), 1317
    silk, 1317
    wool, 1317
Pyrrolidine, determination of, 1196
2-Pyrrolidone, analysis of, for *N*-vinylpyrrolidone, 1168, 1175

Qualitative analysis. *See special techniques and materials.*
Quantitative analysis. *See special techniques and materials.*
Quarter-wave potential, chronopotentiometry, 407
Quartz, analysis of, for manganese, 576
Quercetin, fluorometric reagent, 99
Quincke method, magnetic susceptibility, 593
Quinhydrone electrode, for pH measurements, 524
Quinoline, determination of, in gasoline, 1189
8-Quinolinol. *See* 8-Hydroxyquinoline.

R_f values, of esters of fatty acids, table of, 1093
Radiation buffers in flame emission spectrometry, 127
Radiation energy, units of, 542
Radioactivation analysis. *See* Activation analysis *and* Neutron activation.

Radioactive disintegration, 541
  alpha-particle emission, 542
  electron capture, 542
  growth and decay rates of radioelements, table of, 544
  positron emission, 542
  rate of decay, 542, 544
Radioactive emission, beta-particle, 542
Radioactive transition, isomeric transition, 542
Radioactivity, 543
  half life, 543
  measurement of, 544
    by Geiger-Müller counter, 545
    by ionization chamber, 545
    by liquid scintillation counter, 545
    by semiconductor counters, 545
    by solid crystal scintillation, 545
    errors in, 546
    statistics in, 546
  nature of, 541
  specific activity, 544
Radioactivity, added, measurement of, 552
Radioactivity, natural, measurement of, 551
Radiochemical methods, 552. *See also* Activation analysis, Isotope dilution, Radiometric methods, *and* Radiometric titration.
  analysis of,
    acrylonitrile-vinyl acetate copolymers, 1588
    antimony, 1791
    plastics, 1588
    rubber, 1758
    water, 1907
  applications of, 581
  determination of,
    ethylene, combined, in polymers, 1588
    monomer content in ethylene-propylene copolymers, 1687
    nonmetallic compounds in ferrous materials, 865
    propylene, combined, in polymers, 1588
    sulfur, blooming of, in rubber, 1730
    sulfur, diffusivity of, in rubber, 1730
    sulfur, solubility of, in rubber, 1730
    uranium, 865
    water, 1940–1
Radiochemistry units, 544
Radioisotopes. *See also* Radionuclides.
  analytical applications of, 551
  detection sensitivities of, table, 548
Radioisotopes, uses of,
  as radioactive reagents, 552
  in carrier techniques, 552
  in chemical analysis, table of, 549, 550
  in isotope dilution, 552
  in tracer chemistry, 547
  selection of, 548
Radiometric methods,
  for elements, table of, 556
  for organic compounds, table of, 559
Radiometric titrations, table of, 559

Radionuclides, analysis of mixtures of, 545
  neutron-induced, gamma-ray energies of, 570–2
  table of, 566–9
Radioreagent methods,
  for elements, table of, 553
  for organic compounds, table of, 555
Radium, determination of, in water, 556, 1913–5
Radium-226, determination of, in water, 1915–24
Raman spectra,
  applications in analysis, 59
    difficulties in, 60
  depolarization ratio, 64
  nature of, 60
  origin of, 59–60
  polarization of, 62
  recording of, 72
  standard intensity, 70
Raman spectra of,
  aqueous solutions, 77
  benzene and substituted benzenes, 77
  biacetyl, 66
  diamines, 77
  hydrocarbons, 76
  stearolic acid, 76
  sulfhydryl compounds, 77
Raman spectrometer, Cary Model 81, 67
Raman spectrometry, 59
  advantages of, 75
  analysis of functional groups, 1208
  applications, 75
  experimental technique, 65
  instrumentation, 65
    Cary Model 81 spectrometer, 67, 73
    detectors, 74
    monochromator, 65, 74
    source of excitation, 65
  intensity measurement of, 69
  intensity standards, 70
  limitations of, 75
  quantitative analysis, 69
  resonance Raman effect, 75
  sample preparation, 66
  simple phases and cells, 67–8
Rancidity, determination of, in natural fats, 1059
Rankine method, magnetic susceptibility, 593
Rapid dropping mercury electrode polarography, 348
Rapid linear scan polarography, 348
Rare earth chloride hydrates, characterization of, 659
Rare earth metals,
  determination by,
    activation analysis, 576
    electrophoresis, 714
    emission spectrometry, 865, 900–5
    potentiometric titration, 293
    ultraviolet spectrometry, 33
  determination of,
    in ferrous materials, 865
    in graphite, 576

Rare earth metals, determination of (Cont.)
    in magnesium alloys, 900–5
    in soil, 576
  separation of, 714
Reaction kinetics, determination of, 473
Reaction mechanisms, determination of, 473
Reagents, for compounds, 21
  for metals, table of, 21
  for nonmetals, 21
Ream, analysis of, 1263
Reference electrodes,
  for amperometric titrations, 385
  for chronopotentiometry, 413
  for pH measurements, 527
    calomel electrode, 527
    silver-silver chloride electrode, 527, 528
    thallium amalgam-thallous chloride electrode, 528, 577
Reference materials, in iron and steel analysis, 854–5
Reflectance spectrometry, analysis of paints, 1271
Reflected β-radiation, determination of,
  iron, 864
  manganese, 864
Reformed gas, analysis of, 1211
Reforming catalysts, analysis of, 1537
Refractive index, 250
  of fats, determination of, 1076
    table of, 1075
  of sucrose solutions, table of, 1149–51
Refractivities of atoms, table of, 252
Refractometry, 250
  analysis of,
    fats, 256, 1075–7
    structural groups of mineral oil, 254
  applications, 252, 255
  determination of,
    albumens, 256
    composition of solutions, 255
    globulins, 256
    nonalbuminous constituents of serum, 256
    oil content of flax seed, 1076
    sugar in food, 1148
    water, added in milk, 1134
  instrumentation, 250
  physical separation techniques, 253
  process analysis equipment, 251
  qualitative analysis, 252
  quantitative aspects, 255
Refrigerants, analysis of, for water, 1939
Relative retention, 722
Resins. See also Polymers.
  identification of, in paints, 1285
  infrared spectra of, 1281
Resins, nitrogen, analysis of, for melamine, 1278
Resins, phenolic. See Phenolic resins.
Resins, polyester. See Polyester resins.
Resins, urea, analysis of, for urea, 1269
Resonance Raman effect, 75
Retention data for gas chromatography, 1562–74

Reversed-phase partition-thin layer chromatography. *See* Thin-layer chromatography.
Reverse isotope dilution, 554
Reversible waves, polarographic, 337
Reynold's number, 803
Rhenium, determination of, 33
Rhodamine B, fluorometric reagent, 98
Rhodamine SDGN, detection of, 78
Rhodium, determination of, 1514
Riboflavin, determination of, 102, 1154–5
Rocks. *See also* Silicates *and* Siliceous materials.
  analysis of, 110, 561–2, 575–7, 1228
Ronnel, 1478, 1484, 1492, 1497, 1499
Rosin, analysis of, for iron, 1266
Rotating platinum electrode, 384
  amperometric titrations, 384
Rotography, 268
Rubber, 1664, 1666. *See also* Natural rubber.
  analysis by,
    amperometry, 1695, 1742–3
    chromatography, 1695–9, 1701–6
    conductivity, 1695
    electron microscopy, 1761
    fluorometry, 1695
    gas chromatography, 1738–40
    infrared spectrometry, 1695, 1706, 1719
    isotope dilution, 562
    microscopy, 1751, 1758
    microtoming techniques, 1758
    near-infrared spectrometry, 1599
    nephelometry, 1695
    photometric titration, 1695
    polarography, 1695, 1729, 1746
    potentiometric titration, 1695, 1761–3
    pyrolysis, 1731–3
    radiometric methods, 1758
    ultraviolet spectrometry, 1695, 1696–9, 1699–1706, 1713–7, 1722–4, 1733–5, 1740–2, 1744–6, 1748
    visible spectrometry, 1717–9, 1733, 1735–8, 1743
    x-ray diffraction, 1706–12, 1713–7, 1719–22, 1747
  analysis for,
    accelerators, 1695, 1695–9, 1699–1706, 1740–2
    aldehyde-amine accelerators, 1699–1701
    amines, 1706–12
    antioxidants, 1695–6
    antioxidants, amine, 1713–7, 1717–9, 1735–8, 1738–40
    antioxidants, phenolic, 1733–5
    carbon black, 1695, 1731–3
    cis-1,4-content, 1599
    dithiocarbamate accelerators, 1696–9, 1699–1701
    extenders, 1695
    fillers, dispersion, 1757
    fillers, inorganic, 1695, 1719
    fluorine, 1752–6
    guanidine accelerators, 1699–1701
    isocyanate group, 1761–3
    lead, 1748

Rubber, analysis for (Cont.)
  magnesium carbonate, 1719–22
  magnesium oxide, 1719–22
  mercaptobenzothiazole, 1742–3
  organic acid, 1749–52
  processing oils, 1695
  rubber hydrocarbon, total, 1691
  sulfur, 562, 1695, 1722–4, 1724–9
  sulfur, free, 1729
  tetramethyl thiuram disulfide, 1743
  thiazole accelerators, 1699–1701
  thiruam accelerators, 1699–1701
  zinc, 1746
  zinc oxide, 1744–6, 1747
  solvents for, 1666
Rubber accelerators,
  absorbance characteristics of, table of, 1704–5
  aldehyde–amines, identification of, 1699–1701
  determination of, 1695, 1740–2
  dithiocarbamates, determination of, 1740–2
  identification of, 1696–9, 1699–1701
  guanidines, identification of, 1699–1701
  identification of, 1695–9, 1699–1706
  thiazoles, identifications of, 1699–1701
  thiurams, identification of, 1699–1701
Rubber compounds, 1695
  accelerators. *See* Rubber accelerators.
  antioxidants, determination of, 1695
  antioxidants, identification of, 1695
  antioxidants, amine, determination of, 1713–7, 1735–8, 1738–40
  antioxidants, amine, identification of, 1713–7, 1717–9
  antioxidants, phenolic, determination of, 1733–5
  carbon black, determination of, 1695, 1731–3
  extender, determination of, 1695
  fillers, inorganic, determination of, 1695
  identification of, 1695, 1719–22
  processing oils, determination of, 1695
  sulfur, determination of, 1695, 1722–4, 1724–9
  sulfur, free, determination of, 1729
Rubber hydrocarbons total, determination of, 1691
Rubber-modified polystyrene, examination of, 1592
Rubber, natural. *See* Natural rubber.
Rubber polymers. *See also individual polymers.*
Rubber polymers,
  composition of, 1667
  copolymer composition of, 1667
  identification of, 1667, 1669–70, 1671, 1673–5
  mixtures of, analysis, 1691–5
    natural rubber and SBR, analysis of, 1692
  nomenclature of, 1665
  pyrolysis temperatures, table of, 1669
  structural composition of, 1667
Rubber products, 1664, 1666

Rubidium, determination of,
in glass, 1219–26, 1227
in semiconductor materials, 1772–5
Rudolph, O.C., and Sons, photoelectric polarimeter, 262
Rutile, 1303

Saccharimeter, 266
Saccharimetry, 258, 265. *See also* Polarimetry.
determination of sucrose, 267
Safflower oil, absorptivity value, 1289
fatty acid composition of, 1322
Salad dressing, analysis of, for disodium
EDTA, 1121
Salicylate, determination of, 35
Salicylidene-*o*-aminophenol, fluorometric reagent, 99
Salinity of soil, determination of, 1880
Salts, molten, analysis of, 422
Sample preparation,
of biological materials, 134
of ferroalloys, 853–4
for atomic absorption spectrometry, 112,
1218
for electron probe x-ray microanalyzer,
193, 1229–30
for emission spectrometry, 153, 859
for flame spectrometry, 132, 134, 1213
for infrared spectrometry, 45, 1602–4,
1606
by internal reflectance, 1283
liquid phase, 46
materials used, table of, 46
solutions, 46
solids, 48
vapor phase, 45
for nuclear magnetic resonance, 612
for Raman spectrometry, 66
for x-ray spectrometry, 176, 906, 1247
Sampling,
of fluxes, 853–4
of glass, 132, 1218, 1229–30, 1247, 1258–
60
of iron and steel, 859
of molten metals, 853–4
of ores, 853–4
of plastics, 1602–4, 1606
of rubber and rubber products, 1666
of sinters, 853–4
of soaps and detergents, 1812
of water,
for flame emission spectrometry, 132
Sand, analysis of, for water, 1946
Sand equation, 406, 409
Sandoptal-proponal mixtures, analysis of,
239
Sargent automatic analyzer, 439
Sargent oscillometer, 497
Sargent Slomin electrolytic analyzer, 441
Saturated hydrocarbons. *See also* Alkanes *and*
Cycloalkanes.
determination of, in fats, 1089
SBR. *See* Styrene-butadiene copolymer.
analysis of, for organic acid, 1749–52

Scandium, determination of,
by potentiometric titration, 293
by ultraviolet spectrometry, 33
Schopper folding endurance of paper, 1408
Scintillation detector, 176
Scintillation spectrometers, 546
Sea sediments, analysis of, 576
Sea water. *See also* Water.
analysis of, 305, 561, 576, 577
Second-order transition of polymers, 1642
Sedimentation analysis, 781
characterization of ultracentrifugation,
784
density gradient sedimentation equilibrium, 785, 792
sedimentation equilibrium methods, 784,
787, 788
sedimentation velocity methods, 784,
785
methods of, 783
methods of separation, 781
Sedimentation balances, 813
Sedimentation methods,
particle size analysis, 803
centrifugal sedimentation techniques,
818–21
cumulative-homogeneous suspensions,
813–6
cumulative two-layer systems, 816–8
incremental-homogeneous methods,
805–13
theory of, 803
Seeman-Bohlin x-ray diffraction camera, 199
Selenate. *See* Selenium.
Selenite. *See* Selenium.
Selenium,
analysis of, 575
determination by,
activation analysis, 576, 1791
amperometric titration, 396
isotope dilution, 562
polarography, 1234
determination of,
in feeds and plant products, 576
in fertilizers, 576
in gallium arsenide, 1791
in glass, 1234
in sulfur, 576
Selleger's stain, in paper analysis, 1382, 1387
Semiconductor counters, radioactivity, 545
Semiconductor materials, 1764
analysis by,
activation analysis, 1789, 1790, 1791,
1792–80
emission spectrometry, 1770–82
infrared spectrometry, 1809
isotope dilution, 1791
mass spectrometry, 1782–9
polarography, 1800–7
vacuum fusion, 1807
analysis for,
antimony, 1780–2, 1802, 1792–1800
arsenic, 1790, 1792–1800, 1802
bismuth, 1792–1800, 1801, 1802–7
cadmium, 1800

Semiconductor materials, analysis for (Cont.)
  cobalt, 1792–1800
  copper, 1790, 1792–1800, 1801, 1802–7
  elements, 1772–82
  gallium, 1792–1800
  gold, 1792–1800
  hydrogen, 1807
  indium, 1792–1800, 1801, 1802–7
  iron, 1800, 1801
  lead, 1800, 1801, 1802–7
  magnesium, 1791
  nickel, 1801
  oxygen, 1791, 1807
  phosphorus, 1790
  selenium, 1791
  silicon, 1771, 1791
  silicon carbide, 1771
  silver, 1801
  sulfur, 1791
  tellurium, 1791
  thallium, 1801, 1802–7
  tin, 1801, 1802–7
  zinc, 1791, 1800, 1801, 1802–7
  carrier concentrations determination of, 1767
  conduction in, 1764
  dopants in, 1766
  impurities in identification of, 1768
  problems of analysis, 1769
Separated electrode, 463
Separation, by gas chromatography, 720
Sequestrene. See EDTA and Disodium EDTA.
Serotonin, determination of, in blood, 1036–7
Serum. See also Biological fluids.
  analysis for,
    acid phosphatase, 981–4
    alkaline phosphatase, 984–7
    albumin, 1007–9
    barbiturates, 1039
    bilirubin, 987–60
    carbon dioxide, 992–4
    cholesterol, total, 997–1000
    creatinine, 1000–2
    insulin, 564
    lipids, 1039–41
    pesticides, 1503
    protein, total, 1004–7
    SGOT, 1011–4
    sodium, 1027–31
Serum glutamic-oxalacetic transaminase. See SGOT.
Serum proteins, separation of, 710–14
Sesamin, determination of, in fats, 1060
Sewage, analysis of, for alkyl benzene sulfonates, 1833–6
SFC. See Solid fat content.
SGOT, determination of, in serum, 1011–4
Sharples micromerograph, 817
Sieves, for particle size analysis, 799–801
  National Standard Specifications, table of, 800
Sigma electrons, 82
Silanes, analysis of, 1199
  determination of, 1197

Silicates. See also Rocks and Siliceous materials.
  analysis by,
    amperometric titration, 394
    flame spectrometry, 1228
    fluorometric method, 101
  analysis for,
    aluminum, 1228
    beryllium, 101
    potassium, 394
Siliceous materials, analysis of, for iron, 1228
Silicomanganese, analysis of, for silicon, 865
Silicon,
  analysis by,
    activation analysis, 575, 1790, 1791, 1792–1800
    emission spectrometry, 1780–2
    infrared spectrometry, 1810
    mass spectrometry, 1784–8
    polarography, 1802–7
    vacuum fusion, 1807
  analysis for,
    antimony, 575, 1792–1800
    arsenic, 1792–1800
    bismuth, 1792–1800, 1802–7
    boron, 1791
    cadmium, 1802–7
    cobalt, 1792–1800
    copper, 575, 1792–1800, 1802–7
    gallium, 1792–1800
    gold, 575, 1792–1800
    indium, 1792–1800, 1802–7
    lead, 1802–7
    oxygen, 1807, 1811
    phosphorus, 1790
    thallium, 1802–7
    tin, 1802–7
    zinc, 1802–7
  determination by,
    activation analysis, 576, 865, 1791
    emission spectrometry, 865, 1771, 1772–5, 1778–80, 1780–2
    ultraviolet spectrometry, 33
    x-ray spectrometry, 865, 969–73, 1253
  determination of,
    in beryllium, 576
    in cast iron, 865
    in cement, 969–73
    in ferromanganese, 865
    in ferrotungsten, 865
    in ferrous materials, 865
    in gallium arsenide, 576
    in glass, 1253
    in sea sediments, 576
    in semiconductor materials, 1771, 1772–5, 1778–80, 1780–2, 1791
    in silicomanganese, 865
    in steel, 865
  reagents for, 99
Silicon carbide, analysis of, 1800
  determination of, in semiconductors, 1771
Silicon chelates, fluorescent, 99
Silicone resins, infrared spectra of, 1683
Silicone rubbers, structural characteristics of, 1681–3

Silicon polymers, fractionation of, 1647
Silk, characterization of, 1317
Silver,
  determination by,
    activation analysis, 576
    amperometric titration, 390
    atomic absorption spectrometry, 110, 116
    coulometric method, 562
    electrogravimetry, 455, 456
    emission spectrometry, 1772–5, 1778–80, 1780–2, 1892–4
    flame spectrometry, 136, 880–4
    polarography, 1801
    radiometric titration, 560
    radioreagent method, 553
  determination of,
    in black copper, 390
    in copper alloys, 391
    in film, 553
    in germanium, 1801
    in iron raw materials, 390
    in lead concentrates, 116, 390
    in magnesium-base alloys, 880–4
    in noble metals, 110
    in nonferrous metals, 110, 136
    in ores and concentrates, 110
    in petroleum and petroleum products, 110
    in photographic emulsions, 576
    in semiconductor materials, 1772–5, 1778–80, 1780–2
    in steel, 576
    in sulfides, 576
    in water, 1892–4
Silver nitrate,
  reagents,
  for acetate, 221
    reagent for arsenite, 221
    reagent for chloride, 217
    reagent for cyanide, 219
Silver-silver chloride electrode, for pH measurements, 527, 528
Silver-tarnishing test of paper, 1432–3
Silvex, determination of, in water, 1926
Simple polarization, 266
Sinters, sampling of, 853–4
Slags,
  analysis by,
    atomic absorption spectrometry, 864
    flame spectrometry, 864
    radiometric method, 556
    x-ray spectrometry, 860, 864
  analysis for,
    calcium, 864
    iron, 864
    magnesium, 864
    phosphorus, 556
Slater and Cohen disc centrifuge, 819
Slow linear scan polarography, 346
Slush pulp, bacteriological examination of, 1458–60
Soaps,
  analysis by, 1812
    flame spectrometry, 1837

Soaps, analysis by (Cont.)
    ultraviolet spectrometry, 1826–8
    visible spectrometry, 1816–7
    x-ray spectrometry, 1826–8
  analysis for,
    copper, 1816–7
    germicides, 1826–8
    insoluble materials, 1838–9
    potassium, 1837
    sodium, 1837
  determination by,
    conductivity method, 1080, 1756
    flame spectrometry, 1073–4
    potentiometric titration, 1843–4
  determination of,
    in commercial products containing detergents, 1843–4
    in latex, 1756
    in oil, 1073–4, 1080
  sampling of, 1812
Sodium,
  determination by,
    activation analysis, 576, 1537
    atomic absorption spectrometry, 109, 110, 1228, 1514, 1516, 1517, 1876
    emission spectrometry, 1772–5
    flame spectrometry, 132, 134, 135, 137, 965–7, 1009–11, 1027–31, 1073–4, 1219–26, 1227, 1294, 1837, 1875
    glass electrode, 1877
    isotope dilution, 562
    polarography, 1235
    x-ray emission spectrometry, 1255
  determination of,
    in aluminum and aluminum alloys, 135
    in biological materials, 134, 576, 1009–11
    in blood serum, 109
    in body, total, 562
    in boiler deposits, 110
    in cast iron, 135
    in cement, 132, 137, 965–7
    in coal ash, 110
    in detergents, 1837
    in fertilizers, 109
    in fused salt, 557
    in glass, 132, 1219–26, 1227, 1235, 1255
    in limestone, 137
    in lithium, 135
    in metals and alloys, 576
    in nodular iron, 135
    in oil, 1073–4
    in paint, 1294
    in petroleum and petroleum products, 110
    in phosphorus, 135
    in plant materials, 109
    in sea water, 576
    in semiconductor materials, 1772–5
    in serum, 1027–31
    in soaps, 1837
    in soils, 109, 1228, 1875–7
    in solutions, 576

Sodium, determination of (Cont.)
  in sulfuric acid, 1537
  in tissue, 109
  in tungsten metal, 135
  in worn lube oils, 1516, 1517
  in urine, 109
  microtest for, 213
Sodium alkyl benzene sulfonate. *See* Alkyl benzene sulfonates.
Sodium chloride, determination of, in meat and meat products, 1127
Sodium thermionic detector, in gas chromatography, 1488
Sodium toluene sulfonate, 1823–5. *See* Toluene sulfonic acid, Sodium salt.
Sodium xylene sulfonate. *See* Xylene sulfonic acid, Sodium salt.
Soil,
  analysis by, 1865
    activation analysis, 576
    atomic absorption spectrometry, 109, 114, 1228, 1876
    column chromatography, 1880
    conductivity method, 1946, 1947
    dielectric method, 1950
    electrodialysis, 1878
    emission spectrometry, 1827–4, 1873
    flame spectrometry, 133, 1874, 1875, 1879
    gas chromatography, 1879
    glass electrode, 1877, 1878
    ion exchange, 1880
    isotope dilution, 561
    neutron scattering, 1940
    paper chromatography, 1879
    polarography, 1876, 1877
    thermogravimetry, 1880
    visible spectrometry, 1865, 1866–8, 1869–71, 1879
  analysis for,
    aluminum, 1865, 1873
    bismuth, 1873
    boron, 1866
    cadmium, 1873
    calcium, 109, 561, 1228, 1873, 1875, 1876, 1879, 1880
    carbon, 1879
    carbonate, 1880
    chromium, 1873
    cobalt, 1866–8, 1873, 1879
    copper, 109, 1866–7, 1873, 1876, 1879
    gallium, 1873
    iron, 109, 1868, 1873
    lead, 1873
    magnesium, 109, 1228, 1868, 1873, 1875, 1876, 1879, 1880
    magnesium, exchangeable, 114
    manganese, 109, 1869, 1876
    molybdenum, 109, 1869–71, 1873
    nickel, 1873, 1879
    nitrate, 1871, 1877
    nitrogen, 1878–9
    organic matter, 1880
    phosphate, 561
    phosphorus, 1871–2, 1879

Soil, analysis for (Cont.)
    potassium, 109, 1228, 1873, 1875, 1876, 1878, 1879
    rare earths, 576
    salinity, 1880
    sodium, 109, 1228, 1875–7
    strontium, 109, 1228, 1873
    tin, 1873
    titanium, 1873
    vanadium, 1873
    water, 1940, 1946, 1947, 1950
    water, hygroscopic, 1880
    zinc, 109, 1866–8, 1873, 1876, 1879
Soil salinity, determination of, 1880
Solid crystal scintillation radioactivity, 545
Solid fat content, determination of, in plastic fats, 1082
Solid fat index, determination of, in fats, 1096–8
Solid solutions, analysis of, 208
Solutions, aqueous, Raman spectra of, 77
Solvents,
  for flame emission spectrometry, 124
  for Raman spectrometry, 67
  for ultraviolet spectrometry, 29
  table of, 29
  paint, analysis of, 1309–14
  residual, determination of, in spice oleoresins, 1115
Somogyi method for sugars in food, 1146
Sorbic acid, determination of, in foods, 1112
Sorbitol, determination of, 1323–4
Soya bean oil,
  absorptivity value of, 1289
  analysis of, for neutral oil, 1085–7
  fatty acid composition of, 1322
Specific activity, radiochemistry, 544
Specific conductance, 298
  of standard KCl solutions, table of, 298
Specific gravity, determination of, pulpwood, 1326–32
Specific ionic conductances, table of, 300
Specific retention, 721
Specific rotation, 260
Specific susceptibility, 585
  Wiedemann's additivity law, 587
Spectral lines for the elements, table of, 156–7
Spectral reflectivity of paper, 1429–32
Spectrofluorometers, 92
Spectrometer-absorptiometer, for x-ray emission and absorption analysis, 171
Spectrometers,
  for analysis of radionuclides, 546
  for electron probe x-ray microanalyzer, 189
  for electron spin resonance, 619, 624–7
  for emission spectrometry, 142
    air, 857
    classification of, 143
    grating, 143
    prism, 143
    rating of, 142
    vacuum, 857
Spectrometry. *See special methods.*
Spectrophotometric terminology, 6

Spectropolarimeters, 268
  automatic recording, 270
    Bendix Model 460C, 271
    Cary Model 60, 270
    Durrum-Jasco ORD-5, 270
  Bendix Model 460C, 271
  Cary Model 60, 270
  manual, 269
  semiautomatic, 269
Spectropolarimetry, 268
  configuration, determination of, 275
  conformational analysis, 273
  functional groups, location of, 272
  instrumentation, 269
  method, 271
  optical activity, recognition of, 271
  quantitative analysis, 272
Spectroscopic splitting factor, 616
Sphalerite, analysis of, for indium, 393
Spherulitic crystallization of polyers, determination of, 1591
Spherulitic structure of polymers, determination of, 1592
Spice oleoresins, analysis of, for residual solvents, 1115
Square wave polarography, 350
Stabilizers in polymers, determination of, 1606–10
Stahl applicator, 743–6
Stainless steel, analysis of, 451, 864
Standard electrode potentials, table of, 429
Standard electrodes, for polarography, 358
Standard pH values, table of, 523
Starch,
  determination of,
    in cereals, 1109
    in flour, 1108
    reagent for, 218
Stationary electrode, polarography, 346
Statistics, in radioactive measurements, 546
Stearic acid, determination of in cement, 963–5
Stearolic acid, Raman spectrum of, 76
Steel. *See also* Ferrous materials *and* Iron and steel.
  analysis,
    reference materials, 854–5
    techniques, 855
  analysis by, 853
    activation analysis, 575, 576, 577, 862, 864, 865
    amperometric titration, 390, 395, 397, 562
    atomic absorption spectrometry, 115, 864
    differential thermal analysis, 865
    electrogravimetry, 448, 450, 453
    electron probe microanalyzer, 863
    emission spectrometry, 856, 859, 864
    fluorescence method, 100
    high-temperature oxidation, 861
    high-temperature reduction, 861, 862
    isotope dilution, 561, 865
    mass spectrometry, 862

Steel, analysis by (Cont.)
    polarography, 865
    radiometric methods, 556, 557
    vacuum fusion, 862
    x-ray spectrometry, 859, 864, 865
  analysis for,
    aluminum, 100, 448, 864
    antimony, 575
    arsenic, 575
    bismuth, 575
    boron, 575
    calcium, 575
    carbon, 556, 575
    chromium, 115, 575, 864
    cobalt, 575
    copper, 453, 864
    hydrogen, 862
    manganese, 576
    molybdenum, 561, 576, 865
    nickel, 576, 865
    niobium, 865
    nonmetallic compounds, 865
    oxygen, 862
    phosphorus, 395, 556, 576
    silicon, 865
    silver, 576
    sulfur, 557, 577, 865
    tantalum, 577, 865
    titanium, 397, 865
    tungsten, 577, 865
    vanadium, 397, 450, 562, 577
    zinc, 865
    zirconium, 450
Steel, high-alloy, analysis of, 390
Stereoregular polymers, 1617
Steroids,
  analysis by,
    gas chromatography, 733
    thin-layer chromatography, 754, 761
  configuration of, 275
Sterols, analysis of, 760
Stoke's diameter, 803
Stoke's equation, 803
Stretch of paper, 1446–9
Stripping analysis, 423
Stripping coulometry, 489
Strobane, 1464, 1480, 1485
Strontium. *See also* Alkaline earth metals.
  determination by,
    activation analysis, 577
    atomic absorption spectrometry, 109, 110, 1228
    emission spectrometry, 1873
    flame spectrometry, 133, 135, 967–8
    isotope dilution, 562
    radiometric titration, 560
    x-ray emission spectrometry, 1256
  determination of,
    in biological materials, 577, 1228
    in boiler deposits, 110
    in cement, 133, 967–8
    in coal ash, 110
    in fertilizers, 109
    in glass, 1256
    in lubricating oils, 135

Strontium, determination of (Cont.)
  in phosphors, 562
  in plant materials, 109
  in soils, 109, 1228, 1873
Strontium-90, determination of, in water, 1909–12
Strontium, radioactive, total, determination of, in water, 1907–9
Structure identification, by x-ray diffraction, 203
Strychnine sulfate, reagent for perchlorate, 219
Styrene,
  determination by,
    amperometric titration, 399
    gas chromatography, 1658
    polarography, 1308
    ultraviolet spectrometry, 35
  determination of, in polymers, 1308, 1658
Styrene-acrylonitrile copolyers, analysis of, 1611
Styrene-butadiene copolymer, identification of, 1670, 1673–5
Styrene, combined, determination of, in polymers, 1597
Styrene content, determination of, in polymers, 1611
Styrene monomer, determination of, in polymers, 1315
Styrene polymers, analysis of, for residual styrene monomer, 1658
Sucrose. See also Sugars.
  determination of,
    by saccharimetry, 267
    in sugar beets, 564
Sugars,
  analysis of,
    by thin-layer chromatography, 755, 760
    by visible spectrometry, 1939
    for water, 1939
  determination of,
    by ultraviolet spectrometry, 35
    in cereals, 1109
    in food, 1145, 1146, 1148
  hydrazone derivatives, microtest, 230
  identification of, 230
  properties of, table, 231
Sulfate,
  determination by,
    amperometric titration, 396
    nephelometry, 842
    radiometric titration, 560
    turbidimetry, 282, 842
  determination of, in air, 842
  microtest for, 220
Sulfate detergents, identification of, 1831
  infrared absorption data, table of, 1832
Sulfhydryl compounds, Raman spectra of, 77
Sulfhydryl group, determination of, 399
Sulfides, analysis of, for silver, 576
  determination of, 394
Sulfides, organic, determination of, 1197
Sulfonate detergents, identification of, 1831
  infrared absorption data, table of, 1832

Sulfotepp, 1492, 1497, 1499
Sulfur. See also Sulfate.
  analysis for, selenium,
  determination by,
    activation analysis, 577, 865
    amperometric titration, 396
    combustion method, 1695, 1724–9
    emission spectrometry, 865
    isotope dilution, 562
    photometric titration, 1695
    polarography, 1695
    radiometric methods, 557, 1730
    ultraviolet spectrometry, 1722–4
    x-ray spectrometry, 969–73, 1256, 1540
  determination of,
    in cement, 969–73
    in ferrous materials, 865
    in gallium arsenide, 1791
    in glass, 1256
    in organic substances, 396
    in petroleum hydrocarbons, 1540
    in rubber, 562, 1695, 1722, 1722–4, 1724–9, 1730
    in steel, 577, 865
    in water, 577
  solubility of, in rubber, 1730
Sulfur, blooming of, in rubber, 1730
Sulfur compounds, determination of, 1189, 1211
Sulfur dioxide, analysis of, for water, 1936
  determination of, 847, 1112, 1211
Sulfur, free, determination of, in rubber accelerators, 1729
Sulfuric acid,
  analysis of, 1537
  determination of, in synthetic detergents, 1840
Sulfuric acid areosol, determination of, in air, 842
Superparamagnetism, 586
Supporting electrolyte, 325
  in polarography, table of, 926–9
Surface wettability of paper, 1449–51
Surfactants. See Detergents.
  biodegradability of, 1819–21
Surfactants, anionic. See Detergents.
Surfactants, low level. See Low level surfactants.
Susceptibility,
  atomic, 585
  electronic magnetic, 584
  ionic, 585
  mass, 585
  molar, 585
  nuclear magnetic, 584
  specific, 585
Syndet. See Detergents.
Syndiotactic polymers, 1618
Syndiotactic structures, 1580
Systox, 1497, 1485, 1499

Tall oil, fatty acid composition of, 1322
Tannins, analysis of, 763
Tantalum,
  determination by,

Tantalum, determination by (Cont.)
  activation analysis, 577, 865
  isotope dilution, 562
  ultraviolet spectrometry, 33
  determination of,
    in alloys, 577
    in ferroalloys, 865
    in rocks and minerals, 577
    in steel, 577, 865
Tantalum metal, analysis of,
  by emission spectrometry, 889–91
  by inert gas fusion, 951
  by vacuum fusion, 951
  for oxygen, 951
Tantalum oxide, analysis of, 889–91
Tarnish films on metals, measurement of thickness of, 424
TBA. See Thiobarbituric acid.
2,3,6-TBA herbicide, 1470
TCNB pesticide, 1464, 1478, 1483
TDE pesticide, 1464
2,4-TDI. See 2,4-Toluene diisocyanate.
2,6-TDI. See 2,6-Toluene diisocyanate.
Teflon, analysis of, for fluorine, 575
Tellurium,
  determination by,
    activation analysis, 1791
    amperometric titration, 396
    emission spectrometry, 1777–8, 1778–80, 1780–2
    ultraviolet spectrometry, 33
  determination of,
    in anodic sludge, 396
    in fly-dust, 396
    in gallium arsenide, 1791
    in semiconductor materials, 1777–8, 1778–80, 1780–2
Tensile breaking strength of paper, 1395–8
Terephthalic acid. See Phthalic acid isomers.
Terminal unsaturation, determination of, in alkenes, 1178
Terminology, spectrophotometric, 6
Terpene alcohols, analysis of, 761
3,5,3′,4′-Tetrachlorosalicylanilide, determination of, in soaps and detergents, 1827
Tetraethyllead, determination of, in gasoline, 134
1,2,3,4-Tetrahydro-6-methoxyquinoline, reagent for osmium, 216
Tetramethylsilane, internal standard for NMR spectrometry, 603
Tetramethyl thiuram disulfide, determination of, in rubber, 1743
Textiles, analysis of, for water, 1946, 1950
TGA. See Thermogravimetric analysis.
Thallium,
  determination by,
    amperometric titration, 397
    chronopotentiometry, 422, 423
    coulometric analysis, 491
    electrogravimetry, 457
    radiometric titration, 560
    ultraviolet spectrometry, 33

Thallium (Cont.)
  determination of,
    in cadmium, 397
    in gallium arsenide, 1802–7
    in germanium, 1802–7
    in indium, 1801, 1802–7
    in indium antimonide, 1802–7
    in indium arsenide, 1802–7
    in silicon, 1802–7
Thallium amalgam-thallous chloride electrode, for pH measurements, 527, 528
2,4,5–T herbicide, 1470, 1501
Thermal analysis, 644
  applications, 647
  calorimetric methods, 644
  dynamic methods, 644
  instrumentation, 645–6
  by mass spectrometry, 538
  melting curves, 645
  purity determination by, 647
  static methods, 644
  thermometric methods, 644
Thermal-neutron activation analysis, 1531, 1535
Thermobalance, 662, 663, 1631–4
Thermography. See Differential thermal analysis.
Thermogravimetric analysis, 661
  analysis of,
    plastics, 1630–7
    soil, 1880
  applications, 665–7
  automatic, 662
  determination of,
    carbonate, 1880
    organic matter, 1880
    thermal degradation of polymers, 1630
    water, 1942
    water, hygroscopic, 1880
  factors affecting results, 664
  instrumentation, 663
  weight-loss curves, 662
    ammonium phosphomolybdate, 666
    oxine phosphomolybdate, 667
    quinolinium phosphomolybdate, 667
Thermogravimetry. See Thermogravimetric analysis.
Thermometric titrations, 636
  acid-base titrations, 641
    table of, 640
  applications, 640
  complexation titrations, 641
    table of, 642
  nonaqueous titrations, 641
  oxidation-reduction titrations, 641
    table of, 642
  precipitation titrations, 641
    table of, 641
  end point detection, 637
  experimental procedure, 640
  instrumentation, 638–40
  titration curves, 636–7
Thiamine, determination of, 1152–4
Thiazole accelerators, identification of, 1699–1701

Thin-layer chromatography, 738
  analysis of,
    alkaloids, 754, 760
    amino acids, 757, 760, 958–60
    antioxidants, 763
    carbohydrates, 760
    carotenoids, 754, 761
    chlorinated pesticides, 1492–9
    clinical materials, 1037
    coumarins, 763
    detergents, 757, 760
    dyes, 755, 760, 761
    essential oils, 754
    fats and waxes, 754, 761
    fatty acids, 757
    flavone glycosides, 763
    gallic acid esters, 763
    glycosides, 760
    insecticides, 755
    nucleotides, 757
    peptides, 760
    petroleum products, 754, 761
    plastics, 1650–3
    steroids, 754, 761
    sterols, 760
    sugars, 755, 760
    tannins, 763
    terpene alcohols, 761
    vitamins, 754, 760, 761
  apparatus for, 741–8
  applications of, 753
  coating materials and solvents,
    adsorption TLC, 754–7
    on dextran gels, 765–6
    ion exchange TLC, 757–9
    partition TLC, 760–1
    on polyamides, 763–5
    reversed phase TLC, 761–3
  detection methods, 767–70
    table of, 768
  determination of,
    amino acids, 1038
    barbiturates, 1039
    chlorinated pesticides, 1493
    lipids, 1039–41
    organothiophosphate pesticides, 1497–9
  experimental conditions, table of, 740
  experimental procedure, 739, 741
    chromatoplates, development of, 751–3
    chromatoplates, preparation of, 741–7
    sample, application of, 749–51
  physical principles,
    adsorption, 754–7
    ion exchange, 757–9
    partition, 760–1
    reversed-phase partition, 761–3
  preparative methods, 775–9
  quantitative analysis by, 770–5
  separation by,
    of cis-trans.-isomers, 757
    of polymer additives, 1650
Thin-layer electrophoresis, 766
Thin-layer ionophoresis, 766
Thinners, hydrocarbon, analysis of, for antioxidants, 1308

Thiobarbituric acid method, for determination of rancidity in fats, 1059
2,2'-thiobis(4,4'-chlorophenol), determination of, in soaps and detergents, 1828
2,2'-thiobis(4,6-dichlorophenol), determination of, in soaps and detergents, 1828
Thiodan, 1479, 1484
Thiodan I, 1464, 1479, 1484
Thiols, determination by,
    amperometric titration, 399
    gas chromatography, 1197
    nuclear magnetic resonance, 1202
    ultraviolet spectrometry, 1189–90
Thiopesticides, determination of, 1485–7
Thiophosphate insecticides, determination of, 1503
Thiuram accelerators, identification of, 1699–1701
Thorium,
  determination by,
    activation analysis, 577
    amperometric titration, 396
    emission spectrometry, 562
    isotope dilution, 562
  determination of,
    in monazite melt, 396
    in rocks and minerals, 577
    in solutions, 577
  reagents for, 99
Thorium chelates, fluorescent, 99
Tigogenin, determination of, in hecogenin, 1208
Time-of-flight mass spectrometer, 535
Tin,
  determination by,
    activation analysis, 865
    amperometric titration, 396
    atomic absorption spectrometry, 110
    electrogravimetry, 440, 455, 457
    emission spectrometry, 865, 1772–5, 1778–80, 1780–2, 1873
    polarography, 865, 947, 1081, 1801, 1802–7
  determination of,
    in aluminum, 947
    in antimony, 1801
    in brasses and bronzes, 440
    in fats, 1081
    in ferrous materials, 865
    in ferrotungsten, 865
    in germanium, 1802–7
    in gallium arsenide, 1802–7
    in indium, 1802–7
    in indium antimonide, 1802–7
    in indium arsenide, 1802–7
    in iron, 865
    in nonferrous metals, 110
    in semiconductor materials, 1772–5, 1778–80, 1780–2
    in silicon, 1802–7
    in soil, 1873
  reagents for, fluorometric, 99
Tin alloys, analysis of, for copper, 944
Tin-base alloys, analysis of, for copper, 875–9

Tin chelates, fluorescent, 99
Tissue,
    analysis by,
        atomic absorption spectrometry, 109
        fluorometric method, 102
    analysis of, 102, 109
Titanium,
    determination by,
        activation analysis, 865
        amperometric titration, 397
        emission spectrometry, 1772–5, 1778–80, 1873
        polarography, 865, 947
        ultraviolet spectrometry, 33
        visible spectrometry, 1270
        x-ray emission spectrometry, 1250
    determination of,
        in aluminum, 947
        in ferrous materials, 865
        in glass, 1250
        in paint pigments, 1270
        in semiconductor materials, 1772–5, 1778–80
        in soil, 1873
        in steel, 397, 865
Titanium alloys, analysis of, 940–3
Titanium metal, analysis for,
    copper diffusion, 911
    hydrogen, 951
    oxygen, 951
Titanium dioxide, analysis of, for anatase, 1303
Titration curves, amperometric titrations, 379–84
    conductometric, 309–19
Titrations,
    amperometric, 377
    polarographic, 381
    potentiometric, 290–4
    turbidmetric, 279
Titrator, for amperostatic coulometry, 479
    for potentiostatic coulometry, 464
TLC. See Thin-layer chromatography.
TMS. See Tetramethylsilane.
TMTD. See Tetramethyl thiuram disulfide.
TNPP. See Tris(nonylated phenyl phosphite).
Tobacco, analysis of, for water, 1946
α-Tocopherol, determination of, 399
Tocopherols, determination of, in fats, 1062, 1096
Tollen's reagent, 223
Toluene, determination of, in poly(methyl vinyl ether), 1186
2,4-Toluene diisocyanate, determination of,
    by infrared spectrometry, 1175
    in polymers, 1316
Toluene sulfonic acid, sodium salt, determination of, in detergents, 1823–5
Toxaphene, 1464, 1480, 1485, 1493
    determination of, in water, 1924–5
2,4,5-TP herbicide, 1470, 1501
Trans-crotonaldehyde, NMR spectrum of, 608
Trans-isomers, isolated, determination of, in fats, 1072–3

Transition time, chronopotentiometry, 406
Transmittance, definition of, 6
3,4,4'-trichlorocarbanilide, determination of, in soaps and detergents, 1827
Triethylene glycol, determination of, 1323–4
Triga Mark I reactor, 1535, 1537
Trimethylolethane, determination of, 1323–4
2,4,6-Trinitrotoluene, determination of, 35
Triphenylamine, determination of, 103
Triphosphate. See Tripolyphosphates.
Triple bond. See Unsaturation.
Tripolyphosphate. See also Polyphosphates.
    determination of, 1846–54
Tris(nonylated phenyl)phosphite, determination of, 1597
Trithion, 1479, 1486, 1492, 1497, 1499
Tung oil, absorptivity value, 1289
    analysis of, for eleostearic acid, 1071
    fatty acid composition of, 1322
Tungstate. See Tungsten.
Tungsten,
    determination by,
        activation analysis, 577, 1537
        amperometric titration, 397
        isotope dilution, 865
        ultraviolet spectrometry, 34
        x-ray emission spectrometry, 865
    determination of,
        in ferrotungsten, 397
        in high-alloy steels, 865
        in hydrodesulfurization catalysts, 1537
        in rocks, 577
        in sea water, 577
        in steel, 577
Tungsten lamp, for fluorometric analysis, 85
Tungsten metal, analysis of, 135, 951
Turbidimeters,
    Hellige, 279
    Parr, 279
Turbidimetric titration, 279
    of polymers, for molecular weight distribution, 1306
Turbidimetry, 277
    air pollutants analysis, 842
    applications, 280
    determination by,
        of cloud point of detergents, 1839
        of sulfate, 842
    instrumentation, 279

Ultracentrifugation,
    molecular weight determination, 1661
    sedimentation analysis, 784
Ultracentrifuge, 1661
Ultraviolet absorption characteristics of amine antioxidants, table of, 1715
Ultraviolet spectra, origin of, 23
Ultraviolet spectrometers, 26
Ultraviolet spectrometry, 23
    analysis of,
        air pollutants, 837, 843–4
        detergents, 1821–3, 1825–8
        fats, 1066–71
        foods, 1111–2

Ultraviolet spectrometry, analysis of (Cont.)
  functional groups, 1182–91
  gasoline, 1189
  hydrocarbons, 1182–7, 1548, 1550
  inorganic substances, 32–4
  iron and steel, 860
  oils, 1011, 1277–8
  organic substances, 35
  paints, varnishes, and lacquers, 1272–81
  plastics, 1595–9
  polymers, 1186, 1272–8, 1596–7
  rubber, 1667, 1695, 1699–1706, 1713–7, 1733–5, 1744–6
  soaps, 1826–8
  water, 1890–1
 applications of, 30
 characterization of,
  hydrocarbons, aromatic, 1550
  hydrocarbons, olefin, 1548
 chromophoric groups, 31
 determination of,
  accelerators in rubber, 1695, 1740–2
  additives in polymers, 1596
  aldehydes, 1187
  alkenes, 1182
  alkyl benzene sulfonates, 1821–3, 1891
  alkyl phenoxypolyoxyethylene ethanol detergents, 1828
  alkynes, 1184
  amines, aromatic, 1188
  anhydrides, 1187
  antioxidants in polymers, 1596–7
  antioxidants in rubber, 1695
  antioxidants, phenolic, in rubber, 1733–5
  antiozonants in polymers, 1596
  benzene, 1186
  benzoic acid in alkyd resins, 1274–6
  benzoic acid in food, 1111
  carbon disulfide, 1190
  carbonyl group, 1187
  carboxylic acids, 1187
  conjugated dienoic acids, 1071
  copolymer composition of rubber polymers, 1667
  diene value of castor oil, dehydrated, 1277
  diphenylamine, 1280
  divinyl sulfone, 1190
  eleostearic acid in tung oil, 1071
  esters, 1187
  fatty acids in oils, 1277
  germicides in detergents, 1826–8
  hydrocarbons, 1182–7
  hydroquinone, 1280
  inhibitors in vinyl monomers, 1280
  ketones, 1187
  lead in rubber, 1748
  lead in zinc oxide, 1748
  light stabilizers in polymers, 1596
  melamine, 1278
  mercaptobenzothiazol, 1190
  2,2-methylene bis(3,4,6-trichlorophenol), 1826
  methylisopropenyl ketone, 1597

Ultraviolet spectrometry, determination of (Cont.)
  molecular weight of polymers, average, 1597
  nitrate, 1890–1
  m-nitroaniline, 1188
  nonionic detergents, 1828
  nonylphenol, 1188
  oxidants in air, 843–4
  ozone in air, 843–4
  phenanthrene, 1186
  phenols, 1187
  m-phenylenediamine, 1188
  phthalic acid isomers, 1274–6
  phthalic anhydride, 1272
  polyunsaturated fatty acids, 1066–71, 1183, 1278
  pyridine, 1189
  quinoline, 1189
  sorbic acid, 1112
  styrene, combined in polymers, 1597
  sulfur, 1722–4
  sulfur compounds, 1189
  p-tert.-butylbenzoic acid, 1278
  3,5,3′,4′-tetrachlorosalicylanilide, 1827
  2,2′-thiobis(4,4′-chlorophenol), 1828
  2,2′-thiobis(4,6-dichlorophenol), 1828
  thiols, 1189–90
  toluene, 1186
  toluene sulfonic acid, sodium salt, 1823–5
  3,4,4′-trichlorocarbanilide, 1827
  tris(nonylated phenyl) phosphite, 1597
  water, 1952
  xylene sulfonic acid, sodium salt, 1825–6
  zinc oxide, 1744–6
 differentiation of bleached unbleached lard, 1071
 identification of,
  accelerators in rubber, 1695, 1699–1706
  aldehyde-amine accelerators, 1699-1701
  antioxidants in rubber, 1695
  antioxidants, amine, in rubber, 1713–7
  dithiocarbamate accelerators, 1699–1701
  guanidine accelerators, 1699–1701
  thiazole accelerators, 1699–1701
  thiuram accelerators, 1699–1701
 instrumentation, 25
  absorption cells, 28
  detectors, 28
  radiation source, 25
  spectrophotometers, 25, 26, 27
 methodology, special, 29
 solvents used, 29
 spectra, origin of, 23
Unit pole, 582
Univector polarograph, 364
Unsaturated compounds, characterization of, 680
Unsaturated hydrocarbons. See Alkenes, Alkynes, and individual hydrocarbons.
Unsaturation, determination of,
 by amperometric titration, 399
 in fats, 1202, 1306
 in polybutadienes, 1621–2

Unsaturation, determination of (Cont.)
  in polyethylene, 1613
Uranium,
  determination by,
    activation analysis, 577
    amperometric titration, 397
    chronopotentiometry, 422
    emission spectrometry, 562
    fluorometric analysis, 102, 865
    isotope dilution, 562
    potentiostatic coulometry, 471
    radiometric methods, 865
    ultraviolet spectrometry, 34
  determination of,
    in biological materials, 577
    in ferrous materials, 865
    in graphite, 577
    in metals, 577
    in rocks and minerals, 577
    in solutions, 577
  microtest for, 217
Uranium compounds, analysis of, for phos-
    phorus, 561
Uranium metal, analysis of, for copper, 908
Uranium-235 reactor fuel, 1533
Urea,
  determination of, 1269
  microtest for, 227
Urea nitrogen. See Nitrogen, urea.
Urethane intermediates, analysis of, for iso-
    cyanate, 1292–4
Urethane rubber, identification of, 1670
Uric acid, determination of, 1015–9
Urine. See also Biological fluids.
  analysis by,
    atomic absorption spectrometry, 109,
      115
    flame spectrometry, 1027–31
    fluorometric analysis, 1032–6
    gas chromatography, 1044–9
    thin-layer chromatography, 1038
  analysis for,
    adrenaline, 1033
    amino acids, 1038
    cadmium, 109
    calcium, 109
    catecholamines, 1032–3
    copper, 109
    corticosteroids, 1032
    estrogens, 1033–6, 1047–8
    homovanillic acid, 1044
    17-hydroxycorticosteroids, 1048–9
    iron, 109
    17-ketosteroids, 1046–7
    lead, 109, 115
    magnesium, 109
    mercury, 109
    3-methoxy-4-hydroxymandelic acid,
      1044
    3-methoxy-4-hydroxyphenylacetic acid,
      1044
    nickel, 109
    nitrogen, urea, 1014–5
    potassium, 109, 1027–31
    pregnanediol, 1045–6

Urine, analysis for (Cont.)
    sodium, 109
    vanilmandelic acid, 1044
    zinc, 109

Vacuum extraction, determination of,
  hydrogen in nonferrous metals, 949–52
  oxygen in nonferrous metals, 949–52
Vacuum fusion,
  analysis of,
    iron and steel, 862
    nonferrous metals, 949
    semiconductor materials, 1807
  determination of,
    hydrogen in nonferrous metals, 949
    nitrogen in nonferrous metals, 949
    oxygen in nonferrous metals, 949–52
Vacuum spectrometer, 857
Vanadate. See Vanadium.
Vanadium,
  determination by,
    activation analysis, 577
    amperometric titration, 397, 562, 865
    electrogravimetry, 450
    electron-spin resonance, 632, 634
    emission spectrometry, 1873
    potentiometric titration, 293
    ultraviolet spectrometry, 34
    x-ray emission spectrometry, 1543
  determination of,
    in aluminum, 577
    in cracking catalysts, 1543
    in ferrous materials, 865
    in graphite, 577
    in petroleum, 577
    in petroleum oils, 632, 634
    in sea water, 577
    in soil, 1873
    in steel, 397, 450, 562, 577
Vanadium metal, analysis of, for oxygen,
    951
van Deemter equation, 724
Van de Graaff accelerators, 1535
Vanillin, determination of, 35
Vanilmandelic acid, determination of, 1044
Van Vleck's equation, for dimagnetism, 589
  for paramagnetism, 590
Varian V-4502 spectrometer, for ESR, 624
Varnish. See also Paint.
  analysis of, for oil content, 1288
  characterization of, 1323–4
Vegadex, 1478, 1483
Vegetable oils, analysis for,
  pesticides, 1470
  phosphorus, 1271
Vehicles. See Paint vehicles.
Vibrating platinum electrode, 385
  amperometric titrations, 385
Vinsol resin. See Abietic acid derivatives.
Vinyl acetate, analysis of, for diphenylamine,
    1280
Vinyl monomers, analysis of, 1268, 1280
N-vinylpyrrolidone, analysis of, for 2-pyr-
    rolidone, 1175
  determination of, in 2-pyrrolidone, 1168

Vinyl resins, analysis of,
for poly(vinyl acetate), 1287
Vinyl toluene, determination of, in polymers, 1315
Visible spectrometry, 3
analysis of,
air pollutants, 837, 843, 845–6
clinical materials, 978–1009, 1011–9
fats, 1054–66
fertilizers, 1103–5
foods, 1109–10, 1111–3, 1116–20, 1121, 1127–31, 1133, 1137–9, 1146–57
paint, varnish, and lacquer, 1265–72
rubber and rubber products, 1733, 1735–8, 1743–6, 1748–56
soaps and detergents, 1815–21
soils, 1865–72
water, 1883–90
applications in analysis, 18, 21
errors, sources of, 14
instrumentation, 7
laws of absorption, 5
methods, 4–5, 14, 17, 21
terminology, 6
Vitamin A, determination of,
by ultraviolet spectrometry, 35
in food products, 1148–52
Vitamin B$_{12}$, determination of, 564
Vitamin C, determination of, 1155
Vitamin D, determination of, 564
Vitamins, analysis of, 754, 760, 761
VMA. See Vanilmandelic acid.
V-n-d method of analysis of oil fractions, 255
Voltage-scanning coulometry, 490

Wagner's reagent, 235, 236
Water, 1881. See also Moisture, Mineral water, and Sea water.
analysis by,
activation analysis, 576–7
amperometric titration, 392–3
emission spectrometry, 1892–4
flame spectrometry, 132
gas chromatography, 1924–6
microelectrophoresis, 1927–34
polarography, 1898–1907
potentiometric titration, 1894–8
radiometric methods, 553, 556, 1907–24
ultraviolet spectrometry, 1890–1
visible spectrometry, 1884–5
analysis for,
Aldrin, 1924–5
alkyl benzene sulfonate, 1891
barium, radioactive, 1912
BHC, 1924–5
cadmium, 1902–7
chloride, 1894–5
chlorinated hydrocarbon pesticides, 1926
chlorine, active, 392
color, 1883–90
copper, 1902–7
DDT, 1924–5
Diazinon, 1924–5
Dieldrin, 1924–5
fluoride, 393

Water, analysis for (Cont.)
herbicides, aquatic, 1926
lead, 1902–7
mercury, 576
nickel, 1902–7
nitrate, 1890–1, 1898–1900
osmium, 132
oxygen, dissolved, 1895–8
Parathion, 1924–5
pesticides, 1924
phosphate, 553
plutonium, 556
radioactive strontium, total, 1907–9
radium, 556, 1913–5
radium-226, 1915–24
silver, 1892–4
Silvex, 1926
strontium-90, 1909–12
sulfur, 577
Toxaphene, 1924–5
zinc, 1901–7
determination by, 1935
conductivity, 1946–9
coulometry, 1950–1
critical solution temperatures, 242
dielectric methods, 1949–50
differential thermal analysis, 1943
gas chromatography, 1945
infrared spectrometry, 1181, 1935–7
Karl Fischer titration, 1159–61, 1841
mass spectrometry, 1941
neutron scattering, 1940
nuclear magnetic resonance, 1936–9
radiometric methods, 556, 1941
thermogravimetry, 1880, 1942
ultraviolet spectrometry, 1952
visible spectrometry, 1938–40
x-ray diffraction, 1952
determination of,
in acetic acid, glacial, 242
in air, 1947–8
in alcohols, 1936, 1949
in amines, 1936, 1946
in ammonia, liquid, 1951
in bauxite, 1939
in butane gas, 1945
in cement slurries, 1941
in cereals, 1939
in chlorine, liquid, 1936
in concrete mix, 1946
in cotton, 1939
in crystalline substances, 1952
in detergents, 1841
in foods, 1159–61, 1938, 1939
in Freon, 1936
in fuels, 1941
in gases, 1936, 1947, 1950, 1952
in gasoline, 1939
in glycerol, 1936
in glycols, 1936
in grain, 1946
in hydrocarbons, 1936, 1939, 1941, 1945
in hydrogen fluoride, 1946
in jet fuels, 1939
in jute, 1946

Water, determination of (Cont.)
  in ketones, 1939
  in leather, 1946, 1949
  in meat products, 1950
  in natural gas, 1947–8
  in nitric acid, fuming, 1936
  in nitrogen, 1947–8
  in oils, 1939
  in oxygen, 1947–8
  in paper, 1946, 1950
  in paperboard pulp, 1939
  in petroleum products, 1946
  in pharmaceutical products, 1945
  in plastics, 1946
  in refrigerants, halogenated, 1939
  in sand, 1946
  in soaps, 1841
  in soil, 1880, 1940, 1946, 1947, 1950
  in sugar, 1939
  in sulfur dioxide, 1936
  in textiles, 1946, 1950
  in tobacco, 1946
  in varnish films, 556
  in wood, 1939, 1946
Water absorption of bibulous paper, 1422
Water absorptiveness of nonbibulous paper, 1427–9
Water, added, determination of, in milk, 1134–6, 1136–7
Water resistance of paper, 1423–7
Water vapor permeability of paper, 1434–6
Wave height, polarographic, 328
Waves, polarographic. See Polarography.
Waxes, analysis of, 754, 761
Weber, unit, 583
Weiss magneton, 583
Weston cell, 286
Wheat, analysis of, for pesticides, 1471
Wheatstone bridge, 302
Whitby sedimentation tube, 817
White metal, analysis of, for copper, 923
Wiedmann's additivity law, mass(or specific) susceptibility, 587
Wilson and Jay method, for blood gases, 1043
Wilson's stain, in paper analysis, 1382, 1387
Wines, analysis of, 109
Wood, analysis of, 1326
  for water, 1939, 1946
Wool, characterization of, 1317
Working electrode, 463

Xanthydrol, reagent for urea, 227
  derivatives of amides, properties of, 230
Xenon arc lamp, 85
X-ray absorption, 169, 170
  applications in analysis, 183
  instrumentation, 171–6
  types of, 170
X-ray absorption analysis, 180
  advantages of, 183
  differential absorption, 180
  limitations of, 183
  monochromatic, 180
  polychromatic absorptiometry, 180
  sample preparation, 176

X-ray diffraction, 198, 202
  ASTM index, 203
  Debye-Scheerer camera, 199
  FINK index, 203
  Guinier camera, 201
  Hanawalt index, 1839
  instrumentation, 199
    cameras, 199
    diffractometer, 202
  lattice parameter measurement, 208
  Matthews index, 204
  powder diffraction patterns, 203
  preferred orientation, 208
  qualitative analysis, 198, 203
  quantitative analysis, 198, 204
    binary mixtures, 206
    by combined diffraction-absorption technique, 207
    mixtures by internal standard method, 207
    multicomponent mixtures, 205
  Seeman-Bohlin camera, 199
X-ray diffraction analysis,
  analysis of,
    fats, 1075
    paints, 1303–5
    plastics, 1582–6
    rubber, 1747
  determination of,
    anatase in titanium dioxide pigments, 1303
    crystallinity of polymers, 1584–6
    water, 1952
    zinc oxide in rubber, 1747
  identification of,
    amines, 1706–12
    antioxidants, amine, in rubber, 1713–7
    compounds, 204
    insoluble materials in detergents, 1838–9
    magnesium carbonate in rubber, 1719–22
    magnesium oxide in rubber, 1719
  structure, 203
X-ray diffraction data,
  for amine hydrochlorides, table of, 1710–2
  for quanidines, table of, 1716
X-ray emission, 169
  applications in analysis, 183
  counting statistics, 1245
  instrumentation, 171, 1243, 1539
    analyzer crystals, table of, 1244, 174–5, 1261
    detectors, 176
    dispersion, 174
    excitation source, 172
  sample preparation, 176
X-ray emission analysis, 177
  addition technique, 179
  advantages of, 183
  comparison standards, 177
  dilution technique, 180
  elements determined by, 1539
  internal standard, 178
  limitations of, 183

X-ray emission analysis (Cont.)
  qualitative analysis by, 1540
  thin films, 180
X-ray fluorescence,
  analysis by, of plastics, 1586
  determination of,
    arsenic, 864
    zinc stearate, 1587
X-ray powder cameras, 199
X-ray spectrometer-absorptiometer, 171
X-ray spectrometry,
  analysis of,
    alloy steels, 864–5
    cement, 969–73
    copper, 908
    cracking catalysts, 1543
    ferromanganese, 864
    ferrous materials, 864
    fertilizers, 1102
    gasoline, 1542
    glass, 1243–57
    hafnium-zirconium alloys, 906–8
    iron and steel, 859
    lubricating oils, 1543
    nodular cast iron, 864
    organic matrices, 1541
    paint, 1299–1302
    paint pigments, 1300
    paint vehicles, 1301
    petroleum and petroleum products, 1539–44
    slags, 864
    steel, 864
    titanium, 911
    zinc, 909
  determination of,
    aluminum, 864, 969–73, 1248
    antimony, 1248
    arsenic, 1250
    barium, 1250, 1543
    bromine, 1541
    calcium, 969–73, 1251, 1543
    chlorine, 1251, 1541
    chromium, 864
    cobalt, 1252, 1541
    copper, 1252
    copper diffusion in titanium, 911
    elements, 1248
    iodine, 1541
    iron, 864, 969–73, 1252, 1541, 1543
    lead, 864, 1542
    magnesium, 864, 969–73, 1252
    manganese, 864, 969–73, 1252
    mercury, 909
    metals, instrumental conditions, table of, 1249
    nickel, 1252, 1543
    potassium, 969–73, 1253
    silicon, 865, 969–73, 1253
    sodium, 1255
    strontium, 1256
    sulfur, 969–73, 1256, 1540
    titanium, 1250
    tungsten, 865
    uranium, 908

X-ray spectrometry, determination of (Cont.)
    vanadium, 1543
    zinc, 865, 1252, 1541, 1543
    zirconium, 1256
  instrumentation for,
    small area masks, 1260
    small area probes, 1259
    ultra-thin-window counter tubes, 1261
X-rays, detection of, 198
  diffraction of, 199
  generation of, 169
  K spectra, 198
  KX units, 199
  production of, 198
X-ray tubes, 1260
Xylenes, isomeric, analysis of, 1170
Xylene sulfonic acid, sodium salt, determination of, in detergents, 1825–6

Yttrium, determination of, 293

Zeisel method, 1318
Zeiss Endter particle size analyzer, 797, 799
Zeiss photoelectric polarimeter, 263
Zinc,
  determination by,
    activation analysis, 577, 1791
    amperometric titration, 109, 110, 865, 916–20, 922–3, 1106, 1514, 1516, 1517
    chronopotentiometry, 422
    coulogravimetry, 491
    electrogravimetry, 455, 456
    emission spectrometry, 1777–8, 1778–80, 1780–2, 1873
    isotope dilution, 562, 1791
    paper chromatography, 1879
    polarography, 865, 937–43, 946, 947, 948, 1235, 1746, 1800, 1801, 1802–7, 1876, 1901–7
    potentiometric titration, 292, 293
    radiometric titration, 560
    ultraviolet spectrometry, 34
    visible spectrometry, 1866–8
    x-ray spectrometry, 865, 1252, 1541, 1543
  determination of,
    in aluminum alloys, 937–43
    in aluminum-base alloys, 916–20
    in aluminum-copper alloys, 947
    in blood, 577
    in blood serum, 109
    in brass, 946, 948
    in bronze, 923, 946
    in copper-base alloys, 916–20
    in copper, electrolytic, 922–3
    in electroplating solutions, 110
    in ferromanganese, 865
    in ferrous materials, 865
    in fertilizers, 109, 1106
    in fly-dust, 398
    in gallium, 562
    in gallium arsenide, 577, 1802–7
    in germanium, 1801, 1802–7

Zinc, determination of (Cont.)
  in glass, 1235, 1252
  in gunmetal, 923
  in indium, 1800, 1801, 1802–7
  in indium antimonide, 1802–7
  in indium arsenide, 1802–7
  in iron and steel, 110
  in lubricating oils, 1543
  in nickel-plating baths, 398
  in nonferrous metals, 110
  in ores and concentrates, 110, 398, 577
  in organic matrices, 1541
  in plant materials, 109
  in rocks, 110
  in rubber, 1746
  in sea water, 577
  in semiconductor materials, 1777–8, 1778–80, 1780–2, 1791
  in silicon, 1802–7
  in soil, 109, 1866–8, 1873, 1876, 1879
  in steel, 865
  in tissue, 109
  in urine, 109
  in water, 1901–7
  in worn lube oils, 1516, 1517
  in zirconium alloys, 923
  in zirconium-base alloys, 916–20
  microtest for, 214
  reagent for, fluorometric, 99
Zinc-base alloys,
  analysis by,
    electrogravimetry, 449
    flame spectrometry, 137, 875–9
  analysis for,
    aluminum, 449
    copper, 137, 875–9
    magnesium, 449
Zinc chelates, fluorescent, 99

Zinc metal,
  analysis by,
    isotope dilution, 561
    polarography, 944, 945, 947
    x-ray spectrometry, 909
  analysis for,
    arsenic, 561
    cadmium, 944
    indium, 945
    lead, 947
    mercury, 909
Zinc oxide, analysis of, for lead, 1748
  determination of, in rubber, 1744–6, 1747
Zinc stearate, determination of, in polymers, 1587
Zinc uranyl acetate, reagent for sodium, 213
Zirconium,
  determination by,
    activation analysis, 577
    amperometric titration, 398
    electrogravimetry, 450
    fluorometric analysis, 99, 102
    radiometric titration, 560
    ultraviolet spectrometry, 34
    x-ray emission spectrometry, 1256
  determination of,
    in glass, 1256
    in meteorites, 577
    in ores, 398
    in steel, 450
  reagents for, fluorometric, 99
Zirconium alloys, analysis of, 923
Zirconium-base alloys, analysis of, for zinc, 916–20
Zirconium chelates, fluorescent, 99
Zirconium metal, analysis for,
  hafnium, 576, 561
  oxygen, 951
Zone electrophoresis, 688